CME PROJECT

Algebra 2

Solutions Manual

PEARSON

Boston, Massachusetts
Chandler, Arizona
Glenview, Illinois
Shoreview, Minnesota
Upper Saddle River, New Jersey

Copyright © by Pearson Education, Inc., or its affiliates. All rights reserved. Printed in the United States of America. This publication is protected by copyright, and permission should be obtained from the publisher prior to any prohibited reproduction, storage in a retrieval system, or transmission in any form or by any means, electronic, mechanical, photocopying, recording, or likewise. For information regarding permission(s), write to Pearson School Rights & Permissions, One Lake Street, Upper Saddle River, New Jersey 07458.

Pearson® is a trademark, in the U.S. and/or in other countries, of Pearson plc or its affiliates.

Prentice Hall® is a trademark, in the U.S. and/or in other countries, of Pearson Education, Inc., or its affiliates.

13-digit ISBN 978-0-13-364411-1

10-digit ISBN 0-13-364411-1

1 2 3 4 5 6 7 8 9 10   12 11 10 09 08

To the Teacher

This *Solutions Manual* provides complete step-by-step solutions for exercises in CME Project *Algebra 2*.

Answers are also given in the Teacher's Edition, either in the margins of the pages where the exercises occur, or in the Additional Answers section located in the back of the Teacher's Edition.

Selected answers are provided in the back of the Student Edition.

Contents

1.1   Getting Started

For You to Explore

1. There are a number of answers that would work for each table. Here is a sample.

Table A

- Each output is 2 times the input, so $A(n) = 2n$.
- Each output is 2 more than the previous output, so $A(n) = A(n-1) + 2$.

Table B

- Each output is equal to the input multiplied by the next input, so $B(n) = n(n+1)$.
- Each output is $2n$ more than the previous output, so $B(n) = B(n-1) + 2n$.

Table C

- Each output is equal to the opposite of the input added to 2, so $C(n) = -n + 2$.
- Each output is one less than the previous output, starting at 2, so $C(n) = C(n-1) - 1$, where $C(0) = 2$.

Table D

- Each output is equal to the input multiplied by 2 more than the input, so $D(n) = n(n+2)$.
- Each output is $2n + 1$ more than the previous output, so $D(n) = D(n-1) + 2n + 1$.
- Find any output by squaring the next input then subtracting 1, so $D(n) = (n+1)^2 - 1$.

2. (a)

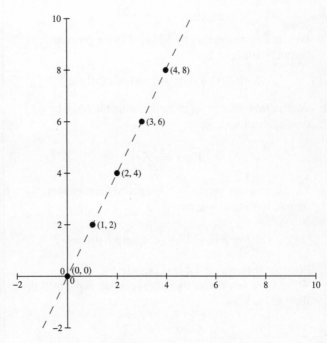

(b) There are other ways to draw a function through the 5 points. Here is one way to do it:

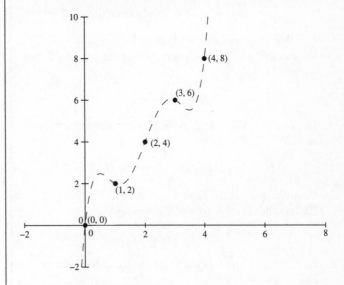

Many other answers are possible.

(c) There are many possible answers here. One is, "double the input if the input is less than 5 and otherwise output 17." Another is this rule:

$$A(n) = 2n + n(n-1)(n-2)(n-3)(n-4)$$

The second part of this rule for $A(n)$ will be zero when $n = 0, 1, 2, 3, 4$ but will be different for any other input n. Similar rules can assign any arbitrary number for the next output(s).

On Your Own

3. Possible answers for Table E include:
   We can find any output by multiplying the input by 2, then adding 3, so

   $$E(n) = 2n + 3$$

   We can find any output by adding 2 to the previous output, starting at 3, so

   $$E(n) = E(n - 1) + 2, \text{ where } E(0) = 3$$

4. We can find any output by multiplying the input by $\frac{1}{2}$, then subtracting 2, so

   $$F(n) = \frac{1}{2}n - 2$$

   We can find any output by adding $\frac{1}{2}$ to the previous output, starting at -2, so

   $$F(n) = F(n - 1) + \frac{1}{2}, \text{ where } F(0) = -2$$

5. Possible answers for Table G include:
   We can find any output by multiplying the input by 3 then subtracting 7, so

   $$G(n) = 3n - 7$$

   We can find any output by adding 3 to the previous output, starting at -7, so

   $$G(n) = G(n - 1) + 3, \text{ where } G(0) = -7$$

6. Possible answers for Table H include:
   We can find any output by multiplying the input by 5 then adding 3, so

   $$H(n) = 5n + 3$$

   Each output is 5 more than the previous output, starting at 3, so

   $$H(n) = H(n - 1) + 5, \text{ where } H(0) = 3$$

7. Possible answers for Table I include:
   Each output is the square of the input, so

   $$I(a) = a^2$$

8. Each output $J(p)$ is equal to the square of the input p multiplied by 2, so

   $$J(p) = 2p^2$$

9. We can find any output by taking the square of the input then adding 1, so

   $$K(x) = x^2 + 1$$

10. We can find any output by taking the square of the input then subtracting 25, so

    $$L(x) = x^2 - 25$$

    Alternately, each answer is a product of two numbers. Finding rules for the two numbers that multiply to make the output leads to

    $$L(x) = (x - 5)(x + 5)$$

    which is the same as $L(x) = x^2 - 25$.

11. We can find any output by multiplying the input by 6 then adding 9, so

    $$M(n) = 6n + 9$$

    Each output is 6 more than the previous output, starting at 9, so

    $$M(n) = M(n - 1) + 6, \text{ where } M(0) = 9$$

12. The outputs $N(t)$ are all perfect squares. Since each output is the square of 3 more than the input t, we write

    $$N(t) = (t + 3)^2$$

    Also, the outputs in Table N are the sum of the ones in Table I and Table M. This gives the alternate form

    $$N(t) = t^2 + 6t + 9$$

13. Each output $O(n)$ is equal to the square of the input n multiplied by 5, so

    $$O(n) = 5n^2$$

14. We can find any output by multiplying the input by 4 then adding 1, so

    $$P(b) = 4b + 1$$

    Each output is 4 more than the previous output, starting at 1, so

    $$P(b) = P(b - 1) + 4, \text{ where } P(0) = 1$$

15. The outputs in Table Q are the sum of the outputs in Tables O and P. So, their rules can be added together to get

    $$Q(n) = 5n^2 + 4n + 1$$

16. Each output $R(w)$ is equal to the cube of the input w, so

    $$R(w) = w^3$$

17. Each output $S(c)$ is equal to 3 more than the cube of the input c, so

    $$S(c) = c^3 + 3$$

    One way to notice this is that the outputs in Table S are three larger than the outputs in Table R.

18. Each output $T(n)$ is equal to 3 raised to the power of the input n, so

    $$T(n) = 3^n$$

19. Each output $U(x)$ is equal to 2 raised to the power of the input x, so

    $$U(x) = 2^x$$

20. Each output $V(n)$ is equal to 1 less than 2 raised to the power of the input n, so

$$V(n) = 2^n - 1$$

Also, the outputs in Table V are each one less than the outputs in Table U. So, any rule for Table U can be used to build a rule for Table V.

Maintain Your Skills

21. (a)

x	$a(x)$
0	0
1	1
2	4
3	9
4	16
5	25

(b)

x	$b(x)$
0	−1
1	0
2	3
3	8
4	15
5	24

(c)

x	$c(x)$
0	−4
1	−3
2	0
3	5
4	12
5	21

(d)

x	$d(x)$
0	−9
1	−8
2	−5
3	0
4	7
5	16

22. Replace $f(x)$ with 0 and x with 5:

$$0 = 5^2 - c$$
$$25 = c$$

23.

$$(x + 1)^2 - x^2 = 2x + 1$$

Multiply out the first expression in the identity.

$$x^2 + 2x + 1 - x^2 = 2x + 1$$

Then combine like terms to get

$$2x + 1 = 2x + 1$$

The expressions on both sides of this equation are identical. This shows that the original identity is true for every value of x.

Check Your Understanding

1.

Table B

Input: n	Output: $B(n)$	Δ
0	0	2
1	2	4
2	6	6
3	12	8
4	20	

2. (a) The outputs agree at $B(0) = 0$ and $B(1) = 2$, but this recursive rule gives $b(2) = 4$, which is incorrect.
  (b) The output does not agree at $B(1)$. The rule gives $b(1) = 0$, but $b(1)$ should equal 2.
  (c) This agrees with the table.
  (d) The output does not agree at $B(0)$. The rule gives $b(0) = 2$, but $b(0)$ should equal 0.

3. (a) Try rule (a) with the input 0 and output 0:

$$b(n) = 2n$$
$$0 = 2(0)$$
$$0 = 0$$

Rule (a) works with the input 0 and output 0. Now try the input 1 and output 2:

$$b(n) = 2n$$
$$2 = 2(1)$$
$$2 = 2$$

Rule (a) works with the input 1 and output 2. Now try the input 2 and output 6:

$$b(n) = 2n$$
$$6 = 2(2)$$
$$6 \neq 4$$

Rule (a) does not work with the input 2 and output 6, so it does not match Table B.
  (b) Rule (b) works with every input, so it fits Table B.
  (c) Rule (c) works with every input, so it fits Table B.
  (d) Rule (d) works for the first three inputs, but then fails. This rule gives $b(3) = 14$, but the table says $B(3) = 12$.

4.

Input	Output	Δ
0	5	6
1	11	8
2	19	10
3	29	15
4	44	

5.

Input	Output	Δ
0	**6**	3
1	**9**	3
2	**12**	3
3	**15**	3
4	18	

6.

Input	Output	Δ
0	5	−3
1	**2**	**15**
2	17	−13
3	**4**	−5
4	−1	

7. (a)
$$f(1) = f(0+1)$$
$$= f(0) \cdot (0+1)$$
$$= 1 \cdot 1$$
$$= 1$$

$$f(2) = f(1+1)$$
$$= f(1) \cdot (1+1)$$
$$= 1 \cdot 2$$
$$= 2$$

Continue this method to find $f(3)$ through $f(6)$. You will get $f(3) = 6$, $f(4) = 24$, $f(5) = 120$ and $f(6) = 720$.

(b) The factorial function on the calculator gives these outputs. Mathematically, the notation uses an exclamation mark. For example,
$$5! = 5 \cdot 4 \cdot 3 \cdot 2 \cdot 1 = 120$$

8. (a)

Input	Output
0	2
1	6
2	10
3	14
4	18

(b)

Input	Output
0	2
1	6
2	18
3	54
4	162

(c)

Input	Output
0	2
1	6
2	18
3	54
4	162

(d)

Input	Output
0	2
1	6
2	10
3	14
4	18

9. Here are some possible answers.

- Tables E, F, and G are all related because each has a constant difference in the difference table.
- Tables I, J, and K are all related because they include an x^2 term in the rule.

There are many more, such as the fact that some tables are multiples of others, some are the sum of others, some are the reciprocals of others, and so forth.

On Your Own

10.

Side Length	# Dots	Δ
0	0	1
1	1	2
2	3	3
3	6	4
4	10	5
5	15	

11. (a) Each output is equal to the previous output added to the new input, so
$$T(n) = T(n-1) + n$$

Here, n is the number of dots and $T(n)$ is the triangular number.

(b) You can think of the triangular number $T(n)$ as the sum of the integers $1 + 2 + 3 + \cdots + (n-2) + (n-1) + (n)$. (Note that this expression only makes sense for $n \geq 6$. If you use an argument like this to find a closed form function, you will have to check that function for smaller values of n to be sure that it works.) You could reverse the order of the addends without changing the sum.

$$T(n) = 1 + 2 + 3 + \cdots + (n-2)$$
$$+ (n-1) + (n)$$
$$T(n) = (n) + (n-1) + (n-2) + \cdots + 3 + 2 + 1$$

Add these two equations term by term to get

$$2 \cdot T(n) = (n+1) + (n+1) + (n+1)$$
$$+ \cdots + (n+1) + (n+1) + (n+1)$$

Because each of the previous equations had n addends, their sum also has n addends.

$$2 \cdot T(n) = n(n+1)$$
$$T(n) = \frac{n(n+1)}{2}$$

12. (a)

Input: x	Output: $ax + b$	Δ
0	b	a
1	$a + b$	a
2	$2a + b$	a
3	$3a + b$	a
4	$4a + b$	a
5	$5a + b$	

(b)
$$f(x + 1) - f(x) = (a(x + 1) + b) - (ax + b)$$
$$= ax + a + b - ax - b = a$$

13.

Input: x	Output: $ax^2 + bx + c$	Δ
0	c	$a + b$
1	$a + b + c$	$3a + b$
2	$4a + 2b + c$	$5a + b$
3	$9a + 3b + c$	$7a + b$
4	$16a + 4b + c$	$9a + b$
5	$25a + 5b + c$	

$$f(x + 1) - f(x)$$
$$= (a(x + 1)^2 + b(x + 1) + c) - (ax^2 + bx + c)$$
$$= a((x + 1)^2 - x^2) + b(x + 1 - x) + (c - c)$$
$$= a(2x + 1) + b$$
$$= 2ax + a + b$$

14. You are given that $g(1) = 1$. From the definition, $g(2) = g(1) + 3 = 4$. Then $g(3) = g(2) + 5 = 9$. Finally, $g(4) = g(3) + 7 = 16$. The correct answer choice is **D**.

Maintain Your Skills

15. (a) Plug in two points in the equation to find slope. Here we use the first two points:
$$m = \frac{\Delta y}{\Delta x}$$
$$= \frac{-4 - (-7)}{1 - 0}$$
$$= 3$$

(b)
$$m = \frac{\Delta y}{\Delta x}$$
$$= \frac{-11 - (-7)}{1 - 0}$$
$$= -4$$

(c)
$$m = \frac{\Delta y}{\Delta x}$$
$$= \frac{1\frac{1}{2} - 2}{1 - 0}$$
$$= \frac{-\frac{1}{2}}{1}$$
$$= -\frac{1}{2}$$

(d) A linear function has a constant difference for each input. The value of this difference is the slope. Thus, if you subtract any output from the next output, you find the slope. Note that the inputs must be consecutive integers to find the slope directly from the difference in outputs.

1.3 Constant Differences

Check Your Understanding

1.

Table G		
n	$G(n)$	Δ
0	-7	3
1	-4	3
2	-1	3
3	2	3
4	5	

2. Each output is 3 more than the previous output, starting at -7, so:
$$f(n) = \begin{cases} -7 & \text{if } n = 0 \\ f(n - 1) + 3 & \text{if } n > 0 \end{cases}$$

3. The "hockey stick" property of difference tables lets you find any output by adding all the differences up to that output to the initial output of the function. Since this function has a constant difference of 3, the sum of all the differences up to the n-th output will be $3n$. This means you can find the n-th output directly by multiplying the input by 3, then adding -7, so:
$$g(n) = 3n - 7$$

4. (a) • Using the closed form rule:
$$g(n) = 3n - 7$$
$$g(10) = 3(10) - 7$$
$$g(10) = 30 - 7$$
$$g(10) = 23$$

• Using the recursive rule:
$$f(10) = f(9) + 3$$
$$= (f(8) + 3) + 3$$
$$= (f(7) + 3) + 3 + 3$$
$$= \cdots$$
$$= f(0) + 10 \cdot 3$$
$$= -7 + 30$$
$$= 23$$

(b) Using the closed form rule:
$$g(n) = 3n - 7$$
$$g(10.1) = 3(10.1) - 7$$
$$= 30.3 - 7$$
$$= 23.3$$

The recursive rule cannot be used here. The recursive rule starts with $f(0)$, and could be used to find $f(1)$, then $f(2)$, then $f(3)$, and so on. However, it can't be used to find any values of $f(n)$ when n is negative, or when n isn't an integer.

5. The difference when the input n is 0 can be calculated by subtracting $f(0)$ from $f(1)$, or $5 - 11$. $5 - 11$ is equal to -6, not 6. The flaw in Leslie's logic is that some of the differences are -6, not 6.

6. The constant differences will cause the output to decrease by 7 in four steps. The constant difference must be $\frac{-7}{4}$.

n	$p(n)$	Δ
0	3	$-\frac{7}{4}$
1	$\frac{5}{4}$	$-\frac{7}{4}$
2	$-\frac{1}{2}$	$-\frac{7}{4}$
3	$-\frac{9}{4}$	$-\frac{7}{4}$
4	-4	

7. • Each output $p(n)$ is $\frac{7}{4}$ less than the previous output. Subtract this constant difference 10 times to reach the value of $p(10)$:

$$p(10) = p(0) - 10 \cdot \frac{7}{4}$$
$$= 3 - \frac{70}{4}$$
$$= -\frac{29}{2}$$

• Subtract the constant difference 100 times to reach the value of $p(100)$:

$$p(100) = p(0) - 100 \cdot \frac{7}{4}$$
$$= 3 - 175$$
$$= -172$$

• Subtract the constant difference 263 times to reach the value of $p(263)$:

$$p(263) = p(0) - 263 \cdot \frac{7}{4}$$
$$= 3 - \frac{1841}{4}$$
$$= \frac{12}{4} - \frac{1841}{4}$$
$$= -\frac{1829}{4}$$

8. Since 2 yields 11 and 3 yields 14, the constant difference is 3. From input 3 to input 7, you add that 4 times. That is, you add 12 to 14, to obtain 26. The correct answer choice is **D**.

9. (a)

n	$F(n)$	Δ
0	1	0
1	1	1
2	2	1
3	3	2
4	5	3
5	8	5
6	13	

(b) The set of differences is the same as the set of outputs, moved one step down, with 0 for the first difference, $F(1) - F(0)$. More formally, for $n > 1$,

$$F(n) - F(n-1) = F(n-2)$$

The reason you have to specify the first difference, is that you can't use this equation for $n < 2$, because $F(-1)$ is not defined.

(c) Continue the pattern in the table until you reach $F(10)$.

n	$F(n)$	Δ
0	1	0
1	1	1
2	2	1
3	3	2
4	5	3
5	8	5
6	13	8
7	21	13
8	34	21
9	55	34
10	89	

$F(10) = 89$ if the pattern in the table continues.

On Your Own

10.

Table M		
n	$M(n)$	Δ
0	9	6
1	15	6
2	21	6
3	27	6
4	33	

11. The differences are constant, so each output is 6 more than the last. This leads to the recursive definition

$$m(n) = \begin{cases} 9 & \text{if } n = 0 \\ m(n-1) + 6 & \text{if } n > 0 \end{cases}$$

12. The method presented in this lesson should lead directly to $m(n) = 6n + 9$ as a rule that fits the table.

13. • Using the closed-form rule:

$$m(n) = 6n + 9$$
$$m(7) = 6(7) + 9$$
$$= 42 + 9$$
$$= 51$$

• Using the recursive rule:

$$m(7) = m(6) + 6$$
$$= (m(5) + 6) + 6$$
$$= (m(4) + 6) + 6 + 6$$
$$= \cdots$$
$$= m(0) + 7 \cdot 6$$
$$= 9 + 42$$
$$= 51$$

Using the closed-form rule:

$$m(n) = 6n + 9$$
$$m(-7) = 6(-7) + 9$$
$$= -42 + 9$$
$$= -33$$

The recursive rule cannot be used, since its rule starts at $m(0)$ and tells you how to get to the next output. It is not possible to find $m(-1)$ or any output from a negative input.

The two models agree for any nonnegative integer input. However, for negative numbers and nonintegers, the recursive form is undefined.

14. (a)

n	$D(n)$	Δ
0	1	1
1	2	2
2	4	4
3	8	8
4	16	16
5	32	32
6	64	

(b) The differences are the same as the outputs. More formally,

$$D(n) - D(n - 1) = D(n - 1)$$

This can be rewritten as $D(n) = 2 \cdot D(n - 1)$, which helps to explain why the closed form rule $D(n) = 2^n$ fits the table.

(c) Continue the table until $D(10)$ is found.

n	$D(n)$	Δ
0	1	1
1	2	2
2	4	4
3	8	8
4	16	16
5	32	32
6	64	64
7	128	128
8	256	256
9	512	512
10	1024	

If the pattern continues, $D(10)$ will be 1024.

15. A closed form rule shows how to directly calculate the output from the input. So, the output must equal some expression that includes the input. To fit a table that has constant differences, the input must be multiplied by the constant difference in the closed form definition of the function. This makes sense, because when the input is increased by 1, which is the next entry in the table, the output changes by this constant difference. The output of 0 is important, because it shows the value when no constant difference has been added. Thus, at the end of the closed form rule the output of 0 is added.

Examples will vary.

16. One way is to look for tables with linear closed form rules. Another is to take common differences for each table and see what happens. Only tables A, C, E, F, G, H, M, and P have constant differences and can be matched by linear rules.

17. The difference between the two inputs is 8 and the difference between the two outputs is -12. To get the output of 11, you'll add the constant difference eight times to the output of 3. The constant difference is one-eighth of the difference between the two outputs. This is $\frac{1}{8} \cdot -12 = -\frac{3}{2}$.

18. (a) When the input increases by 6, the output increases by 1. Thus, when the input increases by 1, the output must increase by $\frac{1}{6}$. To get the output for an input of 0, subtract $\frac{1}{6}$ nine times from the output of 9:

$$0 - \frac{1}{6}(9) = -\frac{3}{2}$$

So, a closed-form rule for the Inverse of Table M would be

$$\text{Output} = \frac{1}{6} \cdot \text{Input} + -\frac{3}{2}$$

(b)

Inverse of Table M		
Input	Output	Δ
0	$-\frac{3}{2}$	$\frac{1}{6}$
1	$-\frac{4}{3}$	$\frac{1}{6}$
2	$-\frac{7}{6}$	$\frac{1}{6}$
3	-1	$\frac{1}{6}$
4	$-\frac{5}{6}$	

(c) The constant difference in this table, $\frac{1}{6}$, is the reciprocal of the constant difference of 6 found in Table M.

Maintain Your Skills

19. The difference between the output of 2 and the output of 5 is 27, while the difference between the inputs 2 and 5 is 3. Since the output increases by 27 when the input increases by 3, the constant difference is 9. The rest of the numbers in the table can be found using this difference.

Input	Output	Δ
0	-23	9
1	-14	9
2	-5	9
3	4	9
4	13	9
5	22	9
6	31	

20. (a)

$$m = \frac{\Delta y}{\Delta x}$$
$$= \frac{22 - (-5)}{5 - 2}$$
$$= \frac{27}{3} = 9$$

(b)

$$m = \frac{\Delta y}{\Delta x}$$

$$= \frac{22 - (-5)}{10 - 7}$$

$$= \frac{27}{3} = 9$$

(c)

$$m = \frac{\Delta y}{\Delta x}$$

$$= \frac{5 - 2}{22 - (-5)}$$

$$= \frac{3}{27} = \frac{1}{9}$$

1.4 Tables and Slope

Check Your Understanding

1. (a) The constant difference is the change in the output divided by the change in the input.

$$m = \frac{24 - 10}{7 - 3}$$

$$= \frac{14}{4}$$

$$= \frac{7}{2}$$

(b) Trace the constant difference back three steps. The output is 10 when the input is 3. Subtract the constant difference $\frac{7}{2}$ three times from the output:

$$10 - 3 \cdot \frac{7}{2} = \frac{20}{2} - \frac{21}{2} = \frac{-1}{2}$$

(c) Since the constant difference is $\frac{7}{2}$ and the output is $\frac{-1}{2}$ when the input is zero, the information in this lesson leads to the rule

$$\text{Output} = \frac{7}{2} \cdot (\text{Input}) - \frac{1}{2}$$

2. (a)

$$m = \frac{\Delta y}{\Delta x}$$

$$= \frac{24 - 10}{7 - 3}$$

$$= \frac{7}{2}$$

(b) The equation is $\frac{y-10}{x-3} = \frac{7}{2}$. This can be simplified to $2y = 7x - 1$.

3. In order for this table to come from a linear rule, the slope between any two points must be the same. Since the slope between $(0, -12)$ and $(3, 5)$ is $\frac{17}{3}$ and the slope between $(3, 5)$ and $(4, 10)$ is 5, this table could not have come from a linear rule.

4. The slope between any two points on a line is the same, because a line has a constant slope. Since the slope between $(0, -12)$ and $(3, 5)$ is $\frac{17}{3}$ and the slope between $(3, 5)$ and $(4, 10)$ is 5, there is not a line that passes through these three points.

5. Between the inputs 1 and 6 (a difference of 5) the output changes by -25. So the constant difference must be -5. Then, $(2, a)$ is one constant difference below $(1, 4)$, and $a = -1$. Similarly $b = -26$ is one constant difference below $(6, -21)$.

6. The constant difference, or slope, is $\frac{1}{2}$ and the output at 0 is -4. This means that one rule that agrees with this table is

$$F(n) = \frac{1}{2}n - 4$$

7. (a) Add the constant difference once to the output for 6 to get the output for 7:

$$-3 + 5 = 2$$

(b) Subtract the constant difference three times from the output for 6 to get the output for 3:

$$-3 - 3(5) = -18$$

(c) Subtract the constant difference three more times to get the output for 0:

$$-18 - 3(5) = -33$$

And since the constant difference is 5,

$$\text{Output} = 5 \cdot \text{Input} - 33$$

You might also approach this problem by noting that the linear function must be of the form

$$\text{Output} = 5 \cdot \text{Input} - \text{Output for Zero}$$

Use any input-output pair to solve for the output for 0, and then use the linear function to compute any missing values.

8.

Table K

x	$K(x)$	Δ
0	1	1
1	2	3
2	5	5
3	10	7
4	17	

Tables that come from linear rules have a constant difference, so the values in the Δ column in the difference table are all the same if the rule is linear. In Table K, the values in the Δ column are not all the same, so this Table cannot come from a linear rule.

9.

x	$K(x)$	Δ	Δ^2
0	1	1	2
1	2	3	2
2	5	5	2
3	10	7	
4	17		

10. (a)
$$m = \frac{\Delta y}{\Delta x}$$
$$= \frac{-21 - 4}{6 - 1}$$
$$= -5$$

(b) Since the slope of the line is -5, the linear function for which this line is the graph must have a constant difference equal to this slope. To find the output for an input of 2, you can just add the constant difference to the output for 1. This gives you $a = 4 - 5 = -1$.

(c) To find the output for an input of 7, you can just add the constant difference to the output for 6. This gives you $b = -21 - 5 = -26$.

11. Yes, all the outputs are the same, so all the differences are 0.

12. (a)

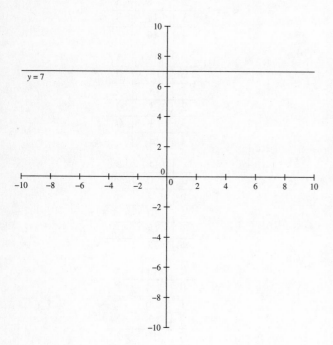

(b)
$$m = \frac{\Delta y}{\Delta x}$$
$$= \frac{0}{-5}$$
$$= 0$$

(c) Examine the graph of this line. Since for every value of x the value of y is always 7, the equation is

$$y = 7$$

13. (a)

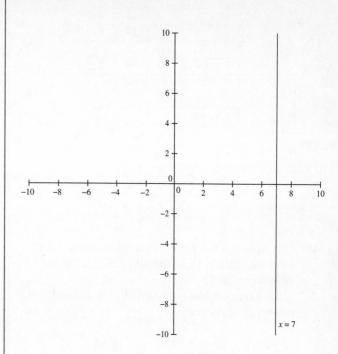

(b) Answers may vary. Slope is defined as the change in the value of y (Δy) divided by the change in the value of x (Δx). In this example, this fraction is $\frac{5}{0}$. There is no value for such a fraction—division by zero is undefined. Therefore, you can say there is "no slope," or that the slope is undefined.

(c) Since the value of x is always 7, no matter what value y takes on, an equation for this line is

$$x = 7$$

14.

Table O		
n	$O(n)$	Δ
0	0	5
1	5	15
2	20	25
3	45	35
4	80	

Table O cannot come from a linear rule because the differences are not constant.

15. There is a constant difference of 4 and $P(0) = 1$, so a linear rule is

$$P(b) = 4b + 1$$

16. (a) The outputs in Table Q are the sum of the outputs in Tables O and P.

(b) The differences in Table Q are the sum of the differences in Tables O and P.

17.

w	$R(w)$	Δ	Δ^2	Δ^3
0	0	1	6	**6**
1	1	**7**	**12**	6
2	8	19	**18**	6
3	27	**37**	24	6
4	64	61	30	**6**
5	125	91	**36**	
6	216	**127**		
7	343			

18. (a)

x	$d(x)$	Δ
0	3	2
1	5	2
2	7	2
3	9	

(b) One answer is that the constant difference doesn't continue. $d(4) = 35$, so the next difference in the table would be 26.

$d(x)$ acts just like $x \mapsto 2x + 3$ on 0, 1, 2 and 3, but nowhere else. In fact,

$$d(x) - (2x + 3) = x^4 - 6x^3 + 11x^2 - 6x$$
$$= x(x^3 - 6x^2 + 11x - 6)$$
$$= x(x - 1)(x - 2)(x - 3)$$

So, $d(x) - (2x + 3)$ will be 0 at 0, 1, 2, and 3, and nowhere else.

19. The slope is the difference of the outputs (21) divided by the difference of the inputs (9). Thus it is $\frac{21}{9} = \frac{7}{3}$. The correct answer choice is **C**.

Maintain Your Skills

20. (a)

x	$a(x)$	Δ
0	0	**1**
1	1	**3**
2	4	**5**
3	9	**7**
4	16	

(b)

x	$b(x)$	Δ
0	0	**2**
1	2	**6**
2	8	**10**
3	18	**14**
4	32	

(c)

x	$c(x)$	Δ
0	0	**5**
1	5	**15**
2	20	**25**
3	45	**35**
4	80	

(d)

x	$d(x)$	Δ
0	0	**−10**
1	−10	**−30**
2	−40	**−50**
3	−90	**−70**
4	−160	

(e)(f) The function $e(x) = x^2$ has all positive odd integers in its difference column, including 25 if you work enough rows. As a result, $e(x) = 2x^2$ has 50 in its difference column because $2 \cdot 25 = 50$. Thus, with the function $e(x) = kx^2$, 50 will be in the difference column if $\frac{50}{k}$ is a positive odd integer.

Identify all odd factors of 50: 1, 5 and 25.

$1 \cdot 50 = 50$, so $e(x) = 50x^2$ also has 50 in its difference column.

$5 \cdot 10 = 50$, so $e(x) = 10x^2$ also has 50 in its difference column.

21. (a)

x	$f(x)$	Δ
0	2	3
1	5	3
2	8	3
3	11	3
4	14	

(b)

x	$g(x)$	Δ
0	3	0
1	3	0
2	3	0
3	3	0
4	3	

(c)

x	$h(x)$	Δ
0	0	4
1	4	6
2	10	8
3	18	10
4	28	

(d)

x	$k(x)$	Δ
0	4	2
1	6	2
2	8	2
3	10	2
4	12	

(e)

x	$r(x)$	Δ
0	0	1
1	1	7
2	8	19
3	27	37
4	64	

(f)

x	$s(x)$	Δ
0	1	6
1	7	12
2	19	18
3	37	24
4	61	

Check Your Understanding

1.

n	$y(n)$	Δ	Δ^2
0	-2	8	**10**
1	6	18	**10**
2	24	28	**10**
3	52	38	
4	90		

Since the second differences are constant, this table could have come from a quadratic rule. Continue the table to find the matching quadratic

n	$y(n) - 5n^2$	Δ
0	-2	3
1	1	3
2	4	3
3	7	3
4	10	

Now, since $y(n) - 5n^2$ has a constant difference of 3, you can match it to the linear function $y(n) - 5n^2 = 3n - 2$. This tells you that $y(n) = 5n^2 + 3n - 2$, which matches the original table.

2. Start by calculating the constant second differences:

n	$y(n)$	Δ	Δ^2
0	10	12	-6
1	22	6	-6
2	28	0	-6
3	28	-6	
4	22		

The constant second difference is -6, so if the function is defined by $y(x) = an^2 + bn + c$, the value of a is equal to -6 divided by 2, or -3.
Next, subtract $-3n^2$ from the values of $y(n)$. This cancels out the an^2 term, giving a table that can be used to calculate the values of b and c:

Input: n	Output: $y(n)$	Output: $-3n^2$	$y(n) - (-3n^2)$
0	10	0	**10**
1	22	-3	**25**
2	28	-12	**40**
3	28	-27	**55**
4	22	-48	**70**

A rule for the $y(n) - (-3n^2)$ column is $15n + 10$. Then b is 15 (the constant difference for the $y(n) - (-3n^2)$ column) and c is 10 (the first term in the $y(n) - (-3n^2)$ column). A quadratic function that fits this table is

$$y(n) = -3n^2 + 15n + 10$$

3.

w	$R(w)$	Δ	Δ^2	Δ^3
0	0	1	6	**6**
1	1	**7**	**12**	**6**
2	8	19	**18**	**6**
3	27	**37**	24	6
4	64	61	30	**6**
5	125	91	**36**	
6	216	**127**		
7	343			

4.

x	$m(x)$	Δ	Δ^2	Δ^3
0	4	-3	**34**	**30**
1	1	**31**	**64**	**30**
2	32	**95**	**94**	**30**
3	127	**189**	**124**	**30**
4	316	**313**	**154**	**30**
5	629	**467**	**184**	
6	1096	**651**		
7	1747			

5. (a) Cubic functions appear to yield constant third differences (Δ^3). Testing other cubics confirms this.
(b) This constant third difference is equal to the leading coefficient multiplied by 6.

6. Try it with Exercise 4: To get the Δ of $f(x)$, you need to compute $f(x + 1) - f(x)$. But

$$f(x + 1) - f(x)$$
$$= (5(x + 1)^3 + 2(x + 1)^2 - 10(x + 1) + 4)$$
$$\quad - (5x^3 + 2x^2 - 10x + 4)$$
$$= 5((x + 1)^3 - x^3) + 2((x + 1)^2 - x^2)$$
$$\quad - 10((x + 1) - x) + 4(1 - 1)$$
$$= 5(3x^2 + 3x + 1) + 2(2x + 1) - 10(1) + 4(0)$$

and this is Sasha's method.

7.

x	$f(x)$	Δ	Δ^2	Δ^3
0	d	$a + b + c$	$6a + 2b$	$6a$
1	$a + b + c + d$	$7a + 3b + c$	$12a + 2b$	$6a$
2	$8a + 4b + 2c + d$	$19a + 5b + c$	$18a + 2b$	$6a$
3	$27a + 9b + 3c + d$	$37a + 7b + c$	$24a + 2b$	$6a$
4	$64a + 16b + 4c + d$	$61a + 9b + c$	$30a + 2b$	
5	$125a + 25b + 5c + d$	$91a + 11b + c$		
6	$216a + 36b + 6c + d$			

8. (a) Anything multiplied by 0 is equal to 0, so any value of x that makes the factors $(x - 3)$, $(x - 5)$ or $(x - 6)$ equal to 0 will satisfy the equation. If $x = 3$ the factor $(x - 3)$ turns into $(3 - 3)$, which is equal to 0. The whole equation looks like

$$(3 - 3)(3 - 5)(3 - 6) = 0$$
$$(0)(-2)(-3) = 0$$
$$0 = 0$$

So $x = 3$ satisfies this equation. Similarly, when $x = 5$, the factor $(x - 5)$ is equal to 0, and when $x = 6$, the factor $(x - 6)$ is equal to 0. $x = 5$ and $x = 6$ also satisfy this equation.

(b) Multiply out the factors. First multiply two together and then multiply the result by the third factor:

$$(x-3)(x-5)(x-6)$$
$$= (x^2 - 5x - 3x + 15)(x-6)$$
$$= (x^2 - 8x + 15)(x-6)$$
$$= x^3 - 8x^2 + 15x - 6x^2 + 48x - 90$$
$$= x^3 - 14x^2 + 63x - 90$$

9.

x	$v(x)$	Δ	Δ^2	Δ^3
0	-90	50	-22	6
1	-40	28	-16	6
2	-12	12	-10	6
3	0	2	-4	6
4	2	-2	2	6
5	0	0	8	
6	0	8		
7	8			

10. Start by calculating the constant second differences. This solution uses x for the input and y for the output:

x	y	Δ	Δ^2
0	7	-13	20
1	-6	7	20
2	1	27	20
3	28	47	
4	75		

The constant second difference is 20, so if the function is $f(x) = ax^2 + bx + c$, the value of a is equal to 20 divided by 2, or 10.

Next, subtract the values of $10x^2$ from the values of y (the output). This cancels out the ax^2 term and gives a table that can be used to find b and c:

x	y	$10x^2$	$y - 10x^2$
0	7	0	7
1	-6	10	-16
2	1	40	-39
3	28	90	-62
4	75	160	-85

A rule for the $y - 10x^2$ column is $-23x + 7$. The value of b is -23 and the value of c is 7. A quadratic function that fits this table is

$$y = 10x^2 - 23x + 7$$

11. (a)

n	$F(n)$	Δ	Δ^2	Δ^3
0	1	0	1	-1
1	1	1	0	1
2	2	1	1	0
3	3	2	1	1
4	5	3	2	
5	8	5		
6	13			

Since the third differences are not constant, this table could not have come from a cubic function.

(b) The Δ value for any n is the same as the $F(n)$ value for the previous n. Similarly, the Δ^2 value for any n is the same as the Δ value of the previous n and the $F(n)$ value of $n - 2$. This diagonal down-and-right pattern continues forever.

12. Begin by trying to find a constant difference. This solution uses x for the input and y for the output.

x	y	Δ	Δ^2	Δ^3
0	-3	-2	2	**12**
1	-5	0	14	**12**
2	-5	14	26	**12**
3	9	40	38	
4	49	78		
5	127			

The table has a constant third difference of 12, so a cubic function can generate this table. In a cubic function $ax^3 + bx^2 + cx + d$, the value of a is equal to the constant difference divided by 6. So, in this table, the value of a is 2.

Subtract the outputs of $2x^3$ from the outputs of the table. This effectively "cancels out" the ax^3 term and gives a table of values from a quadratic function. From this table, continue by using Tony's method to find the values of b, c and d.

x	y	$2x^3$	$y - 2x^3$
0	-3	0	-3
1	-5	2	-7
2	-5	16	-21
3	9	54	-45
4	49	128	-79
5	127	250	-123

The column $y - 2x^3$ can be matched by a quadratic rule. The input is x and the output is $bx^2 + cx + d$ is the output. Find the constant second difference:

x	$bx^2 + cx + d$	Δ	Δ^2
0	-3	-4	-10
1	-7	-14	
2	-21		

The constant second difference is -10, so if the rule is $y = bx^2 + cx + d$, the value of b is equal to -10 divided by 2, or -5.

Then, subtract the values of $-5x^2$ from the values of $bx^2 + cx + d$ (the output). This cancels out the $-5x^2$ term and gives a table that can be used to find c and d. The next table is a linear function, so two points are enough:

x	$-5x^2 + cx + d$	$-5x^2$	$-5x^2 + cx + d - (-5x^2)$
0	-3	0	-3
1	-7	-5	-2

A rule for the $5x^2 + cx + d - (-5x^2)$ column is $x - 3$. The value of c is 1 and the value of d is -3.

The polynomial that fits the original table is

$$\text{Output} = 2(\text{Input})^3 - 5(\text{Input})^2 + \text{Input} - 3$$

13.

n	$y(n)$	Δ	Δ^2
0	−7	2	**6**
1	−5	8	**12**
2	3	20	**18**
3	23	38	
4	61		

Since the second differences are not constant, this table cannot have come from a quadratic rule.

14.

Input: a	Output: b	Δ
0	25	−14
1	11	−14
2	−3	−14
3	−17	−14
4	−31	

Since the first difference is constant, this table comes from a linear rule. The constant difference is −14 and the output for 0 is 25, so a rule that agrees with this table is:

$$b = -14a + 25$$

15.

n	$c(n)$	Δ	Δ^2
0	−8	8	−4
1	0	4	−4
2	4	0	−4
3	4	−4	
4	0		

The second difference is constant, so this table comes from a quadratic rule. Since the constant second difference is −4, the value of a in the rule $an^2 + bn + c$ is −2. Subtract $-2n^2$ from $c(n)$ to get a table of a linear rule that can be used to find b and c. Two points are enough for the next table:

n	$c(n)$	$-2n^2$	$c(n) - -2^2$
0	−8	0	−8
1	0	−2	2

The constant difference is 10 and the output for 0 is −8, so the linear rule is $10n - 8$. Then the rule that fits the original table is

$$c(n) = -2n^2 + 10n - 8$$

16. (a) If this table comes from a cubic function, the third differences will be constant. Here is a difference table:

n	$D(n)$	Δ	Δ^2	Δ^3
0	1	1	1	**1**
1	2	2	2	**2**
2	4	4	4	**4**
3	8	8	8	**8**
4	16	16	16	
5	32	32		
6	64			

Since the third differences are not constant, this table does not come from a cubic function.

(b) Each time, the numbers in the difference column are identical to the numbers in the previous column. This will continue for as many columns as you make.

17.

Input: x	Output: y	Δ	Δ^2	Δ^3
0	1	0	3	−3
1	1	3	0	2
2	4	3	2	
3	7	5		
4	12			

The first differences are not constant, so this table cannot come from a linear rule. The second differences are not constant, so this table cannot come from a quadratic rule. And, the third differences are not constant, so this table cannot come from a cubic rule.

18. Answers will vary. One way to do this is to draw the graphs and the data points together. Another is to decide how far away the data points are from the curves. Because you've used tables so much, you might make a table to compare the four alternatives.

x	y	$2x - 5$	$2.8x - 0.6$	$x^2 - x + 1$	$x^3 - 3x^2 + 2x + 1$
0	1	−5	−0.6	1	1
1	1	−3	2.2	1	1
2	4	−1	5	3	1
3	7	1	7.8	7	7
4	12	3	10.6	13	25

Rule 3 seems to be the best fit.

19. Follow the process of taking differences until a constant appears, which in this case means you have to find all the differences you can—up to the fourth difference. Since you haven't yet done a problem with a fourth difference, you'll also need to figure out what the constant difference tells you about the coefficient of the term raised to the fourth power in the polynomial. You can do this by making difference tables for quartic polynomials that you know and looking for a relationship between the constant difference you get and the known coefficient, or you can make a difference table for the general quartic polynomial—$q(x) = ax^4 + bx^3 + cx^2 + dx + e$. Then you can subtract the term ax^4 from the outputs and you'll have a cubic polynomial, which you know how to deal with.

$$y = \frac{5}{24}x^4 - \frac{7}{4}x^3 + \frac{127}{24}x^2 - \frac{15}{4}x + 1$$

20. The constant third differences of a cubic will be the leading coefficient times 6. Since that coefficient is 1, the correct answer choice is **C**.

Maintain Your Skills

21. (a)

x	$f(x)$
0	14
1	6
2	0
3	−4
4	−6
5	−6

(b)

x	g(x)
0	78
1	60
2	44
3	30
4	18
5	8

(c)

x	h(x)
0	0
1	−8
2	−14
3	−18
4	−20
5	−20

(d)

x	j(x)
0	9
1	0
2	−3
3	0
4	9
5	24

(e) When x is set to 5, $k(x)$ must be equal to 0. The rule for $k(x)$ must then include $(x - 5)$ as a factor, because $(x - 5)$ is equal to 0 when $x = 5$, and anything multiplied by 0 is equal to 0. The same logic applies when x is 6, so one possible rule for $k(x)$ is:

$$k(x) = (x - 5)(x - 6)$$

The table for this rule would be

x	k(x)
0	30
1	20
2	12
3	6
4	2
5	0

Many other rules are possible!

(f) Because of the same logic applied to part (e), the rule for $m(x)$ must have x, $(x - 1)$, and $(x - 2)$ as factors. The simplest rule for these three criteria would be $m(x) = x(x - 1)(x - 2)$. However, for this rule, $m(3) = 6$. To get the output you want, multiply your rule by 4 to get $m(x) = 4x(x - 1)(x - 2)$. Now $m(3) = 24$, and all the other outputs you want are still zero. This is only one of many possible solutions. Here is its input-output table:

x	m(x)
0	0
1	0
2	0
3	24
4	96
5	240

22. (a)

x	f(x)
0	0
1	3
2	6
3	9
4	12

(b)

x	g(x)
0	0
1	4
2	8
3	12
4	16

(c)

x	h(x)
0	0
1	3
2	8
3	15
4	24

(d)

x	j(x)
0	0
1	3
2	6
3	15
4	36

(e) You can create a function that matches $f(x)$ for the inputs 0 through 4, but not for other inputs, by adding on a term for $k(x)$ that will equal zero at the inputs whose outputs you want to match, but won't be zero for other inputs. For example, $x(x - 1)(x - 2)$ is zero when $x = 0$, 1, or 2, so the table for $j(x) = 2x + x(x - 1)(x - 2)$ was identical to the table for $f(x)$ when $x = 0$, 1, or 2.

Extending the product you add to the function will allow it to match more entries in the table for $f(x)$. So a function $k(x)$ that matches all the entries for $f(x)$ from 0 through 4 could be

$$k(x) = 3x + x(x - 1)(x - 2)(x - 3)(x - 4)$$

The input-output table for this function would be identical to that for $f(x)$, but $f(5) = 15$ and $k(5) = 135$. There are other possibilities for $k(x)$.

1A   MATHEMATICAL REFLECTIONS

1. Create a difference table for the function.

Input: n	Output: B(n)	Δ
0	1	2
1	3	4
2	7	6
3	13	8
4	21	

The difference you add to an output to get the n-th output is equal to twice the value of n. For example, to get $B(3)$, you add $2 \cdot 3$ to $B(2)$. This leads to a recursive definition for $g(n)$.

$$g(n) = \begin{cases} 1 & \text{if } n = 0 \\ g(n-1) + 2n & \text{if } n > 0 \end{cases}$$

2. Extend the difference table to show the second difference.

Input: n	Output: $B(n)$	Δ	Δ^2
0	1	2	2
1	3	4	2
2	7	6	2
3	13	8	
4	21		

Because the second difference is constant, you know that a quadratic rule will match this table. The coefficient of the n^2 term in the quadratic rule will be half the constant difference from the table or 1. Add a new column to your table showing $B(n) - n^2$. You will be able to match this new column with a linear rule.

Input: n	Output: $B(n)$	Δ	Δ^2	$B(n) - n^2$	Δ
0	1	2	2	1	1
1	3	4	2	2	1
2	7	6	2	3	1
3	13	8		4	1
4	21			5	

Look at the $B(n) - n^2$ column. Its output for 0 is 1 and it has a constant difference of 1. That means this column matches the linear rule $n + 1$. Since $B(n) - n^2 = n + 1$, you know that a closed-form rule that matches the table is $B(n) = n^2 + n + 1$.

3. The slope between any two points on a line is constant. That means the slope between any point (x, y) on the line and $(2, 5)$ will be equal to the slope between $(2, 5)$ and $(-4, 8)$. This relationship gives an equation for the line containing these two points.

$$\frac{y - 5}{x - 2} = \frac{8 - 5}{-4 - 2}$$

$$\frac{y - 5}{x - 2} = \frac{3}{-6}$$

$$\frac{y - 5}{x - 2} = \frac{-1}{2}$$

$$y - 5 = \frac{-1}{2}(x - 2)$$

$$y - 5 = \frac{-1}{2}x + 1$$

$$\frac{1}{2}x + y = 6$$

$$x + 2y = 12$$

4. Find the difference between an output and the previous output. If that difference is constant for every pair of sequential outputs, the table can be matched by a linear rule $a(\text{Input}) + b$, where a is the constant difference and b is the output for the input 0.

5. If the first difference is constant, the function will be linear. If the second difference is constant, the function will be quadratic. If the third difference is constant, the function will be cubic.

6. Create a difference table, and compute differences until you find a constant difference.

Input	Output	Δ	Δ^2
0	1	4	2
1	5	6	2
2	11	8	2
3	19	10	2
4	29	12	
5	41		

Since the second difference is constant, this table will be matched by a quadratic rule. Half the constant difference, or 1, is the coefficient of the leading term.

Extend the table by including a column for Output $-$ (Input)^2 and its differences.

Input	Output	Output $-$ (Input)^2	Δ
0	1	1	3
1	5	4	3
2	11	7	3
3	19	10	3
4	29	13	3
5	41	16	

The Output $-$ (Input)^2 column has a constant first difference, so it can be matched by a linear rule. Its output for input 0 is 1 and the constant difference is 3, so the rule is $3(\text{Input}) + 1$, and the quadratic rule for the original table is Output $=$ (Input)$^2 + 3(\text{Input}) + 1$.

INVESTIGATION 1B   FITTING AND DATA

1.6   Getting Started

For You to Explore

1. Results will vary, but should be consistent within each table.
2. It is extremely unlikely, but possible, for the tables to agree with a linear function. Tables generated by linear rules have constant differences. Most tables that come from this experiment could *not* have come from a linear rule, since their Δ values vary as the results of each number cube roll after the first.
3. One way to come up with a reasonable estimate is to take your total for 20 rolls, and multiply it by 5. Another way is to take 5 groups' totals from 20 rolls and add them up. Another way is to use the class mean and multiply it by 100. In any case, your estimate will probably be between 300 and 400, and (c) is the only answer in this range.

In fact, the first answer (98) is impossible! The lowest possible total after 100 rolls is 100, and this is for the extremely unlikely situation where a 1 is rolled 100 times in a row.

4. Answers will vary slightly, but all the graphs should be nearly linear. Some of the things the graph shows is that the total increases as the number of rolls increases, but the amount of the increase is variable. The average increase in the total with each roll of the number cube (the approximate slope of the approximate line) will be about 3.5 but will vary from group to group.

5. Answers will vary, but the best line for most data sets should be $T = 3.5r$. The other possible answers here are $T = 2.5r$ and $T = 4.5r$, but those correspond to especially lucky runs of low or high numbers. The line $T = r + 30$ is too high for low values of r and too low for high values of r. The worst line is $T + 3r = 60$, which has a negative slope. It decreases as the number of rolls grows, while the data does the opposite.

6. (a) You must hold your finger an equal distance from each of the two weights if they are to balance. The mark for 5.5 inches is 2.5 inches from both 3 and 8.
   (b) The ruler's balance point is an equal distance from x and from y. This point will be located at the marking equal to the average of x and y, which is

   $$\frac{x + y}{2}$$

   (c) The average of 1, 3, and 8 will be the balance point. $\frac{1+3+8}{3}$ is equal to 4, so the balance point is at the 4 inch mark.

On Your Own

7. You might graph the data for surrounding years and look for trends. You might even find the equation of a line that seems to be a good fit for the data you have and then use the equation of that line to figure out the y-coordinate when x is equal to the missing year.

8. (a) $\frac{85+82+91}{3} = 86$
   (b) As in Exercise 6, the balance point will be at the mark for the average of the three locations of the identical weights. $\frac{85 \text{ cm}+82 \text{ cm}+91 \text{ cm}}{3} = 86 \text{ cm}$

9. (a) The trend shows a migration of the U.S. population westward. Some reasons include the addition of states to the U.S. from the original 13, and the increasing population in Western states such as California, Arizona, and Nevada.
   (b) This function is the mean.

10. (a) Calculating the slope between any two of the five points always gives the same answer, 3. By Theorem 1.1 on page 19, a single line will pass through all the points.
    (b) The slope between any two of the points in the data is 3, and the slope between any point (x, y) on the line and $(0, 4)$, for example, must also be 3.

$$\frac{y - 4}{x - 0} = 3$$
$$y - 4 = 3x$$
$$y = 3x + 4$$

(c) Calculate the mean of the inputs and the mean of the outputs.

$$\frac{0 + 1 + 2 + 5 + 8}{5} = \frac{16}{5} = 3.2$$
$$\frac{4 + 7 + 10 + 19 + 28}{5} = \frac{68}{5} = 13.6$$

The balance point is $(3.2, 13.6)$.

(d) Here is a plot of the five points and the balance point:

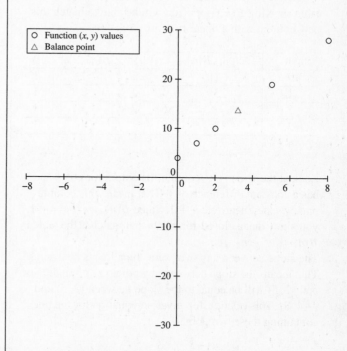

The balance point is on the same line as the original five points because $13.6 = 3 \cdot 3.2 + 4$.

11. (a) See the plot below. Also, $m((3, 2), (6, 3)) = \frac{1}{3}$ but $m(6, 3), (8, 5)) = 1$, and three points are collinear if and only if the slope between any two of them is the same as the slope between any other two of them.
    (b) Answers may vary. One way to proceed is to pick two points as samples and find the slope connecting them. Selecting $(6, 3)$ and $(12, 6)$ gives a slope of $\frac{1}{2}$. Other answers are possible.
    (c)
    $$x : \frac{3 + 6 + 8 + 11 + 12}{5} = 8$$
    $$y : \frac{2 + 3 + 5 + 5 + 6}{5} = 4.2$$

The balance point is $(8, 4.2)$.

(d) Here is the graph of the data and the balance point:

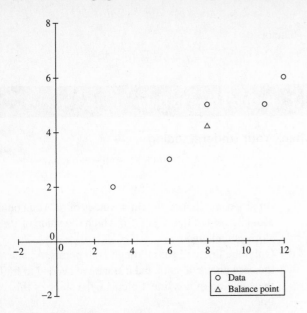

The balance point lies along the trend in the data, so you'd want it to lie on the line of best fit.

12. You know that the value of b that will result in the minimum value of the function will be halfway between its two roots (assuming the function has roots). And you know that to find the roots of a quadratic, you can use the quadratic formula. However, a close look at the quadratic formula will tell you how to find the point halfway between the two roots without actually computing the roots.

The values of p that solve the equation $ap^2 + bp + c = 0$ are:

$$p = \frac{-b \pm \sqrt{b^2 - 4ac}}{2a}$$

Because of the "plus or minus square root" term, the value of p that is midway between the two roots will always be $\frac{-b}{2a}$.

(a) For the function $p \mapsto 158.86 - 47.2\,p + 4\,p^2$ the value $p = \frac{47.2}{8} = 5.9$ will minimize the function.

(b) For the function $p \mapsto 52.26 - 27.2\,p + 4\,p^2$ the value $p = \frac{27.2}{8} = 3.4$ will minimize the function.

(c) For the function $p \mapsto 5.66 - 7.2\,p + 4\,p^2$ the value $p = \frac{7.2}{8} = 0.9$ will minimize the function.

(d) For the function $p \mapsto 19.06 + 12.8\,p + 4\,p^2$ the value $p = \frac{-12.8}{8} = -1.6$ will minimize the function.

Maintain Your Skills

13.

$$\bar{x} = \frac{0 + 1 + 2 + 5 + 8}{5} = 3.2$$

$$\bar{y} = \frac{4 + 7 + 10 + 19 + 28}{5} = 13.6$$

$x - \bar{x}$	$y - \bar{y}$
−3.2	−9.6
−2.2	−6.6
−1.2	−3.6
1.8	5.4
4.8	14.4

$$\overline{x - \bar{x}} = \frac{-3.2 + -2.2 + -1.2 + 1.8 + 4.8}{5} = 0$$

$$\overline{y - \bar{y}} = \frac{-9.6 + -6.6 - 3.6 + 5.4 + 14.4}{5} = 0$$

The balance point for the new table is $(0, 0)$. You might conjecture that this will always be the balance point for a table computed in this way.

One way to justify this conjecture is to look at the calculations in this way.

$$\overline{x - \bar{x}} = \frac{x_1 - \bar{x} + x_2 - \bar{x} + \cdots + x_n - \bar{x}}{n}$$

$$\overline{x - \bar{x}} = \frac{(x_1 + x_2 + \cdots + x_n) - n\bar{x}}{n}$$

$$\overline{x - \bar{x}} = \frac{x_1 + x_2 + \cdots + x_n}{n} - \frac{n\bar{x}}{n}$$

$$\overline{x - \bar{x}} = \bar{x} - \bar{x}$$

$$\overline{x - \bar{x}} = 0$$

(You could do a similar calculation for $\overline{y - \bar{y}}$.) This shows that the balance point for any table of $x - \bar{x}$ and $y - \bar{y}$ values, where $\bar{x}$ and $\bar{y}$ are the means of the x and y coordinates, respectively, will be $(0, 0)$.

14.

$$\bar{x} = \frac{3 + 6 + 8 + 11 + 12}{5} = 8$$

$$\bar{y} = \frac{2 + 3 + 5 + 5 + 6}{5} = 4.2$$

$x - \bar{x}$	$y - \bar{y}$
−5	−2.2
−2	−1.2
0	0.8
3	0.8
4	1.8

$$\overline{x - \bar{x}} = \frac{-5 + -2 + 0 + 3 + 4}{5} = 0$$

$$\overline{y - \bar{y}} = \frac{-2.2 + -1.2 + 0.8 + 0.8 + 1.8}{5} = 0$$

The balance point for the new table is $(0, 0)$. See the solution for Exercise 13 for more about conjectures you may have and how to justify them.

15.

$$\bar{x} = \frac{1900 + 1904 + 1908 + 1912 + 1920 + 1924 + 1928}{7}$$

$$\approx 1913.7$$

$$\bar{y} = \frac{246.2 + 245.4 + 243.4 + 236.8 + 241.8 + 233.6 + 233.2}{7}$$

$$\approx 240.057$$

$x - \bar{x}$	$y - \bar{y}$
−13.7	6.143
−9.7	5.343
−5.7	3.343
−1.7	−3.257
6.3	1.743
10.3	−6.457
14.3	−6.857

$$\overline{x - \bar{x}}$$
$$= \frac{-13.7 + -9.7 + -5.7 + -1.7 + 6.3 + 10.3 + 14.3}{7} \approx 0$$

$$\overline{y - \bar{y}}$$
$$= \frac{6.143 + 5.343 + 4.343 + -3.257 + 1.743 + -6.457 + -6.857}{7} \approx 0$$

The balance point for the new table is approximately $(0, 0)$. See the solution for Exercise 13 for more about conjectures you may have and how to justify them.

16.

$$\bar{x} = \frac{73 + 22 + 16 + 60 + 6 + 73 + 10 + 6 + 8 + 33}{10} = 30.7$$

$$\bar{y} = \frac{6 + 66 + 54 + 18 + 9 + 13 + 82 + 85 + 73 + 57}{10} = 46.3$$

$x - \bar{x}$	$y - \bar{y}$
42.3	−40.3
−8.7	19.7
−14.7	7.7
29.3	−28.3
−24.7	−37.3
42.3	−33.3
−20.7	35.7
−24.7	38.7
−22.7	26.7
2.3	10.7

$$\overline{x - \bar{x}}$$
$$= \frac{42.3 + -8.7 + -14.7 + 29.3 + -24.7 + 42.3 + -20.7 + -24.7 + -22.7 + 2.3}{10}$$
$$= 0$$

$$\overline{y - \bar{y}}$$
$$= \frac{-40.3 + 19.7 + 7.7 + -28.3 + -37.3 + -33.3 + 35.7 + 38.7 + 26.7 + 10.7}{10}$$
$$= 0$$

The balance point for the new table is $(0, 0)$. See the solution for Exercise 13 for more about conjectures you may have and how to justify them.

17.

$$(a - b)^2 = 2(a^2 + b^2) - (a + b)^2$$

Multiply expressions on the right hand side of the equation.

$$(a - b)^2 = 2a^2 + 2b^2 - (a^2 + 2ab + b^2)$$

Simplify to remove parentheses.

$$(a - b)^2 = 2a^2 + 2b^2 - a^2 - 2ab - b^2$$

Combine like terms.

$$(a - b)^2 = a^2 - 2ab + b^2$$

Factor.

$$(a - b)^2 = (a - b)^2$$

1.7 Fitting Lines to Data

Check Your Understanding

1. (a) Any line passing through $(3, 6)$ has the form

$$y - 6 = m(x - 3)$$

for slope m. Choose any three values of m. You could also choose the line $x = 3$ for which the value of its slope is undefined.

(b) Only one line will pass through both points. As was the case above, a point and a slope are needed to find the equation of this line. Calculate the slope of this line:

$$m = \frac{\Delta y}{\Delta x}$$
$$= \frac{-1 - 6}{8 - 3}$$
$$= -\frac{7}{5}$$

The equation of the line with slope $-\frac{7}{5}$ that passes through $(3, 6)$ is

$$y - 6 = -\frac{7}{5}(x - 3)$$

You might also write this equation as

$$y = \frac{-7}{5}x + \frac{51}{5}$$

or

$$7x + 5y = 51$$

2. (a)

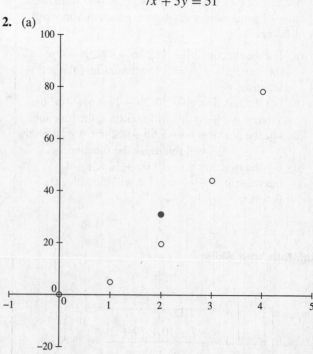

(b)
$$\frac{0+1+2+3+4}{5}=2$$

and

$$\frac{0+4.9+19.6+44.1+78.4}{5}=29.4$$

The balance point is (2, 29.4).

(c) The data points appear to lie on a curve rather than a line, so a fitting line would not be appropriate. You can also see that the balance point is not close to the other data points. It is not possible to fit a line to this data set while still representing it well.

3. (a)

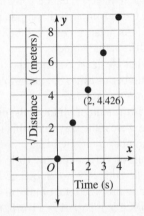

(b)
$$\frac{0+1+2+3+4}{5}=2$$
$$\frac{0+2.21+4.43+6.64+8.85}{5}=4.426$$

The balance point is (2, 4.426).

(c) A fitting line is reasonable for this data. Unlike the data in Exercise 2, this data seems to produce an approximate straight line. The balance point seems to lie on this line. Using a line to represent this data is appropriate.

4.

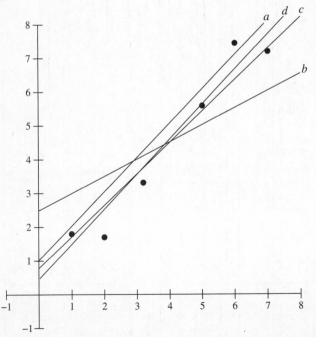

Answers will vary, but only (c) $y = 0.9x + 0.9$ and (d) $y = x + 0.5$ follow the trend well. Line (a) $y = x + 1$ is above most data points, and line (d) $y = 0.5x + 2.5$ is not steep enough to follow the trend.

5. (a) The "population center" for these three cities can be found by finding the center of the set of data consisting of their locations. $\frac{300+700+1000}{3} = 666\frac{2}{3}$ and $\frac{20+100+-400}{3} = -93\frac{1}{3}$, so the population center is $(666\frac{2}{3}, -93\frac{1}{3})$.

(b) If the cities do not have equal populations, then the population center should be weighted by population. If you use the population of city C as your base, then point C is weighted 1, point A, with twice as many people as C is weighted 2, and point B, with four times as many people as C is weighted 4. Multiply each coordinate by its weight and then divide by the sum of the weights to find the weighted average.

$$\frac{2 \cdot 300 + 4 \cdot 700 + 1 \cdot 1000}{7} = 628\frac{4}{7}$$

$$\frac{2 \cdot 20 + 4 \cdot 100 + 1 \cdot -400}{7} = 5\frac{5}{7}$$

So the population center is $(628\frac{4}{7}, 5\frac{5}{7})$.

6. The balance point for the times from 1900–1960 is (1929.2, 233.2). You can make any reasonable choice for the slope based on how you see the data, but one possible choice is $\frac{-1}{2}$. This slope would give the equation $t = -\frac{1}{2}(y - 1929.2) + 233.2$ for $y < 1960$.

The balance point for the times from 1960–2000 is (1980, 216.3). The assumption that the times are "static" would suggest slope 0, and the equation $t = 216.3$. You could also assume that this trend continues into the future.

These two equations lead to the following results.

(a) 1916: 239.8, 1940: 227.8, 1944: 225.8
(b) 2624: 216.3

On Your Own

7. (a) The predicted values in the table are points on the line $y = x + 1$. Since none of the predicted values are equal to the actual values, the line $y = x + 1$ does not pass through any of the six data points. Another way to find this answer is by using the error column. If the error is 0 then the line passes through the point, but none of the errors are 0.

(b) When the **Error** column is negative, the actual value is less than the predicted value. These points are below the line $y = x + 1$.

(c) The predicted values are too high in almost every case. This is probably a poor fit, since almost all the errors are on one side.

8. (a)

Data vs. Line Fit for Line (b)

Input	Actual	Predicted: y = 0.5x + 2.5	Error: Actual − Predicted
1	1.8	3	−1.2
2	1.7	3.5	−1.8
3	3.6	4	−0.4
5	5.4	5	0.4
6	7.3	5.5	1.8
7	7.2	6	1.2

Data vs. Line Fit for Line (c)

Input	Actual	Predicted: y = 0.9x + 0.9	Error: Actual − Predicted
1	1.8	1.8	0
2	1.7	2.7	−1
3	3.6	3.6	0
5	5.4	5.4	0
6	7.3	6.3	1
7	7.2	7.2	0

Data vs. Line Fit for Line (d)

Input	Actual	Predicted: y = 1x + 0.5	Error: Actual − Predicted
1	1.8	1.5	0.3
2	1.7	2.5	−0.8
3	3.6	3.5	0.1
5	5.4	5.5	−0.1
6	7.3	6.5	0.8
7	7.2	7.5	−0.3

(b) Line (c) makes only two errors; the other four points are exactly right.

(c) Line (d) has the smallest errors and the smallest maximum error, but does not match any data exactly.

9. (a) Answers vary depending on students' choice of slope. The balance point is (4, 4.5), and if the choice for the slope is $m = 1$, the equation of the line is $y = x + 0.5$ (line (d) from the original exercise). If the student chooses $m = 0.9$, that gives $y = 0.9x + 0.9$ (line (c) for the original exercise).

(b) For any slope, the sum of the errors should be 0. If students chose $m = 1$, they compute $0 - 1 + 0 + 0 + 1 + 0 = 0$. If students chose $m = 0.9$, they compute $0.3 - 0.8 + 0.1 - 0.1 + 0.8 - 0.3 = 0$

(c) The equation of a fit line through the balance point must be of the form $y - \overline{y} = m(x - \overline{x})$, or $y = m(x - \overline{x}) + \overline{y}$. So, the error for any point (x_i, y_i) is $m(x_i - \overline{x}) + \overline{y} - y_i$. Add up all the errors, and you'll get:

$$mx_1 - m\overline{x} + \overline{y} - y_1 + mx_2 - m\overline{x}$$
$$+ \overline{y} - y_2 + \cdots + mx_n - m\overline{x} + \overline{y} - y_n$$

Collect all the like terms together.

$$m(x_1 + x_2 + \cdots + x_n) - nm\overline{x} + n\overline{y}$$
$$- (y_1 + y_2 + \cdots + y_n)$$

Remember that $\overline{x} = \frac{x_1 + x_2 + \cdots + x_n}{n}$ and $\overline{y} = \frac{y_1 + y_2 + \cdots + y_n}{n}$. This means that $x_1 + x_2 + \cdots + x_n = n\overline{x}$ and $y_1 + y_2 + \cdots + y_n = n\overline{y}$. Substituting these facts into your expression, you get:

$$m(n\overline{x}) - nm\overline{x} + n\overline{y} - (n\overline{y})$$

And this simplifies to 0.

10. (a) The balance point is the center of the ruler (at 6 inches for a 12-inch ruler, for example, and halfway from top to bottom).

(b) The balance point is the center of the circular coin.

(c) It is possible to have a balance point that isn't within the object. One example is a boomerang. Another is a cup or mug: its balance point will be in the center, but not part of the actual object.

11. (a) Harvey rolled 14 sixes. You can find this by taking the total number of rolls (85) and subtracting the count of ones through fives (71).

(b) The mean is the sum of all the rolls, divided by how many there were. One way to do this is to multiply each roll number by its frequency. For example, there were 10 rolls of 1, for a total of $10 \times 1 = 10$, and there were 15 rolls of 2, for a total of $15 \times 2 = 30$.

Continuing this, the total of all rolls is $10 \times 1 + 15 \times 2 + 19 \times 3 + 16 \times 4 + 11 \times 5 + 14 \times 6 = 10 + 30 + 57 + 64 + 55 + 84 = 300$. The mean is $\frac{300}{85} \approx 3.53$.

The median is the middle number in the sorted list. With 85 numbers, there are 42 numbers above and below the median; find this by dividing 85 by 2 and rounding down. Then, the 43rd number in the list is the median. Counting through the 10 ones and 15 twos gives 25 numbers, and 19 threes gives 46. So, the 43rd number will be toward the end of the list of threes, and this makes 3 the median.

The mode is 3, since it occurs the most times (19).

12. (a)

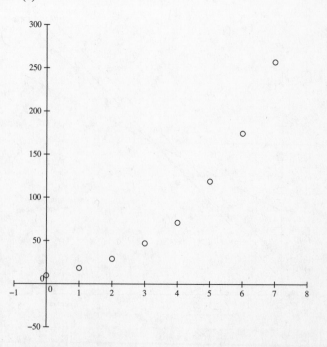

(b) The mean of Hours is 3.5 and the mean of Yeast Density is 90.8, so the balance point is (3.5, 90.8). This plot includes the balance point:

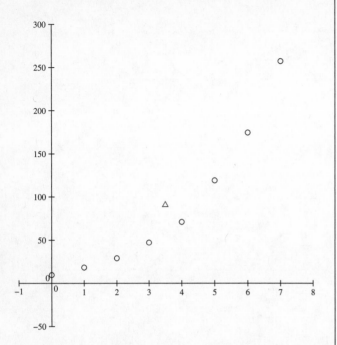

(c) No, a fitting line is not reasonable for this data. These points do not appear to seem to lie along (or approximately along) a line in the scatter plot. Consequently, the trend in the Yeast Density is not linear, so a fitting line is not appropriate.

13. (a) Here is the completed table:

Data vs. Line Fit: $y = 33.4476x - 26.2917$			
Hours: x	Actual Yeast: y	Predicted	**Error**
0	9.6	−26.3	35.9
1	18.3	7.2	11.1
2	29.0	40.6	−11.6
3	47.2	74.1	−26.9
4	71.1	107.5	−36.4
5	119.1	140.9	−21.8
6	174.6	174.4	0.2
7	257.3	207.8	49.5

(b) The sum of the errors, and therefore the average, through any line that contains the balance point will be 0, so this is the smallest of the three measures of error. Making all the errors positive, adding, and dividing by 8, yields 24.175. Squaring all the errors, adding, and dividing by 8 yields 815.085. Note that not only is $24.175 < 815.085$, it's also true that $24.175 < \sqrt{815.085}$. In general, the mean absolute error is bounded by the square root of the mean square error, and the proof of this fact involves some classical algebraic identities.

14. Choices A, C, and D all have a slope of 4, but only the last contains $(-1, 2)$. The correct answer choice is **D**.

Maintain Your Skills

15. (a)

Input	Output
0	1
1	4
2	7
3	10
4	13

(b)

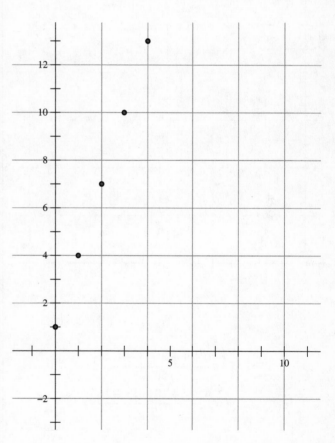

(c)
$$\bar{x} = \frac{0 + 1 + 2 + 3 + 4}{5} = 2$$
$$\bar{y} = \frac{1 + 4 + 7 + 10 + 13}{5} = 7$$

(d) $(2, 7)$ is on the graph.

16. (a)

Input	Output
0	4
1	7
2	10
3	13
4	16

(b)

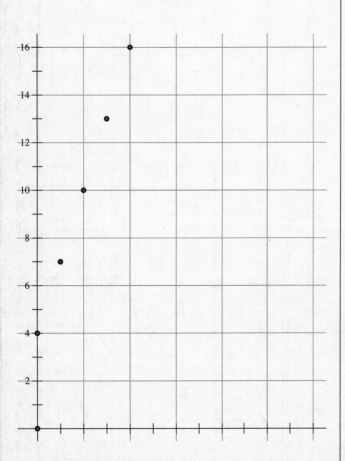

(b)

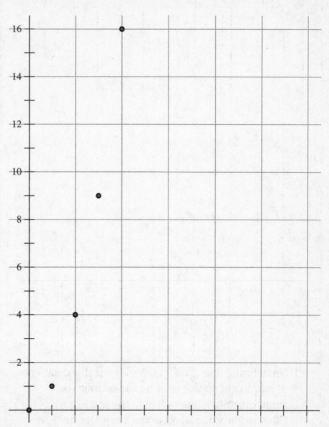

(c)

$$\bar{x} = \frac{0 + 1 + 2 + 3 + 4}{5} = 2$$

$$\bar{y} = \frac{0 + 1 + 4 + 9 + 16}{5} = 6$$

(d) $(2, 6)$ is above the graph.

(c)

$$\bar{x} = \frac{0 + 1 + 2 + 3 + 4}{5} = 2$$

$$\bar{y} = \frac{4 + 7 + 10 + 13 + 16}{5} = 10$$

(d) $(2, 10)$ is on the graph.

17. (a)

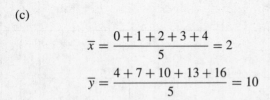

Input	Output
0	0
1	1
2	4
3	9
4	16

18. (a)

Input	Output
0	3
1	4
2	7
3	12
4	19

(b)

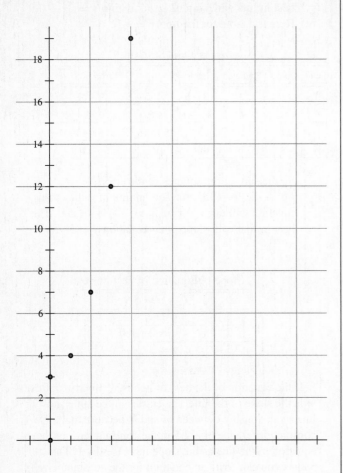

(c)

$$\bar{x} = \frac{0 + 1 + 2 + 3 + 4}{5} = 2$$

$$\bar{y} = \frac{3 + 4 + 7 + 12 + 19}{5} = 9$$

(d) $(2, 9)$ is above the graph.

1.8 The Line of Best Fit, Part 1

Check Your Understanding

1. Here is a graph of the data points, along with the line $y = 2x + 3$:

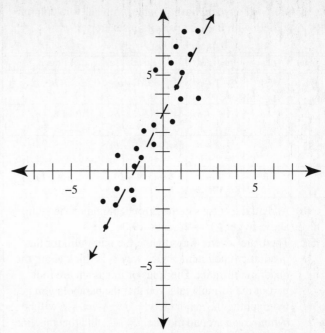

You can see that it follows a linear trend with a positive slope that is greater than 1, and that a best fit line should intersect the y-axis at some positive value of y. Option (a) $y = 2x + 3$ is the only one that meets these criteria. $y = 2x - 3$ is below the trend, while the other lines do not follow it at reasonable slopes.

2. (a) Graph A is the better fit, because if the data is considered to have a linear trend, that trend should have a positive slope.

   (b) Here is a table showing the data values, the values for each of the proposed fitting lines, and the error for each proposed line:

Input	Output	$y = 3x - 1$	Error	$y = -x + 8.4$	Error
1	3	2	1	7.4	−4.4
2	4.5	5	−0.5	6.4	−1.9
3	8.1	8	0.1	5.4	2.7
4	8	11	−3	4.4	3.6

The sum of the errors is $1 + -0.5 + 0.1 + -3 = -2.4$ for graph A and $-4.4 + -1.9 + 2.7 + 3.6 = 0$ for graph B. For this measure of errors, graph A seems to be a worse fit for the data than graph B, because in the calculation of the sum of the errors for graph B, the effects of large positive errors are cancelled out by large negative errors for a total error closer to 0 than the total for graph A.

The mean absolute error is $\frac{1 + 0.5 + 0.1 + 3}{4} = 1.15$ for graph A and $\frac{4.4 + 1.9 + 2.7 + 3.6}{4} = 3.15$ for graph B. By introducing absolute value, the "cancelling" effect present in the sum of the errors is taken care of, and you can see that graph A is a better fit.

The mean squared error is $\frac{1^2 + 0.5^2 + 0.1^2 + 3^2}{4} = 2.565$ for graph A and $\frac{4.4^2 + 1.9^2 + 2.7^2 + 3.6^2}{4} = 10.805$ for graph B. When you square the errors, error values less than 1 actually have an effect less than their absolute value in the calculation of the mean while the effect of errors greater than 1 is magnified. It's even easier to choose graph A as the better fit.

3. (a) Here is Tony and Sasha's table, with an extra column to help with the next part of this exercise.

Data vs. Line Fit: $y = 3x + b$

Input	Output	Predicted:	Error:	Error^2:
1	3	$3 \cdot 1 + b$ $= 3 + b$	$3 - (3 \cdot 1 + b)$ $= -b$	b^2
2	4.5	$3 \cdot 2 + b$ $= 6 + b$	$4.5 - (3 \cdot 2 + b)$ $= -1.5 - b$	$(-1.5 - b)^2$ $= 2.25 + 3b + b^2$
3	8.1	$3 \cdot 3 + b$ $= 9 + b$	$8.1 - (3 \cdot 3 + b)$ $= -0.9 - b$	$(-0.9 - b)^2$ $= 0.81 + 1.8b + b^2$
4	8	$3 \cdot 4 + b$ $= 12 + b$	$8 - (3 \cdot 4 + b)$ $= -4 - b$	$(-4 - b)^2$ $= 16 + 8b + b^2$

(b) Add all the entries in the Error^2 column of the table above to get $4b^2 + 12.8b + 19.06$.

(c) There are several ways to find the minimum for this quadratic function in b. One way is to think about the quadratic formula. The "plus or minus square root" part of the formula tells you that the parabola you get by graphing the quadratic $y = ax^2 + bx + c$ will be symmetrical around the line $y = \frac{-b}{2a}$, and that this line will go through the minimum value of the function.

Don't be confused by the fact that b is used as the coefficient of the x term in the standard presentation of the quadratic formula and that b is the variable in this exercise. You still just divide the opposite of the coefficient of the x term by two times the coefficient of the x^2 term to find the line of symmetry. The function $4b^2 + 12.8b + 19.06$ will take on its minimum value at $b = \frac{-12.8}{2 \cdot 4} = -1.6$.

(d) Substitute your answer from the previous part into the equation of the line to get $y = 3x - 1.6$.

4. (a) Here is a table for the line $y = x + b$

Data vs. Line Fit: $y = x + b$

Input	Output	Predicted:	Error:	Error^2:
1	3	$1 + b$	$3 - (1 + b)$ $= 2 - b$	$(2 - b)^2$ $= 4 - 4b + b^2$
2	4.5	$2 + b$	$4.5 - (2 + b)$ $= 2.5 - b$	$(2.5 - b)^2$ $= 6.25 - 5b + b^2$
3	8.1	$3 + b$	$8.1 - (3 + b)$ $= 5.1 - b$	$(5.1 - b)^2$ $= 26.01 - 10.2b + b^2$
4	8	$4 + b$	$8 - (4 + b)$ $= 4 - b$	$(4 - b)^2$ $= 16 - 8b + b^2$

So the sum of the squares of the errors is $4b^2 - 27.2b + 52.26$. The minimum value of this function will occur for $b_{\min} = \frac{-(-27.2)}{8} = 3.4$. The best-fit line with slope 1 has equation $y = x + 3.4$.

(b) Here is a table for the line $y = 2x + b$.

Data vs. Line Fit: $y = 2x + b$

Input	Output	Predicted:	Error:	Error^2:
1	3	$2 + b$	$3 - (2 + b)$ $= 1 - b$	$(1 - b)^2$ $= 1 - 2b + b^2$
2	4.5	$4 + b$	$4.5 - (4 + b)$ $= 0.5 - b$	$(0.5 - b)^2$ $= 0.25 - b + b^2$
3	8.1	$6 + b$	$8.1 - (6 + b)$ $= 2.1 - b$	$(2.1 - b)^2$ $= 4.41 - 4.2b + b^2$
4	8	$8 + b$	$8 - (8 + b)$ $= -b$	b^2

So the sum of the squares of the errors is $4b^2 - 7.2b + 5.66$. The minimum value of this function will occur for $b_{\min} = \frac{-(-7.2)}{8} = 0.9$. The best fit line with slope 2 has equation $y = 2x + 0.9$

(c) Here is a table for the line $y = b$.

Data vs. Line Fit: $y = b$

Input	Output	Predicted:	Error:	Error^2:
1	3	b	$3 - b$	$(3 - b)^2 = 9 - 6b + b^2$
2	4.5	b	$4.5 - b$	$(4.5 - b)^2 = 20.25 - 9b + b^2$
3	8.1	b	$8.1 - b$	$(8.1 - b)^2 = 65.61 - 16.2b + b^2$
4	8	b	$8 - b$	$(8 - b)^2 = 64 - 16b + b^2$

So the sum of the squares of the errors is $4b^2 - 47.2b + 158.86$. The minimum value of this function will occur for $b_{\min} = \frac{-(-47.2)}{8} = 5.9$. The best fit line with slope 0 has equation $y = 5.9$.

5.

Slope	Equation of best line
0	$y = 5.9$
1	$y = x + 3.4$
2	$y = 2x + 0.9$
3	$y = 3x - 1.6$

If the equation of the best fit line is $y = mx + b$, then m is the slope of the line. The entries in the table show a linear relationship between m and b, because there is a constant difference of -2.5 in the constant term of the equation of the line as the slope increases by 1. This means you can write an equation for the constant term b in terms of the slope m.

$$b = -2.5m + 5.9$$

On Your Own

6. (a)

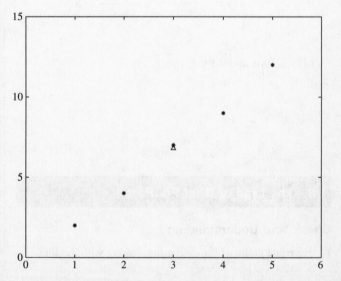

(b)

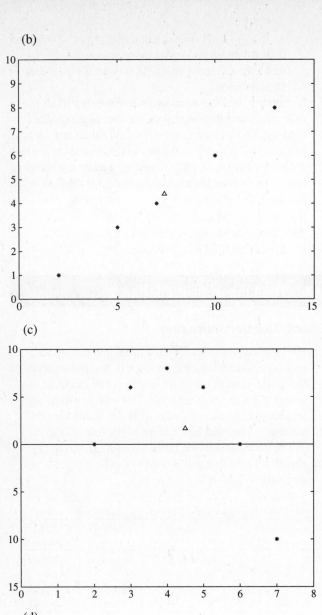

(c)

(d)

Tables 1, 2, and 4 show linear trends. Table 3 does not. The graphs display the data points as stars and the centroid of the data (see Exercise 7) as triangles.

7. Table 1: Balance point $(3, 6.8)$
   Table 2: Balance point $(7.4, 4.4)$
   Table 3: Balance point $(4.5, 1\frac{2}{3})$
   Table 4: Balance point $(2.4, 1.8)$

   You can see the balance points graphed with the data in the solution for Exercise 6.

   In all but Table 3, the balance point lies along the trend in data. Table 3 is the only table that cannot be fit well with a line. The data for Table 3 comes from a quadratic function.

8. To find the intersection of the lines $y = 5.9$ and $y = x + 3.4$, substitute $y = 5.9$ into the second equation. You get $5.9 = x + 3.4$, so $x = 2.5$ and the lines intersect in the point $(2.5, 5.9)$. If the four lines are concurrent, this same point will be on the other two lines. We can check by substituting its coordinates into their equations.

$$5.9 = 2(2.5) + 0.9$$
$$5.9 = 3(2.5) - 1.6$$

In both cases, the point satisfies the equation for the line. The lines are concurrent at $(2.5, 5.9)$.

This point is also the centroid of the data.
$\bar{x} = \frac{1+2+3+4}{4} = \frac{10}{4} = 2.5$ and $\bar{y} = \frac{3+4.5+8.1+8}{4} = \frac{23.6}{4} = 5.9$

9. (a) The mean absolute error for line $y = x + 3$ is 1.25. Here is a table you could use to calculate it:

Mean Absolute Error for $y = x + 3$				
Input	Output	Predicted	**Error**	Abs. Error
0	4	3	1	1
2	4	5	−1	1
4	5	7	−2	2
5	7	8	−1	1
5	9	8	1	1
6	11	9	2	2
8	12	11	1	1
10	12	13	−1	1

$\frac{1+1+2+1+1+2+1+1}{8} = 1.25$. The mean of the absolute values of all the errors is 1.25.

   (b) The mean absolute error for line $y = x + 2$ is $\frac{2+0+1+0+2+3+2+0}{8} = 1.25$.

   (c) The mean absolute error for line $y = x + 4$ is $\frac{0+2+3+2+0+1+0+2}{8} = 1.25$.

   (d) The mean absolute error for line $y = 2x - 2$ is $\frac{6+2+1+1+1+1+2+6}{8} = 2.5$.

10. Find the standard error by calculating the mean squared error, then taking the square root. Here is the calculation for the first line:

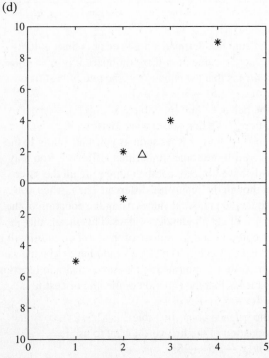

Mean Squared Error for $y = x + 3$				
Input	Output	Predicted	Error	Sqd. Error
0	4	3	1	1
2	4	5	−1	1
4	5	7	−2	4
5	7	8	−1	1
5	9	8	1	1
6	11	9	2	4
8	12	11	1	1
10	12	13	−1	1

The mean of the squared errors is 1.75, and the standard error is the square root, or about 1.32.

The mean squared error for the line $y = x + 2$ is 2.75. The standard error is about 1.66 (the square root of 2.75).

The mean squared error for the line $y = x + 4$ is also 2.75, and the standard error is about 1.66.

Ranked by standard error, line $y = x + 3$ is the best fit, and lines $y = x + 2$ and $y = x + 4$ are equally good.

11. $\frac{5+6+14+23+34+38}{6} = 20$ and $\frac{1+22+17+29+27+42}{6} = 23$, so the balance point is (20, 23). The correct answer choice is **B**.

12. (a) The reason the mean squared error downplays a small error is that when you square a number that is less than one, the square is smaller than the original number. When you square an error less than one in the course of calculating the means squared error, its final effect will be less than in the mean absolute error. Similarly the mean squared error magnifies large errors in comparison to the mean absolute error. This is because the square of any number greater than one is larger than the original number and the larger the original number gets, the greater the difference between that number and its square.

(b) If small errors are minimized and large ones maximized, you will choose a line of best fit that's closest to most of the data points.

13. (a) $y = 6.103x^2 - 9.277x + 16.433$
(b) $y = 10.976(1.590)^x$
(c) The standard error for the quadratic fit is around 5.4, while the standard error for the exponential fit is about 9.3. The quadratic fit has a smaller standard error.

Maintain Your Skills

14. There are many data sets that meet the requirements. Here are some examples of possible answers.

(a) 27, 27, 25, 20, 16
(b) 27, 27, 25, 20, 16
(c) 27, 27, 25, 20, 16
(d) 27, 27, 25, 21, 15

15. (a) 30
(b) 46
(c) 5, 5, 3, −2, −6; your solution to this part will depend on the data set you found to solve Exercise 13. To make the mean 1, you would subtract 22 from each of your numbers.

(d) 4, 4, 2, −3, −7; your solution to this part will depend on the data set you found to solve Exercise 13. To make the mean 0, you would subtract 23 from each of your numbers.

16. Remember: find the mean by finding the sum of all the data values and dividing by the number of data values. Find the median by arranging the data values from least to greatest. Then choose the one in the middle (or average the two nearest the middle if you have an even number of data values.) Find the mode by looking for the data value that appears most frequently.

(a) Mean = 8; Median = 7; Mode = 10
(b) Mean = 8; Median = 7; Mode = 10
(c) Mean = 8; Median = 7; Mode = 10

1.9 The Line of Best Fit, Part 2

Check Your Understanding

1. Find the balance point for each table, and then write a general equation for a line of slope m that passes through that point. Find the error for that line, and calculate the sum of the squares of the error. This will be a quadratic in m, and you can find the value of m that minimizes that quadratic. That will be the slope of the line of best fit.

The balance point for Table 1 is (2.5, 3), so the equation of the line you'll want to use is $y = m(x - 2.5) + 3$.

Table 1

Input	Output	$y = m(x - 2.5) + 3$	Error	Error^2
1	−10	$-1.5m + 3$	$1.5m - 13$	$2.25m^2 -39m + 169$
2	8	$-0.5m + 3$	$0.5m + 5$	$0.25m^2 +5m + 25$
3	12	$0.5m + 3$	$-0.5m + 9$	$0.25m^2 -9m + 81$
4	2	$1.5m + 3$	$-1.5m - 1$	$2.25m^2 +3m + 1$

The sum of the squares of the error is $5m^2 - 40m + 276$, and the value of m that minimizes it is $m = \frac{40}{2.5} = 4$. This means that the equation of the line of best fit is $y = 4(x - 2.5) + 3 = 4x - 7$.

The balance point for Table 2 is (5.5, 3), so the equation of the line you'll want to use is $y = m(x - 5.5) + 3$. As soon as you start filling in the table, you'll see some similarities to Table 1. You may already have noticed that the outputs are all the same even though the inputs are different. Then, when you compute the predicted values using the equation of the line, you'll get all identical values. This means that the error column (and the square of the error column) will be identical to Table 1. The slope would have to be the same (4), because it's minimizing the same quadratic function. This means that the equation of the line of best fit is $y = 4(x - 5.5) + 3 = 4x - 19$.

The balance point for Table 3 is (2.5, 25), so the equation of the line you'll want to use is $y = m(x - 2.5) + 25$.

Table 3

Input	Output	$y = m(x - 2.5) + 25$	Error	Error²
1	−22	$-1.5m + 25$	$1.5m - 47$	$2.25m^2 - 141m + 2209$
2	58	$-0.5m + 25$	$0.5m + 33$	$0.25m^2 + 33m + 1089$
3	40	$0.5m + 25$	$-0.5m + 15$	$0.25m^2 - 15m + 225$
4	24	$1.5m + 25$	$-1.5m - 1$	$2.25m^2 + 3m + 1$

The sum of the squares of the error is $5m^2 - 120m + 3524$, and the value of m that minimizes it is $m = \frac{120}{2.5} = 12$. This means that the equation of the line of best fit is $y = 12(x - 2.5) + 25 = 12x - 5$.

 The balance point for Table 4 is $(4.5, 25)$, so the equation of the line you'll want to use is $y = m(x - 4.5) + 25$. As with Tables 1 and 2, Tables 3 and 4 have the same list of outputs and will have the same error columns, and therefore the same slope for their line of best fit. The line of best fit is thus $y = 12x - 29$.

2. The balance point for the data is $(2.5, 5.9)$, so the equation of the line you'll want to use is
$y = m(x - 2.5) + 5.9$.

Input	Output	$y = m(x - 2.5) + 5.9$	Error	Error²
1	3	$-1.5m + 5.9$	$1.5m - 2.9$	$2.25m^2 - 8.7m + 8.41$
2	4.5	$-0.5m + 5.9$	$0.5m - 1.4$	$0.25m^2 - 1.4m + 1.96$
3	8.1	$0.5m + 5.9$	$-0.5m + 2.2$	$0.25m^2 - 2.2m + 4.84$
4	8	$1.5m + 5.9$	$-1.5m + 2.1$	$2.25m^2 - 6.3m + 4.41$

The sum of the squares of the error is $5m^2 - 18.6m + 19.62$, and the value of m that minimizes it is $m = \frac{18.6}{2.5} = 1.86$. This means that the equation of the line of best fit is $y = 1.86(x - 2.5) + 5.9 = 1.86x + 1.25$.

3. (a) This data does not follow a linear trend, so the best fit line does not represent it well. It is
$y = 53.69x - 85.36$.

 (b) Find the best fit quadratic and exponential using the calculator, then compare their measures of error. The quadratic is $y = 7.56x^2 - 14.35x + 28.04$; the exponential is $y = 13.9(1.55)^x$. The best fit quadratic has far smaller errors than the best fit exponential. Its standard error is about 6.05, while the standard error of the best fit exponential is about 25.2.

On Your Own

4. (a) The balance point for Table 1 is $(2.5, 50)$, so the equation of the line you'll want to use is
$y = m(x - 2.5) + 50$.

Table 3

Input	Output	$y = m(x - 2.5) + 50$	Error	Error²
1	0	$-1.5m + 50$	$1.5m - 50$	$2.25m^2 - 150m + 2500$
2	90	$-0.5m + 50$	$0.5m + 40$	$0.25m^2 + 40m + 1600$
3	50	$0.5m + 50$	$-0.5m$	$0.25m^2$
4	60	$1.5m + 50$	$-1.5m + 10$	$2.25m^2 - 30m + 100$

The sum of the squares of the error is $5m^2 - 140m + 4200$, and the value of m that minimizes it is $m = \frac{140}{2.5} = 14$. This means that the equation of the line of best fit is
$y = 14(x - 2.5) + 50 = 14x + 15$.

 (b) The balance point for Table 2 is $(0.5, 50)$, so the equation of the line you'll want to use is
$y = m(x - 0.5) + 50$. As in Exercise 1, this table has the same list of outputs as Table 1, so it will have the same error column, and therefore the same slope for the line of best fit. The equation for the line of best fit is $y = 14(x - 0.5) + 50 = 14x + 43$.

 You can also think of this as a *translation* of the data points. Each new data point is two units to the left of the corresponding data point from Table 1. (Notice that the balance point is also two units to the left of the one for Table 1.) So the line of best fit will have to be parallel to the line of best fit for Table 1, and since it will also be two units to the left of the line for Table 1, it will have a larger y-intercept and a smaller x-intercept than the line for that table. However, the key conclusion is that the lines of best fit for these two tables are parallel—they have the same slope.

 (c) In Table 3, the data points have been translated down one unit from Table 2. Again the slope of the line of best fit must be the same, 14, and it must pass through the balance point for this table, which is $(0.5, 49)$. The equation for the line of best fit is $y = 14(x - 0.5) + 49 = 14x + 42$.

 (d) In Table 4, the data points have been translated to the left 0.5 units and down 49 units from Table 3. Again the slope of the line of best fit must be the same, 14, and it must pass through the balance point for this table, which is $(0, 0)$. The equation for the line of best fit is $y = 14(x - 0) + 0 = 14x$.

5. In each of these graphs, the data points are marked as stars, while the balance point (computed in Exercise 6) is marked as a triangle.

 (a)

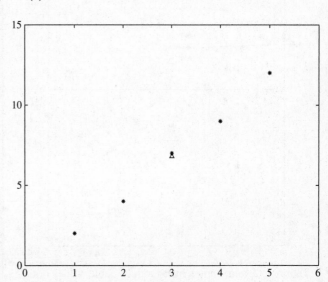

(b)

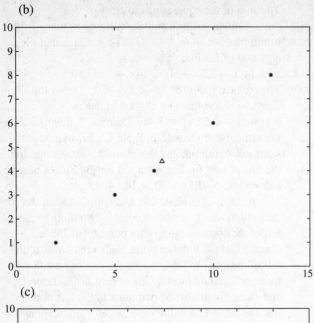

(c)

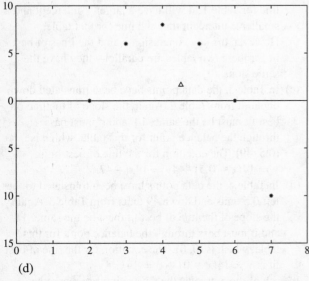

(d)

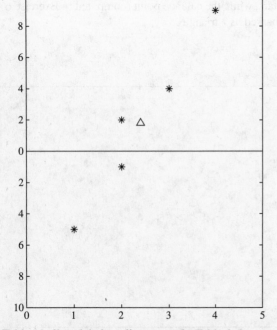

Tables 1, 2, and 4 show linear trends. Table 3 does not.

6. See the graphs in the solution for Exercise 5.
   - Table 1: Balance point $(3, 6.8)$
   - Table 2: Balance point $(7.4, 4.4)$
   - Table 3: Balance point $(4.5, 1\frac{2}{3})$
   - Table 4: Balance point $(2.4, 1.8)$

   In all but Table 3, the balance point lies along the trend in data. Table 3 is the only table that cannot be fit well with a line. The data for Table 3 comes from a quadratic function.

7. For Table 1, a reasonable guess at the slope of the trend is anywhere between 2 and 3. A line connecting the first and last data points has slope 2.5 (rise of 10 divided by run of 4), so 2.5 is a very good guess. Using this estimate for the trend line's slope, the equation is

$$y - 6.8 = 2.5(x - 3)$$

which simplifies to $y = 2.5x - 0.7$. It turns out that this is the exact line returned as best fit from a calculator. Here is the graph:

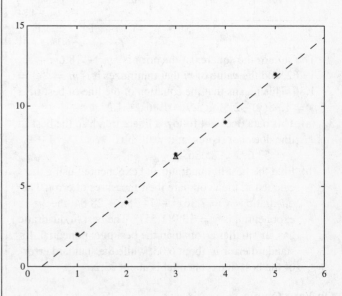

For Table 2, a reasonable guess at the slope of the trend is between $\frac{1}{2}$ and $\frac{2}{3}$. The slope between the endpoints is $\frac{7}{11} \approx 0.64$ (rise of 7 divided by run of 11). If slope 0.6 is used, the equation through the balance point is

$$y - 4.4 = 0.6(x - 7.4)$$

which simplifies to $y = 0.6x - 0.04$. Here is the graph:

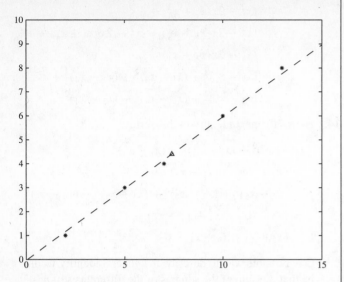

The actual best fit slope is $\frac{77}{122} \approx 0.6312$, and one equation for the best fit line is

$$y - 4.4 = \frac{77}{122}(x - 7.4)$$

For Table 4, a reasonable guess at the slope of the trend is between 4 and 5. The slope between the endpoints is $4\frac{2}{3}$ (rise of 14 divided by run of 3), so anything between 4.5 and 5 is an excellent guess. Using the estimate 4.7 for the trend line's slope, the equation is

$$y - 1.8 = 4.7(x - 2.4)$$

which simplifies to $y = 4.7x - 9.48$. Here is the graph:

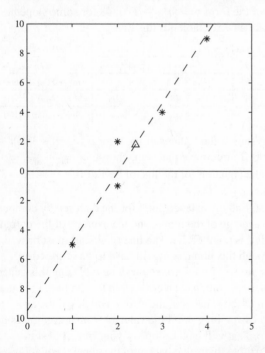

The actual best fit slope is 4.5, and the best fit line is $y = 4.5x - 9$.

8. (a) The mean absolute error for line $y = x + 3$ is 1.25. Here is a table you could use to calculate it:

Mean Absolute Error for $y = x + 3$				
Input	Output	Predicted	**Error**	Abs. Error
0	4	3	1	1
2	4	5	−1	1
4	5	7	−2	2
5	7	8	−1	1
5	9	8	1	1
6	11	9	2	2
8	12	11	1	1
10	12	13	−1	1

The mean of all the absolute errors is 1.25.

(b) The mean absolute error for line $y = x + 2$ is 1.25.

(c) The mean absolute error for line $y = x + 4$ is 1.25.

(d) The mean absolute error for line $y = 2x - 2$ is 2.5.

9. Find the standard error by calculating the mean squared error, then taking the square root. Here is the calculation for the first line:

Mean Squared Error for $y = x + 3$				
Input	Output	Predicted	Error	Sqd. Error
0	4	3	1	1
2	4	5	−1	1
4	5	7	−2	4
5	7	8	−1	1
5	9	8	1	1
6	11	9	2	4
8	12	11	1	1
10	12	13	−1	1

The mean of the squared errors is 1.75, and the standard error is the square root, or about 1.32.

The mean squared error for the line $y = x + 2$ is 2.75. The standard error is about 1.66 (the square root of 2.75).

The mean squared error for the line $y = x + 4$ is also 2.75, and the standard error is about 1.66.

Ranked by standard error, line $y = x + 3$ is the best fit, and lines $y = x + 2$ and $y = x + 4$ are equally good.

10. The line of best fit might pass through all, some, or none of the points in the data set. It must, however, contain the balance point. The correct answer choice is **C**.

11. Solutions will vary, depending both on the table that you use as well as on the method you choose for producing a table with a given line of best fit. Here's an example of a different table with the same line of best fit as Table 1, $y = 14x + 15$.

Table 1A

Input	Output
1	29
2	43
3	57
4	71

The data in this table exactly fits the line $y = 14x + 15$.

12. Any set for which the data lies on a vertical line will work. To see why this is so, look at a table where the data comes from a vertical line.

Fitting a Vertical line

Input	Output	$y = m(x-1)+6$
1	4	6
1	5	6
1	7	6
1	8	6

If you go through the process, you find that the balance point of the data is $(1, 6)$, which gives you the equation $y = m(x-1)+6$ as the starting point for your line of best fit. However, when you compute the predicted values using this equation, those values do not depend on the slope of the line. This means that the error also does not depend on the slope you choose for the line of best fit. All the lines through the balance point give the same mean squared error.

Maintain Your Skills

13. (a)
$$(x_1 - x_2)^2 = 2(x_1^2 + x_2^2) - (x_1 + x_2)^2$$
$$= 2x_1^2 + 2x_2^2 - (x_1^2 + 2x_1x_2 + x_2^2)$$
$$= 2x_1^2 + 2x_2^2 - x_1^2 - 2x_1x_2 - x_2^2$$
$$= x_1^2 - 2x_1x_2 + x_2^2$$
$$= (x_1 - x_2)^2$$

(b) $(x_1 - x_2)^2 + (x_1 - x_3)^2 + (x_2 - x_3)^2$
$$= 3(x_1^2 + x_2^2 + x_3^2) - (x_1 + x_2 + x_3)^2$$
$$= 3x_1^2 + 3x_2^2 + 3x_3^2 - (x_1^2 + x_1x_2 + x_1x_3 +$$
$$x_1x_2 + x_2^2 + x_2x_3 + x_1x_3 + x_2x_3 + x_3^2)$$
$$= 3x_1^2 + 3x_2^2 + 3x_3^2 -$$
$$(x_1^2 + x_2^2 + x_3^2 + 2x_1x_2 + 2x_1x_3 + 2x_2x_3)$$
$$= 3x_1^2 + 3x_2^2 + 3x_3^2 - x_1^2 - x_2^2 - x_3^2 -$$
$$2x_1x_2 - 2x_1x_3 - 2x_2x_3)$$
$$= 2x_1^2 + 2x_2^2 + 2x_3^2 - 2x_1x_2 - 2x_1x_3 - 2x_2x_3)$$
$$= (x_1^2 - 2x_1x_2 + x_2^2) + (x_1^2 - 2x_1x_3 + x_3^2) +$$
$$(x_2^2 - 2x_2x_3 + x_3^2)$$
$$= (x_1 - x_2)^2 + (x_1 - x_3)^2 + (x_2 - x_3)^2$$

(c)
$$(x_1 - x_2)^2 + (x_1 - x_3)^2 + (x_1 - x_4)^2 + (x_2 - x_3)^2 +$$
$$(x_2 - x_4)^2 + (x_3 - x_4)^2$$
$$= 4(x_1^2 + x_2^2 + x_3^2 + x_4^2) - (x_1 + x_2 + x_3 + x_4)^2$$
$$= 4x_1^2 + 4x_2^2 + 4x_3^2 + 4x_4^2 - (x_1^2 + x_2^2 + x_3^2 + x_4^2 +$$
$$2x_1x_2 + 2x_1x_3 + 2x_1x_4 + 2x_2x_3 +$$
$$2x_2x_4 + 2x_3x_4)$$
$$= 3x_1^2 + 3x_2^2 + 3x_3^2 + 3x_4^2 - 2x_1x_2 - 2x_1x_3 -$$
$$2x_1x_4 - 2x_2x_3 - 2x_2x_4 - 2x_3x_4)$$

$$= (x_1^2 - 2x_1x_2 + x_2^2) + (x_1^2 - 2x_1x_3 + x_3^2) +$$
$$(x_1^2 - 2x_1x_4 + x_4^2) +$$
$$(x_2^2 - 2x_2x_3 + x_3^2) + (x_2^2 - 2x_2x_4 + x_4^2) +$$
$$(x_3^2 - 2x_3x_4 + x_4^2)$$
$$= (x_1 - x_2)^2 + (x_1 - x_3)^2 + (x_1 - x_4)^2 +$$
$$(x_2 - x_3)^2 + (x_2 - x_4)^2 + (x_3 - x_4)^2$$

14. Here's the next identity in this series:
$$(x_1 - x_2)^2 + (x_1 - x_3)^2 + (x_1 - x_4)^2 +$$
$$(x_1 - x_5)^2 + (x_2 - x_3)^2 + (x_2 - x_4)^2 +$$
$$(x_2 - x_5)^2 + (x_3 - x_4)^2 + (x_3 - x_5)^2 + (x_4 - x_5)^2$$
$$= 5(x_1^2 + x_2^2 + x_3^2 + x_4^2 + x_5^2) -$$
$$(x_1 + x_2 + x_3 + x_4 + x_5)^2$$

One possible way to describe the general identity would be that the sum of the squares of the differences of n numbers, two at a time, is n times the sum of their squares minus the square of their sum.

1B MATHEMATICAL REFLECTIONS

1. First find the balance point for the data set.
$$\bar{x} = \frac{-1 + 2 + 5 + 6}{4} = \frac{12}{4} = 3$$
$$\bar{y} = \frac{-2 + 88 + 48 + 58}{4} = \frac{192}{4} = 48$$

So the balance point is $(3, 48)$.

You know that the line of best fit must pass through the balance point, so the equation for the line of best fit must be of the form $y = m(x - 3) + 48$ for some slope m. Make an error table for this line.

Input	Output	$y = m(x-3)+48$	Error	Error^2
-1	-2	$-4m + 48$	$4m - 50$	$16m^2 - 400m + 2500$
2	88	$-m + 48$	$m + 40$	$m^2 + 80m + 1600$
5	48	$2m + 48$	$-2m$	$4m^2$
6	58	$3m + 48$	$-3m + 10$	$9m^2 - 60m + 100$

The sum of the squares of the error is $30m^2 - 380m + 4200$. To minimize that sum, choose $m = \frac{-(-380)}{2 \cdot 30} = \frac{19}{3}$. So the equation for the line of best fit is $y = \frac{19}{3}(x - 3) + 48$ or $y = \frac{19}{3}x + 29$.

2. First, find the balance point for the data set, by computing the average of the inputs and the average of the outputs. Call this point $(\bar{x}, \bar{y})$. The line of best fit must pass through this point, so it will have to be of the form $y = m(x - \bar{x}) + \bar{y}$ for some slope m. Using this general equation, complete an error table for the line. Find the sum of the squares of the errors, which will be an expression in m. Find the value of m that minimizes this sum. That will be the slope of your line of best fit. Substitute that value back into the general equation you used in your error table to get the complete equation for the line of best fit.

3. Given a set of data, the *line of best fit* is the line that minimizes the sum of the squares of the errors—it minimizes the mean squared error.

4. To find the line of best fit, enter the data into a spreadsheet on your calculator and use the linear regression feature to have it calculate the line of best fit.
$\text{Time} = -0.39377(\text{Year}) + 995.627$

MID-CHAPTER TEST

1. The slope is $\frac{6-5}{-2-1} = -\frac{1}{3}$. If the missing output is 7, then $\frac{y-5}{7-1} = -\frac{1}{3}$, or $y - 5 = -\frac{1}{3} \cdot 6 = -2$. Thus $y = 3$. The correct answer choice is **B**.

2. The line goes up, so that eliminates D. It is not very steep, so that eliminates B. The y-intercept would be between 0 and 2, so that eliminates A. The correct answer choice is **C**.

3. The average x-value is $\frac{-1+2+3+8}{4} = \frac{12}{4} = 3$. The average y-value is $\frac{4+6-2+8}{4} = \frac{16}{4} = 4$. The correct answer choice is **B**.

4. As n increases by 1, $d(n)$ increase by 2.5. So it is a line with slope 2.5, starting at -7. A closed-form would thus be $d(n) = 2.5n - 7$. A recursive function would be

$$d(n) = \begin{cases} -7 & \text{if } n = 0 \\ d(n-1) + 2.5 & \text{if } n \geq 1 \end{cases}$$

5.

x	$e(x)$	Δ	Δ^2
0	5	5	2
1	10	7	2
2	17	9	2
3	26	11	2
4	37	13	
5	50		

Since the second differences are constant, it could be described with a quadratic. This constant is 2; divide by 2 to obtain a leading coefficient of 1. Subtract x^2 from each value of $e(x)$; find a linear function to match this. The function $e(x) - x^2$ increases by 4 as x increases by 1, and it starts at 5. The linear function is therefore $4x + 5$. Hence, $e(x) = x^2 + 4x + 5$.

6. If the line is $y = 2x + b$, then for inputs = 0, 1, 2, 3, it has outputs = $b, 2 + b, 4 + b, 6 + b$. The errors are then $4 + b, b, 1 + b, 1 + b$. The sum of the squares = $(4 + b)^2 + b^2 + (1 + b)^2 + (1 + b)^2 = 4b^2 + 12b + 18$. This is minimized when $b = \frac{-12}{8} = \frac{-3}{2}$. Hence the line is $y = 2x - 1.5$. The balance point is $(1.5, 1.5)$; this is on the line.

INVESTIGATION 1C   MORE ABOUT RECURSIVE MODELS

For You to Explore

1.

n	$g(n)$
0	5
1	12
2	19
3	26
4	33
5	40
6	47
7	54
8	61
9	68
10	75

To find the closed form for this table, use the techniques you learned in Investigation 1A. The entries here have a constant difference, so this is a linear function and the constant difference of 7 is the coefficient of the variable in the linear expression. You also know that the value of the function at zero is the constant term in the linear expression, so $g(n) = 7n + 5$.
$g(103) = 7(103) + 5 = 726$
$g(104) = 7(104) + 5 = 733$
$g(245) = 7(245) + 5 = 1720$

2.

n	$t(n)$
0	1
1	2
2	4
3	8
4	16
5	32
6	64
7	128
8	256
9	512
10	1024

You may have recognized this function, but if not, think about this idea—how could you compute the fifth entry in the table without computing the four before it? Work back through the recursive definition.

$$t(4) = 2 \cdot t(3) = 2 \cdot 2 \cdot t(2) = \dots$$

This may help you see that the closed form for this table is $t(n) = 2^n$.
$t(103) = 2^{103} \approx 1.014 \times 10^{31}$
$t(104) = 2^{104} \approx 2.028 \times 10^{31}$
$t(245) = 2^{245} \approx 5.654 \times 10^{73}$

3.

n	$j(n)$
0	0
1	1
2	4
3	9
4	16
5	25
6	36
7	49
8	64
9	81
10	100

You probably recognized this function, but you could also use the difference table techniques from Investigation 1A to find the closed form for this table. $j(n) = n^2$.

$j(103) = 103^2 = 10609$

$j(104) = 104^2 = 10816$

$j(245) = 245^2 = 60025$

4.

n	$k(n)$
0	0
1	2
2	6
3	12
4	20
5	30
6	42
7	56
8	72
9	90
10	110

You could use the difference table techniques from Investigation 1A to find the closed form for this table, or you may have recognized the pattern by thinking about some of the entries in the table as products. For example, $k(6) = 42 = 6 \times 7$ or $k(7) = 56 = 7 \times 8$. Closed form rules for this table include $k(n) = n^2 + n$ and $k(n) = (n)(n + 1)$.

$k(103) = 103 \cdot 104 = 10712$

$k(104) = 104 \cdot 105 = 10920$

$k(245) = 245 \cdot 246 = 60270$

5.

n	$\ell(n)$
0	0
1	1
2	3
3	6
4	10
5	15
6	21
7	28
8	36
9	45
10	55

You could use the difference table techniques from Investigation 1A to find the closed form for this table, or

you might have noticed that each of the entries in this table is half of the corresponding entry in the table for Exercise 4. A closed form for this table is $\ell(n) = \frac{(n)(n+1)}{2}$.

$\ell(103) = \frac{103 \cdot 104}{2} = 5356$

$\ell(104) = \frac{104 \cdot 105}{2} = 5460$

$\ell(245) = \frac{245 \cdot 246}{2} = 30135$

6. Notice that there is a constant difference of 3 between outputs. Define your recursive function by giving a starting point, in this case the value of the function at $n = 0$, and then telling how to compute the next entry from the current one, by adding the constant difference.

$$a(n) = \begin{cases} 6 & \text{if } n = 0 \\ a(n-1) + 3 & \text{if } n > 0 \end{cases}$$

Input	Output
0	6
1	9
2	12
3	15
4	18
5	21
6	24
7	27
8	30
9	33
10	36

7. Notice that there is a constant difference of 4 between outputs. Define your recursive function by giving a starting point, in this case the value of the function at $n = 0$, and then telling how to compute the next entry from the current one, by adding the constant difference.

$$b(n) = \begin{cases} 7 & \text{if } n = 0 \\ b(n-1) + 4 & \text{if } n > 0 \end{cases}$$

Input	Output
0	7
1	11
2	15
3	19
4	23
5	27
6	31
7	35
8	39
9	43
10	47

8. There is not a constant difference between outputs, but the differences may look familiar. In fact, the differences are equal to the entries in the table for Exercise 7. This means that this table is the running total of the one in Exercise 7.

This can help you define your recursive function, especially if you find a closed form representation for the table in Exercise 7. Since that's a linear function, the constant difference is the coefficient of the variable and the output at zero is the constant term, so a closed form for the table in the previous exercise is $4n + 7$. This expression gives you the difference between terms in the *current* table, so

$$c(n) = \begin{cases} 7 & \text{if } n = 0 \\ c(n-1) + 4n + 7 & \text{if } n > 0 \end{cases}$$

To compute the entries for your table, just use the expression $4n + 7$ to calculate the difference. For example, $c(6) = c(5) + 4(6) + 7 = 102 + 24 + 7 = 133$.

Input	Output
0	7
1	18
2	33
3	52
4	75
5	102
6	133
7	168
8	207
9	250
10	297

On Your Own

9.

n	$g(n)$
0	0
1	1
2	2
3	3
4	4
5	5
6	6
7	7
8	8
9	9
10	10

The closed form for this table is $g(n) = n$.
$g(103) = 103$
$g(104) = 104$
$g(245) = 245$

10.

n	$t(n)$
0	0
1	3
2	9
3	27
4	81
5	243
6	729
7	2187
8	6561
9	19683
10	59049

Each of the entries is equal to three times the previous entry, so if you work backwards through the recursion,

when you're computing $t(5)$, you end up multiplying 3 by itself 5 times. In other words, $t(n) = 3^n$.
$t(103) = 3^{103} \approx 1.392 \times 10^{49}$
$t(104) = 3^{104} \approx 4.175 \times 10^{49}$
$t(245) = 3^{245} \approx 7.847 \times 10^{116}$

11.

n	$j(n)$
0	1
1	4
2	9
3	16
4	25
5	36
6	49
7	64
8	81
9	100
10	121

You may have recognized the outputs in this table as perfect squares, and found the closed form from that—$j(n) = (n + 1)^2$. If not, you could still use the difference table techniques from Investigation 1A.
$j(103) = 104^2 = 10816$
$j(104) = 105^2 = 11025$
$j(245) = 246^2 = 60516$

12.

n	$k(n)$
0	0
1	0
2	1
3	4
4	10
5	20
6	35
7	56
8	84
9	120
10	165

To find the closed form for this table, you will want to use the difference table techniques from Investigation 1A. The third differences for this table are constant and equal to 1, which means that the coefficient of the n^3 term in the closed form representation will be $\frac{1}{6}$ of that constant difference, or $\frac{1}{6}$. Make a new column in your difference table for $k(n) - \frac{1}{6}n^3$, and then the differences for this column are constant and equal to $-\frac{1}{6}$. This gives you a closed form for this table of $\frac{1}{6}(n^3 - n)$.
$k(103) = \frac{1}{6}(103^3 - 103) = 182104$
$k(104) = \frac{1}{6}(104^3 - 104) = 187460$
$k(245) = \frac{1}{6}(245^3 - 245) = 2450980$

13. Using the difference table techniques from Investigation 1A won't be helpful here, but you may notice that each output is a *factor* of the subsequent output. Instead of looking at differences, you could look at quotients. As it happens, there is a multiplicative pattern in the table.

n	$d(n)$	$\frac{d(n+1)}{d(n)}$
0	1	1
1	1	2
2	2	3
3	6	4
4	24	5
5	120	

From this you can see that to get the n-th output, you multiply the previous output by n.

$$d(n) = \begin{cases} 1 & \text{if } n = 0 \\ nd(n-1) & \text{if } n > 0 \end{cases}$$

n	$k(n)$
0	1
1	1
2	2
3	6
4	24
5	120
6	720
7	5040
8	40320
9	362880
10	3628800

14. You might find it easier to create this table if you take a minute to interpret the notation of the recursive definition. It tells you what the first two outputs will be, and then says that each subsequent output is the sum of the two outputs before it.

n	$f(n)$
0	1
1	1
2	2
3	3
4	5
5	8
6	13
7	21
8	34
9	55
10	89

15. (a) Use your function-modeling language to model this function. Then evaluate it for different values of n, watching what happens to the output as you change the value of n. The value of $b(n)$ will decrease until, at $n = 24$, $b(24) = 0.10$. Then $b(25) = -438.61$, so $n = 24$ gives you the value of $b(n)$ that is the closest to zero.

(b) If you enter the function into your function modeling language exactly as it's written in the Student Edition, and ask it to evaluate $b(36)$, it will return this expression in x:

$$10617.84 - 37.07x$$

Because you are looking for the value of x that will make $b(n)$ as close to zero as possible, you want to set this expression equal to zero and solve for x.

$$x = \frac{10617.84}{37.07} = 286.43$$

Maintain Your Skills

16. To solve this exercise, you can think of the letters as alphabet blocks and imagine a series of blank spaces (as many spaces as blocks) in which you are to place the blocks. For example, to find all the arrangements for the blocks M, O, and P you'd have three blank spaces.

You're going to place a block in the first space, and you have 3 blocks to choose from. Then you have 2 choices for the block in the second space, and 1 left for the third blank. You would multiply all of these numbers to get the total number of choices. Here is a tree diagram to help you see why you'd multiply.

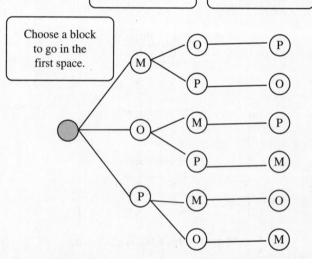

This gives you the list: MOP, MPO, OMP, OPM, PMO, POM for the three blocks M, O, and P.

(a) 2 choices for the first letter, 1 for the second, for a total of $2 \times 1 = 2$ possible arrangements.

(b) 3 choices for the first letter, 2 for the second, and 1 for the last for a total of $3 \times 2 \times 1 = 6$ possible arrangements.

(c) $4 \times 3 \times 2 \times 1 = 24$ arrangements

(d) $5 \times 4 \times 3 \times 2 \times 1 = 120$ arrangements

(e) $6 \times 5 \times 4 \times 3 \times 2 \times 1 = 720$ arrangements

17. $9 \times 8 \times \cdots \times 2 \times 1 = 362880$

18.

$$\frac{n(n+1)}{2} - \frac{(n-1)n}{2} = n$$

Multiply both sides of the equation by 2.

$$n(n+1) - (n-1)n = 2n$$

Multiply out all the expressions on the left-hand side of the equation.

$$n^2 + n - n^2 + n = 2n$$

Combine like terms.

$$2n = 2n$$

1.11 Monthly Payments

Check Your Understanding

1. Use the function you have set up in your function-modeling language:

$$b(n) = \begin{cases} 9000 & \text{if } n = 0 \\ \left(1 + \frac{.05}{12}\right) b(n-1) - 250 & \text{if } n > 0 \end{cases}$$

In this function, n is the number of months and $b(n)$ is the amount you owe at the end of the n-th month. $b(12) = \$6390.74$

2. No, you cannot pay off this loan in 36 months. At the end of 36 months, you would still owe $764.92.

3. Use your CAS to define the monthly payment function, but with a variable p in place of the monthly payment:

$$b(n) = \begin{cases} 9000 & \text{if } n = 0 \\ \left(1 + \frac{.05}{12}\right) b(n-1) - p & \text{if } n > 0 \end{cases}$$

When you evaluate this function for different numbers of months, the CAS will output an expression in p. Because you want to know the payment p that will pay off the loan in the number of months that you input, set this expression equal to 0 and solve for p. That will tell you the necessary monthly payment.

(a) $b(36) = \$10,453.3 - 38.7533p$, so $p = \$269.74$.
(b) $b(39) = \$10,584.5 - 42.2523p$, so $p = \$250.51$.
(c) $b(48) = \$10,988.1 - 53.0149p$, so $p = \$207.26$.

4. This time, you want to set up the monthly payment function with a variable in place of the loan amount.

$$c(n) = \begin{cases} r & \text{if } n = 0 \\ \left(1 + \frac{.05}{12}\right) c(n-1) - 250 & \text{if } n > 0 \end{cases}$$

When you evaluate this function for different numbers of months, the CAS will output an expression in r. Because you want to know the payment r that will allow you to pay off the loan in the number of months that you input at a payment of $250, set this expression equal to 0 and solve for r. That will tell you the amount of money that you could borrow under these terms.

$c(36) = 1.16147r - \$9688.33$, so $r = \$8341.44$. You could borrow up to $8341.44 at an interest rate of 5% and pay it off in 36 months with a monthly payment of $250.

5. Set up the monthly payment function for the given information. You are borrowing $11,000, you pay $310 per month, and you're evaluating the function for $n = 36$. You will not be able to input a variable for the interest rate as you did for the loan and payment amounts, because the expression that the function would return is

really too complex for you solve. (Go ahead and see what happens if you are curious.)

You can start by substituting any interest rate you think is likely. The example below shows 4%.

$$f(n) = \begin{cases} 11,000 & \text{if } n = 0 \\ \left(1 + \frac{.04}{12}\right) d(n-1) - 310 & \text{if } n > 0 \end{cases}$$

When you evaluate $f(36)$ for this interest rate, you get $536.71. This means you still owe money on the loan and that you would need a lower interest rate to pay off the loan in 36 months.

For an interest rate of 1%, $f(36) = \$10.56$, so you still are not low enough. When you try an interest rate of 0.9%, you end up with $f(36) = -\$6.80$. This means that the last payment would be just a little less than the regular $310, and you would have paid off the loan in 36 months for an interest rate of 0.9%.

On Your Own

6. Solutions will vary depending on the interest rate you choose. The following example is worked with a 7% interest rate. Set up a monthly payment function in your function modeling language, leaving the starting amount as a variable, and using a variable for the monthly payment amount as well.

$$f(a, n) = \begin{cases} 1000 \, a & \text{if } n = 0 \\ \left(\frac{12.07}{12}\right) f(n-1) - p & \text{if } n > 0 \end{cases}$$

Then evaluate this function for a equal to the cost of the car in thousands of dollars and $n = 36$ months. You will get an expression in p, which you can set equal to zero and solve for the value p of the monthly payment.

(a) Here is the table that would result:

Cost of car (thousands of dollars)	Monthly payment
10	$308.771
11	$339.648
12	$370.525
13	$401.402
14	$432.279
15	$463.156
16	$494.034
17	$524.911
18	$555.788

(b) The monthly payments have a constant first difference of 30.877, so you could either write the closed form $p = 30.877a + 308.771$ or the recursive form:

$$p = \begin{cases} 308.771 & \text{if } a = 10 \\ g(a-1) + 30.877 & \text{if } a > 10 \end{cases}$$

(c) For a $26,000 car, the monthly payment would be $30.877(26) + \$308.771 = \$1111.57$.

7. Set up a function with a variable p for the price of the car and a variable n for the number of months for each of the two deals. Here is an example of a function for the rebate deal:

$$r(p, n) = \begin{cases} (p - 2) \cdot 1000 & \text{if } n = 0 \\ \left(\frac{12.05}{12}\right) r(p, n-1) - m & \text{if } n > 0 \end{cases}$$

Here is an example of a function for the low interest rate deal:

$$s(p, n) = \begin{cases} 1000p & \text{if } n = 0 \\ \left(\frac{12.009}{12}\right) s(p, n-1) - m & \text{if } n > 0 \end{cases}$$

For each price, evaluate $r(p, 36)$ and $s(p, 36)$. You will get expressions in m, the monthly payment, that you can set equal to zero and solve for m. Then you can find the total amount paid over the life of the loan by multiplying m by 36, the number of months.

Price in Thousands	Rebate Total	Low Interest Total
20	19,421	20,279
21	20,500	21,293
22	21,579	22,307
23	22,658	23,321
24	23,737	24,335
25	24,816	25,349
26	25,895	26,363
27	26,974	27,377
28	28,053	28,391
29	29,132	29,405
30	30,211	30,419
31	31,290	31,433
32	32,369	32,447
33	33,448	33,461
34	34,527	34,474
35	35,606	35,488
36	36,685	36,502
37	37,764	37,516
38	38,843	38,530
39	39,922	39,544
40	41,001	40,558

At some point, you might choose to find the linear function for the monthly payment in terms of the price of the car by using the entries in your table, so that you will have a simpler function to evaluate. For the rebate deal, that linear function would be $m = 1079p - \$2159$. For the low interest rate deal the linear function would be $m = 1014p - \$1$. Solving the system of these two equations will give you the break-even point.

$$m = 1079p - \$2159$$
$$m = 1014p - \$1$$

Subtract the second equation from the first to get

$$0 = 65p - \$2158$$

Then solve for p, finding $p = \$33,200$. For cars that cost less than \$33,200, you would pay less over the life of the loan if you chose the rebate deal. For cars that cost more than \$33,200, you would pay less if you chose the low interest rate deal.

8. After 1 month, you owe $\$10,000 \left(\frac{12.05}{12}\right) - \$500 = \$9541.67$. After 2 months, you owe $\$9541.67 \left(\frac{12.05}{12}\right) - \$500 = \$9081.42$. After 3 months, you owe $\$9081.42 \left(\frac{12.05}{12}\right) - \$500 = \$8619.26$. The correct answer choice is **C**.

Maintain Your Skills

9. (a) $1 + 2 = 3$
    (b) $1 + 2 + 2^2 = 7$
    (c) $1 + 2 + 2^2 + 2^3 = 15$
    (d) $1 + 2 + 2^2 + 2^3 + 2^4 = 31$
    (e) $1 + 2 + 2^2 + 2^3 + 2^4 + 2^5 = 63$
    (f) $1 + 2 + 2^2 + 2^3 + 2^4 + 2^5 + \cdots + 2^9 = 1023$ To find this sum, you might choose to type all of this into your calculator, or you might look for a pattern in the previous sums, or you might complete the following exercise first. It asks you to find both a recursive and a closed form definition for this function. You could use your answer to Exercise 10 to find this sum.

10. (a) To find the recursive definition, you need to express the difference between successive outputs as a function of n. Your results from Exercise 9 should also be helpful, as the sums in that exercise are several of the outputs from an input-output table for this function. The difference between successive outputs is 2^n which leads to the following recursive definition:

$$s(n) = \begin{cases} 1 & \text{if } n = 0 \\ s(n-1) + 2^n & \text{if } n > 0 \end{cases}$$

   (b) If you create an input-output table for this function using your recursive definition, the outputs may begin to look familiar. They are each one less than a power of 2. You might also notice that the difference that you add to find the next output in the table is always one more than the output you're adding it to. For example, $s(6) = s(5) + 2^5 = 31 + 32 = 63$. One closed form definition of this function is $s(n) = 2^{n+1} - 1$.

1.12 The Factorial Function

Check Your Understanding

1. You may have approached this exercise with a table like this:

n	$n!$	$(n-1)!$	$g(n) = \frac{n!}{(n-1)!}$
2	2	1	2
3	6	2	3
4	24	6	4
5	120	24	5
6	720	120	6
7	5040	720	7
8	40,320	5040	8
9	362,880	40,320	9
10	3,628,800	362,880	10

A closed form for the function is $g(n) = n$. Another way you might have seen this answer is to think of the expression for the factorial function shown on page 104. Expand $g(n)$ using this definition.

$$\frac{n!}{(n-1)!} = \frac{n \times (n-1) \times (n-2) \times \cdots \times 2 \times 1}{(n-1) \times (n-2) \times \cdots \times 2 \times 1}$$

Everything cancels out in this expression except for n.

2. Expand $h(n)$ using the expression for the factorial function shown on page 104.

$$\frac{n!}{(n-2)!} = \frac{n \times (n-1) \times (n-2) \times (n-3) \cdots \times 2 \times 1}{(n-2) \times (n-3) \times \cdots \times 2 \times 1}$$

Everything cancels out in this expression except for $n(n-1)$.

n	$h(n)$
3	6
4	12
5	20
6	30
7	42
8	56
9	72
10	90

$h(n) = n(n-1)$

3. $k(n) = n(n-1)(n-2)(n-3)$ looks like $n!$, but with all the terms from $(n-4)$ down to 1 missing from the product. The product of the numbers from 1 to $(n-4)$ is just $(n-4)!$, so $k(n) = \frac{n!}{(n-4)!}$.

4. You might start by computing a few values for the function.

n	$q(n)$
1	1
2	4
3	36
4	576
5	14400

These are all perfect squares, so you might include another column for the square root of each output.

n	$q(n)$	$\sqrt{q(n)}$
1	1	1
2	4	2
3	36	6
4	576	24
5	14400	120

And now you can recognize the factorial function, so $q(n) = (n!)^2$

You could also approach this problem by working backward through the recursive definition for some particular value. For example, $q(5) = 5^2 \times q(4) = 5^2 \times 4^2 \times q(3) = \ldots$. This would help you see that $q(5)$ is the product of all the squares from 1^2 to 5^2. You could rearrange the factors to get this:

$$q(5) = (5 \times 4 \times 3 \times 2 \times 1)(5 \times 4 \times 3 \times 2 \times 1) = (5!)^2$$

5. To get a zero, you would need to have either a factor equal to 10 (or a multiple of 10) or a pair of factors, one of which is a multiple of 2 and the other of which is an odd multiple of 5. To find out how many zeroes will be at the end of $n!$, you can look at a list of the numbers from 1 to n and look for these configurations. In the picture below, the multiples of 10 are marked in bold and the pairs of multiples of 2 and odd multiples of 5 are marked by connectors.

$$1\ 2\ 3\ 4\ 5$$

$$1\ 2\ 3\ 4\ 5\ 6\ 7\ 8\ 9\ \mathbf{10}$$

$$1\ 2\ 3\ 4\ 5\ 6\ 7\ 8\ 9\ \mathbf{10}\ 11\ 12\ 13\ 14\ 15\ 16\ 17\ 18\ 19\ \mathbf{20}$$

If we got as far as 25, there would be something more to think about, because with 25 as a factor, you could pair it with two multiples of 2 to make two zeroes at the end of $n!$.

(a) 5! ends in 1 zero.
(b) 10! ends in 2 zeroes.
(c) 20! ends in 4 zeroes.

On Your Own

6. (a) Expand the factorial expressions $\frac{n!}{(n-2)!} = 56$ in the equation. The denominator of the fraction will cancel out everything in the numerator except for the factors n and $n-1$. Now you have $n(n-1) = 56$. You can either solve this with the quadratic formula or by remembering that $8 \times 7 = 56$. Either method will lead you to conclude that $n = 8$. Note that the quadratic equation also has a root of -7, but this cannot be a solution to the original equation, because $n!$ is not defined for negative integers. Likewise, in parts (b) and (c), the quadratic has a second root, but it does not satisfy the original equation.

(b) After expanding the factorials in $\frac{(n-1)!}{(n-3)!} = 56$ and simplifying the fraction, you have $(n-1)(n-2) = 56$, so $n-1 = 8$ and $n = 9$.

(c) After expanding the factorials in $\frac{(n+1)!}{(n-1)!} = 56$ and simplifying the fraction, you have $(n+1)(n) = 56$, so $n = 7$.

(d) After expanding the factorials in $\frac{(n+1)!}{n!} = 56$ and simplifying the fraction, you have $n + 1 = 56$, so $n = 55$.

7. To get a clearer picture of what's going on in this table, you might want to look at ratios of $\frac{f(n+1)}{f(n)}$.

n	$f(n)$	$\frac{f(n+1)}{f(n)}$
1	2	2
2	4	3
3	12	4
4	48	5
5	240	6
6	1440	

This pattern can be reflected in the recursive definition like this:

$$f(n) = \begin{cases} 2 & \text{if } n = 1 \\ n \cdot f(n-1) & \text{if } n > 1 \end{cases}$$

8. The number of ways is

$$\frac{8!}{3!5!} = \frac{8 \cdot 7 \cdot \cancel{6} \cdot \cancel{5} \cdot \cancel{4} \cdot \cancel{3} \cdot \cancel{2} \cdot \cancel{1}}{\cancel{3} \cdot \cancel{2} \cdot \cancel{1} \cdot \cancel{5} \cdot \cancel{4} \cdot \cancel{3} \cdot \cancel{2} \cdot \cancel{1}} = 56$$

The correct answer choice is **B**.

9. As in Exercise 5, you will end up with one zero at the end of 150! for every positive multiple of 5 that's less than or equal to 150. There are 30 such multiples.

6 of these, however, are also multiples of 25. By pairing a multiple of 25 with one even factor in the factorial expression, you'll create one ending zero, but since it has a second factor of 5, you can pair a multiple of 25 with two even factors and create two ending zeroes. You've already paired one of the 5s with an even number, now you can pair the other 5s with another even number, creating 6 more ending zeroes.

There's also one multiple of 125 that's less than 150, and it has yet another factor of 5 that can be paired with an even factor to account for another ending zero. $30 + 6 + 1 = 37$, so there will be 37 zeroes at the end of 150!.

10. (a)

n	$r(n)$
1	1
2	3
3	6
4	10
5	15

(b) To find the recursive form for this function, look at the first differences in the table you just made. In each case, to find $r(n)$, you add n to $r(n-1)$, so the recursive form is:

$$r(n) = \begin{cases} 1 & \text{if } n = 1 \\ r(n-1) + n & \text{if } n > 1 \end{cases}$$

(c) Yes, there is a closed form. To find it, you can use the difference table techniques from Investigation 1A. You might also remember the following technique for finding the sum of the numbers from 1 to n:

$$S = 1 + 2 + 3 + \cdots + (n-2) + (n-1) + n$$
$$S = n + (n-1) + (n-2) + \cdots + 3 + 2 + 1$$

Add these two equations to get:

$$2S = (n+1) + (n+1) + (n+1) + \cdots +$$
$$(n+1) + (n+1) + (n+1)$$
$$2S = n(n+1)$$
$$S = \frac{n(n+1)}{2}$$

Either technique will help you arrive at a closed form for the function that will be equivalent to $r(n) = \frac{n(n+1)}{2}$.

11. (a)

n	$s(n)$
1	4
2	9
3	16
4	25
5	36

(b) To find the recursive form for this function, look at the first differences in the table you just made. In

each case, to find $s(n)$, you add $2n + 1$ to $s(n-1)$, so the recursive form is:

$$s(n) = \begin{cases} 4 & \text{if } n = 1 \\ s(n-1) + 2n + 1 & \text{if } n > 1 \end{cases}$$

(c) Yes, there is a closed form. You probably recognized these outputs as perfect squares, and were able to identify the function's closed form as $s(n) = (n+1)^2$.

12. (a)

n	$t(n)$
1	3
2	15
3	105
4	945
5	10,395

(b) This is another function for which the difference table techniques in Investigation 1A will not be helpful. But there is a pattern in the *quotients* between successive outputs that you can use to find a recursive definition. To find the next output, multiply the current output by the next odd number in sequence. Or, in symbols:

$$t(n) = \begin{cases} 3 & \text{if } n = 1 \\ t(n-1) \cdot (2n+1) & \text{if } n > 1 \end{cases}$$

(c) This function is very similar to the factorial function. It's a product with a list of factors determined by the input value, and as such, there is no closed form for this function. It could, however, be written without an ellipsis as $\frac{(2n+1)!}{2^n \cdot n!}$.

13. (a)

n	$r(n)$
1	4
2	13
3	40
4	121
5	364

(b) To find the next output from the previous output, just add the next power of 3 in the sequence.

$$r(n) = \begin{cases} 4 & \text{if } n = 1 \\ r(n-1) + 3^n & \text{if } n > 1 \end{cases}$$

(c) To find the closed form for this function, call the sum of the powers of 3 from 1 ($= 3^0$) to 3^n S. Then write another equation for $3S$. You'll have this:

$$3S = 3 + 3^2 + \cdots + 3^{n-1} + 3^n + 3^{n+1}$$
$$S = 1 + 3 + 3^2 + \cdots + 3^{n-1} + 3^n$$

Now you can subtract the second equation from the first to get an equation for $2S$. Most of the powers of three will be eliminated in this process.

$$2S = -1 + 3^{n+1}$$

Divide both sides by 2 and you'll have the closed form $r(n) = \frac{3^{n+1} - 1}{2}$.

14. You might start by thinking about how a large factorial would compare to a large power of 100. The power of 100 is a series of factors of 100, all multiplied together. The factorial is a list of counting numbers in sequence, all multiplied together. There would be the same number of factors in each of these products. If enough of the factors in the factorial expression are greater than 100, it should eventually make up for the fact that the first 99 factors are less than 100. You will need a fairly powerful computational tool to compute these large values. A standard non-graphing scientific calculator will not be able to display 70!, and the number you're looking for must at least be greater than 100. Through experimentation, you can eventually find that for $n = 269$, $100^{269} = 1 \times 10^{538}$ and $269! \approx 2.46745 \times 10^{538}$.

Maintain Your Skills

15. $(x - 1)(x - 2) = x^2 - 3x + 2$, so the coefficient of x is -3 and the constant term is 2.

16. $(x - 1)(x - 2)(x - 3) = (x^2 - 3x + 2)(x - 3) = x^3 - 6x^2 + 11x - 6$, so the coefficient of x^2 is -6 and the constant term is -6.

17. $(x - 1)(x - 2)(x - 3)(x - 4) = (x^3 - 6x^2 + 11x - 6)(x - 4) = x^4 - 10x^3 + 35x^2 - 50x + 24$, so the coefficient of x^3 is -10 and the constant term is 24.

18. Expanding this product is not really practical without a computer algebra system, but there is a pattern in the previous exercises that can help.

In each case, the coefficient of the term with the second-highest degree was always equal to the sum of the constant terms in the factors. This makes sense. Think about this particular product. The only way to get an x^7 term is to multiply seven x's and one constant. Each constant will get a turn, and the coefficient of the x^7 term will be the sum of all the constant terms in the factors. So the coefficient of x^7 will be $-1 + -2 + -3 + -4 + -5 + -6 + -7 + -8 = -36$.

Also, the constant term in the expanded product was always the product of the constant terms in the factors in the previous exercises. This makes sense too. There's only one way to produce a constant in the final product, and that is to multiply all of the constant terms in the factors. That means that the constant term for this expanded product will be $-1 \times -2 \times -3 \times -4 \times -5 \times -6 \times -7 \times -8 = (-1)^8 \cdot 8! = 40320$.

1C MATHEMATICAL REFLECTIONS

1. Create a difference table for the function, and keep taking differences until you find a constant difference.

n	$k(n)$	Δ	Δ^2	$k(n) - 2n^2$
0	0	4	4	0
1	4	8	4	2
2	12	12	4	4
3	24	16		6
4	40			8

As you found, the second difference was constant for this function. That means that this function is quadratic and the coefficient of the x^2 term is half of that constant difference, or 2. Once you know this, you can continue your table with a column computing $k(n) - 2n^2$ as above. This table shows that $k(n) - 2n^2 = 2n$, so you can conclude that $k(n) = 2n^2 + 2n = 2n(n + 1)$.

2. In this table you can see a constant difference of 5 between successive outputs, which leads to the recursive form.

$$a(n) = \begin{cases} 3 & \text{if } n = 0 \\ a(n - 1) + 5 & \text{if } n > 0 \end{cases}$$

Input	Output
0	3
1	8
2	13
3	18
4	23
5	28
6	33
7	38
8	43
9	48
10	53

3. As you begin investigating this function, your first step might be to make a difference table.

Input	Output	Δ
0	3	8
1	11	13
2	24	18
3	42	23
4	65	28
5	93	

The differences are the outputs from the table in Exercise 2, or in other words, the table for this function is a running total of the previous function. This can help you find the recursive form for this function if you know a closed form expression for the previous one.

In Exercise 2, the table shows a function with a constant first difference, so it is a linear function. The constant difference is 5 and the zero term is 3, so a closed form representation of this function would be $a(n) = 5n + 3$. This leads to the following recursive form for the function under consideration:

$$b(n) = \begin{cases} 3 & \text{if } n = 0 \\ b(n - 1) + 5n + 3 & \text{if } n > 0 \end{cases}$$

Input	Output
0	3
1	11
2	24
3	42
4	65
5	93
6	126
7	164
8	207
9	255
10	308

4.

n	$b(n)$
0	12,000
1	11,660
2	11,318.3
3	10,974.9
4	10,629.8
5	10,282.9
6	9934.33
7	9584
8	9231.92
9	8878.08
10	8522.47

(a) The loan amount is $12,000 and the interest rate is 6%.

(b) $n = 33$

5. A sample answer:

To define a function recursively means that values of the function are determined using a starting value and previous values of the function. For example, the recursive definition of the function $f(x) = 4x - 2$ would be

$$f(x) = \begin{cases} -2 & \text{if } x = 0 \\ f(x-1) + 4 & \text{if } x > 0, \end{cases}$$

Here, -2 is the "starting value" for $x = 0$, and you can determine the next value of the function by adding 4 to the previous value.

This recursive definition does not define exactly the same function as the closed form, however, because the closed form of $f(x)$ can be evaluated for any real value of x, and the recursive form can only be evaluated for non-negative integer values of x. It does reveal the constant first difference for this linear function in an explicit way.

There are some functions which cannot be defined in a closed form, such as the factorial function. For functions like this, a recursive definition is the only way for a calculator or computer to evaluate the function.

6.

$$f(n) = \begin{cases} 1 & \text{if } n = 0 \\ f(n-1) \cdot n & \text{if } n > 0 \end{cases}$$

7. Use your function modeling language to create a monthly payment function using a variable as the payment

amount. In this example, p is the payment.

$$g(n) = \begin{cases} 10000 & \text{if } n = 0 \\ \left(\frac{12.05}{12}\right) \cdot g(n-1) - p & \text{if } n > 0 \end{cases}$$

When you evaluate $g(36)$, you'll get the following expression in p:

$$11614.7 - 38.7533p$$

Since the loan should be paid off at 36 months, you'll want to set this expression equal to zero and solve for p, and $p \approx \frac{11614.7}{38.7533} \approx \$299.71$.

CHAPTER REVIEW

1. Each entry is 5 times the previous one, so a recursive rule is

$$a(n) = \begin{cases} 1 & \text{if } n = 0 \\ a(n-1) \cdot 5 & \text{if } n \geq 1 \end{cases}$$

You can rewrite each entry as a power of 5, so a closed form is $a(n) = 5^n$. Therefore, $a(15) = 5^{15} = 30,517,578,125$.

2.

x	$b(x)$	Δ	Δ^2
0	1	2	3
1	3	5	3
2	8	8	3
3	16	11	3
4	27	14	
5	41		

Since the second differences are constant, a quadratic function will agree with the table.

3.

x	$c(x)$	Δ	Δ^2
0	–3	7	4
1	4	11	4
2	15	15	4
3	30	19	
4	49		

The second differences are constant, so this can be matched by a quadratic function. Since the constant is 4, the leading coefficient is 2. The values of $c(x) - 2x^2$ are $-3, 2, 7, 12, 17$. This is matched by the linear function $5x - 3$. Hence, $c(x) = 2x^2 + 5x - 3$.

4.

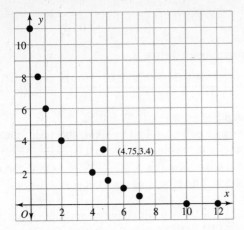

The balance point is found by taking the mean of the x-values ant the mean of the y-values. The points do not appear to be following a linear trend, so a linear function would not be a good fit.

5. The mean absolute error is given by

$$\frac{|0.2 - 1| + |8.8 - 10| + |17 - 16| + |21.1 - 19|}{4}$$
$$= \frac{0.8 + 1.2 + 1 + 2.1}{4} = \frac{5.1}{4} = 1.275$$

The mean squared error is given by

$$\frac{(0.2 - 1)^2 + (8.8 - 10)^2 + (17 - 16)^2 + (21.1 - 19)^2}{4}$$
$$= \frac{0.64 + 1.44 + 1 + 4.41}{4} = \frac{7.49}{4} = 1.8725$$

The standard error is the square root of the mean squared error. Thus it is $\sqrt{1.8725} \approx 1.368$.

6. The balance point has x-coordinate $\frac{1+2+3+4}{4} = 2.5$ and y-coordinate $\frac{-6+2+8+12}{4} = \frac{16}{4} = 4$. So the line of best fit has the form $y = m(x - 2.5) + 4$. At $x = 1, 2, 3, 4$ this line has y-values $-1.5m + 4, -0.5m + 4, 0.5m + 4, 1.5m + 4$. The sum of the squares of the errors will be

$$(1.5m - 10)^2 + (0.5m - 2)^2 + (-0.5m + 4)^2$$
$$\quad + (-1.5m + 8)^2$$
$$= 2.25m^2 - 30m + 100 + 0.25m^2 - 2m + 4 + 0.25m^2$$
$$\quad - 4m + 16 + 2.25m^2 - 24m + 64$$
$$= 5m^2 - 60m + 184$$

This is minimized when $m = \frac{60}{10} = 6$. Hence the line of best fit is $y = 6(x - 2.5) + 4$ or $y = 6x - 11$.

7.

n	$g(n)$
3	3
4	6
5	10
6	15
7	21
8	28
9	36
10	45

8. A recursive function that agrees with this table is

$$g(n) = \begin{cases} 3 & \text{if } n = 3 \\ g(n-1) + n - 1 & \text{if } n \geq 4 \end{cases}$$

To find a closed-form function you can either go through the process you learned in investigation A, or you can simplify the original expression by canceling common factors. This will leave you with $g(n) = \frac{n(n-1)}{2}$ for $n \geq 3$.

9. With an interest rate of 0.03, a payment of $300, and a loan of L dollars, after 36 months you will have a balance of $1.09405L - \$11,286.17$. This will be 0 when $L = \$10,315.95$. With the $1000 down, you could afford to buy a car for $11,315.95.

10. In the first case, with a loan of $11,000, an interest rate of 0.05, and a monthly payment of x, after 36 months the balance will be $\$12,776.19 - 38.7533x = 0$, so $x = \$329.68$.

In the second case, with a loan of $12,000, an interest rate of 0.009, and a monthly payment of x, after 36 months the balance will be $\$12,328.29 - 36.4765x = 0$, so $x = \$337.98$. The first one has the lower payment.

CHAPTER TEST

1. Choices A and C each give a correct amount for $a(1)$, but $a(2)$ is incorrect for both. Choice D gives an incorrect amount for $a(1)$. The correct answer choice is **B**.

2. The points are moving down, so that eliminates choice D. The decrease is not very steep, so that eliminates choice B. The y-intercept would be between 6 and 8, so the correct answer choice is **C**.

3. Since it has constant first differences, it is linear. The slope is $\frac{24-(-3)}{4-1} = \frac{27}{3} = 9$. Using the first given point, $b(n) - (-3) = 9(n - 1)$, or $b(n) + 3 = 9n - 9$, so $b(n) = 9n - 12$. Hence, $b(20) = 180 - 12 = 168$. The correct answer choice is **A**.

4. The line of best fit need not contain any of the data points. The correct answer choice is **C**.

5. The equation simplifies to $(n + 1)n = 72 = 9 \cdot 8$. Therefore, the correct answer choice is **B**.

6. With a loan of $11,000, an interest rate of 4%, and a monthly payment of $$x$, the balance after 36 months is $12,399.99 - 38.1816x = 0$, so $x = \$324.76$. The correct answer choice is **B**.

7.

n	$m(n)$
0	4
1	1
2	-2
3	-5
4	-8
5	-11
6	-14
7	-17
8	-20
9	-23
10	-26

The differences are constant; namely -3. Therefore, the function is linear. Since it starts at 4, $m(n) = -3n + 4$. Thus $m(80) = -240 + 4 = -236$.

8. The differences are the constant 3. So a recursive definition is

$$p(n) = \begin{cases} -8 & \text{if } n = 0 \\ p(n-1) + 3 & \text{if } n \geq 1 \end{cases}$$

This is a linear function, starting at -8, and so $p(n) = 3n - 8$.

9.

x	$g(x)$	Δ	Δ^2
0	4	3	-2
1	7	1	-2
2	8	-1	-2
3	7	-3	
4	4		

Since the second differences are constant, it is quadratic. This constant is -2, so the leading coefficient is -1. Now $g(x) - (-x^2)$ has the values 4, 8, 12, 16, 20. Since this starts at 4 and has 4 for a constant difference, the function $4x + 4$ matches it. Hence $g(x) = -x^2 + 4x + 4$.

10. Substituting the four inputs into $2x - 3$ yields -7.2, -0.4, 5, and 7.4. So the mean absolute error is

$$\frac{|-8.2 + 7.2| + |-0.6 + 0.4| + |4.8 - 5| + |7.4 - 7.4|}{4}$$

$$= \frac{1 + 0.2 + 0.2 + 0}{4} = \frac{1.4}{4} = 0.35$$

The mean squared error is

$$\frac{1^2 + 0.2^2 + 0.2^2 + 0^2}{4} = \frac{1.08}{4} = 0.27$$

The standard error is $\sqrt{0.27} \approx 0.52$.

11. The balance point is found by taking the mean values of the inputs and the outputs. The first is $\frac{-2.1 + 1.3 + 4 + 5.2}{4}$ $= 2.1$ and the second is $\frac{-8.2 - 0.6 + 4.8 + 7.4}{4} = 0.85$. So it is $(2.1, 0.85)$. The given line does not pass through this point.

A line $y = 2x + b$ with inputs from Table R has outputs $-4.2 + b$, $2.6 + b$, $8 + b$, $10.4 + b$. The sum of the squares of the errors would be

$$(b + 4)^2 + (b + 3.2)^2 + (b + 3.2)^2 + (b + 3)^2$$
$$= b^2 + 8b + 16 + b^2 + 6.4b$$
$$+ 10.24 + b^2 + 6.4b + 10.24 + b^2 + 6b + 9$$
$$= 4b^2 + 26.8b + 45.48$$

This is minimized when $b = \frac{-26.8}{8} = -3.35$. The given equation does not minimize the standard error.

12. The balance point is $\left(\frac{5+2+8+5}{4}, \frac{18+12+23+12}{4}\right) = (5, 16.25)$. Say the line of best fit is $y = m(x - 5) + 16.25$. For the given inputs, the outputs are 16.25, $-3m + 16.25$, $3m + 16.25$, 16.25. The sum of the squares of the errors is

$$(1.75)^2 + (3m - 4.25)^2 + (-3m + 6.75)^2 + (4.25)^2$$
$$= 3.0625 + 9m^2 - 25.5m + 18.0625 + 9m^2$$
$$- 40.5m + 45.5625 + 18.0625$$
$$= 18m^2 - 66m + 84.75$$

This is minimized when $m = \frac{66}{36} = \frac{11}{6}$. The line of best fit is therefore $y = \frac{11}{6}(x - 5) + 16.25$ or $y = \frac{11}{6}x + \frac{85}{12}$.

13. The left side simplifies after cancellation to

$$n + \frac{n(n-1)}{2} = \frac{2n}{2} + \frac{n^2 - n}{2} = \frac{n^2 + n}{2} = \frac{(n+1)n}{2},$$

and this equals the right side.

14. If Shawn gets a loan of L dollars at 5% interest for 36 months, paying $300 a month, at the end of that time he will owe $1.16147L - \$11,626 = 0$, so $L = \$10,009.73$. Together with the $1200 down payment, he can pay $11,209.73.

15. He will pay $1200 + \$300(36) = \$12,000$. If he buys a car for $11,210, puts down $1200, pays $350 each month at 5% interest, then after 30 months he will owe $11,339.87 - \$11,159.75 = \$180.12$. Therefore, it will take 31 months to pay off. The last month he will pay $180.12\left(\frac{12.05}{12}\right) = \$180.87$. Add to this $30(\$350) = \$10,500$, plus the original 1200, to get a total expenditure of $11,880.87. He saves about $120.

2.0 Polynomial Basics

Check Your Understanding

1. (a) This is not an identity. There is no constant term when the right side is expanded.

   (b) This is not an identity. One way to "make" it an identity would be to change the right side to $(x + 4)(x - 4)$.

   (c) This is an identity. The right side expands to $x^2 - 16$.

   (d) This is an identity. The right side expands to $4x^2 - 16$.

   (e) This is not an identity. To "make" it an identity, the right side would have to be $8x^2 - 14x - 15$, not $10x^2$.

2. (a) When multiplying this out, there are two ways to get x^{11}. One is to take x^5 from the first term and x^6 from the second, and the other is to take x^6 from the first term and x^5 from the second. In each case, you end up with x^{11} (with a coefficient of 1). Since this happens twice, the coefficient of x^{11} in the normal form of the product will be 2.

   (b) Think about multiplying the factor $x + x^2 + x^3 + x^4 + x^5 + x^6$ by its square. To find all the x^{11} terms in that product, you have to consider which terms from this factor can be matched to terms from the square to get x^{11}.

   If you use an x from this factor, then you'll need the x^{10} term from the square. If you use an x^2 from this factor, then you'll need the x^9 term from the square. So, the total number of times an x^{11} will occur in the product is number of ways to make x^5 through x^{10} in the square.

   In total, there are 3 ways to make x^{10} in the square ($x^4 \cdot x^6$, $x^5 \cdot x^5$, and $x^6 \cdot x^4$), so the coefficient of x^{10} in the square is 3. There are 4 ways to make x^9 in the square, so its coefficient in the square is 4. There are 5 ways to make x^8, 6 ways to make x^7, 5 ways to make x^6, and 4 ways to make x^5.

   Now that you know the coefficients of the terms x^5 through x^{10} in the square, you also know that each of these terms from the square can be matched with exactly one term from the factor $x + x^2 + x^3 + x^4 + x^5 + x^6$ to make an x^{11} term in the product. So the coefficient of x^{11} in the final product will be the sum of the coefficients for x^5 through x^{10} in the square, which is 27.

3. $$\left(\frac{n(n+1)}{2} + \frac{n(n-1)}{2} \right) \left(\frac{n(n+1)}{2} - \frac{n(n-1)}{2} \right)$$
   $$= \left(\frac{n^2 + n}{2} + \frac{n^2 - n}{2} \right) \left(\frac{n^2 + n}{2} - \frac{n^2 - n}{2} \right)$$
   $$= \left(\frac{n^2 + n + n^2 - n}{2} \right) \left(\frac{n^2 + n - n^2 + n}{2} \right)$$
   $$= \left(\frac{2n^2}{2} \right) \left(\frac{2n}{2} \right)$$
   $$= (n^2)(n)$$
   $$= n^3$$

4. (a) $x^3 + x^2 + x + 1$

   (b) $x^7 + x^6 + x^5 + x^4 + x^3 + x^2 + x + 1$

   (c) $x^{15} + x^{14} + x^{13} + x^{12} + x^{11} + x^{10} + x^9 + x^8 + x^7 + x^7 + x^6 + x^5 + x^4 + x^3 + x^2 + x + 1$

   (d) $x^{31} + x^{30} + x^{29} + \cdots + x^3 + x^2 + x + 1$

5. (a) Factor the left side: $(x - 3)(x - 4) = 0$. The solutions come from the Zero Product Property: $x = 3$ or $x = 4$.

   (b) Subtract 50 from each side to get $x^2 + 16x - 80 = 0$. Then use the Quadratic Formula or factor to get $(x + 20)(x - 4) = 0$. The solutions are $x = -20$ or $x = 4$.

   (c) Subtract $10x - 33$ from each side to get $x^2 - 10x + 24 = 0$. Then factor to $(x - 4)(x - 6) = 0$ to find the two solutions $x = 4$ or $x = 6$.

On Your Own

6. (a) Set $x = 1$ to find $f(1) = 1^2 + 4 \cdot 1 - 5 = 0$.

   (b) $f(x)$ factors to $f(x) = (x - 1)(x + 5)$, so $(x - 1)$ is a factor.

7. (a) Set $x = 17$ to find $g(17) = 17^2 - 14 \cdot 17 - 51 = 0$.

   (b) $g(x)$ factors to $g(x) = (x - 17)(x + 3)$, so $(x - 17)$ is a factor.

8. (a) Set $x = 3$ to find $f(3) = 3^2 + 4 \cdot 3 - 5 = 16$.

   (b) $f(x) - f(3) = f(x) - 16 = x^2 + 4x - 21$.

   (c) The polynomial $x^2 + 4x - 21$ factors as $(x + 7)(x - 3)$, so $(x - 3)$ is a factor of $f(x) - f(3)$.

9. (a) Set $x = 5$ to find $g(5) = 5^2 - 14 \cdot 5 - 51 = -96$.

   (b) $g(x) - g(5) = g(x) - (-96) = x^2 - 14x + 45$.

   (c) The polynomial $x^2 - 14x + 45$ factors as $(x - 5)(x - 9)$, so $(x - 5)$ is a factor of $g(x) - g(5)$.

10. (a) Think about how an x^8 term could be built: it could come from an x^3 term and an x^5 term, or from two x^4 terms. In total, there are 3 ways it could happen: a 3 and a 5, a 4 and a 4, or a 5 and a 3.

    (b) Here, think about the third factor $1 + x + x^2 + x^3 + x^4 + x^5$ when you're expanding. If 1 is taken from the third factor, then x^8 must come from the product of the first two factors. If x is taken from the third factor, then x^7 must come from the product of the first two factors. So, the coefficient of x^8 is equal to the number of ways to make x^3 through x^8 when expanding the product of the first two factors.

In total, there are 3 ways to make x^8 in the product of the first two factors, 4 ways to make x^7, 5 ways to make x^6, 6 ways to make x^5, 5 ways to make x^4, and 4 ways to make x^3. In all, there are 27 ways to make a factor of x^8 by multiplying one term from the product of the first two factors and a term from the third factor.

11. (a) Try some examples. The degree of the product is the sum of the degrees of the original polynomials. In symbols, $\deg(fg) = \deg(f) + \deg(g)$.
   (b) Try some examples. The degree of a polynomial is unchanged when it is multiplied by any constant. $\deg(2g) = \deg(g)$.
   (c) The degree of a sum can't be more than the degree of either polynomial. The sum may also be have a smaller degree if the leading term cancels: for example, $f(x) = x^3 + 3$ and $g(x) = -x^3 + x^2$. Here, $\deg(f + g) = 2$, and the degrees of f and g are each 3.

12. There are many possible ways to do this. For example, if the first polynomial is

$$x^6 + x^5 + x - 1 \quad \text{(degree 6)}$$

and the second polynomial is

$$-x^6 - x^5 + 3x^4 + 2x^2 \quad \text{(degree 6)}$$

then the sum is

$$3x^4 + 2x^2 + x + 1 \quad \text{(degree 4)}$$

All solutions can be categorized this way:

Polynomial 1: $a_6x^6 + a_5x^5 + a_4x^4 + a_3x^3 + a_2x^2 + a_1x + a_0$

Polynomial 2: $b_6x^6 + b_5x^5 + b_4x^4 + b_3x^3 + b_2x^2 + b_1x + b_0$

where all of these conditions are met:

- $a_6 \neq 0$ and $b_6 \neq 0$ (both polynomials are degree 6)
- $a_6 + b_6 = 0$ (the degree 6 terms cancel each other out)
- $a_5 + b_5 = 0$ (the degree 5 terms cancel each other out)
- $a_4 + b_4 \neq 0$ (the degree 4 terms do not cancel each other out, and at least one of them is non-zero)

13. Impossible. Adding does not change the degree of any term. It's possible to lose terms when you add two polynomials, so the degree of the sum can be less than the degree of either of the polynomials you're adding. This happens if you the highest degree terms in the addends cancel each other out. (See Exercise 12.) But it's not possible to get terms of a new degree when you add two polynomials, so you can't get new terms with higher degrees.

14. Multiply out each expression:

$$(r + s)^3 = r^3 + 3r^2s + 3rs^2 + s^3$$

$$-3rs(r + s) = -3r^2s - 3rs^2$$

The middle two terms of the $(r + s)^3$ expansion cancel out, leaving $r^3 + s^3$ as the simplified normal form.

Maintain Your Skills

15. Each linear factor contributes 1 to the degree, so count the linear factors. Squared factors count 2, and so forth.
   (a) 1   (b) 2   (c) 3   (d) 4
   (e) 7   (f) 3   (g) 7   (h) 20

16. (a) $a^2 - b^2$
   (b) $a^3 - b^3$
   (c) $a^4 - b^4$
   (d) $a^5 - b^5$
   (e) Here is the general case:

$$(a - b)(a^n + a^{n-1}b + a^{n-2}b^2 + \cdots + a^2b^{n-2}$$
$$+ ab^{n-1} + b^n) = a^{n+1} - b^{n+1}$$

17. (a) $1 - x^2$
   (b) $1 + x^3$
   (c) $1 - x^4$
   (d) Here is the general case:

$$(1 + x)(1 - x + x^2 - x^3 + \cdots + (-1)^n x^n) = 1 + (-1)^n x^{n+1}$$

INVESTIGATION 2A   ABOUT FUNCTIONS

2.1   Getting Started

For You to Explore

1. (a) The product of 3 and 4 is 12.
   (b) The quotient of 3 and 4 is $\frac{3}{4}$.
   (c) The quotient of 6 and 8 is $\frac{6}{8}$, which reduces to $\frac{3}{4}$.
   (d) The quotient of 0 and 23 is $\frac{0}{23}$, or 0.
   (e) The quotient of 23 and 0 can be written as $\frac{23}{0}$, which is not a real number.
   (f) Calculate $SQRT(5)$ first, which is $\sqrt{5}$. Now calculate $SQR(\sqrt{5})$, which is 5.
   (g) $SQR(5)$ is 25, and $SQRT(25)$ is 5.
   (h) Since $SQRT(-5)$ is not defined as a real number, $SQR(SQRT(-5))$ cannot be evaluated.
   (i) $SQR(-5) = 25$, then $SQRT(25) = 5$.
   (j) Calculate $P(3, 4)$ and $P(2, 6)$ first. Both are equal to 12. $Q(12, 12)$ is equal to $\frac{12}{12}$, or 1.
   (k) Pierre de Fermat's birthday is August 17.
   (l) 3 does not have a birthday, so $BD(3)$ cannot be calculated.
   (m) $SUM(9, 16)$ is 25, then $SQRT(25)$ is 5.
   (n) $SQRT(9) = 3$ and $SQRT(16) = 4$, then $SUM(3, 4) = 7$.
   (o) BD(Isaac Newton) is January 4th, but $SQRT$(January 4th) doesn't make sense. Thus, $SQRT(BD(\text{Isaac Newton}))$ cannot be evaluated.
   (p) $SQRT(PR(-2, \frac{1}{3}))$ is $SQRT(\frac{-2}{3})$. You can't take the square root of a negative number, so this is undefined.
   (q) The reciprocal of 2 is $\frac{1}{2}$.
   (r) The reciprocal of 2 is $\frac{1}{2}$, then the reciprocal of $\frac{1}{2}$ is 2.

(s) The reciprocal of 2 is $\frac{1}{2}$, then the reciprocal of $\frac{1}{2}$ is 2, and then the reciprocal of 2 is $\frac{1}{2}$ again.

(t) Zero does not have a reciprocal, so this does not exist.

2. The function $m(x)$ might output the greatest integer that is less than or equal to the input. Remember, though, that this is not the only possible rule that $m(x)$ could follow.

3. (a) No, the statement is not always true. For example, if $a = 16$ and $b = 9$, the statement is false.

   (b) The statement is true whenever one of a or b is zero, and false otherwise.

4. (a) p can be any person.

   (b) Square roots exist for any positive number or 0, so the domain of $SQRT$ is any non-negative number.

   (c) Division by zero is invalid, so the domain of QUO is any pair of real numbers (a, b) when b is not equal to 0.

   (d) n can be any nonzero number.

   (e) x can be any nonnegative number, other than 2.

5. (a) $BD(p)$ can be equal to any day of the year, depending on what person p is the input. Thus, the range of BD is any day of the year.

   (b) $SQRT$ outputs the positive square root of a number, except for $SQRT(0) = 0$. Thus, the range of $SQRT$ is any nonnegative number.

   (c) QUO can output any number, so the range of QUO is all numbers.

   (d) Any positive number is the reciprocal of some other positive number. Likewise for negative numbers. The range of REC is all real numbers other than 0.

   (e) You can try plugging in positive numbers bigger than 2 and smaller than 2, and you will eventually see that you can get any output. The range is all real numbers. This can be shown with algebra as follows: For which c is there a solution to $\frac{\sqrt{x}}{x-2} = c$? If $c = 0$, then $x = 0$ works. If $c \neq 0$, then square both sides, get rid of the fraction, multiply out and combine like terms to obtain: $c^2 x^2 - (4c^2 + 1)x + 4c^2 = 0$. The discriminant of this quadratic equation is $(4c^2 + 1)^2 - 4 \cdot c^2 \cdot 4c^2 = 8c^2 + 1 > 0$ for all c. So it always has two solutions; the larger solution works for $c > 0$ and the smaller solution works for $c < 0$.

On Your Own

6. (a) This is not enough information. The input (a, b) could have been 3 and 3, -1 and -9, $\frac{1}{2}$ and 18, or others.

   (b) Only one number has a square root of 9, and that's 81.

   (c) Two numbers have a square of 9, -3 and 3. The input could have been either, so this is not enough information.

7. (a) -3 and 3 both produce 9. Other examples work.

   (b) There are many examples of people with the same birthday—most twins, for example.

   (c) $(3, 6)$ and $(4, 8)$ both produce $\frac{1}{2}$. Other examples work.

   (d) Impossible. All numbers that have square roots have unique square roots.

   (e) Impossible. No two numbers have the same reciprocal.

8. (a)
$$D(x, y) = \sqrt{x^2 + y^2}$$
$$D(0, 0) = \sqrt{0^2 + 0^2}$$
$$= \sqrt{0}$$
$$= 0$$

(b)
$$D(3, 4) = \sqrt{3^2 + 4^2}$$
$$= \sqrt{9 + 16}$$
$$= \sqrt{25}$$
$$= 5$$

(c)
$$D(-3, 4) = \sqrt{(-3)^2 + 4^2}$$
$$= \sqrt{9 + 16}$$
$$= \sqrt{25}$$
$$= 5$$

(d)
$$D(4, 3) = \sqrt{4^2 + 3^2}$$
$$= \sqrt{16 + 9}$$
$$= \sqrt{25}$$
$$= 5$$

(e) Many answers are possible. One is the input $(5, 0)$. There are many others, such as $(-5, 0)$ and $(-3, -4)$.

(f) Here is the graph:

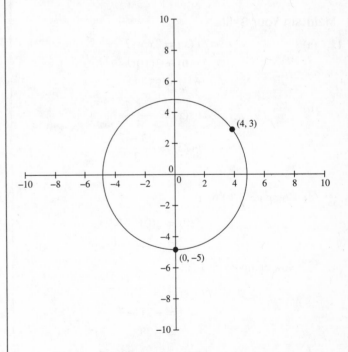

$D(x, y)$ represents the distance from $(0, 0)$ to (x, y). So, all the points that make $D(x, y) = 5$ are the points that are 5 units away from $(0, 0)$. This is a circle with center $(0, 0)$ and radius 5.

9. (a)
$$B(x, y, z) = D(x, y) + z$$
$$B(0, 0, 0) = D(0, 0) + 0$$
$$= 0 + 0$$
$$= 0$$

(b)
$$B(3, 4, 5) = D(3, 4) + 5$$
$$= 5 + 5$$
$$= 10$$

(c)
$$B(4, 3, 5) = D(4, 3) + 5$$
$$= 5 + 5$$
$$= 10$$

(d)
$$B(-3, 4, -5) = D(-3, 4) - 5$$
$$= 5 - 5$$
$$= 0$$

(e)
$$B(5, 12, z) = 7$$
$$D(5, 12) + z = 7$$
$$13 + z = 7$$
$$z = -6$$

(f) The equation is the same as $\sqrt{x^2 + y^2} + z = 0$, so $z = -\sqrt{x^2 + y^2}$. The solutions are all triples $(x, y, -\sqrt{x^2 + y^2})$, where x and y are any real numbers.

10. (a) $D(x, y)$ is defined as $\sqrt{x^2 + y^2}$.
Since $\sqrt{}$ is defined to be nonnegative, $\sqrt{x^2 + y^2}$ is never negative, and $D(x, y)$ is never negative.

(b) $B(x, y, z)$ can be negative if z is negative. One example is $B(3, 4, -12)$.

Maintain Your Skills

11. (a)
$$f(x) = 3x - 7$$
$$f(10) = 3(10) - 7$$
$$= 23$$

(b)
$$g(x) = \frac{x + 7}{3}$$
$$g(23) = \frac{23 + 7}{3}$$
$$= 10$$

(c) Compute $f(0)$ first:
$$f(0) = 3(0) - 7$$
$$= -7$$

Now compute $f(-7)$:
$$f(-7) = 3(-7) - 7$$
$$= -21 - 7$$
$$= -28$$

(d)
$$g(g(-28)) = g\left(\frac{-28 + 7}{3}\right)$$
$$= g\left(\frac{-21}{3}\right)$$
$$= g(-7)$$
$$= \frac{-7 + 7}{3}$$
$$= 0$$

(e)
$$f(g(172)) = f\left(\frac{172 + 7}{3}\right)$$
$$= f\left(\frac{179}{3}\right)$$
$$= 3\left(\frac{179}{3}\right) - 7$$
$$= 179 - 7$$
$$= 172$$

(f)
$$g(f(0.27)) = g(3(0.27) - 7)$$
$$= g(0.81 - 7)$$
$$= g(-6.19)$$
$$= \frac{-6.19 + 7}{3}$$
$$= \frac{0.81}{3}$$
$$= 0.27$$

(g) Expanding this expression would take a lot of work. Instead, it is easier to use the pattern from the previous examples. $f(g(1000))$ must equal 1000, so $f(g(f(g(1000)))) = 1000$.

12. (a)
$$h(x) = (x - 1)^2$$
$$h(4) = (4 - 1)^2$$
$$= 9$$

(b)
$$j(x) = \sqrt{x} + 1$$
$$j(9) = \sqrt{9} + 1$$
$$= 4$$

(c)
$$h(h(3)) = h((3 - 1)^2)$$
$$= h(4)$$
$$= (4 - 1)^2$$
$$= 9$$

(d)
$$j(j(16)) = j(\sqrt{16} + 1)$$
$$= j(5)$$
$$= \sqrt{5} + 1$$

(e)
$$j(h(5)) = j((5 - 1)^2)$$
$$= j(16)$$
$$= \sqrt{16} + 1$$
$$= 5$$

(f) $j(h(-5)) = j((-5 - 1)^2) = j(36) = \sqrt{36} + 1 = 7$

(g) Function $j(x)$ has only nonnegative numbers in its domain, so $j(-3)$ does not exist. Then, $h(j(-3))$ does not exist, either.

13. (a) $f(3) = 3 + 4 = 7$
(b) $f(f(3)) = f(7) = 7 + 4 = 11$
(c) $f(f(f(3))) = f(11) = 11 + 4 = 15$
(d) $f(f(f(f(3)))) = f(15) = 15 + 4 = 19$

(e) Each application of f adds four to the original input. Since f has been applied twelve times, the effect will be to add 4 twelve times.

$$\underbrace{f(f(\dots(f(3))))}_{12\,f\text{'s}} = 51$$

14. (a) $g(1) = \frac{1+1}{1} = \frac{2}{1} = 2$

(b) $g(g(1)) = g(2) = \frac{2+1}{2} = \frac{3}{2}$

(c) $g(g(g(1))) = g\left(\frac{3}{2}\right) = \frac{\frac{3}{2}+1}{\frac{3}{2}} = \frac{5}{3}$

(d) $g(g(g(g(1)))) = g\left(\frac{5}{3}\right) = \frac{\frac{5}{3}+1}{\frac{5}{3}} = \frac{8}{5}$

(e) $g(g(g(g(g(1))))) = g\left(\frac{8}{5}\right) = \frac{\frac{8}{5}+1}{\frac{8}{5}} = \frac{13}{8}$

(f) You may have recognized the sequence of numerators and denominators in this problem as the Fibonacci numbers, defined recursively as

$$F(n) = \begin{cases} 1 & \text{if } n = 0 \\ 1 & \text{if } n = 1 \\ F(n-1) + F(n-2) & \text{if } n \geq 2 \end{cases}$$

In each case, if g is composed n times, the output will be $\frac{F(n+1)}{F(n)}$.

$$\underbrace{g(g(\dots(g(1))))}_{10\,g\text{'s}} = \frac{144}{89}$$

2.2 Getting Precise About Functions

Check Your Understanding

1. (a) The graph of this function is a downward-facing parabola. The vertex is at $(36, 1296)$, so the range is all reals less than or equal to 1296.

(b) Here is the graph:

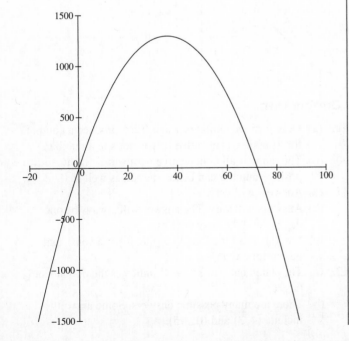

2. (a) If the base is x and the perimeter is 144, the height y can be found using the perimeter. The formula for the perimeter of this rectangle is $P = 2x + 2y$, so $144 = 2x + 2y$. Then solve for y:

$$144 = 2x + 2y$$
$$144 - 2x = 2y$$
$$72 - x = y$$

The area is equal to xy. Since $y = 72 - x$, the area is $A(x) = x(72 - x)$.

(b) Since the shape must be a rectangle, the length of the base must be greater than 0. Also, the length must be less than 72, since the height of the rectangle must also be positive.

(c) The rectangle with the largest area is a square of side length 36, which has area $36^2 = 1296$. A rectangle must also have positive area. The graph shows that any positive area less than or equal to 1296 is possible.

(d)

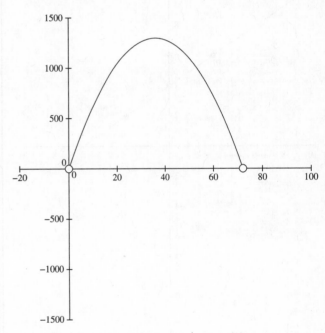

Note that this graph does *not* include the points $(0, 0)$ or $(72, 0)$.

3. No, these functions are not the same because they have different domains and ranges. Even though the functions agree in many places, they are not identical functions.

4. (a) Both tables are the same:

Input	Output
0	3
1	8
2	13
3	18
4	23
5	28

(b) The natural domain of H is all real numbers. Any number can be used as input to H. The natural domain of K is all nonnegative integers, by its definition. Defining $K(0)$ allows the definition of $K(1)$, which allows $K(2)$, and so on, but only integer values of n are allowed.

(c) H and K are not the same function, because they have different domains.

5. (a) Only positive numbers x and 0 can produce an output for $h(x)$. If x is negative, then so is x^3. Then $\sqrt{x^3}$ is not a real number.

(b) The range is all nonnegative numbers $\mathbb{R}^+$. Any positive number can be the output, as well as 0.

6. (a) The statement $f : \mathbb{R}^2 \to \mathbb{R}$ indicates the domain and target.

(b) There are infinitely many pairs that make f equal to 12. Some include $(3, 2)$ and $(0, 4)$. In fact, any number can be picked for a and b can be found.

(c) Since $f(x, y) = 2x + 3y$, any point that makes the equation true satisfies $2x + 3y = 12$. This is the graph of a straight line:

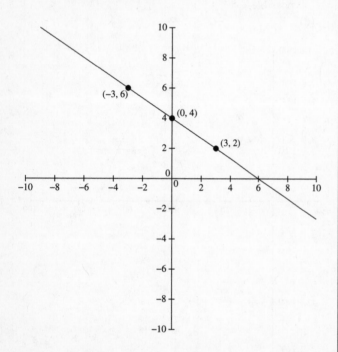

7. (a) $3(3)^2 = 27$ and $3(-3)^2 = 27$

(b)
$$12 = 3x^2$$
$$4 = x^2$$
$$\pm\sqrt{4} = x$$
$$2, -2 = x$$

(c) $f(11) = 3(11)^2 = 363$ and $f(10) = 3(10)^2 = 300$. $363 - 300 = 63$.

(d)
$$f(x + 1) = 3(x + 1)^2$$
$$= 3(x^2 + 2x + 1)$$
$$= 3x^2 + 6x + 3$$

(e) $f(x+1) - f(x) = (3x^2 + 6x + 3) - (3x^2) = 6x + 3$.

(f) Since $g(x) = 6x + 3$, then $g(10) = 6 \cdot 10 + 3 = 63$. Alternately, $g(10) = f(11) - f(10)$, which was calculated earlier in this exercise.

8. (a) 5

(b) 5

(c) 10

(d) A

(e) $g(x) = (x+1)^2 - x^2 = (x^2 + 2x + 1) - (x^2) = 2x + 1$

(f) $6x + 3$

(g) $20x + 10$

(h) $g(x) = (x+1)^2 + 10(x+1) - 12 - (x^2 + 10x - 12) = 2x + 11$

(i) $g(x) = 3(x+1)^2 + 10(x+1) - 12 - (3x^2 + 10x - 12) = 6x + 13$

9. (a) The natural domain for f is the set of inputs for which it is defined. In this case, that's all real numbers such that $x \le 6$.

(b) Here is a sketch of the graph:

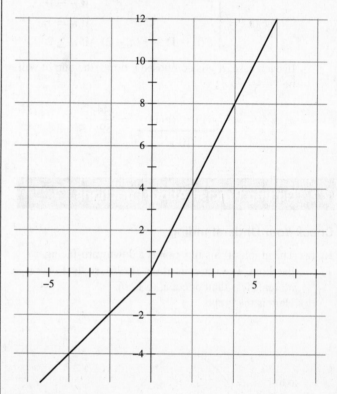

On Your Own

10. (a) Only positive numbers x and 0 can produce an output for $j(x)$. If x is negative, $\sqrt{x}$ is not a real number.

(b) The range is all nonnegative numbers $\mathbb{R}^+$. Any positive number can be the output, as well as 0.

11. (a) Answers will vary.

(b) Answers will vary. The answer will always be one day beyond the answer to part (a).

(c) Yes, this is a function. As a rule, it has a consistent output for any input.

12. (a) The statement $N : \mathbb{R}^2 \to \mathbb{R}$ indicates the domain and target.

(b) There are many possible answers. Some answers include $(4, 3)$ and $(0, -5)$.

(c) The only pair of numbers that makes $x^2 + y^2 = 0$ is $(0, 0)$.

(d) It is the graph of $x^2 + y^2 = 25$, a circle with center $(0, 0)$ and radius 5:

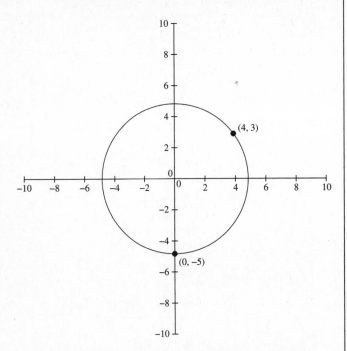

(e) The *range* is all actual outputs of the function. Since squares are never negative, the output of N cannot be negative. The output can be zero, and any output $k > 0$ is the result of $N(\sqrt{k}, 0)$. Therefore the range is $\mathbb{R}^+$, the nonnegative real numbers.

13. The two functions do not have the same domain. The domain of $t(x)$ is $\mathbb{R}^+$, nonnegative real numbers. The domain of $f(x)$ is $\mathbb{R}$, all real numbers. This happens because of the square root in the definition of $t(x)$.

Specifically, $t(-7)$ is undefined, since $\sqrt{-7}$ is not a real number. However, $f(-7) = -7$ is fine. The functions do not behave identically, so they are not the same function.

14. (a) This function is a quadratic with vertex $\left(\frac{1}{12}, \frac{-49}{24}\right)$. Domain: $\mathbb{R}$. Target: $\mathbb{R}$. Range: $f(x) \geq \frac{-49}{24}$.

(b) This function cannot accept numbers less than 3, and outputs cannot be negative. Domain: $x \geq 3$. Target: $\mathbb{R}$. Range: $\mathbb{R}^+$.

(c) You cannot divide by 0, nor take the square root of a negative number, so the domain is all $x > 3$. The target is $\mathbb{R}$ and the range is all positive numbers.

(d) This function cannot accept 0 as input, and cannot output 1 (since $\frac{1}{x}$ cannot equal zero). Domain: $x \neq 0$. Target: $\mathbb{R}$. Range: $f(x) \neq 1$.

(e) The input is any point (x, y). Any real number can be the output. Domain: $\mathbb{R}^2$. Target: $\mathbb{R}$. Range: $\mathbb{R}$.

(f) The input is a value x and the output is a *point*, the point on $y = x^3$ that has that value of x. Domain: $\mathbb{R}$. Target: $\mathbb{R}^2$. Range: all points (x, y) satisfying $y = x^3$.

(g) This function swaps x and y, so any possible input or output is possible. Domain: $\mathbb{R}^2$. Target: $\mathbb{R}^2$. Range: $\mathbb{R}^2$.

15. (a) $f(g(2)) = f(-4) = 32$

(b) $g(f(2)) = g(-4) = -10$

(c) $f(g(z)) = f(z-6) = (z-6)^2 - 4(z-6) = z^2 - 16z + 60$

(d) $g(f(z)) = g(z^2 - 4z) = z^2 - 4z - 6$

(e) $f(f(z)) = f(z^2 - 4z) = (z^2 - 4z)^2 - 4(z^2 - 4z) = z^4 - 8z^3 + 12z^2 + 16z$

(f) $g(g(z)) = g(z-6) = (z-6) - 6 = z - 12$

(g) The equation to solve is $a^2 - 4a = a - 6$. This simplifies to the quadratic

$$a^2 - 5a + 6 = 0$$
$$(a-2)(a-3) = 0$$

So $a = 2$ or $a = 3$.

(h) Rules for $f(g(b))$ and $g(f(b))$ were found in this exercise. The equation to solve is $b^2 - 16b + 60 = b^2 - 4b - 6$. This can be solved for b:

$$b^2 - 16b + 60 = b^2 - 4b - 6$$
$$-16b + 60 = -4b - 6$$
$$60 = 12b - 6$$
$$66 = 12b$$
$$5.5 = b$$

16. (a)
$$2f(a) + 3 = 5$$
$$2(3a + 2) + 3 = 5$$
$$6a + 4 + 3 = 5$$
$$6a + 7 = 5$$
$$6a = -2$$
$$a = -\frac{1}{3}$$

(b)
$$f(2a + 3) = 5$$
$$3(2a + 3) + 2 = 5$$
$$6a + 9 + 2 = 5$$
$$6a + 11 = 5$$
$$6a = -6$$
$$a = -1$$

(c)
$$f(2a + 3) = a + 3$$
$$3(2a + 3) + 2 = a + 3$$
$$6a + 9 + 2 = a + 3$$
$$6a + 11 = a + 3$$
$$5a = -8$$
$$a = -\frac{8}{5}$$

17. (a)
$$12290 = 3x + 2$$
$$12288 = 3x$$
$$4096 = x$$

(b) In this case, you go through the same process but end up with $4096 = x^2$. This has two solutions, $x = 64$ and $x = -64$. That's because when you raise a

negative number to an even power, you get a positive output.
  (c) Solve for the x^3 term in the same manner, $4096 = x^3$. This has only one solution, $x = 16$.
  (d) Solve to get $4096 = x^6$. Because x is raised to an even power, there are two solutions, $x = 4$ and $x = -4$.

18. In Exercise 17, you worked with these same functions and found that for the second and fourth functions, there were some pairs of inputs that could result in the same output. This would mean that Derman's conjecture is false for those functions.

  (a) For $f(x) = 3x + 2$, Derman's conjecture is true.
  (b) For $f(x) = 3x^2 + 2$, Derman's conjecture is false.
  (c) For $f(x) = 3x^3 + 2$, Derman's conjecture is true.
  (d) For $f(x) = 3x^6 + 2$, Derman's conjecture is false.

19. The denominator cannot be 0, so $x^2 - 5x + 4 \neq 0$. This implies that $(x-1)(x-4) \neq 0$, so $x \neq 1$ or 4. The correct answer choice is **D**.

20. The "inverse Spiro trick" would be, "Divide by 4, add 3, multiply by 2, and subtract 3." To undo the trick, you need to work through each of Spiro's functions in reverse order and undo the calculations step by step.

21. (a) To find $f(7)$, you first need to find a. You know that $3a + 1 = 7$, so $a = 2$. Then, $f(7) = 2 - 2 = 0$
  (b) First, find a. $3a + 1 = 14$, so $a = \frac{13}{3}$, and $f(14) = \frac{13}{3} - 2 = \frac{7}{3}$
  (c) $3a + 1 = 16$, so $a = 5$. $f(16) = 5 - 2 = 3$
  (d) Go through the same process that you used for the specific values. $3a + 1 = z$, so $a = \frac{z-1}{3}$.
  $f(z) = \frac{z-1}{3} - 2 = \frac{z-1-6}{3} = \frac{z-7}{3}$

22. Answers will vary. Many answers are possible. Here are some:

$$f(x) = x + 5, g(x) = x - 3$$
$$f(x) = 5x, g(x) = 3x$$
$$f(x) = x^2, g(x) = x^3$$

Most of the time, the two functions should perform related operations, such as adding or subtracting, for example.

Maintain Your Skills

23. Graphing each function shows its behavior. Also, any function with an even exponent, like $f(x) = x^2$, cannot output negative numbers. Then $f(x)$ has $\mathbb{R}^+$ as its range, not $\mathbb{R}$. Functions b, d, and e have a range of $\mathbb{R}$.

24. (a)
$$g(x, y) = \frac{(3x + 5) - (3y + 5)}{x - y}$$
$$= \frac{3x + 5 - 3y - 5}{x - y}$$
$$= \frac{3x - 3y}{x - y}$$
$$= \frac{3(x - y)}{x - y}$$
$$= 3$$

(b)
$$g(x, y) = \frac{(5x + 5) - (5y + 5)}{x - y}$$
$$= \frac{5x + 5 - 5y - 5}{x - y}$$
$$= \frac{5x - 5y}{x - y}$$
$$= \frac{5(x - y)}{x - y}$$
$$= 5$$

(c)
$$g(x, y) = \frac{(12x + 5) - (12y + 5)}{x - y}$$
$$= \frac{12x + 5 - 12y - 5}{x - y}$$
$$= \frac{12x - 12y}{x - y}$$
$$= \frac{12(x - y)}{x - y}$$
$$= 12$$

(d)
$$g(x, y) = \frac{(x^2) - (y^2)}{x - y}$$
$$= \frac{x^2 - y^2}{x - y}$$
$$= \frac{(x + y)(x - y)}{x - y}$$
$$= x + y$$

(e)
$$g(x, y) = \frac{(x^2 + x) - (y^2 + y)}{x - y}$$
$$= \frac{x^2 + x - y^2 - y}{x - y}$$
$$= \frac{(x^2 - y^2) + (x - y)}{x - y}$$
$$= \frac{(x + y)(x - y) + (x - y)}{x - y}$$
$$= \frac{(x + y + 1)(x - y)}{x - y}$$
$$= x + y + 1$$

(f)
$$g(x, y) = \frac{(3x^2 + 2x - 1) - (3y^2 + 2y - 1)}{x - y}$$
$$= \frac{3x^2 + 2x - 1 - 3y^2 - 2y + 1}{x - y}$$
$$= \frac{(3x^2 - 3y^2) + (2x - 2y)}{x - y}$$
$$= \frac{3(x + y)(x - y) + 2(x - y)}{x - y}$$
$$= \frac{(3x + 3y + 2)(x - y)}{x - y}$$
$$= 3x + 3y + 2$$

Check Your Understanding

1. (a)
$$f(x) = 2x + 3$$
$$f(3) = 2(3) + 3$$
$$= 9$$

(b)
$$g(x) = 5x + 1$$
$$g(3) = 5(3) + 1$$
$$= 16$$

(c)
$$f(g(3)) = f(5(3) + 1)$$
$$= f(16)$$
$$= 2(16) + 3$$
$$= 35$$

(d) $f \circ g(3)$ is notation that means exactly the same thing as $f(g(3))$, so $f \circ g(3) = 35$.

(e) $g \circ f(3) = g(9) = 5(9) + 1 = 46$.

(f) If $f(3)$ is 9 and $g(3)$ is 16, then it is $9 \cdot 16 = 144$.

2. (a)
$$g \circ f(x) = g(2x + 3)$$
$$= 5(2x + 3) + 1$$
$$= (10x + 15) + 1$$
$$= 10x + 16$$

(b)
$$f \circ g(x) = f(5x + 1)$$
$$= 2(5x + 1) + 3$$
$$= (10x + 2) + 3$$
$$= 10x + 5$$

3. (a) The formula for the area of a circle is $A = \pi r^2$, where A is the area and r is the radius. Here, A is in square inches.

(b) Since $r = 4t$, substitute r in the previous formula with $4t$ to get
$$A = \pi (4t)^2$$
Another way to write this is $A = 16\pi t^2$.

4. (a) $f \circ g(x) = f(x^2 + 3) = x^2 + 3$.
$g \circ f(x) = g(x) = x^2 + 3$ since $f(x) = x$.

(b) $f \circ g(x) = f(2x - 7) = 2x - 7$, and $g \circ f(x) = 2x - 7$.

(c) $f \circ g(x) = f((x - 4)^3) = (x - 4)^3$, and $g \circ f(x) = (x - 4)^3$.

(d) An *identity* is something that doesn't change the other input. For example, 0 is the identity for addition, since $a + 0 = a$ for any number a. This is the same behavior $f(x) = x$ has under composition. So, $f(x) = x$ is the *identity function* for composition.

5. Use the method of Exercise 7. Since $f(x) = 3x - 1$, the result of $f \circ g(x)$ is
$$3 \cdot g(x) - 1$$

So, to find $g(x)$, solve the equation $3 \cdot g(x) - 1 = x$:
$$3 \cdot g(x) - 1 = x$$
$$3 \cdot g(x) = x + 1$$
$$g(x) = \frac{x + 1}{3}$$

Note that if f and g describe actions, they reverse each other: f multiplies by 3 and subtracts 1, while g adds 1 and divides by 3.

6. Your goal is to find a function g that *undoes f*. f multiplies a number by 2 and then adds 3 to the result. To undo that process, you would first subtract 3 and then divide by 2. Thus, $g(x) = \frac{x-3}{2}$.
Check to see that the composition $g \circ f(x) = x$:
$$g \circ f(x) = g(2x + 3)$$
$$= \frac{(2x + 3) - 3}{2}$$
$$= \frac{2x}{2}$$
$$= x$$

7. (a) If $f(g(x)) = 4x^2 + 1$, then fill in the blanks for what $f(x)$ does:
$$2(\qquad) + 5 = 4x^2 + 1$$
The blank is filled by the expression for $g(x)$. Then solve for $g(x)$:
$$2 \cdot g(x) + 5 = 4x^2 + 1$$
$$2 \cdot g(x) = 4x^2 - 4$$
$$g(x) = 2x^2 - 2$$
Function $g(x)$ must be $g(x) = 2x^2 - 2$. Check it:
$$f(g(x)) = f(2x^2 - 2) = 2(2x^2 - 2) + 5$$
$$= 4x^2 - 4 + 5 = 4x^2 + 1$$

(b) You are given that $g(2x + 5) = 4x^2 + 1$. Let $u = 2x + 5$. Then $u - 5 = 2x$, so $x = \frac{u-5}{2}$. Substituting, you obtain
$$g(u) = 4\left(\frac{u-5}{2}\right)^2 + 1 = 4\left(\frac{u^2 - 10u + 25}{4}\right) + 1$$
$$= u^2 - 10u + 25 + 1 = u^2 - 10u + 26$$

8. (a) $f \circ g(x) = f(cx + d) = a(cx + d) + b = acx + (ad + b)$
$g \circ f(x) = g(ax + b) = c(ax + b) + d = acx + (bc + d)$

(b) The two functions will be identical whenever $(ad + b) = (bc + d)$. This can be simplified a bit by collecting terms:
$$ad + b = bc + d$$
$$ad - d = bc - b$$
$$d(a - 1) = b(c - 1)$$
This last statement is a quick check to see if $f \circ g = g \circ f$. For example, the functions $f(x) = 3x + 4$ and $g(x) = 5x + 8$ have this property. Also, any functions where $d = b = 0$ or $a = c = 1$ have the property.

9. Start with $f(x) = ax + b$ and find $f \circ f(x) = a(ax + b) + b = a^2 x + ab + b$. You want this expression to equal $4x + 9$. The coefficients of the x terms of these expressions must be equal, so you know that $a^2 = 4$. This means that $a = 2, -2$.

You also want the constant terms in both expressions to be equal, so $ab + b = 9$. If $a = 2$, this means that $2b + b = 9$ and $b = 3$. This would give you $f(x) = 2x + 3$, which works because $2(2x + 3) + 3 = 4x + 6 + 3 = 4x + 9$. If $a = -2$, then $-2b + b = 9$ and $b = -9$. This would give you $f(x) = -2x - 9$, which also works because $-2(-2x - 9) - 9 = 4x + 18 - 9 = 4x + 9$.

On Your Own

10. (a) $f(4) = 4^2 - 1 = 15$
(b) $g(4) = 3 \cdot 4 + 1 = 13$
(c) $f(4) \cdot g(4) = 15 \cdot 13 = 195$
(d) $f(g(4)) = f(13) = 13^2 - 1 = 168$
(e) $f \circ g(4)$ has the same meaning as $f(g(4))$, so it's 168.
(f) $g \circ f(4) = g(15) = 3 \cdot 15 + 1 = 46$

11. $h(x)$ outputs the same values as the absolute value function, and has the same domain of $\mathbb{R}$. When x is positive, $h(x) = x$. When x is negative, $h(x)$ is the positive opposite: $h(x) = -x$ when $x < 0$. This is the same as the definition of the absolute value function.

12. (a) $f \circ g(3) = f(1) = 2$
(b) $g \circ f(3) = g(0) = -2$
(c) $f \circ g(a) = f(a - 2) = (a - 2)^2 - 5(a - 2) + 6 = a^2 - 9a + 20$
(d) $g \circ f(a) = g(a^2 - 5a + 6) = (a^2 - 5a + 6) - 2 = a^2 - 5a + 4$
(e) $(f \circ g) \circ f(a) = (f \circ g)(a^2 - 5a + 6)$
Since $f \circ g(a) = a^2 - 9a + 20$, this expression is

$$(a^2 - 5a + 6)^2 - 9(a^2 - 5a + 6) + 20$$

This is a good answer, but the normal form (found by expansion) is $a^4 - 10a^3 + 28a^2 - 15a + 2$.
(f) $f \circ (g \circ f) = f(a^2 - 5a + 4)$. Since $f(a) = a^2 - 5a + 6$, this expression is

$$(a^2 - 5a + 4)^2 - 5(a^2 - 5a + 4) + 6$$

Remarkably, this expression *also* expands to $a^4 - 10a^3 + 28a^2 - 15a + 2$.
(g) To find these, solve $a^2 - 9a + 20 = 0$. The left side factors as $(a - 4)(a - 5) = 0$, giving two solutions $a = 4$ and $a = 5$.
(h) Solve $a^2 - 5a + 4 = 0$. The left side factors as $(a - 1)(a - 4) = 0$, giving two solutions $a = 1$ and $a = 4$.

13. (a) To find $h \circ (f \circ g)(x)$, start by finding $f \circ g(x)$.

$$f \circ g(x) = (x + 3)^2 - 6(x + 3) + 8$$
$$= x^2 + 6x + 9 - 6x - 18 + 8$$
$$= x^2 - 1$$

Now you can compute $h \circ (f \circ g)(x)$.

$$h \circ (f \circ g)(x) = (x^2 - 1) + 1$$
$$= x^2$$

(b) To find $(h \circ f) \circ g(x)$, start by finding $h \circ f(x)$.

$$h \circ f(x) = (x^2 - 6x + 8) + 1$$
$$= x^2 - 6x + 9$$

Now compute $(h \circ f) \circ g(x)$.

$$f \circ g(x) = (x + 3)^2 - 6(x + 3) + 9$$
$$= x^2 + 6x + 9 - 6x - 18 + 9$$
$$= x^2$$

14. (a) You know that $f(x) = x^2 - 10x + 21$, and you want to find $g(x) = ax + b$ so that $f \circ g(x) = x^2 - 4$.

$$f \circ g(x) = x^2 - 4$$
$$(ax + b)^2 - 10(ax + b) + 21 = x^2 - 4$$
$$(a^2)x^2 + (2ab)x + b^2 - (10a)x - 10b + 21 = x^2 - 4$$
$$(a^2)x^2 + (2ab - 10a)x + (b^2 - 10b + 21) = x^2 - 4$$

For these two expressions to be equal, they must have the same coefficients and constant terms. This gives you three equations in a and b:

$$a^2 = 1$$
$$2ab - 10a = 0$$
$$b^2 - 10b + 21 = -4$$

The first equation tells you that $a = 1, -1$. You can handle these two cases separately.

If $a = 1$, then $2ab - 10a = 2b - 10$. $2b - 10 = 0$, so $b = 5$. If $b = 5$ is a solution for the equation $b^2 - 10b + 21 = -4$, then you have found g. $(5)^2 - 10(5) + 21 = 25 - 50 + 21 = -4$, so $g(x) = x + 5$.

You can check this by finding $f \circ g(x)$ for this g.

$$f \circ g(x) = (x + 5)^2 - 10(x + 5) + 21$$
$$= x^2 + 10x + 25 - 10x - 50 + 21$$
$$= x^2 - 4$$

So $g(x) = x + 5$ gives the result you want. Now look at the case where $a = -1$. In this case, $2ab - 10a = -2b + 10$. Since $-2b + 10 = 0$, $b = 5$. You already know that $b = 5$ results in the correct constant term, so this would give you $g(x) = -x + 5$. Check the composition.

$$f \circ g(x) = (-x + 5)^2 - 10(-x + 5) + 21$$
$$= x^2 - 10x + 25 + 10x - 50 + 21$$
$$= x^2 - 4$$

So $g(x) = -x + 5$ also gives the result you want.

(b) You know that $f \circ g(x) = x^2 - 4$, and you want to find $h(x) = ax + b$ so that $h \circ (f \circ g(x)) = x^2$.

$$h \circ (f \circ g(x)) = x^2$$
$$h(x^2 - 4) = x^2$$
$$a(x^2 - 4) + b = x^2$$
$$ax^2 - 4a + b = x^2$$

So $a = 1$ and $-4a + b = 0$. This implies that $-4 + b = 0$, so $b = 4$. Thus $h(x) = x + 4$.

15. Answers will vary. One possible answer is $g(x) = x$, since it satisfies $f \circ g = f = g \circ f$.
    Other answers include $g(x) = x^k$ for any positive integer k.

16. You want g such that $g(x - 5) = 3x^2 - 11x - 20$. Replace x by $x + 5$ everywhere. Then

$$g(x) = 3(x + 5)^2 - 11(x + 5) - 20$$
$$= 3(x^2 + 10x + 25) - 11x - 55 - 20 = 3x^2 + 19x$$

The correct answer choice is **A**.

17. (a) $a \circ b = a(x^2 - 7) = 3(x^2 - 7) + 1 = 3x^2 - 20$
    (b) $b \circ c = b(x - 5) = (x - 5)^2 - 7 = x^2 - 10x + 18$
    (c) $(a \circ b) \circ c = (a \circ b)(x - 5) = 3(x - 5)^2 - 20 = 3x^2 - 30x + 55$
    (d) $a \circ (b \circ c) = a(x^2 - 10x + 18) = 3(x^2 - 10x + 18) + 1 = 3x^2 - 30x + 55$

18. This exercise suggests that function composition is associative:

$$(a \circ b) \circ c = a \circ (b \circ c)$$

One of the best ways to do this proof is to consider a potato-and-arrow diagram of the functions involved. No matter which composition is performed first, an arrow chain leading through the three functions will be preserved. Other methods are possible.

19. Start by graphing $f(x) = 2x + 3$ and $g(x) = x^2$ and the line with equation $y = x$. Then to find a point $(a, f \circ g(a))$ by following this process.

- Move vertically from the point $(a, 0)$ to touch the graph of $y = g(x)$. The coordinates of this point are $(a, g(a))$ or (a, a^2).
- Move horizontally from the point (a, a^2) to the line with equation $y = x$. This new point has coordinates (a^2, a^2).
- Move vertically from the point (a^2, a^2) to touch the graph of $y = f(x)$. This point has coordinates $(a^2, 2(a^2) + 3)$ or $(a^2, f \circ g(a))$. This is the y-coordinate you want to pair with an x-coordinate of a.
- Move horizontally from the point $(a^2, f \circ g(a))$ to the vertical line $x = a$. Mark this point for your graph of $f \circ g(x)$.

Do this for several points until you can see the shape of the graph of the composition.

Maintain Your Skills

20. In each case, function g reverses function f. Use backtracking to find a rule for g.

   (a) $g(x) = x - 3$
   (b) $g(x) = x + 3$
   (c) $g(x) = \frac{x-5}{3}$
   (d) $g(x) = \frac{x+5}{3}$
   (e) $g(x) = \frac{x-5}{2}$
   (f) $g(x) = \frac{x-B}{A}$

21. In each case, function g reverses function f. Use backtracking to find a rule for g.

   (a) $g(x) = x - 3$
   (b) $g(x) = x + 3$
   (c) $g(x) = \frac{x-5}{3}$
   (d) $g(x) = \frac{x+5}{3}$
   (e) $g(x) = \frac{x-5}{2}$
   (f) $g(x) = \frac{x-B}{A}$

2.4 Inverses: Doing and Undoing

Check Your Understanding

1. (a) Yes, the inverse is $f^{-1}(x) = x$.
   (b) Yes, the inverse is $g^{-1}(x) = \frac{1}{x}$.
   (c) No, there are duplicate outputs. For example, the output 16 corresponds to the inputs 4 and -4.
   (d) Yes, the inverse is $k^{-1}(x) = \sqrt[3]{x}$.
   (e) No, there are duplicate outputs. For example, the output 0 corresponds to the inputs 0, 1, and -1.
   (f) Yes, the inverse is $m^{-1}(x) = x^2$ where $x \geq 0$. The domain $x \geq 0$ is required, since the square root returns a positive result.
   (g) No, there are duplicate outputs. For example, the output 5 corresponds to the inputs 5 and -5.

2. (a) If $(1, 5)$ is on the graph of the original function, then the input 1 gives output 5. The inverse function reverses this, so it must have the input 5 giving output 1. Using notation:

$$f(1) = 5 \rightarrow f^{-1}(5) = 1$$

The point $(5, 1)$ must be on the inverse function's graph.
   (b) For every point (x, y) on the original graph, there is a point (y, x) on the graph of the inverse function. The graph has been reflected over the line with equation $y = x$.
   (c) If the graph of f, consisting of points (x, y) is one-to-one, then the graph of $f^{-1}(x)$, consisting of corresponding points (y, x) must also be one-to-one. The operation of taking the inverse resulted in a reflection of the graph over the line with equation $y = x$. If you do this reflection again, the new image will be the original graph of f.

3. (a) The natural domain for f as it's defined is $x \leq 6$.

(b)

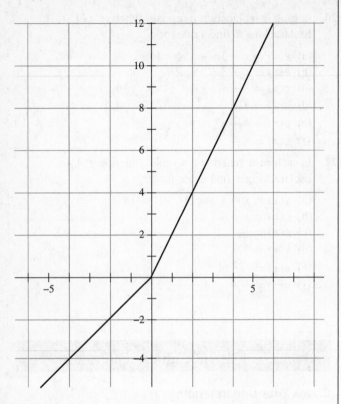

(c) Answers will vary. Here is a possible solution:

$$f(x) = \begin{cases} x & \text{if } x < 0 \\ 2x & \text{if } x \geq 0 \end{cases}$$

(d) Answers will vary. Here is a possible solution:

$$f(x) = \begin{cases} x & \text{if } x < 0 \\ 2x & \text{if } 0 \leq x \leq 6 \\ -x & \text{if } x > 6 \end{cases}$$

4. (a) If you restrict the domain to $x \geq 0$, the function is one-to-one. You could also restrict the domain to $x \leq 0$ to have a one-to-one function.

(b) If you restricted the domain to $x \geq 0$, then the inverse will be $x \mapsto \sqrt{x}$. If you restricted it to $x \leq 0$, the inverse is $x \mapsto -\sqrt{x}$.

5. (a) The domain is $\{1, 5, 9, 13\}$.

(b)

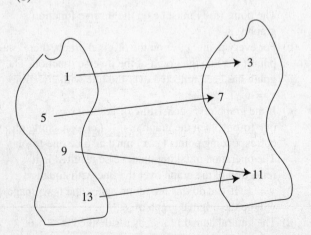

(c) $t(x)$ is a function because each input is matched with exactly one output. No inputs are duplicated.

(d) $t(x)$ does not have an inverse function. In the table of the inverse function the input 11 would have two outputs. The inverse is not a function.

Change the output for the input 13 to some number other than 3, 7, or 11.

6. Rewrite as

$$x = \frac{f^{-1}(x)}{f^{-1}(x) - 1}$$

then solve for $f^{-1}(x)$. To make it simpler, replace $f^{-1}(x)$ with y:

$$x = \frac{y}{y - 1}$$
$$x(y - 1) = y$$
$$xy - x = y$$
$$xy - y = x$$
$$y(x - 1) = x$$
$$y = \frac{x}{x - 1}$$

Remarkably, the inverse function $f^{-1}(x) = \frac{x}{x-1}$ is the same as $f(x)$.

7. Here are the graphs of h and j on the same axes, along with the dotted line $y = x$:

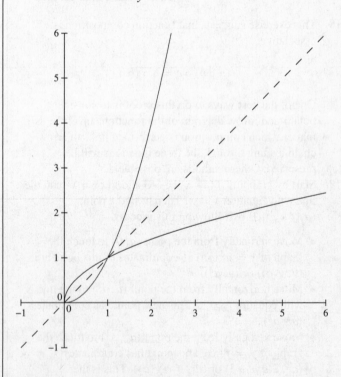

The functions are reflections across the line $y = x$, and any point (a, b) on one corresponds to (b, a) on the other. They are inverse functions.

8. (a)

$$g \circ f(x) = 5(5x^2 - 17x + 6)$$
$$= 25x^2 - 85x + 30$$

(b) $g^{-1}(x) = \frac{x}{5}$, so

$$h(x) = g \circ f \circ g^{-1}(x)$$
$$= 25\left(\frac{x}{5}\right)^2 - 85\left(\frac{x}{5}\right) + 30$$
$$= x^2 - 17x + 30$$

(c)

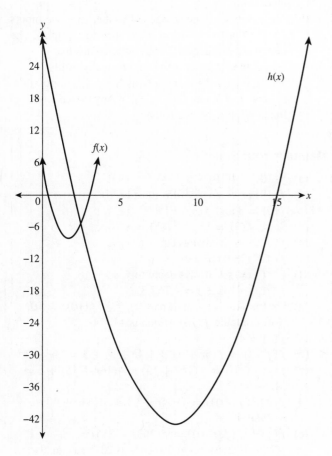

(d) The zeros of h are $x = 2, 15$, and the zeros of f are $x = \frac{2}{5}, 3$.

9. The statement is false. A function can have an inverse which returns the same value as the function for some inputs x, but that doesn't mean that it is the identity function. For example, consider the function $f(x) = 2x + 3$. Its inverse is $f^{-1}(x) = \frac{x-3}{2}$. $f(x) = f^{-1}(x)$ for $x = -3$, and f is not the identity function.

It is even possible for $f(x) = f^{-1}(x)$ for *all* inputs x but still not be the identity function. Such functions include

$$f(x) = 10 - x$$
$$f(x) = \frac{1}{x}$$
$$f(x) = \frac{x}{x-1}$$

These functions are their own inverses, so $f(x) = f^{-1}(x)$ for *all* x, and the functions are still not the identity.

On Your Own

10. Functions (b) and (c) are one-to-one. The others have several places where an output corresponds to multiple inputs. Only in (b) and (c) are the outputs unique.

11. It is important to remember that 3 and 7 are the only known inputs. Switch the inputs and outputs to find information about the inverse function. $f^{-1}(7) = 3$ and $f^{-1}(5) = 7$ are the only known pieces of information about the inverse function. The correct answer choice is **D**.

12. To prove that if functions $f, g : \mathbb{R} \to \mathbb{R}$ are one-to-one, $f \circ g$ is also one-to-one, you can follow an input a through the composition. $f \circ g(a) = f(g(a))$. You know that $g(a)$ is the only output that g produces for an input of a and that no other input produces this output. $f(g(a))$ is the only output that f produces for an input of $g(a)$, and no other input produces this output. That means that when you input a into $f \circ g$, you'll get an output which is produced for no other input, and that you'll get the same output every time. $f \circ g$ is one-to-one.

13. Take an example: if f is a doubling function and g is adding 3, then $f \circ g$ adds 3, then doubles. The inverse function would divide by 2, then subtract 3, so it undoes f then g. The inverse function is

$$g^{-1} \circ f^{-1}(x)$$

The correct answer choice is **B**.

14. Switch the variables as in the examples.

(a)
$$x = 5m^{-1}(x) + 3$$
$$x - 3 = 5m^{-1}(x)$$
$$m^{-1}(x) = \frac{x-3}{5}$$

(b)
$$x = 2n^{-1}(x) - 11$$
$$x + 11 = 2n^{-1}(x)$$
$$n^{-1}(x) = \frac{x+11}{2}$$

(c)
$$x = -3p^{-1}(x) + 4$$
$$x - 4 = -3p^{-1}(x)$$
$$p^{-1}(x) = -\frac{x-4}{3}$$

(d)
$$x = \frac{q^{-1}(x)}{5} - 0.6$$
$$x + 0.6 = \frac{q^{-1}(x)}{5}$$
$$q^{-1}(x) = 5(x + 0.6)$$
$$q^{-1}(x) = 5x + 3$$

15. (a) If the slope is nonzero, the line will always increase or decrease. The line will never have two inputs give the same output. If two inputs *did* give the same output, the slope between those two points would be zero!

(b) $f^{-1}(x)$ undoes the function $f(x) = ax + b$ which multiplies by a and adds b. To undo that process, subtract b and divide by a, so $f^{-1}(x) = \frac{x-b}{a}$

(c) The slope of $f^{-1}(x)$ is $\frac{1}{a}$.

(d) There are many possible answers, but you're looking for something where the slope of the function and its inverse are equal. $a = \frac{1}{a}$. This only happens if $a = 1, -1$.

If $a = 1$, and the function and its inverse are equal, $x + b = x - b$. This is only true if $b = 0$, so the function $f(x) = x$ is its own inverse.

If $a = -1$, and the function and its inverse are equal, $-x + b = -(x - b)$. This equation is an identity, so any linear function of the form $f(x) = -x + b$ will work.

16. (a) $g \circ f(x) = 25(5x^3 - 12x^2 - 11x + 6)$
$$= 125x^3 - 300x^2 - 275x + 150$$

(b) $k^{-1}(x) = \frac{x}{5}$

$$h(x) = g \circ f \circ k^{-1}(x)$$
$$= 125\left(\frac{x}{5}\right)^3 - 300\left(\frac{x}{5}\right)^2 - 275\left(\frac{x}{5}\right) + 150$$
$$= x^3 - 12x^2 - 55x + 150$$

(c)

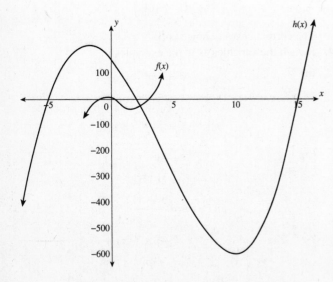

(d) f has zeros at $x = -1, \frac{2}{5}$, and 3. h has zeros at $x = -5, 2$, and 15.

17. You're looking for a linear function $g(x) = ax + b$ so that $g \circ f \circ g^{-1}$ is a monic quadratic. If $g(x) = ax + b$, then $g^{-1}(x) = \frac{x-b}{a}$.

$$g \circ f(x) = a(7x^2 - 15x + 2) + b$$
$$= 7ax^2 - 15ax + 2a + b$$

$$g \circ f \circ g^{-1} = 7a\left(\frac{x-b}{a}\right)^2 - 15a\left(\frac{x-b}{a}\right) + 2a + b$$
$$= \frac{7(x-b)^2}{a} - 15(x-b) + 2a + b$$

Since you just want this to be monic, you can choose any value for b, but it's most practical to choose $b = 0$. a, however, has to be 7. So, if $g(x) = 7x$, $g \circ f \circ g^{-1}$ turns out to be $x^2 - 15x + 14$. However, any function $g(x) = 7x + b$ would work—it would just give you a different monic quadratic.

18. (a) Answers will vary. The graph must always go up and to the right. Graphs (b) and (c) from Exercise 10 are increasing.

(b) The function is one-to-one unless there are two inputs a and b that give $f(a) = f(b)$ (the same output). The fact that the function is increasing means that if $b > a$, then $f(b) > f(a)$ automatically. And if $b < a$, then $f(b) < f(a)$ (why?). So, it's impossible to have $a \neq b$ and $f(a) = f(b)$. Any increasing function *must* be one-to-one.

Maintain Your Skills

19. (a) $f(10) = 4(10) + 3 = 43$

(b) $f(10)$ is 43, so $f^{-1}(43)$ must be 10.

(c) $f(0) = 3$ and $f(3) = 15$.

(d) Since $f(3) = 15$, $f^{-1}(15) = 3$. Next, $f^{-1}(3) = 0$.

(e) $f(f^{-1}(x))$ is always equal to x, so $f(f^{-1}(289)) = 289$.

(f) $f^{-1}(f(x))$ is always equal to x, so $f^{-1}(f(-162.3)) = -162.3$.

(g) For the same reason as part (f), $f^{-1}(f(10)) = 10$. Now compute $f(10)$, which is 43.

20. (a) $f(r) = 4r + 3$

(b) $f(f(r)) = f(4r + 3) = 4(4r + 3) + 3 = 16r + 15$

(c) $f(f(f(r))) = f(16r + 15) = 4(16r + 15) + 3 = 64r + 63$

(d) $f(f(f(f(r)))) = f(64r + 63) = 4(64r + 63) + 3 = 256r + 255$

(e) $f(f(f(f(f(r))))) = f(256r + 255) = 4(256r + 255) + 3 = 1024r + 1023$. You can also write this as $(4^5)r + (4^5 - 1)$.

(f) $f^{12}(r) = (4^{12})r + (4^{12} - 1) = 16777216r + 16777215$.

2A   MATHEMATICAL REFLECTIONS

1. (a) $f(3) = 3(3)^2 - 6(3) + 1 = 27 - 18 + 1 = 10$
$f(-3) = 3(-3)^2 - 6(-3) + 1 = 27 + 18 + 1 = 46$

(b)
$$f(x) = 12$$
$$3x^2 - 6x + 1 = 12$$
$$3x^2 - 6x - 11 = 0$$

Now you can use the quadratic formula to find the solutions to this equation.

$$x = \frac{-(-6) \pm \sqrt{(-6)^2 - 4(3)(-11)}}{2(3)}$$
$$= \frac{6 \pm \sqrt{36 + 132}}{6}$$

$$= \frac{6 \pm \sqrt{168}}{6}$$

$$= \frac{3 \pm \sqrt{42}}{3}$$

(c) $f(11) - f(10) = 3(11)^2 - 6(11) + 1$

$$- (3(10)^2 - 6(10) + 1)$$

$$= (363 - 66 + 1) - (300 - 60 + 1)$$

$$= (298) - (241)$$

$$= 57$$

(d) $\quad f(x + 1) = 3(x + 1)^2 - 6(x + 1) + 1$

$$= 3x^2 + 6x + 3 - 6x - 6 + 1$$

$$= 3x^2 - 2$$

(e) $\quad f(x + 1) - f(x) = 3x^2 - 2 - (3x^2 - 6x + 1)$

$$= 3x^2 - 2 - 3x^2 + 6x - 1$$

$$= 6x - 3$$

(f) $g(x) = f(x + 1) - f(x) = 6x - 3$, so
$g(10) = 6(10) - 3 = 57$.

2. (a) $f(3) = 3(3) + 2 = 11$
   (b) $g(3) = 3 + 5 = 8$
   (c) $f(g(3)) = f(8) = 3(8) + 2 = 26$
   (d) $f \circ g(3) = 26$ (This is just different notation for the calculation in the previous part.)
   (e) $g \circ f(3) = g(11) = 11 + 5 = 16$
   (f) $f(3) \cdot g(3) = 11 \cdot 8 = 88$

3. (a) You want $f \circ g(x) = x$, and this will be true if g is the inverse of f. To find the inverse of f, think about what f does, and then create a g that will undo it. f takes an input, multiplies it by 3 and then adds 2. So the inverse of f will subtract 2 from an input and then divide it by 3. $g(x) = \frac{x-2}{3}$
   (b) For $g \circ f(x) = x$, the inverse function you found in the previous part will also work. $g(x) = \frac{x-2}{3}$
   (c) To find $g(x)$, solve the equation for $g(x)$.

$$f \circ g(x) = x^2$$

$$3(g(x)) + 2 = x^2$$

$$3(g(x)) = x^2 - 2$$

$$g(x) = \frac{x^2 - 2}{3}$$

   (d) You are given that $g(3x + 2) = x^2$ and what you want is $g(\text{input}) = \text{output}$. So replace $3x + 2$ by a simple variable, say $u = 3x + 2$, then rewrite the output. First you find that $x = \frac{u-2}{3}$, so $x^2 = \left(\frac{u-2}{3}\right)^2$. Therefore, $g(u) = \left(\frac{u-2}{3}\right)^2$.
   (e) If $g \circ f(x) = f(x)$, then this g left its input unchanged. A function that does that is $g(x) = x$, the identity function.
   (f) In the equation $f \circ g(x) = f(x)$, g behaves just like x, so the identity function would also work here. $g(x) = x$

4. (a) $g \circ f(x) = 16(-3 + x + 8x^2 + 4x^3) =$
   $-48 + 16x + 128x^2 + 64x^3$

(b) $k^{-1}(x) = \frac{x}{4}$

$$h(x) = g \circ f \circ k^{-1}(x)$$

$$= -48 + 16\left(\frac{x}{4}\right) + 128\left(\frac{x}{4}\right)^2 + 64\left(\frac{x}{4}\right)^3$$

$$= -48 + 4x + 8x^2 + x^3$$

(c)

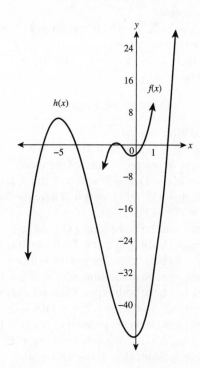

(d) $h(x)$ has zeros at $x = -6, -4$, and 2. $f(x)$ has zeros at $x = -\frac{3}{2}, -1$, and $\frac{1}{2}$.

5. Answers will vary, but should include the following elements.

   • A function accepts inputs and returns outputs. Each input produces the same output every time it is operated on by the function. You can't have more than one output matched to any given input.
   • The set of acceptable inputs for a function is called its domain. The set of all possible outputs for a function is called its range.
   • A function is also an object in its own right, and can be operated on with the Basic Rules of Algebra.

6. Answers will vary. Here is a sample response:
   The composition of two functions f and g can be written as $f \circ g(x)$ or $f(g(x))$. Both types of notation mean the same thing—Take an input x and find its output for the function g; then use that output as the input for the function f and find the final output. If the functions f and g are expressed algebraically, you can use the Basic Rules of Algebra to write $f \circ g(x)$ as a new function. Just substitute the algebraic expression for $g(x)$ into f and simplify.

7. The function $x \mapsto 3x + 7$ takes an input and multiplies it by 3, and then adds 7. To undo that, you want a function that takes an input, subtracts 7, and then divides by 3. In symbols, $x \mapsto \frac{x-7}{3}$.

2.5   Getting Started

For You to Explore

1. The rule $f(n) = 2n + 1$ works for all three points. Other rules are possible.

2. Note that $6 = 2 \cdot 3$, $30 = 5 \cdot 6$, and $56 = 7 \cdot 8$. So you could have $g(n) = n(n + 1)$.

3. Note that $10 = 2 \cdot 5$, $55 = 5 \cdot 11$, and $105 = 7 \cdot 15$. So you could have

$$h(x) = x \cdot f(x) = x(2x + 1)$$

4. (a) One possible answer is
$k(x) = (x - 1)(x - 3) = x^2 - 4x + 3$.
   (b) The roots of any polynomial of the form
$f(x) = k(x - 1)(x - 3)$ will be 1 and 3, and any polynomial with those roots will have the form
$f(x) = k(x - 1)(x - 3)$.

5. (a) The rule must be in the form $j(x) = k(x - 3)(x - 6)$, since 3 and 6 are both zeros. Then use $j(1) = 20$ to find $k = 2$. So $j(x) = 2(x - 3)(x - 6)$.
   (b) The rule must be in the form $n(x) = k(x - 1)(x - 6)$, since 1 and 6 are both zeros. Then use $n(3) = 12$ to find $k = -2$. So $k(x) = -2(x - 1)(x - 6)$.
   (c) The rule must be in the form $m(x) = k(x - 1)(x - 3)$, since 3 and 6 are both zeros. Then use $m(6) = 60$ to find $k = 4$. So $m(x) = 4(x - 1)(x - 3)$.
   (d) Here is the completed table:

x	$j(x) + n(x) + m(x)$
1	20
3	12
6	60

6. This is the same table as part (d) of Exercise 5. To find a rule for $k(x)$, add the rules for $j(x)$, $n(x)$, and $m(x)$. This gives

$$k(x) = 2(x - 3)(x - 6) - 2(x - 1)(x - 6)$$
$$+ 4(x - 1)(x - 3)$$

   Expanding and collecting like terms gives $k(x) = 4x^2 - 20x + 36$.

7. First, find three polynomials, say, g, h, and ℓ, that behave like the special polynomials in Exercise 5. Start with g. This polynomial will have $g(1) = 10$, $g(3) = 0$, and $g(6) = 0$, and one way to do this is to let

$$g(x) = A(x - 3)(x - 6)$$

   This gives the right zeros for any choice of A. Pick A so that

$$10 = g(1) = A(1 - 3)(1 - 6)$$

   so $A = 1$. Similarly, $h(x) = -2(x - 1)(x - 6)$, and $\ell(x) = 3(x - 1)(x - 3)$.

Then $k(x) = g(x) + h(x) + \ell(x)$. So

$$k(x) = (x - 3)(x - 6) - 2(x - 1)(x - 6)$$
$$+ 3(x - 1)(x - 3)$$

Expanding and collecting like terms gives $k(x) = 2x^2 - 7x + 15$.

8. First, find three polynomials, say, g, h, and ℓ that behave like the special polynomials in Exercise 5. Start with g. This polynomial will have $g(1) = 84$, $g(5) = 0$, and $g(8) = 0$, and one way to do this is to let

$$g(x) = A(x - 5)(x - 8)$$

This gives the right zeros for any choice of A. Pick A so that

$$84 = g(1) = A(1 - 5)(1 - 8)$$

and $A = 3$. Similarly, $h(x) = -4(x - 1)(x - 8)$, and $\ell(x) = 2(x - 1)(x - 5)$.

Then $t(x) = g(x) + h(x) + \ell(x)$. So

$$t(x) = 3(x - 5)(x - 8) - 4(x - 1)(x - 8)$$
$$+ 2(x - 1)(x - 5)$$

Expanding and collecting like terms gives $t(x) = x^2 - 15x + 98$.

9. The function is $f(x) = 4x^2 - 20x + 36$. These points are the same as the three points in Exercise 6.

On Your Own

10. (a) When $x = 1$, the equation becomes $f(1) = C(-3)(-5)$, since all other terms are zero. Since $f(1) = 15C$, the value of C must be 3 since $(1, 45)$ is on the graph. Similarly $B = -2$ and $A = 6$ can be found.
    (b) Function f is defined as

$$f(x) = 6(x - 1)(x - 4) - 2(x - 1)(x - 6)$$
$$+ 3(x - 4)(x - 6)$$

   Expanding and collecting like terms gives the normal form, $f(x) = 7x^2 - 46x + 84$. Testing the three given points shows that they do satisfy the function.

11. This function has the same inputs and outputs as $f(x)$. The method used in Exercise 10 could also work here, but the same function will emerge: $r(x) = 7x^2 - 46x + 84$.

12. (a) Here is the completed table:

x	$f(x)$	$g(x)$
-2	-5	499
-1	-2	-2
0	1	-55
1	4	4
2	7	7
3	10	-46
4	13	13
5	16	520

   (b) According to the table, the functions agree at $x = -1, 1, 2$, and 4.

(c) If $f(x) = g(x)$, then $f(x) - g(x) = 0$. But
$f(x) - g(x) = -7(x-1)(x-2)(x-4)(x+1)$.
This only equals zero when $x = 1, 2, 4$, or -1.

(d) Expand to get $7x^4 - 42x^3 + 49x^2 + 45x - 55$.

(e) Here are the graphs of $f(x)$ and $g(x)$:

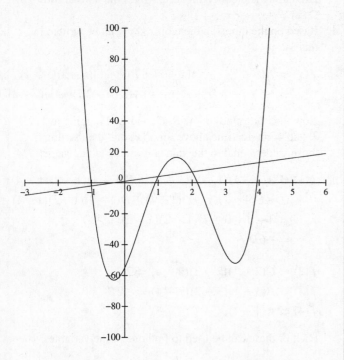

13. (a) Any polynomial with $g(2) = 5$ works here. Some
examples include $g(x) = 10x - 15$, $g(x) = x^2 + 1$,
and $g(x) = x^3 - 3x + 3$.

(b) Use the structure of exercise 12. Function
$g(x) - f(x)$ must be zero when $x = 2, 5, 7$. So,
$g(x) = 4x - 3 + k(x-2)(x-5)(x-7)$ for any
nonzero k. Pick any polynomial for k or just a
constant.

Maintain Your Skills

14. (a) $A = 2, B = 3, C = 4$

(b) $f(x) = 9x^2 - 71x + 122$

(c)

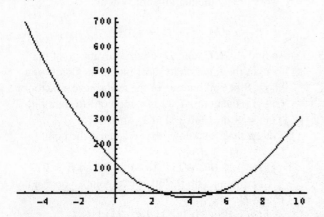

(d) Use the vertex formula $x = \frac{-b}{2a}$ to find the
x-coordinate of the vertex, then input to find the

y-coordinate. This quadratic has a minimum at
$\left(\frac{71}{18}, \frac{-649}{36}\right)$.

15. (a) $A = 1, B = 3, C = 4$

(b) $f(x) = 8x^2 - 66x + 118$

(c)

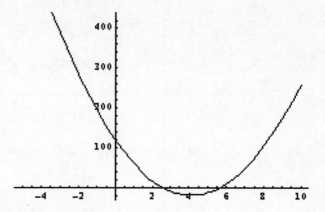

(d) Minimum at $\left(\frac{33}{8}, \frac{-145}{8}\right)$

16. (a) $A = 3, B = -1, C = 0$

(b) $f(x) = 2x^2 - 8x + 6$

(c)

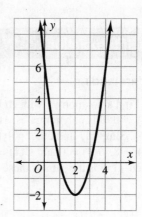

(d) Minimum at $(2, -2)$

17. (a) $A = -3, B = -1, C = 0$

(b) $f(x) = -4x^2 + 22x - 18$

(c)

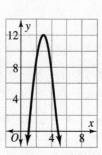

(d) Maximum at $\left(\frac{11}{4}, \frac{49}{4}\right)$

18. (a) $A = -3, B = 1, C = 2$

(b) $f(x) = -12x + 42$

(c)

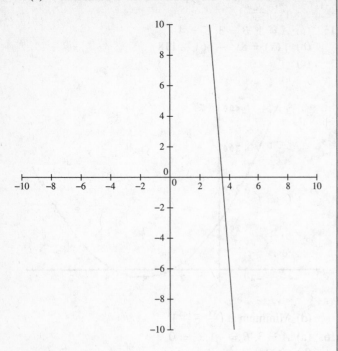

(d) This function is linear, so there is no maximum or minimum.

2.6 Lagrange Interpolation

Check Your Understanding

1. Use Lagrange. Find a polynomial with $A(1) = 12$, $A(2) = 0$, $A(4) = 0$: this polynomial is $A(x) = 4(x - 2)(x - 4)$. Similarly find other polynomials fitting $B(1) = 0$, $B(2) = 8$, $B(4) = 0$ and $C(1) = 0$, $C(2) = 0$, $C(4) = 36$. Then $f(x)$ is the sum of these polynomials:

$$f(x) = 6(x - 1)(x - 2) - 4(x - 1)(x - 4)$$
$$+ 4(x - 2)(x - 4)$$

Expand and collect terms to find the normal form, $f(x) = 6x^2 - 22x + 28$.

2. Although Lagrange can be used, the three data values must lie on the same line (use common differences). The slope is 9, and the point $(1, 2)$ gives the equation

$$v(x) = 9x - 7$$

3. Based on the inputs in the table,

$$\Omega(x) = A(x - 1)(x - 2) + B(x - 1)(x - 3)$$
$$+ C(x - 2)(x - 3)$$

Now find the values of A, B, and C. Plugging in 1, 2, and 3 into the rule above for Ω and then setting those values equal to the values from the table, we get

$$\Omega(1) = 2C = 2 \qquad \text{(Thus, } C = 1\text{)}$$
$$\Omega(2) = -1B = 11 \qquad \text{(Thus, } B = -11\text{)}$$
$$\Omega(3) = 2A = 28 \qquad \text{(Thus, } A = 14\text{)}$$

This gives the rule for $\Omega(x)$ as

$$\Omega(x) = 14(x - 1)(x - 2) - 11(x - 1)(x - 3)$$
$$+ (x - 2)(x - 3)$$

Expanding and collecting terms gives the normal form $\Omega(x) = 4x^2 - 3x + 1$.

4. Based on the inputs in the table, $f(x)$ can be written in this form:

$$f(x) = A(x - 1)(x - 2)(x - 3) + B(x - 1)(x - 2)(x - 4)$$
$$+ C(x - 1)(x - 3)(x - 4) + D(x - 2)(x - 3)(x - 4)$$

Now find the values of A, B, C, and D. Plugging in 1, 2, 3, and 4 into the rule above for $f(x)$ and then setting those values equal to the values from the table, we get

$$f(1) = A(1 - 1)(1 - 2)(1 - 3) + B(1 - 1)(1 - 2)(1 - 4)$$
$$+ C(1 - 1)(1 - 3)(1 - 4) + D(1 - 2)(1 - 3)(1 - 4)$$
$$= 0 + 0 + 0 + D(1 - 2)(1 - 3)(1 - 4)$$
$$= -6D$$

$$f(2) = C(2 - 1)(2 - 3)(2 - 4) = 2C$$
$$f(3) = B(3 - 1)(3 - 2)(3 - 4) = -2B$$
$$f(4) = A(4 - 1)(4 - 2)(4 - 3) = 6A$$

Each of these can be used to find one of the variables:

$$1 = f(1) = -6D \qquad \text{so } D = -\frac{1}{6}$$
$$22 = f(2) = 2C \qquad \text{so } C = 11$$
$$61 = f(3) = -2B \qquad \text{so } B = -\frac{61}{2}$$
$$124 = f(4) = 6A \qquad \text{so } A = \frac{124}{6} = \frac{62}{3}$$

Then $f(x)$ is given by

$$f(x) = \frac{62}{3}(x - 1)(x - 2)(x - 3) - \frac{61}{2}(x - 1)(x - 2)(x - 4)$$
$$+ 11(x - 1)(x - 3)(x - 4) - \frac{1}{6}(x - 2)(x - 3)(x - 4)$$

This is a mess. It cleans up well, though, with either some hard work or a computer algebra system:

$$f(x) = x^3 + 3x^2 + 5x - 8$$

5. (a) To find A, B, C, and D, use the advantage of the form of the function to substitute in the points you know. Since all but one of the terms have a factor of $(x - 1)$, the point $(1, 1)$ is a good one to start with.
$f(1) = A + 0 + 0 + 0 = 1$, so $A = 1$.
    Now that you know A, you can use the point $(2, 22)$ to find B.
$f(2) = 1 + B(2 - 1) + 0 + 0 = 22$, so $B = 21$.
    Continuing with the other two points, you can find C and D.
$f(3) = 1 + 21(3 - 1) + C(3 - 1)(3 - 2) +$
$0 = 61$, so $C = 9$. $f(4) = 1 + 21(4 - 1) +$
$9(4 - 1)(4 - 2) + D(4 - 1)(4 - 2)(4 - 3)$, so $D = 1$.

(b) The polynomial is $f(x) = 1 + 21(x-1) + 9(x-1)(x-2) + (x-1)(x-2)(x-3)$, which in normal form is $f(x) = x^3 + 3x^2 + 5x - 8$. This is the same as the normal form for the function in Exercise 4, so they define the same function.

6. Lagrange gives a form which still requires a lot of expansion and collection of terms. Sometimes, some of the resulting coefficients become zero in the simplifications. If this happens to the highest-degree terms, then the degree of the resulting polynomial may be less than the degree of the parts.

   This applies to polynomials in general: the degree of $f(x) + g(x)$ may be less than or equal to the highest degree between $f(x)$ and $g(x)$, due to this possibility of cancellation.

On Your Own

7. (a) The "common sense" answer is 32, which follows the sequence of powers of 2.
   (b) If the inputs are 0 through 4 and the outputs are the given sequence, Lagrange gives the rule

   $$f(x) = \frac{1}{24}x^4 - \frac{1}{12}x^3 + \frac{11}{24}x^2 + \frac{7}{12}x + 1$$

   It's a messy rule, but it works.

   Then $f(5)$ (the next term) is 31. The following terms are 57 and 99, which are further away from the "common sense" sequence.

8. We'll find a polynomial f of degree at most 5 that agrees with the table. First of all, here's a polynomial that will be *zero* at each of the inputs on the table:

   $$(x-1)(x-3)(x-6)(x-8)(x-9)(x-12)$$

   And, if we remove any one of the factors, the resulting expression will vanish at *all but one* of the inputs. Lagrange's idea is to capitalize on this and to write a polynomial in a form that is easy to evaluate at these particular inputs. He considers

   $$f(x) = A(x-1)(x-3)(x-6)(x-8)(x-9)$$
   $$+ B(x-1)(x-3)(x-6)(x-8)(x-12)$$
   $$+ C(x-1)(x-3)(x-6)(x-9)(x-12)$$
   $$+ D(x-1)(x-3)(x-8)(x-9)(x-12)$$
   $$+ E(x-1)(x-6)(x-8)(x-9)(x-12)$$
   $$+ F(x-3)(x-6)(x-8)(x-9)(x-12) \quad (*)$$

   The numbers A–F will be determined in a minute. Each product is formed by taking

   $$(x-1)(x-3)(x-6)(x-8)(x-9)(x-12)$$

   and "dropping" one factor. So, each product is a polynomial of degree 5, and *that* ensures that the whole expression will be of degree at most 5.

   Why write f in such a messy way? Well, it allows you to easily calculate $f(n)$ for any n from among the given

inputs. For example, from the table, we want $f(1)$ to be -6. So, we calculate in this way:

$$f(1) = -6 = A(1-1)(1-3)(1-6)(1-8)(1-9)$$
$$+ B(1-1)(1-3)(1-6)(1-8)(1-12)$$
$$+ C(1-1)(1-3)(1-6)(1-9)(1-12)$$
$$+ D(1-1)(1-3)(1-8)(1-9)(1-12)$$
$$+ E(1-1)(1-6)(1-8)(1-9)(1-12)$$
$$+ F(1-3)(1-6)(1-8)(1-9)(1-12)$$

But look—all the terms except the last have a factor of 0, so they all vanish. We get

$$-6 = F(-2)(-5)(-7)(-8)(-11) = -6160F$$

So, $F = \frac{-6}{-6160} = \frac{3}{3080}$.

Next, let $x = 3$. From the table, we want $f(3)$ to be 166. But when we replace x by 3 in expression $(*)$, the only term to survive is the E term, and we get

$$166 = E(2)(-3)(-5)(-6)(-9) = 1620E$$

So $E = \frac{83}{810}$.

Similarly, we can pick off the other missing coefficients by replacing x by 6 (producing $D = -\frac{7159}{540}$), 8 (producing $C = \frac{31291}{280}$), 9 (producing $B = -\frac{28469}{216}$), and 12 (producing $A = \frac{243787}{7128}$). So, substituting in $(*)$, we get:

$$f(x) = \frac{243787}{7128}(x-1)(x-3)(x-6)(x-8)(x-9)$$
$$- \frac{28469}{216}(x-1)(x-3)(x-6)(x-8)(x-12)$$
$$+ \frac{31291}{280}(x-1)(x-3)(x-6)(x-9)(x-12)$$
$$- \frac{7159}{540}(x-1)(x-3)(x-8)(x-9)(x-12)$$
$$+ \frac{83}{810}(x-1)(x-6)(x-8)(x-9)(x-12)$$
$$+ \frac{3}{3080}(x-3)(x-6)(x-8)(x-9)(x-12)$$

A CAS simplifies this to $x^5 - 3x^3 + x^2 - 5$. Try it for yourself.

9. Answers will vary. They should contain something about fitting a polynomial function to a table by creating a function f that has undetermined values $A, B, C, \ldots$ and then solving for those unknowns by using the definition of f and the values from the table.

10. Using Lagrange, you would find a sum of five polynomials with four terms zero and the fifth equal to the number from the table. This produces a function that has five pieces like

$$k(x - r_1)(x - r_2)(x - r_3)(x - r_4)$$

where the numbers in $(x - r_1)$ correspond to the four zeros for each piece. Each piece is a fourth-degree polynomial, so the sum of the five pieces can't be any more than a fourth-degree polynomial. However, it can be less than fourth degree if higher-degree terms cancel out.

The degree of the polynomial can be as small as zero, if the entries indicate a constant function. However, if all the entries are zero, Lagrange would give you the zero polynomial $Z(x) = 0$. This particular polynomial has *no* degree. Thus, the smallest degree polynomial that could result is a polynomial of degree 0.

11. There is more than one possible answer, but any such polynomial must have $(x - 1)(x - 2)(x - 3)(x - 4)$ as part of its factored form. One possible answer: $h(x) = (x - 1)(x - 2)(x - 3)(x - 4)$.

12. There is more than one possible answer. Any such polynomial is 3 more than a polynomial that has $h(1) = h(2) = h(3) = 0$. Then $h(x)$ must have the form

$$h(x) = A(x - 1)(x - 2)(x - 3)$$

where A is a constant or another polynomial. Then, since $j(x)$ is 3 more than this,

$$j(x) = A(x - 1)(x - 2)(x - 3) + 3$$

where A is a constant or polynomial. One possible answer is $j(x) = 432(x - 1)(x - 2)(x - 3) + 3$, but there are many others.

13. Using the values from the table and substituting yields $0 = f(-2) = A(-2)(-3)(-5) = -30A$, so $A = 0$. We also obtain $-6 = f(0) = B(2)(-1)(-3) = 6B$, so $B = -1$. The correct answer choice is **B**.

14. (a) $s(n) = 1 + 2 + 3 + \cdots + (n - 1) + n$ by applying the recursive formula over and over until it gets down to $s(1)$.

$$\begin{aligned} s(n) &= n + s(n - 1) \\ &= n + (n - 1) + s(n - 2) \\ &= n + (n - 1) + (n - 2) + s(n - 3) \\ &\quad \vdots \qquad\qquad \vdots \\ &= n + (n - 1) + (n - 2) + \cdots + 2 + s(1) \\ &= n + (n - 1) + (n - 2) + \cdots + 2 + 1 \end{aligned}$$

(b) Tabulate s.

Input: n	Output: $s(n)$
1	1
2	3
3	6
4	10
5	15

There are a few ways to proceed from here. One is to use difference table techniques:

Input: n	Output: $s(n)$	Δ	Δ^2
1	1	2	1
2	3	3	1
3	6	4	1
4	10	5	
5	15		

The second common difference is 1, so the rule is

$$S(n) = \frac{1}{2}n^2 + \cdots$$

By subtracting $\frac{1}{2}n^2$ from each term, the leftover is linear with slope $\frac{1}{2}$. This gives the rule

$$S(n) = \frac{1}{2}n^2 + \frac{1}{2}n = \frac{n^2 + n}{2} = \frac{n(n + 1)}{2}$$

Another method is Lagrange. Taking three or more points will always lead to the rule

$$S(n) = \frac{1}{2}n^2 + \frac{1}{2}n = \frac{n(n + 1)}{2}$$

15. First, make a table for q:

Input: n	Output: $q(n)$
1	1
2	5
3	14
4	30
5	55
6	91

One way to proceed is to use difference table techniques. The third common difference is 2, so the rule is

$$Q(n) = \frac{1}{3}n^3 + \cdots$$

Subtract $\frac{1}{3}n^3$ from each term to produce a quadratic, and proceed from there with second differences.

Knowing that it is a cubic, Lagrange can be used on any four points to determine the rule for $Q(n)$. For example, using the first four points, $Q(n)$ looks like

$$\begin{aligned} Q(n) = {} & A(n - 1)(n - 2)(n - 3) \\ & + B(n - 1)(n - 2)(n - 4) \\ & + C(n - 1)(n - 3)(n - 4) \\ & + D(n - 2)(n - 3)(n - 4) \end{aligned}$$

and the values in the table determine the coefficients A through D:

$$\begin{aligned} Q(1) &= -6D = 1 && \text{(Thus } D = -\tfrac{1}{6}\text{)} \\ Q(2) &= 2C = 5 && \text{(Thus } C = \tfrac{5}{2}\text{)} \\ Q(3) &= -2B = 14 && \text{(Thus } B = -7\text{)} \\ Q(4) &= 6A = 30 && \text{(Thus } A = 5\text{)} \end{aligned}$$

Substituting A, B, C, and D back into Q and simplifying gives the rule

$$Q(n) = \frac{1}{6}n(1 + 3n + 2n^2) = \frac{n(n + 1)(2n + 1)}{6}$$

16. (a) $f(5) = 3$ and $f(7) = 6$. Simplify by multiplying and collecting terms, or by noting that f is a line through the points $(5, 3)$ and $(7, 6)$. The rule is $f(x) = \frac{3}{2}x - \frac{9}{2}$.

(b) $f(5) = -20$ and $f(7) = 12$. This function describes a line through the points $(5, -20)$ and $(7, 12)$. The rule is $f(x) = 16x - 100$.

(c) $f(5) = b_1$ and $f(7) = b_2$. This function describes a line through the points $(5, b_1)$ and $(7, b_2)$. The slope of this line is $\frac{b_2 - b_1}{2}$. An equation is

$$f(x) = \frac{b_2 - b_1}{2}x + \frac{7b_1 - 5b_2}{2}$$

(d) $f(a_1) = b_1$ and $f(a_2) = b_2$. This function describes a line through the points (a_1, b_1) and (a_2, b_2). The slope of this line is $\frac{b_2 - b_1}{a_2 - a_1}$. An equation is

$$f(x) = \frac{b_2 - b_1}{a_2 - a_1}x + \frac{a_1 b_1 - a_1 b_2}{a_2 - a_1}$$

17. (a) $f(3) = 9$, $f(5) = 4$, and $f(7) = 6$. Simplify by multiplying it out and collecting terms, or using a computer algebra system. The rule is $f(x) = \frac{7}{8}x^2 - \frac{19}{2}x + \frac{237}{8}$.

(b) $f(3) = 29$, $f(5) = -9$, and $f(7) = 16$. The rule is $f(x) = \frac{63}{8}x^2 - 82x + \frac{1633}{8}$.

(c) $f(3) = b_1$, $f(5) = b_2$, and $f(7) = b_3$. Simplify by multiplying it out and collecting terms, or using a computer algebra system.

The result is

$$\frac{b_1 - 2b_2 + b_3}{8}x^2 + \frac{-3b_1 + 5b_2 - 2b_3}{2}x$$
$$+ \frac{35b_1 - 42b_2 + 15b_3}{8}$$

(d) $f(a_1) = b_1$, $f(a_2) = b_2$, and $f(a_3) = b_3$. This simplifies to

$$\frac{b_3}{(a_3 - a_1)(a_3 - a_2)} + \frac{b_2}{(a_2 - a_1)(a_2 - a_3)}$$
$$+ \frac{b_1}{(a_1 - a_2)(a_1 - a_3)}x^2 - \frac{b_3(a_1 + a_2)}{(a_3 - a_1)(a_3 - a_2)}$$
$$- \frac{b_2(a_1 + a_3)}{(a_2 - a_1)(a_2 - a_3)} - \frac{b_1(a_2 + a_3)}{(a_1 - a_2)(a_1 - a_3)}x$$
$$+ \frac{b_3 a_1 a_2}{(a_3 - a_1)(a_3 - a_2)} + \frac{b_2 a_1 a_3}{(a_2 - a_1)(a_2 - a_3)}$$
$$+ \frac{b_1 a_2 a_3}{(a_1 - a_2)(a_1 - a_3)}$$

2.7   Agreeing to Disagree

Check Your Understanding

1.

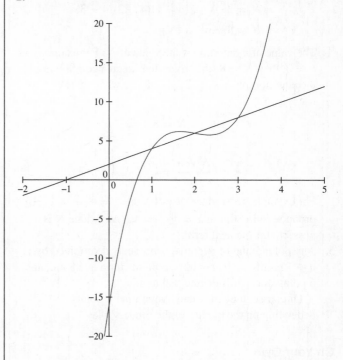

If $f(x) = h(x)$, then $2x + 2 + 3(x - 1)(x - 2)(x - 3) = 2x + 2$. Then

$$3(x - 1)(x - 2)(x - 3) = 0$$

The only values of x that make this true are $x = 1, 2$, and 3.

2. Whatever is chosen for $j(x)$, it must be equal to $h(x)$ for $x = 1, 2, 3$. Then $j(x) - h(x)$ has 1, 2, and 3 as roots. So

$$j(x) = 2x + 2 + (\quad)(x - 1)(x - 2)(x - 3)$$

where the blank is some polynomial or constant. Any such polynomial $j(x)$ will be equal to $h(x) = 2x + 2$ when $x = 1, 2, 3$.

3. (a) The rule "add 2 to each term" works here. The closed rule is $x \mapsto 2x - 1$, and the next term is 7.

(b) Answers will vary.

(c) Use the method of Exercise 2. A polynomial answer would be in the form

$$f(x) = 2x - 1 + k(x - 1)(x - 2)(x - 3)$$

Then find k so that the next output will be 19. That value of k is 2, and $f(x) = 2x^3 - 12x^2 + 24x - 13$ after expanding.

(d) Again, the polynomial is in the form

$$f(x) = 2x - 1 + k(x - 1)(x - 2)(x - 3)$$

Then find k, knowing $f(4) = 1$:

$$f(4) = 2 \cdot 4 - 1 + k(4 - 1)(4 - 2)(4 - 3)$$

This gives the equation $1 = 7 + 6k$, and $k = -1$ is the solution. Then $f(x)$ is known. It expands to $f(x) = -x^3 + 6x^2 - 9x + 5$.

4. Use the method of the previous exercises. Any polynomial matching this sequence would have the form

$$f(x) = 2x + k(x-1)(x-2)(x-3)$$

Now suppose $f(4) = N$, the next term. Then

$$N = 2 \cdot 4 + k(4-1)(4-2)(4-3)$$
$$N = 8 + 6k$$

The value of k determines the value of N. For example, if $k = 0$, then $N = 8$ (the "expected" sequence). Solving the equation $N = 8 + 6k$ for k shows what value of k to use, given N:

$$N = 8 + 6k$$
$$N - 8 = 6k$$
$$\frac{N-8}{6} = k$$

For example, to produce $N = 10$, use $k = \frac{10-8}{6} = \frac{1}{3}$. To produce $N = 80$, use $k = \frac{80-8}{6} = 12$. Any value N is possible for the next term.

5. Any polynomial of degree n is uniquely determined by $n + 1$ points, so it should be 3 points for a quadratic, and 6 points for a fifth-degree polynomial.

   Of course, they may end up with more points, depending on the quality of the Finders' play.

On Your Own

6. Answers vary. All polynomials would be in the form

$$x \mapsto 3x - 1 + kx(x-1)(x-2)(x-3)$$

Here, k can be a constant or polynomial. One example is

$$x \mapsto 3x - 1 + 2x(x-1)(x-2)(x-3)$$

Here are the graphs of $f(x) = 3x - 1$ and $p(x) = 3x - 1 + 2x(x-1)(x-2)(x-3)$ on the same axes:

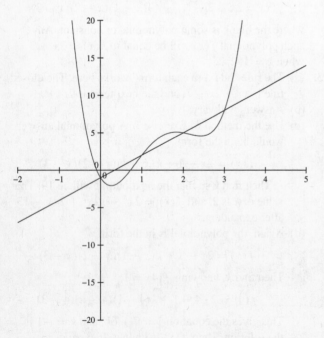

The graphs intersect when $x = 0, 1, 2, 3$ only.

7. Answers vary. One example is

$$q : x \mapsto 3x - 1 - 4x(x-1)(x-2)(x-3)(x-4)$$

Here are the graphs of $f(x) = 3x - 1$ and $q(x) = 3x - 1 - 4x(x-1)(x-2)(x-3)(x-4)$ on the same axes:

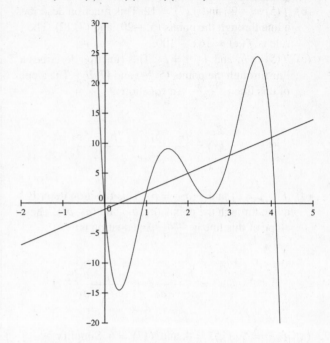

The graphs intersect when $x = 0, 1, 2, 3, 4$ only.

8. Answers vary. An example:

$$x \mapsto 4 - x^2 - 3x(x-1)(x-2)(x-3)$$

Here are the graphs of $f(x) = 4 - x^2$ and $p(x) = 4 - x^2 - 3x(x-1)(x-2)(x-3)$ on the same axes:

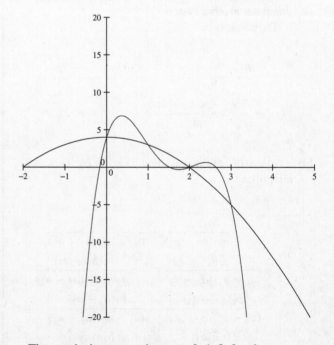

The graphs intersect when $x = 0, 1, 2, 3$ only.

9. Answers vary. An example:

$$x \mapsto 4 - x^2 - 7x(x-1)(x-2)(x-3)(x-4).$$

Here are the graphs of $f(x) = 4 - x^2$ and $q(x) = 4 - x^2 - 7x(x-1)(x-2)(x-3)(x-4)$ on the same axes:

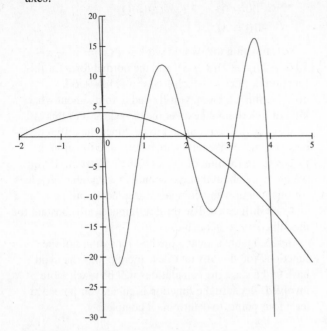

The graphs intersect when $x = 0, 1, 2, 3, 4$ only.

10. No. This would imply there are two different lines through the points $(1, 2)$ and $(2, 5)$. There is exactly one line through any two given points. There can be only one linear function through any two points.

11. (a) Yes. Any quadratic that passes through $(1, 3)$ and $(2, 0)$ works. One possible quadratic is $f(x) = 3(x-2)^2$, which has vertex $(2, 0)$ and passes through $(1, 3)$.

    (b) No. There is only one quadratic through any three given points, so there cannot be a second quadratic that agrees at $(1, 3)$, $(2, 0)$, and $(3, -5)$ that is different from the first.

12. Answers will vary. One method is to use Lagrange on the four points $(1, 1)$, $(2, 4)$, $(3, 9)$, and $(4, 7)$. A cubic (or smaller-degree) polynomial must go through these points, and Lagrange will find it.

    A second method is to note that any polynomial matching $x \mapsto x^2$ at $x = 1, 2, 3$ must have the form

    $$g(x) = x^2 + A(x-1)(x-2)(x-3)$$

    where A is a constant or polynomial. Then, find a suitable A that makes $g(4) = 7$. One possible value is $A = -\frac{3}{2}$.

13. If the line is $\ell(x) = ax + b$, then the function you seek looks like $f(x) = ax + b + k(x - c_1)(x - c_2)(x - c_3)$, where $x = c_1, c_2, c_3$ are the 3 points of agreement, and $k \neq 0$. There is a cubic term that cannot cancel out. The correct answer choice is B.

14. No, there is no such polynomial. Any such polynomial would have to look like

    $$f(x) = k(x-1)(x-2)(x-3)(x-4)\cdots$$

    and its terms would never end. What would be its degree? It would have to be infinite, since each term has a degree of 1 and the terms continue forever. This is impossible: a polynomial cannot have infinite degree. So, no such polynomial can exist.

Maintain Your Skills

15. (a) $x^2 - 3x + 2$
    (b) $x^3 - 6x^2 + 11x - 6$
    (c) $x^4 - 10x^3 + 35x^2 - 50x + 24$
    (d) $x^5 - 15x^4 + 85x^3 - 225x^2 + 274x - 120$
    (e) $x^6 - 21x^5 + 175x^4 - 735x^3 + 1624x^2 - 1764x + 720$
    (f) $x^7 - 28x^6 + 322x^5 - 1960x^4 + 6769x^3 - 13132x^2 + 13068x - 5040$
    (g) $x^8 - 36x^7 + 546x^6 - 4536x^5 + 22449x^4 - 67284x^3 + 118124x^2 - 109584x + 40320$

    There are many possible patterns. For example, the constant terms are the factorial numbers 1, 2, 6, 24, 120, ... The leading coefficient is always 1, and the next coefficients form the triangular numbers 1, 3, 6, 10, 15, ...

    Other answers are possible here, and there are many patterns in the same vein as Pascal's Triangle to be found in these numbers.

2B MATHEMATICAL REFLECTIONS

1. Find a function $g(x)$ to match this table:

Input	Output
1	3
2	0
4	0

$$g(x) = A(x-2)(x-4)$$
$$3 = A(1-2)(1-4)$$
$$1 = A$$

$g(x) = (x-2)(x-4)$

Find a function $h(x)$ to match this table:

Input	Output
1	0
2	7
4	0

$$h(x) = B(x-1)(x-4)$$
$$7 = B(2-1)(2-4)$$
$$-\frac{7}{2} = B$$

$h(x) = -\frac{7}{2}(x-1)(x-4)$

Find a function $j(x)$ to match this table:

Input	Output
1	0
2	0
4	21

$$j(x) = C(x - 1)(x - 2)$$
$$21 = C(4 - 1)(4 - 2)$$
$$\frac{7}{2} = C$$

$j(x) = \frac{7}{2}(x - 1)(x - 2)$

So the function $f(x) = (x - 2)(x - 4) - \frac{7}{2}(x - 1)(x - 4) + \frac{7}{2}(x - 1)(x - 2)$. The normal form for this function is $f(x) = x^2 + x + 1$.

2. Find a function $g(x)$ to match this table:

Input	Output
1	4
3	0
5	0

$$g(x) = A(x - 3)(x - 5)$$
$$4 = A(1 - 3)(1 - 5)$$
$$\frac{1}{2} = A$$

$g(x) = \frac{1}{2}(x - 3)(x - 5)$

Find a function $h(x)$ to match this table:

Input	Output
1	0
3	40
5	0

$$h(x) = B(x - 1)(x - 5)$$
$$40 = B(3 - 1)(3 - 5)$$
$$-10 = B$$

$h(x) = -10(x - 1)(x - 5)$

Find a function $j(x)$ to match this table:

Input	Output
1	0
3	0
5	156

$$j(x) = C(x - 1)(x - 3)$$
$$156 = C(5 - 1)(5 - 3)$$
$$\frac{39}{2} = C$$

$j(x) = \frac{39}{2}(x - 1)(x - 3)$

So the function $f(x) = \frac{1}{2}(x - 3)(x - 5) - 10(x - 1)(x - 5) + \frac{39}{2}(x - 1)(x - 3)$. The normal form for this function is $f(x) = 10x^2 - 22x + 16$.

3. There are many possible solutions. One way to do it is to write a function that has a piece that's equal to zero at 1, 2, and 4, like this one: $h(x) = 7 + (x - 1)(x - 2)(x - 4)$. Another way is to choose some value for the function (other than 7) for an input not equal to 1, 2, or 4 and then use Lagrange interpolation to find a matching function. For example, you might choose to make $h(3) = 2$.

4. $f(x) = x^3 - x + M(x - 1)(x - 2)(x - 3)$ will agree with the function $x \mapsto x^3 - x$ at $x = 1, 2,$ and 3. Now,

to find the value of M that makes $f(4) = 0$, substitute.

$$0 = 4^3 - 4 + M(4 - 1)(4 - 2)(4 - 3)$$
$$0 = 64 - 4 + M(3)(2)(1)$$
$$-10 = M$$

So a function that would work is $f(x) = x^3 - x - 10(x - 1)(x - 2)(x - 3)$, and the normal form for this function is $f(x) = -9x^3 + 60x^2 - 111x + 60$.

5. To solve this problem, you'll need to think about what kind of function you expect the closed form of this recursively defined function to be. Since the differences between successive terms are a quadratic function, it makes sense to think of this as a cubic function. If you weren't sure about that, you could make a table of values for this function and compute differences until you find a constant difference. The third differences are constant for this function, so it's cubic.

Here's a table showing the first four values of the function. You don't want to use more points than you have to, because the calculations will be much more involved. Because the function is cubic, you'll need at least four points to determine it completely.

Input	Output
0	1
1	4
2	15
3	40

Then, to find the cubic function that agrees with the table, use Lagrange interpolation. Find a function $r(x)$ to match this table:

Input	Output
0	1
1	0
2	0
3	0

$$r(x) = A(x - 1)(x - 2)(x - 3)$$
$$1 = A(-1)(-2)(-3)$$
$$-\frac{1}{6} = A$$

$r(x) = -\frac{1}{6}(x - 1)(x - 2)(x - 3)$

Find a function $s(x)$ to match this table:

Input	Output
0	0
1	4
2	0
3	0

$$s(x) = Bx(x - 2)(x - 3)$$
$$4 = B(1)(-1)(-2)$$
$$2 = B$$

$s(x) = 2x(x - 2)(x - 3)$

Find a function $t(x)$ to match this table:

Input	Output
0	0
1	0
2	15
3	0

$$t(x) = Cx(x-1)(x-3)$$
$$15 = C(2)(1)(-1)$$
$$-\frac{15}{2} = C$$

$t(x) = -\frac{15}{2}x(x-1)(x-3)$

Find a function $u(x)$ to match this table:

Input	Output
0	0
1	0
2	0
3	40

$$u(x) = Dx(x-1)(x-2)$$
$$40 = D(3)(2)(1)$$
$$\frac{20}{3} = D$$

$u(x) = \frac{20}{3}x(x-1)(x-2)$

The function you want is the sum of the functions r, s, t, and u.

$$p(x) = -\frac{1}{6}(x-1)(x-2)(x-3) + 2x(x-2)(x-3)$$
$$- \frac{15}{2}x(x-1)(x-3) + \frac{20}{3}x(x-1)(x-2)$$

The normal form for this function is

$$p(x) = x^3 + x^2 + x + 1$$

6. Answers will vary. Here is a sample response:

If you want to find a polynomial function to match a table, the table must define a function—in other words, there must be exactly one output for each input. If this condition is met, you can use Lagrange interpolation to find a polynomial function that agrees with the table. In Lagrange interpolation, you find several functions, each of which agrees with one of the points in the original table and is equal to 0 for every other table input. Then, the function that will agree with the original table is the sum of these functions.

There are other techniques you can use, such as the difference table techniques from Chapter 1, or Sasha's technique using terms that are strategically equal to zero and solving for the coefficients of these terms. (See Exercise 5.)

7. Once you've found one function that agrees with your table, you can create a second function that also agrees with the table for those particular input values, but disagrees elsewhere. To do this, add an expression that is zero for all of the table inputs to your first function. For example, if your table shows outputs for inputs 0, 1, 2,

and 3, and agrees with the function $f(x) = 3x - 5$ for those four inputs, you could create the function $g(x) = 3x - 5 + 43(x)(x-1)(x-2)(x-3)$. This function would also agree with the table for those four points, but it's definitely a different function.

You might also choose an extra point that doesn't result from the first function you find, and then use Lagrange interpolation to find a function that agrees with the new table that includes your extra point.

8. Any number could be next in the sequence. Think of this as a set of three input-output pairs, $(1, 1)$, $(2, 4)$, and $(3, 9)$. Consider any fourth pair (which cannot have input 1, 2, or 3) and use Lagrange interpolation to find a polynomial function that agrees with all of the points.

MID-CHAPTER TEST

1. To find $f(x + 1)$, substitute $x + 1$ for x in f. Then, subtract $f(x)$: $g(x) = f(x+1) - f(x) = 3(x+1)$ $-3x = 3x + 3 - 3x = 3$. The correct answer choice is **B**.

2. Since $N(x, y) = 169$, $x^2 + y^2 = 169$, you do not want the sum of the squares of the two numbers to be 169. The only pair that does not give a sum of 169 is **C**, because $1^2 + 12^2 = 1 + 144 = 145 \neq 169$.

3. The correct choice is **D**, 23 because $f \circ g(2) =$ $f(g(2)) = f(2\cdot2+5) = f(9) = 3\cdot9-4 = 27-4 = 23$

4. Rewrite the equation as $x = 2 \cdot m^{-1}(x) - 7$ and solve for $m^{-1}(x)$:

$$x = 2 \cdot m^{-1}(x) - 7$$
$$x + 7 = 2 \cdot m^{-1}(x)$$
$$\frac{x+7}{2} = m^{-1}(x)$$

The correct answer choice is **C**.

5. The graphs of f and g intersect when $f(x) = g(x)$. $f(x) = g(x) = 3x - 5$ only if $4(x-1)(x-6) = 0$. By the Zero Product Property, this happens only when $x - 1 = 0 \longrightarrow x = 1$ or $x - 6 = 0 \longrightarrow x = 6$. The correct answer choice is **D**.

6. (a) $f(2) = 3(2)^2 + 1 = 12 + 1 = 13$ and
$f(-2) = 3(-2)^2 + 1 = 12 + 1 = 13$

(b)
$$f(x) = 49$$
$$3x^2 + 1 = 49$$
$$3x^2 = 48$$
$$x^2 = 16$$
$$x = \pm 4$$

(c)
$$f(5) - f(4) = (3(5)^2 + 1) - (3(4)^2 + 1)$$
$$= (75 + 1) - (48 + 1)$$
$$= 27$$

(d)
$$f(x+1) = 3(x+1)^2 + 1$$
$$= 3(x^2 + 2x + 1) + 1$$
$$= 3x^2 + 6x + 3 + 1$$
$$= 3x^2 + 6x + 4$$

(e) $f(x+1)-f(x) = (3x^2+6x+4)-(3x^2+1) = 6x+3$

(f) $g(4) = 6(4) + 3 = 24 + 3 = 27$

7. One way to look at this is that you need to undo multiplying by 3 and then adding 4. So, you want to subtract 4 and divide by 3:

$$g(x) = \frac{x-4}{3}$$

8. (a) The natural domain for f, as it is defined, is $x \leq 2$.

(b)

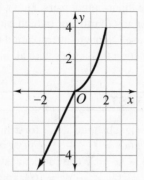

(c) Answers will vary. Here is a possible solution:

$$f(x) = \begin{cases} 2x & \text{if } x < 0 \\ x^2 & \text{if } x \geq 0 \end{cases}$$

(d) Answers will vary. Here is a possible solution:

$$f(x) = \begin{cases} 2x & \text{if } x < 0 \\ x^2 & \text{if } 0 \leq x \leq 2 \\ -2x + 8 & \text{if } x > 2 \end{cases}$$

9. To find the inverse, use the definition of inverse function to rewrite the equation as

$$f(f^{-1}(x)) = x = \frac{1}{f^{-1}(x) + 2}$$

Then, solve for $f^{-1}(x)$. To make it simpler, replace $f^{-1}(x)$ with y:

$$x = \frac{1}{y + 2}$$
$$x(y + 2) = 1$$
$$y + 2 = \frac{1}{x}$$
$$y = \frac{1}{x} - 2$$

So, $f^{-1}(x) = \dfrac{1}{x} - 2$, with $x \neq 0$.

10. First, find three polynomials, say, g, h, and l that behave like $j(x) = k(x - a)(x - b)$. Start with g. This polynomial will have $g(1) = 6$, $g(2) = 0$, and $g(3) = 0$. One way to do this is to let

$$g(x) = A(x - 2)(x - 3)$$

This gives the right zeros for any choice of A. Pick A so that

$$6 = g(1) = A(1 - 2)(1 - 3) \longrightarrow 6 = A(-1)(-2)$$
$$\longrightarrow 3 = A$$

So,

$$g(x) = 3(x - 2)(x - 3)$$

Similarly,

$$h(x) = -15(x - 1)(x - 3)$$

and

$$l(x) = 18(x - 1)(x - 2)$$

The function you are looking for is the sum of these functions:

$$\begin{aligned} f(x) &= g(x) + h(x) + l(x) \\ &= 3(x - 2)(x - 3) - 15(x - 1)(x - 3) \\ &\quad + 18(x - 1)(x - 2) \end{aligned}$$

Expanding and collecting like terms gives

$$f(x) = 6x^2 - 9x + 9$$

11. Answers will vary but should include the following elements.

- A function accepts inputs and returns outputs. Each input produces the same output every time it is operated on by the function. You cannot have more than one output matched to any given input.
- The set of acceptable inputs for a function is called its domain. The set of all possible outputs for a function is called its range.
- A function is an object in its own right, and can be operated on with the Basic Rules of Algebra.

INVESTIGATION 2C   FACTORS, ROOTS, AND ZEROS

2.8   Getting Started

For You to Explore

1. (a) When $x = 5$, $(x - 5)$ is zero. Then $(x - 5)(x - 3)$ $(x^2 - 1)$ will be zero, and the result is 219.

(b) Look for any number that makes $(x - 5)(x - 3)$ $(x^2 - 1) = 0$. The Zero Product Property indicates that either $x - 5 = 0$, $x - 3 = 0$, or $x^2 - 1 = 0$. This gives the four values of x: 5, 3, 1, and -1.

2. (a) One possible answer is $q(x) = (x - 1)(x - 3)$. Any polynomial with $q(1) = 0$ and $q(3) = 0$ works.

(b) Answers vary. The degree of $q(x) = (x - 1)(x - 3)$ is 2.

(c) One possible answer is $r(x) = (x - 1)(x - 3)$ $(x - 5)(x - 7)(x - 9)$. Any polynomial with these five roots works, but you might choose a polynomial that has additional roots.

(d) Answers vary. The degree of $r(x) = (x - 1)(x - 3)$ $(x - 5)(x - 7)(x - 9)$ is 5.

3. (a) Answers will vary. Any polynomial $j(x)$ or $g(x)$ will have $(x - 5)$ as one of its factors, since $j(5) = 0$ and $g(5) = 0$.

(b) Since $h(x) = j(x) - g(x)$, $h(5) = j(5) - g(5)$. Both $j(5)$ and $g(5)$ are zero, so $h(5) = 0$.

4. (a) $t(x) + u(x)$ is $2x^5 + x^2 + 2$, and has degree 5.
   (b) $t(x) - u(x)$ is $-x^2 - 4$, and has degree 2.
   (c) $t(x) + v(x)$ is $x^5 + x^4 + 6$, and has degree 5.
   (d) $t(x) - v(x)$ is $x^5 - x^4 - 8$, and has degree 5.
   (e) $t(x) \cdot u(x)$ is $x^{10} + x^7 + 2x^5 - x^2 - 3$, and has degree 10. Alternately, consider only the highest-degree term that will result: it will come from the highest-degree terms of t and u. This term will be

   $$x^5 \cdot x^5 = x^{10}$$

   so the degree will be 10 regardless of the other (lower-degree) terms in t and u.

5. Evaluate $m(8)$. When $x = 8$, $(x - 8)$ will be zero, so the expression

   $$(x - 8)\left(7x^3 + 12x^2 - 13x + \frac{22}{5}\right)$$

   equals zero. Then

   $$m(8) = 7(k + 1)$$

   You are given $m(8) = 21$, so the value of k is found by solving $21 = 7(k + 1)$. Therefore, $k = 2$.

6. There are a few ways to do this exercise. One is to think about what degree polynomial you'd need to multiply $x - 1$ by to end up with a quotient of degree 3. Since the other factor must have degree 2, you can use a general quadratic expression,

   $$x^3 - 1 = (x - 1)(ax^2 + bx + c)$$

   Expand the right side and solve to find a, b, and c.

   $$\begin{aligned} x^3 - 1 &= (x - 1)(ax^2 + bx + c) \\ &= ax^3 + bx^2 + cx - ax^2 - bx - c \\ &= ax^3 + (b - a)x^2 + (c - b)x - c \end{aligned}$$

   This tells you that $a = 1$, because the coefficients of the x^3-terms must match. Similarly $b - a = 0$, so $b = 1$. $c - b = 0$, so $c = 1$, and this also leads to matching constant terms.

   $$x^3 - 1 = (x - 1)(x^2 + x + 1)$$

7. Although the second factor is not completely written, you can still expand the right side of the identity to see what happens. Each term in that factor must be multiplied by x and then by -1. You can see this in the second and third lines in the display below:

   $$\begin{aligned} x^n - 1 &= (x - 1)(x^{n-1} + x^{n-2} + \cdots + x^2 + x + 1) \\ &= (x^n + x^{n-1} + x^{n-2} + \cdots + x^2 + x) \\ &\quad - (x^{n-1} + x^{n-2} + \cdots + x^2 + x + 1) \\ &= x^n - 1 \end{aligned}$$

   All of the terms in the product from the multiplication by x have a coefficient of 1, and all of the terms from the multiplication by -1 have a coefficient of -1. This means that you get a lot of cancellation. In fact, all of the terms of degree $n - 1$ to 1 cancel out, leaving only $x^n - 1$.

On Your Own

8. (a) The polynomial will be simpler to evaluate whenever the expression $(x - 1)(x - 3)(x^5 + x^4 + x^3 + x^2 + x + 1)$ equals zero. This happens when the input is 1 or -3. For either of these inputs, the output is given by the second part of the rule, which just multiplies the input by 5 and subtracts 2.
   (b) $h(1) = 3$ and $h(-3) = -17$. Other inputs will require evaluation of the longer expression.

9. Expand:

   $$\begin{aligned} (x - a)(x^2 + ax + a^2) &= (x^3 + ax^2 + a^2x) \\ &\quad + (-ax^2 - a^2x - a^3) \end{aligned}$$

   Most terms cancel, leaving only $x^3 - a^3$ as the expanded (normal) form.

10. Expand:

    $$\begin{aligned} (x - a)&(x^3 + ax^2 + a^2x + a^3) \\ &= (x^4 + ax^3 + a^2x^2 + a^3x) \\ &\quad + (-ax^3 - a^2x^2 - a^3x - a^4) \end{aligned}$$

    Most terms cancel, leaving only $x^4 - a^4$ as the expanded (normal) form.

11. The work you did in Exercise 7 helps here. In the earlier exercise, the result is that

    $$(x - 1)(x^4 + x^3 + x^2 + x + 1) = x^5 - 1$$

    Take this expression and divide each side by $(x - 1)$ to get

    $$x^4 + x^3 + x^2 + x + 1 = \frac{x^5 - 1}{x - 1}$$

    The left-hand expression is the polynomial $g(x)$.
    By the way, note that the equation above is not true if $x = 1$.

Maintain Your Skills

12.

   $$\begin{aligned} (x^2 - 1)(x^4 + x^2 + 1) &= x^6 + x^4 + x^2 \\ &= \quad\ \ -x^4 - x^2 - 1 \\ &= x^6 - 1 \end{aligned}$$

13.

   $$\begin{aligned} (x^3 - 1)(x^6 + x^3 + 1) &= x^9 + x^6 + x^3 \\ &= \quad\ \ -x^6 - x^3 - 1 \\ &= x^9 - 1 \end{aligned}$$

14.

   $$\begin{aligned} (x^4 - 1)(x^8 + x^4 + 1) &= x^{12} + x^8 + x^4 \\ &= \quad\ \ -x^8 - x^4 - 1 \\ &= x^{12} - 1 \end{aligned}$$

Check Your Understanding

1. (a) Perform polynomial long division to find the quotient and remainder. Here is a description of the process:
   - Look at the first terms of the divisor and the dividend (the polynomial you're dividing *into*). x^3 divided by x is x^2, so this is the first term in your quotient. Write it above the term with the same degree in the dividend.
   - Multiply x^2 by $x + 2$ and write each term below the term with the same degree in the dividend. Be sure to include the sign of each term.
   - Subtract this product from the dividend. Be sure to include all of the terms from the dividend in your subtraction. Your result is $-3x - 6$.
   - Look at the first terms of the divisor and this new difference (what's left of the dividend). $-3x$ divided by x is -3, so this is the second term in your quotient. Write it above the term with the same degree in the dividend.
   - Multiply -3 by $x + 2$ and write each term below the term with the same degree in the dividend.
   - Subtract this product from what's left of the dividend. Your result is 0. Since this is a constant, it is your remainder and you have finished the division. The quotient is $x^2 - 3$.

   (b) The Remainder Theorem says that $h(-2)$ equals the remainder when dividing by $(x + 2)$, so $h(-2) = 0$.

2. The Remainder Theorem says that the remainder when dividing by $(x - 1)$ is equal to $f(1)$ where $f(x) = x^{105} + x + 1$. Here, it's much simpler to find $f(1)$:

   $$f(1) = 1^{105} + 1 + 1 = 1 + 1 + 1 = 3$$

   So, the remainder is 3.

3. The Remainder Theorem says that the remainder when dividing by $(x + 1)$ is equal to $f(-1)$ where $f(x) = x^{105} + x + 1$. In this case, it's much simpler to find $f(-1)$:

   $$f(1) = (-1)^{105} + (-1) + 1 = (-1) + (-1) + 1 = -1$$

   So, the remainder is -1.

4. This is a direct consequence of the Remainder Theorem. $P(10)$ is the remainder when dividing by $(x - 10)$. Since $(x - 10)$ divides evenly, $P(10) = 0$.

5. (a) There are many ways to approach this exercise, so this is just one way you could approach the problem. Tony's third condition is a good place to start, because in a list of numbers from 1 to 1000, say, there are fewer multiples of 7 (and thus, fewer numbers that are 1 more than a multiple of 7) than there are multiples of 5 or 3. Begin by making a list of numbers that are 1 more than a multiple of 7.

   $$1, 8, 15, 22, 29, 36, 43, 50, 57, 64, 71, 78, \dots$$

   Each of the numbers on this list is 7 more than the previous one.

Now, find the numbers on your list that are 3 more than a multiple of 5. Look for a pattern so you can extend the list of numbers that meet Tony's last two conditions.

$$8, 43, 78, 113, 148, 183, 218, 253, \dots$$

You end up choosing every fifth number after your first choice of 8. Each of the numbers on this new list is 35 more than the previous one. (And 35 is 7×5.)

Look for the numbers on your latest list that are two more than a multiple of 3. These numbers will meet all three of Tony's conditions.

$$8, 113, 218, \dots$$

You end up choosing every third number after your first choice of 8. Each of the numbers on this final list is 105 more than the previous one. (Yes, 105 is $3 \times 5 \times 7$.)

Tony's number might be 8.

   (b) There are infinitely many solutions to Tony's puzzle. 113 and 218 are the next two, and any number of the form $8 + 105n$ where n is a non-negative integer will be a solution.

6. (a) It may not be obvious at first, but Derman has given three input-output pairs for his secret polynomial. That's because the remainder after division by $(x - 3)$ is equal to the output for an input of 3. So, in fact, Derman is giving a table with three input-output pairs and asking the partygoers to figure out a polynomial that agrees with his table. Lagrange interpolation is one way to do that. Here's Derman's table:

x	$d(x)$
3	16
5	42
7	84

   Lagrange interpolation gives you $d(x) = 2(x - 5)(x - 7) - \frac{21}{2}(x - 3)(x - 7) + \frac{21}{2}(x - 3)(x - 5)$. The normal form of this polynomial is $d(x) = 2x^2 - 3x + 7$.

   (b) There are infinitely many polynomials that meet Derman's conditions. In fact, any polynomial of the form $2x^2 - 3x + 7 + p(x)(x - 3)(x - 5)(x - 7)$, where $p(x)$ is any polynomial, will agree with Derman's table. If you choose $p(x) = 1$, you get $x^3 - 13x^2 + 68x - 98$. For $p(x) = 2$, you get $2x^3 - 28x^2 + 139x - 203$. These are both examples of other polynomials that meet his conditions.

On Your Own

7. (a) Perform polynomial long division to find the quotient and remainder.
   - x^3 divided by x is x^2, so this is the first term in your quotient.
   - Multiply x^2 by $x + 2$ to get $x^3 + 2x^2$.
   - Subtract this product from the dividend to get $-x^2 + x$.

- $-x^2$ divided by x is $-x$, so this is the second term in your quotient.
- Multiply $-x$ by $x + 2$ to get $-x^2 - 2x$.
- Subtract this product from what's left of the dividend. Your result is $3x$.
- $3x$ divided by x is 3, so this is the third term in your quotient.
- Multiply 3 by $x + 2$ to get $3x + 6$.
- Subtract this product from what's left of the dividend. Your result is -6. Since this difference has a degree smaller than the degree of the divisor $x + 2$, it is your remainder and you have finished the division. The quotient is $x^2 - x + 3$.

(b) The Remainder Theorem says that $f(-2)$ equals the remainder when dividing by $(x + 2)$, so $f(-2) = -6$.

8. In each case, use the Remainder Theorem. The remainder when dividing by $(x - 3)$ is equal to $f(3)$ for each polynomial function.

(a) $3^3 - 1 = 26$
(b) $3 - 1 = 2$
(c) $3^2 + 3 + 1 = 13$
(d) $3^4 + 3^2 + 1 = 91$
(e) This result is $91 \cdot 2 = 182$.
(f) $3^4 + 3^3 + 3^2 = 117$

9. The remainder when dividing by $(x - 2)$ is equal to the value of the function when $x = 2$.

(a) $3 \cdot f(2) + g(2) = 3 \cdot 5 + (-4) = 11$
(b) $f(2) \cdot (g(2))^2 = 5 \cdot (-4)^2 = 80$
(c) $(2^2 + 2 + 1) \cdot f(2) + g(2) = 7 \cdot 5 + (-4) = 31$

10. (a) $f(2) = 8$, since the first three terms are zero when $x = 2$.
(b) The remainder when $f(x)$ is divided by $(x - 2)$ is equal to $f(2)$, so it is 8.
(c) $g(x) = 5(x - 2)^2 + 3(x - 2) - 6$. Then $g(2) = -6$.
(d) The remainder when $g(x)$ is divided by $(x - 2)$ is equal to $g(2)$, so it is -6.
(e) $h(x) = 5(x - 2) + 3$. Then $h(2) = 3$.
(f) The remainder when $h(x)$ is divided by $(x - 2)$ is equal to $h(2)$, so it is 3.
(g) $m(x) = 5$ always. So $m(2) = 5$ as well.
(h) The quotient when $m(x)$ is divided by $(x - 2)$ is 0. The remainder is 5.

11. You are given that $g(-2) = 0$, so -2 is a zero. You can try substituting the given choices and you will find that $g(7) = 0$ and $g(-7) \neq 0$. Alternately, $x + 2$ must be a factor of $g(x)$; you could divide it by $x + 2$ and obtain a quotient of $x^2 - 14x + 49 = (x - 7)^2$. From this you will see that $x = 7$ is a zero. The correct answer choice is **B**.

12. One polynomial for which $f(2) = 5$ and $f(3) = 7$ is $f(x) = 2x + 1$. Other polynomials that also agree with these input-ouput pairs are of the form $g(x) = 2x + 1 + p(x)(x - 2)(x - 3)$ where $p(x)$ is any polynomial. Think about dividing $g(x) = 2x + 1 + p(x)(x - 2)(x - 3)$ by $(x - 2)(x - 3)$. The quotient would be $p(x)$ and the remainder would have to be $2x + 1$.

13. One method is to use polynomial division by $(x - 1)$. Divide $x^3 + x^2 - 8x + 13$ by $(x - 1)$. The quotient is $x^2 + 2x - 6$ and the remainder is 7. Then $D = 7$.
Divide $x^2 + 2x - 6$ by $(x - 1)$. The quotient is $x + 3$ and the remainder is -3. Then $C = -3$.
Divide $x + 3$ by $(x - 1)$. The quotient is 1, and the remainder is 4. Then $B = 4$.
Alternately, expand $(x - 1)^3 + B(x - 1)^2 + C(x - 1) + D$ to build a system of equations:

$$B - 3 = 1$$
$$C - 2B + 3 = -8$$
$$D - C + B - 1 = 13$$

The solution to this system of equations is $B = 4$, $C = -3$, $D = 7$.

14. By the Remainder Theorem,

$$P(x) = (x - 7) \cdot Q(x) + R \qquad \text{and}$$
$$P(7) = R \qquad \text{so}$$
$$P(x) = (x - 7) \cdot Q(x) + P(7) \qquad \text{so}$$
$$P(x) - P(7) = (x - 7) \cdot Q(x)$$

This shows that $P(x) - P(7)$ has a factor of $(x - 7)$.

15. By the Remainder Theorem,

$$P(x) = (x - a) \cdot Q(x) + R \qquad \text{and}$$
$$P(a) = R \qquad \text{so}$$
$$P(x) = (x - a) \cdot Q(x) + P(a) \qquad \text{so}$$
$$P(x) - P(a) = (x - a) \cdot Q(x)$$

This shows that $P(x) - P(a)$ has a factor of $(x - a)$.

Maintain Your Skills

16. (a) $x + 1$
(b) $x^2 + x + 1$
(c) $x^3 + x^2 + x + 1$
(d) $x^4 + x^3 + x^2 + x + 1$
(e) A reasonable guess is $x^{11} + x^{10} + x^9 + x^8 + x^7 + x^6 + x^5 + x^4 + x^3 + x^2 + x + 1$, and it turns out to be right.

17. (a) $f(1) = 6$, so the numerator is $2x^2 + 5x - 7$. This factors to $(x - 1)(2x + 7)$. The quotient is
$$\frac{(x - 1)(2x + 7)}{x - 1} = 2x + 7$$

(b) $f(2) = 17$, so the numerator is $2x^2 + 5x - 18$. This factors to $(x - 2)(2x + 9)$. The quotient is
$$\frac{(x - 2)(2x + 9)}{x - 2} = 2x + 9$$

(c) $f(3) = 32$, so the numerator is $2x^2 + 5x - 33$. This factors to $(x - 3)(2x + 11)$. The quotient is
$$\frac{(x - 3)(2x + 11)}{x - 3} = 2x + 11$$

(d) $f(4) = 51$, so the numerator is $2x^2 + 5x - 52$. This factors to $(x - 4)(2x + 13)$. The quotient is
$$\frac{(x - 4)(2x + 13)}{x - 4} = 2x + 13$$

(e) $f(5) = 74$, so the numerator is $2x^2 + 5x - 75$. This factors to $(x - 5)(2x + 15)$. The quotient is

$$\frac{(x - 5)(2x + 15)}{x - 5} = 2x + 15$$

(f) $f(6) = 101$, so the numerator is $2x^2 + 5x - 102$. This factors to $(x - 6)(2x + 17)$. The quotient is

$$\frac{(x - 6)(2x + 17)}{x - 6} = 2x + 17$$

2.10 The Factor Theorem

Check Your Understanding

1. Suppose $P(x)$ has degree 2, but three real roots $a, b,$ and c. The Factor Theorem says that $(x - a)$, $(x - b)$, and $(x - c)$ are all factors of $P(x)$. But then $(x - a)(x - b)(x - c)$ must also be a factor of $P(x)$. And that's impossible, since $(x - a)(x - b)(x - c)$ has higher degree than $P(x)$.

   Therefore, $P(x)$ can't have 3 roots. It can certainly have 2 roots, and there are many examples.

2. (a) These are degree 4, so check 5 different values for x:

$$
\begin{array}{ll}
P(0) = -2 & R(0) = -2 \\
P(1) = -2 & R(1) = -2 \\
P(-1) = -2 & R(-1) = -2 \\
P(\sqrt{2}) = 0 & R(\sqrt{2}) = 0 \\
P(-\sqrt{2}) = 0 & R(-\sqrt{2}) = 0
\end{array}
$$

   They are identical.

(b) These are degree 3, so check 4 different values for x:

$$
\begin{array}{ll}
P(1) = 0 & R(1) = 0 \\
P(0) = 0 & R(0) = 0 \\
P(-1) = 0 & R(-1) = 0 \\
\mathbf{P(2) = 6} & \mathbf{R(2) = -6}
\end{array}
$$

   Since $P(2) \neq R(2)$, the polynomials are *not* identical. Any other numeric choice could also be used here.

(c) These are degree 2, so check 3 different values for x:

$$
\begin{array}{ll}
P(-3) = -7 & R(-3) = -7 \\
P(0) = 2 & R(0) = 2 \\
P(-2) = -6 & R(-2) = -6
\end{array}
$$

   They are identical.

3. If $x - 1$ is a factor of the polynomial, then 1 must be a root. That means that $(1)^3 + a(1)^2 - 1 + 5 = 0$, so $a = -5$.

4. If $x^2 + x - 6 = (x + 3)(x - 2)$ is a factor of the polynomial, then both -3 and 2 must be roots of the polynomial.

$$(-3)^4 + (-3)^3 - a(-3)^2 - b(-3) + a - b = 0$$
$$81 - 27 - 9a + 3b + a - b = 0$$
$$54 - 8a + 2b = 0$$

$$(2)^4 + (2)^3 - a(2)^2 - b(2) + a - b = 0$$
$$16 + 8 - 4a - 2b + a - b = 0$$
$$24 - 3a - 3b = 0$$

So you have two equations in the two unknowns a and b. Multiply the first by 3 and the second by 2 to get

$$162 - 24a + 6b = 0$$
$$48 - 6a - 6b = 0$$

Add the two equations to get $210 - 30a = 0$, so $a = 7$. Substitute into either original equation. For example, $54 - 8(7) + 2b = 0$ which means that $b = 1$.

5. There are several ways to approach this exercise. You might notice that the polynomial in this equation is the one you just found the coefficients for in Exercise 4, so you know two of its factors already—$x - 2$ and $x + 3$. Use polynomial long division to divide $x^4 + x^3 - 7x^2 - x + 6$ by $x^2 + x - 6$ and you'll get at most a quadratic polynomial quotient to finish the factoring. (If you don't feel comfortable dividing by a quadratic, you could do the division in two steps, dividing by one of the linear factors you know and then dividing the resulting quotient by the other linear factor.)

   Here is a description of the process of dividing by $x^2 + x - 6$.

   - x^4 divided by x^2 is x^2, so x^2 is the first term of your quotient.
   - Multiply x^2 by $x^2 + x - 6$ to get $x^4 + x^3 - 6x^2$.
   - Subtract this from $x^4 + x^3 - 7x^2 - x + 6$ to get $-x^2 - x + 6$.
   - $-x^2$ divided by $-x^2$ is -1, so -1 is the next term of your quotient.
   - Multiply -1 by $x^2 + x - 6$ to get $-x^2 - x + 6$.
   - Subtract this from $-x^2 - x + 6$ and you get 0, so there is no remainder and $x^2 + x - 6$ is confirmed as a factor of the original polynomial.

   You know how to factor this quotient, so the complete factorization of $x^4 + x^3 - 7x^2 - x + 6$ is $(x + 3)(x - 2)(x - 1)(x + 1)$ and the solutions to the equation are $x = -3, -1, 1,$ and 2.

   If you didn't notice that the polynomial in this equation is the one you just found the coefficients for in Exercise 4, you could still factor it by substituting various factors of the constant term of the original polynomial, 6, into the polynomial and seeing if you can find roots. Finding a root tells you a factor of the polynomial, and then you can divide by that factor to get a smaller-degree polynomial to factor.

6. Since both left and right sides are quadratic polynomials, test three inputs. Since the left side has factors of $(x - 1)$, $(x - 2)$, and $(x - 3)$, the three values to test are 1, 2, and 3.

   Testing $x = 1$ gives the result 2 on each side. Testing $x = 2$ gives the result -1 on each side. Testing $x = 3$ gives the result 2 on each side.

7. Since both left and right sides are quadratic polynomials, test three inputs. The simplest values to test are 1, 3, and 6.

Testing $x = 1$ gives 20 on the left side, since the first term cancels to leave 20 and the others are zero. The right side is also 20.

Testing $x = 3$ gives 12 on the left side, since the second term cancels to leave 12 and the others are zero. The right side is also 12.

Testing $x = 6$ gives 60 on the left side, since the third term cancels to leave 60 and the others are zero. The right side is also 60.

8. When $x = 1, 2, 3$ the value of $P(x)$ is 1. Since P can be no more than quadratic, and it agrees with $P(x) = 1$ on three points, then $P(x) = 1$ exactly.

On Your Own

9. If $x - 1$ is a factor of $x^3 + ax^2 - x + 8$, then 1 is a root of the polynomial. So $(1)^2 + a(1)^2 - (1) + 8 = 0$, and $a = -8$.

10. If $x^2 + x - 6$ is a factor of $x^4 + x^3 - ax^2 - bx + 2a + b$, then 2 and -3 are both roots of the polynomial.

$$(2)^4 + (2)^3 - a(2)^2 - b(2) + 2a + b = 0$$
$$16 + 8 - 4a - 2b + 2a + b = 0$$
$$24 - 2a - b = 0$$

$$(-3)^4 + (-3)^3 - a(-3)^2 - b(-3) + 2a + b = 0$$
$$81 - 27 - 9a + 3b + 2a + b = 0$$
$$54 - 7a + 4b = 0$$

Multiply the first of the two resulting equations by 4 and add it to the second equation to get $150 - 15a = 0$, so $a = 10$. Substitute this value into either equation to solve for b. For example, $24 - 2(10) - b = 0$ and then $b = 4$.

11. There are several ways to approach this exercise. You might notice that the polynomial in this equation is the one you just found the coefficients for in Exercise 10, so you know two of its factors already—$x - 2$ and $x + 3$. Use polynomial long division to divide $x^4 + x^3 - 10x^2 - 4x + 24$ by $x^2 + x - 6$ and you'll get at most a quadratic polynomial quotient to finish the factoring. (If you don't feel comfortable dividing by a quadratic, you could do the division in two steps, dividing by one of the linear factors you know and then dividing the resulting quotient by the other linear factor.)

Here is a description of the process of dividing by $x^2 + x - 6$.

- x^4 divided by x^2 is x^2, so x^2 is the first term of your quotient.
- Multiply x^2 by $x^2 + x - 6$ to get $x^4 + x^3 - 6x^2$.
- Subtract this from $x^4 + x^3 - 10x^2 - 4x + 24$ to get $-4x^2 - 4x + 24$.
- $-4x^2$ divided by x^2 is -4, so -4 is the next term of your quotient.
- Multiply -4 by $x^2 + x - 6$ to get $-4x^2 - 4x + 24$.
- Subtract this from $-4x^2 - 4x + 24$ and you get 0, so there is no remainder and $x^2 + x - 6$ is confirmed as a factor of the original polynomial.

You know how to factor this quotient, so the complete factorization of $x^4 + x^3 - 10x^2 - 4x + 24$ is

$(x + 3)(x - 2)(x - 2)(x + 2)$, and the solutions to the equation are $x = -3, -2,$ and 2.

If you didn't notice that the polynomial in this equation is the one you just found the coefficients for in Exercise 10, you could still factor it by substituting various factors of the constant term of the original polynomial, 24, into the polynomial and seeing if you can find roots. Finding a root tells you a factor of the polynomial, and then you can divide by that factor to get a smaller-degree polynomial to factor.

12. (a) $x - 2$ is a factor of $f(x)$ if and only if $f(2) = 0$. Check by substituting $x = 2$ to get $4 - 4(2) + 13(2)^2 - 12(2)^3 + 3(2)^4 = 4 - 8 + 52 - 96 + 48 = 0$. Therefore $x - 2$ is a factor.

(b)(c) Divide $f(x)$ by $x - 2$ to find the quotient $q(x)$. Then you can check to see if 2 is also a root of the quotient. Polynomial long division yields a quotient of $3x^3 - 6x^2 + x - 2$ with no remainder (so your previous answer was correct). Substituting $x = 2$, you get $3(2)^3 - 6(2)^2 + (2) - 2 = 24 - 24 + 2 - 2 = 0$, so $x - 2$ is also a factor of the quotient.

You've shown that $3x^4 - 12x^3 + 13x^2 - 4x + 4 = (x - 2)(3x^3 - 6x^2 + x - 2)$ and $3x^3 - 6x^2 + x - 2 = (x - 2)p(x)$ for a polynomial $p(x)$ that you haven't necessarily solved for explicitly. This means that $3x^4 - 12x^3 + 13x^2 - 4x + 4 = (x - 2)(x - 2)p(x)$, so $(x - 2)^2$ is a factor of $f(x)$.

13. Expand the right side by multiplying the binomial:

$$(x^n + ax^{n-1} + a^2 x^{n-2} + \cdots + a^{n-1}x)$$
$$+ (-ax^{n-1} - a^2 x^{n-2} - \cdots - a^{n-1}x - a^n)$$

All terms cancel except $x^n - a^n$.

14. (a) Note that

$$f(r) = a_n r^n + a_{n-1} r^{n-1} + \cdots + a_1 r + a_0$$

So $f(x) - f(r)$ can be written as

$$f(x) - f(r) = a_n(x^n - r^n) + a_{n-1}(x^{n-1} - r^{n-1}) + \cdots + a_1(x - r)$$

Since each term is of the form $x^k - r^k$, all of these terms include an $(x - r)$ factor. Therefore, $(x - r)$ is a factor of $f(x) - f(r)$. Alternately, note that if you substitute r into the polynomial $f(x) - f(r)$, you obtain $f(r) - f(r) = 0$. By the Factor Theorem, $x - r$ is a factor of this polynomial.

(b) To find the explicit expression for the resulting quotient g, use the result of Exercise 13 to factor each part of $f(x) - f(r)$:

$$f(x) - f(r) = a_n(x - r)(x^{n-1} + rx^{n-2} + r^2 x^{n-3} + \cdots)$$
$$+ a_{n-1}(x - r)(x^{n-2} + rx^{n-1} + \cdots)$$
$$+ \cdots + a_1(x - r)$$

Then factor out the $(x - r)$ and combine like terms as powers of x.

$$g(x) = (a_n)x^{n-1} + (a_n r + a_{n-1})x^{n-2}$$
$$+ (a_n r^2 + a_{n-1}r + a_{n-2})x^{n-3} + \cdots$$
$$+ (a_n r^{n-1} + a_{n-1} r^{n-2} + \cdots + a_1)$$

15. This is a fairly direct consequence of the result in Exercise 14. Since $f(x) - f(a)$ has a factor $(x - a)$, it can be written as

$$f(x) - f(a) = g(x) \cdot (x - a)$$

Then rewrite as

$$f(x) = g(x) \cdot (x - a) + f(a)$$

This fits the format of quotient and remainder: the quotient is $g(x)$ and the remainder is $f(a)$. This proves the theorem: when $f(x)$ is divided by $(x - a)$, the remainder is $f(a)$.

16. One way to do this is to include the data that if $n = 0$, the result is 0 (no squares to add). Then, use the difference table techniques from Chapter 1.

 The other is to use Lagrange interpolation on any four points in the set.

 In either case, the result is

$$f(n) = \frac{1}{3}n^3 + \frac{1}{2}n^2 + \frac{1}{6}n$$

This formula can also be written as

$$f(n) = \frac{n(n + 1)(2n + 1)}{6}$$

17. Since $x + a$ is a factor, it follows that $f(-a) = 0$. It does not follow that $f(a) = 0$. The correct answer choice is **B**.

Maintain Your Skills

18. Since the numerator $f(x)$ is factored, cancel the appropriate factors in each rational expression.

  (a) $(x^2 + 1)(x - 2)(x - 3)(x - 4)$
  (b) $(x^2 + 1)(x - 3)(x - 4)$
  (c) $(x^2 + 1)(x - 1)(x - 2)(x - 4)$
  (d) $(x^2 + 1)(x - 1)(x - 2)(x - 3)$
  (e) $(x^2 + 1)(x - 4)$
  (f) $x^2 + 1$

19. (a)

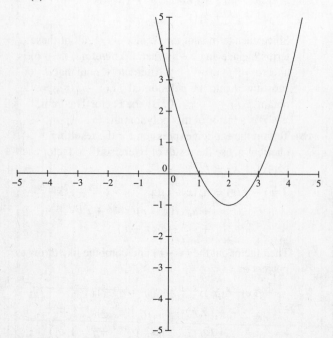

(b)

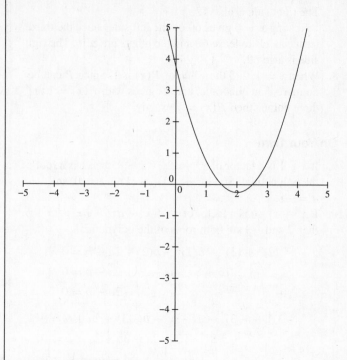

(c)

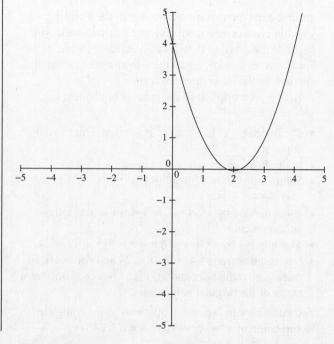

(d)

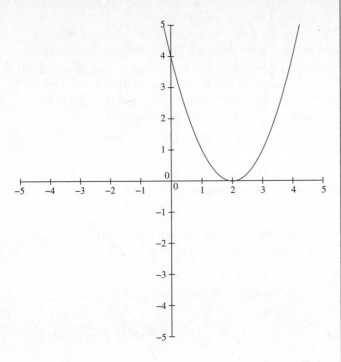

(e)

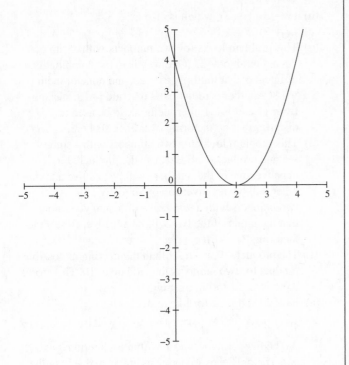

2C   MATHEMATICAL REFLECTIONS

1. To solve this problem, you can use polynomial long division or the identity you established in Exercise 13 of lesson 2.10 to find $g(x) = x^7 + x^6 + x^5 + x^4 + x^3 + x^2 + x + 1$.

2. One way to solve this problem is to use polynomial division to divide the quotient $x^7 + x^6 + x^5 + x^4 +$

$x^3 + x^2 + x + 1$ from the previous problem by $x + 1$. Here is a description of that process:

- x^7 divided by x is x^6, so this is the first term of the new quotient.
- Multiply x^6 by $x + 1$ to get $x^7 + x^6$.
- Subtract this from $x^7 + x^6 + x^5 + x^4 + x^3 + x^2 + x + 1$ to get $x^5 + x^4 + x^3 + x^2 + x + 1$.
- x^5 divided by x is x^4, so this is the next term of the quotient.
- Multiply x^4 by $x + 1$ to get $x^5 + x^4$.
- Subtract this from $x^5 + x^4 + x^3 + x^2 + x + 1$ to get $x^3 + x^2 + x + 1$.
- x^3 divided by x is x^2, so this is the next term of the quotient.
- Multiply x^2 by $x + 1$ to get $x^3 + x^2$.
- Subtract this from $x^3 + x^2 + x + 1$ to get $x + 1$.
- x divided by x is 1, so this is the last term of the quotient.
- Multiply 1 by $x + 1$ to get $x + 1$.
- Subtract this from $x + 1$ to get 0, so $x + 1$ is a factor of the quotient from the previous problem.

$g(x) = x^6 + x^4 + x^2 + 1$

3. The Remainder Theorem says that the remainder when $x^{105} - 3x + 1$ is divided by $x + 1$ is equal to $(-1)^{105}$ $-3(-1) + 1 = -1 + 3 + 1 = 3$

4. You could solve this problem by expanding the right side of the equation and making the corresponding coefficients of like-degree terms equal, or you can substitute strategic values in for x to simplify the calculations. For example, if $x = 1$, then the equation becomes $1 + 2 = 0 + 0 + C$, so $C = 3$. Then, for $x = 0$, $0 + 0 = 1 - B + C$, so $B = 4$.

5. From the given information, you know $2x^3 + rx^2 + sx + 4 = (x - 2)^2 p(x)$. You also know that $p(x)$ must be a linear polynomial, so that the degree of the polynomials on either side of this equation will be equal. Use $p(x) = ax + b$ and expand the right side.

$$2x^3 + rx^2 + sx + 4 = (x - 2)^2(ax + b)$$
$$= (x^2 - 4x + 4)(ax + b)$$
$$= ax^3 - 4ax^2 + 4ax + bx^2 - 4bx + 4b$$
$$= ax^3 + (b - 4a)x^2 + (4a - 4b)x + 4b$$

Coefficients of like-degree terms must be equal, so the x^3-term and the constant term coefficients yield $a = 2$ and $b = 1$. This makes the coefficient of the x^2-term $b - 4a = 1 - 4(2) = -7$, so $r = -7$. Now look at the coefficients for the x-term. $4a - 4b = 8 - 4 = 4$, so $s = 4$.

6. If a number a is a zero or root of a polynomial, the Factor Theorem says that $(x - a)$ is a factor of the polynomial. And, if $x - a$ is a factor of a polynomial $f(x)$, the Remainder Theorem says that $f(a) = 0$.

7. You could use Corollary 2.5 which says that if two polynomials of degree n agree for $n + 1$ inputs, they are equivalent. (This is the "Function Implies Form" Theorem.)

8. You need a polynomial of degree 3 or less. This is because four input-output pairs are enough to completely determine a cubic polynomial.

2.11   Getting Started

For You to Explore

1. (a) $(x+5)(x+5)$

(b) $(x+6)(x+4)$

(c) There are no integers with sum 10 and product 23. So, $z^2 + 10z + 23$ has no factorization over $\mathbb{Z}$. There are *real numbers* that add to 10 and multiply to 23: they are $5 + \sqrt{2}$ and $5 - \sqrt{2}$.

(d) $(u+7)(u+3)$

(e) If two numbers sum to 10, their maximum product is 25 when both are 5. There is no way to take two real numbers that sum to 10 and have a product of 26. So, there is no factorization of $y^2 + 10y + 26$ over $\mathbb{Z}$ or even $\mathbb{R}$.

2. (a) $(x+3)(x+15)$

(b) Use the scaling method. Pull out $2x$ from each term:

$$4x^2 + 36x + 45 = (2x)^2 + 18(2x) + 45$$

Then, the polynomial factors like the one in (a) to $(2x+3)(2x+15)$.

(c) This polynomial factors like the one in (a), using the expression $(x-3)$. The factorization is

$$((x-3)+3)((x-3)+15).$$

This simplifies a bit to $x(x+12)$.

Another way to do this problem is to expand the expressions $(x-3)^2$ and $18(x-3)$ before trying to factor:

$$(x-3)^2 + 18(x-3) + 45$$
$$= (x^2 - 6x + 9) + (18x - 54) + 45$$
$$= x^2 + 12x$$

This gives the same factorization.

(d) $(z+11)(z-11)$ by difference of squares.

(e) $(3u+11)(3u-11)$ by difference of squares, since $9u^2 = (3u)^2$.

(f) This is also difference of squares, factoring to

$$(y+5+11)(y+5-11).$$

Combining terms gives $(y+16)(y-6)$ as the factorization.

(g) Both terms have a common factor of $(y+5)$, so pull it out to get

$$(y+5)(y^2-4).$$

The other factor, (y^2-4), factors as a difference of squares to the final factorization, $(y+5)(y+2)(y-2)$.

(h) As with (g), the common factor $(y+5)$ can be pulled out to get

$$(y+5)(y^2-3).$$

This time, the other factor does not factor, since 3 is not a perfect square of an integer. It would factor over $\mathbb{R}$, however.

3. One way to do this problem is to find the two numbers. The roots of the equation are 1 and 5. The sum of the roots is 6 and the product is 5.

Another way is to recall that in a quadratic equation $Ax^2 + Bx + C = 0$, the sum of the roots is given by $\frac{-B}{A}$ and the product is given by $\frac{C}{A}$. Here, $A = 1$, $B = -6$, and $C = 5$, and the sum and product of roots can be found.

4. If α and β are roots, then $(x - \alpha)$ and $(x - \beta)$ are factors of the quadratic expression. Multiplying this out gives

$$(x - \alpha)(x - \beta) = x^2 - (\alpha + \beta)x + (\alpha \cdot \beta)$$

Since we have $\alpha + \beta = 6$ and $\alpha \cdot \beta = -3$ from the problem, the quadratic is $x^2 - 6x - 3$. These two numbers are solutions to the equation

$$x^2 - 6x - 3 = 0$$

Alternately, find the two numbers α and β, then verify that they are solutions. The values are

$$3 \pm 2\sqrt{3}$$

Their sum is $(3 + 2\sqrt{3}) + (3 - 2\sqrt{3}) = \mathbf{6}$, and their product is

$$(3 + 2\sqrt{3})(3 - 2\sqrt{3}) = 3^2 - (2\sqrt{3})^2 = 9 - 12 = \mathbf{-3}$$

On Your Own

5. (a) $(x+1)(x+5)$

(b) $(x-3)(x-3)$, which is also $(x-3)^2$.

(c) $(x+2)(x+10)$

(d) This problem looks for two numbers with a sum of 10 and product -20. One way is to list combinations of integers that multiply to -20, and none of them work. Another is to list pairs that add to 10, starting from 11 and -1. Either method can be used to discover that no factoring over $\mathbb{Z}$ exists here.

(e) This problem looks for two numbers with a sum of -5 and product -24. Because the product is negative, one of the numbers will be positive and the other will be negative, so you're really looking for two numbers with a *difference* of 5, and you know that the larger of the two will be negative. Here's the factoring: $(x-8)(x+3)$.

(f) The product, 30, is larger than the maximum possible product for two numbers that add up to 10. Therefore, there is no factoring over either $\mathbb{Z}$ or $\mathbb{R}$.

6. (a) Expand and look for like terms:

$$(x-1)(x^2+x+1) = (x^3+x^2+x) - (x^2+x+1)$$

The like terms x^2 and x within each term *cancel out*. The only remaining terms are x^3 and -1, so the expansion gives

$$(x-1)(x^2+x+1) = x^3 - 1$$

(b) Expand and look for like terms:

$$(x+1)(x^2-x+1) = (x^3-x^2+x) + (x^2-x+1)$$

The like terms x^2 and x within each term *cancel out*. The only remaining terms are x^3 and $+1$, so the expansion gives

$$(x+1)(x^2-x+1) = x^3 + 1$$

7. Any of the answers can be confirmed by multiplying the factored expressions.

   (a) The factored form is from the first part of the previous exercise: $(x - 1)(x^2 + x + 1)$.
   (b) The previous exercise gives this factoring: $(x + 1)(x^2 - x + 1)$.
   (c) $(x - 2)(x^2 + 2x + 4)$
   (d) $(x + 2)(x^2 - 2x + 4)$
   (e) $(2x - 1)(4x^2 + 2x + 1)$
   (f) $(2x + 1)(4x^2 - 2x + 1)$
   (g) $(x - a)(x^2 + ax + a^2)$
   (h) $(x + a)(x^2 - ax + a^2)$
   (i) Here, the factoring from this problem gives

   $$((x + 1) - 1)((x + 1)^2 + (x + 1) + 1)$$

   This can be simplified to $x(x^2 + 3x + 3)$. Alternately, you could expand $(x + 1)^3$ at the start to give $x^3 + 3x^2 + 3x + 1$, then subtract 1. The expression $(x^2 + 3x + 3)$ cannot be factored further.
   (j) Use a similar method to the previous part. The factoring is $x(x^2 - 3x + 3)$.

8. If p and q are roots, then $(x - p)$ and $(x - q)$ are factors (possibly in $\mathbb{Z}$, possibly in $\mathbb{R}$ . . .). Then

   $$x^2 - 10x + 7 = (x - p)(x - q)$$

   Expanding the right side gives

   $$x^2 - 10x + 7 = x^2 - px - qx + pq$$

   Then $-10 = -p - q$ and $7 = pq$. The first statement is equivalent to saying $p + q = 10$, and the second directly says $pq = 7$.
   The actual values of p and q are $5 \pm \sqrt{18} = 5 \pm 3\sqrt{2}$.

9. This exercise is the reverse of Exercise 8. Given the roots, calculate their sum and product.

   $$\text{sum} = (3 + \sqrt{7}) + (3 - \sqrt{7}) = \mathbf{6}$$
   $$\text{product} = (3 + \sqrt{7})(3 - \sqrt{7}) = 3^2 - (\sqrt{7})^2 = \mathbf{2}$$

   Then if the quadratic equation is in the form $x^2 - bx + c = 0$, $b = 6$ and $c = 2$. This gives the equation

   $$x^2 - 6x + 2 = 0$$

   Any equation you can produce by multiplying this equation by any constant is also a solution.

10. One way to solve this problem is to expand the right side:

    $$A(x - 2)^3 = A(x^3 - 6x^2 + 12x - 8)$$
    $$= Ax^3 - 6Ax^2 + 12Ax - 8A$$
    $$B(x - 2)^2 = B(x^2 - 4x + 4) = Bx^2 - 4Bx + 4B$$
    $$C(x - 2) = Cx - 2C$$

    Then the right side can be rewritten as

    $$Ax^3 + (-6A + B)x^2 + (12A - 4B + C)x$$
    $$+ (-8A + 4B - 2C + D)$$

This gives a set of equations to solve:

$$A = 3$$
$$-6A + B = -18$$
$$12A - 4B + C = 40$$
$$-8A + 4B - 2C + D = -37$$

Each equation gives you enough information to solve the next. The first equation gives $\mathbf{A = 3}$. Knowing A in the second equation gives $\mathbf{B = 0}$. Knowing A and B in the third equation gives $\mathbf{C = 4}$. Finally, using all three of these, the final equation gives $\mathbf{D = -5}$.

Other methods are possible, including the use of polynomial division from the previous investigation. Dividing the polynomial on the left by $(x - 2)$ and taking the remainder gives each successive term.

Here's how this method would play out. $3x^3 - 18x^2 + 40x - 37$ divided by $x - 2$ gives the quotient $3x^2 - 12x + 16$ with remainder -5. This remainder must be D from the original equation, because each of the other terms on the right side includes a factor of $x - 2$.

Now, divide the quotient you got in the first step, $3x^2 - 12x + 16$, by $x - 2$. This gives a new quotient of $3x - 6$ with remainder 4. This remainder must be C from the original equation. This is because you've now effectively divided the original polynomial by $(x - 2)^2$ (although you did not include the remainder from the first division in this second division). The term $C(x - 2)$ on the right side of the original equation is the only one left that does not include a factor of $(x - 2)^2$.

Divide the latest quotient, $3x - 6$, by $x - 2$. This gives a quotient of 3 with remainder 0. This means that A from the original equation must be 3, and B must be 0. ($B(x - 2)^2$ is the term left that does not include a factor of $(x - 2)^3$, and $A\frac{(x-2)^3}{(x-2)^3} = A$.)

Maintain Your Skills

11. Multiply out each expression as needed, then arrange the terms from highest to lowest degree.

    (a) $x^2 - 9$
    (b) $4x^2 - 9$
    (c) $-x^2 + 9$
    (d) $x^2 + 2x - 8$
    (e) $2x + 1$
    (f) $x^4 + x^2 + 1$
    (g) $x^6 + 3x^4 - x^3 + 3x^2 + 1$
    (h) $3x^4 + 3x^2 + 1$

12. (a) This factors as difference of squares. $(x + 3)(x - 3)$
    (b) This is a difference of squares. $(2x + 3)(2x - 3)$
    (c) This is a difference of squares. $(3 + x)(3 - x)$
    (d) This is a difference of squares, giving $((x + 1) + 3)((x + 1) - 3)$, which simplifies to $(x + 4)(x - 2)$. The expanded version from Exercise 11 could also be used here.
    (e) This is a difference of squares, giving $((x + 1) + x)((x + 1) - x)$, which simplifies to $(2x + 1)(1)$. The "1" factor can then be ignored,

leaving $2x + 1$ as the final expression. No further factoring is possible.

(f) This is a difference of squares, giving $((x^2 + 1) + x)$ $((x^2 + 1) - x)$. The terms within the parentheses can be rearranged to form $(x^2 + x + 1)(x^2 - x + 1)$.

(g) This is a difference of cubes: $(x^2 + 1 - x)$ $((x^2 + 1)^2 + (x^2 + 1) \cdot x + x^2)$. Collecting terms gives the factoring $(x^2 - x + 1)(x^4 + x^3 + 3x^2 + x + 1)$.

(h) This is a difference of cubes: $(x^2 + 1 - x^2)$ $((x^2 + 1)^2 + (x^2 + 1) \cdot x^2 + x^4)$. Collecting terms gives $(1)(3x^4 + 3x^2 + 1)$. The "1" factor can be ignored. No further factoring is possible.

2.12   Quadratics

Check Your Understanding

1. (a) Pull out a $(3x)$ to make a new quadratic: $(3x)^2 + 6(3x) - 7$. This new quadratic $M^2 + 6M - 7$ factors as $(M + 7)(M - 1)$. So the factoring is $(3x + 7)$ $(3x - 1)$.

(b) Use scaling. Introduce a factor of 6 to get

$$36x^2 - 186x + 210$$

This can be rewritten as $(6x)^2 - 31(6x) + 210$. This new quadratic $M^2 - 31M + 210$ factors as $(M - 21)(M - 10)$. So, the factoring of $36x^2 - 186x + 210$ is $(6x - 21)(6x - 10)$. Pull out the common factors to get $6(2x - 7)(3x - 5)$.

So, the factoring of $6x^2 - 31x + 35$ is $(2x - 7)$ $(3x - 5)$.

Alternately, you could use the quadratic formula to find the roots of the equation $6x^2 - 31x + 35 = 0$. These two roots are $\frac{7}{2}$ and $\frac{5}{3}$, which then lead to the factors.

(c) Use scaling. Introduce a factor of 15 to get

$$225x^2 + 240x - 105$$

This can be rewritten as $(15x)^2 + 16(15x) - 105$. This new quadratic $M^2 + 16M - 105$ factors as $(M - 5)(M + 21)$. So, the factoring of $225x^2 + 240x - 105$ is $(15x - 5)(15x + 21)$. Pull out the common factors to get $15(3x - 1)(5x + 7)$.

So, the factoring of $15x^2 + 16x - 7$ is $(3x - 1)$ $(5x + 7)$.

(d) Scaling works here. Equally valid is looking at the middle term, $62x$. There aren't many ways to make $62x$ out of just 9 and 7. In fact, it has to be that the 9 and 7 get multiplied in order to build anything big enough to make $62x$.

The product must be $(9x - 1)(x + 7)$.

(e) Scaling works here, and so does the quadratic formula. The roots of $-18x^2 - 65x - 7$ are given by

$$x = \frac{65 \pm \sqrt{65^2 - 4 \cdot (-18) \cdot (-7)}}{2 \cdot (-18)}$$

The values of x are $\frac{-1}{9}$ and $\frac{-7}{2}$. These lead to the factoring $-(9x + 1)(2x + 7)$. The negative sign

accounts for the fact that

$$-18x^2 - 65x - 7 = -(18x^2 + 65x + 7)$$

(f) Again, use scaling or the quadratic formula. Scaling leads to the quadratic $-M^2 + 61M + 126$, which factors as $(M - 63)(-M - 2)$. The factorization of $-18x^2 + 61x + 7$ is $(9x + 1)(-2x + 7)$.

(g) This polynomial is related to the one in part (d). The difference is that each x has been replaced by x^2. So, use the factoring from that quadratic to get

$$9x^4 + 62x^2 - 7 = (9x^2 - 1)(x^2 + 7)$$

Ah, there's more. $9x^2 - 1$ is a difference of squares, so its part factors to $(3x + 1)(3x - 1)$. The expression $x^2 + 7$ is a sum of squares and does not factor. The final factoring is

$$9x^4 + 62x^2 - 7 = (3x + 1)(3x - 1)(x^2 + 7)$$

(h) This is a regular difference-of-squares factoring. The factoring is

$$25 - 4x^2 = (5 + 2x)(5 - 2x)$$

(i) This is related to the expression of part (f). Here, each term has been multiplied by $-x$. Pull out this common factor:

$$18x^3 - 61x^2 - 7x = -x(-18x^2 + 61x + 7)$$

The factoring of $-18x^2 + 61x + 7$ is already known. The overall factoring is

$$18x^3 - 61x^2 - 7x = -x(9x + 1)(-2x + 7)$$

As a final option, you can choose distribute the negative through to the final factor:

$$18x^3 - 61x^2 - 7x = x(9x + 1)(2x - 7)$$

2. The key to this exercise is that the factorings in Exercise 1 apply here. Since the coefficients of terms are the same as the earlier exercise, the only difference lies in the variables used. For example, consider part (a):

$$9x^2 + 18x - 7 = (3x + 7)(3x - 1)$$
$$9x^2 + 18xy - 7y^2 = (3x + 7y)(3x - y)$$

The other solutions are very similar to their corresponding parts in the previous exercise.

(a) $(3x + 7y)(3x - y)$
(b) $(2x - 7y)(3x - 5y)$
(c) $(3x - a)(5x + 7a)$
(d) $(9x - b)(x + 7b)$
(e) $(9x + a)(-2x - 7a)$
(f) $(9x + y)(-2x + 7y)$
(g) $(5y + 2x)(5y - 2x)$
(h) $x(9x + y)(2x - 7y)$

On Your Own

3. **(a)** Although the factoring can be found directly, it's a little more difficult because of the odd coefficient in the linear term. Scaling provides a way to factor this without dealing with fractional coefficients.

Multiply by 4 to get $16x^2 - 52x + 12 = (4x)^2 - 13(4x) + 12$. The monic polynomial is $M^2 - 13M + 12$, which factors to $(M - 1)(M - 12)$.

Then $16x^2 - 52x + 12 = (4x - 1)(4x - 12) = 4(4x - 1)(x - 3)$, so the original quadratic factors as

$$4x^2 - 13x + 3 = (4x - 1)(x - 3)$$

(b) This one can be scaled without multiplying:

$$4x^2 - 8x + 3 = (2x)^2 - 4(2x) + 3$$

Then the reduced quadratic leads to the factoring $(2x - 1)(2x - 3)$.

(c) Again, this can be scaled without multiplying:

$$4x^2 + 4x - 3 = (2x)^2 + 2(2x) - 3$$

This reduced quadratic leads to the factoring $(2x + 3)(2x - 1)$.

(d) This is the same quadratic as part (c), where the variable x has been replaced by $(x + 1)$. So, the factoring is

$$(2(x + 1) + 3)(2(x + 1) - 1)$$

Expanding and collecting gives a simpler factored form:

$$4(x + 1)^2 + 4(x + 1) - 3 = (2x + 5)(2x + 1)$$

Alternately, expand the expressions $4(x + 1)^2$ and $4(x + 1)$ to get the quadratic $4x^2 + 12x + 5$, which has the same factorization.

(e) This is a similar polynomial to part (a), but x has been replaced by x^2. The factoring is performed the same way:

$$4x^4 - 13x^2 + 3 = (4x^2 - 1)(x^2 - 3)$$

This is not a complete factoring, since $4x^2 - 1$ is a difference of squares: $4x^2 - 1 = (2x + 1)(2x - 1)$. The other expression, $x^2 - 3$, is not a difference of squares and does not factor. The final factoring is

$$4x^4 - 13x^2 + 3 = (2x + 1)(2x - 1)(x^2 - 3)$$

(f) This polynomial is similar to the one in part (e), but x has been replaced by $x - 1$.

If you perform this substitution in the final factoring, you get

$$4(x - 1)^4 - 13(x - 1)^2 + 3$$
$$= (2(x - 1) + 1)(2(x - 1) - 1)((x - 1)^2 - 3)$$

Multiply and combine terms in the factors to get

$$4(x-1)^4 - 13(x-1)^2 + 3 = (2x-1)(2x-3)(x^2-2x-2)$$

(g) This polynomial is also similar to the one in part (e), but x has been replaced by $(x - 1)^3$. If you make this substitution in the final factoring for that part, you get

$$4(x - 1)^{12} - 13(x - 1)^6 + 3$$
$$= ((x - 1)^6) - 3)(2(x - 1)^3 - 1)(2(x - 1)^3 + 1)$$

If you multiply out and combine like terms in the factors, you end up with

$$4(x - 1)^{12} - 13(x - 1)^6 + 3$$
$$= (x^6 - 6x^5 + 15x^4 - 20x^3 + 15x^2 - 6x - 2)$$
$$(2x^3 - 6x^3 + 6x - 3)(2x^3 - 6x^3 + 6x - 1)$$

(h) This is a difference of two squares, so you get:

$$(x^2 + 1)^2 - x^2 = ((x^2 + 1) - x)((x^2 + 1) + x)$$

Combine like terms in the factors to get the final factoring:

$$(x^2 + 1)^2 - x^2 = (x^2 - x + 1)(x^2 + x + 1)$$

4. Solve for x by first multiplying through by x, then moving terms to one side to produce a quadratic:

$$2x - \frac{3}{x} = 5$$
$$2x^2 - 3 = 5x$$
$$2x^2 - 5x - 3 = 0$$

In multiplying by x, check to see that $x \neq 0$. $x = 0$ is not a solution to this equation, so everything is fine. Now factor to find x:

$$2x^2 - 5x - 3 = 0$$
$$(2x + 1)(x - 3) = 0$$

The two solutions are $x = 3$ and $x = \frac{-1}{2}$. Check:

$$2 \cdot 3 - \frac{3}{3} = 5 \textbf{ True!}$$
$$2 \cdot \frac{-1}{2} - \frac{3}{\frac{-1}{2}} = -1 + 6 = 5 \textbf{ True!}$$

5. **(a)** Replace x by $z + 3$ and simplify.

$$x^2 - 6x + 7 = 0$$
$$(z + 3)^2 - 6(z + 3) + 7 = 0$$
$$z^2 + 6z + 9 - 6z - 18 + 7 = 0$$
$$z^2 - 2 = 0$$

The new equation is $z^2 - 2 = 0$.

(b) Solutions can be found by solving for z directly:

$$z^2 - 2 = 0$$
$$z^2 = 2$$
$$z = \pm\sqrt{2}$$

There are two solutions. Alternately, factor $z^2 - 2$ as a difference of squares over $\mathbb{R}$:

$$z^2 - 2 = (z + \sqrt{2})(z - \sqrt{2})$$

This also gives the same solutions.

(c) Since $z = x - 3$, substitute to solve for x. Then
$$(x - 3) = \sqrt{2} \text{ or } (x - 3) = -\sqrt{2}$$
The two solutions are $x = 3 + \sqrt{2}$ and $x = 3 - \sqrt{2}$, which can be written as $x = 3 \pm \sqrt{2}$.

6. Since $\frac{c}{a}$ is the product of the roots, A is true. If $a = 1$ and d is a root, then $x - d$ is a factor of the polynomial, so B is true (the other pieces of information are red herrings). If a, b, and c are positive, then $\frac{-b}{a} < 0$ and $\frac{c}{a} > 0$. In this case, the sum of the roots is negative and their product is positive. Hence they must both be negative and D is true. The correct answer choice is **C**.

7. It will work, but it will require working with fractional coefficients. He'd have an easier time if he multiplied through by 18. Here's Derman's solution:

   Multiply by 2 to get $36x^2 + 14x - 2$.
   Replace $6x$ by M to get $M^2 + \frac{7}{3}M - 2$.
   This isn't a nice quadratic to factor, but the quadratic formula gives roots of -3 and $\frac{2}{3}$, so it does factor as $M^2 + \frac{7}{3}M - 2 = (M + 3)(M - \frac{2}{3})$
   Replace the M to get $(6x + 3)(6x - \frac{2}{3}) =$
   $(6x + 3)(2)(3x - \frac{1}{3})$.
   Divide by 2 to get the factoring for the original polynomial $(6x + 3)(3x - \frac{1}{3})$. You can make it look nicer by factoring a 3 out of the first factor and multiplying the second factor by it. This leaves you with $(2x + 1)$ $(9x - 1)$ as the final factoring.
   For contrast, here's what would happen if Derman had multiplied through by 18 instead:
   Multiply by 18 to get $324x^2 + 126x - 18$.
   Replace $18x$ by M to get $M^2 + 7M - 18$.
   This factors as $M^2 + 7M - 18 = (M + 9)(M - 2)$
   Unreplace the M to get $(18x + 9)(18x - 2) =$
   $9(2x + 1)(2)(9x - 1)$
   Divide by 9 to get the final factoring $(2x + 1)(9x - 1)$.

Maintain Your Skills

8. (a) The solutions to the first equation are $x = 1$ and $x = 7$. The solutions to the second equation are $x = 3$ and $x = 21$. The solutions to the second equation are three times larger.
   (b) The solutions to the first equation are $x = -7$ and $x = \frac{3}{2}$. The solutions to the second equation are $x = -14$ and $x = 3$. The solutions to the second equation are two times larger.
   (c) The solutions to the first equation are $x = -7$ and $x = \frac{3}{2}$. The solutions to the second equation are $x = -21$ and $x = \frac{9}{2}$. The solutions to the second equation are three times larger.
   (d) The solutions to the first equation are $x = -7$ and $x = \frac{3}{2}$. The solutions to the second equation are $x = -35$ and $x = \frac{15}{2}$. The solutions to the second equation are five times larger.
   (e) The solutions to the first equation are $x = -7$ and $x = \frac{3}{2}$. The solutions to the second equation are $x = -14$ and $x = 3$. The solutions to the second equation are two times larger.

(f) The solutions to the first equation are $x = -7$ and $x = \frac{5}{3}$. The solutions to the second equation are $x = -21$ and $x = 5$. The solutions to the second equation are three times larger.
(g) The solutions to the first equation are $x \approx -6.88304$ and $x \approx 1.5497$. The solutions to the second equation are approximately $x \approx -20.649$ and $x \approx 4.649$. The solutions to the second equation are three times larger.

9. There are two methods:
   - Multiply the coefficient of x by the multiplier, and multiply the constant term by the square of the multiplier.
   - Divide the coefficient of x^2 by the multiplier, and multiply the constant term by the multiplier.

   Here are some possible answers. There are many others.
   (a) $x^2 - 56x + 343 = 0$
   (b) $2x^2 + 77x - 1029 = 0$
   (c) $x^2 + 11x - 42 = 0$ or $2x^2 + 22x - 84 = 0$
   (d) $x^2 + 11x - 63 = 0$ or $3x^2 + 33x - 189 = 0$
   (e) $x^2 + 11x - 105 = 0$ or $5x^2 + 55x - 525 = 0$

2.13 Factoring Cubics

Check Your Understanding

1. Expand the left-side expressions in each case.
$$\begin{aligned}(x + y)^3 &= (x + y)(x + y)(x + y) \\ &= (x^2 + 2xy + y^2)(x + y) \\ &= x^3 + 2x^2y + xy^2 + x^2y + 2xy^2 + y^3 \\ &= x^3 + 3x^2y + 3xy^2 + y^3\end{aligned}$$

$$\begin{aligned}(x - y)^3 &= (x - y)(x - y)(x - y) \\ &= (x^2 - 2xy + y^2)(x - y) \\ &= x^3 - 2x^2y + xy^2 - x^2y + 2xy^2 - y^3 \\ &= x^3 - 3x^2y + 3xy^2 - y^3\end{aligned}$$

2. (a) This factoring uses difference of cubes. The first thing being cubed is x, and the second is 4.
   $(x - 4)(x^2 + 4x + 16)$
   (b) This factoring uses sum of cubes. The first thing being cubed is x, and the second is 4.
   $(x + 4)(x^2 - 4x + 16)$
   (c) This factoring uses difference of cubes. The first thing being cubed is $3x$, and the second is 4.
   $(3x - 4)(9x^2 + 12x + 16)$
   (d) This factoring uses sum of cubes. The first thing being cubed is $3x$, and the second is 4.
   $(3x + 4)(9x^2 - 12x + 16)$
   (e) This factoring uses difference of cubes. The first thing being cubed is $(x + 1)$, and the second is 4. This gives $(x + 1 - 4)((x + 1)^2 + 4(x + 1) + 4^2)$, which can be simplified to $(x - 3)(x^2 + 6x + 21)$.

(f) This factoring uses sum of cubes. The first thing being cubed is $(2x - 3)$, and the second is 4. This gives $(2x - 3 + 4)((2x - 3)^2 - 4(2x - 3) + 4^2)$. This can be simplified to $(2x + 1)(4x^2 - 20x + 37)$.

(g) This factoring uses grouping. Group the first two terms, and the last two:

$$x^3 + 3x^2 - 9x - 27$$
$$(x^3 + 3x^2) + (-9x - 27)$$
$$x^2(x + 3) - 9(x + 3)$$
$$(x + 3)(x^2 - 9)$$

The second factor, $x^2 - 9$, is a difference of squares, so it factors. The final factoring is

$$(x + 3)(x + 3)(x - 3)$$

or $(x + 3)^2(x - 3)$.

(h) This factoring uses grouping, and is similar to the previous part. Group the first two terms and the last two:

$$x^3 + ax^2 - a^2x - a^3$$
$$(x^3 + ax^2) + (-a^2x - a^3)$$
$$x^2(x + a) - a^2(x + a)$$
$$(x + a)(x^2 - a^2)$$

The second factor, $x^2 - a^2$, is a difference of squares, so it factors. The final factoring is

$$(x + a)(x + a)(x - a)$$

or $(x + a)^2(x - a)$.

(i) This is a difference of squares factoring. The first thing being squared is x, and the second is $(3x + 1)$. The factoring is

$$(x + (3x + 1))(x - (3x + 1))$$

This simplifies to

$$(4x + 1)(-2x - 1)$$

Alternately, expand the second expression and then factor the resulting non-monic quadratic.

(j) This factors by grouping. Group the last three terms together:

$$-y^2 + 2yz - z^2 = -(y^2 - 2yz + z^2) = -(y - z)^2$$

Then the expression is $x^2 - (y - z)^2$, and factors as a difference of squares to

$$(x + y - z)(x - (y - z)) = (x + y - z)(x - y + z)$$

(k) This one requires you to find a factor, since grouping won't work. The equation $x^3 - 4x^2 - 31x + 70 = 0$ has three roots, $x = 2$, $x = -5$, and $x = 7$. Using the root $x = 2$, the expression $(x - 2)$ is a factor. Then use polynomial division to find that

$$x^3 - 4x^2 - 31x + 70 = (x - 2)(x^2 - 2x - 35)$$

Then the remaining quadratic factors to give the final factored form, $(x - 2)(x + 5)(x - 7)$.

(l) This is related to the previous part. Its related factoring is

$$(x - 2y)(x + 5y)(x - 7y)$$

(m) The two terms here have a common factor of $(x + 1)$, so pull it out:

$$(x + 1)((x + 1)^2 - 3x)$$

Then simplify the second factor to $x^2 - x + 1$. The final factored form is

$$(x + 1)(x^2 - x + 1)$$

Alternately, expand $(x + 1)^3$ and $-3x(x + 1)$, then cancel the like terms to leave the expression $x^3 + 1$. This expression can then be factored as a sum of cubes.

3. The first term must be multiplied to make a cube, so multiply through by 25 to produce $125x^3$:

$$125x^3 + 75x^2 + 75x - 50 = (5x)^3 + 3(5x)^2 + 15(5x) - 50.$$

The related monic cubic is $M^3 + 3M^2 + 15M - 50$. The "find a root" method works here. The only easily-found root is $M = 2$. Then $(M - 2)$ is a factor, and polynomial division gives the factoring as

$$(M - 2)(M^2 + 5M + 25).$$

The second factor cannot be factored further. Now, replace M with $5x$:

$$(5x - 2)((5x)^2 + 5(5x) + 25)$$
$$= (5x - 2)(25x^2 + 25x + 25)$$
$$= 25(5x - 2)(x^2 + x + 1)$$

The factoring of the original polynomial is

$$5x^3 + 3x^2 + 3x - 2 = (5x - 2)(x^2 + x + 1)$$

On Your Own

4. (a) This factoring uses difference of cubes. The first thing being cubed is x, and the second is 3. $(x - 3)$ $(x^2 + 3x + 9)$

(b) This factoring uses sum of cubes. The first thing being cubed is x, and the second is 3. $(x + 3)(x^2 - 3x + 9)$

(c) This factoring uses difference of cubes. The first thing being cubed is $4x$, and the second is 3. $(4x - 3)$ $(16x^2 + 12x + 9)$

(d) This factoring uses sum of cubes. The first thing being cubed is $4x$, and the second is 3. $(4x + 3)$ $(16x^2 - 12x + 9)$

(e) This factoring uses difference of cubes. The first thing being cubed is $(x - 1)$, and the second is 5. This gives $(x - 1 - 5)((x - 1)^2 + 5(x - 1) + 5^2)$, which can be simplified to $(x - 6)(x^2 + 3x + 21)$.

(f) This factoring uses sum of cubes. The first thing being cubed is $(2x - 3)$, and the second is 5. This gives $(2x - 3 + 5)((2x - 3)^2 - 5(2x - 3) + 5^2)$. This can be simplified to $(2x + 2)(4x^2 - 22x + 49)$. Lastly, pull a common factor of 2 from the terms in the first factor to get the final factored form,

$$2(x + 1)(4x^2 - 22x + 49)$$

(g) This factoring uses grouping. Group the first two terms, and the last two:

$$x^3 + 5x^2 - 25x - 125$$
$$(x^3 + 5x^2) + (-25x - 125)$$
$$x^2(x + 5) - 25(x + 5)$$
$$(x + 5)(x^2 - 25)$$

The second factor, $x^2 - 25$, is a difference of squares, so it factors. The final factoring is

$$(x + 5)(x + 5)(x - 5)$$

or $(x + 5)^2(x - 3)$.

(h) Find a root of $5x^3 - 7x^2 + 7x - 2 = 0$ to find this factoring. The root is $x = \frac{2}{5}$, so $(x - \frac{2}{5})$ is a factor (over $\mathbb{Q}$). The factor over $\mathbb{Z}$ is $(5x - 2)$. Use polynomial long division to find the other factor. The factorization is

$$(5x - 2)(x^2 - x + 1)$$

Alternately, you could use scaling to build the corresponding polynomial $125x^3 - 175x^2 + 175x - 50 = (5x)^3 - 7(5x)^2 + 35(5x) - 50$.

(i) This is a difference of squares factoring. The first thing being squared is x^2, and the second is $(3x + 1)^2$. The factoring is

$$(x^2 + (3x + 1)^2)(x^2 - (3x + 1)^2)$$

The first factor simplifies to $10x^2 + 6x + 1$ and does not factor further. The second factor is another difference of squares (also Exercise 2i from Check Your Understanding). It factors to $(x + (3x + 1))$ $(x - (3x + 1))$. The final factoring is

$$(10x^2 + 6x + 1)(4x + 1)(-2x - 1)$$

(j) This factors by grouping. Group the last three terms together:

$$-y^2 - 2yz - z^2 = -(y^2 + 2yz + z^2) = -(y + z)^2$$

Then the expression is $x^2 - (y + z)^2$, and factors as a difference of squares to

$$(x + (y + z))(x - (y + z)) = (x + y + z)(x - y - z)$$

(k) This is a sum of cubes. The first thing being cubed is $(x + 1)$, and the second is x. The factoring is

$$(2x + 1)((x + 1)^2 - x(x + 1) + x^2)$$

which simplifies to $(2x + 1)(x^2 + x + 1)$.

(l) Find a factor works here: the factor is $(x - 2)$ and long division gives the factorization

$$(x - 2)(x^2 - x + 1)$$

Alternately, the form $x^3 - 3x^2 + 3x - 1$ would be $(x - 1)^3$, so the whole thing can be rewritten as

$$(x - 1)^3 - 1$$

Then it can factor as a difference of cubes to
$((x - 1) - 1)((x - 1)^2 + (x - 1) + 1) =$
$(x - 2)(x^2 - x + 1)$.

(m) This is related to the previous part. Its related factoring is

$$(x - 2z)(x^2 - xz + z^2)$$

(n) The final term is a cube, -64. This fits the form in Exercise 1 of Check Your Understanding: it is the cube of the binomial $(x - 4)$. The factoring is

$$(x - 4)(x - 4)(x - 4)$$

or $(x - 4)^3$. This could also be found by the "find a root" method. The only root is $x = 4$.

5. Use root-finding to factor. One method is to sketch the graph of $y = x^3 - 15x - 4$ on a calculator, and find any x-intercepts. The graph passes through the point $(4, 0)$, so 4 is a solution to $x^3 - 15x - 4 = 0$ and $x - 4$ is a factor of the polynomial. Use polynomial division to find the other factor:

$$x^3 - 15x - 4 = (x - 4)(x^2 + 4x + 1)$$

The other factor cannot be factored over $\mathbb{Z}$.

6. The expression is the same as the one in Exercise 5, with $(x - 1)$ instead of x. So, use the factoring:

$$(x-1)^3 - 15(x-1) - 4 = ((x-1)-4)((x-1)^2 + 4(x-1) + 1)$$

The factors can be simplified, giving the result $(x - 5)(x^2 + 2x - 2)$.

7. Several methods are possible. One method is to use root-finding. Two roots are $x = 1$ and $x = -1$, giving the factors $(x - 1)$ and $(x + 1)$. Then, find the remaining factor by polynomial division.

A second method is to group the terms:

$$(x^4 - 2x^2 + 1) + (-x^3 + x)$$

The first group is a perfect square trinomial, and the second group has a common factor of $-x$:

$$(x^4 - 2x^2 + 1) + (-x^3 + x)$$
$$(x^2 - 1)^2 - x(x^2 - 1)$$
$$(x^2 - 1)(x^2 - 1 - x)$$
$$(x + 1)(x - 1)(x^2 - x - 1)$$

8. $(x + 4)^3 - (x^3 + 4^3) = x^3 + 3 \cdot x^2 \cdot 4 + 3 \cdot x \cdot 4^2 + 4^3 - x^3 - 4^3 = 12x^2 + 48x$. The correct answer choice is **D**.

Maintain Your Skills

9. (a) $x + 1$
   (b) $x^2 + 2x + 1$
   (c) $x^3 + 3x^2 + 3x + 1$
   (d) $x^4 + 4x^3 + 6x^2 + 4x + 1$
   (e) $x^5 + 5x^4 + 10x^3 + 10x^2 + 5x + 1$

   The numbers in each expansion correspond to the numbers in Pascal's Triangle. Each coefficient is the sum of two coefficients in the previous expansion, based on the fact that (for example)

$$(x + 1)^5 = (x + 1)(x + 1)^4$$

   Each coefficient comes from either an x or a 1 in the first factor, and the coefficients found in the second factor.

Check Your Understanding

1. (a) This is a quadratic in x^2. If $M = x^2$, the expression can be rewritten as $M^2 - M - 6$. The factoring is $(M + 2)(M - 3)$, so the factoring of the original is $(x^2 + 2)(x^2 - 3)$. Neither factor can be factored further.

   (b) This is a quadratic in x^3. The factoring is $(x^3 - 1)(x^3 - 8)$. Each of these factors can be factored further as a difference of cubes:

   $$x^3 - 1 = (x - 1)(x^2 + x + 1)$$
   $$x^3 - 8 = (x - 2)(x^2 + 2x + 4)$$

   The final factoring is $(x - 1)(x^2 + x + 1)(x - 2)(x^2 + 2x + 4)$.

   (c) This is a difference of squares. The factoring is $(x^2 + 4)(x^2 - 4)$. The second factor is another difference of squares, so the final factoring is $(x^2 + 4)(x + 2)(x - 2)$.

   (d) This is a difference of cubes. The first thing being cubed is x^2, and the second is 2. The factoring is

   $$(x^2 - 2)(x^4 + 2x^2 + 4)$$

   This does not factor further.

   (e) This is a difference of squares, similar to part (c). The initial factoring is $(x^2 + 4y^2)(x^2 - 4y^2)$, and the second factor is a difference of squares. The final factoring is $(x^2 + 4y^2)(x + 2y)(x - 2y)$.

   (f) This is a sum of cubes. The first thing being cubed is x^2, and the second is 2. The factoring is

   $$(x^2 + 2)(x^4 - 2x^2 + 4)$$

   This does not factor further.

   (g) This is a difference of squares. A perfect square trinomial would be $x^4 - 8x^2 + 16 = (x^2 - 4)^2$, so the expression can be rewritten:

   $$x^4 - 9x^2 + 16 = (x^4 - 8x^2 + 16) - x^2$$
   $$= (x^2 - 4)^2 - x^2$$

   Now this is a difference of squares. The factoring is

   $$(x^2 - 4 + x)(x^2 - 4 - x)$$

   Rewriting factors gives $(x^2 + x - 4)(x^2 - x - 4)$.

   (h) This is a difference of squares, like part (g). A perfect square trinomial would be $x^4 + 2x^2 + 1 = (x^2 + 1)^2$. Rewrite the expression as

   $$x^4 + x^2 + 1 = (x^4 + 2x^2 + 1) - x^2$$
   $$= (x^2 + 1)^2 - x^2$$

   The factoring is $(x^2 + 1 + x)(x^2 + 1 - x)$, which can be rewritten to $(x^2 + x + 1)(x^2 - x + 1)$.

2. (a) Use the quadratic formula to find the roots. The roots are

   $$x = \frac{2 \pm \sqrt{2^2 + 16}}{2} = \frac{2 \pm 2\sqrt{5}}{2} = 1 \pm \sqrt{5}$$

The factorization is in the form $(x - a)(x - b)$, where a and b are the roots. The factorization is

$$(x-(1+\sqrt{5}))(x-(1-\sqrt{5})) = (x-1-\sqrt{5})(x-1+\sqrt{5})$$

(b) Find the roots:

$$x = \frac{1 \pm \sqrt{1^2 + 4}}{2} = \frac{1 \pm \sqrt{5}}{2}$$

The factorization is

$$\left(x - \left(\frac{1 + \sqrt{5}}{2}\right)\right)\left(x - \left(\frac{1 - \sqrt{5}}{2}\right)\right)$$

Alternately, the form in the second expression means the roots will be half the roots in the first form, which can be used in place of the quadratic formula here.

3. There is more than one possible answer for each part.

   (a) If $2 + \sqrt{3}$ is a root of a polynomial with integer coefficients, it can't be the only root. Maybe it's a quadratic. If so, you'd need to have another root so that the sum with $2 + \sqrt{3}$ is an integer, and so is the product with $2 + \sqrt{3}$. The logical candidate is $2 - \sqrt{3}$, because the $\sqrt{3}$s in both roots will cancel each other out when you add them and when you take the product, the difference of squares identity guarantees that the $\sqrt{3}$ term will be squared. This quadratic would have the sum of roots equal to 4, and the product of roots would be

   $$(2 + \sqrt{3})(2 - \sqrt{3}) = 4 - 3 = 1$$

   You can use this information and the sum-product identity to find the quadratic $x^2 - 4x + 1$ with the appropriate roots.

   (b) If $2 - \sqrt{3}$ is a root, then $2 + \sqrt{3}$ must also be a root. These are the same roots as in part (a), so the same quadratic results.

   (c) This is a little trickier. If $\sqrt{2} + \sqrt{3}$ is a root, so must $\sqrt{2} - \sqrt{3}$, $-\sqrt{2} + \sqrt{3}$, and $-\sqrt{2} - \sqrt{3}$. The polynomial is

   $$(x-\sqrt{2}-\sqrt{3})(x-\sqrt{2}+\sqrt{3})(x+\sqrt{2}-\sqrt{3})(x+\sqrt{2}+\sqrt{3})$$

   Expand this expression using radical arithmetic (best done in pairs or with a CAS). The expanded expression is $x^4 - 10x^2 + 1$, which has the correct root.

   Another way to approach this problem is to start by letting $a = \sqrt{2} + \sqrt{3}$. This is an equation that has the root you want, but it definitely doesn't have integer coefficients. Square both sides. Then you have

   $$a^2 = 2 + 2\sqrt{6} + 3$$
   $$a^2 = 5 + 2\sqrt{6}$$

   You still don't have integer coefficients, so isolate the radical and square again.

$$a^2 - 5 = 2\sqrt{6}$$
$$a^4 - 10a^2 + 25 = 24$$
$$a^4 - 10a^2 + 1 = 0$$

This is an equation with integer coefficients that has $\sqrt{2} + \sqrt{3}$ as one of its roots.

4. Yes, this can happen if the coefficients are elements of $\mathbb{Q}$. For example, the expression

$$x^2 - \frac{1}{4}$$

does not factor over $\mathbb{Z}$ but factors over $\mathbb{Q}$ as $\left(x + \frac{1}{2}\right)$ $\left(x - \frac{1}{2}\right)$.

On Your Own

5. (a) This expression is quadratic in x^2, and the quadratic $M^2 - 11M + 28$ factors as $(M - 4)(M - 7)$. When you put x^2 back in for M, you can factor some more, because $(x^2 - 4)$ is the difference of two squares. $(x - 2)(x + 2)(x^2 - 7)$ is the final factoring.
   (b) This expression is a perfect square trinomial, since $M^2 - 6M + 9 = (M - 3)^2$. This factors to $(x^3 - 3)^2$ and no further.
   (c) This is a difference of cubes. It factors to $(x^2 - 3)$ $(x^4 + 3x^2 + 9)$.
   (d) This is a polynomial in x^2:

$$(x^2)^3 + 3(x^2)^2 + 3(x^2) + 1$$

   This is the form that appears in Exercise 1 of lesson 2.13, the cube of a binomial. The factoring is $(x^2 + 1)^3$.
   (e) This would be a perfect square if the $9x^2$ were $10x^2$, so rewrite it as

$$(x^4 + 10x^2 + 25) - x^2 = (x^2 + 5)^2 - x^2$$

   This factors as a difference of squares to $(x^2 + 5 + x)$ $(x^2 + 5 - x)$, or $(x^2 + x + 5)(x^2 - x + 5)$.
   (f) The expression $x^4 - 2a^2x^2 + a^4$ is a perfect square, so rewrite the original expression as

$$(x^4 - 2a^2x^2 + a^4) - a^2x^2 = (x^2 - a^2)^2 - (ax)^2$$

   This factors as a difference of squares to $(x^2 - a^2 + ax)$ $(x^2 - a^2 - ax)$ or $(x^2 + ax - a^2)(x^2 - ax - a^2)$.
   (g) This factors as difference of squares to $(x^3 + 1)(x^3 - 1)$. Ah, but these factors can be factored further using cubes. The factorization is

$$(x + 1)(x^2 - x + 1)(x - 1)(x^2 + x + 1)$$

   (h) This factors as a difference of squares to $(x^4 + 1)$ $(x^4 - 1)$. Ah, the second factor is another difference

of squares, so a further factoring is $(x^4 + 1)$ $(x^2 + 1)(x^2 - 1)$. The third factor is yet another difference of squares, so the final factorization is $(x^4 + 1)(x^2 + 1)(x + 1)(x - 1)$.

6. Whenever you square both sides of an equation in order to solve it, you must check the answers in the original equation. When you square both sides of an equation, the resulting equation may have *more* solutions than the original.

   (a) Square both sides to get $x = 49$ as the solution.
   (b) Square both sides to get $x - 3 = 49$, which has $x = 52$ as solution.
   (c) Square both sides to get $x - 3 = 78$. The solution is $x = 81$.
   (d) Square both sides to get $x - 3 = x^2 - 15$. This can be rewritten as the quadratic $0 = x^2 - x - 12$, which has roots 4 and -3.
      But there is only one correct root, since the negative root -3 results in a negative number under the square root sign on each side of the original equation. This solution is rejected, leaving only the positive solution 4.
   (e) This problem is difficult to solve directly. One way to do it is to rewrite the equation as

$$\sqrt{2x - 5} = \sqrt{x - 2} + 2$$

   then solve by squaring each side:

$$\sqrt{2x - 5} = \sqrt{x - 2} + 2$$
$$2x - 5 = (x - 2) + 4\sqrt{x - 2} + 4$$
$$2x - 5 = x + 2 + 4\sqrt{x - 2}$$
$$x - 7 = 4\sqrt{x - 2}$$
$$x^2 - 14x + 49 = 16(x - 2)$$
$$x^2 - 14x + 49 = 16x - 32$$
$$x^2 - 30x + 81 = 0$$
$$(x - 3)(x - 27) = 0$$

   This gives two possible solutions, $x = 3$ and $x = 27$. Testing $x = 3$ shows it does not work, but $x = 27$ does work, giving $\sqrt{49} - \sqrt{25} = 2$.
      Alternately, graph the equation $y = \sqrt{2x - 5} - \sqrt{x - 2}$ and see where that graph intersects the horizontal line $y = 2$. The only intersection is at the point $(27, 2)$, so the only solution is $x = 27$.

7. No, Derman's factoring isn't complete. The six terms in the second factor can be grouped in several ways to produce a further factoring. One such way is

$$(x^5 + x^4 + x^3) + (x^2 + x + 1) = x^3(x^2 + x + 1) + 1(x^2 + x + 1)$$

This factors as $(x^3 + 1)(x^2 + x + 1)$. From there, $x^3 + 1$ factors as a sum of cubes to give the complete factoring of $x^6 - 1$.

8. This can be factored using "difference of squares" twice. Namely,

$$x^4-1 = (x^2)^2-1 = (x^2+1)(x^2-1) = (x^2+1)(x+1)(x-1)$$

This cannot be factored further over $\mathbb{Z}$. The correct answer choice is **B**.

9. You can either expand the right side of the equation, or think about how that expansion would yield terms of degree 3, 2, and 1 to get the following equations:

$$a+b = 1$$
$$2+ab = 1$$

Substituting $b = 1 - a$ into the second equation gives you

$$2+a(1-a) = 1$$
$$0 = a^2 - a - 1$$

The quadratic formula gives you two real solutions for this equation, and you choose one to call a and the other is b. $a = \frac{1+\sqrt{5}}{2}$, $b = \frac{1-\sqrt{5}}{2}$

Maintain Your Skills

10. In each case, factor by grouping or use a CAS.
   (a) $(x+1)(x^2+1)$
   (b) $(x+1)(x^2-x+1)(x^2+x+1)$
   (c) $(x+1)(x^2+1)(x^4+1)$
   (d) $(x+1)(x^4-x^3+x^2-x+1)(x^4+x^3+x^2+x+1)$

2.15 Rational Expressions

Check Your Understanding

1. (a) The common factor of $5x$ can be divided out of the numerator and denominator, leaving $\frac{3}{x}$.
   (b) The numerator factors to $(x+y)(x-y)$. Then, cancel $(x+y)$ from top and bottom to leave only $x-y$ on top.
   (c) Factoring gives

$$\frac{(x+y)(x-y)}{(x+y)(x+y)}$$

Canceling $(x+y)$ from top and bottom leaves $\frac{x-y}{x+y}$.
   (d) Factoring gives

$$\frac{(x+1)(x-1)}{(x^2+1)(x+1)(x-1)}$$

Canceling leaves $\frac{1}{x^2+1}$.
   (e) Factor the numerator and denominator as quadratics. This gives

$$\frac{(x+2)(2x-3)}{(x+2)(3x-2)}$$

Canceling $(x+2)$ from top and bottom leaves $\frac{2x-3}{3x-2}$.

(f) Factor the numerator and denominator by grouping. The numerator is $(x-3)(x^4-1)$ and the denominator is $(x-3)(x^3-1)$. Each of these can be factored further. When all the factoring is done, the expression can be written as

$$\frac{(x-1)(x-3)(x+1)(x^2+1)}{(x-1)(x-3)(x^2+x+1)}$$

The expression $(x-1)(x-3)$ can be cancelled from top and bottom, leaving

$$\frac{(x+1)(x^2+1)}{x^2+x+1}$$

2. To find the rule for $g(x)$, factor the numerator and denominator as quadratics. This gives

$$\frac{(x+2)(2x-3)}{(x+2)(3x-2)}$$

The factor $(x+2)$ is cancelled from top and bottom giving:

$$g(x) = \frac{2x-3}{3x-2}$$

Since the only difference is the cancellation of $(x+2)$, the expressions must be identical unless $x+2 = 0$, when $x = -2$. For this value of x, f is undefined. However, $g(-2) = \frac{7}{8}$ is defined with no problem. Here is the graph of $g(x)$:

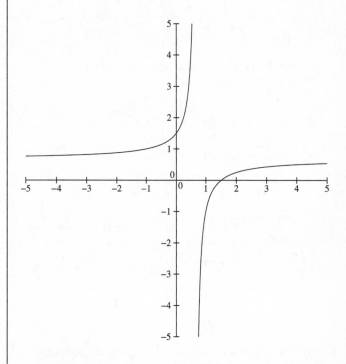

The graph of $f(x)$ is the same as the graph of $g(x)$, but the point $(-2, \frac{7}{8})$ is removed since $f(-2)$ is undefined.

This appears on the graph as a hole:

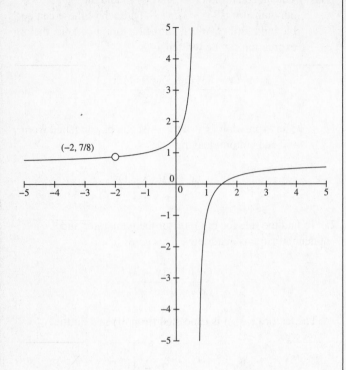

This type of point is often called a *hole discontinuity*.

3. (a) You can use $b - a$ as your common denominator, because $a - b = -(b - a)$.

$$\frac{b}{b-a} + \frac{a}{a-b} = \frac{b}{b-a} + \frac{a}{a-b} \cdot \frac{-1}{-1}$$

$$= \frac{b}{b-a} + \frac{-a}{b-a}$$

$$= \frac{b-a}{b-a}$$

$$= 1$$

(b) For this part, a common denominator is $(x-a)(x-b)(a-b)$.

$$\frac{1}{(x-a)(a-b)} + \frac{1}{(x-b)(b-a)}$$

$$= \frac{1}{(x-a)(a-b)} \cdot \frac{(x-b)}{(x-b)}$$

$$+ \frac{1}{(x-b)(b-a)} \cdot \frac{-(x-a)}{-(x-a)}$$

$$= \frac{x-b}{(x-a)(x-b)(a-b)} + \frac{-(x-a)}{(x-a)(x-b)(a-b)}$$

$$= \frac{x-b-x+a}{(x-a)(x-b)(a-b)}$$

$$= \frac{a-b}{(x-a)(x-b)(a-b)}$$

$$= \frac{1}{(x-a)(x-b)}$$

4. (a) The first denominator is $3(x-1)$ and the second is $(x-1)(x-4)$. To get a common denominator, multiply the first fraction (on top and bottom) by $(x-4)$ and the second by 3.

That is

$$\frac{(1+2x)}{3(x-1)} \cdot \frac{(x-4)}{(x-4)} + \frac{(5-x)}{(x-1)(x-4)} \cdot \frac{3}{3}$$

$$= \frac{2x^2 - 7x - 4 + 15 - 3x}{3(x-1)(x-4)}$$

$$= \frac{2x^2 - 10x + 11}{3(x-1)(x-4)}$$

(b) The common denominator is $x(x-3)(x+3)$. Multiply the first fraction (on top and bottom) by $x(x+3)$, the second by $x(x-3)$, and the third by $(x-3)(x+3)$. The combined numerator is

$$2x(x+3) - 2x(x-3) - (x-3)(x+3) = -x^2 + 12x + 9$$

(c) The common denominator for these expressions will be $(a-b)(b-c)(c-a)$.

$$\frac{1}{(a-b)(b-c)} + \frac{1}{(b-c)(c-a)} + \frac{1}{(c-a)(a-b)}$$

$$= \frac{1}{(a-b)(b-c)} \cdot \frac{c-a}{c-a} + \frac{1}{(b-c)(c-a)} \cdot \frac{a-b}{a-b}$$

$$+ \frac{1}{(c-a)(a-b)} \cdot \frac{b-c}{b-c}$$

$$= \frac{(c-a) + (a-b) + (b-c)}{(a-b)(b-c)(c-a)}$$

$$= 0$$

5. First, find a common denominator $((x-1)(x-3))$, and express the right side as a single rational expression.

$$\frac{1}{(x-1)(x-3)} = \frac{A}{x-1} + \frac{B}{x-3}$$

$$= \frac{A}{x-1} \cdot \frac{x-3}{x-3} + \frac{B}{x-3} \cdot \frac{x-1}{x-1}$$

$$= \frac{A(x-3)}{(x-1)(x-3)} + \frac{B(x-1)}{(x-1)(x-3)}$$

$$= \frac{A(x-3) + B(x-1)}{(x-1)(x-3)}$$

$$= \frac{Ax + Bx - 3A - B}{(x-1)(x-3)}$$

$$= \frac{(A+B)x + (-3A-B)}{(x-1)(x-3)}$$

Now compare the rational expression on the left and that on the right. They have the same denominator, so they're only equivalent if their numerators are equal. This gives you two equations in A and B:

$$A + B = 0$$

$$-3A - B = 1$$

Substitute $B = -A$ into the second equation to get $-3A + A = 1$. Solve this for $A = -\frac{1}{2}$, and then $B = \frac{1}{2}$

On Your Own

6. Use difference of squares factoring in each case.

(a) $x^2 - 1 = (x+1)(x-1)$, then

$$\frac{(x+1)(x-1)}{x-1} = x+1$$

(b) $x^4 - 1 = (x^2 + 1)(x^2 - 1)$, then
$$\frac{(x^2 + 1)(x^2 - 1)}{x^2 - 1} = x^2 + 1$$

(c) $x^6 - 1 = (x^3 + 1)(x^3 - 1)$, then
$$\frac{(x^3 + 1)(x^3 - 1)}{x^3 - 1} = x^3 + 1$$

(d) $x^8 - 1 = (x^4 + 1)(x^4 - 1)$, then
$$\frac{(x^4 + 1)(x^4 - 1)}{x^4 - 1} = x^4 + 1$$

(e) $x^{10} - 1 = (x^5 + 1)(x^5 - 1)$, then
$$\frac{(x^5 + 1)(x^5 - 1)}{x^5 - 1} = x^5 + 1$$

7. (a)
$$1 + \frac{1}{x - 1} - \frac{1}{1 + x}$$
$$= 1 \cdot \frac{x^2 - 1}{x^2 - 1} + \frac{1}{x - 1} \cdot \frac{x + 1}{x + 1} - \frac{1}{1 + x} \cdot \frac{x - 1}{x - 1}$$
$$= \frac{x^2 - 1 + x + 1 - x + 1}{x^2 - 1}$$
$$= \frac{x^2 + 1}{x^2 - 1}$$

(b)
$$1 - \frac{2}{1 + x^2} = 1 \cdot \frac{1 + x^2}{1 + x^2} - \frac{2}{1 + x^2}$$
$$= \frac{1 + x^2 - 2}{1 + x^2}$$
$$= \frac{x^2 - 1}{x^2 + 1}$$

(c)
$$\frac{1}{x - 2} - \frac{1}{x - 1} = \frac{1}{x - 2} \cdot \frac{x - 1}{x - 1} - \frac{1}{x - 1} \cdot \frac{x - 2}{x - 2}$$
$$= \frac{x - 1 - x + 2}{(x - 1)(x - 2)}$$
$$= \frac{1}{(x - 1)(x - 2)}$$

(d)
$$\frac{1}{2(x - 3)} - \frac{1}{x - 2} + \frac{1}{2(x - 1)}$$
$$= \frac{1}{2(x - 3)} \cdot \frac{x^2 - 3x + 2}{x^2 - 3x + 2} - \frac{1}{x - 2} \cdot \frac{2x^2 - 8x + 6}{2x^2 - 8x + 6}$$
$$+ \frac{1}{2(x - 1)}$$
$$= \frac{x^2 - 3x + 2 - (2x^2 - 8x + 6) + x^2 - 5x + 6}{2(x - 3)(x - 2)(x - 1)}$$
$$= \frac{2}{2(x - 3)(x - 2)(x - 1)}$$
$$= \frac{1}{(x - 3)(x - 2)(x - 1)}$$

(e)
$$\frac{2}{(x - 1)^2} + \frac{1}{x - 1} - \frac{1}{x - 2}$$
$$= \frac{2}{(x - 1)^2} \cdot \frac{x - 2}{x - 2} + \frac{1}{x - 1} \cdot \frac{x^2 - 3x + 2}{x^2 - 3x + 2}$$
$$- \frac{1}{x - 2} \cdot \frac{x^2 - 2x + 1}{x^2 - 2x + 1}$$
$$= \frac{2x - 4 + x^2 - 3x + 2 - x^2 + 2x - 1}{(x - 1)^2(x - 2)}$$
$$= \frac{x - 3}{(x - 1)^2(x - 2)}$$

8. Find a single rational expression for the right side:
$$\frac{1}{(x - 1)(x - 2)} = \frac{A}{x - 1} + \frac{B}{x - 2}$$
$$= \frac{A}{x - 1} \cdot \frac{x - 2}{x - 2} + \frac{B}{x - 2} \cdot \frac{x - 1}{x - 1}$$
$$= \frac{Ax - 2A + Bx - B}{(x - 1)(x - 2)}$$
$$= \frac{(A + B)x + (-2A - B)}{(x - 1)(x - 2)}$$

For these two fractions to be equal, they must have the same numerator. So $A + B = 0$ and $-2A - B = 1$. Solve these two equations to obtain $A = -1$ and $B = 1$.
$$\frac{1}{(x - 1)(x - 2)} = \frac{-1}{x - 1} + \frac{1}{x - 2}$$

9.
$$\frac{x^2 - 9x + 20}{-x^2 + 6x - 8} = \frac{(x - 5)(x - 4)}{-(x - 2)(x - 4)} = \frac{x - 5}{2 - x}$$

The correct answer choice is **A**.

Maintain Your Skills

10. Each of these reductions relies on factoring the numerator. All the denominator factors are part of the full factoring of the numerator, leaving one remaining factor that cannot be canceled out.

(a) The numerator factors to $(x - 1)(x^2 + x + 1)$.
(b) The numerator factors to $(x^2 + 1)(x + 1)(x - 1)$.
(c) The numerator factors to $(x - 1)$ $(x^4 + x^3 + x^2 + x + 1)$.
(d) The numerator factors to $(x^3 + 1)(x^3 - 1)$. Both factors of $x^3 - 1$ are present in the denominator. Then, $x^3 + 1$ factors to $(x + 1)(x^2 - x + 1)$. The full factoring of $x^6 - 1$ is $(x - 1)(x + 1)$ $(x^2 + x + 1)(x^2 - x + 1)$. The final result, after you cancel common factors of $x + 1$, is $x^2 - x + 1$.
(e) The numerator factors to $(x^4 + 1)(x^4 - 1)$, and the denominator gives all the factors of $x^4 - 1$.
(f) The numerator is a difference of cubes, and factors to $(x^3 - 1)(x^6 + x^3 + 1)$. The denominator includes all the factors of $x^3 - 1$, so the remaining factor is $x^6 + x^3 + 1$.

(g) The numerator is a difference of squares, and factors to $(x^5 + 1)(x^5 - 1)$. The denominator includes all factors of $x^5 - 1$, but also includes $(x + 1)$. Use polynomial long division to find that

$$x^5 + 1 = (x + 1)(x^4 - x^3 + x^2 - x + 1).$$

So the final result is $x^4 - x^3 + x^2 - x + 1$.

(h) The numerator is a difference of squares, factoring as $(x^6 + 1)(x^6 - 1)$. The denominator includes all factors of $x^6 - 1$, but also includes $x^2 + 1$. The remaining factor in the numerator, $x^6 + 1$, factors as a sum of cubes:

$$x^6 + 1 = (x^2 + 1)(x^4 - x^2 + 1)$$

Only the $x^4 - x^2 + 1$ factor remains after cancellation.

11. (a) $f(3) + f(4) + f(5) = \frac{1}{2} + \frac{1}{6} + \frac{1}{12} =$
$\frac{6}{12} + \frac{2}{12} + \frac{1}{12} = \frac{9}{12} = \frac{3}{4}$

(b) $f(3) + f(4) + f(5) + f(6) = \frac{3}{4} + \frac{1}{20} = \frac{16}{20} = \frac{4}{5}$

(c) $f(3) + f(4) + f(5) + f(6) + f(7) = \frac{4}{5} + \frac{1}{30} = \frac{25}{30} = \frac{5}{6}$

(d) Using the pattern in the previous parts of the exercise, $f(3) + f(4) + f(5) + f(6) + f(7) + \cdots + f(23) = \frac{21}{22}$

(e) $f(3) + f(4) + f(5) + f(6) + f(7) + \cdots + f(n) = \frac{n-2}{n-1}$

2D MATHEMATICAL REFLECTIONS

1. (a) Multiply $6x^2 - x - 15$ by 6, to get $36x^2 - 6x - 90$. Replace $6x$ with M and factor.

$$M^2 - M - 90 = (M - 10)(M + 9)$$

Unreplace M in the factored form, and factor out a 6.

$$(6x - 10)(6x + 9) = 2(3x - 5)(3)(2x + 3)$$

Divide by 6 for the factoring of the original polynomial: $(3x - 5)(2x + 3)$.

(b) This part is very similar to the previous one, but you'll factor it as $(M + 10)(M - 9)$, ending up with $(3x + 5)(2x - 3)$.

(c) Multiply $35x^2 + 79x + 42$ by 35, to get $1225x^2 + 2765x + 1470$. Replace $35x$ with M and factor.

$$M^2 + 79M + 1470 = (M + 30)(M + 49)$$

Unreplace M in the factored form, and factor out a 35.

$$(35x + 30)(35x + 49) = 5(7x + 6)(7)(5x + 7)$$

Divide by 35 for the factoring of the original polynomail: $(7x + 6)(5x + 7)$.

2. (a) $x^3 - 125 = x^3 - 5^3 = (x - 5)(x^2 + 5x + 25)$

(b) $x^3 + 125 = x^3 + 5^3 = (x + 5)(x^2 - 5x + 25)$

(c) $27x^3 - 64 = (3x)^3 - 4^3 = (3x - 4)(9x^2 + 12x + 16)$

(d) $27x^3 + 64 = (3x)^3 + 4^3 = (3x + 4)(9x^2 - 12x + 16)$

(e) $(x-1)^3 - 27 = ((x-1)-3)((x-1)^2 + 3(x-1) + 9) = (x - 4)(x^2 + x + 7)$

(f) $(2x - 3)^3 + 27 = ((2x - 3) + 3)((2x - 3)^2 - 3(2x - 3) + 9) = (2x)(4x^2 - 18x + 27)$

(g) 3 is a root of $x^3 + 3x^2 - 9x - 27$, because $27 + 27 - 27 - 27 = 0$. Divide $x^3 + 3x^2 - 9x - 27$ by $x - 3$ to get $x^2 + 6x + 9$. This is $(x + 3)^2$, so the complete factorization of the original polynomial is $(x - 3)(x + 3)^2$.

(h) 3 is a root of $x^3 - 4x^2 + 4x - 3$, because $27 - 36 + 12 - 3 = 0$. Divide $x^3 - 4x^2 + 4x - 3$ by $x - 3$ to get $x^2 - x + 1$. This doesn't factor over $\mathbb{Z}$, so the complete factorization of the original polynomial is $(x - 3)(x^2 - x + 1)$.

(i)
$$x^4 - (2x + 1)^4 = (x^2 - (2x + 1)^2)(x^2 + (2x + 1)^2)$$
$$= (x - (2x + 1))(x + (2x + 1))$$
$$(x^2 + 4x^2 + 4x + 1)$$
$$= (-x - 1)(3x + 1)(5x^2 + 4x + 1)$$

(j)
$$x^2 - y^2 + 2yz - z^2 = x^2 - (y - z)^2$$
$$= (x - y + z)(x + y - z)$$

3. (a) You can factor $35x^4 + 79x^2 + 42$ by using your result for 1(c) and substituting x^2 for x in that factoring. $(7x^2 + 6)(5x^2 + 7)$

(b) You can factor $6x^6 + x^3 - 15$ by using your result for 1(b) and substituting x^3 for x in that factoring. $(3x^3 + 5)(2x^3 - 3)$

(c) $x^4 - 81$ is a difference of squares. $x^4 - 81 = (x^2 + 9)(x^2 - 9)$ Now the second factor is also a difference of squares. So the complete factoring is $(x^2 + 9)(x + 3)(x - 3)$

(d) $x^6 - 27$ is a difference of two cubes. $(x^2 - 3)(x^4 + 3x^2 + 9)$

(e) Multiply $4x^4 - 5x^2 + 1$ by 4 to get $16x^4 - 20x^2 + 4$. Replace $4x^2$ with M. Now you have $M^2 - 5M + 4$, and this factors as $(M - 4)(M - 1)$. Unreplace and factor out a 4. $(4x^2 - 4)(4x^2 - 1) = 4(x^2 - 1)(4x^2 - 1)$. Divide by 4 to get this factoring of the original polynomial: $(x^2 - 1)(4x^2 - 1)$. Both of these factors are differences of two squares, so this can be factored further to $(x + 1)(x - 1)(2x + 1)(2x - 1)$

(f) $x^4 + 5x^2 + 9 = (x^2 - x + 3)(x^2 + x + 3)$

4. (a)
$$x = \sqrt{5}$$
$$x^2 = 5$$
$$x^2 - 5 = 0$$

(b)
$$x = \sqrt{5} + \sqrt{7}$$
$$x^2 = 5 + 2\sqrt{35} + 7$$
$$x^2 - 12 = 2\sqrt{35}$$
$$x^4 - 24x^2 + 144 = 140$$
$$x^4 - 24x^2 + 4 = 0$$

(c)
$$x = 3 + \sqrt{5} + \sqrt{7}$$
$$x - 3 = \sqrt{5} + \sqrt{7}$$
$$x^2 - 6x + 9 = 5 + 2\sqrt{35} + 7$$
$$x^2 - 6x - 3 = 2\sqrt{35}$$
$$x^4 - 12x^3 + 30x^2 + 36x + 9 = 140$$
$$x^4 - 12x^3 + 30x^2 + 36x - 131 = 0$$

5. (a) $1 - \frac{x+2}{x^2+x+1} = \frac{x^2+x+1-x-2}{x^2+x+1} = \frac{x^2-1}{x^2+x+1}$

(b)
$$1 - \frac{2}{3(1+x)} + \frac{2(x-2)}{3(1-x+x^2)}$$
$$= 1 \cdot \frac{3+3x^3}{3+3x^3} - \frac{2}{3(1+x)} \cdot \frac{1-x+x^2}{1-x+x^2}$$
$$+ \frac{2(x-2)}{3(1-x+x^2)} \cdot \frac{1+x}{1+x}$$
$$= \frac{3+3x^3 - 2 + 2x - 2x^2 + 2x^2 - 2x - 4}{3(x^3+1)}$$
$$= \frac{x^3-1}{x^3+1}$$

6. There are several ways to factor non-monic quadratics. Sometimes you can see a factoring right away, or you can use the quadratic formula. Or you can use scaling. For example, if you want to factor $ax^2 + bx + c$, multiply through by a to create a quadratic with a perfect square as its x^2 term. You have $a^2x^2 + abx + ac$. Replace ax with M to get $M^2 + bM + ac$. Now you can use your factorization techniques for monic quadratics to factor this. Then unreplace M, factor an a out of the factored form, and you'll have a factorization for the original quadratic polynomial.

7. Use the identities:
$$(x^3 - y^3) = (x - y)(x^2 + xy + y^2)$$
$$(x^3 + y^3) = (x + y)(x^2 - xy + y^2)$$

8.
$$x^4 + 4 = x^4 + 4x^2 - 4x^2 + 4$$
$$= x^4 + 4x^2 + 4 - 4x^2$$
$$= (x^2 + 2)^2 - (2x)^2$$
$$= ((x^2 + 2) - (2x))((x^2 + 2) + (2x))$$
$$= (x^2 + 2x + 2)(x^2 - 2x + 2)$$

CHAPTER REVIEW

1. (a) $f(2) = 3(2) + 7 = 6 + 7 = 13$
   (b) $g(2) = \frac{2+1}{3} = 1$
   (c) $f(g(2)) = f(1) = 3(1) + 7 = 3 + 7 = 10$
   (d) $g(f(2)) = g(13) = \frac{13+1}{3} = \frac{14}{3}$
   (e) $f \circ g(2) = f(g(2)) = 10$
   (f) $f(2) \cdot g(2) = 13 \cdot 1 = 13$

2. (a) $f \circ g(x) = f(g(x)) = f(x^2 + 4x + 1) = (x^2 + 4x + 1) - 2 = x^2 + 4x - 1$

(b) $g \circ f(x) = g(x - 2) = (x - 2)^2 + 4(x - 2) + 1 = x^2 - 4x + 4 + 4x - 8 + 1 = x^2 - 3$

3. (a)

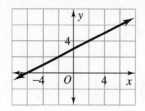

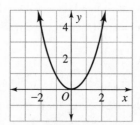

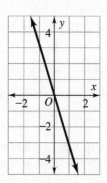

(b) f and h are one-to-one. g is not one-to-one.

(c) To find $f^{-1}(x)$, rewrite the equation as $x = \frac{f^{-1}(x)}{2} + 3$, and solve for $f^{-1}(x)$:
$$x = \frac{f^{-1}(x)}{2} + 3$$
$$x - 3 = \frac{f^{-1}(x)}{2}$$
$$2(x - 3) = f^{-1}(x)$$
$$2x - 6 = f^{-1}(x)$$

Similarly, $x = -3h^{-1}(x) \longrightarrow h^{-1}(x) = -\frac{x}{3}$.

4. If $h(1) = 0$, then $(x - 1)$ is a factor of h. Similarly, $(x - 3)$ and $(x - 4)$ are factors of h. One possible solution is
$$h(x) = (x - 1)(x - 3)(x - 4) = x^3 - 8x^2 + 19x - 12$$

Other solutions will be in the form $h(x) = A \cdot (x - 1)(x - 3)(x - 4)$, where A is any polynomial expression.

5. First, find four polynomials, say, g, h, k, and l that behave like $j(x) = m(x - a)(x - b)(x - c)$. Start with g. This polynomial will have $g(1) = -24$, $g(3) = 0$, $g(4) = 0$ and $g(5) = 0$. One way to do this is to let
$$g(x) = A(x - 3)(x - 4)(x - 5)$$

This gives the right zeros for any choice of A. Pick A so that

$$-24 = g(1) = A(1-3)(1-4)(1-5)$$
$$-24 = A(-2)(-3)(-4)$$
$$1 = A$$

So,

$$g(x) = 1(x-3)(x-4)(x-5)$$

Similarly,

$$h(x) = 4(x-1)(x-4)(x-5)$$
$$k(x) = -3(x-1)(x-3)(x-5)$$

and

$$l(x) = -1(x-1)(x-3)(x-4)$$

The function you are looking for is the sum of these functions:

$$f(x) = g(x) + h(x) + k(x) + l(x)$$
$$= 1(x-3)(x-4)(x-5) + 4(x-1)(x-4)(x-5)$$
$$+ -3(x-1)(x-3)(x-5)$$
$$+ -1(x-1)(x-3)(x-4)$$

Expanding and collecting like terms gives:

$$f(x) = x^3 - 17x^2 + 75x - 83$$

6. (a) Answers will vary. One possible answer is $g(x) = 3x -5 + (x+1)(x-2)$ Other answers will be in the form $g(x) = 3x - 5 + ($ any constant$)(x+1)(x-2)$ The expression added at the end will be zero when $x = -1$ or $x = 2$. The output for $x = -1$ will be $g(-1) = 3(-1)-5+0 = 3(-1)-5 = -8 = f(-1)$. Similarly, the output for $x = 2$ will be $g(2) = 3(2) -5 + 0 = 1 = f(2)$.

(b)

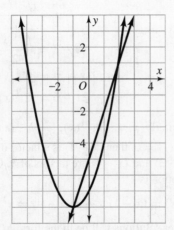

7. (a) Use your CAS to divide $x^3 - 8x^2 + 3x - 5$ by $x+3$, or, perform the long division. The quotient is $x^2 - 11x + 36$ and the remainder is -113.

(b) By the Remainder Theorem, the remainder when you divide $p(x)$ by $x+3$ is $p(-3)$. So, $p(-3) = -113$

8. By the Factor Theorem, $x - 2$ is a factor of $p(x)$ if and only if $p(2) = 0$. To find a let $p(2) = 0$:

$$p(2) = 0$$
$$2^3 + 3 \cdot 2^2 + 4 \cdot 2 + a = 0$$
$$8 + 12 + 8 + a = 0$$
$$28 + a = 0$$
$$a = -28$$

9. To find C, let $x = 1$:

$$1^2 - 8(1) = (1-1)^2 + B(1-1) + C \longrightarrow -7 = C$$

So, $x^2 - 8x = (x-1)^2 + B(x-1) - 7$ Expand and solve for B:

$$x^2 - 8x = (x-1)^2 + B(x-1) - 7$$
$$x^2 - 8x + 7 = (x-1)^2 + B(x-1)$$
$$x^2 - 8x + 7 = x^2 - 2x + 1 + B(x-1)$$
$$-6x + 6 = B(x-1)$$
$$-6(x-1) = B(x-1)$$
$$-6 = B$$

10. (a) Write the quadratic as a monic:

$$4x^2 + 4x - 3 = (2x)^2 + 2(2x) - 3$$

Let $H = 2x$ and factor:

$$H^2 + 2H - 3 = (H-1)(H+3)$$

Replace H with $2x$:

$$(2x-1)(2x+3)$$

(b) Write the quadratic as a monic. First multiply by 6:

$$6(6x^2 + 23x + 21) = (6x)^2 + 23(6x) + 126$$

Let $H = 6x$ and factor:

$$H^2 + 23H + 126 = (H+14)(H+9)$$

Replace H with $6x$ and remove any common factors:

$$(6x + 14)(6x + 9) = 2(3x+7) \cdot 3(2x+3)$$

Divide by 6 to undo multiplying by 6:

$$6(3x+7)(2x+3) \div 6 = (3x+7)(2x+3)$$

(c) Factor as the difference of two squares:

$$36x^2 - 49y^2 = (6x)^2 - (7y)^2 = (6x+7y)(6x-7y)$$

(d) The expression is in quadratic form. Let $H = x - 2$:

$$3(x-2)^2 + 5(x-2) + 2 = 3H^2 + 5H + 2 = (3H+2)(H+1)$$

Replace H with $x - 2$ and simplify:

$$(3(x-2)+2)((x-2)+1) = (3x-6+2)(x-1)$$
$$= (3x-4)(x-1)$$

(e) Factor as the sum of two cubes:

$$x^3 + 8 = x^3 + 2^3 = (x+2)(x^2 - 2x + 4)$$

(f) Factor by grouping terms:

$$x^3 - 2x^2 + 3x - 6 = (x^3 - 2x^2) + (3x - 6)$$
$$= x^2(x - 2) + 3(x - 2)$$
$$= (x - 2)(x^2 + 3)$$

11. (a) Write the polynomial as a quadratic in x^2 and factor:

$$x^4 - 2x^2 + 1 = (x^2)^2 - 2(x^2) + 1$$
$$= (x^2 - 1)(x^2 - 1)$$
$$= (x + 1)(x - 1)(x + 1)(x - 1)$$
$$= (x + 1)^2(x - 1)^2$$

(b) Use the Quadratic Formula and the Factor Theorem:

$$x^2 - x - 4 = 0$$

$$\longrightarrow x = \frac{1 \pm \sqrt{1 - 4(1)(-4)}}{2(1)} = \frac{1 \pm \sqrt{17}}{2} \text{ So,}$$

$$x^2 - x - 4 = \left(x - \left(\frac{1 + \sqrt{17}}{2}\right)\right)\left(x - \left(\frac{1 - \sqrt{17}}{2}\right)\right)$$

12. (a)

$$\frac{2}{x - 4} + \frac{x}{x + 4} = \frac{2}{x - 4} \cdot \frac{(x + 4)}{(x + 4)} + \frac{x}{x + 4} \cdot \frac{(x - 4)}{(x - 4)}$$
$$= \frac{2(x + 4) + x(x - 4)}{(x + 4)(x - 4)}$$
$$= \frac{2x + 8 + x^2 - 4x}{(x + 4)(x - 4)}$$
$$= \frac{x^2 - 2x + 8}{(x + 4)(x - 4)}$$

(b)

$$2 - \frac{x + 3}{x - 2} = 2 \cdot \frac{(x - 2)}{(x - 2)} - \frac{x + 3}{x - 2}$$
$$= \frac{2(x - 2) - (x + 3)}{x - 2}$$
$$= \frac{2x - 4 - x - 3}{x - 2}$$
$$= \frac{x - 7}{x - 2}$$

CHAPTER TEST

1. $f \circ g(3) = f(g(3)) = f(4(3) + 1) = f(13) = 2(13) - 3 = 26 - 3 = 23$. So, the correct choice is **C**.

2. To find the inverse, rewrite the equation as:

$$f(f^{-1}(x)) = x = \sqrt[3]{f^{-1}(x)} + 1$$

To make the work simpler, replace $f^{-1}(x)$ with y. Solve for y:

$$x = \sqrt[3]{y} + 1$$
$$x - 1 = \sqrt[3]{y}$$
$$(x - 1)^3 = (\sqrt[3]{y})^3$$
$$(x - 1)^3 = y$$
$$(x - 1)^3 = f^{-1}(x)$$

So, the correct choice is **B**.

3. Each of the ordered pairs $(2, 0)$ and $(3, 0)$ satisfy the equation, $f(x) = A(x - 2)(x - 3)$, no matter what the value of A. To find A use the ordered pair $(4, -6)$:

$$f(4) = -6 = A(4-2)(4-3) \longrightarrow -6 = 2A \longrightarrow A = -3$$

The current choice is **B**.

4. Since the remainder when you divide by $x - 2$ is the number $p(2)$, you only need to evaluate $p(2) = 2(2)^3 - 3(2)^2 + 5(2) - 1 = 16 - 12 + 10 - 1 = 13$. The correct choice is **C**.

5. Multiply $x^2 + 2x + 4$ by $x - 2$:

$$(x - 2)(x^2 + 2x + 4) = x(x^2 + 2x + 4) - 2(x^2 + 2x + 4)$$
$$= x^3 + 2x^2 + 4x - 2x^2 - 4x - 8$$
$$= x^3 - 8$$

None of the other choices give a product of $x^3 - 8$. The correct choice is **C**.

6. (a) $f \circ g(x) = f(g(x)) = f(x^2 - 1) = \frac{2(x^2 - 1) + 1}{3} = \frac{2x^2 - 2 + 1}{3} = \frac{2x^2 - 1}{3}$

(b) $g \circ f(x) = g(f(x)) = g\left(\frac{2x+1}{3}\right) = \left(\frac{2x+1}{3}\right)^2 - 1 = \frac{4x^2 + 4x + 1}{9} - 1 = \frac{4x^2 + 4x + 1}{9} - \frac{9}{9} = \frac{4x^2 + 4x - 8}{9}$

(c) Use the definition of inverse function:

$$f(f^{-1}(x)) = x = \frac{2 \cdot f^{-1}(x) + 1}{3}$$

Replace $f^{-1}(x)$ with y to make it simpler. Solve for $y = f^{-1}(x)$:

$$x = \frac{2 \cdot f^{-1}(x) + 1}{3}$$
$$x = \frac{2y + 1}{3}$$
$$3x = 2y + 1$$
$$3x - 1 = 2y$$
$$\frac{3x - 1}{2} = y$$

So, $y = f^{-1}(x) = \frac{3x-1}{2}$. Now, show that $f(f^{-1}(x)) = x$:

$$f \circ f^{-1}(x) = f(f^{-1}(x)) = f\left(\frac{3x-1}{2}\right) = \frac{2 \cdot \frac{3x-1}{2} + 1}{3} = \frac{3x - 1 + 1}{3} = \frac{3x}{3} = x$$

7. Write f as a sum of functions g, h, and k, defined by:

$$g(x) = A(x - 1)(x - 2)$$
$$h(x) = B(x - 1)(x - 3)$$
$$k(x) = C(x - 2)(x - 3)$$

So,

$$f(x) = A(x-1)(x-2) + B(x-1)(x-3) + C(x-2)(x-3)$$

To find A, B, and C:

$$f(1) = 4 = A(1 - 1)(1 - 2) + B(1 - 1)(1 - 3)$$
$$+ C(1 - 2)(1 - 3)$$
$$= A \cdot 0 + B \cdot 0 + C \cdot 2 \longrightarrow 2C = 4 \longrightarrow C = 2$$

$$f(2) = -2 = A(2-1)(2-2) + B(2-1)(2-3)$$
$$+ C(2-2)(2-3)$$
$$= A \cdot 0 + B \cdot (-1) + C \cdot 0 = -1 \cdot B \longrightarrow -B$$
$$= -2 \longrightarrow B = 2$$
$$f(3) = 20 = A(3-1)(3-2) + B(3-1)(3-3)$$
$$+ C(3-2)(3-3)$$
$$= A \cdot 2 + B \cdot 0 + C \cdot 0 = 2 \cdot A \longrightarrow 2A$$
$$= 20 \longrightarrow A = 10$$

So,

$$f(x) = A(x-1)(x-2) + B(x-1)(x-3)$$
$$+ C(x-2)(x-3)$$
$$= 10(x-1)(x-2) + 2(x-1)(x-3)$$
$$+ 2(x-2)(x-3)$$
$$= 14x^2 - 48x + 38$$

8. (a) Use your CAS to expand $\frac{2x^3 + 4x^2 - 5x + 6}{x-3} =$ $2x^2 + 10x + 25 + \frac{81}{x-3}$ So, the quotient is $2x^2 + 10x + 25$ and the remainder is 81. You may also perform long division.

(b) By the Remainder Theorem, the remainder when you divide $f(x)$ by $x-3$ is $f(3)$. So, $f(3) = 81$.

9. (a) Multiply by 8, to write the expression as a monic quadratic:

$$8(8x^2 + 22x + 15) = (8x)^2 + 22(8x) + 120$$

Let $H = 8x$ and factor:

$$H^2 + 22H + 120 = (H + 10)(H + 12)$$

Replace H with $8x$ and remove any common factors:

$$(8x + 10)(8x + 12) = 2(4x + 5) \cdot 4(2x + 3)$$
$$= 8(4x + 5)(2x + 3)$$

Divide by 8 to undo multiplying by 8:

$$\frac{8(4x + 5)(2x + 3)}{8} = (4x + 5)(2x + 3)$$

So, $8x^2 + 22x + 15 = (4x + 5)(2x + 3)$

(b) $x^4 - 13x^2 + 36 = (x^2)^2 - 13(x^2) + 36 =$ $(x^2 - 4)(x^2 - 9) = (x + 2)(x - 2)(x + 3)(x - 3)$

(c) $x^3 + 1 = x^3 + 1^3 = (x + 1)(x^2 - x + 1)$

10. Change each rational expression to one with a common denominator and subtract:

$$\frac{x}{x+3} - \frac{3}{x-2} = \frac{x}{x+3} \cdot \frac{(x-2)}{(x-2)} - \frac{3}{x-2} \cdot \frac{(x+3)}{(x+3)}$$
$$= \frac{x^2 - 2x}{(x+3)(x-2)} - \frac{3x+9}{(x+3)(x-2)}$$
$$= \frac{(x^2 - 2x) - (3x + 9)}{(x+3)(x-2)}$$
$$= \frac{x^2 - 5x - 9}{(x+3)(x-2)}$$

11. If a number a is a zero or root of a polynomial, the Factor Theorem says that $(x - a)$ is a factor of the polynomial. And, if $x - a$ is a factor of a polynomial, $f(x)$, the Remainder Theorem says that $f(a) = 0$.

CUMULATIVE REVIEW

1. The first line tells you that $a(0) = 3$, which eliminates A and D. The outputs increase by 2, which eliminates C. The correct answer choice is **B**.

2. One way to do this is to find the linear function that the two given points fit. Another is to note that an increase of 5 in the input yields a decrease of 80 in the output. So an increase of 50 yields a decrease of 800. Thus $a(50) = 58 - 800 = -742$. An increase of 100 yields a decrease of 1600, so $a(100) = 58 - 1600 = -1542$.

3. Noting the different scales on the axes, you can see that the slope would be at least 2. Continuing the trend to the left shows that the y-intercept would be negative. These two pieces of information imply that the best choice would be **C**.

4. Be careful to note that the numerator is $2 \cdot n!$, and not $(2n)!$ The factors of the denominator get completely canceled out, and what is left in the numerator is $2 \cdot n$.

(a) $2 \cdot 100 = 200$
(b) $2 \cdot 500 = 1000$

5. With a loan of $20,000 at 3.5%, and a payment of $400, after 50 months the amount left will be $1636.95. After 54 months the amount left will be $49. So she will finish paying the following month. The correct answer choice is **C**.

6. The outputs are 4, 12, 23, 37, and 54. The Δ column is 8, 11, 14, and 17. The Δ^2 column is given.

7. The outputs are 1, 4, 9, 16, and 25. The Δ column is 3, 5, 7, and 9. The Δ^2 column is 2, 2, 2. This constant tells us that the function is quadratic, and that the leading coefficient is 1. Subtract n^2 from the outputs to get: 1, 3, 5, 7, 9. This is a linear function starting at 1 with difference 2. Hence it is $2n + 1$. Therefore, $f(n) = n^2 + 2n + 1$.

8. Note that $4 = 2 \cdot 2$, $12 = 3 \cdot 4$, $48 = 4 \cdot 12$, $240 = 5 \cdot 48$. So a recursive relationship could be

$$a(n) = \begin{cases} 2 & \text{if } n = 0 \\ (n+1) \cdot a(n-1) & \text{if } n \geq 1 \end{cases}$$

9. The outputs for this line would be: $-1, 0, 1, 2, 3$. These yield respective errors of: $-2, -1, 1, 2, 2$. Therefore, the mean absolute error $= \frac{2+1+1+2+2}{5} = \frac{8}{5} = 1.6$. The mean squared error $= \frac{2^2 + 1^2 + 1^2 + 2^2 + 2^2}{5} = \frac{14}{5} = 2.8$. The standard error would be $\sqrt{2.8} \approx 1.673$.

10. Let $y = 2x + b$. For the given values of x, this has outputs $4 + b, 10 + b, 16 + b, 22 + b, 28 + b$. We wish to minimize:

$$(1 + b)^2 + (3 + b)^2 + (4 + b)^2 + (7 + b)^2 + (9 + b)^2$$
$$= 156 + 48b + 5b^2$$

The minimum occurs when $b = \frac{-48}{10} = -4.8$. The line is $y = 2x - 4.8$.

11. First find the balance point. The average x-value is $\frac{3+7+9+14+20}{5} = 10.6$, and the average y-value is $\frac{48+27+15+9+1}{5} = 20$. So the line of best fit looks like

$$y = m(x - 10.6) + 20$$

For the given inputs, the outputs are $-7.6m + 20$, $-3.6m + 20$, $-1.6m + 20$, $3.4m + 20$, $9.4m + 20$. We wish to minimize

$$(28 + 7.6m)^2 + (7 + 3.6m)^2 + (-5 + 1.6m)^2$$
$$+ (11 + 3.4m)^2 + (19 + 9.4m)^2$$
$$= 1340 + 892m + 173.2m^2$$

The minimum occurs when $m = \frac{-892}{2(173.2)} = -2.575$. The line of best fit is therefore

$$y = -2.575x + 47.296$$

12. The outputs are $1, 3, 6, 10, 15, 21, 28, 36, 45, 55$. A recursive relationship is

$$r(n) = \begin{cases} 1 & \text{if } n = 1 \\ r(n-1) + n & \text{if } n \geq 2 \end{cases}$$

A closed form for this function is

$$r(n) = \frac{(n+1)n}{2}$$

13. (a) Paying \$12,000 over 48 months comes to \$250 per month.
(b) If x is her monthly payment, then the balance after 48 months, at 5% interest, is \$14,650.74 − 53.015x = 0. Therefore $x = \$276.35$.
(c) She will pay a total of $48x = \$13,264.80$, so her total interest will be \$1264.80.

14. If L is the amount of the loan, then after 48 months at 3% interest, paying \$450 per month, the balance will be $1.127328L - \$22,919.04 = 0$. So $L = \$20,330.41$. Adding the down payment of \$2500 yields \$22,830 to the nearest dollar.

15. (a) $f(-1) = (-1)^2 + 1 = 2$
(b) $f(g(4)) = f(8-3) = f(5) = 5^2 + 1 = 26$
(c) $g(f(x)) = g(x^2 + 1) = 2(x^2 + 1) - 3 = 2x^2 - 1$
(d) $x = 2 \cdot g^{-1}(x) - 3$, so $x + 3 = 2 \cdot g^{-1}(x)$, $g^{-1}(x) = \frac{x+3}{2}$

16. Plugging in the first point yields $A(2)(-3) = -18$, or $-6A = -18$. So $A = 3$.

17. According to the Remainder Theorem, this would be

$$p(-2) = 2(-2)^3 - 3(-2)^2 + (-2) - 2$$
$$= -16 - 12 - 2 - 2 = -32$$

18. (a) $27x^3 - 64 = (3x)^3 - 4^3 =$
$(3x - 4)((3x)^2 + (3x) \cdot 4 + 4^2) =$
$(3x - 4)(9x^2 + 12x + 16)$
(b) $125x^3 + 8y^3 = (5x)^3 + (2y)^3 =$
$(5x + 2y)((5x)^2 - (5x)(2y) + (2y)^2) =$
$(5x + 2y)(25x^2 - 10xy + 4y^2)$

19. This function multiplies the input by -3 and then adds 1. To undo this, subtract 1 and then divide by -3:

$$f^{-1}(x) = \frac{x-1}{-3} = \frac{1-x}{3}$$

Now

$$f(f^{-1}(x)) = f\left(\frac{1-x}{3}\right) = -3\left(\frac{1-x}{3}\right) + 1$$
$$= -(1-x) + 1 = -1 + x + 1 = x$$

20. Use Lagrange interpolation. Let

$$f(x) = A(x-1)(x-2) + Bx(x-2) + Cx(x-1)$$

Now

$$3 = f(0) = A(-1)(-2) + 0 + 0 = 2A$$

so $A = \frac{3}{2}$. Also

$$7 = f(1) = 0 + B(1)(-1) + 0 = -B$$

so $B = -7$. Finally

$$15 = f(2) = 0 + 0 + C \cdot 2(1) = 2C$$

so $C = \frac{15}{2}$. Therefore

$$f(x) = \frac{3}{2}(x-1)(x-2) - 7x(x-2) + \frac{15}{2}x(x-1)$$
$$= \frac{3}{2}(x^2 - 3x + 2) - 7(x^2 - 2x) + \frac{15}{2}(x^2 - x)$$
$$= \frac{3}{2}x^2 - \frac{9}{2}x + 3 - 7x^2 + 14x + \frac{15}{2}x^2 - \frac{15}{2}x$$
$$= 2x^2 + 2x + 3$$

21. (a)

$$
\begin{array}{r}
-x^2 + 5x - 12 \\
x + 3 \overline{\smash{)}\ -x^3 + 2x^2 + 3x - 1} \\
\underline{-x^3 - 3x^2} \\
5x^2 + 3x - 1 \\
\underline{5x^2 + 15x} \\
-12x - 1 \\
\underline{-12x - 36} \\
35
\end{array}
$$

So the quotient is $-x^2 + 5x - 12$, and the remainder is 35.
(b) By the Remainder Theorem, $p(-3)$ is the remainder you just found, 35.

22. (a) Multiply by 12, then let $A = 12x$ to obtain

$$144x^2 - 36x - 108 = A^2 - 3A - 108$$
$$= (A + 9)(A - 12)$$
$$= (12x + 9)(12x - 12)$$
$$= 12 \cdot 3(4x + 3)(x - 1)$$

Divide by 12 to obtain $3(4x + 3)(x - 1)$.
(b) Multiply by 10, then let $A = 10x$ to obtain

$$100x^2 + 110x + 30 = A^2 + 11A + 30$$
$$= (A + 5)(A + 6)$$
$$= (10x + 5)(10x + 6)$$
$$= 5(2x + 1)2(5x + 3)$$

Divide by 10 to obtain $(2x + 1)(5x + 3)$.
(c) This is a "quadratic in x^4."

$$x^8 - 5x^4 + 4 = (x^4)^2 - 5(x^4) + 4$$
$$= (x^4 - 4)(x^4 - 1)$$

Both factors are differences of squares. This equals

$$(x^2 + 2)(x^2 - 2)(x^2 + 1)(x^2 - 1)$$
$$= (x^2 + 2)(x^2 - 2)(x^2 + 1)(x + 1)(x - 1)$$

23. This is a sum of cubes.

$$x^6 + 64 = (x^2)^3 + 4^3 = (x^2 + 4)((x^2)^2 - (x^2)(4) + 4^2)$$
$$= (x^2 + 4)(x^4 - 4x^2 + 16)$$

24. (a)

$$2 + \frac{x-1}{x+1} = 2 \cdot \left(\frac{x+1}{x+1}\right) + \frac{x-1}{x+1}$$
$$= \frac{2x+2}{x+1} + \frac{x-1}{x+1} = \frac{3x+1}{x+1}$$

(b)

$$\frac{3x}{2x+3} - 1 = \frac{3x}{2x+3} - \frac{2x+3}{2x+3}$$
$$= \frac{3x - 2x - 3}{2x+3} = \frac{x-3}{2x+3}$$

Complex Numbers

INVESTIGATION 3A   INTRODUCTION TO
                   COMPLEX NUMBERS

3.1   Getting Started

For You to Explore

1. (a) Answers will vary. One explanation is that squaring a
       positive number gives a positive number, and
       squaring a negative number gives a positive number.
       Squaring 0 gives zero. Since any real number is either
       positive, negative, or zero, it's impossible for the
       square to equal -16.
   (b) The same argument applies for -1 as for -16.
2. (a) The roots are 9 and 3, so their sum is 12.
   (b) The roots are 9 and 3, so their product is 27.
   (c) The sum of the squares of the roots is $9^2 + 3^2 = 90$.
3. (a) Using the quadratic formula, you find the roots

$$x = \frac{12 \pm \sqrt{144 - 4(1)(34)}}{2} = \frac{12 \pm \sqrt{8}}{2}$$

$$= \frac{12 \pm 2\sqrt{2}}{2} = 6 \pm \sqrt{2}$$

   The two roots are $6 + \sqrt{2}$ and $6 - \sqrt{2}$. The sum of
   the roots is $(6 + \sqrt{2}) + (6 - \sqrt{2}) = 12$.
   (b) The product of the roots is $(6 + \sqrt{2})(6 - \sqrt{2}) =$
       $36 - 2 = 34$. (You can multiply this out more quickly
       if you recognize the product as a factoring of the
       difference of two squares.)
   (c) The sums of the squares of the roots is

$$(6 + \sqrt{2})^2 + (6 - \sqrt{2})^2 = (36 + 12\sqrt{2} + 2)$$
$$+ (36 - 12\sqrt{2} + 2) = 76$$

4. (a) Expand the right side:

$$(x + y)^2 - 2xy = (x^2 + 2xy + y^2) - 2xy = x^2 + y^2$$

   (b) The identity is $x^3 + y^3 = (x + y)^3 - 3xy(x + y)$. Start
       by expanding $(x + y)^3$ and seeing what is needed:

$$(x + y)^3 = x^3 + 3x^2y + 3xy^2 + y^3$$

   Then $(x + y)^3 = (x^3 + y^3) + 3xy(x + y)$ by splitting
   up the four terms. Subtracting from each side gives
   the solution

$$(x + y)^3 - 3xy(x + y) = x^3 + y^3$$

   To see this more clearly as an expression in the sum
   and product of the two numbers, replace the sum of

the two numbers by S and the product by P. This
gives you $x^3 + y^3 = S^3 - 3PS$.

5. (a) The roots are 7 and 5, then calculate the three results.
       The sum is 12, the product is 35, the sum of squares
       is 74.
   (b) The roots are 8 and 4. The sum is 12, the product is
       32, the sum of squares is 80.
   (c) The roots are $6 + \sqrt{3}$ and $6 - \sqrt{3}$. Calculate the sum
       of squares by using the identity in Exercise 4. The
       sum is 12, the product is 33, the sum of squares is 78.
   (d) The roots are -8 and -4. Only the sum changes from
       the situation when the roots are positive as in part (b)
       of this exercise. The sum is -12, the product is 32,
       the sum of squares is 80.
   (e) The roots are 5 and -5. The sum is 0, the product is
       -25, the sum of squares is 50.
   (f) The roots are $\sqrt{10}$ and $-\sqrt{10}$. The sum is 0, the
       product is -10, the sum of squares is 20.
   (g) The roots are 3 and -11. The sum is -8, the product
       is -33, the sum of squares is 130.
6. (a) The sum of the roots is $-b$. This can be done using the
       quadratic formula or earlier results from polynomials.
   (b) The product of the roots is c. Again, the quadratic
       formula could be used.
   (c) Use the identity from Exercise 4. If the roots are x
       and y, the sum of squares is

$$(x + y)^2 - 2xy$$

   This is $b^2 - 2c$.
7. Use the values of the roots, or the identity from
   Exercise 4:

$$x^3 + y^3 = (x + y)^3 - 3xy(x + y)$$

   (a) $12^3 - 3 \cdot 35(12) = 468$
   (b) $12^3 - 3 \cdot 32(12) = 576$
   (c) $12^3 - 3 \cdot 33(12) = 540$

8. (a) Two real numbers have the greatest product when
       they are the same number. So, if the sum is 14, the
       largest product is $7 \cdot 7 = 49$.
   (b) The quadratic formula gives the roots as

$$\frac{14 \pm \sqrt{14^2 - 200}}{2} = \frac{14 \pm \sqrt{-4}}{2}$$

   The roots cannot be real numbers, since $\sqrt{-4}$ is not a
   real number.

On Your Own

9. (a) The identity is $a^2 + b^2 = (a + b)^2 - 2ab$ (when a and b are used in place of x and y). Then

$$a^2 + b^2 = 14^2 - 2(47) = 196 - 94 = 102$$

(b) Use the quadratic formula to find a and b. The roots of the quadratic $x^2 - 14x + 47 = 0$ are

$$x = 7 \pm \sqrt{2}$$

There is no way to decide which root is a and which is b, but $a^2 + b^2$ can still be calculated using either:

$$a^2 + b^2 = (7 + \sqrt{2})^2 + (7 - \sqrt{2})^2$$
$$= (49 + 14\sqrt{2} + 2) + (49 - 14\sqrt{2} + 2)$$
$$= 102$$

10. (a) Since $x^2 + y^2 = (x + y)^2 - 2xy$ is true, this becomes a statement about integers. The expressions $r + s$ and rs are integers, so

$$r^2 + s^2 = (\text{some integer})^2 - 2(\text{some integer})$$

Since integers are closed under multiplication and subtraction, this result is an integer. The statement is true.

(b) This statement is not true. To see why, choose $r = 2 + 5i$ and $s = 2 - 5i$. Then $r + s = 4$, which is an integer, and $rs = 29$ which is also an integer, but neither r nor s is an integer.

11. The graph is a parabola with vertex $(5, 4)$:

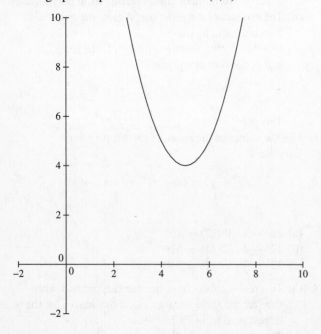

The graph crosses the x-axis whenever $y = 0$. These are the solutions to $0 = x^2 - 10x + 29$. But there are no real solutions to this equation, since the quadratic formula gives a negative under the square root sign:

$$x = \frac{10 \pm \sqrt{100 - 4 \cdot 29}}{2}$$

12. (a) The identity states $a^2 + b^2 = (a + b)^2 - 2ab$, so the result is

$$10^2 - 2 \cdot 29 = 100 - 58 = 42$$

(b) There are no real solutions to the quadratic equation $x^2 - 10x + 29 = 0$, since the quadratic formula gives a negative under the square root sign:

$$x = \frac{10 \pm \sqrt{100 - 4 \cdot 29}}{2}$$

The variables a and b cannot represent real numbers, though it may still be possible to calculate $a^2 + b^2$.

13. If the roots are a and b, then the new quadratic will have roots a^2 and b^2. The sum of the roots is $a^2 + b^2$ and the product is a^2b^2.

$$a^2 + b^2 = (a + b)^2 - 2ab = (10)^2 - 2(22) = 56$$
$$a^2b^2 = (ab)^2 = (22)^2 = 484$$

The new quadratic is $x^2 - 56x + 484$.

14. (a) The numbers are 5 and 2, and are the roots of the quadratic $x^2 - 7x + 10 = 0$.

(b) The numbers are 5 and -3 and are the roots of the quadratic $x^2 - 2x - 15 = 0$.

(c) The numbers are $\frac{3}{2}$ and $\frac{1}{2}$ and are the roots of the quadratic $x^2 - 2x + \frac{3}{4} = 0$.

(d) The numbers are $1 + \sqrt{2}$ and $1 - \sqrt{2}$ and are the roots of the quadratic $x^2 - 2x - 1 = 0$.

(e) These are the roots of the quadratic $x^2 - px + q = 0$. Use the quadratic formula:

$$x = \frac{p \pm \sqrt{p^2 - 4q}}{2}$$

The two numbers are $\frac{p + \sqrt{p^2 - 4q}}{2}$ and $\frac{p - \sqrt{p^2 - 4q}}{2}$.

Maintain Your Skills

15. These expansions use the difference of squares rule

$$(a + b)(a - b) = a^2 - b^2$$

For example,

$$(\sqrt{7} + \sqrt{3})(\sqrt{7} - \sqrt{3}) = 7 - 3 = 4$$

Here, $a = \sqrt{7}$ and $b = \sqrt{3}$. This is used in all six expansions.

(a) 4

(b) 3

(c) 2

(d) 7

(e) $m - n$

(f) $a^2 - b$

16. (a) $\frac{1}{\sqrt{7}+\sqrt{3}} \cdot \frac{\sqrt{7}-\sqrt{3}}{\sqrt{7}-\sqrt{3}} = \frac{\sqrt{7}-\sqrt{3}}{4}$

(b) $\frac{1}{\sqrt{5}+\sqrt{2}} \cdot \frac{\sqrt{5}-\sqrt{2}}{\sqrt{5}-\sqrt{2}} = \frac{\sqrt{5}-\sqrt{2}}{3}$

17. (a) Expand each expression. $(\sqrt{2})^2 = 2$ and $(-\sqrt{2})^2 = 2$. The sum is 4.

(b) Expand each expression. $(1 + \sqrt{2})^2 = 3 + 2\sqrt{2}$ and $(1 - \sqrt{2})^2 = 3 - 2\sqrt{2}$. The sum is 6.
Each of these uses the rule $\sqrt{x} \cdot \sqrt{y} = \sqrt{xy}$.

(c) Here, $x = 2$ and $y = 5$. The result is $\sqrt{10}$.

(d) Here, $x = 3$ and $y = 5$. The result is $\sqrt{15}$.

(e) Here, $x = 7$ and $y = 7$. The result is 7.

(f) The result is $2b^2$.

(g) Here, $x = a$ and $y = b$. This is $\sqrt{ab}$.

(h) Here, $x = k$ and $y = k$, so $\sqrt{k} \cdot \sqrt{k} = k$.

3.2 Extending Number Systems

Check Your Understanding

1. Use factoring to find the solution sets. In several cases, there are other solutions outside the natural numbers.

(a) 6 and 4

(b) 10

(c) no solution

(d) no solution

(e) no solution

(f) no solution

(g) no solution

(h) 1

2. Additional solutions in $\mathbb{Z}$ (the integers) but not in $\mathbb{N}$ include zero and negative integers.

(a) no additional solutions

(b) 0

(c) -4 and -6

(d) no additional solutions

(e) no additional solutions

(f) no additional solutions

(g) no additional solutions

(h) no additional solutions

3. Additional solutions in $\mathbb{Q}$ (the rational numbers) but not in $\mathbb{Z}$ include fractions, both positive and negative.

(a) no additional solutions

(b) no additional solutions

(c) no additional solutions

(d) $\frac{1}{4}$ and $\frac{1}{6}$

(e) no additional solutions

(f) no additional solutions

(g) no additional solutions

(h) no additional solutions

4. These additional solutions are real, irrational numbers.

(a) no additional solutions

(b) no additional solutions

(c) no additional solutions

(d) no additional solutions

(e) $\sqrt{10}$ and $-\sqrt{10}$

(f) no additional solutions

(g) no additional solutions

(h) no additional solutions

5. These additional solutions are non-real numbers.

(a) no additional solutions

(b) no additional solutions

(c) no additional solutions

(d) no additional solutions

(e) no additional solutions

(f) $\sqrt{-10}$ and $-\sqrt{-10}$

(g) $\frac{-1\pm\sqrt{-3}}{2}$

(h) $\frac{-1\pm\sqrt{-3}}{2}$

6. For each answer, determine whether the discriminant $b^2 - 4ac$ is positive, negative, or zero.

(a) The discriminant is positive, so there are two roots. This quadratic also factors to $(x + 1)(x + 3)$, identifying the roots.

(b) The discriminant is zero, so there is one root. This quadratic factors to $(x + 2)(x + 2)$.

(c) The discriminant is negative. There are no real roots.

(d) The discriminant is positive, so there are two roots. This quadratic factors to $(3x - 4)(x - 2)$.

7. (a)

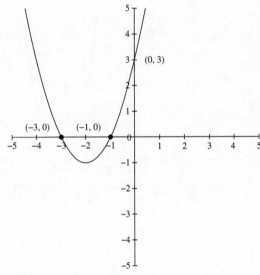

(b)

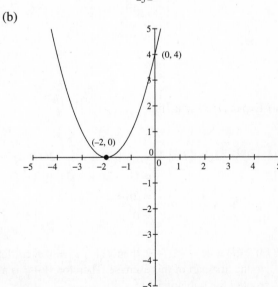

(c)

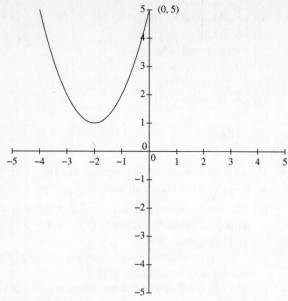

(d)

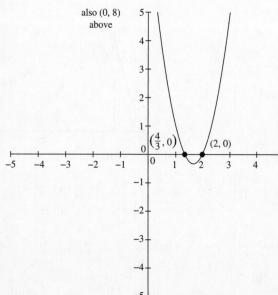

8. (a) Expand the square first.

$$(1+i)^2 - 2(1+i) + 2 = (1+2i+i^2) - 2(1+i) + 2$$
$$= (1+2i+(-1)) - 2 - 2i + 2$$
$$= 2i - 2 - 2i + 2$$
$$= 0$$

(b) If $f(x) = x^2 - 2x + 2$, then $f(1+i) = 0$ according to the first part of this exercise. Therefore $1 + i$ is a root of the polynomial $x^2 - 2x + 2$.

9. (a) Here is the table:

Input: n	Output: $a(n)$
0	2
1	0
2	6
3	0
4	18
5	0
6	54

(b) When $n = 10$, $a(n) = 3^5 + 3^5$. Since $3^5 = 243$, then $a(10) = 486$.

When $n = 101$, the first term is positive and the second is its opposite. These cancel, so $a(101) = 0$.

In general $a(n) = 0$ whenever n is odd.

(c) Note that $a(n) = 0$ for any odd $n = 1, 3, 5, \ldots$ This function has an infinite number of roots. Remember that a polynomial of degree n can have at most n roots. Since the number of roots for a polynomial is limited, no polynomial could agree with $a(n)$ for all natural numbers.

10. (a) Any number to the zero power is 1, so this is rational.

(b) $1 + \sqrt{2}$ is irrational.

(c) $(1 + \sqrt{2})^2 = 3 + \sqrt{2}$ is irrational.

(d) Here is the completed table:

Input: n	Output: $f(n)$
0	2
1	2
2	6
3	14
4	34
5	82
6	198

(e) Answers vary here. One way to find such an equation is to start with $x = 1 + \sqrt{2}$. This equation certainly has $1 + \sqrt{2}$ as a root, but it doesn't have integer coefficients. Rewrite it as $x - 1 = \sqrt{2}$ and square both sides. This will get rid of the square root operation. You get $x^2 - 2x + 1 = 2$, which you can write as $x^2 - 2x - 1 = 0$. This equation has $1 + \sqrt{2}$ as a root. To get more equations that also have this root, you can multiply the function you have by any polynomial.

(f) One way to show this is by starting with the statement you want to prove and using expansion and the Basic Rules, show that it gives you the original definition of the function.

$$f(n) = 2f(n-1) + f(n-2)$$

Use the definition of the function to expand the right side.

$$= 2(1 + \sqrt{2})^{n-1} + 2(1 - \sqrt{2})^{n-1}$$
$$\quad + (1 + \sqrt{2})^{n-2} + (1 - \sqrt{2})^{n-2}$$

Collect all the terms with factor $(1 + \sqrt{2})$ and those with $(1 - \sqrt{2})$.

$$= 2(1 + \sqrt{2})^{n-1} + (1 + \sqrt{2})^{n-2} + 2(1 - \sqrt{2})^{n-1}$$
$$+ (1 - \sqrt{2})^{n-2}$$

Factor out any common factors in these pairs of terms you collected.

$$= (1 + \sqrt{2})^{n-2}[2(1 + \sqrt{2}) + 1]$$
$$+ (1 - \sqrt{2})^{n-2}[2(1 - \sqrt{2}) + 1]$$

Multiply out the second factor in each term.

$$= (1 + \sqrt{2})^{n-2}[2 + 2\sqrt{2} + 1]$$
$$+ (1 - \sqrt{2})^{n-2}[2 - 2\sqrt{2} + 1]$$

Notice that $(1 + \sqrt{2})^2 = 1 + 2\sqrt{2} + 2$
and $(1 - \sqrt{2})^2 = 1 - 2\sqrt{2} + 2$.

$$= (1+\sqrt{2})^{n-2}(1+\sqrt{2})^2 + (1-\sqrt{2})^{n-2}(1-\sqrt{2})^2$$

Simplify using the rules for exponents.

$$= (1 + \sqrt{2})^n + (1 - \sqrt{2})^n$$

This is the original function definition.

11. (a) Here is the completed table:

Input: n	Output: $g(n)$
0	2
1	4
2	6
3	4
4	−14
5	−76
6	−234

As in the previous exercise, the peculiar terms don't appear in the final function values.

(b) $(2 + \sqrt{-1})^2 = 2^2 + 2 \cdot 2 \cdot \sqrt{-1} + (-1)$. Then, simplify and combine terms to get $3 + 4\sqrt{-1}$.

(c) One possible answer is $x^2 - 4x + 5 = 0$. Here's how to get that answer. Start from an equation that you *know* has $2 + \sqrt{-1}$ as a root. Isolate the square root, and square both sides.

$$x = 2 + \sqrt{-1}$$
$$x - 2 = \sqrt{-1}$$
$$x^2 - 4x + 4 = -1$$
$$x^2 - 4x + 5 = 0$$

You can get different solutions to the exercise by multiplying this quadratic by any other polynomial.

(d) Use the definition of $g(n)$ to expand the right side. Collect terms and factor as in the previous exercise to work towards the original definition of the function. The second part of this exercise is helpful when you want to recognize terms like $(2 + \sqrt{-1})^2$ and $(2 - \sqrt{-1})^2$ in their unfactored forms. The solution follows the same pattern as that for the corresponding part of the previous exercise.

$$g(n) = 4g(n - 1) - 5g(n - 2)$$
$$= 4(2 + \sqrt{-1})^{n-1} + 4(2 - \sqrt{-1})^{n-1} -$$
$$5(2 + \sqrt{-1})^{n-2} - 5(2 - \sqrt{-1})^{n-2}$$
$$= (2 + \sqrt{-1})^{n-2}[4(2 + \sqrt{-1}) - 5] +$$
$$(2 - \sqrt{-1})^{n-2}[4(2 - \sqrt{-1}) - 5]$$
$$= (2 + \sqrt{-1})^{n-2}(8 + 4\sqrt{-1} - 5) +$$
$$(2 - \sqrt{-1})^{n-2}(8 - 4\sqrt{-1} - 5)$$
$$= (2 + \sqrt{-1})^{n-2}(3 + 4\sqrt{-1}) +$$
$$(2 - \sqrt{-1})^{n-2}(3 - 4\sqrt{-1})$$
$$= (2 + \sqrt{-1})^{n-2}(2 + \sqrt{-1})^2 +$$
$$(2 - \sqrt{-1})^{n-2}(2 - \sqrt{-1})^2$$
$$= (2 + \sqrt{-1})^n + (2 - \sqrt{-1})^n$$

On Your Own

12. Answers will vary. Here are some possibilities.
   (a) $(-2)(-5) = 10$. $\frac{3}{4} \cdot \frac{8}{3} = 2$
   (b) $\frac{9}{4} \cdot \frac{16}{3} = 12$. $\frac{1}{4} + \frac{3}{4} = 1$
   (c) $\sqrt{2} \cdot \sqrt{8} = 4$. $\frac{\sqrt{5}}{2\sqrt{5}} = \frac{1}{2}$
   (d) $(2 + \sqrt{-1}) + (2 - \sqrt{-1}) = 4$
       $(1 + \sqrt{-3})(1 - \sqrt{-3}) = 4$
   (e) $4 \div 9$. $4 - 9$
   (f) $4 \div 3$. $\sqrt{15}$
   (g) $\sqrt{\frac{1}{2}} \cdot \sqrt{5}$
   (h) $\sqrt{-4} \cdot \sqrt{-2}$

13. (a) 1 and 5
   (b) no solution
   (c) no solution
   (d) 1
   (e) no solution
   (f) no solution

14. (a) These solutions include zero and negative integers.
   (a) no additional solutions
   (b) −1 and −5
   (c) no additional solutions
   (d) no additional solutions
   (e) no additional solutions
   (f) no additional solutions

   (b) These solutions include fractions of integers.
   (a) no additional solutions
   (b) no additional solutions
   (c) no additional solutions
   (d) $\frac{-6}{5}$
   (e) no additional solutions
   (f) no additional solutions

   (c) These solutions include all real numbers.
   (a) no additional solutions
   (b) no additional solutions
   (c) $-2 + \sqrt{2}$ and $-2 - \sqrt{2}$

    (d) no additional solutions

    (e) $\sqrt{5}$ and $-\sqrt{5}$

    (f) no additional solutions

  (d) These solutions include non-reals.

    (a) no additional solutions

    (b) no additional solutions

    (c) no additional solutions

    (d) no additional solutions

    (e) no additional solutions

    (f) $3 + \sqrt{-2}$ and $3 - \sqrt{-2}$

15. (a) The sum is -10 and the product is -299.

   (b) The sum is 2 and the product is -8.

   (c) The sum is 2 and the product is -2.

   (d) The sum is 2 and the product is $1 - n$.

   (e) The sum is 2 and the product is 4.

16. $(3 + \sqrt{-2})(3 - \sqrt{-2}) = 9 - (-2) = 9 + 2 = 11$. The correct answer choice is **D**.

Maintain Your Skills

17. (a) $(2 + \sqrt{-1}) + (2 - \sqrt{-1}) = 4$, a real number.

   (b) $(2 + \sqrt{-1}) - (2 - \sqrt{-1}) = 2\sqrt{-1}$, not a real number.

   (c) $(2 + \sqrt{-1})(2 + \sqrt{-1}) = 3 + 4\sqrt{-1}$, not a real number.

   (d) $(2 + \sqrt{-1})(2 - \sqrt{-1}) = 5$ by difference of squares, a real number.

   (e) $\frac{2+\sqrt{-1}}{2+\sqrt{-1}} = 1$, a real number.

18. (a) $(2 + 3x) + (5 + 6x) = 7 + 9x$

   (b) $(2 + 3x) + (2 - 3x) = 4$

   (c) $(2 + 3x) - (2 - 3x) = 6x$

   (d)

$$\begin{aligned}(2 + 3x)(5 + 6x) &= 10 + 15x + 12x + 18x^2 \\ &= 10 + 27x + 18(-1) \\ &= -8 + 27x\end{aligned}$$

   (e)

$$\begin{aligned}(2 + 3x)^2 &= 4 + 12x + 9x^2 \\ &= 4 + 12x + 9(-1) \\ &= -5 + 12x\end{aligned}$$

   (f)

$$\begin{aligned}(2 + 3x)(2 - 3x) &= 4 + 6x - 6x - 9x^2 \\ &= 4 - 9(-1) \\ &= 13\end{aligned}$$

3.3 Making the Extension: $\sqrt{-1}$

Check Your Understanding

1. Use difference of squares factoring for each.

   (a) $a^2 - b^2$

   (b) $a^2 - 2b^2$

   (c) $a^2 - 3b^2$

   (d) $a^2 - cb^2$

   (e) $a^2 + b^2$

2. The two graphs do not intersect. Here are the graphs:

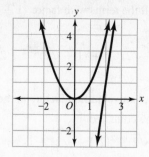

3. (a) Rewrite the equation: $x^2 - 6x + 11 = 0$. Then use the quadratic formula:

$$x = \frac{6 \pm \sqrt{36 - 44}}{2} = \frac{6 \pm \sqrt{-8}}{2}$$

   This simplifies to $3 \pm \sqrt{-2}$.

  (b) The solutions are $3 + \sqrt{-2}$ and $3 - \sqrt{-2}$. The sum is

$$(3 + \sqrt{-2}) + (3 - \sqrt{-2}) = 6$$

   and the product is

$$(3 + \sqrt{-2})(3 - \sqrt{-2}) = 3^2 - (\sqrt{-2})^2 = 9 + 2 = 11$$

   Notice the correspondence between the sum and product of the roots and the coefficients of the original equation.

4. Answers will vary. The quadratic formula gives the solutions for any quadratic equation, and its solutions are always in the form

$$\frac{x + \sqrt{y}}{z}$$

  where x, y, and z are real numbers derived from the coefficients of the quadratic. These will always be real numbers, so the only possible "problem" comes when y is negative. Including square roots of negatives means these solutions will always be present.

5. The exact expressions for these numbers are $\sqrt{34}$ and $-\sqrt{34}$. To three significant digits, the numbers are ± 5.83.

6. No, since 0 has only one square root: $0^2 = 0$ and no other number squares to zero. For any *positive* real number a, there are two numbers whose squares equal a.

7. Show that each number is a solution by calculating the value of $x^3 - 5x^2 + 8x - 6$. The number r is a solution if and only if this equals zero. When $x = 3$,

$$3^3 - 5 \cdot 3^2 + 8 \cdot 3 - 6 = 27 - 45 + 24 - 6 = 0$$

When $x = 1 + \sqrt{-1}$,

$$\begin{aligned}(1+\sqrt{-1})^3 &- 5(1 + \sqrt{-1})^2 + 8(1 + \sqrt{-1}) - 6 \\ &= (-2 + 2\sqrt{-1}) - 5(2\sqrt{-1}) + 8(1 + \sqrt{-1}) - 6 \\ &= -2 + 2\sqrt{-1} - 10\sqrt{-1} + 8 + 8\sqrt{-1} - 6 \\ &= 0\end{aligned}$$

When $x = 1 - \sqrt{-1}$,

$$(1-\sqrt{-1})^3 - 5(1 - \sqrt{-1})^2 + 8(1 - \sqrt{-1}) - 6$$

$$= (-2 - 2\sqrt{-1}) - 5(-2\sqrt{-1}) + 8(1 - \sqrt{-1}) - 6$$

$$= -2 - 2\sqrt{-1} + 10\sqrt{-1} + 8 - 8\sqrt{-1} - 6$$

$$= 0$$

All three numbers are solutions to the equation.

8. (a) $3 + (1 + \sqrt{-1}) + (1 - \sqrt{-1}) = 5$.

(b)

$$3(1+\sqrt{-1}) + 3(1 - \sqrt{-1}) + (1 + \sqrt{-1})(1 - \sqrt{-1})$$

$$= 3 + 3\sqrt{-1} + 3 - 3\sqrt{-1} + 2 = 8$$

(c) $3(1 + \sqrt{-1})(1 - \sqrt{-1}) = 3 \cdot 2 = 6$.

On Your Own

9. In each part, use the result $\sqrt{-n} = \sqrt{-1} \cdot \sqrt{n}$ while simplifying. For example, $\sqrt{-4} \cdot \sqrt{-9} = \sqrt{-1} \cdot \sqrt{4} \cdot \sqrt{-1} \cdot \sqrt{9}$. Then simplify and combine to get $6 \cdot -1 = -6$. Here are the results:

(a) -6

(b) -6

(c) -9

(d) -9

(e) $-3 + 2\sqrt{-3}$

(f) $-3 + 2\sqrt{-3}$

10. Answers may vary. The examples in Exercise 9 can be used to justify this statement, or you could use a generic example with variables. Proof relies on the fact that the any-order property works in $\mathbb{R}$, and the arithmetic in this new system is reliant on $\mathbb{R}$.

11. (a) Combine like terms to make $7 + 9\sqrt{-1}$.

(b) Rewrite $\sqrt{-16}$ as $\sqrt{16}\sqrt{-1} = 4\sqrt{-1}$ and $\sqrt{-25}$ as $5\sqrt{-1}$. Then the expression becomes $(3 + 4\sqrt{-1}) + (4 + 5\sqrt{-1})$, the same as the previous part.

(c)

$$(5 + \sqrt{-1})(5 + 2\sqrt{-1})$$

$$= 25 + 10\sqrt{-1} + 5\sqrt{-1} + 2(-1)$$

$$= 23 + 15\sqrt{-1}$$

(d) The sum is 6, since the $\sqrt{-2}$ terms cancel out. Written in the form $a + b\sqrt{-1}$, $a = 6$ and $b = 0$.

(e) The product is 11. This is a difference of squares, so the product is

$$3^2 - \sqrt{-2}^2 = 9 - (-2) = 11$$

Written in $a + b\sqrt{-1}$ form, this is $11 + 0\sqrt{-1}$.

12. Using the quadratic formula, you obtain

$$x = \frac{10 \pm \sqrt{100 - 104}}{2} = \frac{10 \pm \sqrt{-4}}{2} = 5 \pm \sqrt{-1}$$

The correct answer choice is **C**.

13. (a) Factor as difference of cubes:

$$x^3 - 8 = (x - 2)(x^2 + 2x + 4)$$

(b) Since $(x - 2)(x^2 + 2x + 4) = 0$, use the Zero Product Property. Either $x = 2$ or $x^2 + 2x + 4 = 0$. Then you can use the quadratic formula to find the roots of the quadratic.

$$x = \frac{-2 \pm \sqrt{4 - 16}}{2} = \frac{-2 \pm \sqrt{-12}}{2}$$

This simplifies to

$$\frac{-2 \pm 2\sqrt{-3}}{2} = -1 \pm \sqrt{-3}$$

So, the three solutions are $x = 2$ and $x = -1 \pm \sqrt{-3}$.

(c) Factor as the difference of cubes to get $x^3 - 1 = (x - 1)(x^2 + x + 1)$ This gives you $x = 1$ as one of the roots by the ZPP. The quadratic formula gives you

$$x = \frac{-1 \pm \sqrt{-3}}{2}$$

for the other two roots. (They're exactly half of the roots for $x^3 - 8$.)

14. (a) Factor as difference of cubes:

$$x^3 - 64 = (x - 4)(x^2 + 4x + 16)$$

Then $x = 4$ or $x^2 + 4x + 16 = 0$. The quadratic is solved via the quadratic formula:

$$x = \frac{-4 \pm \sqrt{-48}}{2} = \frac{-4 \pm 4\sqrt{-3}}{2} = -2 \pm 2\sqrt{-3}$$

(b) Each solution to $x^3 - 64 = 0$ is exactly twice a corresponding solution to $x^3 - 8 = 0$ and four times a solution to $x^3 - 1 = 0$. This makes sense, since doubling a number multiplies its cube by 8. Since 64 is eight times as large as 8, the solutions from $x^3 - 64 = 0$ are the solutions from $x^3 - 8 = 0$ doubled. The effect of quadrupling a number is to multiply its cube by 64. Since 64 is 64 times as large as 1, the solutions from $x^3 - 64 = 0$ are the solutions from $x^3 - 1$ multiplied by 4.

15. First, factor as difference of squares:

$$x^6 - 64 = (x^3 + 8)(x^3 - 8)$$

Each of these factors can be further factored as the sum and difference of cubes:

$$x^3 + 8 = (x + 2)(x^2 - 2x + 4)$$

$$x^3 - 8 = (x - 2)(x^2 + 2x + 4)$$

The full factoring is $x^6 - 64 = (x + 2)(x - 2)(x^2 - 2x + 4)(x^2 + 2x + 4)$. The first two factors give the solutions $x = -2$ and $x = 2$. The second factors, run through the quadratic formula, give four other solutions:

$$x = 1 + \sqrt{-3}, 1 - \sqrt{-3}, -1 + \sqrt{-3}, -1 - \sqrt{-3}$$

In total, there are six solutions, four of which are nonreal.

Maintain Your Skills

16. Each is a difference of squares factoring.

(a) $(3 + 4\sqrt{-1})(3 - 4\sqrt{-1}) = 9 - 16(-1) = 25$

(b) $(12 + 5\sqrt{-1})(12 - 5\sqrt{-1}) = 144 - 25(-1) = 169$

(c) $(7 + \sqrt{-1})(7 - \sqrt{-1}) = 49 - (-1) = 50$

(d) $(x + y\sqrt{-1})(x - y\sqrt{-1}) = x^2 - y^2(-1) = x^2 + y^2$

17. (a) This equals -1 by definition.

(b) Break them up by pairs:

$$(\sqrt{-1} \cdot \sqrt{-1}) \cdot (\sqrt{-1} \cdot \sqrt{-1})$$

Then the product is $-1 \cdot -1 = 1$.

(c) Rewrite to $(\sqrt{-1}^2)^3 = (-1)^3 = -1$.

(d) Rewrite to $(\sqrt{-1}^2)^4 = (-1)^4 = 1$.

(e) Rewrite to $(\sqrt{-1}^8) \cdot \sqrt{-1} = 1 \cdot \sqrt{-1} = \sqrt{-1}$.

3.4 Making the Extension: Complex Numbers

Check Your Understanding

1. (a) $(3 + 2i) + (9 - i) = 12 + i$

(b) $(3 + 2i)(9 + i) = 27 + 18i + 3i + 2i^2 = 27 + 21i - 2 = 25 + 21i$

(c) $(5 + 2i) + (5 - 2i) = 10$. Written as $a + bi$, it is $10 + 0i$.

(d) $(5 + 2i)(5 - 2i) = 25 + 10i - 10i - 4i^2 = 25 - (-4) = 29$ or $29 + 0i$.

(e) $(4 + 2i) + (2 + 4i) = 6 + 6i$

(f) $(4 + 2i)(2 + 4i) = 8 + 4i + 16i + 8i^2 = 8 + 20i - 8 = 20i$ or $0 + 20i$.

2. (a) $(3 + 5i) + (3 - 5i) = 6$ or $6 + 0i$.

(b) $(3 + 5i)(3 - 5i) = 9 + 15i - 15i - 25(-1) = 34$ or $34 + 0i$.

(c) $(-7 + 2i) + (-7 - 2i) = -14$

(d) $(-7 + 2i)(-7 - 2i) = 49 - 14i + 14i - 4(-1) = 53$

(e) $(12 + 5i) + (12 - 5i) = 24$

(f) $(12 + 5i)(12 - 5i) = 144 + 60i - 60i - 25(-1) = 169$

3. (a) The conjugate of $(a + bi)$ is $(a - bi)$.

(b) Add $(a + bi)$ and $(a - bi)$:

$$(a + bi) + (a - bi) = 2a$$

Since a is a real number, and multiplying by 2 doesn't change that, the sum of a complex number and its conjugate is real.

(c) Multiply $(a + bi)$ and $(a - bi)$:

$$(a + bi)(a - bi) = a^2 + abi - abi - b^2(-1) = a^2 + b^2$$

Since a and b are real numbers, so is $a^2 + b^2$, because the real numbers are closed under the operations of squaring and addition. This means that the product of a complex number and its conjugate is real.

(d) The sum of a number and its conjugate is equal to 0 if $2a = 0$. This implies that $a = 0$ and the real part of the complex number is 0. In other words, the sum of a number and its conjugate is zero if the complex number is a real multiple of i.

(e) The product of a number and its conjugate is equal to 0 if $a^2 + b^2 = 0$. Since a and b are both real numbers, $a^2 \geq 0$, $b^2 \geq 0$, so this will only happen if $a = b = 0$ and the number in question is $0 + 0i$.

4. Derman is wrong, since the statement about complex numbers requires that a and b are *real* numbers when a complex number is written as $a + bi$. Derman's example uses values for a and b that are not real numbers. His substitution makes $a + bi = i + ii$, which would actually be written as $-1 + i$ if correctly written in $a + bi$ form. So, Derman made the mistake of using complex values for a and b in the $a + bi$ form of a complex number.

5. Multiply out to set up a system of equations.

$$(a + bi)(1 + i) = 11 - 3i$$
$$a + ai + bi + bi^2 = 11 - 3i$$
$$(a - b) + (a + b)i = 11 - 3i$$

This gives the system of equations $a - b = 11$ and $a + b = -3$. Solve by adding the equations together:

$$\begin{aligned} a - b &= 11 \\ +) \quad a + b &= -3 \\ \hline 2a &= 8 \\ a &= 4 \end{aligned}$$

Knowing that $a = 4$, substitute in either equation to find $b = -7$. The complex number is $4 - 7i$.

6. (a) Find a complex number $(a + bi)$ so that $(2 + 3i) + (a + bi) = 0$:

$$(2 + a) + (3 + b)i = 0 + 0i$$

Then $2 + a = 0$ implies $a = -2$, and $3 + b = 0$ implies $b = -3$. The complex number $(-2 - 3i)$ is the opposite of $2 + 3i$.

(b) For any complex number $(x + yi)$, the complex number $(-x - yi)$ is the opposite, since $(x + yi) + (-x - yi) = 0$. All nonzero members of $\mathbb{C}$ have distinct negatives or opposites, and zero is its own negative.

7. If $z = a + bi$, then $\bar{z} = a - bi$. Calculate $z^2 + \bar{z}^2$:

$$\begin{aligned} z^2 + \bar{z}^2 &= (a + bi)^2 + (a - bi)^2 \\ &= (a^2 + 2abi + b^2i^2) + (a^2 - 2abi + b^2i^2) \\ &= (a^2 - b^2 + 2abi) + (a^2 - b^2 - 2abi) \\ &= 2(a^2 - b^2) \end{aligned}$$

Since a and b are real numbers, so is $2(a^2 - b^2)$. The result is a real number.

8. The solution here relies on the fact that when you add or multiply conjugates, the result is real. This allows you to find quadratics that have a specific complex root.

(a) The sum of $3 + 2i$ and $3 - 2i$ is 6, and the product is 13. Then the equation $x^2 - 6x + 13 = 0$ has solutions $x = 3 + 2i$ and $x = 3 - 2i$.

(b) See the previous part: $x^2 - 6x + 13 = 0$ is one possible answer.

(c) The sum of $1 + 5i$ and $1 - 5i$ is 2, and the product is 26. Then the equation $(x^2 - 6x + 13)(x^2 - 2x + 26) = 0$ has both $3 + 2i$ and $1 + 5i$ as solutions.

(d) The sum of $1 + 5i$ and $1 - 5i$ is 2 and the product is 26. Meanwhile, the sum of $-1 + 5i$ and $-1 - 5i$ is -2 and the product is 26. The equation $(x^2 - 2x + 26)(x^2 + 2x + 26) = 0$ has both $1 + 5i$ and $-1 + 5i$ as solutions.

(e) The sum of $1 + i\sqrt{3}$ and $1 - i\sqrt{3}$ is 2, and the product is 4. The equation $x^2 - 2x + 4 = 0$ has $1 + i\sqrt{3}$ as a solution. One other equation is $x^3 + 8 = 0$, since $x^3 + 8 = (x + 2)(x^2 - 2x + 4)$.

(f) The equation $x - (\sqrt{2} + \sqrt{3}) = 0$ has real coefficients, so you could use that. You might have instinctively continued the calculation to find this equation that has integer coefficients and the required root: $x^4 - 10x^2 + 1 = 0$. (To get this equation, start from $x - \sqrt{2} = \sqrt{3}$, square both sides, isolate the remaining radical, and square both sides again.)

(g) The sum of $\sqrt{2} + i\sqrt{3}$ and its conjugate $\sqrt{2} - i\sqrt{3}$ is $2\sqrt{2}$ and their product is 5, so $x^2 - 2\sqrt{2}x + 5 = 0$ is one possible answer.

On Your Own

9.

$$(a + bi)(b - ai) = ab - a^2 i + b^2 i = bai^2$$
$$= ab + (b^2 - a^2)i - ba(-1) = 2ab + (b^2 - a^2)i$$

The correct answer choice is **D**.

10. (a) $i^3 = i^2 \cdot i = -1 \cdot i = -i$

(b) $i^4 = i^2 \cdot i^2 = -1 \cdot -1 = 1$

(c) Use $i^4 = 1$. Then $i^5 = i^4 \cdot i = i$. Also $i^6 = i^2 = -1$, $i^7 = i^3 = -i$, and $i^8 = i^4 = 1$.

(d) Extract a multiple of 4. $i^{210} = i^{208} \cdot i^2 = (i^4)^{52} \cdot i^2$. Since $i^4 = 1$, this result equals $i^2 = -1$.

(e) Multiply the top and bottom of the fraction through by i:

$$\frac{1}{i} \cdot \frac{i}{i} = \frac{i}{i^2} = \frac{i}{-1} = -i$$

Or, note that $\frac{1}{i} = i^{-1}$ and use the exponent properties in this exercise.

11. (a) Subtract $3 - i$ from each side to find z.

$$z + (3 - i) = 6 + 2i$$
$$z = (6 + 2i) - (3 - i)$$
$$z = 3 + 3i$$

(b) Add 3 to each side to find w.

$$w - 3 = 6 + i$$
$$w = (6 + i) + 3$$
$$w = 9 + i$$

(c) Use square roots, or let $x = a + bi$. Then $x^2 = a^2 + 2abi - b^2$ must equal $-9 + 0i$. Then $2ab = 0$ implies either a or b is zero.

If b is zero, then x is a real number and x^2 cannot equal -9. If a is zero, then the value of b comes from

$$a^2 - b^2 = -9$$

With $a = 0$, $b = \pm 3$. The two possible values of x are $x = 3i$ and $x = -3i$. Both numbers square to equal -9.

(d) Solve using the quadratic formula. The equation can be transformed to $z^2 - 6z + 34 = 0$. The roots are

$$z = \frac{6 \pm \sqrt{36 - 4 \cdot 34}}{2} = \frac{6 \pm \sqrt{-100}}{2}$$

Simplifying, $z = \frac{6 \pm 10i}{2} = 3 \pm 5i$ are the two solutions.

12. If $z = a + bi$, then the product is

$$(a + bi)(3 + 2i) = (3a - 2b) + (2a + 3b)i$$

For this to be a *real* number, the imaginary part of the product must be zero. Then $2a + 3b = 0$. There are many possible solutions to this. One example is $a = 3$ and $b = -2$, giving $z = 3 - 2i$. In general,

$$2a + 3b = 0$$
$$2a = -3b$$
$$a = \frac{-3}{2}b$$

This gives a rule that can generate other possible answers.

13. (a) One possible answer is i. There are many others.

(b) Any rational number is also real.

(c) One possible answer is $\sqrt{2}$, another is π. There are many others (any irrational number).

(d) This is not possible. Any rational number is real, and any real number is also complex.

(e) All real numbers are also complex numbers, they just have imaginary part 0.

14. (a) Multiply out the right side as a difference of squares, and then use the fact that $i^2 = -1$.

$$x^2 + 1 = (x + i)(x - i)$$
$$= x^2 - i^2$$
$$= x^2 + 1$$

(b) The expression $x^2 + 1$ has no factoring in the system of *real* numbers. Now, with complex numbers, there is a factoring. This is not a contradiction, since these are different number systems.

15. (a) The quadratic formula gives the solutions

$$x = \frac{10 \pm \sqrt{100 - 4 \cdot 34}}{2} = \frac{10 \pm \sqrt{-36}}{2} = \frac{10 \pm 6i}{2}$$

The two solutions are $5 + 3i$ and $5 - 3i$.

(b) The sum is $(5 + 3i) + (5 - 3i) = 10$, and the product is $(5 + 3i)(5 - 3i) = 34$.

(c) To find the sum of the squares, either calculate the squares or use the identity

$$x^2 + y^2 = (x + y)^2 - 2xy$$

Using the identity, the sum of the squares is $10^2 - 2(34) = 32$. The actual squares are $16 + 30i$ and $16 - 30i$, and their sum is 32.

16. The square of $(a + bi)$ is $(a^2 - b^2) + 2abi$. Then a system of equations is built:

$$a^2 - b^2 = -11$$

$$2ab = 60$$

Since $ab = 30$, the substitution $a = \frac{30}{b}$ can be made in the first equation:

$$\left(\frac{30}{b}\right)^2 - b^2 = -11$$

Multiply through by b^2 to produce

$$900 - b^4 = -11b^2$$

which is a quadratic in b^2. It factors:

$$b^4 - 11b^2 - 900 = (b^2 - 36)(b^2 + 25) = 0$$

Either $b^2 = 36$, giving $b = 6$ and $b = -6$ as solutions. Or $b^2 = -25$, which is not possible (since b must be a real number).

Then substitute $b = 6$ and $b = -6$ into the equation $2ab = 60$ to find that the two pairs of solutions are

$$a = 5, b = 6 \text{ or } a = -5, b = -6$$

The two possible complex numbers are $5 + 6i$ and $-5 - 6i$.

Maintain Your skills

17. (a) $(2 + i) + (3 + i) = 5 + 2i$
    (b) $(3 + i) + (2 + i) = 5 + 2i$
    (c) $(5 + i) - (4 + 3i) = 1 - 2i$
    (d) $(4 + 3i) - (5 + i) = -1 + 2i$
    (e) $(5 + 3i) + (8 - 3i) = 13$
    (f) $(3 + i\sqrt{2}) + (3 - i\sqrt{2}) = 6$

18. (a) $(2+i)(3+i) = 6+3i+2i+i^2 = 6+5i-1 = 5+5i$
    (b) $(3+i)(2+i) = 6+2i+3i+i^2 = 6+5i-1 = 5+5i$
    (c) $(5+i)(5-i) = 25+5i-5i-i^2 = 25+1 = 26$
    (d) $(2+i)^2 = 4+2i+2i+i^2 = 4+4i-1 = 3+4i$
    (e) $(3+2i)^2 = 9+6i+6i+4i^2 = 9+12i-4 = 5+12i$
    (f) $(4+i)^2 = 16+4i+4i+i^2 = 16+8i-1 = 15+8i$

19. In each, let $z = a + bi$. Then

$$(a + bi)(2 - i) = (2a + b) + (-a + 2b)i$$

This sets up a system of equations to find a and b.

(a) The system is $2a + b = 3$, $-a + 2b = 1$. Solve by elimination:

$$
\begin{array}{r}
2a + b = 3 \\
+) \quad -2a + 4b = 2 \\
\hline
5b = 5 \\
b = 1
\end{array}
$$

Using $b = 1$, substitute to find $a = 1$.

(b) The system is $2a + b = 6$, $-a + 2b = 2$. Solve by elimination:

$$
\begin{array}{r}
2a + b = 6 \\
+) \quad -2a + 4b = 4 \\
\hline
5b = 10 \\
b = 2
\end{array}
$$

Using $b = 2$, substitute to find $a = 2$. Alternately note that this system is exactly double the system from the first part, so the solution will be double as well.

(c) The system is $2a + b = 9$, $-a + 2b = 3$. Solve by elimination:

$$
\begin{array}{r}
2a + b = 9 \\
+) \quad -2a + 4b = 6 \\
\hline
5b = 15 \\
b = 3
\end{array}
$$

Using $b = 3$, substitute to find $a = 3$. Alternately note that this system is exactly triple the system from the first part, so the solution will be triple as well.

(d) The system is $2a + b = 5$, $-a + 2b = 0$. Solve by elimination:

$$
\begin{array}{r}
2a + b = 5 \\
+) \quad -2a + 4b = 0 \\
\hline
5b = 5 \\
b = 1
\end{array}
$$

Using $b = 1$, substitute to find $a = 2$.

(e) The system is $2a + b = 10$, $-a + 2b = 0$. Solve by elimination:

$$
\begin{array}{r}
2a + b = 10 \\
+) \quad -2a + 4b = 0 \\
\hline
5b = 10 \\
b = 2
\end{array}
$$

Using $b = 2$, substitute to find $a = 4$. Alternately note that this system is double the system from the previous part, so the solution will be double as well.

(f) The system is $2a + b = 15$, $-a + 2b = 0$. Solve by elimination:

$$
\begin{array}{r}
2a + b = 15 \\
+) \quad -2a + 4b = 0 \\
\hline
5b = 15 \\
b = 3
\end{array}
$$

Using $b = 3$, substitute to find $a = 6$.

3.5   Reciprocals and Division

Check Your Understanding

1. Answers may vary. Show that for any complex number z, $z + \bar{z}$ is a real number.

2. (a) The conjugate of $a + bi$ is $a - bi$. Here, the conjugate of $0 + 2i$ is $0 - 2i$, usually written as just $-2i$.

(b) The conjugate of $7 + 0i$ is $7 - 0i$, or just 7.

(c) Calculate $z + w = 7 + 2i$ and its conjugate, $7 - 2i$. Then $\overline{z + w} = 7 - 2i$, while $\bar{z} + \bar{w} = (-2i) + (7) = 7 - 2i$. They are equal.

3. (a) The conjugates are $\bar{z} = a - bi$ and $\bar{w} = c - di$.

(b) Calculate $\overline{z + w}$ and $\bar{z} + \bar{w}$:

$$\overline{z + w} = \overline{(a + c) + (b + d)i} = (a + c) - (b + d)i$$

$$\bar{z} + \bar{w} = (a - bi) + (c - di) = (a + c) + (-b - d)i$$

These two expressions are equivalent for any choices of z and w.

4. (a) $\bar{z} = 3 - 2i$

(b) The conjugate of $3 - 2i$ is $3 + 2i$.

(c) The conjugate of the sum $7 - 3i$ is $7 + 3i$.

(d) The sum of the conjugates is $(3 - 2i) + (4 + 5i) = 7 + 3i$. Or, use the result from Exercise 3.

(e) The conjugate of the product $(3 + 2i)(4 - 5i) = 22 - 7i$ is $22 + 7i$.

(f) The product of the conjugates is $(3 - 2i)(4 + 5i) = 22 + 7i$.

(g) The sum is $(3 + 2i) + (3 - 2i) = 6$.

(h) The product is $(4 - 5i)(4 + 5i) = 41$.

5. (a) Multiply by $1 - i$:

$$\frac{11 - 3i}{1 + i} \cdot \frac{1 - i}{1 - i} = \frac{8 - 14i}{2} = 4 - 7i$$

(b) Multiply by $2 + i$:

$$\frac{4 + i}{2 - i} \cdot \frac{2 + i}{2 + i} = \frac{7 + 6i}{5}$$

(c) Multiply by $2 - i$:

$$\frac{8 + 4i}{2 + i} \cdot \frac{2 - i}{2 - i} = \frac{20}{5} = 4$$

Another way to do this is to recognize that the numerator is exactly 4 times as large as the denominator.

(d) Multiply by $3 + i$:

$$\frac{3 + i}{3 - i} \cdot \frac{3 + i}{3 + i} = \frac{8 + 6i}{10} = \frac{4 + 3i}{5}$$

(e) Multiply by $3 - i$:

$$\frac{3 - i}{3 + i} \cdot \frac{3 - i}{3 - i} = \frac{8 - 6i}{10} = \frac{4 - 3i}{5}$$

(f) Multiply by $a - bi$:

$$\frac{c + di}{a + bi} \cdot \frac{a - bi}{a - bi} = \frac{ac - bci + adi + bd}{a^2 + b^2}$$

$$= \frac{(ac + bd) + (ad - bc)i}{a^2 + b^2}$$

6. Compute each product using the rule $i^2 = -1$.

(a) $-9 + 38i$

(b) $-9 - 38i$

(c) $37 + 50i$

(d) $37 - 50i$

(e) $1 + 76i$

(f) $1 - 76i$

7. Let $z = a + bi$ and $w = c + di$. Then

$$\overline{zw} = \overline{(a + bi)(c + di)}$$
$$= \overline{(ac - bd) + (ad + bc)i}$$
$$= (ac - bd) - (ad + bc)i$$

$$(\bar{z})(\bar{w}) = (a - bi)(c - di)$$
$$= (ac - bd) + (-ad - bc)i$$
$$= (ac - bd) - (ad + bc)i$$

This proves that $\overline{zw} = (\bar{z})(\bar{w})$ for any complex numbers z and w.

8. (a) Let $z = a + bi$. Then

$$z + \bar{z} = (a + bi) + (a - bi) = 2a$$

(b) Let $z = a + bi$. Then

$$z\bar{z} = (a + bi)(a - bi) = a^2 + abi - abi + b^2 = a^2 + b^2$$

9. (a) Since $2a = 14$, $a = 7$. Then substitute into $a^2 + b^2 = 74$ to give $b^2 = 25$. There are two possible values of b, either 5 or -5.

(b) One way is to use the results from the first part along with the results from Exercise 8. The results $a = 7$ and $b = 5$ suggest that $7 + 5i$ and $7 - 5i$ satisfy the two properties. (Using $a = 7$ and $b = -5$ give the same pair of answers.)

Another method is to use the quadratic formula, since the two numbers satisfy the equation $x^2 - 14x + 74 = 0$. Again, the solutions are $7 + 5i$ and $7 - 5i$.

On Your Own

10. In each fraction, multiply the numerator and denominator of the fraction by the conjugate of the denominator. In general,

$$\frac{1}{a + bi} \cdot \frac{a - bi}{a - bi} = \frac{a - bi}{a^2 + b^2}$$

This general result applies to the four specific cases given in the first four parts of the exercise.

(a) $\frac{1-i}{2}$

(b) $\frac{1+i}{2}$

(c) $\frac{2-3i}{13}$

(d) $\frac{5-6i}{61}$

11. $z = a + bi$ for real numbers a and b. (a and b are not both zero.)

$$\frac{1}{z} = \frac{1}{a+bi} \cdot \frac{a-bi}{a-bi}$$

$$= \frac{a-bi}{a^2+b^2}$$

$$= \frac{a}{a^2+b^2} - \frac{b}{a^2+b^2}i$$

This reciprocal exists as long as $a^2 + b^2 \neq 0$. The only way for $a^2 + b^2$ to equal zero is if $a = 0$ and $b = 0$.

This means that all complex numbers other than $0 + 0i$ have reciprocals.

12. (a) -1

(b) -1

(c) $3 + 4i$

(d) $3 - 4i$

(e) $8 + 6i$

(f) $8 - 6i$

(g) $9 - 40i$

(h) $9 + 40i$

13. (a) Let $z = a + bi$. Then $\bar{z} = a - bi$. Calculate both $\overline{z^2}$ and $(\bar{z})^2$:

$$\overline{z^2} = \overline{(a+bi)^2}$$

$$= \overline{(a^2-b^2) + (2ab)i}$$

$$= (a^2-b^2) - (2ab)i$$

$$(\bar{z})^2 = (a-bi)^2$$

$$= (a^2-b^2) - (2ab)i$$

The statement is true for any complex number z.

(b) In the previous statement,

$$\overline{zw} = (\bar{z})(\bar{w})$$

let $w = z$. Then the result reads

$$\overline{zz} = (\bar{z})(\bar{z})$$

which is equivalent to saying

$$\overline{z^2} = (\bar{z})^2$$

14. (a) Multiply by $4 + i$:

$$\frac{4+i}{4-i} \cdot \frac{4+i}{4+i} = \frac{15+8i}{17}$$

(b) Multiply by $2 + 3i$:

$$\frac{2+3i}{2-3i} \cdot \frac{2+3i}{2+3i} = \frac{-5+12i}{13}$$

(c) Multiply by $a + bi$:

$$\frac{a+bi}{a-bi} \cdot \frac{a+bi}{a+bi} = \frac{(a^2-b^2) + (2ab)i}{a^2+b^2}$$

15. This is essentially the same as Exercise 11. The correct answer choice is **B**.

16. (a)

$$(a+bi)^2 = a^2 + 2abi + b^2i^2$$

$$= a^2 + 2abi - b^2$$

$$= (a^2 - b^2) + (2ab)i$$

(b)

$$(a^2+b^2)^2 = a^4 + 2a^2b^2 + b^4$$

$$= (a^4 - 2a^2b^2 + b^4) + 4a^2b^2$$

$$= (a^2 - b^2)^2 + (2ab)^2$$

Alternatively, expand the right side completely.

(c) If $a = 3$ and $b = 2$, then $a^2 + b^2 = 13$, $a^2 - b^2 = 5$, and $2ab = 12$.

17. Answers will vary, but the roots will always be conjugates of one another.

18. Suppose $z = m + ni$ is a root of the quadratic

$$p(x) = ax^2 + bx + c$$

Then $p(z) = az^2 + bz + c = 0$. But consider $p(\bar{z})$:

$$p(\bar{z}) = a(\bar{z})^2 + b(\bar{z}) + c$$

$$= a\overline{z^2} + b\bar{z} + c$$

Since the sum of conjugates is the conjugate of the sum, and conjugates of the real numbers a, b, and c are equal to themselves,

$$p(\bar{z}) = \overline{p(z)}$$

But $p(z) = 0$, so $\overline{p(z)} = 0$ as well. This means that $\bar{z}$ must be a root of the quadratic.

Maintain Your Skills

19. Multiply top and bottom by the conjugate of the denominator in each case.

(a) $\frac{17-6i}{5}$

(b) $\frac{17+6i}{5}$

(c) $\frac{-9+19i}{13}$

(d) $\frac{-9-19i}{13}$

(e) $2 + i$

(f) $2 - i$

20. (a) Get a common denominator.

$$\frac{1}{1+i} + \frac{1}{1-i} = \frac{(1+i) + (1-i)}{(1+i)(1-i)} = \frac{2}{2} = 1$$

(b) Get a common denominator.

$$\frac{1}{2+3i} + \frac{1}{2-3i} = \frac{(2+3i) + (2-3i)}{(2+3i)(2-3i)} = \frac{4}{13}$$

(c) Get a common denominator.

$$\frac{1}{5+i} + \frac{1}{5-i} = \frac{(5+i)+(5-i)}{(5+i)(5-i)} = \frac{10}{26} = \frac{5}{13}$$

(d) Let $z = a + bi$. Note that since z is non-zero then a and b cannot both be zero. Then get a common denominator.

$$\frac{1}{a+bi} + \frac{1}{a-bi} = \frac{(a+bi)+(a-bi)}{(a+bi)(a-bi)} = \frac{2a}{a^2+b^2}$$

Since a and b are real, this fraction must also be real. (Remember that $z \neq 0$.)

You could also do this without writing $z = a + bi$:

$$\frac{1}{z} + \frac{1}{\overline{z}} = \frac{z + \overline{z}}{z\overline{z}}$$

Then, use previous results that establish that the sum and product of conjugates is always real.

3A MATHEMATICAL REFLECTIONS

1. Factor the left side as the difference of squares.

$$(x^2 - 11)(x^2 + 11) = 0$$

From this you can conclude that either $x^2 - 11 = 0$ or $x^2 + 11 = 0$. If $x^2 - 11 = 0$, the expression on the left can be factored as

$$(x - \sqrt{11})(x + \sqrt{11}) = 0$$

which gives you the solutions $x = \pm\sqrt{11}$. If $x^2 + 11 = 0$, the expression on the left can be factored as

$$(x - i\sqrt{11})(x + i\sqrt{11}) = 0$$

which gives you the solutions $x = \pm i\sqrt{11}$.

(a) There are no solutions in $\mathbb{N}$.
(b) There are no solutions in $\mathbb{Z}$.
(c) There are no solutions in $\mathbb{Q}$.
(d) The real solutions are $x = \sqrt{11}$ and $-\sqrt{11}$.
(e) The nonreal solutions are $x = i\sqrt{11}$ and $-i\sqrt{11}$.

2. (a) Use the quadratic formula.

$$x = \frac{-(-4) \pm \sqrt{(-4)^2 - 4(1)(13)}}{2(1)}$$

$$= \frac{4 \pm \sqrt{16 - 52}}{2}$$

$$= \frac{4 \pm 6i}{2}$$

$$= 2 \pm 3i$$

The roots are $2 + 3i$ and $2 - 3i$.

(b) Either read off the sum (4) from the coefficients of the original polynomial, or calculate $(2 + 3i) + (2 - 3i) = 4$.

(c) Either read off the product (13) from the coefficients of the original polynomial, or calculate $(2 + 3i)(2 - 3i) = 4 + 9 = 13$.

(d) You can use the identity $a^2 + b^2 = (a+b)^2 - 2ab$ to find the sum of the squares of the roots r and s from their sum and product, $r^2 + s^2 = (4)^2 - 2(13) = -10$. Or you can compute it directly from the two roots. $(2+3i)^2 + (2-3i)^2 = 4 + 12i - 9 + 4 - 12i - 9 = -10$.

3. Factor the polynomial as the difference of two cubes.

$$x^3 - 64 = (x - 4)(x^2 + 4x + 16)$$

The first factor gives you one solution: $x = 4$. Then you can use the quadratic formula on the other factor.

$$x = \frac{-4 \pm \sqrt{(4)^2 - 4(1)(16)}}{2(1)}$$

$$= \frac{-4 \pm \sqrt{-48}}{2}$$

$$= \frac{-4 \pm 4i\sqrt{3}}{2}$$

$$= -2 + 2i\sqrt{3}, -2 - 2i\sqrt{3}$$

4. (a) Starting with $z + (4 - 3i) = 6 + 8i$, subtract 4 from both sides and add $3i$ to both sides to get $z = 2 + 11i$.

(b) To solve $z \cdot (4 - 3i) = 6 + 8i$, substitute $a + bi$ for z and multiply everything out.

$$(a + bi)(4 - 3i) = 6 + 8i$$

$$4a - 3ai + 4bi + 3b = 6 + 8i$$

$$(4a + 3b) + (-3a + 4b)i = 6 + 8i$$

This gives you a system of two equations in two unknowns:

$$4a + 3b = 6$$
$$-3a + 4b = 8$$

One way to solve this is to multiply the first equation by 3 and the second by 4.

$$12a + 9b = 18$$
$$-12a + 16b = 32$$

Add the two equations to get $25b = 50$, which tells you that $b = 2$. Substituting this into either of the original equations gives you $a = 0$, so the complex number you want is $z = 2i$.

You could also have solved this by thinking of the original equation as $z = \frac{6+8i}{4-3i}$. Multiply the top and bottom of this fraction by the conjugate of the denominator to get

$$z = \frac{6+8i}{4-3i} \cdot \frac{4+3i}{4+3i}$$

$$= \frac{24 + 18i + 32i - 24}{16 + 9}$$

$$= \frac{50i}{25}$$

$$= 2i$$

5. $\bar{z} = 2 + 5i$ and $\bar{w} = -3 - 7i$. $(\bar{z})(\bar{w}) =$
$(2 + 5i)(-3 - 7i) = -6 - 14i - 15i + 35 = 29 - 29i$;
$zw = (2-5i)(-3+7i) = -6+14i+15i+35 = 29+29i$
The conjugate of this product is $29 - 29i$ which is the
same as the product of the conjugates.

6. The complex numbers, $\mathbb{C}$, is the set of all numbers
$a + bi$ where a and b are real numbers and $i = \sqrt{-1}$.

7. There are several ways to approach this problem. One
way is to use the relationship between the coefficients of
a quadratic equation and the sum and product of its
solutions to realize that the two numbers you're looking
for must be the solutions to the quadratic equation

$$x^2 - 20x + 109 = 0$$

Use the quadratic formula to find $x = \frac{20 \pm \sqrt{400-436}}{2} = 10 \pm 3i$.

Another way is to realize that in the real numbers, the
maximum product for two numbers with a sum of 20 is
100, so these two solutions must be a complex conjugate
pair. $(a + bi) + (a - bi) = 20$, so $2a = 20$, and $a = 10$.
$(a + bi)(a - bi) = a^2 + b^2 = 100 + b^2 = 109$, so
$b^2 = 9$ and $b = 3$. Then you see that the two numbers are
$10 + 3i$ and $10 - 3i$.

8. You can use the quadratic formula to solve any quadratic
equation $ax^2 + bx + c = 0$, but when the discriminant,
$b^2 - 4ac$, is negative, there is no real solution to the
equation. However, since square roots of negative
numbers are possible in the complex numbers, you don't
have to throw out solutions which have them, and you
will find solutions to every quadratic equation.

- If $b^2 - 4ac > 0$, there are two real solutions.
- If $b^2 - 4ac = 0$, there is one real solution. (The
  quadratic is a perfect square.)
- If $b^2 - 4ac < 0$, there are two solutions in the
  complex numbers with a non-zero imaginary part.

INVESTIGATION 3B   THE COMPLEX PLANE

3.6   Getting Started

For You to Explore

1. (a) One explanation is that $\overline{OA}$ is horizontal and $\overline{AB}$ is
vertical, so angle OAB is right. Another is to check
the side lengths and see that they satisfy the
Pythagorean Theorem.

(b) Use the distance formula. The length of OB is

$$\sqrt{3^2 + 4^2} = \sqrt{25} = 5$$

(c) Since this is a right triangle, angles B and O are
complementary. The measures of these angles sum to
90 degrees, so angle O's measure is

$$90 - 53.13 \approx 36.87$$

(d) The calculator's result is 36.87.

2. (a) Measure each length using the distance formula.

$$OP = \sqrt{1^2 + \sqrt{3}^2} = 2$$
$$PQ = \sqrt{0^2 + 2^2} = 2$$
$$OQ = \sqrt{1^2 + \sqrt{3}^2} = 2$$

All three sides have the same length, 2.

(b) Since this is an equilateral triangle, each angle
measures 60 degrees. The marked angle is half of
this, since the axis is a median (and an angle bisector)
in this triangle. The marked angle measures
30 degrees.

3. (a) The slope is the change in y divided by the change in
x, which is $\frac{24}{7}$.

(b) The distance formula can be used to find the length of
the segment. $\sqrt{(7 - 0)^2 + (24 - 0)^2} = \sqrt{49 + 576} = \sqrt{625} = 25$

(c) Answers will vary. A reasonable guess is about 70
degrees, considering the location of the segment.

(d) The calculator gives the result: 73.74 degrees.

4. (a) Use the distance formula to find the length of each
side.

$$AP = \sqrt{3^2 + \sqrt{3}^2} = \sqrt{12}$$
$$PQ = \sqrt{0^2 + (2\sqrt{3})^2} = \sqrt{12}$$
$$AQ = \sqrt{3^2 + \sqrt{3}^2} = \sqrt{12}$$

All three sides have the same length.

(b) One way to do this is to think of the marked angle as
one-third of the full circle around the circumcenter of
the triangle. Since the triangle is equilateral, this
marked angle must be 120 degrees.

Another way is to look at triangle AOP, which is
isosceles. Angle OAP is 30 degrees, since it is half of
angle PAQ (which is 60°). The same is true of angle
APO, so the angle at the circumcenter must be 120
degrees.

5. In each part of this exercise, use the property of the
30-60-90 triangle that the shortest leg (opposite the 30°
angle) is half the hypotenuse, and the longer leg is $\sqrt{3}$
times as long as the shorter leg.

(a) The shortest leg is 5, so the hypotenuse is 10 and the
other leg is $5\sqrt{3}$. The coordinates are $A(5, 0)$ and
$B(5, 5\sqrt{3})$.

(b) The shortest leg is 4, so the hypotenuse is 8 and the
other leg is $4\sqrt{3}$. The coordinates are $A(-4\sqrt{3}, 0)$
and $B(-4\sqrt{3}, 4)$.

(c) The hypotenuse is 12, so the shortest leg is 6 and the
other leg is $6\sqrt{3}$. The coordinates are $A(6\sqrt{3}, 0)$ and
$B(6\sqrt{3}, -6)$.

6. If $(1, 0)$ is a vertex, then $(-1, 0)$ must be another. This is
true because $(0, 0)$ is the center of the square.

To find the other vertices, recall that the diagonals in a
square are perpendicular, equal in length, and bisect one
another. The other diagonal must be vertical, and the

other vertices must be one unit from the center (above and below it). The other vertices must be (0, 1) and (0, −1).

On Your Own

7. One way to find these lengths is to draw the horizontal and vertical projections of the line segment, then use the Pythagorean Theorem on the resulting right triangle. The distance formula is based on this same principle.

   (a) The legs measure 4 and 1, and the hypotenuse measures $\sqrt{4^2 + 1^2} = \sqrt{17}$.
   (b) The legs measure 2 and 1, and the hypotenuse measures $\sqrt{2^2 + 1^2} = \sqrt{5}$.
   (c) The legs measure 7 and 6, and the hypotenuse measures $\sqrt{7^2 + 6^2} = \sqrt{85}$.
   (d) The legs measure 3 and 4, and the hypotenuse measures $\sqrt{3^2 + 4^2} = \sqrt{25} = 5$.
   (e) The legs measure 6 and 8, and the hypotenuse measures $\sqrt{6^2 + 8^2} = \sqrt{100} = 10$.
   (f) The legs measure 1 and $\sqrt{3}$, and the hypotenuse measures $\sqrt{1^2 + \sqrt{3}^2} = \sqrt{4} = 2$.

8. Most products are conjugate pairs, so their product is a real number. The only exception is (c).

   (a) 17
   (b) 5
   (c) $(7 + 6i)$
   (d) 85
   (e) 25
   (f) 4

9. For each part, evaluate the tangent of the angle using the appropriate ratio of sidelengths in the right triangle that has the segment as its hypotenuse. (The tangent in each case is equal to the slope of the line segment.) Then use the calculator's inverse tangent ($\tan^{-1}$) button to get an estimate of the angle measure.

   (a) The slope is $\frac{1}{4}$, so the calculation is $\tan^{-1}\frac{1}{4} \approx 14.03$ degrees.
   (b) The slope is $\frac{1}{2}$, so the calculation is $\tan^{-1}\frac{1}{2} \approx 26.57$ degrees.
   (c) The slope is $\frac{6}{7}$, so the calculation is $\tan^{-1}\frac{6}{7} \approx 40.60$ degrees.
   (d) The slope is $\frac{4}{3}$, so the calculation is $\tan^{-1}\frac{4}{3} \approx 53.13$ degrees.

10. In general, the hypotenuse in an isosceles right triangle is $\sqrt{2}$ times as long as either leg. So, either multiply or divide by $\sqrt{2}$, depending on the given information. To express the result of division by $\sqrt{2}$ as a fraction with an integer denominator, multiply the entire fraction by $\frac{\sqrt{2}}{\sqrt{2}}$.

$$\frac{1}{\sqrt{2}} \cdot \frac{\sqrt{2}}{\sqrt{2}} = \frac{\sqrt{2}}{2}$$

   (a) $4\sqrt{2}$
   (b) $10\sqrt{2}$
   (c) $a\sqrt{2}$
   (d) $2\sqrt{2}$
   (e) $5\sqrt{2}$
   (f) $\frac{b}{2}\sqrt{2}$

11. (a) Because the given angle measures 45 degrees, the triangle is an isosceles right triangle. Each leg has length 8, so the coordinates are $A(8, 0)$ and $B(8, 8)$.
    (b) The hypotenuse of this isosceles right triangle has length 12, so each leg has length $\frac{12}{\sqrt{2}} = 6\sqrt{2}$. The coordinates are $A(-6\sqrt{2}, 0)$ and $B(-6\sqrt{2}, -6\sqrt{2})$.

12. This triangle will look exactly like the one in Exercise 4, but will be half as large in each direction. This means that its vertices will have coordinates that are half the coordinates of the other triangle.

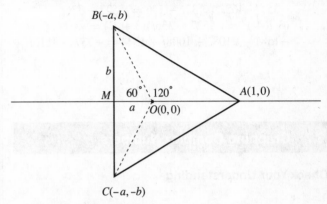

You know that the distance from the circumcenter $O(0, 0)$ to one of the vertices $A(1, 0)$ is 1. This is also the distance from the circumcenter to each of the other vertices. The triangle BOM in the figure is a 30-60-90 triangle with hypotenuse 1. This means that its horizontal leg (opposite the 30 degree angle) measures $a = \frac{1}{2}$, and its vertical leg (opposite the 60 degree angle) measures $b = \frac{\sqrt{3}}{2}$.

The coordinates of the other vertices are $B\left(\frac{-1}{2}, \frac{\sqrt{3}}{2}\right)$ and $C\left(\frac{-1}{2}, \frac{-\sqrt{3}}{2}\right)$.

Maintain Your Skills

13. (a)
$$(-1 + i\sqrt{3})^3 = (-1 + i\sqrt{3})(-1 + i\sqrt{3})^2$$
$$= (-1 + i\sqrt{3})(-2 - 2i\sqrt{3})$$
$$= 2 + 2i\sqrt{3} - 2i\sqrt{3} - 2i^2 \cdot 3$$
$$= 2 + 6 = 8$$

(b)
$$(-1 - i\sqrt{3})^3 = (-1 - i\sqrt{3})(-1 - i\sqrt{3})^2$$
$$= (-1 - i\sqrt{3})(-2 + 2i\sqrt{3})$$
$$= 2 - 2i\sqrt{3} + 2i\sqrt{3} - 2i^2 \cdot 3$$
$$= 2 + 6 = 8$$

(c) $2^3 = 8$
(d) $2(-1 + i\sqrt{3})(-1 - i\sqrt{3}) = 2(1 + i\sqrt{3} - i\sqrt{3} - 3i^2) = 2 \cdot 4 = 8$
(e) $2 + (-1 + i\sqrt{3}) + (-1 - i\sqrt{3}) = (2 - 1 - 1) + (i\sqrt{3} - i\sqrt{3}) = 0$

14. In general, the point (x, y) is mapped to $(-y, x)$.

   (a) $A' = (0, 1)$
   (b) $A' = (1, 0)$
   (c) $A' = (-5, 3)$
   (d) $A' = (1, 6)$

15. (a) $(3 + 4i)^2 = 9 + 12i + 12i - 16 = -7 + 24i$
   (b) $(3 + 4i)^3 = (-7 + 24i)(3 + 4i) = -21 - 28i + 72i - 96 = -117 + 44i$
   (c) $(3 + 4i)^4 = (-117 + 44i)(3 + 4i) = -351 - 468i + 132i - 176 = -527 - 336i$
   (d) $(3 + 4i)^5 = (-527 - 336i)(3 + 4i) = -1581 - 2108i - 1008i + 1344 = -237 - 3116i$

3.7 Graphing Complex Numbers

Check Your Understanding

1.

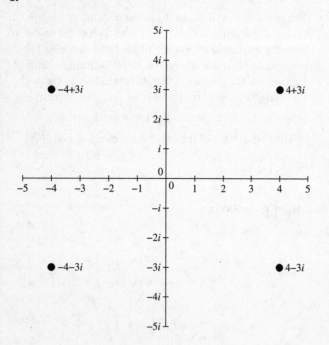

2. (a) In Quadrant I, a and b are both positive.
   (b) In Quadrant II, a is negative and b is positive.
   (c) In Quadrant III, a and b are both negative.
   (d) In Quadrant IV, a is positive and b is negative.

3. (a) The equation can be written as $x^2 - 4x + 13 = 0$. Then use the quadratic formula:

$$x = \frac{4 \pm \sqrt{4^2 - 4 \cdot 13}}{2} = \frac{4 \pm \sqrt{-36}}{2} = \frac{4 \pm 6i}{2} = 2 \pm 3i$$

The two solutions are $2 + 3i$ and $2 - 3i$.

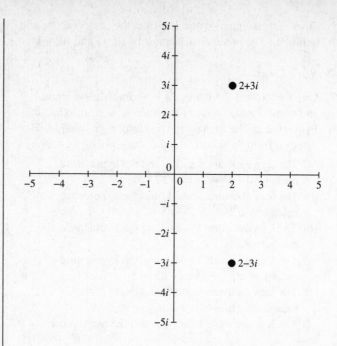

   (b) The sum is $(2 + 3i) + (2 - 3i) = 4$ and the product is $(2 + 3i)(2 - 3i) = 4 - 9i^2 = 13$. Note that these could be found by using the original quadratic's sum and product properties.

4. (a) $x^3 - 8 = (x - 2)(x^2 + 2x + 4)$. Then $x = 2$ or $x^2 + 2x + 4 = 0$ gives the solutions $x = -1 \pm i\sqrt{3}$.

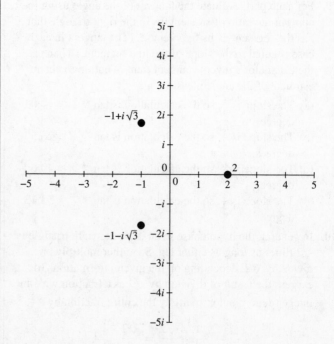

   (b) Look at the diagram in Exercise 4 of Lesson 3.6; the points here are the same as the ones there, except in the complex plane. So, the triangle is equilateral. Alternately, calculate the distance between the points: each distance is $2\sqrt{3}$.

(c) The sum is $2 + (-1 + i\sqrt{3}) + (-1 - i\sqrt{3}) = 0$. The product is $2(-1 + i\sqrt{3})(-1 - i\sqrt{3}) =$
$2(1 - 3i^2) = 2 \cdot 4 = 8$.

5. There is more than one possible answer. One answer is $1 + i$, $1 - i$, $-1 + i$, and $-1 - i$:

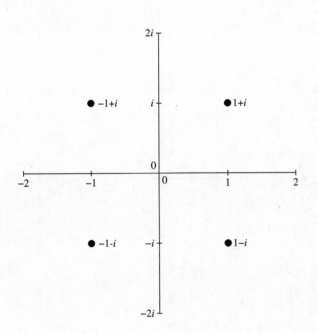

Another is 1, i, -1, and $-i$.

6.

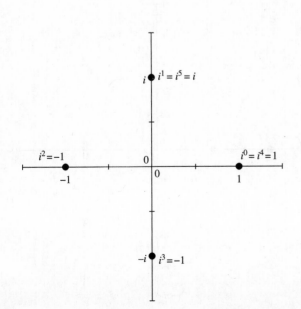

7.

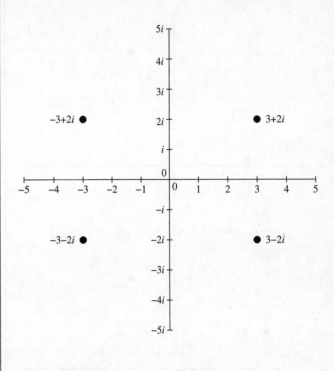

8.

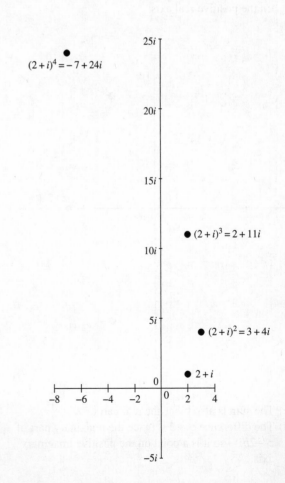

9. (a) The graph of $a + bi$ will be in Quadrant I, and the graph of $a - bi$ will be in Quadrant IV:

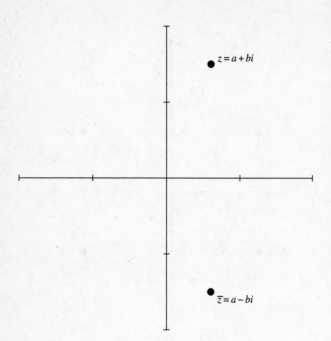

The conjugate is the image of the original point after reflection over the real axis.

(b) The sum $z + \bar{z} = (a + bi) + (a - bi) = 2a$, so it lies on the positive real axis:

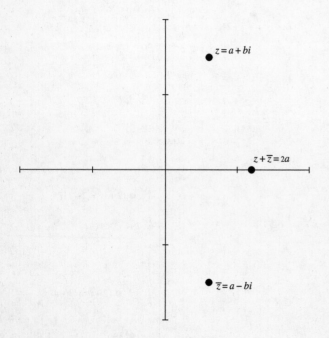

(c) The sum is also twice the real part of z.

(d) The difference $z - \bar{z}$ is twice the imaginary part of z—$2bi$—so it is a point on the positive imaginary axis.

10. Use factoring or the quadratic formula to find the roots.

(a)

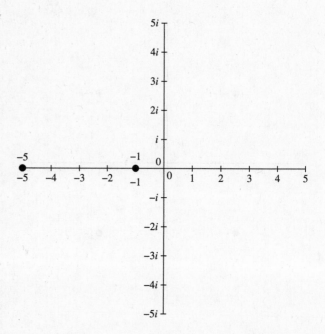

(b)

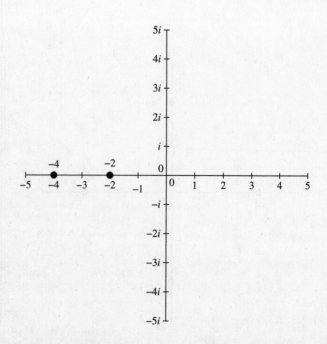

(c)

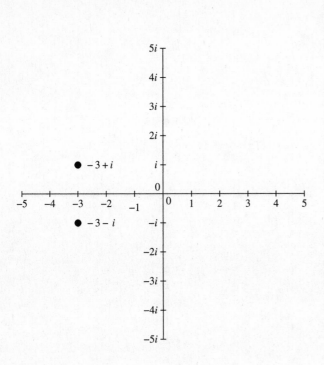

(d)

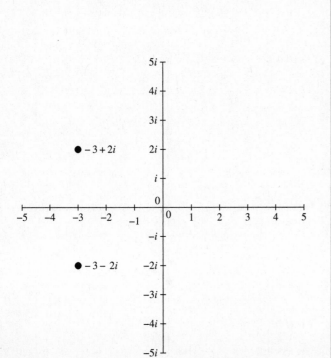

(e)

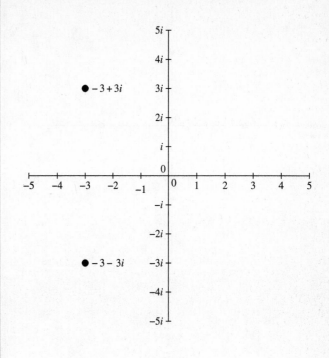

11. Use factoring to find the roots.

(a) $x^4 - 1 = (x^2 + 1)(x^2 - 1)$. The first factor leads to $x^2 = -1$ and the roots $x = \pm i$, and the second leads to $x^2 = 1$ and the roots $x = \pm 1$:

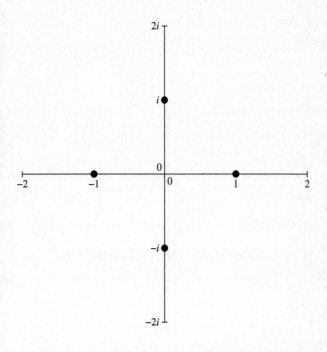

(b) $x^4 - 16 = (x^2 + 4)(x^2 - 4)$. The first factor leads to $x^2 = -4$ and the roots $x = \pm 2i$, and the second leads to $x^2 = 4$ and the roots $x = \pm 2$:

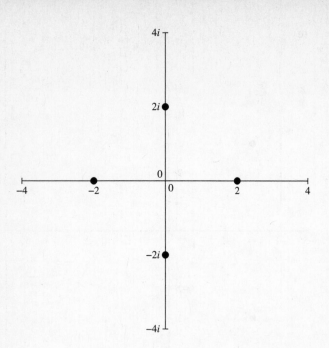

(d) $x^4 - 256 = (x^2 + 16)(x^2 - 16)$. The first factor leads to $x^2 = -16$ and the roots $x = \pm 4i$, and the second leads to $x^2 = 16$ and the roots $x = \pm 4$:

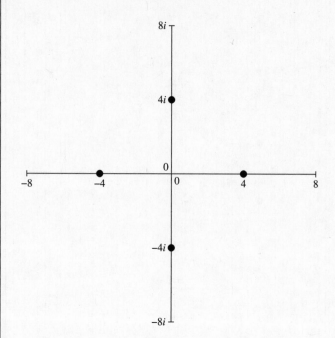

(c) $x^4 - 81 = (x^2 + 9)(x^2 - 9)$. The first factor leads to $x^2 = -9$ and the roots $x = \pm 3i$, and the second leads to $x^2 = 9$ and the roots $x = \pm 3$:

12.

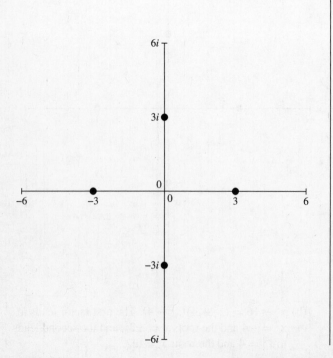

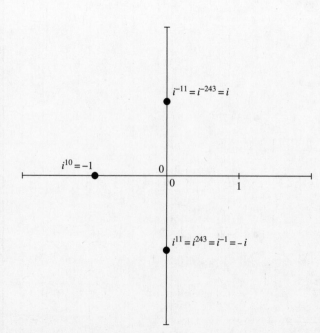

13. (a) $w = 2 - i$, $2w = 4 - 2i$, and $3w = 6 - 3i$:

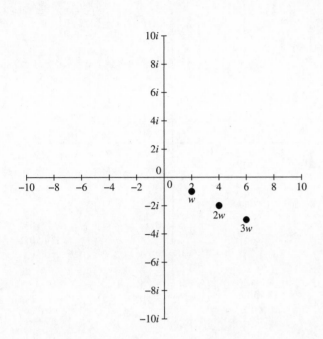

(c) $\overline{w} = 2 + i$, $\overline{2w} = 4 + 2i$, and $\overline{3w} = 6 + 3i$:

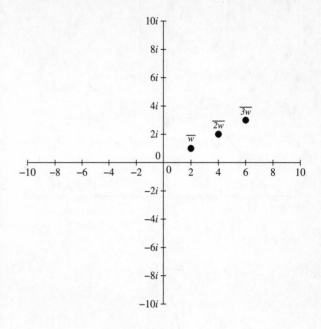

(d) $\overline{z + w} = 5$, $\overline{z + 2w} = 7 + i$, and $\overline{z + 3w} = 9 + 2i$:

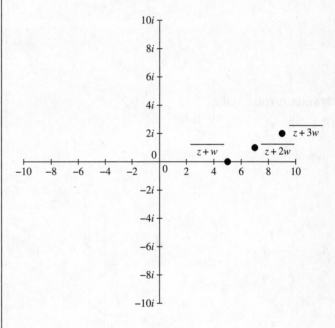

(b) $z + w = 5$, $z + 2w = 7 - i$, and $z + 3w = 9 - 2i$:

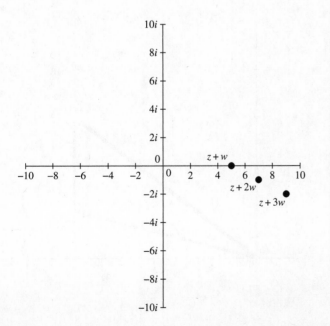

14.

$$zw = (5 + i)(4 - i) = 21 - i$$
$$w^2 = (4 - i)(4 - i) = 15 - 8i$$
$$\overline{z} = 5 - i$$
$$3z + 2w = 15 + 3i + 8 - 2i = 23 + i$$

The correct answer choice is **D**.

15 One key here is that $z^2 = i$. Then $z^3 = i \cdot z$, and $z^4 = i^2 = -1$.

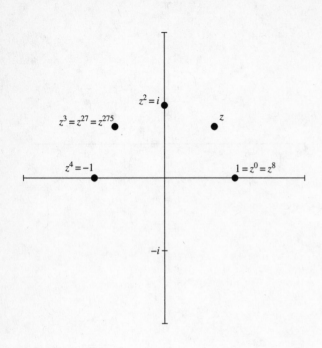

17.

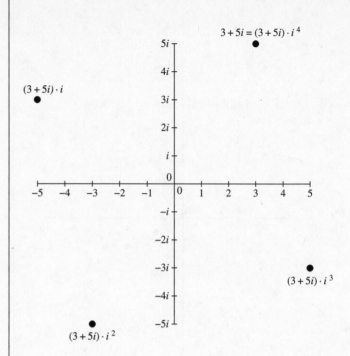

Check Your Understanding

1. (a)

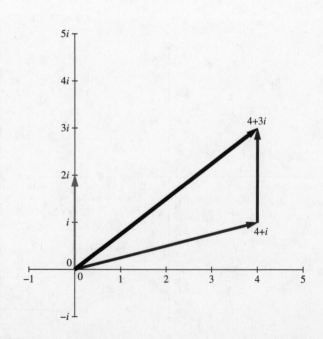

Maintain Your Skills

16.

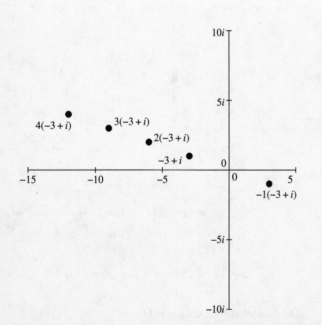

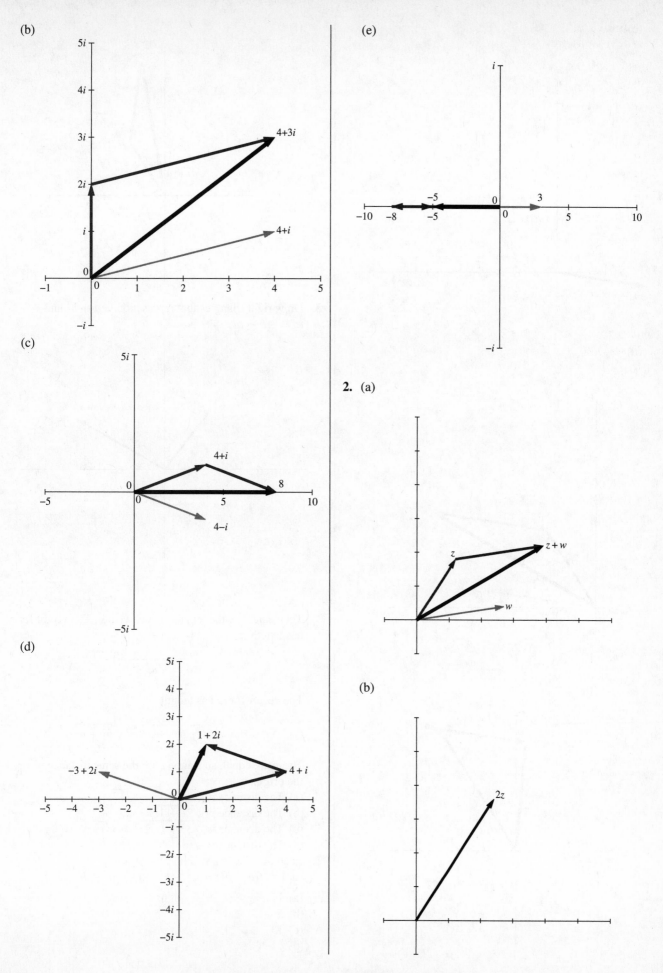

(c)

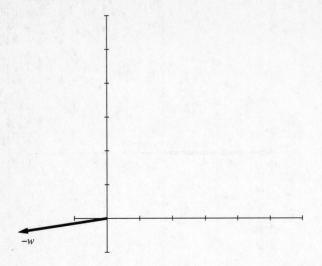

(d)

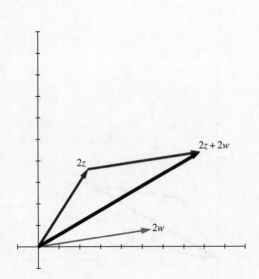

(e)

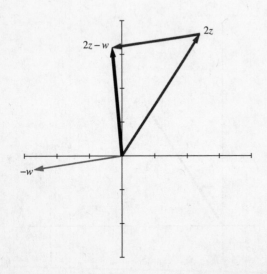

(f)

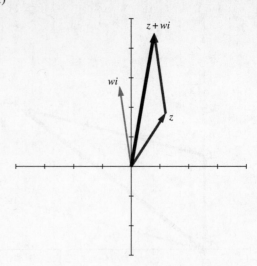

3. Draw right triangles that represent $z = a + bi$ and $iz = -b + ai$:

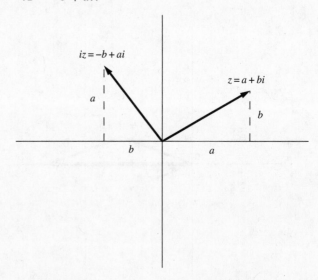

Then calculate the length of each vector. The vector for z has length

$$d = \sqrt{a^2 + b^2}$$

The vector for iz has length

$$d = \sqrt{(-b)^2 + a^2} = \sqrt{b^2 + a^2}$$

These are equal, so z and iz are the same distance from the origin.

4. (a) The distance is $\sqrt{4^2 + 1^2} = \sqrt{17}$.
  (b) The distance is $\sqrt{2^2 + 1^2} = \sqrt{5}$.
  (c) The distance is $\sqrt{3^2 + (-2)^2} = \sqrt{13}$.
  (d) The distance is $\sqrt{6^2 + 5^2} = \sqrt{61}$.

5. Each of these is a special case of
  $(a + bi)(a - bi) = a^2 - b^2(-1) = a^2 + b^2$.

  (a) 17
  (b) 5
  (c) 13
  (d) 61

6. (a) Calculate the distance between each pair of vertices. The distances are

$$\sqrt{33^2 + 56^2} = \sqrt{4225} = 65$$

$$\sqrt{15^2 + 8^2} = \sqrt{289} = 17$$

$$\sqrt{48^2 + 64^2} = \sqrt{6400} = 80$$

(b) The new vertices are $18 - 49i, -15 + 7i, -30 + 15i$. Here is a graph of the original triangle and the triangle formed by multiplying each vertex by -1:

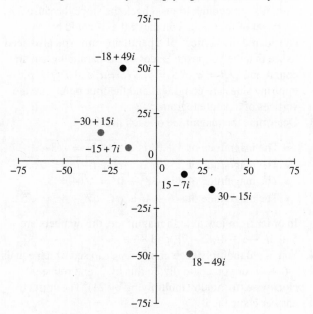

The triangle is rotated 180 degrees.

(c) The new vertices are $-49 - 18i, 7 + 15i, 15 + 30i$. Here is a graph of the original triangle and the triangle formed by multiplying each vertex by i:

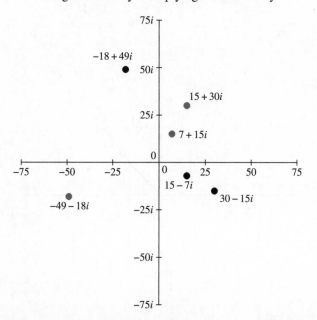

The triangle is rotated 90 degrees.

7. (a) The numbers are $z = 3 + 2i$ and $iz = -2 + 3i$:

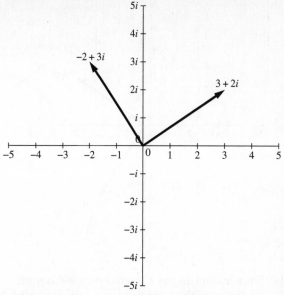

(b) The numbers are $z = -1 + 4i$ and $iz = -4 - i$:

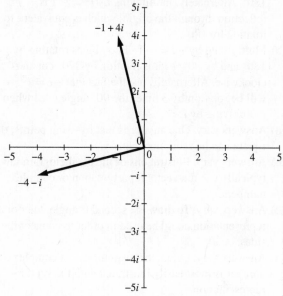

(c) The numbers are $z = -1 - 3i$ and $iz = 3 - i$:

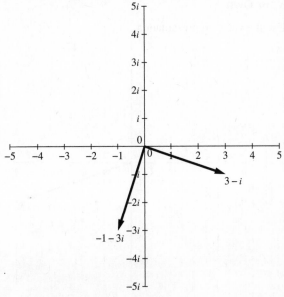

(d) The numbers are $z = 2 - 3i$ and $iz = 3 + 2i$:

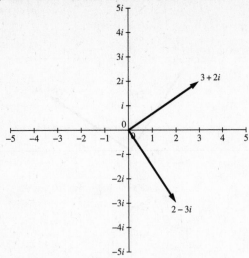

8. (a) Since multiplying by i is rotation by 90° counter-clockwise, multiplying by $i^2 = i \cdot i$ is rotation by 180°. Alternately, multiplying by $i^2 = -1$ is reflection through the origin, which is equivalent to a rotation by 180°.

   (b) Multiplying by $-i = -1 \cdot i$ combines rotating by 180° and by 90°, so it is rotation by 270° counter-clockwise. Alternately, use the fact that $-i = i^3$, so it will be rotation by 3 times the 90° angle used when multiplying by i.

9. (a) Answers vary. One answer is that by using points, the square can be seen more clearly.

   (b) Answers vary. Illustrations of the parallelogram law typically use the vector representation of complex numbers.

   (c) Answers vary. To draw the second triangle, the point representation could be used in order to connect the sides.

   (d) Answers vary. Often, the magnitude of a complex number is most easily illustrated with the vector representation.

On Your Own

10. Use the vector representation.

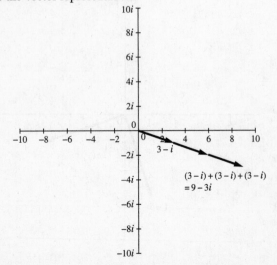

11. (a) The magnitude of $3 + i$ is $\sqrt{3^2 + 1^2} = \sqrt{10}$.

    (b) The magnitude of $4 - i$ is $\sqrt{4^2 + (-1)^2} = \sqrt{17}$.

    (c) The product is $(3 + i)(4 - i) = 13 + i$. The magnitude of $13 + i$ is $\sqrt{13^2 + 1^2} = \sqrt{170}$.

    (d) The calculation gives $(2 + i)^2 = 3 + 4i$. The magnitude of $3 + 4i$ is $\sqrt{3^2 + 4^2} = \sqrt{25} = 5$.

    (e) The calculation gives $(2 + i)^3 = 2 + 11i$. The magnitude of $2 + 11i$ is $\sqrt{2^2 + 11^2} = \sqrt{125} = 5\sqrt{5}$.

12. If you use the Parallelogram Theorem on two real numbers, the four "vertices" of the parallelogram $QRST$ all lie on the real axis, at $Q(0, 0)$, $R(a, 0)$, $S(a + b, 0)$, and $T(b, 0)$. Since these points are all on the real axis, the slope between any pair of them is 0. But in this strange case, it's not enough to just check the slope, because not every set of four points on the real axis could be considered the vertices of a parallelogram. You also need to see that the "opposite" sides of the parallelogram are congruent. $QR = a$, $RS = b$, $ST = a$, and $TQ = b$, so opposite sides are congruent and the four points are the vertices of a parallelogram.

13. Determine the magnitude of each number:

    - The magnitude of $5 + 3i$ is $\sqrt{5^2 + 3^2} = \sqrt{34}$.
    - The magnitude of $2 - 7i$ is $\sqrt{2^2 + (-7)^2} = \sqrt{53}$.
    - The magnitude of 8 is $\sqrt{8^2 + 0^2} = \sqrt{64} = 8$.
    - The magnitude of $-6 + 4i$ is $\sqrt{(-6)^2 + 4^2} = \sqrt{52}$.

    In order from low to high magnitude, the numbers are $5 + 3i$, $-6 + 4i$, $2 - 7i$, and 8.

14. You could multiply each choice by $2i$ to see which equals $-6 + 4i$, or you could divide this by 2, and rotate 90° clockwise (to "undo" multiplying by 21). The correct answer choice is **B**.

15. (a) $(1 + i) \cdot z = i\sqrt{2}$

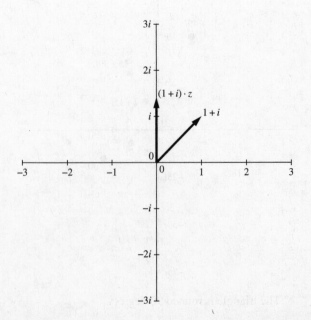

(b) $(3 + 5i) \cdot z = -\sqrt{2} + 4i\sqrt{2}$

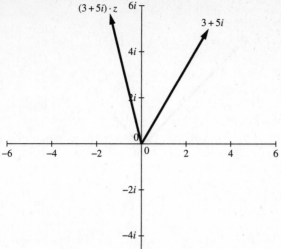

(c) $(-2 + i) \cdot z = -\frac{3\sqrt{2}}{2} - \frac{\sqrt{2}}{2}i$

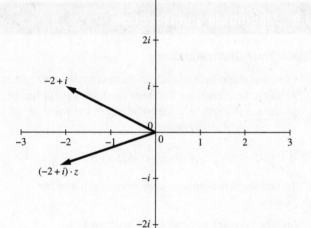

(d) $(-3 - 4i) \cdot z = \frac{\sqrt{2}}{2} - \frac{7\sqrt{2}}{2}i$

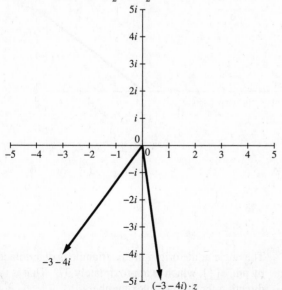

16. (a) The magnitude is unchanged, but there is a rotation of 45° counterclockwise. This seems to happen with each example in Exercise 15.

(b) Multiplying by z is a rotation of 45°, so multiplying by $z^2 = z \cdot z$ is a rotation of 45° *twice*. That's a rotation of 90°.　Alternately, note that $z^2 = i$ by calculation, so this multiplication should lead to a rotation by 90°. There is no change in magnitude.

Maintain Your Skills

17. All solutions use difference of cubes factoring.

(a) $x^3 - 1 = (x - 1)(x^2 + x + 1)$. The real solution is $x = 1$, and the quadratic leads to the complex roots

$$x = \frac{-1}{2} \pm \frac{\sqrt{3}}{2}i$$

(b) $x^3 - 8 = (x - 2)(x^2 + 2x + 4)$. The real solution is $x = 2$, and the quadratic leads to the complex roots

$$x = -1 \pm i\sqrt{3}$$

(c) $x^3 = 27$ leads to $x^3 - 27 = 0$. Use factoring: $x^3 - 27 = (x - 3)(x^2 + 3x + 9)$. The real solution is $x = 3$, and the quadratic leads to the complex roots

$$x = \frac{-3}{2} \pm \frac{3\sqrt{3}}{2}i$$

(d) $x^3 = 64$ leads to $x^3 - 64 = 0$. Use factoring: $x^3 - 64 = (x - 4)(x^2 + 4x + 16)$. The real solution is $x = 4$, and the quadratic leads to the complex roots

$$x = -2 \pm 2i\sqrt{3}$$

(e) There is more than one possible answer, but using the pattern in this exercise leads to the cubic equation $x^3 - 512 = 0$, which has roots $x = 8$ and $x = -4 \pm 4i\sqrt{3}$.

18. (a) $zw = -1 + 7i$

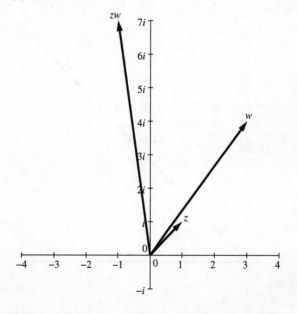

(b) $zw = -7 + i$

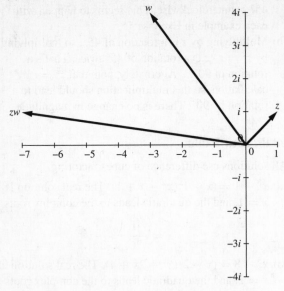

(c) $zw = -17 + 7i$

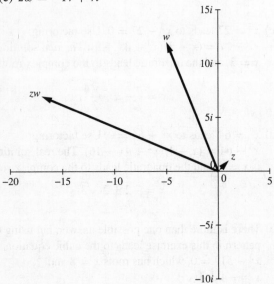

(d) $zw = 7 + 7i$

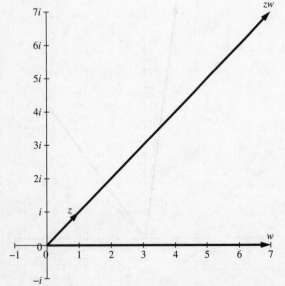

(e) $zw = -3 + 3i$

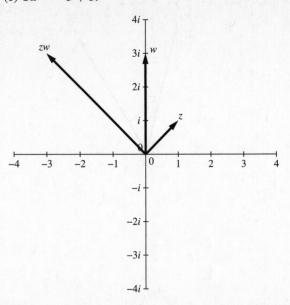

Check Your Understanding

1. First, the magnitude of each of these complex numbers is 5. Since these complex numbers are equal except for the positive and negative values of a and b, the value of $\sqrt{a^2 + b^2}$ will always equal

$$\sqrt{4^2 + 3^2} = \sqrt{25} = 5$$

To find the direction, consider where each number is located.

(a) The complex number is in Quadrant I:

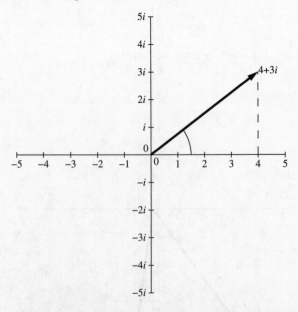

The angle at the origin in this triangle is determined by $\tan^{-1}\left(\frac{3}{4}\right)$, which is approximately $37°$. That is the direction for this complex number.

(b) The complex number is in Quadrant IV:

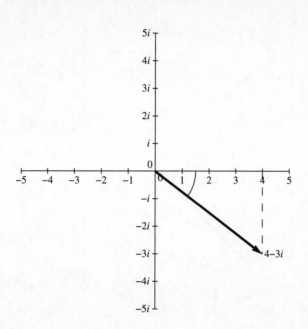

The angle at the origin in this triangle is determined by $\tan^{-1}\left(\frac{3}{4}\right)$, which is approximately 37°. The direction is 360° minus this angle, so the direction is approximately 323°.

(c) The complex number is in Quadrant II:

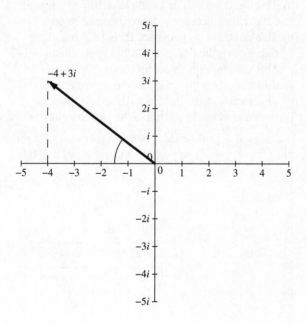

The angle at the origin in this triangle is determined by $\tan^{-1}\left(\frac{3}{4}\right)$, which is approximately 37°. The direction is 180° minus this angle, so the direction is approximately 143°.

(d) The complex number is in Quadrant III:

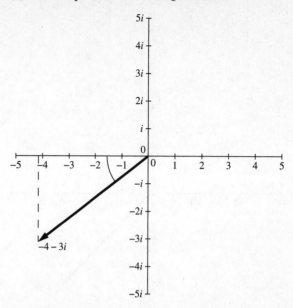

The angle at the origin in this triangle is determined by $\tan^{-1}\left(\frac{3}{4}\right)$, which is approximately 37°. The direction is 180° plus this angle, so the direction is approximately 217°.

2. First, the magnitude of each of these complex numbers is $2\sqrt{2}$. Since these complex numbers are equal except for the positive and negative values of a and b, the value of $\sqrt{a^2 + b^2}$ will always equal

$$\sqrt{2^2 + 2^2} = \sqrt{8} = 2\sqrt{2}$$

To find the direction, consider where each number is located.

(a) The complex number is in Quadrant I:

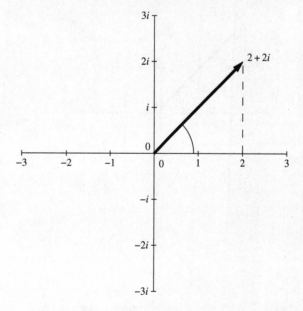

Note that this complex number forms an isosceles right triangle when an altitude is added, so the angle at the origin is exactly 45°. This is the direction angle for $2 + 2i$.

(b) The complex number is in Quadrant IV:

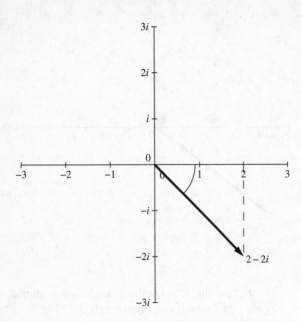

Note that this complex number forms an isosceles right triangle when an altitude is added, so the angle at the origin is exactly 45°. The direction angle for $2 - 2i$ is $360 - 45 = 315°$.

(c) The complex number is in Quadrant II:

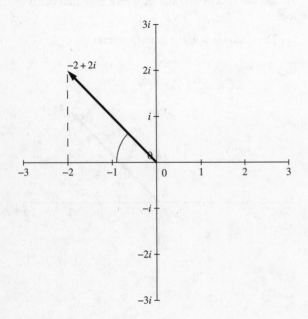

Note that this complex number forms an isosceles right triangle when you include an altitude in the figure, so the angle at the origin is exactly 45°. The direction angle for $-2 + 2i$ is $180 - 45 = 135°$.

(d) The complex number is in Quadrant III:

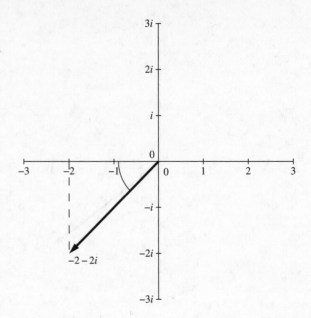

Note that this complex number forms an isosceles right triangle when an altitude is added, so the angle at the origin is exactly 45°. The direction angle for $-2 - 2i$ is $180° + 45° = 225°$.

3. Draw each complex number and estimate the direction.

(a) This direction will be a little less than 45°, say 40°. (The actual measure is approximately 38.66°.

(b) This direction (in Quadrant II) is 180° minus the direction of the first number. So, approximately 140°.

(c) This direction (in Quadrant IV) is 360° minus the direction of the first number. So, approximately 320°.

(d) This direction (in Quadrant III) is 180° plus the direction of the first number. So, approximately 220°.

4. The magnitude is doubled. There are many ways to prove this. One way is to compare the magnitude of $a + bi$ to that of $2a + 2bi$:

$$|a + bi| = \sqrt{a^2 + b^2}$$
$$|2a + 2bi| = \sqrt{(2a)^2 + (2b)^2} = \sqrt{4a^2 + 4b^2}$$
$$= \sqrt{4(a^2 + b^2)} = 2\sqrt{a^2 + b^2}$$

The direction is unchanged. Since the origin and the points (a, b) and $(2a, 2b)$ are collinear, the direction of the complex number $2a + 2bi$ must be the same as that of $a + bi$.

5. Answers will vary. The property is still true when x and y are complex numbers.

6. (a) Here are $z = 2i$ and $z^2 = -4$ on the same axes:

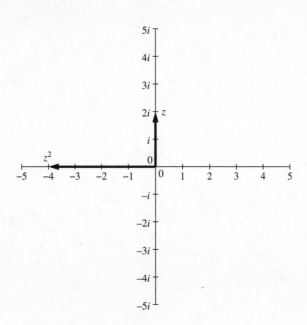

The magnitude of z is 2, and the direction is 90°. The magnitude of z^2 is 4, and the direction is 180°.

(b) Here are $z = -1 + i$ and $z^2 = -2i$ on the same axes:

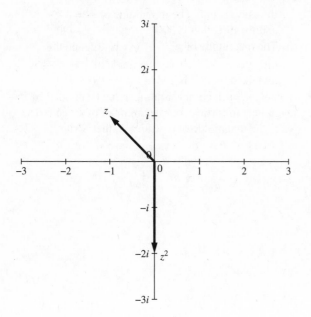

The magnitude of z is $\sqrt{2}$, and the direction is 135°. The magnitude of z^2 is 2, and the direction is 270°.

(c) Here are $z = 4 + i$ and $z^2 = 15 + 8i$ on the same axes:

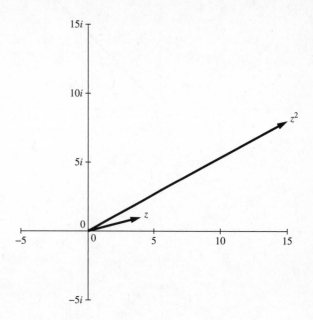

The magnitude of z is $\sqrt{17}$, and the direction is approximately 14°. The magnitude of z^2 is 17, and the direction is approximately 28°.

(d) Here are $z = -4 + i$ and $z^2 = 15 - 8i$ on the same axes:

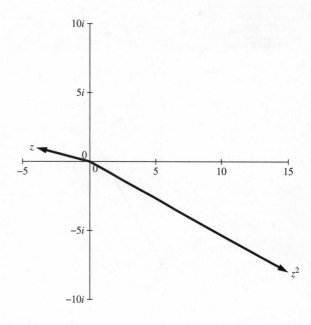

The magnitude of z is $\sqrt{17}$, and the direction is approximately 166°. The magnitude of z^2 is 17, and the direction is approximately 332°.

7. (a)

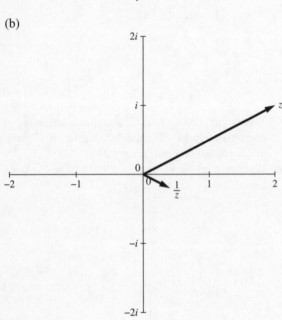

(b)

(c)

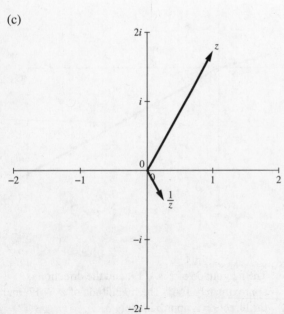

(d)

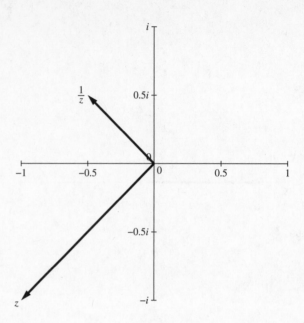

8. (a) The magnitude of $z = 1 + i$ is $\sqrt{2}$, and the direction is $45°$. The magnitude of $\frac{1}{z} = \frac{1-i}{2}$ is $\frac{\sqrt{2}}{2}$ and the direction is $315°$.

(b) The magnitude of $z = 2 + i$ is $\sqrt{5}$, and the direction is approximately $26.6°$. The magnitude of $\frac{1}{z} = \frac{2-i}{5}$ is $\frac{\sqrt{5}}{5}$ and the direction is approximately $333.4°$.

(c) The magnitude of $z = 1 + i\sqrt{3}$ is 2, and the direction is $60°$. The magnitude of $\frac{1}{z} = \frac{1-i\sqrt{3}}{4}$ is $\frac{1}{2}$ and the direction is $300°$.

(d) The magnitude of $z = -1 - i$ is $\sqrt{2}$, and the direction is $225°$. The magnitude of $\frac{1}{z} = \frac{-1+i}{2}$ is $\frac{\sqrt{2}}{2}$ and the direction is $135°$.

9. In general, each complex number can be divided by its magnitude to form a complex number of magnitude 1. So, if the magnitude of $a + bi$ is k, then write $a + bi$ as

$$k \cdot \frac{a + bi}{k} = k \cdot \left(\frac{a}{k} + \frac{b}{k}i \right)$$

(a) $5 \cdot \left(\frac{4}{5} + \frac{3}{5}i \right)$

(b) $13 \left(\frac{5}{13} + \frac{12}{13}i \right)$

(c) $\sqrt{2} \cdot \left(\frac{1}{\sqrt{2}} + \frac{1}{\sqrt{2}}i \right)$

(d) $\sqrt{2} \cdot \left(\frac{1}{\sqrt{2}} - \frac{1}{\sqrt{2}}i \right)$

(e) $\sqrt{13} \cdot \left(\frac{2}{\sqrt{13}} + \frac{3}{\sqrt{13}}i \right)$

(f) $2 \cdot \left(\frac{-1}{2} + \frac{\sqrt{3}}{2}i \right)$

10. Suppose $z = a + bi$ has magnitude k (note $k > 0$). Then we'll show that $\frac{z}{k} = \frac{a}{k} + \frac{b}{k}i$ has magnitude 1:

$$\left|\frac{z}{k}\right| = \sqrt{\left(\frac{a}{k}\right)^2 + \left(\frac{b}{k}\right)^2}$$

$$= \sqrt{\frac{a^2}{k^2} + \frac{b^2}{k^2}}$$

$$= \sqrt{\frac{a^2 + b^2}{k^2}}$$

$$= \frac{\sqrt{a^2 + b^2}}{k} \qquad = \frac{k}{k} = 1$$

The numerator $\sqrt{a^2 + b^2}$ equals the magnitude k, so this new complex number has magnitude 1.

So any $z = a + bi$ can be written as $z = k\left(\frac{a}{k} + \frac{b}{k}i\right)$, the product of a positive real number and a complex number of magnitude 1.

On Your Own

11. First, the magnitude of each of these complex numbers is $\sqrt{13}$. Since these complex numbers are equal except for the positive and negative values of a and b, the value of $\sqrt{a^2 + b^2}$ will always equal

$$\sqrt{3^2 + 2^2} = \sqrt{13}$$

To find the direction, consider where each number is located.

(a) The complex number is in Quadrant I:

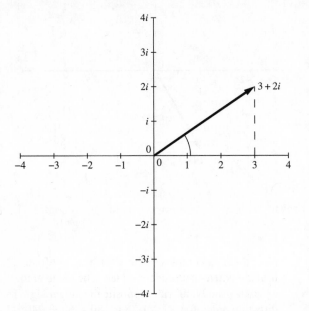

The angle at the origin in this triangle is determined by $\tan^{-1}\left(\frac{2}{3}\right)$, which is approximately $34°$. That is the direction for this complex number.

(b) The complex number is in Quadrant IV:

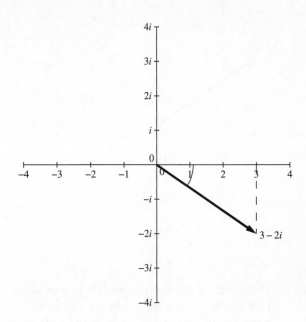

The angle at the origin in this triangle is determined by $\tan^{-1}\left(\frac{2}{3}\right)$, which is approximately $34°$. The direction is $360°$ minus this angle, so the direction is approximately $326°$.

(c) The complex number is in Quadrant III:

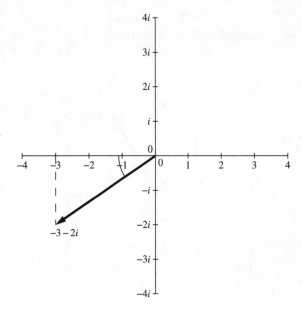

The angle at the origin in this triangle is determined by $\tan^{-1}\left(\frac{2}{3}\right)$, which is approximately $34°$. The direction is $180°$ plus this angle, so the direction is approximately $214°$.

(d) The complex number is in Quadrant II:

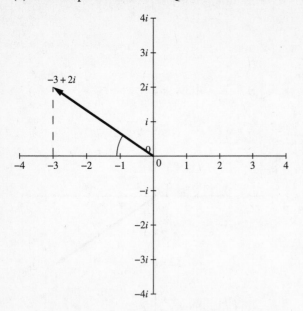

The angle at the origin in this triangle is determined by $\tan^{-1}\left(\frac{2}{3}\right)$, which is approximately 34°. The direction is 180° minus this angle, so the direction is approximately 146°.

12. First, the magnitude of each of the first three complex numbers is 2. Since these complex numbers are equal except for the positive and negative values of a and b, the value of $\sqrt{a^2 + b^2}$ will always equal

$$\sqrt{1^2 + (\sqrt{3})^2} = \sqrt{4} = 2$$

To find the direction, consider where each number is located.

(a) The complex number is in Quadrant I:

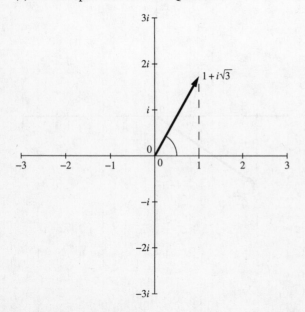

Note that this complex number forms a 30-60-90 triangle when an altitude is added. The angle at the origin is exactly 60° (it is opposite the longer leg). This is the direction angle for $1 + i\sqrt{3}$.

(b) The complex number is in Quadrant IV:

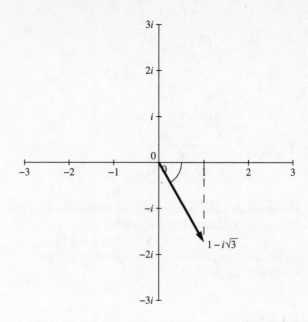

Note that this complex number forms a 30-60-90 triangle when an altitude is added. The angle at the origin is exactly 60° (it is opposite the longer leg). The direction angle for $1 - i\sqrt{3}$ is $360 - 60 = 300°$.

(c) The complex number is in Quadrant III:

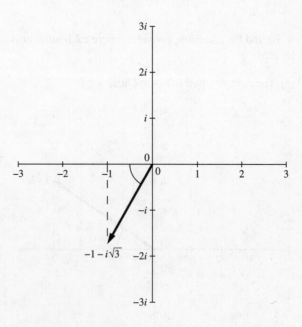

Note that this complex number forms a 30-60-90 triangle when an altitude is added. The angle at the origin is exactly 60° (it is opposite the longer leg). The direction angle for $-1 - i\sqrt{3}$ is $180 + 60 = 240°$.

(d) Calculate the product: $(1 + i\sqrt{3})(1 - i\sqrt{3}) = 1 - 3i^2 = 4$. The number 4 has magnitude 4 and direction 0°, since it lies along the positive real axis.

13. Here's a plot with $-2 + 5i$ and $-2 - 5i$ drawn as vectors:

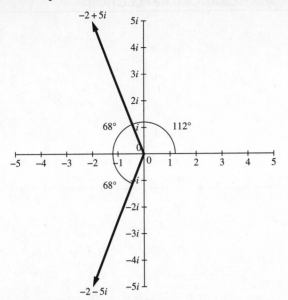

The direction angle for $-2 + 5i$ is $112°$, so the supplementary angle is $68°$. Since $-2 - 5i$ is just as far *below* the axis as $-2 + 5i$ is *above*, the direction for $-2 - 5i$ is

$$112 + 68 + 68 = 248°$$

The correct answer choice is **C**.

14. Here is a graph of z and $\bar{z}$ on the same complex plane:

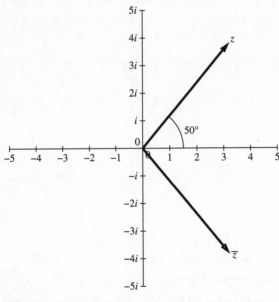

Since $\bar{z}$ is in Quadrant IV, its direction angle is $360 - 50 = 310°$. Alternatively, the angle between $\bar{z}$ and the positive real axis is $50°$, and the direction angle is the entire rest of a $360°$ full rotation. So, the direction is $310°$. The magnitude of $\bar{z}$ is the same as z.

15. Multiplying by i doesn't change the magnitude of a complex number.

Multiplying by i is a rotation of $90°$ counterclockwise, which adds $90°$ to the direction angle. One possible exception is that if the direction angle is already larger than $270°$, then adding $90°$ should include an extra

subtraction of $360°$ for the full rotation. This is optional: it's okay for the direction to be larger than $360°$ (or smaller than $0°$!).

16. Calculate each direction angle using inverse tangent. For $(2 + i)^4 = -7 + 24i$, drop an altitude to find the angle to the axis is $73.74°$, then subtract from $180°$ (because this number is in the second quadrant).

(a) $0°$
(b) $\approx 26.57°$
(c) $\approx 53.13°$
(d) $\approx 79.70°$
(e) $\approx 106.26°$

17. (a) $|z| = \sqrt{2^2 + 1^2} = \sqrt{5}$
   $|w| = \sqrt{3^2 + 1^2} = \sqrt{10}$
   $zw = 5 + 5i$, so $|zw| = \sqrt{5^2 + 5^2} = \sqrt{50} = 5\sqrt{2}$.
(b) $|z| = \sqrt{2^2 + 1^2} = \sqrt{5}$
   $|w| = \sqrt{3^2 + 2^2} = \sqrt{13}$
   $zw = 4 + 7i$, so $|zw| = \sqrt{4^2 + 7^2} = \sqrt{65}$.
(c) $|z| = \sqrt{0^2 + 5^2} = \sqrt{25} = 5$
   $|w| = \sqrt{0^2 + 3^2} = \sqrt{9} = 3$
   $zw = -15$, a real number, so $|zw| = 15$.
(d) $|z| = \sqrt{2^2 + 1^2} = \sqrt{5}$
   $|w| = \sqrt{(\frac{2}{5})^2 + (\frac{-1}{5})^2} = \sqrt{\frac{5}{25}} = \frac{\sqrt{5}}{5}$
   $zw = 1$, a real number, so $|zw| = 1$. Note that in this situation, z and w are reciprocals.

18. (a) The examples suggest that $|z| \cdot |w| = |zw|$.
(b) As you already know from Theorem 3.4,

$$|zw| = \sqrt{zw\,\overline{zw}}$$

Since conjugation is multiplicative (the conjugate of the product is equal to the product of the conjugates), you can rewrite the equation this way:

$$|zw| = \sqrt{zw\,\bar{z}\,\bar{w}}$$

Multiplication is commutative in the complex numbers, so you can collect like factors inside the square root.

$$|zw| = \sqrt{z\bar{z}\,w\bar{w}}$$

You now have the square root of two *real* numbers, because the product of a complex number and its conjugate is always real. Because these two numbers, $z\bar{z}$ and $w\bar{w}$, are real you can use the old real-number theorem, $\sqrt{ab} = \sqrt{a}\sqrt{b}$, to write

$$|zw| = \sqrt{z\bar{z}}\sqrt{w\bar{w}}$$

Now you can use Theorem 3.4 again.

$$|zw| = |z|\,|w|$$

Another way to approach this part of the exercise is to use $z = a + bi$ and $w = c + di$, and crunch out the calculations. First, find $zw = (ac - bd) + (ad + bc)i$. Then,

$$|z| \cdot |w| = \sqrt{a^2 + b^2} \cdot \sqrt{c^2 + d^2}$$
$$= \sqrt{(a^2 + b^2)(c^2 + d^2)}$$
$$= \sqrt{(a^2c^2 + a^2d^2 + b^2c^2 + b^2d^2}$$
$$|zw| = \sqrt{(ac - bd)^2 + (ad + bc)^2}$$
$$= \sqrt{(a^2c^2 - 2abcd + b^2d^2) + (a^2d^2 + 2abcd + b^2c^2)}$$
$$= \sqrt{a^2c^2 + a^2d^2 + b^2c^2 + b^2d^2}$$

The expressions are equal for any choice of the variables, so $|z| \cdot |w| = |zw|$ always.

Maintain Your Skills

19. One way to do this exercise is to use $|z| \cdot |w| = |zw|$, but another is to calculate the squares and then the magnitude.

   (a) $(1 + i)^2 = 2i$, and $\sqrt{0^2 + 2^2} = \sqrt{4} = 2$
   (b) $(2 + i)^2 = 3 + 4i$, and $\sqrt{3^2 + 4^2} = \sqrt{25} = 5$
   (c) $(3 + i)^2 = 8 + 6i$, and $\sqrt{8^2 + 6^2} = \sqrt{100} = 10$
   (d) $(7 + i)^2 = 48 + 14i$, and $\sqrt{48^2 + 14^2} = \sqrt{2500} = 50$
   (e) $(2 + 3i)^2 = -5 + 12i$, and $\sqrt{(-5)^2 + 12^2} = \sqrt{169} = 13$
   (f) In each case, the magnitude is an integer, and the square of the original number's magnitude. So, think of a number with magnitude $\sqrt{29}$. One is $5 + 2i$ (another is $2 + 5i$). Then square it: $(5 + 2i)^2 = 21 + 20i$. This number has magnitude 29.

20. The magnitudes of all the solutions are 1.

   (a) The solutions are $x = 1$ and $x = -1$. The direction of $x = 1$ is $0°$, and the direction of $x = -1$ is $180°$.
   (b) The solutions are $x = 1$, which has direction $0°$, and $x = \frac{-1}{2} \pm \frac{\sqrt{3}}{2}i$. The complex solutions' directions are determined using 30-60-90 triangles.

   For $x = \frac{-1}{2} + \frac{\sqrt{3}}{2}i$, the vector representing this complex number is in Quadrant II. It forms an angle with the negative real axis, which measures $\tan^{-1}\left(\frac{\frac{\sqrt{3}}{2}}{\frac{1}{2}}\right) = \tan^{-1}(\sqrt{3}) = 60°$. This means that the angle from the positive real axis to this vector is $180° - 60° = 120°$, which is the direction of this complex number.

   The situation is similar for $x = \frac{-1}{2} - \frac{\sqrt{3}}{2}i$, except this time the vector is in Quadrant III, so its direction is $180° + 60° = 240°$.
   (c) The solutions are $x = 1$, $x = -1$, and $x = \pm i$. These are the four quadrant angles at 0, 90, 180, and 270 degrees.

3B   MATHEMATICAL REFLECTIONS

1.

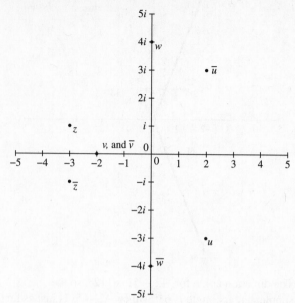

2.

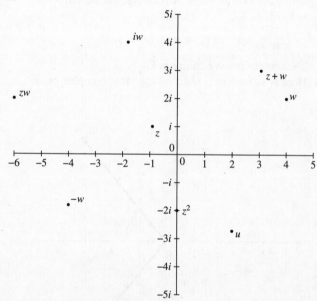

$$z + w = (-1 + 4) + (1 + 2)i = 3 + 3i$$
$$-w = -(4 + 2i) = -4 - 2i$$
$$iw = i(4 + 2i) = 4i - 2 = -2 + 4i$$
$$zw = (-1 + i)(4 + 2i) = -4 - 2i + 4i - 2 = -6 + 2i$$
$$z^2 = (-1 + i)(-1 + i) = 1 - i - i - 1 = -2i$$

3. $z = a + bi$ with a and b real numbers and not both equal to zero. $rz = ra + rbi$. The slope between the points $(0, 0)$ and (a, b) is $\frac{b}{a}$. The slope between $(0, 0)$ and (ra, rb) is $\frac{rb}{ra} = \frac{b}{a}$, so the three points are collinear in the complex plane.

   However, if $a = 0$, the slope between the points $(0, 0)$ and (a, b) is undefined because the line is vertical. In this case, $ra = 0$ too. That slope is also undefined, and the three points are collinear on a vertical line through 0.

Some students may also verify that the slope between the points (a, b) and (ra, rb) is also equal to $\frac{b}{a} \cdot \frac{rb-b}{ra-a} = \frac{(r-1)b}{(r-1)a} = \frac{b}{a}$. Again, you need to consider the case of $a = 0$, but this case also requires considering what to do if $r = 1$, because then when you calculate the slope between the points (a, b) and (ra, rb), you end up with $\frac{0}{0}$. However, this case can be handled by realizing that if $r = 1$, then $(ra, rb) = (a, b)$, so there are really only two points to consider. Any two points define a line, so two points are always collinear.

4. (a) The magnitude of $1 + 2i$ is $\sqrt{1^2 + 2^2} = \sqrt{5}$, and its direction is $\tan^{-1}\left(\frac{2}{1}\right) \approx 63.43°$.

(b) $(1 + 2i)^2 = 1 + 2i + 2i - 4 = -3 + 4i$. The magnitude of $-3 + 4i$ is 5. To find the direction of this number, realize that it is in Quadrant II, so since $\tan^{-1}\left(\frac{4}{3}\right) \approx 53.13°$, the direction of this complex number is approximately $180° - 53.13° = 126.87°$.

(c) $(1 + 2i)^3 = (-3 + 4i)(1 + 2i) = -3 - 6i + 4i - 8 = -11 - 2i$. The magnitude of $-11 - 2i$ is $\sqrt{121 + 4} = \sqrt{125} = 5\sqrt{5}$. To find the direction of $-11 - 2i$, realize that it is in Quadrant III, so since $\tan^{-1}\left(\frac{2}{11}\right) \approx 10.30°$, the direction of this complex number is approximately $180° + 10.30° = 190.30°$.

5. With direction 120°, this number is in Quadrant II of the complex plane. By dropping an altitude from this complex number to the real axis, a 30-60-90 triangle is formed, and its hypotenuse has length 4, the magnitude of the complex number. a is negative, because the number is in Quadrant II, and its absolute value is equal to the length of the horizontal leg of this triangle. Since that leg is opposite the 30° angle of the triangle, it will have length $\frac{4}{2} = 2$. b is positive for this number in Quadrant II, and its absolute value is equal to the length of the vertical leg of this triangle. Since this leg is opposite the 60° angle, it has length $\frac{4\sqrt{3}}{2} = 2\sqrt{3}$. So the number is $-2 + 2\sqrt{3}i$.

6. Answers may vary. Sample answer: You can graph a complex number $z = a + bi$ either as a point (a, b) on the complex plane, or as a vector with tail at 0 and head at (a, b) on the complex plane. The complex plane is a coordinate system where the horizontal axis is the number line for the real numbers, and the vertical axis is the imaginary axis.

7. Answers may vary. Sample answer: The three points 0, (a, b), (c, d) are the three vertices of a parallelogram, and the point $(a + c, b + d)$ is the fourth vertex of the parallelogram. This is the graphical representation of the complex numbers $z = a + bi$, $w = c + di$, and the sum $z + w = (a + c) + (b + d)i$.

8. Answers my vary. Sample answer: If you multiply a complex number $z = a + bi$ by i, the result is $iz = -b + ai$. If you visualize z as a vector, then iz is the image of that vector after a rotation of 90° counterclockwise about the origin. The new vector has the same magnitude, and has a direction that is 90° more than the original.

MID-CHAPTER TEST

1. $\sqrt{-5} \cdot \sqrt{-20} = \sqrt{5} \cdot \sqrt{-1} \cdot \sqrt{20} \cdot \sqrt{-1} = \sqrt{5} \cdot \sqrt{20} \cdot \sqrt{-1} \cdot \sqrt{-1} = \sqrt{5 \cdot 20} \cdot \sqrt{-1} \cdot \sqrt{-1} = \sqrt{100} \cdot (-1) = (10)(-1) = -10$
The correct answer choice is **B**.

2.
$$2(1 + \sqrt{-1}) + 2(-\sqrt{-1}) + (1 + \sqrt{-1})(1 - \sqrt{-1})$$
$$= (2 + 2\sqrt{-1}) + (-2\sqrt{-1}) + (1^2 - (\sqrt{-1})^2)$$
$$= (2+) + (\sqrt{-1} - 2\sqrt{-1}) + (1 - (-1))$$
$$= 2 + 0 + 2$$
$$= 4$$

The correct answer choice is **A**.

3. All of the choices are complex numbers. 2 and 0 are real numbers. $3i^2 = 3(-1) = -3$ is also a real number. Only **C**, $4 - 2i$ is *not* a real number.

4. The magnitude is $\sqrt{a^2 + b^2} = \sqrt{2^2 + 3^2} = \sqrt{4 + 9} = \sqrt{13}$. The correct choice is **B**.

5. $2 + 3i$ makes an angle with the positive real axis that is more than 45° but less than 90°. So, the best estimate is choice **B**, 56.3°.

6. (a) Use the Quadratic Formula to find the roots:
$$x^2 + 2x + 5 = 0$$
$$x = \frac{-2 \pm \sqrt{2^2 - 4(1)(5)}}{2(1)}$$
$$= \frac{-2 \pm \sqrt{-16}}{2}$$
$$= \frac{-2 \pm 4i}{2}$$
$$= -1 \pm 2i$$

(b) $(-1 + 2i) + (-1 - 2i) = -2$. Or, remember the Sum and Product Theorem: $x^2 - (\text{the sum of the roots})x + (\text{the product of the roots}) = 0$ So, $x^2 + 2x + 5 = 0 \longrightarrow x^2 - (-2)x + 5 = 0$. The sum is -2.

(c) The product of the roots is 5 (by the Sum and Product Theorem. Or, you can multiply: $(-1 + 2i)(-1 - 2i) = 1 - 4i^2 = 1 - (-4) = 1 + 4 = 5$.

(d) The sum of the squares of the roots: $r^2 + s^2 = (r + s)^2 - 2rs = (-2)^2 - 2(5) = 4 - 10 = -6$. Or, you can expand: $(-1 + 2i)^2 + (-1 - 2i)^2 = 1 - 4i + 4i^2 + 1 + 4i + 4i^2 = 1 - 4i - 4 + 1 + 4i - 4 = -6$.

7. (a) First factor $x^3 + 27$ as the sum of two cubes:
$$x^3 + 27 = x^3 + 3^3 = (x + 3)(x^2 - 3x + 9)$$

Now solve the equation:
$$x^3 + 27 = 0$$
$$(x + 3)(x^2 - 3x + 9) = 0$$
$$x + 3 = 0 \text{ or } x^2 - 3x + 9 = 0$$

So, $x + 3 = 0 \longrightarrow x = -3$ is one solution. Use the Quadratic Formula to find the other two solutions:

$$x^2 - 3x + 9 = 0$$

$$x = \frac{-(-3) \pm \sqrt{(-3)^2 - 4(1)(9)}}{2(1)}$$

$$= \frac{3 \pm \sqrt{9 - 36}}{2}$$

$$= \frac{3 \pm \sqrt{-27}}{2}$$

$$= \frac{3 \pm \sqrt{9} \cdot \sqrt{-3}}{2}$$

$$= \frac{3 \pm 3\sqrt{-3}}{2}$$

$$= \frac{3 \pm 3\sqrt{3} \cdot i}{2}$$

(b)

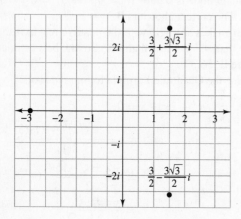

8. (a) $(3 + 4i) + (3 - 4i) = (3 + 3) + (4i - 4i) = 6$
(b) $(3 + 4i) - (3 - 4i) = 3 + 4i - 3 + 4i = 8i$
(c) $(3 + 4i)(3 - 4i) = 9 - 16i^2 = 9 - (16)(-1) = 9 - (-16) = 25$
(d) $\left(\frac{3+4i}{3-4i}\right) \cdot \left(\frac{3+4i}{3+4i}\right) = \frac{9+12i+12i+16i^2}{9-16i^2} = \frac{-7+24i}{25} = -\frac{7}{25} + \frac{24}{25}i$
(e) $\left(\frac{3-4i}{3+4i}\right) \cdot \left(\frac{3-4i}{3-4i}\right) = \frac{9-12i-12i+16i^2}{9-16i^2} = \frac{-7-24i}{25} = -\frac{7}{25} - \frac{24}{25}i$

9. (a)

$$z + (3 - 2i) = 5 - 8i$$

$$z = (5 - 8i) - (3 - 2i)$$

$$= 5 - 8i - 3 + 2i$$

$$= 2 - 6i$$

(b)

$$x^2 = -25$$

$$x = \pm\sqrt{-25}$$

$$= \pm\sqrt{25} \cdot \sqrt{-1}$$

$$= \pm 5i$$

(c)

$$2x^2 + 3x = -5$$

$$2x^2 + 3x + 5 = 0$$

$$x = \frac{-3 \pm \sqrt{3^2 - 4(2)(5)}}{2(2)}$$

$$= \frac{-3 \pm \sqrt{9 - 40}}{4}$$

$$= \frac{-3 \pm \sqrt{-31}}{4}$$

$$= \frac{-3 \pm \sqrt{31} \cdot \sqrt{-1}}{4}$$

$$= \frac{-3 \pm \sqrt{31} \cdot i}{4}$$

(d)

$$z \cdot (3 + i) = 4 - i$$

$$z = \frac{4 - i}{3 + i}$$

$$= \left(\frac{4 - i}{3 + i}\right) \cdot \left(\frac{3 - i}{3 - i}\right)$$

$$= \frac{12 - 4i - 3i + i^2}{9 - i^2}$$

$$= \frac{12 - 7i + (-1)}{9 - (-1)}$$

$$= \frac{11 - 7i}{10}$$

10. (a) $\bar{z} = 1 - \sqrt{3} \cdot i$
(b) $2z = 2(1 + \sqrt{3} \cdot i) = 2 + 2\sqrt{3} \cdot i$
(c) $z^2 = (1 + \sqrt{3} \cdot i)^2 = 1 + 2\sqrt{3} \cdot i + 3i^2 = 1 + 2\sqrt{3} \cdot i + (-3) = -2 + 2\sqrt{3} \cdot i$
(d)

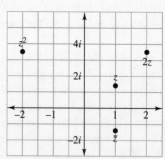

(e) For each of these complex numbers you can use a 30-60-90 triangle to find the direction as well as the magnitude. You can also use $\sqrt{a^2 + b^2}$ to find the magnitude.

	magnitude	direction
z	$\sqrt{1^2 + (\sqrt{3})^2} = \sqrt{1 + 3} = \sqrt{4} = 2$	60°
$\bar{z}$	$\sqrt{1^2 + (-\sqrt{3})^2} = \sqrt{1 + 3} = \sqrt{4} = 2$	300°
$2z$	$\sqrt{2^2 + (2\sqrt{3})^2} = \sqrt{4 + 4 \cdot 3} = \sqrt{16} = 4$	60°
z^2	$\sqrt{(-2)^2 + (2\sqrt{3})^2} = \sqrt{4 + 4 \cdot 3} = \sqrt{16} = 4$	120°

11. The complex numbers, $\mathbb{C}$, is the set of all numbers $a + bi$ where a and b are real numbers and $i = \sqrt{-1}$.

3.10   Getting Started

For You to Explore

1. (a) The magnitude is $\sqrt{3^2 + 1^2} = \sqrt{10}$. For the direction, use $\tan^{-1}\left(\frac{1}{3}\right)$, which is approximately 18.4°.

   (b) The magnitude is $\sqrt{2^2 + 1^2} = \sqrt{5}$. For the direction, use $\tan^{-1}\left(\frac{1}{2}\right)$, which is approximately 26.6°.

   (c) The product is $5 + 5i$. The magnitude is $\sqrt{5^2 + 5^2} = \sqrt{50} = 5\sqrt{2}$. This direction forms a 45° angle with the axis, so the direction is *exactly* 45°.

   (d) The magnitude is $\sqrt{4^2 + 3^2} = \sqrt{25} = 5$. For the direction, use $\tan^{-1}\left(\frac{3}{4}\right)$, which is approximately 36.9°.

   (e) The magnitude is $\sqrt{1^2 + 2^2} = \sqrt{5}$. For the direction, use $\tan^{-1}\left(\frac{2}{1}\right)$, which is approximately 63.4°.

   (f) The product is $-2 + 11i$. The magnitude is $\sqrt{(-2)^2 + 11^2} = \sqrt{125} = 5\sqrt{5}$. The direction angle is in Quadrant II:

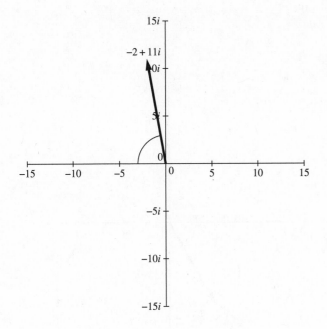

The marked angle is $\tan^{-1}\left(\frac{11}{2}\right)$, which is approximately 79.7°. That means the direction angle is the supplement, which is approximately 100.3°.

2. (a)

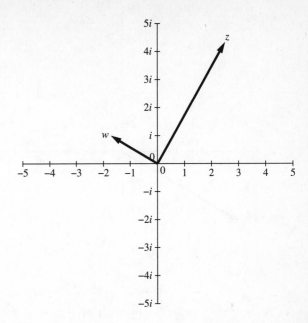

   (b) Answers vary, depending on the accuracy of z and w used. Using the pattern from Exercise 1, the magnitude of zw should be 10 and the direction should be 210°.

   (c) There are two ways to proceed. First, you could find z and w and compute the product zw. By using 30-60-90 triangles,

$$z = \frac{5}{2} + \frac{5\sqrt{3}}{2}i \text{ and } w = -\sqrt{3} + i$$

Then

$$zw = \left(\frac{5}{2} + \frac{5\sqrt{3}}{2}i\right)\left(-\sqrt{3} + i\right)$$

$$= -\frac{5\sqrt{3}}{2} + \frac{5}{2}i - \frac{15}{2}i - \frac{5\sqrt{3}}{2}$$

$$= -\frac{10\sqrt{3}}{2} + \frac{10}{2}i$$

$$= -5\sqrt{3} + 5i$$

The second method is to determine that the magnitude of zw should be 10, and the direction should be 210°. Then a 30-60-90 triangle determines the real and imaginary parts:

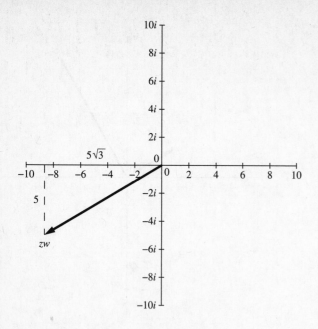

In either case, $zw = -5\sqrt{3} + 5i$.

3. (a)

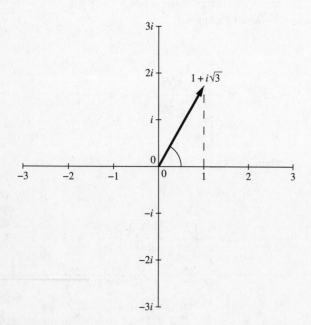

The vector forms a 30-60-90 right triangle, so the direction is 60°.

(b)

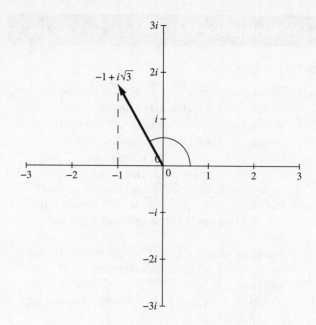

The vector forms a 30-60-90 right triangle, so the direction is $180 - 60 = 120°$.

(c)

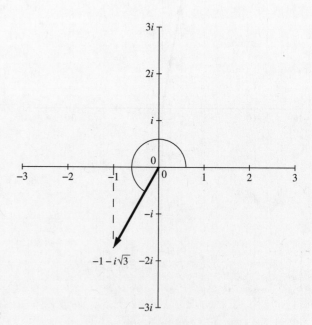

The vector forms a 30-60-90 right triangle, so the direction is $180 + 60 = 240°$.

(d)

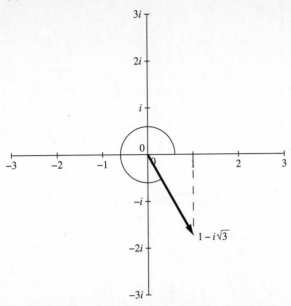

The vector forms a 30-60-90 right triangle, so the direction is $360 - 60 = 300°$.

4. Expand the left side and then factor by grouping.

$$(ac - bd)^2 + (bc + ad)^2 =$$
$$(a^2c^2 - 2abcd + b^2d^2) + (b^2c^2 + 2abcd + a^2d^2) =$$
$$a^2c^2 + b^2d^2 + b^2c^2 + a^2d^2 =$$
$$a^2c^2 + a^2d^2 + b^2c^2 + b^2d^2 =$$
$$a^2(c^2 + d^2) + b^2(c^2 + d^2) =$$
$$(a^2 + b^2)(c^2 + d^2)$$

Other methods are possible, including expanding each side until the expressions are equal.

5. (a) Expand the right side fully:

$$(x - r)(x - s)(x - t) =$$
$$(x - r)(x^2 - sx - tx + st) =$$
$$x(x^2 - sx - tx + st) - r(x^2 - sx - tx + st) =$$
$$x^3 - sx^2 - tx^2 + stx - rx^2 + rsx + rtx - rst =$$
$$x^3 - (r + s + t)x^2 + (rs + rt + st)x - rst$$

(b) Since two polynomials are equal only when each coefficient is equal, the expansion of $(x - r)$ $(x - s)(x - t)$ means that

$$a = -(r + s + t)$$

(c) $b = rs + rt + st$, according to the expansion.

(d) $c = -rst$, according to the expansion.

6. (a) $f(2 + i) = 6 - 7i$ and $f(2 - i) = 6 + 7i$. They are conjugates.

(b) $f(4 + i) = 4 + 13i$ and $f(4 - i) = 4 - 13i$. They are conjugates.

(c) $f(-1 + 3i) = 80$ and $f(-1 + 3i) = 80$. They are conjugates.

(d) $f(3 + i) = 0$, so $f(3 - i) = 0$ (the conjugate).

7. (a) The two numbers satisfy the quadratic equation $x^2 - \frac{-1+\sqrt{5}}{2}x + 1 = 0$. Use the quadratic formula or a calculator with CAS to find the roots. The roots are $x \approx 0.309 + 0.951i$ and $x \approx 0.309 - 0.951i$. As exact answers they are

$$x = \frac{-1 + \sqrt{5}}{4} \pm \frac{\sqrt{10 + 2\sqrt{5}}}{4} i$$

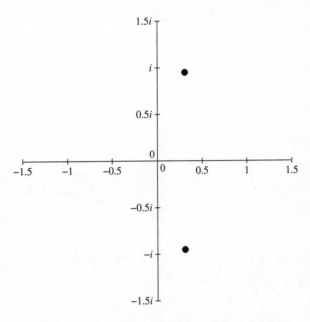

(b) The two numbers satisfy the quadratic equation $x^2 - \frac{-1-\sqrt{5}}{2}x + 1 = 0$. Use the quadratic formula or a calculator with CAS to find the roots. The roots are $x \approx -0.809 + 0.588i$ and $x \approx -0.809 + 0.588i$. As exact answers they are

$$x = \frac{-1 - \sqrt{5}}{4} \pm \frac{\sqrt{10 - 2\sqrt{5}}}{4} i$$

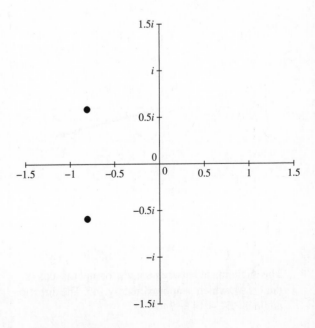

(c) Expand the product of quadratics first:

$$\left(x^2 + \frac{1+\sqrt{5}}{2}x + 1\right)\left(x^2 + \frac{1-\sqrt{5}}{2}x + 1\right)$$
$$= x^4 + x^3 + x^2 + x + 1$$

Then the overall product is $(x-1)(x^4 + x^3 + x^2 + x + 1) = x^5 - 1$. You could also use your CAS to do the expansion.

On Your Own

8. (a)

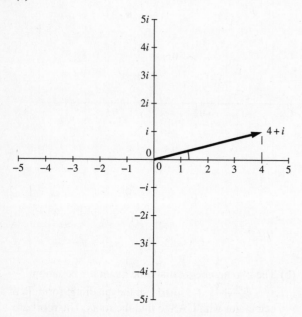

The angle is found by using $\tan^{-1}\left(\frac{1}{4}\right)$, which is approximately $14°$.

(b)

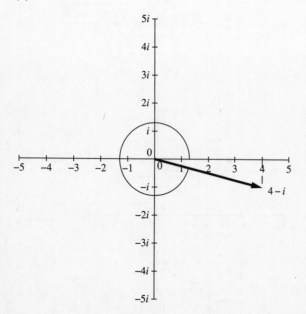

The angle made between the vector and the axis is $\tan^{-1}\left(\frac{1}{4}\right)$, which is approximately $14°$. The direction angle is $360 - 14 = 346°$.

(c)

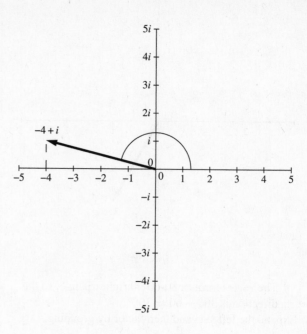

The angle made between the vector and the axis is $\tan^{-1}\left(\frac{1}{4}\right)$, which is approximately $14°$. The direction angle is $180 - 14 = 166°$.

(d)

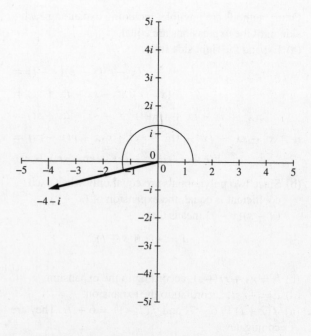

The angle made between the vector and the axis is $\tan^{-1}\left(\frac{1}{4}\right)$, which is approximately $14°$. The direction angle is $180 + 14 = 194°$.

9. (a)

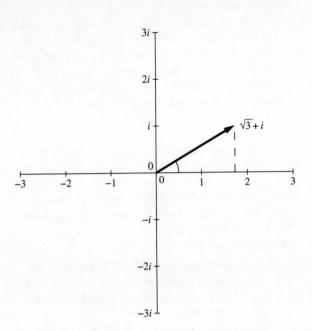

This vector forms a 30-60-90 right triangle, so its direction angle is 30°.

(b)

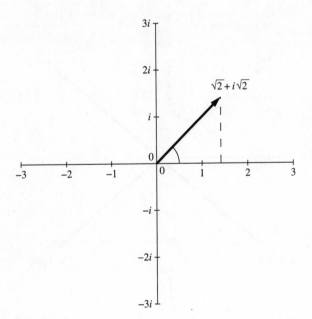

This vector forms a 45-45-90 right triangle, so its direction angle is 45°.

(c)

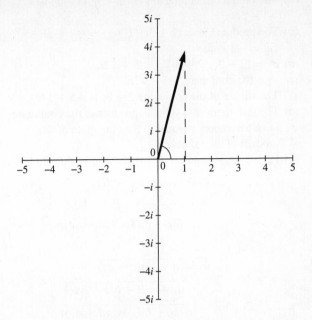

The product is $(\sqrt{6} - \sqrt{2}) + (\sqrt{6} + \sqrt{2})i$. Use a calculator to find

$$\tan^{-1} \frac{\sqrt{6} + \sqrt{2}}{\sqrt{6} - \sqrt{2}} = 75°$$

Alternately, the direction of a product is the sum of the directions, so the direction is $30 + 45 = 75°$.

(d)

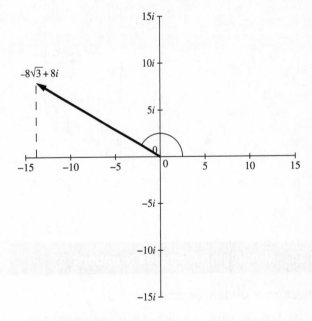

The calculation gives the result $-8\sqrt{3} + 8i$, which forms a 30-60-90 right triangle in Quadrant II. The direction angle is $180 - 30 = 150°$.

Alternately, the direction of a square is twice the direction, so the direction is $2 \cdot 75 = 150°$.

10. (a) The conjugate of $2 + 3i$ is $2 - 3i$.
   (b) The product of conjugates is $(2 - 3i)(1 - i) = -1 - 5i$.
   (c) The product $zw = (2 + 3i)(1 + i) = -1 + 5i$, so $\overline{zw} = -1 - 5i$.
   (d) $z^2 = (2 + 3i)(2 + 3i) = -5 + 12i$.
   (e) $\overline{z^2}$ is the conjugate, $-5 - 12i$.
   (f) The square of the conjugate $2 - 3i$ is $-5 - 12i$.

11. (a) The statement says that the product of the conjugates of two numbers is equal to the conjugate of the product of the numbers.
   (b) Let $z = a + bi$ and $w = c + di$. Then calculate both.

$$\overline{z} \cdot \overline{w} = (a - bi)(c - di)$$
$$= ac - adi - bci + bdi^2$$
$$= (ac - bd) - (ad + bc)i$$

$$\overline{zw} = \overline{(a + bi)(c + di)}$$
$$= \overline{ac + adi + bci + bdi^2}$$
$$= \overline{(ac - bd) + (ad + bc)i}$$
$$= (ac - bd) - (ad + bc)i$$

Therefore, $\overline{z} \cdot \overline{w} = \overline{zw}$.

Maintain Your Skills

12.

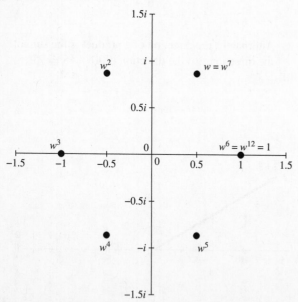

3.11 Multiplying Complex Numbers

Check Your Understanding

1. (a) The magnitude of z^2 is $3 \cdot 3 = 9$, and the direction is $120 + 120 = 240°$. Find this by writing $z^2 = z \cdot z$ and using the multiplication properties.
   (b) The magnitude of z^3 is $3 \cdot 3 \cdot 3 = 27$, and the direction is $120 + 120 + 120 = 360°$, which is the same as $0°$. Find this by writing $z^3 = z \cdot z \cdot z$.

(c) Picture z in the complex plane. You can write this complex number in $a + bi$ form by using the 30-60-90 triangle that it forms with the negative real axis. $z = -\frac{3}{2} + \frac{3\sqrt{3}}{2}i$

To find an equation with integer coefficients that has this complex number as a root, realize that the conjugate must also be a root of any such equation. Then, you can use the sum-product rules for quadratics to find the correct equation. $z + \overline{z} = -3$ and $z \cdot \overline{z} = 9$, so the equation you want is $x^2 + 3x + 9 = 0$. (You can use the quadratic formula to check your work if you like.)

2. For z^2, square the magnitude and double the direction. For z^3, cube the magnitude and triple the direction. In general for z^n, raise the magnitude to the nth power and multiply the direction by n. For example, if z has magnitude 2 and direction $25°$, then z^6 has magnitude $2^6 = 64$ and direction $6 \cdot 25 = 150°$.

3. Take each given z and calculate z^3.
   (a) z^3 would have magnitude $9^3 = 729$ and direction $3 \cdot 60 = 180°$. This doesn't match.
   (b) z^3 would have magnitude $3^3 = 27$ and direction $3 \cdot 60 = 180°$. That's a match.
   (c) z^3 would have magnitude $3^3 = 27$ and direction $3 \cdot 180 = 540°$. That's a match, since $540°$ and $180°$ are the same direction.
   (d) z^3 would have magnitude $3^3 = 27$ and direction $3 \cdot 300 = 900°$. That's a match, since $900°$ and $180°$ are the same direction. $900°$ is two and a half times around; or, $900 - 180 = 720°$, an exact multiple of $360°$.

So, any of (b), (c), or (d) are possible.

4.

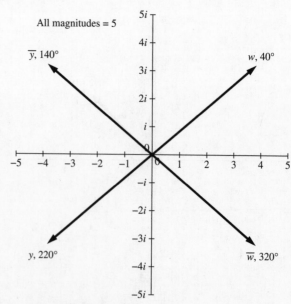

5. (a) The product wx has magnitude $5 \cdot \sqrt{2} = 5\sqrt{2}$. This is because w has magnitude 5 and x has magnitude $\sqrt{2}$.

The product wx has direction $40 + 315 = 355°$. This is because w has direction $40°$ and x has direction $315°$ (in Quadrant IV).

(b) The product yz has magnitude $5 \cdot \sqrt{2} = 5\sqrt{2}$. This is because y has magnitude 5 and z has magnitude $\sqrt{2}$. (Taking the opposite of a complex number does not change its magnitude.)

The product yz has direction $220 + 135 = 355°$. This is because y has direction $220°$ and z has direction $135°$ (in Quadrant II). Taking the opposite of a complex number is a $180°$ rotation, which adds or subtracts $180°$ to the direction angle.

(c) Use the definitions of y and z:

$$yz = (-w)(-x) = -(-wx) = wx$$

6. Answers will vary depending on estimates for the magnitude and direction of z and w. One estimate for the magnitude is

$$3.5 \cdot 5.5 \approx 19$$

One estimate for the direction is

$$50° + 110° \approx 160°$$

7. To find the magnitude of the product, multiply the magnitudes as you normally would.

To find the direction of the product, add the directions, then subtract $360°$ so that the direction of the product is between $0°$ and $360°$.

8. (a)

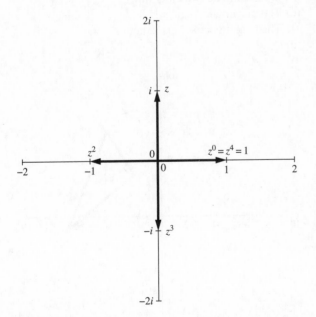

The powers of i rotate $90°$ counter-clockwise, and $i^4 = 1$.

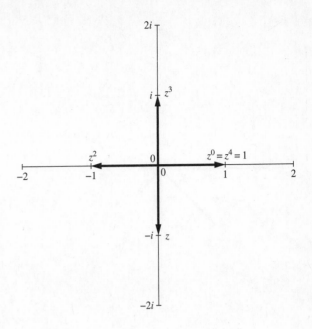

The powers of $-i$ rotate $90°$ *clockwise*, and $(-i)^4 = 1$. One reason this happens is that $-i$ is the conjugate of i.

(c)

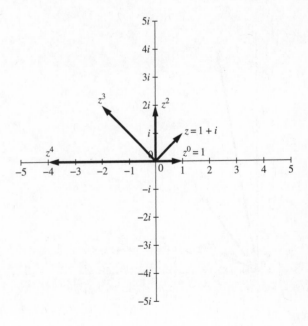

The powers of $1 + i$ rotate $45°$ counter-clockwise, and each power has $\sqrt{2}$ times the magnitude of the one before it. A full rotation happens at $(1 + i)^8 = 16$, and this can be found using the fact that $45 \cdot 8 = 360$.

(d)

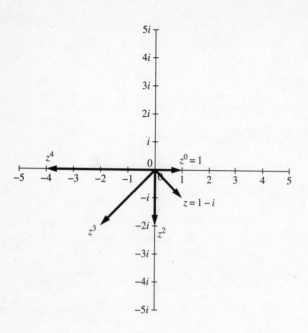

The powers of $1 - i$ rotate $45°$ *clockwise*, and each power has $\sqrt{2}$ times the magnitude of the one before it. This occurs since $1 - i$ is the conjugate of $1 + i$.

(e)

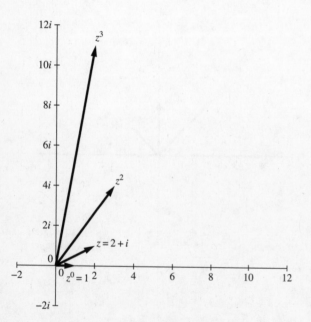

The powers of $2 + i$ rotate about $26.6°$ counter-clockwise, and each has $\sqrt{5}$ times the magnitude of the one before it.

(f)

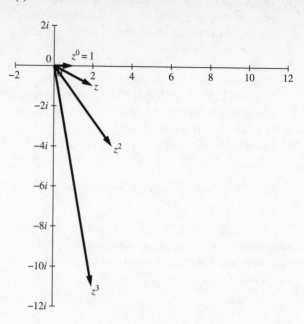

The powers of $2 - i$ rotate about $26.6°$ *clockwise*, and each has $\sqrt{5}$ times the magnitude of the one before it. This occurs since $2 - i$ is the conjugate of $2 + i$.

On Your Own

9. (a) The product has magnitude $1 \cdot 1 = 1$.
    (b) This sum has unknown magnitude. The magnitude could be anything from 0 to 2.
    (c) The magnitude of the conjugate $a - bi$ is always the same as that of $a + bi$, so the magnitude of $\overline{w}$ must be 1.
    (d) The magnitude of the reciprocal is the reciprocal of the magnitude, which is still 1.
    (e) The magnitude of z^2 is $1^2 = 1$.
    (f) The magnitude of $2z$ is 2, not 1.

10. (a)

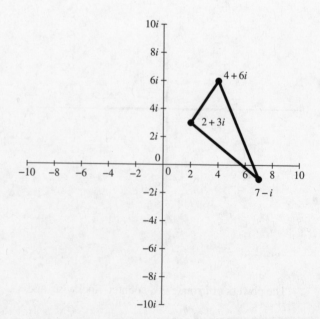

(b)

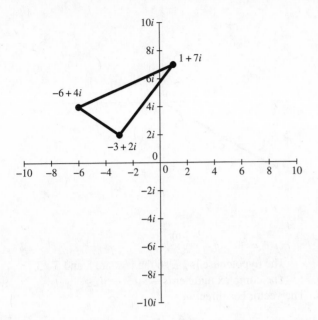

This triangle is rotated 90°.

(c)

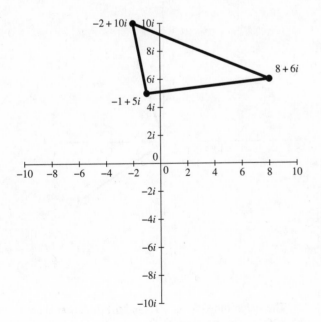

This triangle is rotated 45° and each side is $\sqrt{2}$ times as long.

(d)

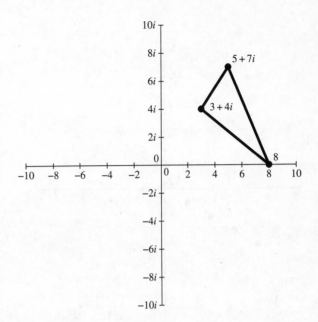

This triangle is *translated* one unit right and one unit up.

11. (a) Answers vary. One possible answer is $1 + i$ and $5 + 5i$. In general, the product must have magnitude 10 and direction 90°, so there are a lot of possibilities.

(b) If $zw = 10i$, then $w = \frac{10i}{z}$. To divide, multiply by the conjugate:

$$w = \frac{10i}{z} \cdot \frac{\bar{z}}{\bar{z}} = \frac{10\bar{z}i}{z\bar{z}}$$

Alternatively, find the magnitude and direction of w. The magnitude would be 10 divided by the magnitude of z, and the direction would be 90° minus the direction of z.

12. Answers vary, depending on the estimates for the magnitude and direction for z and w. One estimate is that z has magnitude 3 and direction 200° and w has magnitude 2.5 and direction 50°. Then the estimate for zw gives its magnitude as $3 \cdot 2.5 = 7.5$ and its direction as $200 + 50 = 250°$. These are estimates, so answers will vary quite a bit.

13. (a) Answers will vary. Here are 4 points with direction 210° and magnitude 1, 2, 3, 4:

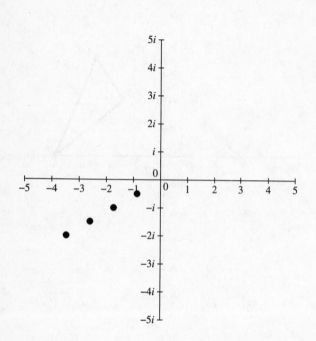

(b) The set is a ray from the origin pointing in the direction of 210°:

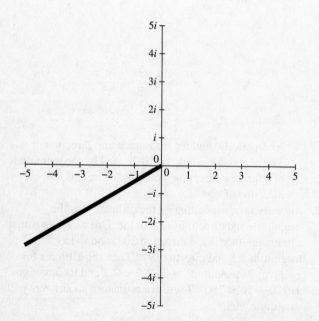

(c) Draw a 30-60-90 right triangle:

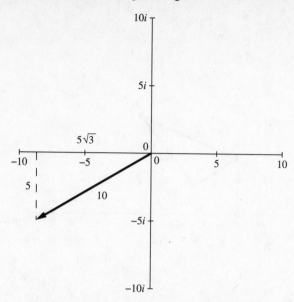

The hypotenuse is 10, so the legs are 5 and $5\sqrt{3}$. The complex number is $-5\sqrt{3} - 5i$.

14. The vector has direction

$$\tan^{-1}\left(\frac{4}{4}\right) = \tan^{-1} = 45°$$

and magnitude

$$\sqrt{4^2 + 4^2} = \sqrt{32} = 4\sqrt{2}$$

Therefore, the correct answer choice is **C**.

15. (a)

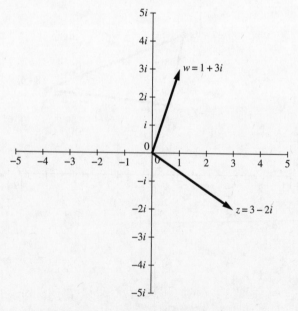

The magnitude of z is $\sqrt{13}$ and the direction is about 326.3°. The magnitude of w is $\sqrt{10}$ and the direction is about 71.6° (in Quadrant IV).

(b) You can find the magnitude and direction of the product using the results from this lesson. Magnitude: $\sqrt{10} \cdot \sqrt{13} = \sqrt{130}$; Direction: 71.6° + 326.3° = 397.9° or ≈ 37.9°

(c) For $\overline{zw}$, the magnitude of the conjugate will be the same as the magnitude of the original complex number. To find the direction, think of reflecting it over the real axis. In this case, that will put the vector in Quadrant IV, but it will still make a 37.9° angle with the real axis. Magnitude: $\sqrt{130}$, Direction: $\approx 322.1°$. For $\frac{1}{zw}$, you can use the fact that the product of zw and $\frac{1}{zw}$ is 1, so their product has magnitude 1 and direction 0°. So if m is the magnitude of $\frac{1}{zw}$, $\sqrt{130}m = 1$, which makes $m = \frac{1}{\sqrt{130}}$, which is the magnitude of $\frac{1}{zw}$. Then if d is the direction of $\frac{1}{zw}$, $37.9° + d = 0°$ and $d = -37.9°$ or $322.1°$.

16. (a)

$$\frac{4+2i}{3+i} \cdot \frac{3-i}{3-i} = \frac{14+2i}{10} = \frac{7}{5} + \frac{1}{5}i$$

(b) The magnitude is given by

$$\sqrt{\left(\frac{7}{5}\right)^2 + \left(\frac{1}{5}\right)^2} = \sqrt{\frac{49}{25} + \frac{1}{25}} = \sqrt{\frac{50}{25}} = \sqrt{2}$$

To find the direction, use inverse tangent. This complex number is in the same direction as $7 + i$, so its direction is

$$\tan^{-1}\left(\frac{1}{7}\right) \approx 8.13°$$

(c) The magnitude of $\frac{z}{w}$ is the magnitude of z divided by the magnitude of w. The direction of $\frac{z}{w}$ is the direction of z minus the direction of w.

17. (a) Answers will vary. Some examples include 13, $12 + 5i$, and $-5 - 12i$.

(b) The complete set of complex numbers whose magnitudes are 13 is a circle, centered at the origin, with radius 13:

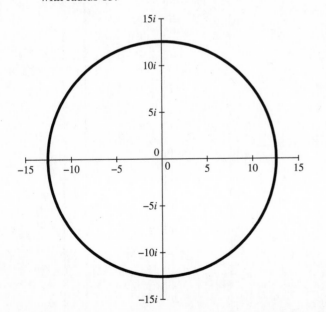

18. (a) $|z| = 3$ is a circle with radius 3:

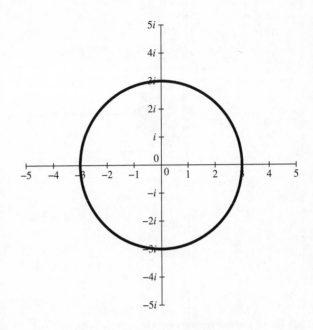

(b) $|z| = 1$ is a circle with radius 1:

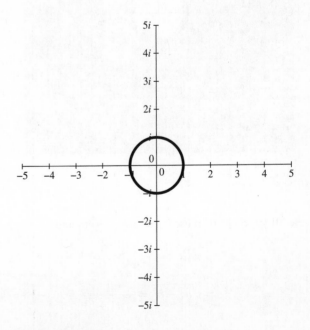

(c) $|z| < 1$ is the region inside a circle with radius 1:

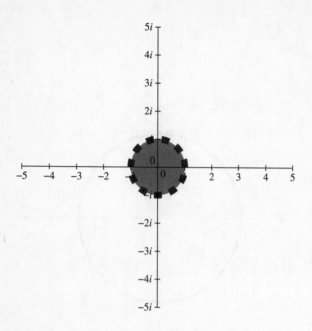

(d) $|z| > 1$ is the region outside a circle with radius 1:

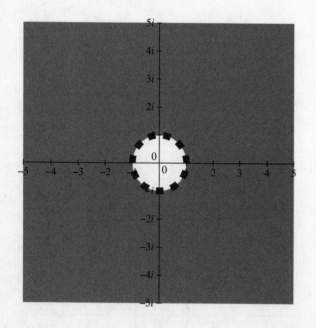

(e) If $|z| = |\frac{1}{z}|$, then use $|z| = \sqrt{a^2 + b^2}$ to find

$$\sqrt{a^2 + b^2} = \frac{1}{\sqrt{a^2 + b^2}}$$

Then $a^2 + b^2 = 1$, the same circle as $|z| = 1$:

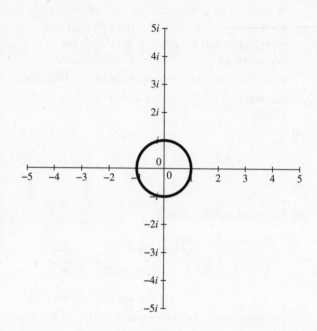

(f) Solve by factoring. If $z^2 = z$, then $z^2 - z = 0$.
Then $z(z - 1) = 0$, and either $z = 0$ or $z = 1$:

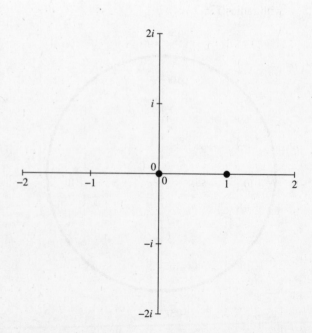

(g) $\bar{z} = z$ if and only if z is a real number, so the solution is the real number line:

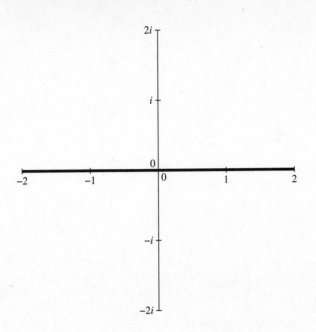

(h) If $|z^2| = |z|$, then either $|z| = 0$ or $|z| = 1$. The only point where $|z| = 0$ is the origin, and $|z| = 1$ is a circle with radius 1.

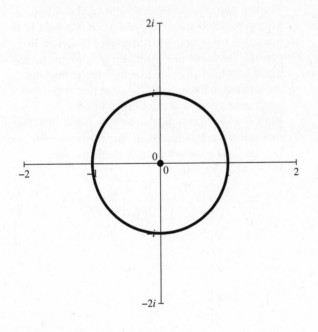

Maintain Your Skills

19. (a) $p(2 + i) = 3 + 4i$ and $p(2 - i) = 3 - 4i$
    (b) $p(2 + i) = 20 + 9i$ and $p(2 - i) = 20 - 9i$
    (c) $p(2 + i) = 2 + 11i$ and $p(2 - i) = 2 - 11i$
    (d) $p(2 + i) = 5 + 15i$ and $p(2 - i) = 5 - 15i$
    (e) $p(2 + i) = 0$ and $p(2 - i) = 0$
    (f) $p(2 + i) = 0$ and $p(2 - i) = 0$

20. (a) $1 + i + (-1) = i$
    (b) $1 + i + (-1) + (-i) = 0$
    (c) The sum of 1 through i^3 is zero, so $i^4 = 1$ is the sum.
    (d) $i^4 + i^5 = 1 + i$ is the sum.
    (e) $i^4 + i^5 + i^6 = 1 + i + (-1) = i$ is the sum.
    (f) Each set of four sums to 0, and this sum ends with an exact set of four. The sum is zero.

21. (a) The sum is $1 + \left(-\frac{1}{2} + \frac{\sqrt{3}}{2}i\right) + \left(-\frac{1}{2} - \frac{\sqrt{3}}{2}i\right)$, and all terms cancel out to leave 0.
    (b) Since $1 + \omega + \omega^2 = 0$, the sum is ω^3, which equals 1.
    (c) The sum is $\omega^3 + \omega^4 = 1 + \left(-\frac{1}{2} + \frac{\sqrt{3}}{2}i\right) = \frac{1}{2} + \frac{\sqrt{3}}{2}i$.
    (d) The sum is zero, since each set of three terms adds to 0.
    (e) The sum is 1, since $\omega^6 = 1$ and the other terms add to 0.
    (f) Use the pattern established in the earlier parts. The sum to ω^{67} will be the same as the sum to ω^4, which is $\frac{1}{2} + \frac{\sqrt{3}}{2}i$. Each set of three terms cancels, and there are a total of 68 terms.

3.12   Conjugates and Roots

Check Your Understanding

1. (a) The graph passes through the point $(-2, 0)$, so $f(-2) = 0$. Then $x = -2$ is a root.
   (b) Use polynomial division to find
   $$x^3 + 6x + 20 = (x + 2)(x^2 - 2x + 10)$$
   Or you could use the sum and product properties: the sum of the three roots is 0, so the sum of the remaining two roots is 2. The product of the three roots is -20, so the product of the remaining two roots is 10.
   Then use the quadratic formula to find the other roots, where $x^2 - 2x + 10 = 0$:
   $$x = \frac{2 \pm \sqrt{4 - 40}}{2} = \frac{2 \pm 6i}{2} = 1 \pm 3i$$

2. If $4 - i$ is a root, then $4 + i$ must also be a root. These roots have a sum of 8 and a product of 17, so a quadratic polynomial with these roots is $x^2 - 8x + 17$. The quadratic equation $x^2 - 8x + 17 = 0$ has $4 - i$ as a solution.
   Alternately, multiply $(x - (4 - i))(x - (4 + i))$ to get $x^2 - 8x + 17$.

3. As seen in the previous exercise, the polynomial $x^2 - 8x + 17$ has $4 - i$ as a root. To add 7 as an additional root, multiply by $(x - 7)$:
   $$(x - 7)(x^2 - 8x + 17) = x^3 - 15x^2 + 73x - 119$$
   The equation $x^3 - 15x^2 + 73x - 119 = 0$ has $x = 7$ and $x = 4 - i$ as solutions.

4. (a) To show that $-1 + 2i$ is a root, find $g(-1 + 2i)$.

$$\begin{aligned} g(-1+2i) &= (-1+2i)^3 - 4(-1+2i)^2 - 7(-1+2i) - 30 \\ &= (11 - 2i) - 4(-3 - 4i) - 7(-1 + 2i) - 30 \\ &= 11 - 2i + 12 + 16i + 7 - 14i - 30 \\ &= 0 + 0i \end{aligned}$$

(b) Since $-1 + 2i$ is a root, $-1 - 2i$ must also be a root. There are a few ways to find the third root. One is to use the sum property: the sum of the three roots is 4. If the third root is r, then

$$(-1 + 2i) + (-1 - 2i) + r = 4$$

This gives 6 as the third root, and $g(6) = 0$.

5. (a) Test $x = 3 + i$:

$$(3 + i)^2 - (8 + 6i) = (8 + 6i) - (8 + 6i) = 0$$

This value of x makes the equation true, so it is a solution.

(b) The equation does not have *real* coefficients, which is a requirement for the conjugate to be a root. When you test $x = 3 - i$, it does not make the equation true.

6. If p is a polynomial with real coefficients, then the complex roots come in conjugate pairs. That is, if $a + bi$ is a root, then $a - bi$ is also a root (note $b \neq 0$). The product of these roots is

$$(a + bi)(a - bi) = a^2 + b^2 > 0, \text{ since } b \neq 0.$$

The product of each pair of complex roots will always be positive, no matter how many there are. Therefore, the product of all the roots is positive if and only if the product of all the *non-complex* roots is positive. And those are the real roots.

On Your Own

7. (a) z has magnitude $\sqrt{26}$ and direction approximately $11°$, and w has magnitude $\sqrt{13}$ and direction approximately $56°$.

(b) Multiply the magnitudes and add the directions. zw has magnitude $13\sqrt{2}$ and direction $67°$.

(c) Square the magnitudes and double the direction. z^2 has magnitude 26 and direction $22°$, and w^2 has magnitude 13 and direction $112°$.

8. (a) Calculate the left side when $x = 4 - i$:

$$\begin{aligned} (4 - i)^3 &- 5(4 - i)^2 - 7(4 - i) + 51 = \\ (52 - 47i) &- 5(15 - 8i) - 7(4 - i) + 51 = \\ 52 - 47i &- 75 + 40i - 28 + 7i + 51 = 0 + 0i \end{aligned}$$

(b) Since $4 - i$ is a root, $4 + i$ must also be a root. The sum of the roots is 5, so

$$(4 - i) + (4 + i) + r = 5$$

gives -3 as the third root.

(c)

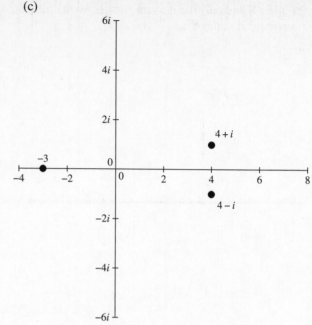

9.

(a) Calculate $p(7 - i)$.

$$\begin{aligned} p(7 - i) &= (7 - i - 3)^3 - 5(7 - i - 3)^2 - 7(7 - i - 3) + 51 \\ &= (4 - i)^3 - 5(4 - i)^2 - 7(4 - i) + 51 \\ &= 0 \end{aligned}$$

The last step comes from Exercise 8. Alternately, expand the expression fully and write in $a + bi$ form.

(b) Since $7 - i$ is a root, $7 + i$ must also be a root. In general, the use of $(x - 3)$ in this polynomial means that the roots of $p(x)$ are exactly 3 larger than the roots found in Exercise 8. The third root is 0.

Alternately, expand $p(x)$ fully to find $p(x) = x^3 - 14x^2 + 50x = x(x^2 - 14x + 50)$. The root $x = 0$ can be found here, and the other roots can be found using the quadratic formula to solve $x^2 - 14x + 50 = 0$.

(c)

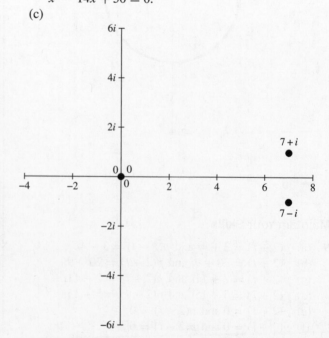

This is the same graph as appears in Exercise 8, but each root is shifted to the right by 3 units.

10. The value of $f(\bar{z})$ must be the conjugate of the value of $f(z)$.

(a) The conjugate of 0 is 0.
(b) The conjugate of 7 is 7 (not $-7\dots$).
(c) The conjugate of $1 + 3i$ is $1 - 3i$.
(d) The conjugate of $-5i$ is $5i$.

11. If $4 - i$ is a root, then $4 + i$ is also a root. These two are the roots of the quadratic $x^2 - 8x + 17$ since their sum is 8 and product is 17. The other root is -5, so one polynomial with these roots is

$$(x^2 - 8x + 17)(x + 5) = x^3 - 3x^2 - 23x + 85$$

A polynomial equation with these solutions is $x^3 - 3x^2 - 23x + 85 = 0$.

12. Since it has real coefficients, the conjugate, or $3 - 4i$, must also be a root. The coefficient of x^2 shows that the sum of the roots is 2, so the third root must be -4. The correct answer choice is **D**.

13. (a) If $2 + 7i$ is a root, then $2 - 7i$ is a root. The sum of these roots is 4, so the third root must be -4. Then one possible equation is

$$(x - (2 + 7i))(x - (2 - 7i))(x + 4) = 0$$

The product $(x - (2 + 7i))(x - (2 - 7i))$ is $x^2 - 4x + 53$ since the numbers $2 + 7i$ and $2 - 7i$ add up to 4 and multiply together to make 53. Then the equation is

$$(x^2 - 4x + 53)(x + 4) = 0$$

which expands to $x^3 + 37x + 212 = 0$.

(b) If $2 + 7i$ is a root, then $2 - 7i$ is a root. The product of these roots is 53, so the third root must be 2. Then one possible equation is

$$(x^2 - 4x + 53)(x - 2) = 0$$

which expands to $x^3 - 6x^2 + 61x - 106 = 0$.

14. (a) $g(-1) = (-1)^6 - 1 = 1 - 1 = 0$

(b) $g(w) = \left(\frac{1+i\sqrt{3}}{2}\right)^6 - 1 = 1 - 1 = 0$

(c) $g(w^2) = \left(\frac{-1+i\sqrt{3}}{2}\right)^6 - 1 = 1 - 1 = 0$

You could also do this using what you know about powers of complex numbers. $w = \frac{1+i\sqrt{3}}{2}$ has magnitude 1 and direction 60°, so $\left(\frac{1+i\sqrt{3}}{2}\right)^6$ has magnitude $(1)^6 = 1$ and direction $6 \cdot (60°) = 360°$ which is the same as direction 0°. Since $\left(\frac{1+i\sqrt{3}}{2}\right)^6$ is equal to the real number 1 (magnitude 1, direction 0°), then $\left(\frac{1+i\sqrt{3}}{2}\right)^6 - 1 = 1 - 1 = 0$

(d) If a number is a root, then its conjugate is also a root. 1 is also a root since $1^6 = 1$.

This graph shows all six roots drawn as points:

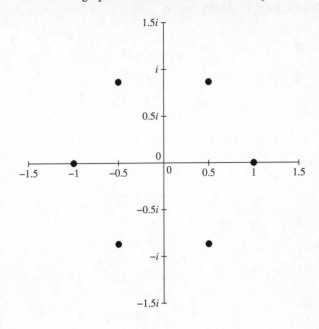

Maintain Your Skills

15. (a) The magnitude of $z = 1 + i$ is $\sqrt{2}$ and the direction is 45°. Then the magnitude of z^4 is $(\sqrt{2})^4 = 4$ and the direction is $4 \cdot 45 = 180°$.

(b) The magnitude of $z = 1 - i$ is $\sqrt{2}$ and the direction is 315°. Then the magnitude of z^4 is $(\sqrt{2})^4 = 4$ and the direction is $4 \cdot 315 = 1260°$ Subtract multiples of 360: $1260 - 1080 = 180°$.

(c) The magnitude of $z = -1 + i$ is $\sqrt{2}$ and the direction is 135°. Then the magnitude of z^4 is $(\sqrt{2})^4 = 4$ and the direction is $4 \cdot 135 = 540°$ Subtract multiples of 360: $540 - 360 = 180°$.

(d) The magnitude of $z = -1 - i$ is $\sqrt{2}$ and the direction is 225°. Then the magnitude of z^4 is $(\sqrt{2})^4 = 4$ and the direction is $4 \cdot 225 = 900°$ Subtract multiples of 360: $900 - 720 = 180°$.

16. For each, calculate z^5 by taking the fifth power of the magnitude and multiplying the direction by 5.

(a) $1^5 = 1$, so this could be z.
(b) z^5 would have magnitude 1 and direction $5 \cdot 72 = 360° = 0°$, so it could be z.
(c) z^5 would have magnitude 1 and direction $5 \cdot 120 = 600° = 240°$, so this *cannot* be z.
(d) z^5 would have magnitude 1 and direction $5 \cdot 144 = 720° = 0°$, so it could be z.
(e) $(-1)^5 = -1$, so this *cannot* be z.
(f) z^5 would have magnitude 1 and direction $5 \cdot 216 = 1080° = 0°$, so it could be z.

Check Your Understanding

1. (a)

$$(w^2)^n = w^{2n}$$
$$= (w^n)^2$$
$$= 1^2 = 1$$

(b) The proof for any positive integer is very similar to the proof for w^2:

$$(w^k)^n = w^{kn}$$
$$= (w^n)^k$$
$$= 1^k = 1$$

2.

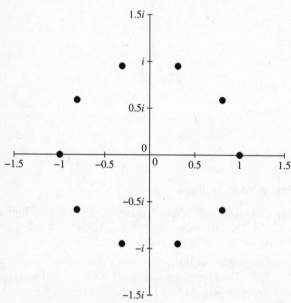

3. (a) Here are the 12th roots of unity:

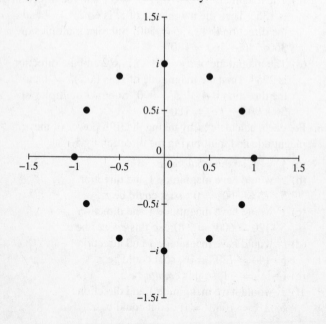

(b) Yes, it is a solution. Answers vary, but one way is to find the magnitude and direction of x. Its magnitude is 1, which is necessary for any root of unity. Its direction is 240°. Since the twelve solutions to $x^{12} = 1$ come every 30°, and 240 is a multiple of 30, this number is a solution.

Alternatively, find x^{12} (preferably on a calculator). Sure enough, $x^{12} = 1$.

Also, x is one of the solutions to $x^3 = 1$ (and $x^6 = 1$). Then it must also be a solution to $x^{12} = 1$, since $x^{12} = (x^3)^4$.

4. (a) Rewrite as $x^3 - 8 = 0$ and factor: $(x - 2)(x^2 + 2x + 4) = 0$. The three solutions are $x = 2$ and $x = -1 \pm i\sqrt{3}$.

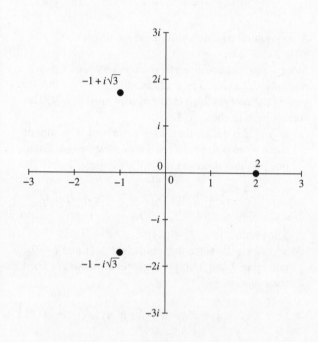

Alternatively, use magnitude and direction: if x^3 has magnitude 8, then x has magnitude 2. There are three possible directions: 0°, 120°, and 240°.

(b) Each solution has magnitude 2, but otherwise the solutions are the same (in direction) as the solutions to $x^3 = 1$.

5. The number i has magnitude 1 and direction 90°. A solution to $z^2 = i$ must have magnitude $\sqrt{1} = 1$. There are two possible directions: $\frac{90}{2} = 45°$ and $\frac{90+360}{2} = 225°$. So, the two possible solutions are

- Magnitude 1, Direction 45° → $z = \frac{\sqrt{2}}{2} + \frac{\sqrt{2}}{2}i$
- Magnitude 1, Direction 225° → $z = -\frac{\sqrt{2}}{2} - \frac{\sqrt{2}}{2}i$

Note that the two solutions are opposites of each other, just like the solutions to $x^2 = 9$ in real numbers.

6. (a) The number i has magnitude 1 and direction 90°, so one answer is that z has magnitude 1 and direction $\frac{90}{3} = 30°$. This complex number is

$$z = \frac{\sqrt{3}}{2} + \frac{1}{2}i$$

(b) The other solutions have different directions by adding $\frac{360}{3} = 120°$ to the direction of a previous solution. The two other solutions are

- Magnitude 1, Direction $150° \to z = -\frac{\sqrt{3}}{2} + \frac{1}{2}i$
- Magnitude 1, Direction $270° \to z = -i$

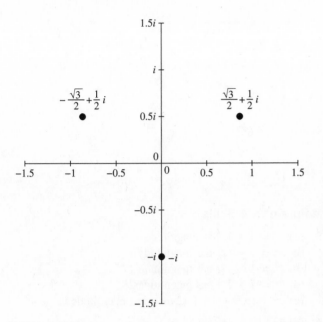

(c) Answers vary. Each solution to $x^3 = i$ is rotated $30°$ counterclockwise from a solution to $x^3 = 1$. The three solutions still are the same distance from 0, and still form the vertices of an equilateral triangle.

7. There are several ways to show that the sum is zero.

Solution 1. The sixth roots of unity are listed on page 105. Add them up directly; the sum is zero.

Solution 2. If z is a sixth root of unity, then $z^6 = 1$. But then so is $-z$, since $(-z)^6 = (-1)^6 \cdot z^6 = z^6$. So the roots come in pairs of opposites, and the sum of opposites is always zero.

Solution 3. A sixth root of unity satisfies the equation $z^6 - 1 = 0$. The *sum of the roots* would be the opposite of the coefficient of z^5 in this polynomial equation. But there is no z^5 term, so the sum of the roots is zero.

Solution 4. Factor $x^6 - 1$ as $(x - 1)(1 + x + x^2 + x^3 + x^4 + x^5)$ If $w = \frac{1+\sqrt{3}}{2}i$, $w^6 - 1 = 0$ but $w \neq 1$. So, for this w, the second factor must be 0:
$1 + w + w^2 + w^3 + w^4 + w^5 = 0$
The right side is the sum of the sixth roots of unity.

8. Yes, Sasha is correct. One way is to test the fifth roots of unity, by finding the magnitude and direction of a root's conjugate.

A second method is to note that a fifth root of unity w is a solution to the polynomial equation $w^5 - 1 = 0$. Since this is a polynomial with real coefficients, if w is a root, then $\overline{w}$ must also be a root. Then $(\overline{w})^5 - 1 = 0$, and $\overline{w}$ must be a fifth root of unity, too.

9. (a) Here is the completed table:

Equation	# New Roots
$x = 1$	1
$x^2 = 1$	1
$x^3 = 1$	2
$x^4 = 1$	2
$x^5 = 1$	4
$x^6 = 1$	2
$x^7 = 1$	6
$x^8 = 1$	4
$x^9 = 1$	6
$x^{10} = 1$	4

(b) There are many answers here. First, the number of new roots is always even (beginning with $x^3 = 1$). This can be proven: if z is a new root, then so is $\overline{z}$, and as long as z is non-real (which can only happen when $z = 1$ or $z = -1$), they must come in pairs. Second, if p is prime, the number of new roots of $x^p = 1$ is $p - 1$.

One strong claim (related to the claim about primes) is that the number of new roots of $x^n = 1$ is the number of values in $\{1, 2, 3, \ldots, n - 1\}$ that do not have common factors with n. For example, consider the solutions to $x^{10} = 1$. If w is the first (principal) root of unity found, the "new roots" are w, w^3, w^7, and w^9. These numbers $(1, 3, 7, 9)$ have no common factors with 10. Numbers that share common factors aren't "new roots": for example, w^6 in tenth roots is the same as w^3 in fifth roots (why?).

On Your Own

10. There are nine roots evenly spaced out over $360°$, so they are $40°$ apart. The correct answer choice is **C**.

11. Each power of z adds $20°$ to the direction. For example, z^5 has direction $5 \cdot 20 = 100°$. To complete the regular polygon, the direction must be $360°$ (or an integer multiple). The equation

$$20n = 360$$

has the solution $n = 18$, so z^{18} completes the regular polygon.

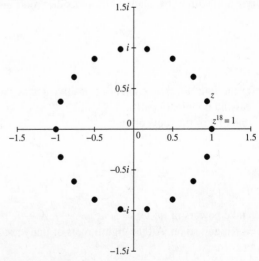

12. (a) z has magnitude 1 and direction 60°.

(b) Since z has direction 60°, z^n has direction $60n$. For $z^n = 1$, then $60n$ must be 360 (or a multiple). Then $z^6 = 1$ is the smallest possible such n. (This means that z is a sixth root of unity.)

(c)

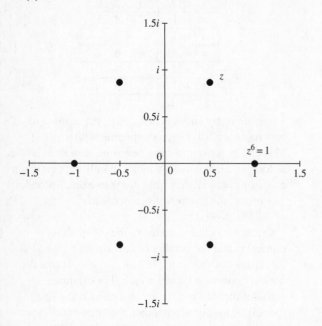

13. (a) All the roots have magnitude 1. The direction will be multiples of $\frac{360}{8} = 45°$:

$$0°, 45°, 90°, 135°, 180°, 225°, 270°, 315°$$

(b) Four of the roots are on the real and imaginary axes: $1, -1, i$, and $-i$. The others form 45-45-90 right triangles. For example, the number with magnitude 1 and direction 45° is

$$\frac{\sqrt{2}}{2} + \frac{\sqrt{2}}{2}i$$

The others are in other quadrants but the same position within the quadrant. So, the other roots are

$$\pm\frac{\sqrt{2}}{2} + \pm\frac{\sqrt{2}}{2}i$$

for the four different choices of positive and negative real and imaginary parts.

14. Pick the first of the roots of unity,

$$w = \frac{\sqrt{2}}{2} + \frac{\sqrt{2}}{2}i$$

Then take powers of w: $w^2 = i$, $w^3 = -\frac{\sqrt{2}}{2} + \frac{\sqrt{2}}{2}i$, $w^4 = -1$, and so on. All the eighth roots of unity are powers of w:

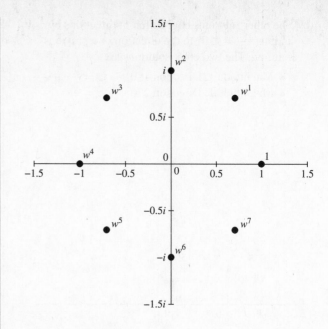

Maintain Your Skills

15. (a) $z^2 = 3 + 4i$ has magnitude 5.

(b) $z^2 = 5 + 12i$ has magnitude 13.

(c) $z^2 = 15 + 8i$ has magnitude 17.

(d) $z^2 = 7 + 24i$ has magnitude 25.

(e) $z^2 = (m^2 - n^2) + (2mn)i$ has magnitude $m^2 + n^2$.

16. (a) $1 + i + i^2 + i^3 + i^4 = 1 + i - 1 - i + 1$, so the result is 1.

(b) If $w^3 = 1$, then $w^3 - 1 = 0$ and $(w - 1)(w^2 + w + 1) = 0$. This means that either the sum is 0 or that $w = 1$ and the sum is 3.

(c) If $z^5 = 1$, then $z^5 - 1 = 0$ and $(z - 1)(z^4 + z^3 + z^2 + z + 1) = 0$. This means that either $z = 1$ and the sum is 5, or that the sum is 0.

(d) If $w^6 = 1$, then $w^6 - 1 = 0$ and $(w - 1)(w^5 + w^4 + w^3 + w^2 + w + 1) = 0$. This means that either $w = 1$ and the sum is 6, or that the sum is 0.

3C   MATHEMATICAL REFLECTIONS

1. (a) $|z| = |1 - \sqrt{3}i| = \sqrt{(1)^2 + (-\sqrt{3})^2} = \sqrt{4} = 2$. It is in Quadrant IV, and makes an angle of $\tan^{-1}\left(\frac{\sqrt{3}}{1}\right) = 60°$ with the real axis, so its direction is 300°.

(b) $|z^2| = |z|^2 = 2^2 = 4$. $\arg(z^2) = 2 \cdot \arg(z) = 2 \cdot 300° = 600°$ or 240°.

(c) $|z^3| = |z|^3 = 2^3 = 8$. (You could also find the product $|z^2| \cdot |z|$.) $\arg(z^3) = 3 \cdot \arg(z) = 3 \cdot 300° = 900°$ or 180°. (Similarly you could find the sum $\arg(z^2) \cdot \arg(z)$.)

(d) $|z^4| = |z|^4 = 2^4 = 16$. $\arg(z^4) = 4 \cdot \arg(z) = 4 \cdot 300° = 1200°$ or 120°.

(e) z^3 is a real number (-8). Its direction is 180°, so it lies on the real axis.

2. (a) $|zw| = |z| \cdot |w| = (6)(2) = 12$. $\arg(zw) = \arg(z) + \arg(w) = 135° + 240° = 375°$ or $15°$.

(b) $|zv| = 3 = |z| \cdot |v|$, so $3 = 6 \cdot |v|$ and $|v| = \frac{1}{2}$. $\arg(zv) = 30° = \arg(z) + \arg(v)$, so $30° = 135° + \arg(v)$ and $\arg(v) = -105°$ or $255°$.

3. If $2 - i$ is a root of a polynomial with real coefficients, then $2 + i$ is also a root. To find a polynomial with these two roots, you can use the sum-and-product rule for quadratics. The sum of these two roots is 4 and their product is 5, so they are roots of the quadratic polynomial $x^2 - 4x + 5$. For 3 to also be a root, multiply this quadratic by $x - 3$ to get $x^3 - 7x^2 + 17x - 15$. This is a polynomial of smallest degree with real coefficients that has the required roots. It is not the only solution, though, because $p(x) \cdot (x^3 - 7x^2 + 17x - 15)$, where $p(x)$ is any polynomial with real coefficients, will also have $2 - i$ and 3 among its roots.

4. To show that $6i$ is a root of the polynomial, substitute $x = 6i$ and show that the value of the polynomial is zero at this value of x.

$(6i)^3 + 2(6i)^2 + 36(6i) + 72 = -216i - 72 + 216i + 72 = 0$

To find the other roots, use the fact that $-6i$ is also a root, because the polynomial has real coefficients. You might then choose to use polynomial long division to divide out the quadratic that has roots $6i$ and $-6i$—$x^2 + 36$—to get the quotient $x + 2$. This tells you the third root is -2.

Instead, you could use the fact that in the original cubic polynomial the coefficient of the x^2-term is equal to the negative of the sum of the three roots of the polynomial. $6i + (-6i) + r = -2$, and $r = -2$. Still another way to find the last root would be to use the fact that the constant term in the original polynomial is the negative of the product of its three roots. $(6i)(-6i)r = -72$, so $r = -2$.

5. In this investigation, you found that the solutions to equations of this type all lie on a circle of radius 1 in the complex plane, equally spaced around the origin. Since this polynomial has degree 5, it has five solutions. All five solutions have magnitude 1, and their directions are $0°$, $72°$, $144°$, $216°$, and $288°$.

Of these, the solution with direction $144°$ lies in Quadrant II. The vector representing this complex number forms a $36°$ angle with the negative real axis. The length of the horizontal leg of this triangle is $\cos(36°) \approx 0.81$ and the length of its vertical leg is $\sin(36°) \approx 0.59$. In $a + bi$ form this solution is $-0.81 + 0.59i$.

6. The magnitude of the product of two complex numbers is equal to the product of the magnitudes of the two complex numbers. The direction of the product of two complex numbers is equal to the sum of the directions of the two complex numbers.

7. $-2 - i$, the conjugate of the given root, must also be a root. Corollary 3.8 states that if a polynomial with real coefficients has a complex root, the conjugate of that root is also a root.

8. The solutions will all lie on a circle of radius 1 centered at the origin of the complex plane. They will be evenly spaced around the origin. $(1, 0)$ is one solution to this equation. It has magnitude 1 and direction $0°$. The other solutions will also have magnitude 1 and their directions are $36°$, $72°$, $108°$, $144°$, $180°$, $216°$, $252°$, $288°$, and $324°$.

CHAPTER REVIEW

1. First solve the equation:

$$x^5 - 36x = 0$$
$$x(x^4 - 36) = 0$$
$$x(x^2 - 6)(x^2 + 6) = 0$$

So, $x = 0$ or

$$x^2 - 6 = 0$$
$$x^2 = 6$$
$$x = \pm\sqrt{6}$$

or

$$x^2 + 6 = 0$$
$$x^2 = -6$$
$$x = \pm\sqrt{-6}$$
$$x = \pm i\sqrt{6}$$

The five solutions are 0, $\pm\sqrt{6}$, and $\pm i\sqrt{6}$.

(a) There are no solutions in $\mathbb{N}$.

(b) The only integer solution is $x = 0$

(c) There are no solutions that are in $\mathbb{Q}$, but not in $\mathbb{Z}$.

(d) The real solutions that are not rational are $x = \sqrt{6}$ and $x = -\sqrt{6}$

(e) The non-real solutions are $x = i\sqrt{6}$ and $x = -i\sqrt{6}$

2. (a) Use the Quadratic Formula:
$$2x^2 - x + 5 = 0$$

$$x = \frac{-(-1) \pm \sqrt{(-1)^2 - 4(2)(5)}}{2(2)}$$
$$= \frac{1 \pm \sqrt{1 - 40}}{4}$$
$$= \frac{1 \pm \sqrt{-39}}{4}$$
$$= \frac{1 \pm i\sqrt{39}}{4}$$

(b) Solve using the Basic Rules:
$$z + (3 - 7i) = -2 - 11i$$
$$z = (-2 - 11i) - (3 - 7i)$$
$$= -2 - 11i - 3 + 7i$$
$$= -5 - 4i$$

(c) Solve using the Basic Rules:

$$(1 - i) \cdot z = 3$$

$$z = \frac{3}{1 - i}$$

$$= \left(\frac{3}{1 - i}\right) \cdot \left(\frac{1 + i}{1 + i}\right)$$

$$= \frac{3 + 3i}{1 - i^2}$$

$$= \frac{3 + 3i}{1 - (-1)}$$

$$= \frac{3 + 3i}{2}$$

$$= \frac{3}{2} + \frac{3}{2} \cdot i$$

3. (a) $z + w = (-1 + 3i) + (4 + 2i) = 3 + 5i$

(b) $\overline{w} = 4 - 2i$

(c) $z \cdot w = (-1 + 3i)(4 + 2i) = -4 - 2i + 12i + 6i^2 = -4 + 10i - 6 = -10 + 10i$

(d) $2z \cdot \overline{w} = 2(-1+3i)(4-2i) = 2(-4+2i+12i-6i^2) = 2(-4 + 14i + 6) = 2(2 + 14i) = 4 + 28i$

(e) $z^2 = (-1+3i)^2 = 1 - 6i + 9i^2 = 1 - 6i - 9 = -8 - 6i$

(f) $\frac{1}{z} = \frac{1}{-1+3i} = \left(\frac{1}{-1+3i}\right) \cdot \left(\frac{-1-3i}{-1-3i}\right) = \frac{-1-3i}{1-9i^2} = \frac{-1-3i}{1+9} = \frac{-1-3i}{10} = -\frac{1}{10} - \frac{3}{10} \cdot i$

4. (a)

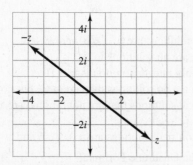

(b)

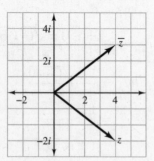

(c)

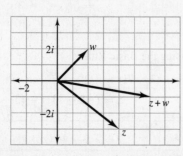

(d)

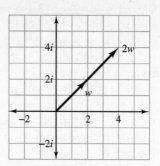

(e)

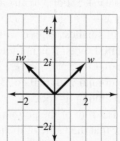

(f)

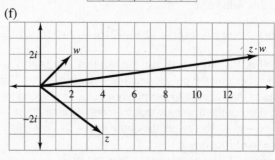

5.

$$(2i)^2 = 4i^2 = 4(-1) = -4$$

$$(2i)^3 = 8i^3 = 8(i)(i^2) = 8(i)(-1) = -8i$$

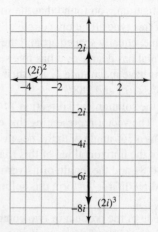

6.

	$a + bi$	Magnitude	Direction
z	$-1 + i$	$\sqrt{(-1)^2 + 1^2} = \sqrt{2}$	$180° - 45° = 135°$
$-z$	$1 - i$	$\sqrt{1^2 + (-1)^2} = \sqrt{2}$	$360° - 45° = 315°$
$\overline{z}$	$-1 - i$	$\sqrt{(-1)^2 + (-1)^2} = \sqrt{2}$	$180° + 45° = 225°$
$i \cdot z$	$-1 - i$	$\sqrt{(-1)^2 + (-1)^2} = \sqrt{2}$	$180° + 45° = 225°$
$3z$	$-3 + 3i$	$\sqrt{(-3)^2 + (3)^2} = \sqrt{18} = 3\sqrt{2}$	$180° - 45° = 135°$
z^2	$-2i$	$\sqrt{0^2 + (-2)^2} = \sqrt{4} = 2$	$270°$

7. (a) When you multiply two complex numbers, you multiply the magnitudes and add the directions. So, the magnitude $= 3 \cdot 2 = 6$, and the direction $= 30° + 120° = 150°$.

(b) $z^2 = z \cdot z$. So, the magnitude $= 3 \cdot 3 = 9$, and the direction $= 30° + 30° = 60°$.

(c) $z^3 = z^2 \cdot z$. So, the magnitude $= 9 \cdot 3 = 27$, and the direction $= 60° + 30° = 90°$.

(d) $-w$ does not change the magnitude, but rotates the complex number 180°. So, the magnitude $= 2$ and the direction $= 120° + 180° = 300°$.

(e) Multiplying by 4 multiplies the magnitude ny 4, but does not change the direction. So, the magnitude $= 4 \cdot 2 = 8$ and the direction $= 120°$.

(f) The conjugate is a reflection over the real axis. So, the magnitude $= 3$, and the direction $= 360° - 30° = 330°$.

8. Since $2 + 3i$ is a solution and the coefficients are real, you know that $2 - 3i$ is a solution. Write the equation using the Factor Theorem and expand:

$$(x - (2 + 3i))(x - (2 - 3i)) = 0$$
$$(x - 2 - 3i)(x - 2 + 3i) = 0$$
$$((x - 2) - 3i)((x - 2) + 3i) = 0$$
$$(x - 2)^2 - (3i)^2 = 0$$
$$x^2 - 4x + 4 - 9i^2 = 0$$
$$x^2 - 4x + 4 + 9 = 0$$
$$x^2 - 4x + 13 = 0$$

9. Each solution has a magnitude of 1 because the magnitude of a product (in this case $x^6 = x \cdot x \cdot x \cdot x \cdot x \cdot x$) is the product of the magnitudes (in this case $1 \cdot 1 \cdot 1 \cdot 1 \cdot 1 \cdot 1 = 1$). The sum of the directions is the direction of the product, so you need a direction such that $6 \cdot$ direction $=$ a multiple of 360°. So, the directions are:

$$\frac{0}{6} = 0°$$
$$\frac{360}{6} = 60°$$
$$\frac{720}{6} = 120°$$
$$\frac{1080}{6} = 180°$$
$$\frac{1440}{6} = 240°$$
$$\frac{1800}{6} = 300°$$

CHAPTER TEST

Multiple Choice

1. $\sqrt{-4} \cdot \sqrt{-9} = i\sqrt{4} \cdot i\sqrt{9} = i^2 \cdot 2 \cdot 3 = -1 \cdot 6 = -6$. The correct choice is **B**.

2. $z - \bar{z} = (4 + 6i) - (4 - 6i) = 4 + 6i - 4 + 6i = 12i$. The correct choice is **C**.

3. Since $i \cdot z$ is a 90° rotation of z, $i \cdot z$ will be in Quadrant IV when z is in Quadrant III. The correct choice is **D**.

4. $|5 - 12i| = \sqrt{5^2 + (-12)^2} = \sqrt{25 + 144} = \sqrt{169} = 13$. The correct choice is **C**.

5. The other solution will be the conjugate of $4 - 6i$, or $4 + 6i$. The correct choice is **D**.

Open Response

6. Use the quadratic formula.

$$x^2 - 2x + 10 = 0$$
$$x = \frac{-(-2) \pm \sqrt{(-2)^2 - 4(1)(10)}}{2(1)}$$
$$= \frac{2 \pm \sqrt{4 - 40}}{2}$$
$$= \frac{2 \pm \sqrt{-36}}{2}$$
$$= \frac{2 \pm 6i}{2}$$
$$= 1 \pm 3i$$

(a) There are no solutions in $\mathbb{R}$.

(b) The solutions in $\mathbb{C}$ are $x = 1 + 3i$ or $x = 1 - 3i$.

7. (a)

$$z + 4i = 2(3 - i)$$
$$z + 4i = 6 - 2i$$
$$z = 6 - 2i - 4i$$
$$z = 6 - 6i$$

(b)

$$z \cdot (5 + i) = 11 - 3i$$
$$z = \frac{11 - 3i}{5 + i}$$
$$z = \left(\frac{11 - 3i}{5 + i}\right) \cdot \left(\frac{5 - i}{5 - i}\right)$$
$$z = \frac{55 - 11i - 15i + 3i^2}{25 - i^2}$$
$$z = \frac{55 - 11i - 15i + (-3)}{25 - (-1)}$$
$$z = \frac{52 - 26i}{26}$$
$$z = 2 - i$$

8. (a) Expand and combine like terms:

$$z \cdot w = (-2 + 2i)(1 + i)$$
$$= -2 - 2i + 2i + 2i^2$$
$$= -2 + (-2)$$
$$= -4$$

Or, to multiply two complex numbers, add their directions and multiply their magnitudes: The direction of z is 135° and the direction of w is 45°. So the direction of $z \cdot w$ is $135° + 45° = 180°$. The magnitude of z is $|-2 + 2i| = \sqrt{(-2)^2 + 2^2} = \sqrt{4 + 4} = \sqrt{8} = 2\sqrt{2}$ and the magnitude of w is $|1 + i| = \sqrt{1^2 + 1^2} = \sqrt{2}$. So the magnitude of $z \cdot w$ $(2\sqrt{2} \cdot \sqrt{2} = 2\sqrt{4} = 2 \cdot 2 = 4$. The complex number with magnitude 4 and direction 180° is -4.

(b)

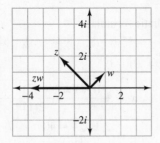

(c)

	$a + bi$	magnitude	direction
z	$-2 + 2i$	$2\sqrt{2}$	$135°$
w	$1 + i$	$\sqrt{2}$	$45°$
$z \cdot w$	-4	4	$180°$

9. (a) Since $z^2 = z \cdot z$, multiply the magnitudes: $4 \cdot 4 = 16$ and add the arguments: $30° + 30° = 60°$. So, the magnitude of z^2 is 16 and the direction is 60°.

(b) Since $z^3 = z \cdot z \cdot z$, multiply the magnitudes: $4 \cdot 4 \cdot 4 = 64$ and add the arguments: $30° + 30° + 30° = 90°$. So, the magnitude of z^3 is 64 and the direction is 90°.

(c) Since $z^4 = z^2 \cdot z^2$, multiply the magnitudes: $16 \cdot 16 = 256$ and add the arguments: $60° + 60° = 120°$. So, the magnitude of z^4 is 256 and the direction is 120°.

10. If $3 - i$ is a solution, then $3 + i$ is a solution. So, $(x - 1)$, $(x - (3 - i))$, and $(x - (3 + i))$ are factors. The cubic equation is

$$(x - 1)(x - (3 - i))(x - (3 + i)) = 0$$
$$(x - 1)((x - 3) + i)((x - 3) - i) = 0$$
$$(x - 1)((x - 3)^2 - i^2) = 0$$
$$(x - 1)(x^2 - 6x + 9 - (-1)) = 0$$
$$(x - 1)(x^2 - 6x + 10) = 0$$
$$x(x^2 - 6x + 10) - 1(x^2 - 6x + 10) = 0$$
$$x^3 - 6x^2 + 10x - x^2 + 6x - 10 = 0$$
$$x^3 - 7x^2 + 16x - 10 = 0$$

INVESTIGATION 4A   GAUSSIAN ELIMINATION

4.1   Getting Started

For You to Explore

1. *Substitution*: Solve the first equation for x, getting $x = 4 - y$. Substitute this into the second equation, getting

$$2(4 - y) - y = -1$$
$$8 - 3y = -1$$
$$9 = 3y$$
$$y = 3$$

Now substitute 3 for y in $x = 4 - y$, so $x = 1$.
Elimination: Subtract two times $x + y = 4$ from $2x - y = -1$, getting $-3y = -9$, or $y = 3$. In display form,

$$2x - y = -1$$
$$(-)\quad 2x + 2y = 8$$
$$\overline{\qquad -3y = -9}$$

Now proceed as before.

2. *Substitution*: Solve the first equation for x to get $x = \frac{1}{2}(1 - y)$. Substitute this in the second equation to get

$$\frac{3(1 - y)}{2} + 2y = 1$$
$$\frac{1}{2}y = -\frac{1}{2}$$
$$y = -1$$

Substitute $y = -1$ into $x = \frac{1-y}{2}$ to get $x = 1$.
   Or, instead of solving for x from the first equation, solve for y: $y = 1 - 2x$; no fractions! Substitute this into the second equation to get $3x + 2(1 - 2x) = 1$, so $2 - x = 1$ and $x = 1$. From this you get $y = 1 - 2 = -1$.
Elimination: It is easiest to eliminate y by subtracting two times the first equation from the second: $-x = -1$, so $x = 1$. Proceed as before.

3. Two lines intersect at the point (x, y) if that point satisfies both equations. In this case, you might choose the substitution method since both equations have already been expressed with y alone on one side. Indeed, just set

the two expressions for y equal:

$$3x + 2 = -2x + 1 \implies 5x = -1 \implies x = -\frac{1}{5}$$

Substitute this value into the equation of either line to get $y = \frac{7}{5}$.

4. If x causes $f(x)$ to equal $g(x)$, then $3x + 2 = -2x + 1$. Now you are back to Exercise 3.

5. Remember that in Lagrange Interpolation, you imagine your polynomial as the sum of terms. You design each term so that it is equal to zero for all but one of the inputs. Then the input-output pairs allow you to figure out the coefficient of each of the terms.

$$p(x) = A(x - 1)(x - 3) + Bx(x - 3) + Cx(x - 1)$$

The A-term of this polynomial is the only one that is not equal to zero if $x = 0$. When $x = 0$, it takes on the value $A(-1)(-3) = 3A$. You know that the output for $x = 0$ is 1, so $3A = 1$ and $A = \frac{1}{3}$. Similarly, the B-term of the polynomial is the only one that is not equal to zero if $x = 1$. When $x = 1$, it takes on the value $B(1)(-2) = -2B$. You know that the output for $x = 1$ is -1, so $-2B = -1$ and $B = \frac{1}{2}$. And the C-term of the polynomial is the only one that is not equal to zero if $x = 3$. When $x = 3$, it takes on the value $C(3)(2) = 6C$. You know that the output for $x = 3$ is 1, so $6C = 1$ and $C = \frac{1}{6}$.
   This gives you

$$p(x) = \frac{1}{3}(x - 1)(x - 3) + \frac{1}{2}x(x - 3) + \frac{1}{6}x(x - 1).$$

You can expand this either by hand or with a CAS to get

$$p(x) = x^2 - 3x + 1$$

6. (a) Substitute $x = 3$ into $1 = q(3) = ax^2 + bx + c$. You get $1 = a3^2 + b3 + c$, that is, $9a + 3b + c = 1$.
   (b) From $q(0) = 1$ you get $a0^2 + b0 + c = 1$, or just $c = 1$. From $q(1) = -1$ the equation is $a + b + c = -1$.
   (c) The values a, b, c must satisfy all three equations, so you have a system of three linear equations in three unknowns. Soon you will learn systematic methods for solving such systems, but here you are lucky; one equation is $c = 1$, so just substitute that into the other two equations, getting

$$9a + 3b = 0$$
$$a + b = -2$$

Now use any method. For instance, subtract three times the second equation from the first, and you get

$6a = 6$, so $a = 1$ and then $b = -3$. So the polynomial is $x^2 - 3x + 1$.

On Your Own

7. Here is an elimination method: First multiply the second equation by 4 to get the system

$$2x + 3y = 1$$
$$2x + \frac{4}{3}y = 4$$

Subtract these equations, and you get $\frac{5}{3}y = -3$, so $y = -\frac{9}{5}$. Substitute this value in the first equation, and you get $2x - \frac{27}{5} = 1$, so $2x = \frac{32}{5}$ and $x = \frac{16}{5}$.

8. The equation of the first line can be written as $y - 1 = 2(x - 1)$, so $y = 2x - 1$.

   For the second equation, if (x, y) is a typical point on the line, then the slope between that point and $(3, 0)$ must be -1. This gives you

$$\frac{y - 0}{x - 3} = -1$$

so $y = -x + 3$. Now set the two expressions for y equal:

$$2x - 1 = -x + 3$$

So $3x = 4$, and $x = \frac{4}{3}$. This gives you $y = -\frac{4}{3} + 3 = \frac{5}{3}$.

9. Since the point $(1, 4)$ satisfies $y = p(x) = ax + b$, it follows that $4 = 1a + b$. Since $(3, 2)$ also satisfies the equation, $2 = 3a + b$. So you have the system

$$3a + b = 2$$
$$a + b = 4$$

Subtract the second equation from the first, and you get $2a = -2$. This gives you $a = -1$, from which you can get $b = 5$. The polynomial (a line) is $p(x) = -x + 5$.

10. This is the main example problem in the text of Lesson 4.2. See the discussion there.

11. (a) $x = 4 - 2y - 3z$, so the second equation becomes

$$2(4 - 2y - 3z) + y - z = -2$$
$$-3y - 7z = -10$$

   (b)

$$\begin{array}{r} 2x + y - z = -2 \\ (-)\quad 2x + 4y + 6z = 8 \\ \hline -3y - 7z = -10 \end{array}$$

   (c) $y = \frac{10 - 7z}{3}$

   (d) $x + \frac{2(10 - 7z)}{3} + 3z = x - \frac{5}{3}z + \frac{20}{3} = \frac{12}{3}$, so $x = -\frac{8}{3} + \frac{5}{3}z$.

   (e) x and y are now expressed in terms of z, and for each value of z, each of these expressions has a unique value. That is, for each value of z, the solution is

$$(x, y, z) = \left(-\frac{8}{3} + \frac{5}{3}z, \frac{10}{3} - \frac{7}{3}z, z\right)$$

12. (a) Substitute $x = 3 - 2y$ into the second equation. You get $(6 - 4y) + 4y = 6$, or $6 = 6$. Since $6 = 6$ is always true, you can just drop it; it adds no further restrictions to the first equation. The first equation is the equation of a line, so it has infinitely many pairs of values (x, y) that solve it.

   A graphical solution shows that both original equations represent the same line.

   (b) Now the substitution gives you $6 = 7$ which is never true, so you can conclude that the system you started with has *no solutions*.

   A graphical solution shows that the two original equations represent parallel lines, so they don't intersect and there is no solution.

Maintain Your Skills

13. From the third equation $z = -1$. You can substitute this into the second equation, getting $3y + 1 = 4$, so $y = 1$. Now substitute the values of y and z into the first equation and solve for x, getting $x = 2$.

14. From the last equation, $t = 4$. Backsubstitute this value in the third equation: $7z - 4 = 3 \implies 7z = 7 \implies z = 1$. Backsubstitute both values into the second equation:

$$5y - 1 + 12 = 1 \implies 5y = -10 \implies y = -2$$

Backsubstitute all three values into the first equation:

$$2x + 6 + 5 - 8 = 9 \implies 2x = 6 \implies x = 3$$

15. There's an obvious order in which to do it, and the computations are not difficult. You never have to deal with more than one variable at a time.

16. Solve for x first; $x = 2$. Substitute 2 for x in the second equation to got $y = -1$. Substituting both x and y values in the third equation gives $z = 6$.

17. This can be solved one variable at a time too. Solve for $z = -1$ first. Then use the first equation to solve for $x = 6$. Then conclude from the third equation that $y = -3$.

18. (a) Triangular form on the left-hand side

   (b) You can solve the second equation for y and substitute into the first. Or you can divide the second equation by -3:

$$x + 2y = 4 - 3z$$
$$y = \frac{10}{3} - \frac{7}{3}z$$

   and then subtract two times the new second equation from the first:

$$x = -\frac{8}{3} + \frac{5}{3}z$$
$$y = \frac{10}{3} - \frac{7}{3}z$$

19. Here's one way to solve it. Eliminate x by subtracting two times the first equation from the second equation and three times the first equation from the third, getting

$$3y + 2z = 3$$
$$4y - z = -7$$

Add two times the new second equation above to the first, getting $11y = -11$. So $y = -1$. Now substitute into $3y + 2z = 3$ to solve for z, and obtain $z = 3$. Then substitute the values of y and z into any of the original equations to solve for x, and obtain $x = 2$.

4.2 Solving Systems Systematically

Check Your Understanding

1. Add Eq. (5) to Eq. (6) and add two times Eq. (5) to Eq. (7):

$$2x + 3z = 1$$
$$x - z = 3$$

The exercise doesn't say which variable to eliminate next; either x or z is fine. To eliminate x next, subtract two times the second equation above from the first: $5z = -5$, and $z = -1$. The second equation above says that $x + 1 = 3$, so $x = 2$. Now substitute both x and z into Eq. (5):

$$2 - y - 1 = 0 \quad \text{so} \quad y = 1$$

To instead eliminate z second instead of x, add 3 times the second equation to the first: $5x = 10$. $x = 2$ and you can substitute to find $z = -1$ and then $y = 1$.

2. Subtract 2 times Eq. (5) from Eq. (6) and add 3 times Eq. (5) to Eq. (7):

$$-x + 3y = 1$$
$$2x - y = 3$$

The exercise doesn't say which variable to eliminate next; either x or y is fine. To eliminate x next, add 2 times the first equation above to the second, getting $5y = 5$, and $y = 1$. Substituting this, say, into the second equation above gives $2x - 1 = 3$, so $x = 2$. Now substitute both x and y into Eq. (5):

$$2 - 1 + z = 0 \quad \text{so} \quad z = -1$$

3. From Eq. (5), $x = y - z$. Substituting in Eq. (6) gives

$$(y - z) + y + 2z = 1$$
$$2y + z = 1$$

Substituting in Eq. (7) gives

$$-(y - z) + 2y - 3z = 3$$
$$y - 2z = 3$$

So you do get the same Eqs. (8–9) as in the example on page 288, where the elimination method was used. The solution may continue exactly as it did there.

4. From Eq. (5), $y = x + z$. Substituting in Eq. (6) gives

$$x + (x + z) + 2z = 1 \tag{1}$$
$$2x + 3z = 1$$

Substituting in Eq. (7) gives

$$-x + 2(x + z) - 3z = 3 \tag{2}$$
$$x - z = 3$$

So you do get the same reduced system as in the solution to Exercise 1. In that exercise, you eliminated y from Eq. (6) by first adding Eq. (5):

$$x - y + z = 0$$
$$x + y + 2z = 1$$
$$\overline{}$$
$$2x + 3z = 1$$

So $x + z$ is added to $x + 2z$ just as in display (1), but it is shown in a different order. Similarly, in that exercise, you eliminated y from Eq. (7) by first adding 2 times Eq. (5):

$$2(x - y + z = 0)$$
$$-x + 2y - 3z = 3$$
$$\overline{}$$
$$x - z = 3$$

So $2(x + z)$ is added to $-x - 3z$ just as in display (2), but it is shown in a different order.

5. The equations for the unknowns a, b, and c are

$$a + b + c = 1 \quad \text{since } f(1) = 1$$
$$4a + 2b + c = 3 \quad \text{since } f(2) = 3$$
$$9a + 3b + c = 6 \quad \text{since } f(3) = 6$$

You might choose to eliminate c first, by subtracting the first equation on the left from the other two:

$$3a + b = 2$$
$$8a + 2b = 5$$

Now you can eliminate b. Subtract two times the first equation from the second to get $2a = 1$. So $a = \frac{1}{2}$, then $b = \frac{1}{2}$, and finally $c = 0$.
So

$$f(x) = \frac{1}{2}(x + x^2) = \frac{x(x + 1)}{2}$$

Is this formula familiar? In hindsight, could you have found the answer another way?

On Your Own

6. If you add the first and third equations, you obtain $-z = -1$, or $z = 1$. This eliminates A, B, and D. Substituting $(-4, 0, 1)$ into the three equations verifies that the correct answer choice is **C**.

7. (a) There is more than one way to eliminate x. You can do it by subtracting the first equation from the others. This is what was done in the text, and what is done in the Gaussian Elimination method of the next lesson. However, it doesn't have to be this way. For instance, you might use the fourth equation, since this can be added to the others, avoiding subtraction.

Subtracting the first equation from the second and third, and adding it to the fourth, replaces the second through fourth equations with

$$-2z + 2w = 1$$
$$-2y + 2w = 2$$
$$2y + 2z = 1$$

(b) Solve for x from the fourth equation: $x = y + z + w - 2$. Substitute this into the other equations, and you get

$$(y+z+w-2)+y+z-w=-1 \Longrightarrow 2y+2z=1$$
$$(y+z+w-2)+y-z+w=0 \Longrightarrow 2y+2w=2$$
$$(y+z+w-2)-y+z+w=1 \Longrightarrow 2z+2w=3$$

Since this solution used the fourth equation to create the substitutions, instead of the first equation you end up with a different 3×3 system in (b) than in (a).

(c) Adding the second equation you got in (a) to the third gives $2z + 2w = 3$. Adding this to the first equation gives $4w = 4$, so $w = 1$. Substitute this value in the first and second equations to get $y = 0$ and $z = \frac{1}{2}$.

(d) Substitute the values of y, z, w from (c) into any one of the original equations and solve for $x = -\frac{1}{2}$.

8. The unknown u only appears in the first equation; neither substitution nor elimination is needed to get a reduced system that does not involve u; just use the last three original equations. Here you could use the elimination method of those equations. Subtract 2 times the first of these from the next and then subtract the first of these from the last, which gives you

$$-3y - z = 1$$
$$y + 2z = 3$$

Next, add 3 times the second equation above to the first, getting $5z = 10$. So $z = 2$, and then substitution in either of these equations gives $y = -1$. Now solve for x, say from $x + y + z = 2$. The result: $x = 1$. Finally, substitute the x, y, z values into the one original equation that involved u:

$$u + 2 + 1 + 2 = 1 \quad \text{so} \quad u = -4$$

9. *Substitution.* $x = 3 - 2y$, so substituting in the second equation,

$$2(3 - 2y) + 4y = 4$$
$$6 = 4$$

Elimination. Subtract two times the first equation from the second, getting $0 = -2$.

Either result is impossible. So the initial assumption, that there *are* values of x and y that satisfy

$$x + 2y = 3$$
$$2x + 4y = 4$$

must be false. Therefore, there is no solution to this system.

10. Subtract two times the first equation from the second; the result is $z = 1$. Substitute this into both equations. The results are

$$x + 2y = 1$$
$$2x + 4y = 2$$

Using both equations doesn't help, because attempts to solve this reduced system don't get anywhere. For instance, subtraction results in $0 = 0$, which is true but

puts no restrictions on x and y. So all you can do with $x + 2y = 1$ is solve it for one variable in terms of the other. For instance, $x = 1 - 2y$. It seems that every triple of the form $(1 - 2y, y, 1)$ is a solution. Indeed, this can be checked by testing these values in the original equations. In particular, there are infinitely many solutions, forming a one-parameter set.

11. (a) Substitute the coordinates of each of the points into the general equation of the circle.

$$(-4 - a)^2 + (0 - b)^2 = r^2$$
$$(0 - a)^2 + (2 - b)^2 = r^2$$
$$(4 - a)^2 + (0 - b)^2 = r^2$$

Multiply everything out, and write each equation so that it has 0 on the right-hand side.

$$16 + 8a + a^2 + b^2 - r^2 = 0$$
$$a^2 + 4 - 4b + b^2 - r^2 = 0$$
$$16 - 8a + a^2 + b^2 - r^2 = 0$$

Subtract the third equation from the first, and you get $16a = 0$, so $a = 0$. Substitute this value into the three equations.

$$16 + b^2 - r^2 = 0$$
$$4 - 4b + b^2 - r^2 = 0$$
$$16 + b^2 - r^2 = 0$$

Subtract the second equation from the first, and you get $12 + 4b = 0$, so $b = -3$. Now, you can use any of the three original equations with $a = 0$ and $b = -3$ to find r.

$$(-4 - 0)^2 + (0 - -3)^2 = r^2$$
$$16 + 9 = r^2$$
$$25 = r^2$$
$$r = 5$$

So $r = 5$ and the center is at $(0, -3)$.

(b) There is a theorem you learned in CME Project *Geometry* that says that if two chords of the same circle intersect, dividing the first into segments of length r, s and the second into segments of length u, v, then $rs = uv$. Note that two of the given points are both on the x-axis and the same distance from the origin. This means that, by symmetry, the center is somewhere on the y-axis, that is, $a = 0$. So let the segment from $(-4, 0)$ to $(4, 0)$ be one chord, and let the other be the diameter $(0, 2)$ to $(0, -y)$. These chords intersect at the origin. This means that $4^2 = 2y$, so $y = 8$. Now you know that the diameter has length 10, so $r = 5$ and the center is $(0, -3)$.

Or, since $a = 0$ you only need to solve for b. The distance from the center $(0, b)$ to the points $(0, 2)$ and $(4, 0)$ must be equal, so you get

$$(2 - b)^2 = 4^2 + b^2$$

and $b = -3$. Then you can find the distance from $(0, -3)$ to any of the three points you know to find the radius. $r = \sqrt{(-4 - 0)^2 + (0 - -3)^2} = \sqrt{25} = 5$.

12. You might choose substitution here, since each variable is already solved for in terms of the others. Substitute the expression for x from the first equation into the others:

$$y = (y + z) + z = y + 2z \quad \text{so} \quad z = 0$$
$$z = (y + z) + y = 2y + z \quad \text{so} \quad y = 0$$

So $x = 0 + 0 = 0$.

13. First, notice that in both parts the first two equations are just the first two equations of Sasha and Derman's system, so you can refer to them as before as Eqs. (1) and (2).

(a) Subtract two times the first equation from the second and subtract 3 times the first equation from the third:

$$-3y - z = 1 \tag{3}$$
$$-2y + z = 4 \tag{4}$$

Now add the two equations to eliminate z:

$$-5y = 5 \quad \text{so} \quad y = -1$$

From this it follows that $z = 2$ and then (from any of the original equations) that $x = 1$.

(b) Subtract 2 times the first equation from both the second and third equations:

$$-3y - z = 1 \tag{5}$$
$$y + 2z = 3 \tag{6}$$

You might also choose to eliminate y, by adding three times Eq. (6) to (5), or to eliminate z, by adding two times (5) to (6). To compare the solution to (b) more easily with the solution to (a), do the latter, getting $-5y = 5$ again. So $y = -1$ again. Furthermore Eqs. (3) and (5) are the same so substitution to get z here in (b) must give the same value as in (a). Then the first equation in (b), as in (a), is Eq. (1) from Sasha and Derman, so substitution in it here gives $x = 1$, just as in part (a).

14. Divide the last equation by 2 and then add the result to the second equation. Subtract 3 times the result from the first equation. Now you have

$$x + 2y = 4$$
$$3y = 3$$
$$z = -1$$

Divide the middle equation by 3 and subtract two times the result from the first equation:

$$x = 2$$
$$y = 1$$
$$z = -1$$

The system is solved.

15. First divide the last equation by 2 and then add or subtract the right multiple of it from the other equations

to eliminate t:

$$2x - 3y + 5z = 17$$
$$5y - z = -11$$
$$7z = 7$$
$$t = 4$$

Repeat the process with z in the first three equations:

$$2x - 3y = 12$$
$$5y = -10$$
$$z = 1$$
$$t = 4$$

Now repeat it with y on the first two equations:

$$2x = 6$$
$$y = -2$$
$$z = 1$$
$$t = 4$$

Finally, scale the first equation:

$$x = 3$$
$$y = -2$$
$$z = 1$$
$$t = 4$$

4.3 Solving Again, in Matrix Form

Check Your Understanding

1. (a) Hopefully, some student will ask, "How do I know what the variables are?" They don't have to be x, y, and z. However, what they are called doesn't really make any difference. The same ordered triple is the solution. Since x, y, z in that order are traditional, the typical answer will be

$$x - y + 2z = 5$$
$$2x - 3y + z = 3$$
$$x + 7z = 16$$

(b) Here is one sequence of matrices. Different sequences are possible depending on when scaling takes place.

$$\begin{pmatrix} 1 & -1 & 2 & | & 5 \\ 2 & -3 & 1 & | & 3 \\ 1 & 0 & 7 & | & 16 \end{pmatrix} \rightarrow \begin{pmatrix} 1 & -1 & 2 & | & 5 \\ 0 & -1 & -3 & | & -7 \\ 0 & 1 & 5 & | & 11 \end{pmatrix} \rightarrow$$

$$\begin{pmatrix} 1 & -1 & 2 & | & 5 \\ 0 & -1 & -3 & | & -7 \\ 0 & 0 & 2 & | & 4 \end{pmatrix} \rightarrow \begin{pmatrix} 1 & -1 & 2 & | & 5 \\ 0 & -1 & -3 & | & -7 \\ 0 & 0 & 1 & | & 2 \end{pmatrix} \rightarrow$$

$$\begin{pmatrix} 1 & -1 & 0 & | & 1 \\ 0 & -1 & 0 & | & -1 \\ 0 & 0 & 1 & | & 2 \end{pmatrix} \rightarrow \begin{pmatrix} 1 & -1 & 0 & | & 1 \\ 0 & 1 & 0 & | & 1 \\ 0 & 0 & 1 & | & 2 \end{pmatrix} \rightarrow$$

$$\begin{pmatrix} 1 & 0 & 0 & | & 2 \\ 0 & 1 & 0 & | & 1 \\ 0 & 0 & 1 & | & 2 \end{pmatrix}$$

So the solution is $(x, y, z) = (2, 1, 2)$.

2. You only need to do the backsubstitution part of the process, shown here in detail. Where blanks are left in the matrix, they represent zeros.

$$\begin{pmatrix} 1 & 1 & 1 & 1 \\ & 2 & 1 & 2 \\ & & 3 & 3 \end{pmatrix} \xrightarrow{\frac{1}{3}(3)} \begin{pmatrix} 1 & 1 & 1 & 1 \\ & 2 & 1 & 2 \\ & & 1 & 1 \end{pmatrix} \xrightarrow[\substack{(2)-(3)}]{(1)-(3)}$$

$$\begin{pmatrix} 1 & 1 & & 0 \\ & 2 & & 1 \\ & & 1 & 1 \end{pmatrix} \xrightarrow{\frac{1}{2}(2)} \begin{pmatrix} 1 & 1 & & 0 \\ & 1 & & \frac{1}{2} \\ & & 1 & 1 \end{pmatrix} \xrightarrow{(1)-(2)}$$

$$\begin{pmatrix} 1 & & & -\frac{1}{2} \\ & 1 & & \frac{1}{2} \\ & & 1 & 1 \end{pmatrix}$$

3. Yes, it will be (if the students do the calculations correctly). It has to be because any basic moves preserve the solution set. Here is the rest of Gaussian elimination done in the standard order.

$$\begin{pmatrix} 1 & 1 & 1 & 2 \\ 0 & -3 & -1 & 1 \\ 0 & 1 & 2 & 3 \end{pmatrix} \xrightarrow{(3)+\frac{1}{3}(2)} \begin{pmatrix} 1 & 1 & 1 & 2 \\ 0 & -3 & -1 & 1 \\ 0 & 0 & \frac{5}{3} & \frac{10}{3} \end{pmatrix}$$

$$\xrightarrow{\frac{3}{5}(3)} \begin{pmatrix} 1 & 1 & 1 & 2 \\ 0 & -3 & -1 & 1 \\ 0 & 0 & 1 & 2 \end{pmatrix} \xrightarrow[\substack{(2)+(3)}]{(1)-(3)} \begin{pmatrix} 1 & 1 & 0 & 0 \\ 0 & -3 & 0 & 3 \\ 0 & 0 & 1 & 2 \end{pmatrix}$$

$$\xrightarrow{-\frac{1}{3}(2)} \begin{pmatrix} 1 & 1 & 0 & 0 \\ 0 & 1 & 0 & -1 \\ 0 & 0 & 1 & 2 \end{pmatrix} \xrightarrow{(1)-(2)} \begin{pmatrix} 1 & 0 & 0 & 1 \\ 0 & 1 & 0 & -1 \\ 0 & 0 & 1 & 2 \end{pmatrix}$$

4. It's the same sequence of matrices as shown in the text on page 517 but in reverse order. Here is the beginning of that reverse sequence with the reasons shown over the arrows.

$$\begin{pmatrix} 1 & 0 & 0 & 1 \\ 0 & 1 & 0 & -1 \\ 0 & 0 & 1 & 2 \end{pmatrix} \xrightarrow[\substack{(1)+(3)}]{(1)+(2)} \begin{pmatrix} 1 & 1 & 1 & 2 \\ 0 & 1 & 0 & -1 \\ 0 & 0 & 1 & 2 \end{pmatrix}$$

$$\xrightarrow{(2)+2(3)} \begin{pmatrix} 1 & 1 & 1 & 2 \\ 0 & 1 & 2 & 3 \\ 0 & 0 & 1 & 2 \end{pmatrix}$$

5. Adding a positive multiple of a row is the same as subtracting the same multiple with the opposite sign. For instance, the matrix operation $(1) + k(2)$ is the same as the basic move $(1) - (k)(-2)$.

6.

$$\begin{pmatrix} 1 & 2 & -3 \\ 2 & -1 & 4 \end{pmatrix} \xrightarrow{(2)-2(1)} \begin{pmatrix} 1 & 2 & -3 \\ 0 & -5 & 10 \end{pmatrix} \xrightarrow{-\frac{1}{5}(2)}$$

$$\begin{pmatrix} 1 & 2 & -3 \\ 0 & 1 & -2 \end{pmatrix} \xrightarrow{(1)-2(2)} \begin{pmatrix} 1 & 0 & 1 \\ 0 & 1 & -2 \end{pmatrix}$$

7. The conditions become

$$2a + 3b = 1 \qquad \text{(because } f(1) = 1\text{)}$$
$$4a + 9b = 10 \qquad \text{(because } f(2) = 10\text{)}$$

Subtracting two times the first equation from the second, and continuing, you get

$$\begin{pmatrix} 2 & 3 & 1 \\ 0 & 3 & 8 \end{pmatrix} \rightarrow \begin{pmatrix} 2 & 3 & 1 \\ 0 & 1 & \frac{8}{3} \end{pmatrix} \rightarrow$$

$$\begin{pmatrix} 2 & 0 & -7 \\ 0 & 1 & \frac{8}{3} \end{pmatrix} \rightarrow \begin{pmatrix} 1 & 0 & -\frac{7}{2} \\ 0 & 1 & \frac{8}{3} \end{pmatrix}$$

So $a = -\frac{7}{2}$, $b = \frac{8}{3}$, and $f(n) = -\frac{7}{2}2^n + \frac{8}{3}3^n$.

8. (a) Each equation represents a line in the plane, and a point satisfies both equations if it is on both lines, that is, if the point is at their intersection. In most cases lines are not parallel, so they intersect at a single point (x, y). However, the two equations could represent parallel lines, in which case there is no intersection and no solution. Or, the two equations could represent the same line, in which case there are infinitely many points of intersection.

(b) Now the system represents m lines in the plane, and it is even more unlikely that they will all share a point in common (or all be the same line), although it remains possible.

(c) Each equation $ax + by + cz = d$ represents a plane in three-dimensional space. Think of it this way. Each equation allows you to solve for one variable in terms of the other two, for instance $z = \frac{1}{c}(d - ax - bx) = \frac{d}{c} - \frac{a}{c}x - \frac{b}{c}y$. So the solution of each equation separately has a point at some height z for every point (x, y). A linear equation represents a flat thing, and a flat thing in three-space with two degrees of freedom (x and y) is a plane. (This is not a proof, but an informal explanation.) The solution(s) to the system are all points (x, y, z) in three-space that are on all m planes. In general (but not always), two planes will have infinitely many intersection points (a whole line's worth), three planes will have a single intersection point, and four or more planes will have no common intersection point.

On Your Own

9. On page 295, the three types of operations are listed. The correct answer choice is **C**.

10.

$$\begin{pmatrix} 1 & 1 & 1 & 3 \\ 2 & -1 & 1 & 2 \\ 1 & 2 & 3 & 6 \end{pmatrix} \xrightarrow{(2)-2(1)} \begin{pmatrix} 1 & 1 & 1 & 3 \\ 0 & -3 & -1 & -4 \\ 1 & 2 & 3 & 6 \end{pmatrix} \xrightarrow{(3)-(1)}$$

$$\begin{pmatrix} 1 & 1 & 1 & 3 \\ 0 & -3 & -1 & -4 \\ 0 & 1 & 2 & 3 \end{pmatrix} \xrightarrow{\text{Switch } (2),(3)} \begin{pmatrix} 1 & 1 & 1 & 3 \\ 0 & 1 & 2 & 3 \\ 0 & -3 & -1 & -4 \end{pmatrix} \xrightarrow{(3)+3(2)}$$

$$\begin{pmatrix} 1 & 1 & 1 & 3 \\ 0 & 1 & 2 & 3 \\ 0 & 0 & 5 & 5 \end{pmatrix} \xrightarrow{\frac{1}{5}(3)} \begin{pmatrix} 1 & 1 & 1 & 3 \\ 0 & 1 & 2 & 3 \\ 0 & 0 & 1 & 1 \end{pmatrix} \xrightarrow[\substack{(2)-2(3)}]{(1)-(3)}$$

$$\begin{pmatrix} 1 & 1 & 0 & 2 \\ 0 & 1 & 0 & 1 \\ 0 & 0 & 1 & 1 \end{pmatrix} \xrightarrow{(1)-(2)} \begin{pmatrix} 1 & 0 & 0 & 1 \\ 0 & 1 & 0 & 1 \\ 0 & 0 & 1 & 1 \end{pmatrix}$$

11. In both cases, the steps to take (what rows to subtract, and what multiples) are the same. In fact, they are the same as in Sasha and Derman's original problem. Here is the work, with both augmented columns shown together to save space.

$$\begin{pmatrix} 1 & 1 & 1 & 1 & 1 \\ 2 & -1 & 1 & -2 & 3 \\ 1 & 2 & 3 & 4 & -1 \end{pmatrix} \xrightarrow{(2)-2(1)} \begin{pmatrix} 1 & 1 & 1 & 1 & 1 \\ 0 & -3 & -1 & -4 & 1 \\ 1 & 2 & 3 & 4 & -1 \end{pmatrix} \xrightarrow{(3)-(1)}$$

$$\begin{pmatrix} 1 & 1 & 1 & 1 & 1 \\ 0 & -3 & -1 & -4 & 1 \\ 0 & 1 & 2 & 3 & -2 \end{pmatrix} \xrightarrow{\text{Switch } (2),(3)} \begin{pmatrix} 1 & 1 & 1 & 1 & 1 \\ 0 & 1 & 2 & 3 & -2 \\ 0 & -3 & -1 & -4 & 1 \end{pmatrix}$$

$$\xrightarrow{(3)+3(2)} \begin{pmatrix} 1 & 1 & 1 & 1 & 1 \\ 0 & 1 & 2 & 3 & -2 \\ 0 & 0 & 5 & 5 & -5 \end{pmatrix} \xrightarrow{\frac{1}{5}(3)} \begin{pmatrix} 1 & 1 & 1 & 1 & 1 \\ 0 & 1 & 2 & 3 & -2 \\ 0 & 0 & 1 & 1 & -1 \end{pmatrix} \xrightarrow[(2)-2(3)]{(1)-(3)}$$

$$\begin{pmatrix} 1 & 1 & 0 & 0 & 2 \\ 0 & 1 & 0 & 1 & 0 \\ 0 & 0 & 1 & 1 & -1 \end{pmatrix} \xrightarrow{(1)-(2)} \begin{pmatrix} 1 & 1 & 0 & -1 & 2 \\ 0 & 1 & 0 & 1 & 0 \\ 0 & 0 & 1 & 1 & -1 \end{pmatrix}$$

12. That $f(x)$ is a linear function means $f(x) = mx + b$, where m and b are to be determined. You know that $f(2) = 2$ and $f(5) = 8$. This gives you

$$2m + b = 2$$
$$5m + b = 8$$

Using Gaussian Elimination in the standard order, write

$$\begin{pmatrix} 2 & 1 & 2 \\ 5 & 1 & 8 \end{pmatrix} \xrightarrow{(2)-\frac{5}{2}(1)} \begin{pmatrix} 2 & 1 & 2 \\ 0 & -\frac{3}{2} & 3 \end{pmatrix} \xrightarrow{-\frac{2}{3}(2)}$$

$$\begin{pmatrix} 2 & 1 & 2 \\ 0 & 1 & -2 \end{pmatrix} \xrightarrow{(1)-(2)} \begin{pmatrix} 2 & 0 & 4 \\ 0 & 1 & -2 \end{pmatrix} \xrightarrow{\frac{1}{2}(1)}$$

$$\begin{pmatrix} 1 & 0 & 2 \\ 0 & 1 & -2 \end{pmatrix}$$

So the linear function is $f(x) = 2x - 2$.

13.

$$\begin{pmatrix} 1 & 1 & 0 & 2 \\ 0 & 1 & 1 & 4 \\ 1 & 0 & 1 & 6 \end{pmatrix} \to \begin{pmatrix} 1 & 1 & 0 & 2 \\ 0 & 1 & 1 & 4 \\ 0 & -1 & 1 & 4 \end{pmatrix} \to$$

$$\begin{pmatrix} 1 & 1 & 0 & 2 \\ 0 & 1 & 1 & 4 \\ 0 & 0 & 2 & 8 \end{pmatrix} \to \begin{pmatrix} 1 & 1 & 0 & 2 \\ 0 & 1 & 1 & 4 \\ 0 & 0 & 1 & 4 \end{pmatrix} \to$$

$$\begin{pmatrix} 1 & 1 & 0 & 2 \\ 0 & 1 & 0 & 0 \\ 0 & 0 & 1 & 4 \end{pmatrix} \to \begin{pmatrix} 1 & 0 & 0 & 2 \\ 0 & 1 & 0 & 0 \\ 0 & 0 & 1 & 4 \end{pmatrix}$$

So $x = 2$, $y = 0$ and $z = 4$.

14. Let the first, second, and third unknown numbers be x, y, z. Then the statements become

$$\frac{x + y}{2} = 1$$
$$\frac{y + z}{2} = 2$$
$$\frac{x + z}{2} = 3$$

This turns into the matrix system

$$\begin{pmatrix} \frac{1}{2} & \frac{1}{2} & 0 & 1 \\ 0 & \frac{1}{2} & \frac{1}{2} & 2 \\ \frac{1}{2} & 0 & \frac{1}{2} & 3 \end{pmatrix}$$

which has the solution $x = 2$, $y = 0$ and $z = 4$, as you can show by Gaussian Elimination, beginning

$$\begin{pmatrix} \frac{1}{2} & \frac{1}{2} & 0 & 1 \\ 0 & \frac{1}{2} & \frac{1}{2} & 2 \\ \frac{1}{2} & 0 & \frac{1}{2} & 3 \end{pmatrix} \to \begin{pmatrix} \frac{1}{2} & \frac{1}{2} & 0 & 1 \\ 0 & \frac{1}{2} & \frac{1}{2} & 2 \\ 0 & -\frac{1}{2} & \frac{1}{2} & 2 \end{pmatrix}$$

$$\to \begin{pmatrix} \frac{1}{2} & \frac{1}{2} & 0 & 1 \\ 0 & \frac{1}{2} & \frac{1}{2} & 2 \\ 0 & 0 & 1 & 4 \end{pmatrix}$$

Or, notice that if you multiply all the equations by 2 to get rid of the fractions, you get exactly the system of Exercise 12.

15. The point is, all the equations need to be written with the variables in the same order, and the constants on the right, so that the equations are ready to be replaced by a matrix. Expanding each of the equations and grouping like terms, you get

$$x + 3y + 2z = 3$$
$$x - \frac{1}{2}y - \frac{1}{2}z = 1$$
$$x + \frac{1}{3}y + \frac{1}{6}z = 1$$

16.

$$\begin{pmatrix} 1 & 1 & 2 & 2 \\ 1 & -1 & 1 & 5 \\ 2 & 2 & 3 & 5 \end{pmatrix} \xrightarrow[(3)-2(1)]{(2)-(1)} \begin{pmatrix} 1 & 1 & 2 & 2 \\ & -2 & -1 & 3 \\ & & -1 & 1 \end{pmatrix} \xrightarrow{-(3)}$$

$$\begin{pmatrix} 1 & 1 & 2 & 2 \\ & -2 & -1 & 3 \\ & & 1 & -1 \end{pmatrix} \xrightarrow[(2)+(3)]{(1)-2(3)} \begin{pmatrix} 1 & 1 & & 4 \\ & -2 & & 2 \\ & & 1 & -1 \end{pmatrix} \xrightarrow{-\frac{1}{2}(2)}$$

$$\begin{pmatrix} 1 & 1 & & 4 \\ & 1 & & -1 \\ & & 1 & -1 \end{pmatrix} \xrightarrow{(1)-(2)} \begin{pmatrix} 1 & & & 5 \\ & 1 & & -1 \\ & & 1 & -1 \end{pmatrix}$$

Notice that there were only a few changes in the original system from Sasha and Derman's system, but that very soon in the solution process it looked very different. The coefficients of the variables play a much more important role in the solution process than the constants on the right.

17.

$$\begin{pmatrix} 1 & -1 & -1 & 0 & 1 \\ 0 & 1 & -1 & -1 & 1 \\ -1 & 0 & 1 & -1 & 1 \\ -1 & -1 & 0 & 1 & 1 \end{pmatrix} \to \begin{pmatrix} 1 & -1 & -1 & 0 & 1 \\ 0 & 1 & -1 & -1 & 1 \\ 0 & -1 & 0 & -1 & 2 \\ 0 & -2 & -1 & 1 & 2 \end{pmatrix} \to$$

$$\begin{pmatrix} 1 & -1 & -1 & 0 & 1 \\ 0 & 1 & -1 & -1 & 1 \\ 0 & 0 & -1 & -2 & 3 \\ 0 & 0 & -3 & -1 & 4 \end{pmatrix} \to \begin{pmatrix} 1 & -1 & -1 & 0 & 1 \\ 0 & 1 & -1 & -1 & 1 \\ 0 & 0 & -1 & -2 & 3 \\ 0 & 0 & 0 & 5 & -5 \end{pmatrix} \to$$

$$\begin{pmatrix} 1 & -1 & -1 & 0 & 1 \\ 0 & 1 & -1 & -1 & 1 \\ 0 & 0 & -1 & -2 & 3 \\ 0 & 0 & 0 & 1 & -1 \end{pmatrix} \to \begin{pmatrix} 1 & -1 & -1 & 0 & 1 \\ 0 & 1 & -1 & 0 & 0 \\ 0 & 0 & -1 & 0 & 1 \\ 0 & 0 & 0 & 1 & -1 \end{pmatrix} \to$$

$$\begin{pmatrix} 1 & -1 & -1 & 0 & | & 1 \\ 0 & 1 & -1 & 0 & | & 0 \\ 0 & 0 & 1 & 0 & | & -1 \\ 0 & 0 & 0 & 1 & | & -1 \end{pmatrix} \rightarrow \begin{pmatrix} 1 & -1 & 0 & 0 & | & 0 \\ 0 & 1 & 0 & 0 & | & -1 \\ 0 & 0 & 1 & 0 & | & -1 \\ 0 & 0 & 0 & 1 & | & -1 \end{pmatrix} \rightarrow$$

$$\begin{pmatrix} 1 & 0 & 0 & 0 & | & -1 \\ 0 & 1 & 0 & 0 & | & -1 \\ 0 & 0 & 1 & 0 & | & -1 \\ 0 & 0 & 0 & 1 & | & -1 \end{pmatrix}$$

18. Let $f(x) = ax^2 + bx + c$. The equations you got using the given points on the function result in the matrix

$$A = \begin{pmatrix} 1 & 1 & 1 & | & 1 \\ 4 & 2 & 1 & | & 3 \\ 9 & 3 & 1 & | & 6 \end{pmatrix}$$

This solution carries out Gaussian elimination in the usual order (clear columns from the left), but it involves some big subtractions. So you might want to try a different approach. One is to feed this matrix into your calculator and use the rref command. You will get the final matrix shown below and can read off the solutions for a, b, c from the rightmost column.

Or, you can do the steps of Gaussian elimination in an unusual order, for instance, subtracting row 1 from rows 2 and 3 to eliminate c instead of a. Or, rewrite the function as $f(x) = c + bx + ax^2$. This reorders the columns of the matrix as well, to

$$B = \begin{pmatrix} 1 & 1 & 1 & | & 1 \\ 1 & 2 & 4 & | & 3 \\ 1 & 3 & 9 & | & 6 \end{pmatrix}$$

and now Gaussian elimination can proceed as usual and get simpler arithmetic.

$$A \rightarrow \begin{pmatrix} 1 & 1 & 1 & | & 1 \\ 0 & -2 & -3 & | & -1 \\ 0 & -6 & -8 & | & -3 \end{pmatrix} \rightarrow$$

$$\begin{pmatrix} 1 & 1 & 1 & | & 1 \\ 0 & -2 & -3 & | & -1 \\ 0 & 0 & 1 & | & 0 \end{pmatrix} \rightarrow \begin{pmatrix} 1 & 1 & 0 & | & 1 \\ 0 & -2 & 0 & | & -1 \\ 0 & 0 & 1 & | & 0 \end{pmatrix} \rightarrow$$

$$\begin{pmatrix} 1 & 1 & 0 & | & 1 \\ 0 & 1 & 0 & | & \frac{1}{2} \\ 0 & 0 & 1 & | & 0 \end{pmatrix} \rightarrow \begin{pmatrix} 1 & 0 & 0 & | & \frac{1}{2} \\ 0 & 1 & 0 & | & \frac{1}{2} \\ 0 & 0 & 1 & | & 0 \end{pmatrix}$$

So $(a, b, c) = \frac{1}{2}(1, 1, 0)$ and $f(x) = \frac{1}{2}(x^2 + x)$.

19. The perimeters are $2(l + w)$, $2(l + h)$ and $2(w + h)$, so these should be set equal to 20, 24, 28 in some order. It doesn't really matter which order, since it is somewhat arbitrary which dimension of the box is called what name. However, since people usually think of $l > w > h$, you can write the equations as follows:

$$2l + 2w = 28$$
$$2l + 2h = 24$$
$$2w + 2h = 20$$

Now switch to matrices. You could divide everything by 2 to start with, but since there will likely be some further

scaling anyway, you might as well wait.

$$\begin{pmatrix} 2 & 2 & 0 & | & 28 \\ 2 & 0 & 2 & | & 24 \\ 0 & 2 & 2 & | & 20 \end{pmatrix} \rightarrow \begin{pmatrix} 2 & 2 & 0 & | & 28 \\ 0 & -2 & 2 & | & -4 \\ 0 & 2 & 2 & | & 20 \end{pmatrix} \rightarrow$$

$$\begin{pmatrix} 2 & 2 & 0 & | & 28 \\ 0 & -2 & 2 & | & -4 \\ 0 & 0 & 4 & | & 16 \end{pmatrix} \rightarrow \begin{pmatrix} 2 & 2 & 0 & | & 28 \\ 0 & -2 & 0 & | & -12 \\ 0 & 0 & 1 & | & 4 \end{pmatrix} \rightarrow$$

$$\begin{pmatrix} 2 & 0 & 0 & | & 16 \\ 0 & 1 & 0 & | & 6 \\ 0 & 0 & 1 & | & 4 \end{pmatrix} \rightarrow \begin{pmatrix} 1 & 0 & 0 & | & 8 \\ 0 & 1 & 0 & | & 6 \\ 0 & 0 & 1 & | & 4 \end{pmatrix}$$

So, the dimensions are 8 in., 6 in., and 4 in.

20. Yes it does. Here are two approaches to show this.
Method 1. You don't know the common perimeter, so call it p. Row reduce the system

$$\begin{pmatrix} 2 & 2 & 0 & | & p \\ 2 & 0 & 2 & | & p \\ 0 & 2 & 2 & | & p \end{pmatrix}$$

Reduction leads to

$$\begin{pmatrix} 1 & 0 & 0 & | & p/4 \\ 0 & 1 & 0 & | & p/4 \\ 0 & 0 & 1 & | & p/4 \end{pmatrix}$$

So all three dimension are the same and the box is a cube.
Method 2. Set each pair of perimeters equal. For example, if $2l + 2w = 2l + 2h$, then $2w - 2h = 0$. Continue this process, and you'll get these three equations:

$$2l - 2w = 0$$
$$2l - 2h = 0$$
$$2w - 2h = 0$$

The reduction in matrix form is

$$\begin{pmatrix} 2 & -2 & 0 & | & 0 \\ 2 & 0 & -2 & | & 0 \\ 0 & 2 & -2 & | & 0 \end{pmatrix} \rightarrow \begin{pmatrix} 2 & -2 & 0 & | & 0 \\ 0 & 2 & -2 & | & 0 \\ 0 & 2 & -2 & | & 0 \end{pmatrix} \rightarrow$$

$$\begin{pmatrix} 2 & -2 & 0 & | & 0 \\ 0 & 1 & -1 & | & 0 \\ 0 & 0 & 0 & | & 0 \end{pmatrix} \rightarrow \begin{pmatrix} 2 & 0 & -2 & | & 0 \\ 0 & 1 & -1 & | & 0 \\ 0 & 0 & 0 & | & 0 \end{pmatrix} \rightarrow$$

$$\begin{pmatrix} 1 & 0 & -1 & | & 0 \\ 0 & 1 & -1 & | & 0 \\ 0 & 0 & 0 & | & 0 \end{pmatrix}$$

Now translate back into equations. Once again, you can drop the equation $0 = 0$ and rewrite the other two with h on the right:

$$l = h$$
$$w = h$$

This means that there are infinitely many solutions (l, w, h), but all three quantities are equal in every one.

21. If the polynomial is $p(x) = a + bx + cx^2 + dx^3$, then you obtain the equations

$$a + b + c + 1d = 1 \qquad \text{since } p(1) = 1$$
$$a + 2b + 4c + 8d = 3 \qquad \text{since } p(2) = 3$$
$$a + 3b + 9c + 27d = 6 \qquad \text{since } p(3) = 6$$
$$1 + 4b + 16c + 64d = 10 \qquad \text{since } p(4) = 10$$

The augmented matrix is

$$\begin{pmatrix} 1 & 1 & 1 & 1 & 1 \\ 1 & 2 & 4 & 8 & 3 \\ 1 & 3 & 9 & 27 & 6 \\ 1 & 4 & 16 & 64 & 10 \end{pmatrix}$$

and the rref is

$$\begin{pmatrix} 1 & 0 & 0 & 0 & 0 \\ 0 & 1 & 0 & 0 & \frac{1}{2} \\ 0 & 0 & 1 & 0 & \frac{1}{2} \\ 0 & 0 & 0 & 1 & 0 \end{pmatrix}$$

So $a = 0$, $b = \frac{1}{2}$, $c = \frac{1}{2}$ and $d = 0$. Notice that the polynomial is a quadratic, not a cubic. In fact, $p(n) = \frac{1}{2}n(n + 1)$, the same formula for the sum of the first n positive integers that you got when you only used three data points.

If the polynomial is written $p(x) = Ax^3 + Bx^2 + Cx + D$, then the matrix is

$$\begin{pmatrix} 1 & 1 & 1 & 1 & 1 \\ 8 & 4 & 2 & 1 & 3 \\ 27 & 9 & 3 & 1 & 6 \\ 64 & 16 & 4 & 1 & 10 \end{pmatrix}$$

and the rref is (again)

$$\begin{pmatrix} 1 & 0 & 0 & 0 & 0 \\ 0 & 1 & 0 & 0 & \frac{1}{2} \\ 0 & 0 & 1 & 0 & \frac{1}{2} \\ 0 & 0 & 0 & 1 & 0 \end{pmatrix}$$

So $p(x) = \frac{1}{2}x^2 + \frac{1}{2}x$ and once again $p(n) = \frac{1}{2}n(n + 1)$. Don't forget to use your calculator when the matrices get big!

22. (a) The reduction is

$$\begin{pmatrix} 1 & 2 & 3 \\ 2 & 4 & 6 \end{pmatrix} \xrightarrow{(2)-2(1)} \begin{pmatrix} 1 & 2 & 3 \\ 0 & 0 & 0 \end{pmatrix}$$

The last matrix represents the system

$$x + 2y = 3$$
$$0 = 0$$

Since $0 = 0$ is always true, you can just drop it; it adds no further restrictions to the first equation. The first equation is the equation of a line, so it has infinitely many pairs of values (x, y) that solve it. Another way to see this is to rewrite it as $x = 3 - 2y$. You can now let y have any value you want, and then there will be one x-value that works with that y-value.

It is instructive to come to the same conclusion using methods of Algebra 1. The two original equations are equations of the same line, so the simultaneous solution is also that line.

(b) Now the reduction is

$$\begin{pmatrix} 1 & 2 & 3 \\ 2 & 4 & 7 \end{pmatrix} \xrightarrow{(2)-2(1)} \begin{pmatrix} 1 & 2 & 3 \\ 0 & 0 & 1 \end{pmatrix}$$

The last matrix represents the system

$$x + 2y = 3$$
$$0 = 1$$

Since $0 = 1$ is always false, you can conclude that the system you started with has *no solutions*: If it did have a solution, that would imply that $0 = 1$.

Again, it is instructive to come to the same conclusion using methods of Algebra 1. The two original equations are equations of parallel lines, so there is no intersection—no simultaneous solution.

Maintain Your Skills

23.

$$x + 3y = 5$$
$$2x + 4y = 6$$

24.

$$\begin{pmatrix} 1 & 3 & 5 \\ 2 & 4 & 6 \end{pmatrix} \rightarrow \begin{pmatrix} 1 & 3 & 5 \\ 0 & -2 & -4 \end{pmatrix} \rightarrow$$
$$\begin{pmatrix} 1 & 3 & 5 \\ 0 & 1 & 2 \end{pmatrix} \rightarrow \begin{pmatrix} 1 & 0 & -1 \\ 0 & 1 & 2 \end{pmatrix}$$

25. To do Gaussian Elimination, you want to put the system into standard form, with the constants on one side (always the right in this book and most books), and the variables in the same order on the other side. In this exercise, one way to rewrite it is as

$$x - y - z = 0$$
$$-x + y - z = 0 \quad \text{(or } x - y + z = 0\text{)}$$
$$-x - y + z = 0$$

You can see that $x = y = z = 0$ is one solution, and Gaussian Elimination shows that it is the only solution, as follows:

$$\begin{pmatrix} 1 & -1 & -1 & 0 \\ -1 & 1 & -1 & 0 \\ -1 & -1 & 1 & 0 \end{pmatrix} \rightarrow \begin{pmatrix} 1 & -1 & -1 & 0 \\ 0 & 0 & -2 & 0 \\ 0 & -2 & 0 & 0 \end{pmatrix}$$

From this you can see that $y = z = 0$, which means that $x = 0$ too, but students should finish the elimination for practice. With two scalings and a row switch, you get the first matrix below, and then do two row subtractions to get the final matrix.

$$\rightarrow \begin{pmatrix} 1 & -1 & -1 & 0 \\ 0 & 1 & 0 & 0 \\ 0 & 0 & 1 & 0 \end{pmatrix} \rightarrow \begin{pmatrix} 1 & 0 & 0 & 0 \\ 0 & 1 & 0 & 0 \\ 0 & 0 & 1 & 0 \end{pmatrix}$$

Note: When the augmentation column starts as all 0's, there is really no point in bothering to write it down. Why not?

26. (a) $\begin{pmatrix} 1 & 0 & -2 \\ 0 & 1 & 3 \end{pmatrix}$

(b) $\begin{pmatrix} 1 & -2 & -2 \\ 0 & 0 & 3 \end{pmatrix}$

(c) $\begin{pmatrix} 1 & -2 & -2 \\ 0 & 0 & 0 \end{pmatrix}$

(d) $\begin{pmatrix} 1 & 0 & -1 & | & 1 \\ 0 & 1 & 2 & | & 2 \\ 0 & 0 & 0 & | & 0 \end{pmatrix}$

(e) same as (d)

(f) $\begin{pmatrix} 1 & 0 & -1 & | & 0 \\ 0 & 1 & 2 & | & 0 \\ 0 & 0 & 0 & | & 1 \end{pmatrix}$

(g) same as (f)

(h) $\begin{pmatrix} 1 & -2 & 0 & | & -2 \\ 0 & 0 & 1 & | & 3 \\ 0 & 0 & 0 & | & 0 \end{pmatrix}$

(i) same as (h)

(j) $\begin{pmatrix} 1 & 3 & 0 & | & -2 \\ 0 & 0 & 1 & | & 3 \\ 0 & 0 & 0 & | & 0 \end{pmatrix}$

(k) same as (j)

(l) $\begin{pmatrix} 1 & 0 & 0 & | & 2 \\ 0 & 1 & -1 & | & 3 \\ 0 & 0 & 0 & | & 0 \end{pmatrix}$

(m) same as (l)

(n) $\begin{pmatrix} 1 & 0 & 0 & | & 2 \\ 0 & 1 & 0 & | & -1 \\ 0 & 0 & 1 & | & 3 \end{pmatrix}$

(o) same as (n)

(p) $\begin{pmatrix} 1 & 0 & 3 & 0 & | & 1 \\ 0 & 1 & 3 & 0 & | & 2 \\ 0 & 0 & 0 & 1 & | & 3 \\ 0 & 0 & 0 & 0 & | & 0 \end{pmatrix}$

(q) $\begin{pmatrix} 1 & 0 & 0 & 3 & | & 1 \\ 0 & 1 & 0 & -1 & | & -2 \\ 0 & 0 & 1 & -2 & | & -1 \\ 0 & 0 & 0 & 0 & | & 0 \end{pmatrix}$

(r) $\begin{pmatrix} 1 & -2 & 3 & 0 & 1 & | & 4 \\ 0 & 0 & 0 & 1 & 3 & | & 5 \end{pmatrix}$ (this matrix equals its rref)

Patterns: The first nonzero entry in any row is a 1 (called the *leading 1*, and that 1 is the only nonzero in its column. All-zero rows appear below any other rows. As you go down the rows, the leading 1 in the row is always farther to the right. In fact, this is what the word *echelon* means. All entries in these rrefs are integers, but examples in the other homework show that this does not always happen.

Another observation: very different-looking matrices can have the same rref.

If the augmentation column has a leading 1, that means the system has no solution.

If students make up matrices at random and find the rrefs, they will discover that the most common result is for the leading 1's to be in consecutive columns. For instance, for a matrix from a 3×3 system, the most common form of a rref on the left of the augmentation line is an identity matrix. Students won't discover this from the specific examples given in the problem, because they were fabricated to show a variety of rrefs, even unusual ones.

27. (d) The original equations are

$$x + 2y + 3z = 5$$
$$2x + 3y + 4z = 8$$
$$3x + 2y + z = 7$$

and the equations represented by the rref are

$$x - z = 1$$
$$y + 2z = 2$$
$$0 = 0$$

If you drop the equation $0 = 0$ (which puts no limitations on the solutions) and rewrite the other equations with the z's on the right (z is the only variable that appears in more than one equation from the rref) you get

$$x = 1 + z$$
$$y = 2 - 2z$$

This form shows that z is a free variable: it can take on any value, but once it does, x and y are completely determined. In this sense you can say the the final set of equations "solves" the problem in way that the original set of equations does not. From the last equations you can state all solutions succinctly and pick out any one solution quickly.

(f) The original equations are

$$x + 2y + 3z = 8$$
$$2x + 3y + 4z = 12$$
$$3x + 2y + z = 6$$

and the equations represented by the rref are

$$x - z = 0$$
$$y + 2z = 0$$
$$0 = 1$$

Since the last equation is impossible, it does not matter what the other equations say. The rref system has no solution, so the original system has no solution.

(h) The original equations are

$$x - 2y + 2z = 4$$
$$2x - 4y + 3z = 5$$
$$3x - 6y + 2z = 0$$

and the equations represented by the rref are

$$x - 2y = -2$$
$$z = 3$$
$$0 = 0$$

Again you can ignore $0 = 0$, but this time the last variable, z is not free. Instead y is. Rewrite the first two equations as

$$x = -2 + 2y$$
$$z = 3$$

This means that for every value of y there is one solution (x, y, z). It happens that the value of z is independent of y, that is, the value of z is fixed. But there is still one solution for each value of y.

(j) The original equations are

$$x + 3y + 2z = 4$$
$$2x + 6y + 3z = 5$$
$$3x + 9y + 2z = 0$$

and the equations represented by the rref are

$$x + 3y = -2$$
$$z = 3$$
$$0 = 0$$

Ignoring $0 = 0$ once again, you find that y, not z, is a free variable, and you may write

$$x = -2 - 3y$$
$$z = 3$$

4A MATHEMATICAL REFLECTIONS

1. (a) There are several ways to solve this system with substitution. One way is to substitute $y = 2x - 3$ from the first equation into the second to get

$$x + 3(2x - 3) = 5$$
$$x + 6x - 9 = 5$$
$$7x = 14$$
$$x = 2$$

$$y = 2(2) - 3$$
$$y = 1$$

Another way is to substitute $x = 5 - 3y$ from the second equation into the first to get

$$2(5 - 3y) - y = 3$$
$$10 - 6y - y = 3$$
$$-7y = -7$$
$$y = 1$$

$$x = 5 - 3(1)$$
$$x = 2$$

(b) Again, there are several ways to solve this system by elimination. Starting with the system

$$2x - y = 3$$
$$x + 3y = 5$$

you might subtract two times the second equation from the first.

$$-7y = -7$$
$$y = 1$$

$$2x - 1 = 3$$
$$x = 2$$

Or, you might add three times the first equation to the second.

$$7x = 14$$
$$x = 2$$
$$2(2) - y = 3$$
$$y = 1$$

2. Because this system is triangular, you can use backsubstitution to solve it, dealing with only one variable at a time.

$$3x - y + 2z = 4$$
$$4y - 3z = 3$$
$$6z = -6$$

Start with the third equation, and find $z = -1$. Substitute this result into the second equation.

$$4y - 3(-1) = 3$$
$$4y = 0$$
$$y = 0$$

Now substitute both of these results into the first equation.

$$3x - 0 + 2(-1) = 4$$
$$3x = 6$$
$$x = 2$$

So your solution is $(x, y, z) = (2, 0, -1)$. You could also write this system as an augmented matrix and use Gaussian Elimination to solve it. That could look like the following sequence of matrices. (Different sequences are possible depending on when scaling takes place.)

$$\begin{pmatrix} 3 & -1 & 2 & | & 4 \\ 0 & 4 & -3 & | & 3 \\ 0 & 0 & 6 & | & -6 \end{pmatrix} \rightarrow \begin{pmatrix} 3 & -1 & 2 & | & 4 \\ 0 & 4 & -3 & | & 3 \\ 0 & 0 & 1 & | & -1 \end{pmatrix} \rightarrow$$

$$\begin{pmatrix} 3 & -1 & 2 & | & 4 \\ 0 & 4 & 0 & | & 0 \\ 0 & 0 & 1 & | & -1 \end{pmatrix} \rightarrow \begin{pmatrix} 3 & -1 & 2 & | & 4 \\ 0 & 1 & 0 & | & 0 \\ 0 & 0 & 1 & | & -1 \end{pmatrix} \rightarrow \begin{pmatrix} 3 & 0 & 2 & | & 4 \\ 0 & 1 & 0 & | & 0 \\ 0 & 0 & 1 & | & -1 \end{pmatrix} \rightarrow$$

$$\begin{pmatrix} 3 & 0 & 0 & | & 6 \\ 0 & 1 & 0 & | & 0 \\ 0 & 0 & 1 & | & -1 \end{pmatrix} \rightarrow \begin{pmatrix} 1 & 0 & 0 & | & 2 \\ 0 & 1 & 0 & | & 0 \\ 0 & 0 & 1 & | & -1 \end{pmatrix}$$

So the solution is $(x, y, z) = (2, 0, -1)$.

3. The most common solution will list the equations in the order they were given, with columns for the variables x, y, and z in alphabetical order. $\begin{pmatrix} 1 & 0 & -3 & | & 5 \\ 0 & 6 & 1 & | & 7 \\ 1 & -2 & 0 & | & 6 \end{pmatrix}$

However, the rows of this matrix could be listed in any order, and the columns for the variables could also be rearranged. If you did rearrange the columns, however, you would have to keep track of the order in which you listed the variables in the matrix *in writing*. Otherwise, when you find the solution, you might assign a value to the wrong variable.

4.
$$\begin{pmatrix} 1 & 1 & 1 & | & 1 \\ 0 & 1 & 2 & | & 4 \\ 3 & 0 & 2 & | & 6 \end{pmatrix} \rightarrow \begin{pmatrix} 1 & 1 & 1 & | & 1 \\ 0 & 1 & 2 & | & 4 \\ 0 & -3 & -1 & | & 3 \end{pmatrix} \rightarrow \begin{pmatrix} 1 & 1 & 1 & | & 1 \\ 0 & 1 & 2 & | & 4 \\ 0 & 0 & 5 & | & 15 \end{pmatrix} \rightarrow$$

$$\begin{pmatrix} 1 & 1 & 1 & | & 1 \\ 0 & 1 & 2 & | & 4 \\ 0 & 0 & 1 & | & 3 \end{pmatrix} \rightarrow \begin{pmatrix} 1 & 1 & 1 & | & 1 \\ 0 & 1 & 0 & | & -2 \\ 0 & 0 & 1 & | & 3 \end{pmatrix} \rightarrow \begin{pmatrix} 1 & 1 & 0 & | & -2 \\ 0 & 1 & 0 & | & -2 \\ 0 & 0 & 1 & | & 3 \end{pmatrix} \rightarrow$$

$$\begin{pmatrix} 1 & 0 & 0 & | & 0 \\ 0 & 1 & 0 & | & -2 \\ 0 & 0 & 1 & | & 3 \end{pmatrix}$$ This final matrix is in row-reduced echelon form, and it gives the solution to the original system of linear equations as $(x, y, z) = (0, -2, 3)$.

5. Sasha should say that there are no solutions to her original system of equations. The last line of the matrix can be interpreted as the equation $0 = 3$. Since this equation is never true, there are no triples (x, y, z) that solve the system of equations represented by this matrix. This matrix, as long as Sasha didn't make any mistakes in her Gaussian Elimination, has to have the same solution set as the original system of equations, so that must also have no solutions.

6. In a system of linear equations, the variables serve only as markers to the coefficients. In solving such an equation you don't need to multiply by the variables or square expressions, but you do need to be sure that you keep all the coefficients that belong to a particular variable associated with that variable. In matrix form, this is done through position. All of the coefficients in any column of the matrix all belong to the same variable in each of the different equations.

7. In Gaussian Elimination, you begin by creating a matrix to represent a system of linear equations. It is conventional to first write each of the equations so that its variables are listed in alphabetical order on the left side with any constant term on the right side, with a vertical line separating the constant terms from the variables—representing the equals sign in the equations.

Then Gaussian Elimination uses the following three steps to change the form of this augmented matrix.

- Scaling: Multiplying a row by a constant
- Switching: Exchanging the order of two of the rows in a matrix
- Subtracting: Replacing a row by its difference with a multiple of another row

Through this process, an augmented matrix is transformed into a matrix in which each row has a leading 1, which means that its first non-zero entry is 1. Then further steps are taken with the goal of making every entry after the leading 1 (except for the entry in the augmentation column) equal to 0. The final matrix is called the row-reduced echelon form, or rref, of the original matrix.

8.
$$\begin{pmatrix} 4 & -1 & 4 & | & 1 \\ 2 & -1 & 8 & | & 11 \\ 2 & -2 & 4 & | & 0 \end{pmatrix} \rightarrow \begin{pmatrix} 4 & -1 & 4 & | & 1 \\ 0 & 1 & -12 & | & -21 \\ 0 & -3 & 4 & | & -1 \end{pmatrix} \rightarrow$$

$$\begin{pmatrix} 4 & -1 & 4 & | & 1 \\ 0 & 1 & -12 & | & -21 \\ 0 & 0 & -32 & | & -64 \end{pmatrix} \rightarrow \begin{pmatrix} 4 & -1 & 0 & | & -7 \\ 0 & 1 & 0 & | & 3 \\ 0 & 0 & 1 & | & 2 \end{pmatrix} \rightarrow$$

$$\begin{pmatrix} 4 & 0 & 0 & | & -4 \\ 0 & 1 & 0 & | & 3 \\ 0 & 0 & 1 & | & 2 \end{pmatrix} \rightarrow \begin{pmatrix} 1 & 0 & 0 & | & -1 \\ 0 & 1 & 0 & | & 3 \\ 0 & 0 & 1 & | & 2 \end{pmatrix}$$ The solution to the original system of linear equations is $(x, y, z) = (-1, 3, 2)$.

INVESTIGATION 4B   MATRIX ALGEBRA

4.4   Getting Started

For You to Explore

1. Since the percentages in the original table are for 1 ounce, multiply each entry by 3 to get the percentages for 3 ounces.

Daily Requirements	
Vitamin A	30%
Vitamin B$_{12}$	75%
carbohydrates	21%

2. Take the entries in the column for cereal with milk and subtract the corresponding entries from the column for cereal to find the entries for the "milk alone" column.

	cereal	with milk	milk alone
Vitamin A	10%	15%	5%
Vitamin B$_{12}$	25%	35%	10%
carbohydrates	7%	9%	2%

3. For the given data, either of the following is fine.

	Boston	Philly	SanFran
Clear	98	93	160
Cloudy	164	160	105

	Clear	Cloudy
Boston	98	164
Philly	93	160
SanFran	160	105

Now, for each city, add the number of clear and cloudy days and subtract from 365. This table shows cloudy days in the middle, between clear and cloudy. The result is either of the following tables.

	Boston	Philly	SanFran
Clear	98	93	160
Part Cldy	103	112	100
Cloudy	164	160	105

	Clear	Part Cldy	Cloudy
Boston	98	103	164
Philly	93	112	160
SanFran	160	100	105

4.
- To find the average number of clear, partly cloudy, and cloudy days for each of the cities for 2 years instead of for 1 year, you could multiply each entry in the original chart by 2 and get a good estimate.
- To find the average number of clear, partly cloudy, and cloudy days for each of the cities for the first half of

the year (January to June), you wouldn't get good results if you just divided each of the entries in the original chart by 2. That's because the months from July to December may have a significantly different average—they're in different seasons.

5. Multiply each entry in the "number" row by the corresponding entry in the "price" row and then add the products to find the total cost.

$$(30)(20) + (25)(15) + (55)(8)$$
$$= 600 + 375 + 440$$
$$= 1415$$

6. Multiply each entry in the "lbs" row by the corresponding entry in the "$/lb" row and add the products to get the total cost.

$$(200)(3.5) + (50)(2) + (250)(1.5) + (100)(3)$$
$$= 700 + 100 + 375 + 300$$
$$= 1475$$

On Your Own

7. Just add entry by entry

All Personal Vehicle Sales in Millions

	A	B	C	D	E
Eur	0.6	0.25	0.3	0.3	1.3
US	4.6	3.3	1.4	2.2	0.4
Asia	0.3	0.15	1.3	4.5	0.1

8. (a) Just subtract expenditure from revenue entry by entry

Revenue in $billions

	A	B	C	D	E
Eur	1	0.5	0	1	6
US	2	−0.5	2	3	0
Asia	−1	−0.5	8	11	−1

(b) Add down columns. The result is a row of profit numbers, which could easily be included as a new bottom row as shown below.

(c) Add across rows. The result is a column of profit numbers. It can easily be included as a new rightmost column as shown below.

Auto Profit in $billions

	A	B	C	D	E	Total
Eur	1	0.5	0	1	6	8.5
US	2	−0.5	2	3	0	6.5
Asia	−1	−0.5	8	11	−1	16.5
Total	2	−0.5	10	15	5	

9. (a) Multiply each entry in the sales table by 1.05.

Passenger Car Sales

	A	B	C	D	E
Eur	0.42	0.21	0.21	0.21	1.05
US	2.1	1.575	0.63	1.05	3.15
Asia	0.21	0.105	0.84	3.675	0.105

(b) Multiply entries in the D column by 1.05, the B column by 1.03, and the E column by 1.02. Leave all the other entries unchanged.

Passenger Car Sales

	A	B	C	D	E
Eur	0.4	0.206	0.2	0.21	1.02
US	2	1.545	0.6	1.05	3.06
Asia	0.2	0.103	0.8	3.675	0.102

(c) Multiply entries in the Europe row by 0.99, the US row by 1.01, and the Asia row by 1.06.

Passenger Car Sales

	A	B	C	D	E
Eur	0.396	0.198	0.198	0.198	0.99
US	2.02	1.515	0.606	1.01	3.03
Asia	0.212	0.106	0.848	3.71	0.106

10. Multiply the size of the tank by the mileage for each truck to find the number of miles possible for that truck. Then add the results to find the total miles for the fleet.

$$20(15) + 18(18) + 12(20) + 15(25)$$
$$= 300 + 324 + 240 + 375$$
$$= 1239$$

11. (a)
$$(30)(20) + (25)(15) + (55)(8) + (25)(20)$$
$$+ (22)(15) + (47)(8)$$
$$= (600 + 375 + 440) + (500 + 330 + 376)$$
$$= (1415) + (1206)$$
$$= 2621$$

The format of the tables might seem confusing at first, and you may have had to look back at the original statement of the problem to interpret them, but you may also have seen the advantage in separating the numbers that had to do with cost per item from those that indicated numbers of items purchased.

(b)
$$(30 + 25)(20) + (25 + 22)(15) + (55 + 47)(8)$$
$$= 1100 + 705 + 816$$
$$= 2621$$

You may have found it simpler to add first and then multiply, because then you only have to do three multiplications instead of six.

Maintain Your Skills

12. Answers will vary, examples are shown.

(a) The first row is 1, 2, 3, the second row is 2, 3, 4, and the third row is 4, 5, 6

(b) $M = \begin{pmatrix} 1\ 2\ 3\ 4 \\ 2\ 3\ 4\ 5 \\ 3\ 4\ 5\ 6 \\ 4\ 5\ 6\ 7 \end{pmatrix}$

(c) This matrix has 10 rows with 12 entries in each row. The rows are numbered from 1 to 10 starting at the top and working down. Each row begins with its row number, and then each subsequent entry is one more than the entry to its left.

(d) The entry in row r and column c is $r + c − 1$.

13. Answers will vary, examples are shown.

(a) The first row is 1, 1, 1, the second row is 2, 4, 8, the third row is 3, 9, 27.

(b) $N = \begin{pmatrix} 1 & 1 & 1 & 1 \\ 2 & 4 & 8 & 16 \\ 3 & 9 & 27 & 81 \\ 4 & 16 & 64 & 256 \end{pmatrix}$

(c) This matrix has 10 rows with 12 entries in each row. The rows are numbered from 1 to 10 starting at the top and working down. Each row begins with its row number, and then each subsequent entry is the row number times the entry to its left.

(d) The entry in row r and column c is r^c.

14. Answers will vary, examples are shown.

(a) The first row is 1, 0, 0, the second row is 0, 1, 0, and the third row is 0, 0, 1.

(b) $I = \begin{pmatrix} 1 & 0 & 0 & 0 & 0 & 0 \\ 1 & 0 & 0 & 0 & 0 & 0 \\ 0 & 1 & 0 & 0 & 0 & 0 \\ 0 & 0 & 1 & 0 & 0 & 0 \\ 0 & 0 & 0 & 1 & 0 & 0 \\ 0 & 0 & 0 & 0 & 1 & 0 \\ 0 & 0 & 0 & 0 & 0 & 1 \end{pmatrix}$

(c) Make an $n \times n$ array of numbers, where every entry is zero except where the row number is equal to the column number—those entries are 1s.

15. (a) If the entries follow the established pattern, the 20th entry would be $10 - 19(3) = -47$.

(b) You could describe this matrix by saying it's a row of 20 numbers, where the first number is 10 and then each number is three less than the number to its left. In symbols, you could say it's a row of 20 numbers where the n-th number is $13 - 3n$. If you think of it as single row of numbers in columns numbered 0 to 19, then you could say that each number is $10 - 3c$, where c is the column number.

(c) You want to multiply corresponding entries and then find the sum of the products. The new matrix has 20 entries, each equal to $2n$ if you count the entries from 1 to 20. So each product would be of the form $2n(13 - 3n) = 26n - 6n^2$. You need to find the sum of these entries for n from 1 to 20, which is $-11,760$.

4.5 Matrix Operations—The Basics

Check Your Understanding

1. (a) 2×3

(b) 2

(c) 4

(d) 6

(e) No such thing! There isn't a third row.

2. (a) $\begin{pmatrix} 3 \\ 6 \\ 11 \\ 18 \end{pmatrix}$

(b) $(3\ 5\ 9\ 17)$

3. (a) $a_{ij} = i + j$. More precisely, $A = (a_{ij})$ where A is 2×3 and $a_{ij} = i + j$.

(b) $b_{ij} = 2(i - 1) + j$

(c) $c_{ij} = (i + j - 1)^i$

Of course, it is not necessary to use i and j. Any other letters that traditionally vary over integers will do.

4. (a) If A and B are both single-row matrices with the same number of entries, then $A + B = C = (c_{ij})$, where $c_{ij} = a_{ij} + b_{ij}$.

(b) If A and B are both single-row matrices with the same number of entries, then $A - B = C = (c_{ij})$, where $c_{ij} = a_{ij} - b_{ij}$.

(c) $kA = C = (c_{ij})$, where $c_{ij} = k \cdot a_{ij}$.

5. You can represent the data as either a row vector (1-row matrix) or a column vector. The box's table is more like a column vector. In fact, students did a very similar exercise before, in column table form, in Exercise 1 in Lesson 4.4. In any event, the matrix operation is scalar multiplication, with scalar 3:

$$3 \begin{pmatrix} 7 \\ 10 \\ 25 \end{pmatrix} = \begin{pmatrix} 21 \\ 30 \\ 75 \end{pmatrix}$$

6. Matrix addition is the operation the teacher should use.
$\begin{pmatrix} 127 & 143 & 107 \\ 181 & 170 & 165 \end{pmatrix} + \begin{pmatrix} 144 & 139 & 126 \\ 184 & 192 & 175 \end{pmatrix}$ This gives you
$\begin{pmatrix} 271 & 282 & 233 \\ 365 & 362 & 340 \end{pmatrix}$

7. You can't just add! A teacher who wants homework (or tests) in each marking period to count equally can average the percentages for each student. But if not, the teacher needs to keep more information about how the tests are supposed to be weighted in order to do the calculation. For instance, a teacher who is adding points needs to know how many points are on each test. Then from the percentages, the teacher can compute the number of points the student got on each test and then add them.

On Your Own

8. $D = \begin{pmatrix} 2 & 4 & 6 \\ 2 & 4 & 6 \\ 2 & 4 & 6 \end{pmatrix}$

9. $\begin{pmatrix} 1 & 2 & 3 & 4 \\ 1 & 4 & 9 & 16 \end{pmatrix}$

10. (a) $\begin{pmatrix} 1 & 0 & 0 & 0 \\ 0 & 1 & 0 & 0 \\ 0 & 0 & 1 & 0 \\ 0 & 0 & 0 & 1 \end{pmatrix}$

(b) $\begin{pmatrix} 1 & 0 \\ 0 & 1 \end{pmatrix}$

(c) $\begin{pmatrix} 1 & 0 & 0 \\ 0 & 1 & 0 \\ 0 & 0 & 1 \\ 0 & 0 & 0 \end{pmatrix}$

11. The question asks for

$$d_{32} + f_{32} = (-3)^{3+2} + 2^{3-2} = -243 + 2 = -241$$

The correct answer choice is **A**.

12. You added the entries for the number of passenger cars to the corresponding entries for other vehicles, which is matrix addition.

13. You subtracted the entries for revenue from the corresponding entries for expenditures, which is matrix subtraction.

14. For the two year averages, you multiplied each entry in the matrix by 2, which is scalar multiplication.

15. The RBI are easy: add the corresponding entries in the first row. You don't have enough information to compute the full-year batting average, though. To find the total average, you'd have to weight the average of the two by the number of at bats used to compute each batting average.

If you had a third row in your table, listing the number of at bats, you could find the total BA, but it would not be a simple operation like addition. Specifically, suppose a player is at bat f times in the first half and s times in the second half. Suppose the player's average in each half is a_f and a_s, respectively. Then the average for the whole season is $(a_f f + a_s s)/(f + s)$.

Maintain Your Skills

16. Substitute the two y-equations on the right into the z-equation on the left:

$$z = 2(3x) + 5(-x)$$
$$= (2 \cdot 3 + 5 \cdot (-1))x$$
$$= x$$

17. Substitute the three y-equations on the right into the z-equation on the left:

$$z = 2(3x) + 5(-x) - 3(4x)$$
$$= (2 \cdot 3 + 5 \cdot (-1) + (-3) \cdot 4)x$$
$$= -11x$$

18. The computation pattern is the same as in several previous exercises, a sum of products. However, in this instance, you have real-number values for y, rather than expressions for y in terms of another variable, x.

$$z = 2(3) + 5(-1) - 3(4)$$
$$= -11$$

19. Bob's spending in dollars is

$$100(1.8) + 150(1.25) + 200(.75) = 517.50.$$

This is exactly parallel to Exercise 18 if you let $z =$ spending in dollars, and

$$y_1 = \text{value in dollars of the pound}$$
$$y_2 = \text{value in dollars of the euro}$$
$$y_3 = \text{value in dollars of the Swiss franc}$$

Then

$$z = 100y_1 + 150y_2 + 200y_3$$
$$y_1 = 1.8, \quad , y_2 = 1.25, \quad y_3 = .75$$

and you just substitute the second line into the first, as in Exercise 18. Only the numerical values are different. You could argue that Exercise 19 is more like Exercise 17, because you should write

$$S = 100p + 150e + 200f \quad \text{and} \quad \begin{array}{l} p = 1.8d \\ e = 1.25d \\ f = .75d \end{array}$$

and substitute to get

$$S = 180d + 187.5d + 150d = 517.5d$$

But this uses p, e, f, d as *units* instead of as *numerical valued variables*. That is, d is just a label for dollars; it is not a number of dollars. In that sense this formulation is not like Exercise 17. However, the substitution rules work the same way for units as for numerical variables.

20.
$$z = a_1b_1x + a_2b_2x + a_3b_3x$$
$$= (a_1b_1 + a_2b_2 + a_3b_3)x$$

21. $\begin{pmatrix} z \\ w \end{pmatrix} = \begin{pmatrix} a_1c_1 + a_2c_2 + a_3c_3 \\ b_1c_1 + b_2c_2 + b_3c_3 \end{pmatrix} x$

4.6 Dot Products

Check Your Understanding

1. Exercises 5, 6, 10, and 11 in Lesson 4.4 are all dot product exercises. In each exercise one row gets dotted with another to get the answer. In Exercise 11 there are two dot products: the varsity number row dotted with the column of prices, and the JV row dotted with the column of prices.

2. In every case except (f) the answer is $1 \cdot 4 + 2 \cdot 5 + 3 \cdot 6 = 32$, even though the computations may be done in a different order. The important point is that dot product commutes and that it doesn't matter whether vectors get written as rows or columns. For (f) the answer is *undefined*, because you can only dot two vectors of the same length.

3. (a) $3^2 + 4^2 = 25$
   (b) $a^2 + b^2$
   (c) $2^2 + 3^2 + 4^2 = 29$
   Hopefully the students will see a connection with the Pythagorean Theorem and with distances in the plane. Maybe they will wonder if (c) has something to do with distances in space. Those who have already seen geometric vectors are more likely to make the connection.

4. In each case there is only one solution of Z. In (a) and (b) it is $Z = (0, 0)$. In (c) it is $Z = (0, 0, 0, 0)$.

5. If X is an n-tuple, then $(0, 0, \ldots, 0)$ is the unique n-tuple that can be added to X without changing its value. So each n-tuple $(0, 0, \ldots, 0)$ is called a zero. There should be no confusion in using the name Z, or $\mathbf{0}$, because only one of them makes sense in any given context. For instance, if you claim that $(1, 2, 3) + Z = (1, 2, 3)$, you must mean $Z = (0, 0, 0)$.

6. (a) $(1, 0, 1) \cdot (x, y, z) + (0, 2, 1) \cdot (x, y, z) - (1, 2, 2) \cdot (x, y, z) = (x + z) + (2y + z) - (x + 2y + 2z) = 0.$

(b) "Factor out" (x, y, z) to get

$$((1, 0, 1) + (0, 2, 1) - (1, 2, 2)) \cdot (x, y, z).$$

This is an instance of the distributive law (of dot product over vector addition) and is valid for dot algebra. But observe: $(1, 0, 1) + (0, 2, 1) - (1, 2, 2) = (0, 0, 0)$. The final answer must be the number 0. See the general solution for Exercise 20.

7. Use the distributive law repeatedly:

$(A + B) \cdot (A + B)$

$= (A + B) \cdot A + (A + B) \cdot B$ (distrib. law)

$= (A \cdot A + B \cdot A) + (A \cdot B + B \cdot B)$ (distrib. law twice)

$= A \cdot A + B \cdot A + A \cdot B + B \cdot B$ (assoc. law for numbers)

$= A \cdot A + A \cdot B + A \cdot B + B \cdot B$ $(B \cdot A = A \cdot B)$

$= A \cdot A + 2A \cdot B + B \cdot B$ (real number grouping)

8. Use the distributive property repeatedly and the commutative property once:

$(A + B) \cdot (A - B) = A \cdot (A - B) + B \cdot (A - B)$

$= (A \cdot A - A \cdot B) + (B \cdot A - B \cdot B)$

$= A \cdot A - A \cdot B + A \cdot B - B \cdot B$

$= A \cdot A - B \cdot B$

9. Let $X = (x_1, x_2, \ldots, x_n)$. By the definition of scalar multiplication, $(-1)X = ((-1)x_1, (-1)x_2, \ldots, (-1)x_n)$. Now you already know for *numbers* that $(-1)x_i = -x_i$. So $(-1)X = (-x_1, -x_2, \ldots, -x_n)$, and $X + (-1)X = (x_1 - x_1, x_2 - x_2, \ldots) = \mathbf{0}$.

10. In light of Exercise 9, the equation in Exercise 10 becomes the special case $k = -1$ of $A \cdot (kB) = k(A \cdot B) = (kA) \cdot B$. and you are done. Note: Exercise 10 says that *negative signs pass through dot products*, and you have just shown that this fact is a special case of the fact that scalars pass through dot products.

On Your Own

11. A dot product is a number, so without calculation you know that A and B are incorrect. It equals

$$3 \cdot 2 + (-5) \cdot 6 + 4 \cdot 7 = 6 - 30 + 28 = 4$$

The correct answer choice is **C**.

12. (a) $1 \cdot x + 0 \cdot y + 0 \cdot z = x.$

(b) y

(c) z

The point here is that dot products can be used to pick out coordinates from a vector.

13. No, because neither side of the proposed equation even makes sense. For instance, since $(B \cdot C)$ is a *number*, it doesn't make sense to dot it with A.

14. (a) $(3, 4) \cdot (4, -3) = 3(4) + 4(-3) = 12 - 12 = 0$

(b) $(3, 4) \cdot (-4, 3) = 3(-4) + 4(3) = -12 + 12 = 0$

(c) $(3, 4) \cdot (8, -6) = 3(8) + 4(-6) = 24 - 24 = 0$

(d) $(a, b) \cdot (b, -a) = ab + b(-a) = ab - ab = 0$

(e) The Zero Product Property says that if $ab = 0$, then either $a = 0$, $b = 0$, or both a and b are equal to zero. In every case above, though, the dot product $A \cdot B = 0$. Yet clearly neither A nor B is a zero vector. (For more on zero vectors, see Exercises 4 and 5). So the Zero Product Property is false for dot products.

15. All the pairs of vectors in Exercise 13 are perpendicular. You can find this out by finding the equation of the line that contains each vector. The slopes of the two lines are negative reciprocals of each other, so the two lines (and the vectors they each contain) are perpendicular.

It turns out that the arrows representing two n-tuples are perpendicular if and only if their dot product is 0. If the dot product is positive, the angle between the tails of the vectors is acute. If the dot product is negative, the angle is obtuse.

16. (a) There are lots of solutions, including $(5, 0)$ and $(1, 2)$.

(b) This has to work because scalars pass through:

$$A \cdot (3, 6) = A \cdot (3(1, 2)) = 3(A \cdot (1, 2)) = 3 \times 5 = 15$$

(c) For one possible answer, set $B = A$. It works because, again, scalars pass through.

(d) If $A = (x, y)$, then $5 = (x, y) \cdot (1, 2) = x + 2y$. Therefore, $y = \frac{5}{2} - \frac{1}{2}x$, and A is any point on this line.

17. Just like Tony and Sasha, write out both $A \cdot B$ and $B \cdot A$ and check that the numbers you get are equal. For ordered pairs, $A \cdot B = a_1b_1 + a_2b_2$ and $B \cdot A = b_1a_1 + b_2a_2$. Further, $a_1b_1 = b_1a_1$ because real number multiplication commutes. Likewise, $a_2b_2 = b_2a_2$, and $A \cdot B = B \cdot A$. For n-tuples,

$$A \cdot B = a_1b_1 + a_2b_2 \cdots + a_nb_n$$
$$= b_1a_1 + b_2a_2 + \cdots + b_na_n$$
$$\text{(real numbers commute)}$$
$$= B \cdot A$$

18. (a) $W = (-1, -2)$

(b) First, note that $\mathbf{0}$ here must be $(0, 0)$, that is, it must have two coordinates. Therefore, $W = (-x, -y)$.

(c) First, $\mathbf{0} = (0, 0, 0, 0)$ and $W = (-1, -2, 3, -\pi)$

19. The condition that $-X$ should satisfy is that $X + (-X) = \mathbf{0}$, where $\mathbf{0}$ has the same length as X. If $X = (x_1, x_2, \ldots, x_n)$ then the one choice that works for $-X$ is $(-x_1, -x_2, \ldots, -x_n)$. Indeed, by the entry-wise rule of vector addition,

$$(x_1, x_2, \ldots, x_n) + (-x_1, -x_2, \ldots, -x_n)$$
$$= (x_1 + -x_1, \ldots, x_n + -x_n) = (0, \ldots, 0) = \mathbf{0}.$$

20. To get a proof for $(B + C)$, replace each $\pm$ with $+$; to get a proof for $(B - C)$ replace each $\pm$ with $-$.

Let $A = (a_1, \ldots, a_n)$, $B = (b_1, \ldots, b_n)$ and $C = (c_1, \ldots, c_n)$. Then by definition

$$B \pm C = (b_1 \pm c_1, \ldots, b_n \pm c_n)$$

and

$$A \cdot (B \pm C) = a_1(b_1 \pm c_1) + \cdots + a_n(b_n \pm c_n)$$

The products on the right are real-number products, so the usual real-number properties apply:

$$A \cdot (B \pm C) = (a_1b_1 \pm a_1c_1) + \cdots + (a_nb_n \pm a_nc_n)$$
$$= (a_1b_1 + \cdots + a_nb_n) \pm (a_1c_1 + \cdots + a_nc_n)$$
$$= A \cdot B \pm A \cdot C,$$

the last line by the definition of dot product.

Note: This exercise asked you to show that dot product distributes over sums on the right. The proof that it distributes over sums on the left is similar. Or, use the commutative property of dot products as follows:

$$(A + B) \cdot C = C \cdot (A + B)$$
$$= C \cdot A + C \cdot B$$
$$= A \cdot C + B \cdot C$$

21. No, there are no dot product inverses, because the expression $A^{-1} \cdot A \cdot X$ doesn't make sense, no matter what n-tuple you propose for A^{-1}. This is because $A \cdot X$ is a *number*, so you can't dot it with any n-tuple. See the solution to Exercise 12.

22. Properties involving the relationship between dots and sums and differences seem to be the same as the number rules for multiplication and sums and differences. But properties involving more than one dot, as in $A \cdot B \cdot C$ generally don't even make sense. Generally properties that involve just one dot product on each side, as in $A \cdot B = B \cdot A$ correspond to real-number properties, but not always. The Zero Product Property is false.

Maintain Your Skills

23. $z_1 = (2, 3, 4) \cdot Y$ and $z_2 = (3, -2, 5) \cdot Y$

24. The common pattern is dot products, but now more of them—one for each z. The computation of z_1 here is exactly the same as the computation of z in Exercise 16:

$$z_1 = 2(3x) + 5(-x) - 3(4x)$$
$$= (2, 5, -3) \cdot (3x, -x, 4x)$$
$$= ((2, 5, -3) \cdot (3, -1, 4))x$$
$$= -11x$$

Second, the computation of z_2 is similar:

$$z_2 = 3(3x) + (-1)(-x) + 1(4x)$$
$$= (3, -1, 1) \cdot (3, -1, 4)x$$
$$= 14x$$

The point is, dot products arise naturally in linear substitutions even if you don't look for them.

Now, given that they do arise, you can do the calculation with dot products from the beginning. For instance, to compute z_1, write

$$Y = (y_1, y_2, y_3) = x(3, -1, 4)$$
$$z_1 = (2, 5, -3) \cdot Y$$
$$= x(2, 5, -3) \cdot (3, -1, 4) \quad \text{(scalars pass through)}$$
$$= -11x$$

A similar calculation can be done for z_2.

25. Substituting the second pair of equations into the first equation, you get

$$a = 3(2x - 3y) + 7(5x + 4y)$$
$$= (3 \cdot 2 + 7 \cdot 5)x + (3 \cdot (-3) + 7 \cdot 4)y$$
$$= (3, 7) \cdot (2, 5)x + (3, 7) \cdot (-3, 4)y$$
$$= 41x + 19y$$

So once again there are dot products, this time two in the same equation.

Here is how to do the calculation with dot products from the beginning, where this time you write the vectors on the right in dot products as columns.

$$a = (3, 7) \cdot \begin{pmatrix} p \\ q \end{pmatrix}$$

$$\begin{pmatrix} p \\ q \end{pmatrix} = x \begin{pmatrix} 2 \\ 5 \end{pmatrix} + y \begin{pmatrix} -3 \\ 4 \end{pmatrix}$$

so a is of the form

$$a = B \cdot (xC + yD) = x(B \cdot C) + y(B \cdot D)$$

26. The calculation for a is exactly the same as in Exercise 24. For b you get

$$b = 1(2x - 3y) + (-2)(5x + 4y)$$
$$= (1 \cdot 2 + (-2) \cdot 5)x + (1 \cdot (-3) + (-2) \cdot 4)y$$
$$= (1, -2) \cdot (2, 5)x + (1, -2) \cdot (-3, 4)y$$
$$= -8x - 11y$$

27. You get the entries of the solution column matrix by dotting the rows of the first given matrix with the column of the second:

$$\begin{pmatrix} -11 \\ 14 \end{pmatrix} = \begin{pmatrix} (2, 5, -3) \cdot (3, -1, 4) \\ (3, -1, 1) \cdot (3, -1, 4) \end{pmatrix}$$

(Note that $(3, -1, 4)$ is a column in the matrix display, but when taking a dot product it is convenient to display it as a row.) If you start with the display

$$\begin{pmatrix} 2 & 5 & -3 \\ 3 & -1 & 1 \end{pmatrix} \begin{pmatrix} 3 \\ -1 \\ 4 \end{pmatrix}$$

you can just go across each row on the left in turn with a finger of your left hand and down the column on the right with a finger of your right hand, multiplying each pair of numbers you point to as you go along.

28. You can get

$$(41, 19) \quad \text{from} \quad (3 \ 7) \begin{pmatrix} 2 & -3 \\ 5 & 4 \end{pmatrix}$$

if you dot the row $(3, 7)$ by each of the columns of the square matrix on its right. That is,

$$(41, 19) = ((3, 7) \cdot (2, 5), \ (3, 7) \cdot (-3, 4))$$

29. (a) From Exercises 25 and 26, read off that the matrix is $\begin{pmatrix} 41 & 19 \\ -8 & -11 \end{pmatrix}$

(b) Every entry in the resulting matrix is a dot product involving a row from the coefficient matrix of the first system and a column from the coefficient matrix of the second system. For instance, the entry in row 2, column 1 of the resulting matrix (the coefficient of x when b is expressed in terms of x and y) is the dot product of the second row of $\begin{pmatrix} 3 & 7 \\ 1 & -2 \end{pmatrix}$ (the row representing b) with the first column of $\begin{pmatrix} 2 & -3 \\ 5 & 4 \end{pmatrix}$ (the column giving the coefficients of x).

4.7 Matrix Multiplication

Check Your Understanding

1. For (a) and (b) the answer is $\begin{pmatrix} a & b \\ c & d \end{pmatrix}$. Multiplying on either side by an identity matrix has no effect. For (c) the product is $\begin{pmatrix} 2a & -3b \\ 2c & -3d \end{pmatrix}$; you have multiplied the first column by 2 and the second by -3. For (d) the product is $\begin{pmatrix} 2a & 2b \\ -3c & -3d \end{pmatrix}$; you have multiplied the first row by 2 and the second by -3.

2. (a)

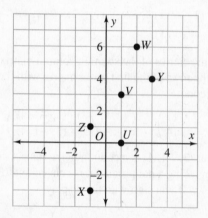

(b) $\begin{pmatrix} 1 \\ 0 \end{pmatrix}, \begin{pmatrix} 1 \\ -3 \end{pmatrix}, \begin{pmatrix} 2 \\ -6 \end{pmatrix}, \begin{pmatrix} -1 \\ 3 \end{pmatrix}, \begin{pmatrix} 3 \\ -4 \end{pmatrix}, \begin{pmatrix} -1 \\ -1 \end{pmatrix}$

(c)

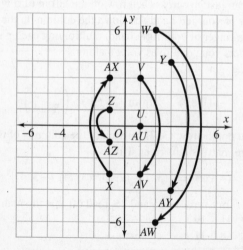

Each point AB is the image after reflection over the x-axis of the point B, where $B = U, \ldots, Z$.

(d) The points BB are

$$\begin{pmatrix} 0 \\ 1 \end{pmatrix}, \begin{pmatrix} -3 \\ 1 \end{pmatrix}, \begin{pmatrix} -6 \\ 2 \end{pmatrix}, \begin{pmatrix} 3 \\ -1 \end{pmatrix}, \begin{pmatrix} -4 \\ 3 \end{pmatrix}, \begin{pmatrix} -1 \\ -1 \end{pmatrix}$$

Each point BB is a 90° counterclockwise rotation of the point B around the origin.

3. (a) $\begin{pmatrix} 2 \\ 5 \\ 6 \end{pmatrix}$; this product picks out the second column in the left factor.

(b) $\begin{pmatrix} 6 \\ 15 \\ 9 \end{pmatrix}$; this product sums the columns in the left factor.

(c) $(5 \; 3 \; 1)$; this product picks out the third row in the right factor.

(d) $(-4 \; -1 \; 2)$; this product subtracts the third row on the right from the first.

(e) and (f) The product in each case is a 3×2 matrix of 0's. Multiplying any matrix by an appropriately sized matrix containing all 0's results in an all 0's matrix, of the size dictated by the factor matrices.

4. (a) $p = x - y$
$q = 3x - 2y$

(b) $2a + b = 3$
$4a + 3b = 5$
$6b = 7$

5. (a) $\begin{pmatrix} x \\ y \\ z \end{pmatrix} = \begin{pmatrix} 2 & -3 & 4 \\ -1 & 2 & \pi \\ 7 & -4 & -2 \end{pmatrix} \begin{pmatrix} u \\ v \\ w \end{pmatrix}$

(b) $\begin{pmatrix} p \\ q \end{pmatrix} = \begin{pmatrix} 2 & 3 & -4 \\ 1 & -3 & 0 \end{pmatrix} \begin{pmatrix} x \\ y \\ z \end{pmatrix}$

(c) $\begin{pmatrix} y_1 \\ y_2 \\ y_3 \end{pmatrix} = x \begin{pmatrix} 3 \\ -1 \\ 4 \end{pmatrix}$

6. The key to all of these is that matrices have to be the same size (shape) for addition, and for multiplication the width (number of columns) of the pre-multiplier, which is the factor on the left, has to be the same as the height (number of rows) of the post-multiplier, which is the factor on the right.

(a) Possible
(b) Not possible
(c) Possible. Any matrix can be multiplied by a scalar.
(d) Not possible. The left matrix needs to have more columns.
(e) Possible; the width of the left matrix is the same as the depth of the right matrix.
(f) Not possible; the right matrix needs to have more rows (longer columns) or else the left matrix needs to be thinner (fewer columns).

(g) Possible; it looks like the left matrix is as wide (as many columns) as the right matrix is deep (number of rows).

(h) Not possible. The left matrix is too wide.

7. Answers will vary, but could include the idea of predicting the size of the product matrix and perhaps checking terms at the corners.

8. (a) Any matrix B with 3 rows, that is, of size $3 \times n$, and now others. This is because A has 3 columns and the post-multiplier matrix must have the same number of rows and the pre-multiplier has columns.

(b) Any matrix B of size $m \times 2$, and no others.

(c) Any matrix B of size 3×2, and no others. Warning: The fact that both AB and BA exist does not mean that $AB = BA$.

9. Suppose A is $m \times n$. Then AB exists whenever B is $n \times p$ for some p. So if AB exists when B is also $m \times n$, that means that $m = n$. So A is square.

A useful consequence is that the only matrices A for which A^2 exists are square matrices.

10. The solution to this exercise is very similar to the solution for Exercise 9. If A is $m \times n$, then B must be $k \times m$ and yet it is also supposed to be $m \times n$. So $m = n$ and A is square.

11. The matrix associated with the equations for z in terms of y is $A = \begin{pmatrix} 1 & 2 \\ 3 & -4 \end{pmatrix}$. The matrix associated with the

equations for y in terms of x is $B = \begin{pmatrix} 2 & -1 \\ 3 & 1 \end{pmatrix}$. The

matrix associated with the equations for z in terms of x is AB (not BA!). Direct calculation gives

$$\begin{pmatrix} 1 & 2 \\ 3 & -4 \end{pmatrix} \begin{pmatrix} 2 & -1 \\ 3 & 1 \end{pmatrix} = \begin{pmatrix} 1 \cdot 2 + 2 \cdot 3 & 1 \cdot -1 + 2 \cdot 1 \\ 3 \cdot 2 + -4 \cdot 3 & 3 \cdot -1 + -4 \cdot 1 \end{pmatrix}$$

$$= \begin{pmatrix} 8 & 1 \\ -6 & -7 \end{pmatrix}$$

The equations you want are

$$z_1 = 8x_1 + x_2$$
$$z_2 = -6x_1 - 7x_2$$

Note: In this case, it probably would have been easier to do the substitution directly. However, given that matrix multiplication is a built-in command for calculators and mathematical software, had there been more variables the matrix method would be the more efficient choice.

12. Let the profit matrix in (a) be P. Adding down columns is a special premultiplication:

$$(1, 1, 1)P$$

Adding across rows is a special postmultiplication:

$$P \begin{pmatrix} 1 \\ 1 \\ 1 \\ 1 \\ 1 \end{pmatrix}$$

13. (a) $\begin{pmatrix} 5 & 10 \\ 1 & 1 \end{pmatrix} \begin{pmatrix} 200 & 150 & 50 \\ 100 & 100 & 85 \end{pmatrix} = \begin{pmatrix} 2000 & 1750 & 1100 \\ 300 & 250 & 135 \end{pmatrix}$.

(b) $\begin{pmatrix} 2000 & 1750 & 1100 \\ 300 & 250 & 135 \end{pmatrix} \begin{pmatrix} 1 \\ 1 \\ 1 \end{pmatrix} = \begin{pmatrix} 4850 \\ 685 \end{pmatrix}$.

14. Let

$$A = \begin{pmatrix} 0.3 & 0.5 \\ 0.3 & 0.2 \\ 0.3 & 0.3 \end{pmatrix}, \qquad B = \begin{pmatrix} 2 & 1 & 3 \\ 3 & 4 & 2 \\ 2 & 2 & 1 \end{pmatrix}$$

The only order in which these can be multiplied is BA, and the size of BA is correct: 3×2. The product is

$$BA = \begin{pmatrix} 1.8 & 2.1 \\ 2.7 & 2.9 \\ 1.5 & 1.7 \end{pmatrix}$$

so for instance, every ounce of cereal A contains 2.7g of vitamin Y.

On Your Own

15. Both products are

$$\begin{pmatrix} a & b & c \\ d & e & f \\ g & h & i \end{pmatrix}$$

one of the original factors.

16. Both products are

$$\begin{pmatrix} a_1 & a_2 \\ b_1 & b_2 \\ c_1 & c_2 \end{pmatrix}$$

one of the original factors.

17. First of all, CA is a 4×2 matrix (rows of the first, columns of the second). Then $B(CA)$ is 2×2. The correct answer choice is **A**.

18. $AB = \begin{pmatrix} 18 & 7 \\ -4 & -11 \end{pmatrix}$, $BA = \begin{pmatrix} 3 & 14 \\ 13 & 4 \end{pmatrix}$.

19. (a) $AB = \begin{pmatrix} 0 \\ 2 \end{pmatrix}$ and $AC = \begin{pmatrix} 11 \\ 25 \end{pmatrix}$. So

$$AB + AC = \begin{pmatrix} 11 \\ 27 \end{pmatrix}.$$

(b) $B + C = \begin{pmatrix} 5 \\ 3 \end{pmatrix}$ and $A \begin{pmatrix} 5 \\ 3 \end{pmatrix} = \begin{pmatrix} 11 \\ 27 \end{pmatrix}$.

The point is that the results are equal because matrix multiplication distributes over addition.

20. (a) $BA = (0 \ 2)$ and $CA = (11 \ 25)$. So $BA + CA = (11 \ 27)$.

(b) $B + C = (5 \ 3)$ and $(5 \ 3)A = (11 \ 27)$.

The point is that the results are equal because matrix multiplication distributes over addition on the left as well as on the right.

21. (a) $BC = \begin{pmatrix} -1 & -6 \\ -1 & -10 \end{pmatrix}$ and $A(BC) = \begin{pmatrix} -3 & -26 \\ -7 & -58 \end{pmatrix}$.

(b) $AB = \begin{pmatrix} 10 & 13 \\ 22 & 29 \end{pmatrix}$ and $(AB)C = \begin{pmatrix} -3 & -26 \\ -7 & -58 \end{pmatrix}$.

It turns out that matrix multiplication does satisfy the associative property, so this exercise gives a first example.

22. Substituting the equations

$$i = 1.1s + 1.3t$$
$$c = 0.5s + 0.3t$$

into the equations

$$p = 120i + 95c$$
$$q = 20i + 52c$$

you get

$$p = 120(1.1s + 1.3t) + 95(.5s + .3t)$$
$$q = 20(1.1s + 1.3t) + 52(.5s + .3t)$$

so

$$p = (120{\cdot}1.1 + 95{\cdot}.5)s + (120{\cdot}1.3 + 95{\cdot}.3)t$$
$$q = (20{\cdot}1.1 + 52{\cdot}.5)s + (20{\cdot}1.3 + 52{\cdot}.3)t$$

which simplifies to

$$p = 179.5s + 184.5t$$
$$q = 48s + 41.6t$$

The substitution method may seem to involve much more writing than the matrix method.

23. Let E (enrollment) be the given matrix.

(a) $(1, 1)E = (316, 303, 286)$ (sum down columns).

(b) $E \begin{pmatrix} 1 \\ 1 \\ 1 \end{pmatrix} = \begin{pmatrix} 438 \\ 467 \end{pmatrix}$ (sum across rows)

(c) You can sum either of the previous two answers: $316 + 303 + 286 = 905 = 438 + 467$. In matrix form this is

$$\left((1, 1)E \right) \begin{pmatrix} 1 \\ 1 \\ 1 \end{pmatrix} = [906] = (1, 1) \left(E \begin{pmatrix} 1 \\ 1 \\ 1 \end{pmatrix} \right)$$

which suggests there is a matrix algebra theorem $(AB)C = A(BC)$.

24. Let S be the matrix

(a) $1.05S$ (scalar multiplication)

(b) $S \begin{pmatrix} 1 & 0 & 0 & 0 & 0 \\ 0 & 1.03 & 0 & 0 & 0 \\ 0 & 0 & 1 & 0 & 0 \\ 0 & 0 & 0 & 1.05 & 0 \\ 0 & 0 & 0 & 0 & 1.02 \end{pmatrix}$

(c) $\begin{pmatrix} 0.99 & 0 & 0 \\ 0 & 1.01 & 0 \\ 0 & 0 & 1.06 \end{pmatrix} S$

25. This arithmetic computation is in an investigation on matrices because it is naturally expressed as a matrix times a column vector:

$$\begin{pmatrix} 5.5 & 0.5 & 3 \\ 5.5 & 0.03 & 0.02 \\ 0.1 & 6 & 1.5 \end{pmatrix} \begin{pmatrix} 9 \\ 20 \\ 5 \end{pmatrix} = \begin{pmatrix} 74.5 \\ 50.2 \\ 128.4 \end{pmatrix}$$
$$= \begin{pmatrix} \text{grams protein} \\ \text{grams fat} \\ \text{grams carbohydrate} \end{pmatrix}$$

26. Let

$$m = \text{number of ounces of meat}$$
$$p = \text{number of ounces of potatoes}$$
$$c = \text{number of ounces of cabbage}$$

Then

(a)
$$5.5m + 0.5p + 3c = 45$$
$$5.5m + 0.03p + 0.02c = 35$$
$$0.1m + 6p + 1.5c = 100$$

(b) $\begin{pmatrix} 5.5 & 0.5 & 3 \\ 5.5 & 0.03 & 0.02 \\ 0.1 & 6 & 1.5 \end{pmatrix} \begin{pmatrix} m \\ p \\ c \end{pmatrix} = \begin{pmatrix} 45 \\ 35 \\ 100 \end{pmatrix}$

27.

$$z_1 = 2y_1 + 5y_2 - 3y_3$$
$$z_2 = 3y_1 - y_2 + y_3$$ becomes

$$\begin{pmatrix} z_1 \\ z_2 \end{pmatrix} = \begin{pmatrix} 2 & 5 & -3 \\ 3 & -1 & 1 \end{pmatrix} \begin{pmatrix} y_1 \\ y_2 \\ y_3 \end{pmatrix}$$

and

$$y_1 = 3x$$
$$y_2 = -x$$ becomes
$$y_3 = 4x$$

$$\begin{pmatrix} y_1 \\ y_2 \\ y_3 \end{pmatrix} = \begin{pmatrix} 3 \\ -1 \\ 4 \end{pmatrix} x$$

The solution was

$$z_1 = -11x$$
$$z_2 = 14x$$

which becomes

$$\begin{pmatrix} z_1 \\ z_2 \end{pmatrix} = \begin{pmatrix} -11 \\ 14 \end{pmatrix} x = \left(\begin{pmatrix} 2 & 5 & -3 \\ 3 & -1 & 1 \end{pmatrix} \begin{pmatrix} 3 \\ -1 \\ 4 \end{pmatrix} \right) x$$

28.

$$a = 3p + 7q$$
$$b = p - 2q$$ becomes $\begin{pmatrix} a \\ b \end{pmatrix} = \begin{pmatrix} 3 & 7 \\ 1 & -2 \end{pmatrix} \begin{pmatrix} p \\ q \end{pmatrix}$

and

$$p = 2x - 3y$$
$$q = 5x + 4y$$ becomes $\begin{pmatrix} p \\ q \end{pmatrix} = \begin{pmatrix} 2 & -3 \\ 5 & 4 \end{pmatrix} \begin{pmatrix} x \\ y \end{pmatrix}$

The solution was

$$a = 41x + 19y$$
$$b = -8x - 11y$$

which becomes

$$\begin{pmatrix} a \\ b \end{pmatrix} = \begin{pmatrix} 41 & 19 \\ -8 & -11 \end{pmatrix} \begin{pmatrix} x \\ y \end{pmatrix} = \left(\begin{pmatrix} 3 & 7 \\ 1 & -2 \end{pmatrix} \begin{pmatrix} 2 & -3 \\ 5 & 4 \end{pmatrix} \right) \begin{pmatrix} x \\ y \end{pmatrix}$$

29. Both equations have to be correct, the first because it restates Theorem 4.1 in matrix form, the second because substitution of equals is always correct. Therefore

$$Z = (AB)X = A(BX)$$

This is an associative property of matrices. It suggests that $(AB)C = A(BC)$ is always true, so long as the matrices are conformable for multiplication. But is it a proof? It really is a proof (assuming a proof of Theorem 4.1) for all A, B, C where C is a column vector, because any matrices A and B can be made to be the matrices of linear systems. In fact, it can be extended to a general proof by arguing that what is true for a single column of a product must be true for every column. This would take some work to state and prove carefully. In any event, from this and earlier exercises you certainly have strong evidence that matrix multiplication is associative.

30. (a) $D = \begin{pmatrix} 1 & 2 & 1 \\ 0 & 1 & -1 \\ 0 & 3 & 3 \end{pmatrix}$

(b) $E = \begin{pmatrix} 1 & 2 & 1 \\ 0 & 1 & -1 \\ 0 & 0 & 6 \end{pmatrix}$

(c) The product is again E.

(d) $A \to D \to E$ are the results of the first two steps of Gaussian Elimination on A. In fact, Gaussian Elimination can always be accomplished by pre-multiplication.

Maintain Your Skills

31. (a) $AB = \begin{pmatrix} 2 \\ 5 \\ 8 \end{pmatrix}$ (the second column of A)

(b) $AB = \begin{pmatrix} -3 \\ -6 \\ -9 \end{pmatrix}$ (minus the third column of A)

(c)
$$AB = \begin{pmatrix} 0 & 0 & 2 \\ 0 & 0 & 5 \\ 0 & 0 & 8 \end{pmatrix}$$

(the only nonzero column is the third, which equals the second column of A)

(d)
$$AB = \begin{pmatrix} 3 & 2 & 1 \\ 6 & 5 & 4 \\ 9 & 8 & 7 \end{pmatrix}$$

(the columns are those of A, but reversed in order)

32. The products are
$$\begin{pmatrix} -4 \\ -6 \\ -8 \end{pmatrix}, \qquad \begin{pmatrix} 2 \\ 4 \\ 6 \end{pmatrix} \text{ and } \begin{pmatrix} -4 & 2 \\ -6 & 4 \\ -8 & 6 \end{pmatrix}$$

33. (a) $(4 \; 5 \; 6)$

(b) $(-7 \; -8 \; -9)$

(c) $\begin{pmatrix} 0 & 0 & 0 \\ 0 & 0 & 0 \\ 4 & 5 & 6 \end{pmatrix}$

(d) $\begin{pmatrix} 7 & 8 & 9 \\ 4 & 5 & 6 \\ 1 & 2 & 3 \end{pmatrix}$

34. The products are
$$EA = (-4 \; -4)$$
$$FA = (0 \; 0)$$
$$GA = \begin{pmatrix} -4 & -4 \\ 0 & 0 \end{pmatrix}$$

35. The product in both cases is
$$\begin{pmatrix} ad - bc & 0 \\ 0 & ad - bc \end{pmatrix} = (ad - bc) \begin{pmatrix} 1 & 0 \\ 0 & 1 \end{pmatrix}$$

36. (a) It exists and equals the dot product $a_1b_1 + a_2b_2 + a_3b_3$. Or rather, AB is the 1×1 matrix whose sole entry is the dot product.

(b) It exists and equals the 3×3 matrix
$$\begin{pmatrix} a_1b_1 & a_2b_1 & a_3b_1 \\ a_1b_2 & a_2b_2 & a_3b_2 \\ a_1b_3 & a_2b_3 & a_3b_3 \end{pmatrix}$$

37. $\begin{pmatrix} 0 & 0 \\ 0 & 0 \end{pmatrix}$ Are you surprised that the Zero Product Property fails? This will be discussed explicitly in a later lesson.

38. Both sides equal $\begin{pmatrix} 11 \\ 22 \end{pmatrix}$. In real-number algebra, if $ab = ac$ then $b = c$, but that's not true for matrices. Cancellation is not a law!

39. $AB = \begin{pmatrix} 1 \\ 1 \end{pmatrix}$ and $A(AB) = \begin{pmatrix} 3 \\ 7 \end{pmatrix}$.

$A^2 = \begin{pmatrix} 7 & 10 \\ 15 & 22 \end{pmatrix}$ and $(A^2)B = \begin{pmatrix} 3 \\ 7 \end{pmatrix}$.

So the answers are the same (associativity holds) but the second method is more work because there is much more to do to compute A^2.

Count the number of operations and see. In fact, if A is $n \times n$ and B is $n \times 1$, the difference in work in computing $(AA)B$ and $A(AB)$ grows more pronounced as n gets large. This exercise is meant to be a concrete low-key introduction to the very large field of efficiency of algorithms.

40. The square of each one of them is I. This shows that the identity matrix, unlike the number 1, can have many square roots (infinitely many, in fact).

4.8 Matrix Inverses

Check Your Understanding

1. The matrix is
$$\begin{pmatrix} 1 & 1 & 1 \\ 2 & -1 & 1 \\ 1 & 2 & 3 \end{pmatrix}$$

The inverse is
$$\begin{pmatrix} 1 & .2 & -.4 \\ 1 & -.4 & -.2 \\ -1 & .2 & .6 \end{pmatrix}$$

Then
$$\begin{pmatrix} 1 & .2 & -.4 \\ 1 & -.4 & -.2 \\ -1 & .2 & .6 \end{pmatrix} \begin{pmatrix} 2 \\ 5 \\ 5 \end{pmatrix} = \begin{pmatrix} 1 \\ -1 \\ 2 \end{pmatrix}$$

as before

2. The equations for the coefficients of the cubic were

$$a + b + c + 1d = 1$$
$$a + 2b + 4c + 8d = 3$$
$$a + 3b + 9c + 27d = 6$$
$$1 + 4b + 16c + 64d = 10$$

so the calculation to do now is

$$\begin{pmatrix} 1 & 1 & 1 & 1 \\ 1 & 2 & 4 & 8 \\ 1 & 3 & 9 & 27 \\ 1 & 4 & 16 & 64 \end{pmatrix}^{-1} \begin{pmatrix} 1 \\ 3 \\ 6 \\ 10 \end{pmatrix} = \begin{pmatrix} 0 \\ \frac{1}{2} \\ \frac{1}{2} \\ 0 \end{pmatrix}$$

So, as before, the polynomial is $\frac{1}{2}(x^2 + x)$.
It is just as well if your calculator doesn't show you the actual inverse matrix, but here it is:

$$\begin{pmatrix} 4 & -6 & 4 & -1 \\ -\frac{13}{3} & \frac{19}{2} & -7 & \frac{11}{6} \\ \frac{3}{2} & -4 & \frac{7}{2} & -1 \\ -\frac{1}{6} & \frac{1}{2} & -\frac{1}{2} & \frac{1}{6} \end{pmatrix}$$

3. (a) The two equations

$$x + 2y = 1$$
$$2x + 4y = 1$$

represent two parallel lines, and therefore there is no solution.

(b)

$$\begin{pmatrix} 1 & 2 & | & 1 \\ 2 & 4 & | & 1 \end{pmatrix} \rightarrow \begin{pmatrix} 1 & 2 & | & 1 \\ 0 & 0 & | & -1 \end{pmatrix}$$

The second row shows that the original system has no solutions.

(c) The calculator tells you that the inverse does not exist.

4. Matrix multiplication is not commutative, so $A^{-1}B$ and BA^{-1} are usually different things, and $\frac{A}{B}$ would be ambiguous. In number algebra, $a^{-1}b = ba^{-1}$, so it is not ambiguous to write $\frac{a}{b}$.

So, which is correct for solving $AX = B$ in matrix algebra, $X = A^{-1}B$ or $X = BA^{-1}$? Well, to undo the A in $AX = B$, you need to get the A^{-1} right next to A. So you multiply on the left (premultiply). Therefore, to preserve the equality, you need to premultiply on the right side as well. So $A^{-1}B$ is the correct expression. Besides, unless A is 1×1, BA^{-1} is not conformable for multiplication anyway.

5. $AM = \begin{pmatrix} 1 & 0 & 0 \\ 3 & 0 & 4 \\ 0 & 0 & 1 \end{pmatrix}$

6. Yes $AM = I$. It turns out that for any square matrix, any *left inverse* is automatically a *right inverse*.

7. Not quite; $a = 0$ is the one exception.

8. No, because for M to be an identity matrix, MX must equal X for all conformable columns X. It is important that M work for all X, because when you solve $AX = B$, you don't know what X is, only its size. See Exercise 11.

On Your Own

9. In matrix form the problem was to solve

$$\begin{pmatrix} 5.5 & 0.5 & 3 \\ 5.5 & 0.03 & 0.02 \\ 0.1 & 6 & 1.5 \end{pmatrix} \begin{pmatrix} m \\ p \\ c \end{pmatrix} = \begin{pmatrix} 45 \\ 35 \\ 100 \end{pmatrix}$$

so the solution is

$$\begin{pmatrix} m \\ p \\ c \end{pmatrix} = \begin{pmatrix} 5.5 & 0.5 & 3 \\ 5.5 & 0.03 & 0.02 \\ 0.1 & 6 & 1.5 \end{pmatrix}^{-1} \begin{pmatrix} 45 \\ 35 \\ 100 \end{pmatrix} = \begin{pmatrix} 6.27 \\ 16.37 \\ 0.77 \end{pmatrix}$$

In other words, feed the recruits 12.22 ounces of meat, 2.22 ounces of potatoes and 22.22 ounces of cabbage!

10. This time the calculation is

$$\begin{pmatrix} 5.5 & 0.5 & 3 \\ 5.5 & 0.03 & 0.02 \\ 0.1 & 6 & 1.5 \end{pmatrix}^{-1} \begin{pmatrix} 45 \\ 35 \\ 120 \end{pmatrix} = \begin{pmatrix} 6.25 \\ 19.84 \\ 0.23 \end{pmatrix}$$

The army should feed the recruits 6.25 ounces of meat, 19.84 ounces of potatoes, and 0.23 ounces of cabbage.

11. You already know that $I = \begin{pmatrix} 1 & 0 \\ 0 & 1 \end{pmatrix}$ is a solution. Now show that it is the only solution. The given matrix equation $\begin{pmatrix} a & b \\ c & d \end{pmatrix} \begin{pmatrix} x \\ y \end{pmatrix} = \begin{pmatrix} x \\ y \end{pmatrix}$ reduces to a system of two linear equations:

$$ax + by = x$$
$$cx + dy = y$$

Remember, the unknowns are a, b, c, and d, and these equations must be satisfied for all x and y. Therefore, you can pick particularly helpful values for x and y, and if these already force $(a, b, c, d) = (1, 0, 0, 1)$, you are done. First pick $x = 1$, $y = 0$. This choice forces $a = 1$, $c = 0$. Now pick $x = 0$, $y = 1$; this forces $b = 0$, $d = 1$.

12. You get the system

$$x + 3y = 1$$
$$2x + 4y = 0$$
$$z + 3w = 0$$
$$2z + 4w = 1$$

So, this system *decomposes* into two 2×2 systems. Each can be solved by traditional methods, but here is a Gaussian elimination solution for the x, y system:

$$\begin{pmatrix} 1 & 3 & | & 1 \\ 2 & 4 & | & 0 \end{pmatrix} \rightarrow \begin{pmatrix} 1 & 3 & | & 1 \\ 0 & -2 & | & -2 \end{pmatrix} \rightarrow$$
$$\begin{pmatrix} 1 & 3 & | & 1 \\ 0 & 1 & | & 1 \end{pmatrix} \rightarrow \begin{pmatrix} 1 & 0 & | & -2 \\ 0 & 1 & | & 1 \end{pmatrix}$$

Similarly, $z = \frac{3}{2}$, $w = -\frac{1}{2}$. Therefore, there is exactly one matrix that solves the original matrix equation:

$$\begin{pmatrix} x & y \\ z & w \end{pmatrix} = \begin{pmatrix} -2 & 1 \\ \frac{3}{2} & -\frac{1}{2} \end{pmatrix}$$

13. This time you get the system

$$x + 2z = 1$$
$$3x + 4z = 0$$
$$y + 2w = 0$$
$$3y + 4w = 1$$

This is quite a different system than in Exercise 12. It still splits into two 2×2 systems, but the variable pairs are different and the coefficients are different. And yet somehow, the solution is the same:

$$\begin{pmatrix} x & y \\ z & w \end{pmatrix} = \begin{pmatrix} -2 & 1 \\ \frac{3}{2} & -\frac{1}{2} \end{pmatrix}$$

Could this be an accident?

14. You want to know when there is a solution $\begin{pmatrix} x & y \\ z & w \end{pmatrix}$ to

$$\begin{pmatrix} x & y \\ z & w \end{pmatrix}\begin{pmatrix} a & b \\ c & d \end{pmatrix} = \begin{pmatrix} 1 & 0 \\ 0 & 1 \end{pmatrix}$$

The first column of the product expands to the system of equations

$$ax + cy = 1$$
$$bx + dy = 0$$

By Theorem 4.6 in CME Project *Algebra 1*, you know this has a solution if and only if $ad - bc \neq 0$ This already shows that $ad - bc \neq 0$ is necessary.

15. The given information says

$$\begin{pmatrix} 1 & 1 & 0 \\ 0 & 1 & 1 \\ 1 & 0 & 1 \end{pmatrix}\begin{pmatrix} x_1 \\ x_2 \\ x_3 \end{pmatrix} = \begin{pmatrix} a_1 \\ a_2 \\ a_3 \end{pmatrix} = \begin{pmatrix} 1 \\ 2 \\ 3 \end{pmatrix}$$

Therefore

$$\begin{pmatrix} x_1 \\ x_2 \\ x_3 \end{pmatrix} = \begin{pmatrix} 1 & 1 & 0 \\ 0 & 1 & 1 \\ 1 & 0 & 1 \end{pmatrix}^{-1}\begin{pmatrix} 1 \\ 2 \\ 3 \end{pmatrix} = \begin{pmatrix} 1 \\ 0 \\ 2 \end{pmatrix}$$

The correct answer choice is **C**.

16. The sum of the three original equations is $2x_1 + 2x_2 + 2x_3 = 6$, so $x_1 + x_2 + x_3 = 3$. Moral: It is often possible to find out something about expressions in unknowns without solving for the unknowns, especially when there is symmetry.

17. No solution. First, the needed inverse matrix does not exist. But this could also mean that there are infinitely many solutions. But here is a way to see that there are not. The sum of the first and third equations is

$$x_1 + x_2 + x_3 + x_4 = 1 + 3 = 4$$

while the sum of the second and fourth equations is

$$x_1 + x_2 + x_3 + x_4 = 2 + 4 = 6$$

These equations are contradictory. (Had the right sides of these two derived equations been the same, then it turns out the exercise would have infinitely many solutions.)

Maintain Your Skills

18. (a) $\begin{pmatrix} 1 & 0 & 0 \\ 0 & \frac{1}{2} & 0 \\ 0 & 0 & 3 \end{pmatrix}$

(b) $\begin{pmatrix} 1 & -1 \\ 0 & 1 \end{pmatrix}$

(c) $\begin{pmatrix} 1 & -\frac{1}{2} & -\frac{1}{12} \\ 0 & \frac{1}{4} & -\frac{5}{24} \\ 0 & 0 & \frac{1}{6} \end{pmatrix}$

(d) $\begin{pmatrix} 1 & 0 & 0 \\ -2 & 1 & 0 \\ 0 & -\frac{1}{2} & \frac{1}{2} \end{pmatrix}$

(e) $\begin{pmatrix} -2 & 1 & 0 & 0 \\ \frac{3}{2} & -\frac{1}{2} & 0 & 0 \\ 0 & 0 & -2 & 1 \\ 0 & 0 & \frac{3}{2} & -\frac{1}{2} \end{pmatrix}$

(f) $\begin{pmatrix} 4 & -6 \\ -6 & 12 \end{pmatrix}$

(g) $\begin{pmatrix} 9 & -36 & 30 \\ -36 & 192 & -180 \\ 30 & -180 & 180 \end{pmatrix}$

4.9 Matrix Properties

Check Your Understanding

1. (a) $I = \begin{pmatrix} 1 & 0 \\ 0 & 1 \end{pmatrix}$

(b) $I = \begin{pmatrix} 1 & 0 & 0 \\ 0 & 1 & 0 \\ 0 & 0 & 1 \end{pmatrix}$

2. If you switch the order of factors in AA, you still get AA, so yes, A and A commute. Also, A and A^2 commute, because $A(A^2) = A(AA) \overset{\text{assoc}}{=} (AA)A = A^2A$.

3. The law is stated in two ways because the commutative law does not hold for matrix multiplication. The number rule $(b + c)a = ba + ca$ need not be stated because it follows from $a(b + c) = ab + ac$ by three applications of $xy = yx$:

$$\begin{aligned} (b + c)a &= a(b + c) \quad \text{(commutative law)} \\ &= ab + ac \quad \text{(given distributive law)} \\ &= ba + ca \quad \text{(commutative law twice)} \end{aligned}$$

However, $(B + C)A = BA + CA$ cannot be gotten from $A(B + C) = AB + AC$ the same way because there is no law $XY = YX$. Nonetheless, both forms of the matrix distributive property are true.

4. (a) Let $B = \begin{pmatrix} b \\ b' \end{pmatrix}$ The first entry of AB is $b + 2b' = 0$. So you know that $b = -2b'$. Plug this into the formula for the second entry of AB and find that it works: $3(-2b') + 6b'$ does equal 0. That is, the second entry adds no further restrictions. So you can

set b' to be anything, say c. This means that B is anything of the form, and only things of the form,
$$\begin{pmatrix} -2c \\ c \end{pmatrix}.$$

(b) Let B_1, B_2 be the two columns of B. They work independently, in that AB_1 is the first column of AB and AB_2 is the second column. So both columns must meet the conditions in (a)—but they may use different c values. This means that B is anything of the form, and only things of the form,
$$B = \begin{pmatrix} -2c & -2d \\ c & d \end{pmatrix}$$

5. Every line is valid except the last:

$(X + Y)^2$

$= (X + Y)(X + Y)$ (meaning of $(X + Y)^2$)

$= X(X + Y) + Y(X + Y)$ $((A + B)C = AC + BC)$

$= (XX + XY) + (YX + YY)$ $(A(B + C) = AB + AC)$

$= X^2 + (XY + YX) + Y^2$ (def of X^2, assoc. prop. addition)

$= X^2 + 2XY + Y^2$ (Error! See below.)

The last step assumes that $YX = XY$ so that $XY + YX$ can be rewritten as $XY + XY = 2XY$. But in general matrices don't commute. So the correct binomial expansion in matrix algebra stops at
$$(X + Y)^2 = X^2 + (XY + YX) + Y^2$$

6. Yes, if as in the example in the text, you write the factors in the order they appear. For instance, in the text, a and b are always after x, y or z, both in the unexpanded form on the left and in the expanded form on the right. In number algebra, the tradition is to rewrite terms in alphabetical order, so xa becomes ax. But in matrix algebra you can't do this, because doing so assumes commutativity.

A careful proof of this expansion principle is by repeated use of the distributive laws.

7.
$$AB = AC$$
$$A^{-1}(AB) = A^{-1}(AC)$$
$$(A^{-1}A)B = (A^{-1}A)C$$
$$IB = IC$$
$$B = C$$

8. If $B = I$ in the pictures, then you have this, where the large dots in I indicate the only places on the two lines where an entry is nonzero. In fact, the entry is 1.

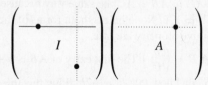

This means that the only entry that matters on the two lines in the A matrix is where the large dot is. That entry gets multiplied by 1 either way. So $AI = IA = A$.

On Your Own

9. By definition of matrix sum, the ij entry of $A + A$ is $a_{ij} + a_{ij}$. By real-number algebra, this is $2a_{ij}$. By definition of scalar multiplication, $2a_{ij}$ is the ij entry of $2A$. So $A + A = 2A$, since the two sides agree entry by entry.

Alternatively, $A + A = 1A + 1A = (1 + 1) = 2A$, where the middle equality is by one of the basic rules.

10. Yes it is. I plays the role of Y in $(X + Y)^2$ in Exercise 5, and I does commute with X, whatever X is. Also, $XI = X$.

11. You already showed in the solution to Exercise 5 that $XY = YX \implies (X + Y)^2 = X^2 + 2XY + Y^2$. As for the converse, suppose $(X + Y)^2 = X^2 + 2XY + Y^2$. You know that in general $(X + Y)^2 = X^2 + XY + YX + Y^2$. So for these assumptions,
$$X^2 + 2XY + Y^2 = X^2 + XY + YX + Y^2$$
Subtracting $X^2 + XY + Y^2$ from both sides, you get $XY = YX$.

12. You need to show that a typical entry of $A(B + C)$, say the ij entry, equals the corresponding entry in $AB + AC$. On the left of $A(B + C) = AB + AC$ you first add $B + C$. Say the result is D. The ij entry of AD is gotten by dotting row i of A with column j of D. Call this dot product $A_i \cdot D_j$. Note that $D_j = B_j + C_j$, where B_j and C_j are the jth columns of B and C. So the ij entry on the left is
$$A_i \cdot (B_j + C_j) = A_i \cdot B_j + A_i \cdot C_j,$$
(distrib. law of dot products)

On the right of $A(B + C) = AB + AC$, compute AB and AC separately and then add. The ij entry of the sum is the sum of the ij entries. The ij entry of AB is $A_i \cdot B_j$; the ij entry of AC is $A_i \cdot C_j$. Then the ij entry on the right is $A_i \cdot B_j + A_i \cdot C_j$, the same as before.

Note that the proof of the distributive law for matrices has been reduced to the distributive law for dot products.

13. (a) $BZ = Z$ no matter what B is. So $BZ = I$ is impossible.

(b) From Exercise 14 of Lesson 4.8, you know that $\begin{pmatrix} a & b \\ c & d \end{pmatrix}$ has a multiplicative inverse if and only if $ad - bc \neq 0$. Any choice of a, b, c, d for which $ad - bc = 0$ gives a noninvertible matrix. For instance setting all 4 values equal to any number r gives such a matrix. More generally
$$ad - bc = 0 \implies \frac{a}{c} = \frac{b}{d}$$
That is, if the ratio of the entries is the same in both columns, the matrix is noninvertible. For instance $\begin{pmatrix} 1 & \pi \\ 7 & 7\pi \end{pmatrix}$ is not invertible.

14. You can either multiply two matrices and then scale, or you can scale the first matrix and then multiply the two resulting matrices, or you can scale the second matrix and multiply the two resulting matrices; you get the same result all 3 ways.

15. The proof here is like the proof of $(X + I)^2 = X^2 + 2X + I$ in Exercise 10, but students will have to observe that $X(bI) = b(XI) = bX$ and $(bI)X = b(IX) = bX$.

16. Answers will vary. Because the commutative property doesn't hold for matrix multiplication and not every matrix has an inverse, there are some differences between matrix algebra and number algebra. For example, when you expand an expression in number algebra, you can rearrange factors in any term and that makes a lot more terms "like terms" that can be combined. In matrix algebra, XY and YX are not like terms. Addition is still commutative for matrices, and both addition and matrix multiplication are still associative. The distributive law still works, but you need two different versions of it because it matters whether the sum is on the left or on the right. Since scalars are different from matrices, you need to also consider how scalar multiplication distributes over a matrix sum, and how scalar products can be associated and pass through matrix products. Every matrix has an additive inverse, and there is always an additive identity matrix of an appropriate size, but some matrices don't have multiplicative inverses and for any non-square matrix the multiplicative identity for multiplication on the left is different from the multiplicative identity for multiplication on the right. The Zero Product Property is false for matrix algebra, and cancellation doesn't work.

17. First $4 = y_{11} = f$. Next $6 = y_{12} = kb = 2k$, so $k = 3$. Then $kc = 3$ and

$$f - k(a - d) = 4 - 3(5 - 4) = 4 - 3 = 1$$

Now

$$YX = \begin{pmatrix} 4 & 6 \\ 3 & 1 \end{pmatrix} \begin{pmatrix} 5 & 2 \\ 1 & 4 \end{pmatrix} = \begin{pmatrix} 26 & 32 \\ 16 & 10 \end{pmatrix}$$

The correct answer choice is **C**.

Maintain Your Skills

18. It's ordinary real-number multiplication: $(a)(b) = (ab)$. Therefore, all 1×1 matrices commute.

19.

$$AD = DA = \begin{pmatrix} ad & & \\ & be & \\ & & cf \end{pmatrix}$$

All $n \times n$ diagonal matrices commute with each other, because all they accomplish is ordinary number multiplication along the main diagonal.

20. (a) If a matrix $\begin{pmatrix} a & b \\ c & d \end{pmatrix}$ commutes under multiplication with $\begin{pmatrix} 0 \\ & 1 \end{pmatrix}$, then

$$\begin{pmatrix} a & b \\ c & d \end{pmatrix} \begin{pmatrix} 0 & 0 \\ 0 & 1 \end{pmatrix} = \begin{pmatrix} 0 & 0 \\ 0 & 1 \end{pmatrix} \begin{pmatrix} a & b \\ c & d \end{pmatrix}$$

$$\begin{pmatrix} 0 & b \\ 0 & d \end{pmatrix} = \begin{pmatrix} 0 & 0 \\ c & d \end{pmatrix}$$

This is true if and only if $b = c = 0$, so any matrix of the form $\begin{pmatrix} a & 0 \\ 0 & d \end{pmatrix}$ will work, and only those.

(b) If a matrix $\begin{pmatrix} a & b & c \\ d & e & f \\ g & h & i \end{pmatrix}$ commutes under multiplication with $\begin{pmatrix} 0 & & \\ & 0 & \\ & & 1 \end{pmatrix}$, then

$$\begin{pmatrix} a & b & c \\ d & e & f \\ g & h & i \end{pmatrix} \begin{pmatrix} 0 & 0 & 0 \\ 0 & 0 & 0 \\ 0 & 0 & 1 \end{pmatrix} = \begin{pmatrix} 0 & 0 & 0 \\ 0 & 0 & 0 \\ 0 & 0 & 1 \end{pmatrix} \begin{pmatrix} a & b & c \\ d & e & f \\ g & h & i \end{pmatrix}$$

$$\begin{pmatrix} 0 & 0 & c \\ 0 & 0 & f \\ 0 & 0 & i \end{pmatrix} = \begin{pmatrix} 0 & 0 & 0 \\ 0 & 0 & 0 \\ g & h & i \end{pmatrix}$$

This is true if and only if $c = f = g = h = 0$, so any matrix of the form $\begin{pmatrix} a & b & 0 \\ d & e & 0 \\ 0 & 0 & i \end{pmatrix}$ will work, and only those.

(c) To expand the expression $(X + I)^3$, the multiplications involved must be possible. This implies that $X + I$ and as a consequence X must be square matrices. The product of a matrix with itself is undefined unless that matrix has the same number of rows as it has columns. Another thing to note is that, although matrix multiplication is not generally commutative, the order of the factors when a square matrix is multiplied by the appropriate identity matrix does not impact the product. In other words, $IX = XI$ for square matrices X. This means that the expansion of $(X + I)^3$ will exactly mirror the number algebra expansion of $(x + 1)^3$.

$$(X + I)^3 = X^3 + 3X^2 + 3X + I$$

(d) As in part (c), X must be square and $XI = IX$, so the expansion of $(X + I)^4$ will exactly mirror the number algebra expansion of $(x + 1)^4$.

$$(X + I)^4 = X^4 + 4X^3 + 6X^2 + 4X + I$$

(e) X and Y must be the same size, so that you can add them, and their sum must be a square matrix, so that you can multiply it by itself. This also means that X and Y must be square. However, you cannot conclude that $XY = YX$, because matrix multiplication is not commutative in general. This means that you will have fewer like terms that you can combine when you compare this expansion to the number algebra expansion of $(x + y)^3$.

$$\begin{aligned} (X + Y)^3 &= (X + Y)(X^2 + XY + YX + Y^2) \\ &= X^3 + X^2Y + XYX + XY^2 + YX^2 \\ &\quad + YXY + Y^2X + Y^3 \\ &= X^3 + X^2Y + XYX + YX^2 + XY^2 \\ &\quad + YXY + Y^2X + Y^3 \end{aligned}$$

As in the correct expansion of $(X + Y)^2$ in Exercise 5, the number of terms of a given degree in each matrix matches the coefficient of the corresponding term in the similar number algebra expansion. For example, the coefficient of the term that has degree 2 in x and degree 1 in y in the expansion of $(x + y)^3$ is 3. There are three terms (X^2Y, XYX, YX^2) with the corresponding degrees in the matrix algebra expansion.

Another pattern you might notice is that there are two terms (2^1) in the expansion of $(X + Y)^1$, four terms (2^2) in $(X + Y)^2$, and eight terms (2^3) in $(X + Y)^3$.

(f) $(X + Y + Z)^2 = X^2 + XY + XZ + YX + Y^2 + YZ$
$$+ ZX + ZY + Z^2$$

A pattern you might notice is that when you square a sum with two addends $((X + Y)^2$ in Exercise 5) you get four terms in the product (2^2), and when you square a sum with three addends $((X + Y + Z)^2)$, you get nine terms in the product (3^2).

4B   MATHEMATICAL REFLECTIONS

1. (a) $3D = \begin{pmatrix} 3(5) & 3(0) \\ 3(1) & 3(-2) \end{pmatrix} = \begin{pmatrix} 15 & 0 \\ 3 & -6 \end{pmatrix}$

   (b) $A + B$ doesn't make sense, because you can only add two matrices if they are of the same size.

   (c) $A - D = \begin{pmatrix} 3-5 & 1-0 \\ -1-1 & 0-(-2) \end{pmatrix} = \begin{pmatrix} -2 & 1 \\ -2 & 2 \end{pmatrix}$

   (d) $B \cdot C = 4(0) + 2(-2) = -4$

   (e) $A \cdot C$ does not make sense. Dot product is an operation defined on n-tuples of equal size. A is not an n-tuple.

   (f) AB does not makes sense, because A has 2 columns and B has only 1 row. To multiply two matrices, the matrix on the left must have the same number of columns as the matrix on the right has rows.

   (g) $AC = \begin{pmatrix} 3(0) + 1(-2) \\ -1(0) + 0(-2) \end{pmatrix} = \begin{pmatrix} -2 \\ 0 \end{pmatrix}$

   (h) $AD = \begin{pmatrix} 3(5) + 1(1) & 3(0) + 1(-2) \\ -1(5) + 0(1) & -1(0) + 0(-2) \end{pmatrix} =$
   $\begin{pmatrix} 16 & -2 \\ -5 & 0 \end{pmatrix}$

2. $E = (a\ b\ c)$ must satisfy the equation $-2a + b + 4c = 0$. There are infinitely many solutions to this equation, including $(0\ 0\ 0)$ and $(2\ 0\ 1)$.

3.
$$F(G + H) = FG + FH$$
$$\begin{pmatrix} 1 & -1 \\ 2 & 0 \end{pmatrix} \begin{pmatrix} -3 & 2 \\ -2 & 4 \end{pmatrix} = \begin{pmatrix} -3 & -3 \\ -6 & 2 \end{pmatrix} + \begin{pmatrix} 2 & 1 \\ 0 & 2 \end{pmatrix}$$
$$\begin{pmatrix} -1 & -2 \\ -6 & 4 \end{pmatrix} = \begin{pmatrix} -1 & -2 \\ -6 & 4 \end{pmatrix}$$

4. $JK \neq KJ$, because JK will be a 3×3 matrix and KJ will be a 2×2 matrix. When you multiply an $a \times b$ matrix by a $b \times c$ matrix, the product is an $a \times c$ matrix.

$$JK = \begin{pmatrix} 2 & 1 & -1 \\ 0 & -4 & 2 \\ 6 & -5 & 1 \end{pmatrix}$$
$$KJ = \begin{pmatrix} 2 & -4 \\ 3 & -3 \end{pmatrix}$$

5. There are many possible 2×2 matrices that don't have an inverse. One example is the matrix $\begin{pmatrix} 1 & 2 \\ 2 & 4 \end{pmatrix}$. You can tell if a 2×2 matrix has no inverse if its discriminant, $ad - bc$, is equal to zero. The discriminant of the example matrix is $1(4) - (2)(2) = 0$, so it has no inverse.

   You could also relate the example matrix to a system of two linear equations, such as
$$x + 2y = 3$$
$$2x + 4y = -1$$

   Such a system of equations either has no solution, or if you choose a system such as
$$x + 2y = 3$$
$$2x + 4y = 6$$

   it has infinitely many solutions. In either case, the matrix has no inverse, because an inverse would imply one unique solution to the system.

   You could also experiment with various matrices on your calculator, until you find one that has no inverse.

6. A dot product is an operation on two n-tuples with the same number of entries that produces a number. To calculate a dot product, find the sum of all the products of corresponding entries from the two n-tuples.

   To multiply the two matrices, the matrix on the left must have the same number of columns as the matrix on the right has rows. Then the entry for the i-th row and j-th column of the product is $R_i \cdot C_j$, the dot product of the i-th row of the matrix on the left and j-th column of the matrix on the right.

7. If $AB = BA$ for two matrices A and B, then you know that A and B are both square matrices of the same size. This is because for the product to exist in both directions, A must have the same number of columns as B has rows and B must have the same number of columns as A has rows. Then, since the two products are equal, you know that the two products are the same size. AB has the same number of rows as A and the same number of columns as B, and BA has the same number of rows as B and the same number of columns as A.

   You also know that a square matrix commutes with itself, with the identity matrix, and with its inverse. So if $B = A$, or I, or A^{-1}, then $AB = BA$.

8. You can write the system of equations as a matrix equation.

$$\begin{pmatrix} 1 & 4 & -1 \\ 2 & -2 & 1 \\ 3 & 1 & -3 \end{pmatrix} \begin{pmatrix} x \\ y \\ z \end{pmatrix} = \begin{pmatrix} -3 \\ 0 \\ 9 \end{pmatrix}$$

Then if you multiply each side on the left by the inverse of the coefficient matrix, you'll solve the system.

$$\begin{pmatrix} 1 & 4 & -1 \\ 2 & -2 & 1 \\ 3 & 1 & -3 \end{pmatrix}^{-1} = \begin{pmatrix} \frac{5}{33} & \frac{1}{3} & \frac{2}{33} \\ \frac{3}{11} & 0 & \frac{-1}{11} \\ \frac{8}{33} & 1 & \frac{-10}{33} \end{pmatrix}$$

so you get

$$\begin{pmatrix} x \\ y \\ z \end{pmatrix} = \begin{pmatrix} \frac{5}{33} & \frac{1}{3} & \frac{2}{33} \\ \frac{3}{11} & 0 & \frac{-1}{11} \\ \frac{8}{33} & 1 & \frac{-10}{33} \end{pmatrix} \begin{pmatrix} -3 \\ 0 \\ 9 \end{pmatrix}$$

$$= \begin{pmatrix} -1 \\ 0 \\ 2 \end{pmatrix}$$

MID-CHAPTER TEST

1. Solve the system by elimination. Multiply the first equation by 3 and the second equation by 2.

$$\begin{cases} 6x - 15y = 3 \\ 6x - 8y = 10 \end{cases}$$

Subtract:

$$-7y = -7$$
$$y = 1$$

Substitute to find x:

$$2x - 5y = 1$$
$$2x - 5(1) = 1$$
$$2x - 5 = 1$$
$$2x = 6$$
$$x = 3$$

The correct choice is **B**, (3, 1).

2. 5 hot dogs at $3.00 each would be $5 \times \$3 = \$15$.
6 hamburgers at $4.00 each would be $6 \times \$4 = \$24$.
11 soft drinks at $1.50 each would be
$11 \times \$1.50 = \$16.50$. So, the total order would cost
$\$15 + \$24 + \$16.50 = \$55.50$. The correct choice is **D**.

3. The dot product of $(-1, 3, 5) \cdot (2, -4, 6)$ is $-1 \cdot 2 + 3 \cdot -4 + 5 \cdot 6 = -2 + -12 + 30 = 16$. The correct choice is **B**.

4. The system represented here is

$$x + 2z = 3$$
$$y = 7$$
$$0 = 0$$

If you drop the equation $0 = 0$ which puts no restrictions on the solutions, you get

$$x = 3 - 2z$$
$$y = 7$$

For every value of z there is one solution. The y value of any solution must be 7. The only choice with $y = 7$ is **B**.

You need to check if $x = 3 - 2z$:

$$x = 3 - 2z$$
$$-1 = 3 - 2(2)$$
$$-1 = 3 - 4$$
$$-1 = -1 \checkmark$$

5. In a_{ij}, i is the row number and j is the column number. So, a_{32} would be the element in the third row and second column, or 11. The correct choice is **D**.

6. First, use the three ordered pairs to write three equations in a, b, and c:

$$a(1)^2 + b(1) + c = 6$$
$$a(2)^2 + b(2) + c = 9$$
$$a(-2)^2 + b(-2) + c = 21$$

or

$$a + b + c = 6 \tag{1}$$
$$4a + 2b + c = 9 \tag{2}$$
$$4a - 2b + c = 21 \tag{3}$$

Subtract equation (1) from equation (2) to get $3a + b = 3$. Subtract equation (1) from equation (3) to get $3a - 3b = 15$. Solve the system:

$$3a + b = 3 \tag{4}$$
$$3a - 3b = 15 \tag{5}$$

by subtracting equation (5) from equation (4) to get:
$4b = -12$ and $b = -3$. Substitute into equation (4) to find a: $3a + (-3) = 3$. So, $3a = 6$ and $a = 2$. Substitute into equation (1) to find c: $2 + (-3) + c = 6$. So, $c = 7$ and $f(x) = 2x^2 - 3x + 7$.

7. (a) The corresponding system is

$$x - 2y + z = -9$$
$$2x + y - 3z = 7$$
$$x + 2y + 4z = -3$$

(b)

$$\begin{pmatrix} 1 & -2 & 1 & | & -9 \\ 2 & 1 & -3 & | & 7 \\ 1 & 2 & 4 & | & -3 \end{pmatrix} \xrightarrow{(3)-(1)} \begin{pmatrix} 1 & -2 & 1 & | & -9 \\ 2 & 1 & -3 & | & 7 \\ 0 & 4 & 3 & | & 6 \end{pmatrix} \xrightarrow{(2)-2(1)}$$

$$\begin{pmatrix} 1 & -2 & 1 & | & -9 \\ 0 & 5 & -5 & | & 25 \\ 0 & 4 & 3 & | & 6 \end{pmatrix} \xrightarrow[5(3)]{4(2)} \begin{pmatrix} 1 & -2 & 1 & | & -9 \\ 0 & 20 & -20 & | & 100 \\ 0 & 20 & 15 & | & 30 \end{pmatrix} \xrightarrow{(3)-(2)}$$

$$\begin{pmatrix} 1 & -2 & 1 & | & -9 \\ 0 & 20 & -20 & | & 100 \\ 0 & 0 & 35 & | & -70 \end{pmatrix} \xrightarrow[(3)\div35]{(2)\div20}$$

$$\begin{pmatrix} 1 & -2 & 1 & | & -9 \\ 0 & 1 & -1 & | & 5 \\ 0 & 0 & 1 & | & -2 \end{pmatrix} \xrightarrow{(2)+(3)} \begin{pmatrix} 1 & -2 & 1 & | & -9 \\ 0 & 1 & 0 & | & 3 \\ 0 & 0 & 1 & | & -2 \end{pmatrix} \xrightarrow[(1)-(3)]{(1)+2(2)}$$

$$\begin{pmatrix} 1 & 0 & 0 & | & -1 \\ 0 & 1 & 0 & | & 3 \\ 0 & 0 & 1 & | & -2 \end{pmatrix}$$ So, the solution is $(-1, 3, -2)$.

8. (a) $A = \begin{pmatrix} 1 + 2(1) = 3 & 1 + 2(2) = 5 & 1 + 2(3) = 7 \\ 2 + 2(1) = 4 & 2 + 2(2) = 6 & 2 + 2(3) = 8 \end{pmatrix}$

(b) $2A = \begin{pmatrix} 2(3)=6 & 2(5)=10 & 2(7)=14 \\ 2(4)=8 & 2(6)=12 & 2(8)=16 \end{pmatrix}$

(c) $A \cdot B = \begin{pmatrix} 3(2)+5(-3)+7(0)=-9 \\ 4(2)+6(-3)+8(0)=-10 \end{pmatrix}$

9. (a) $A + C = \begin{pmatrix} 3+3=6 & -1+1=0 \\ 2+6=8 & 0+-2=-2 \\ -4+0=-4 & 5+4=9 \end{pmatrix}$

(b) $-B = \begin{pmatrix} -2 & 5 & -4 \\ -6 & 4 & 2 \\ -3 & 0 & -8 \\ -4 & -6 & 2 \end{pmatrix}$

(c) Not possible. In order to multiply two matrices, the number of columns in the first matrix must equal the number of rows in the second matrix. Since A has 2 columns and B has 4 rows, you cannot multiply A times B.

(d) $B \cdot A =$
$\begin{pmatrix} 2(3)+-5(2)+4(-4)=-20 & 2(-1)+-5(0)+4(5)=18 \\ 6(3)+-4(2)+-2(-4)=18 & 6(-1)+-4(0)+-2(5)=-16 \\ 3(3)+0(2)+8(-4)=-23 & 3(-1)+0(0)+8(5)=37 \\ 4(3)+6(2)+-2(-4)=32 & 4(-1)+6(0)+-2(5)=-14 \end{pmatrix}$

10. (a) The inverse of a matrix $\begin{pmatrix} a & b \\ c & d \end{pmatrix}$ is $\frac{1}{ad-bc}\begin{pmatrix} d & -b \\ -c & a \end{pmatrix}$

So, the inverse of $D = \begin{pmatrix} 2 & 1 \\ 8 & 3 \end{pmatrix}$ is

$D^{-1} = \frac{1}{6-8}\begin{pmatrix} 3 & -1 \\ -8 & 2 \end{pmatrix} = \begin{pmatrix} -\frac{3}{2} & \frac{1}{2} \\ 4 & -1 \end{pmatrix}$.

(b) $\begin{pmatrix} x \\ y \end{pmatrix} = \begin{pmatrix} -\frac{3}{2} & \frac{1}{2} \\ 4 & -1 \end{pmatrix}\begin{pmatrix} 2 \\ 4 \end{pmatrix} = \begin{pmatrix} -\frac{3}{2}\cdot 2+\frac{1}{2}\cdot 4 \\ 4\cdot 2+-1\cdot 4 \end{pmatrix} = \begin{pmatrix} -1 \\ 4 \end{pmatrix}$

So, $x = -1$ and $y = 4$.

(c) $\begin{cases} 2x + y = 2 \\ 8x + 3y = 4 \end{cases}$

11. In a system of linear equations, the variables serve only as markers to the coefficients. In solving such an equation you don't need to multiply by the variables or square expressions, but you do need to be sure that you keep all the coefficients that belong to a particular variable associated with that variable. In matrix form, this is done through position. All of the coefficients in any column of the matrix all belong to the same variable in each of the different equations.

INVESTIGATION 4C APPLICATIONS OF MATRIX MULTIPLICATION

4.10 Getting Started

For You to Explore

1. (a)

n	0	1	2	3	4	5	6
$s(n)$	1	2	2	4	4	8	8
$t(n)$	1	0	2	0	4	0	8

For n even, $s(n) = 2^{\frac{n}{2}} = t(n)$. For n odd, $s(n) = 2^{\frac{n+1}{2}}$ and $t(n) = 0$.

(b) If you model the function

$$S(n) = \begin{cases} \begin{pmatrix} 1 \\ 1 \end{pmatrix} & \text{if } n = 0 \\ MS(n-1) & \text{if } n > 0 \end{cases}$$

on your calculator, you'll see that it agrees for the first several terms. However, to develop a more complete proof that the two functions are equal you'll need to show that $S(n) = MS(n-1)$ for both n odd and even. For n even, $s(n) = 2^{\frac{n}{2}} = t(n)$. For n odd, $s(n) = 2^{\frac{n+1}{2}}$ and $t(n) = 0$.

If n is odd, then $n - 1$ is even, and $s(n-1) = t(n-1) = 2^{\frac{n-1}{2}}$. This gives you

$S(n) = MS(n-1)$

$= \begin{pmatrix} 1 & 1 \\ 1 & -1 \end{pmatrix}\begin{pmatrix} 2^{\frac{n-1}{2}} \\ 2^{\frac{n-1}{2}} \end{pmatrix}$

$= \begin{pmatrix} 2^{\frac{n-1}{2}} + 2^{\frac{n-1}{2}} \\ 2^{\frac{n-1}{2}} - 2^{\frac{n-1}{2}} \end{pmatrix}$

$= \begin{pmatrix} 2^{\frac{n-1}{2}+1} \\ 0 \end{pmatrix}$

$= \begin{pmatrix} 2^{\frac{n+1}{2}} \\ 0 \end{pmatrix}$

This says that $s(n) = 2^{\frac{n+1}{2}}$ and $t(n) = 0$, which is what you want.

If n is even, then $n - 1$ is odd, and $s(n-1) = 2^{\frac{n}{2}}$ and $t(n-1) = 0$. This gives you

$S(n) = MS(n-1)$

$= \begin{pmatrix} 1 & 1 \\ 1 & -1 \end{pmatrix}\begin{pmatrix} 2^{\frac{n}{2}} \\ 0 \end{pmatrix}$

$= \begin{pmatrix} 2^{\frac{n}{2}} + 0 \\ 2^{\frac{n}{2}} - 0 \end{pmatrix}$

$= \begin{pmatrix} 2^{\frac{n}{2}} \\ 2^{\frac{n}{2}} \end{pmatrix}$

This says that $s(n) = t(n) = 2^{\frac{n}{2}}$, which is what you want.

(c) By calculating, you can show that $S(0) = S(0)$, and in fact that $S(1) = MS(0)$, $S(2) = M^2S(0)$, and so on. Is it true for all n that $S(n) = M^nS(0)$? Assume that it is true for some value $n - 1$ and show that that implies it's true for n.

Given $S(n-1) = M^{n-1}S(0)$. By the definition of the function, you know that $S(n) = MS(n-1)$, but that is equal to $M(M^{n-1}S(0))$. Since matrix multiplication is associative, you can rewrite this expression as $(M^n)S(0)$, and the result is proven.

(d)

$$M = \begin{pmatrix} 1 & 1 \\ 1 & -1 \end{pmatrix}$$

$$M^2 = \begin{pmatrix} 2 & 0 \\ 0 & 2 \end{pmatrix}$$

$$M^3 = \begin{pmatrix} 2 & 2 \\ 2 & -2 \end{pmatrix}$$

$$M^4 = \begin{pmatrix} 4 & 0 \\ 0 & 4 \end{pmatrix}$$

$$M^5 = \begin{pmatrix} 4 & 4 \\ 4 & -4 \end{pmatrix}$$

and so on.

2.

$$A = \begin{pmatrix} 1 & 1 \\ 0 & 1 \end{pmatrix}$$

$$A^2 = \begin{pmatrix} 1 & 2 \\ 0 & 1 \end{pmatrix}$$

$$A^3 = \begin{pmatrix} 1 & 3 \\ 0 & 1 \end{pmatrix}$$

$$A^4 = \begin{pmatrix} 1 & 4 \\ 0 & 1 \end{pmatrix}$$

$$A^5 = \begin{pmatrix} 1 & 5 \\ 0 & 1 \end{pmatrix}$$

$$A^n = \begin{pmatrix} 1 & n \\ 0 & 1 \end{pmatrix}.$$

3. (a)

n	0	1	2	3	4	5	6
$u(n)$	1	2	3	4	5	6	7
$v(n)$	1	1	1	1	1	1	1

$u_n = n + 1$ and $v_n = 1$.

(b) $M = A = \begin{pmatrix} 1 & 1 \\ 0 & 1 \end{pmatrix}$, the same matrix called A in Exercise 2.

(c) From Exercise 2,

$$M^n = \begin{pmatrix} 1 & n \\ 0 & 1 \end{pmatrix}$$

$$M^n U(0) = \begin{pmatrix} 1 & n \\ 0 & 1 \end{pmatrix} \begin{pmatrix} 1 \\ 1 \end{pmatrix} = \begin{pmatrix} n+1 \\ 1 \end{pmatrix} = U(n) \text{ as}$$

claimed.

4. (a) (b)

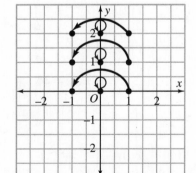

(c) This mapping reflects lines and polygons over the y-axis.

(d) Multiplying by M reflects the plane over the y-axis.

(e) Figures will vary, but whatever figure you draw, it will be reflected over the y-axis.

5. (a) If you reflect the plane over the y-axis, and then reflect it again, every point will be mapped back to itself. This is the identity mapping.

(b)

$$M^2 = \begin{pmatrix} -1 & 0 \\ 0 & 1 \end{pmatrix} \begin{pmatrix} -1 & 0 \\ 0 & 1 \end{pmatrix}$$

$$= \begin{pmatrix} 1 & 0 \\ 0 & 1 \end{pmatrix}$$

$$M^2 X = \begin{pmatrix} 1 & 0 \\ 0 & 1 \end{pmatrix} \begin{pmatrix} x \\ y \end{pmatrix}$$

$$= \begin{pmatrix} x \\ y \end{pmatrix}$$

Every point is mapped to itself, as expected.

6. (a) $\begin{pmatrix} 2 \\ -1 \end{pmatrix}, \begin{pmatrix} -1 \\ 2 \end{pmatrix}, \begin{pmatrix} 0 \\ 0 \end{pmatrix}, \begin{pmatrix} x \\ -y \end{pmatrix}$

(b) $\begin{pmatrix} x \\ y \end{pmatrix} \mapsto \begin{pmatrix} x \\ -y \end{pmatrix} = \begin{pmatrix} 1 & 0 \\ 0 & -1 \end{pmatrix} \begin{pmatrix} x \\ y \end{pmatrix}$. So

$M = \begin{pmatrix} 1 & 0 \\ 0 & -1 \end{pmatrix}$, because it gives the correct X' for every X.

(c) You reflect and reflect back, which results in the identity map, $(x, y) \mapsto (x, y)$. In matrix form you want $X \mapsto R^2 X$, where R is the square matrix in (b). Direct calculation confirms that $R^2 = \begin{pmatrix} 1 & 0 \\ 0 & 1 \end{pmatrix}$, the 2×2 identity matrix.

7. (a) $(1, 2, -3), (1, 2, 3), (2, -1, -4), (0, 0, 0), (x, y, -z)$

(b) $\begin{pmatrix} x \\ y \\ z \end{pmatrix} \mapsto \begin{pmatrix} x \\ y \\ -z \end{pmatrix} = \begin{pmatrix} 1 & 0 & 0 \\ 0 & 1 & 0 \\ 0 & 0 & -1 \end{pmatrix} \begin{pmatrix} x \\ y \\ z \end{pmatrix}$.

(c) You reflect and reflect back, which results in the identity map, $(x, y, z) \mapsto (x, y, z)$. In matrix form you want $X \mapsto R^2 X$, where R is the matrix in (a). Direct calculation confirms that $R^2 = \begin{pmatrix} 1 & 0 & 0 \\ 0 & 1 & 0 \\ 0 & 0 & 1 \end{pmatrix}$.

8. See the example at the beginning of Lesson 4.12, on page 372.

On Your Own

9. (a) (b)

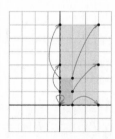

(c) This mapping dilates line segments and polygons by a factor of 3, with the origin as the center of dilation.

(d) M dilates the plane by a factor of 3, with the origin as the center of dilation.

(e) Figures will vary, but the mapping will dilate the figure by a factor of 3, with the center of dilation at the origin.

(f) This mapping scales figures by a factor of 3.

10. (a) If you scale by a factor of 3 twice, you still end up scaling, but by a factor of 9 (not 6, because you *multiply* coordinates by 3 each time).

(b) $M^2 = \begin{pmatrix} 9 & 0 \\ 0 & 9 \end{pmatrix}$, and $M^2 X = \begin{pmatrix} 9x \\ 9y \end{pmatrix}$, as predicted

(c) If you repeat the mapping a third time, you'll end up scaling the plane by a factor of $3^3 = 27$. And this is confirmed by matrix multiplication:
$$M^3 = \begin{pmatrix} 27 & 0 \\ 0 & 27 \end{pmatrix}, \quad M^3 X = \begin{pmatrix} 27x \\ 27y \end{pmatrix}.$$

11. (a) $\begin{pmatrix} -2 \\ -1 \end{pmatrix}, \begin{pmatrix} 1 \\ 2 \end{pmatrix}, \begin{pmatrix} 0 \\ 0 \end{pmatrix}, \begin{pmatrix} -x \\ -y \end{pmatrix}$

(b) $\begin{pmatrix} x \\ y \end{pmatrix} \mapsto \begin{pmatrix} -x \\ -y \end{pmatrix} = \begin{pmatrix} -1 & 0 \\ 0 & -1 \end{pmatrix} \begin{pmatrix} x \\ y \end{pmatrix}$. So the matrix M is $\begin{pmatrix} -1 & 0 \\ 0 & -1 \end{pmatrix}$, and rotating 180° has the same effect as scaling by the factor -1.

(c) Rotating twice by 180° in the same direction amounts to a rotation of 360°, which results in the identity map, $(x, y) \mapsto (x, y)$. In matrix form you want $X \mapsto R^2 X$, where R is the square matrix in (a). Direct calculation confirms that $R^2 = \begin{pmatrix} 1 & 0 \\ 0 & 1 \end{pmatrix}$, the 2×2 identity matrix.

12. If you rotate by 30° counterclockwise and then do it again, the effect is to rotate by 60° counterclockwise.

13. Countryside and city both begin with c, so let's talk about rural and urban. Let $r(n)$ be the rural population n years from the start of 2007; let $u(n)$ be the urban population then. If 35% of the rural population at year n moves to the cities, that means that 65% stays in the countryside, since you're told to assume that there are no births and death or movement in or out of the country. Similarly, 95% of the city dwellers stay there. Therefore you have
$$r(n + 1) = 0.65r(n) + 0.05u(n)$$
$$u(n + 1) = 0.35r(n) + 0.95u(n)$$
$$r(0) = 8$$
$$u(0) = 4$$

With this information you can compute, but a matrix helps further.
$$\begin{pmatrix} r(n+1) \\ u(n+1) \end{pmatrix} = \begin{pmatrix} 0.65 & 0.05 \\ 0.35 & 0.95 \end{pmatrix} \begin{pmatrix} r(n) \\ u(n) \end{pmatrix}$$

So, define $A = \begin{pmatrix} 0.65 & 0.05 \\ 0.35 & 0.95 \end{pmatrix}$ and $P(n) = \begin{pmatrix} r(n) \\ u(n) \end{pmatrix}$ Then
$$P(1) = A\,P(0), \quad P(2) = A\,P(1)$$
$$= A^2\,P(0), \ldots, P(n) = A^n\,P(0)$$

Here are the first 10 years worth of values of $P(n)$, to two decimal places:
$$\begin{pmatrix} 5.4 \\ 6.6 \end{pmatrix}, \begin{pmatrix} 3.84 \\ 8.16 \end{pmatrix}, \begin{pmatrix} 2.90 \\ 9.10 \end{pmatrix}, \begin{pmatrix} 2.34 \\ 9.66 \end{pmatrix}, \begin{pmatrix} 2.01 \\ 9.99 \end{pmatrix},$$
$$\begin{pmatrix} 1.80 \\ 10.20 \end{pmatrix}, \begin{pmatrix} 1.68 \\ 10.32 \end{pmatrix}, \begin{pmatrix} 1.61 \\ 10.39 \end{pmatrix}, \begin{pmatrix} 1.57 \\ 10.43 \end{pmatrix}, \begin{pmatrix} 1.54 \\ 10.46 \end{pmatrix},$$
$$P(100) \text{ is } \begin{pmatrix} 1.50 \\ 10.50 \end{pmatrix}.$$

Pretty clearly the population is heading to a steady state in numbers, even though individual people continue to move around. 1.5 million people are rural at any given time in this steady state; that's exactly $\frac{1}{8}$ of the total population of 12 million. Notice that the country's population very rapidly switches over to being mostly a city population (straining urban resources).
You can see stability in the powers of A as well:
$$A^{10} = \begin{pmatrix} 0.130 & 0.124 \\ 0.870 & 0.876 \end{pmatrix}, \quad A^{100} = \begin{pmatrix} 0.125 & 0.125 \\ 0.875 & 0.875 \end{pmatrix}$$

Hmm. In the long run, it doesn't matter whether you started in the city or the country; the chances are $\frac{1}{8}$, $\frac{7}{8}$ that you will be rural or urban.

Maintain Your Skills

14. (a)
$$X(0) = \begin{pmatrix} 1 + \sqrt{2} \\ 1 \end{pmatrix}$$
$$X(1) = \begin{pmatrix} \sqrt{2} + 2 \\ \sqrt{2} \end{pmatrix}$$
$$X(2) = \begin{pmatrix} 2\sqrt{2} + 2 \\ 2 \end{pmatrix}$$
$$X(3) = \begin{pmatrix} 2\sqrt{2} + 4 \\ 2\sqrt{2} \end{pmatrix}$$
$$X(4) = \begin{pmatrix} 4\sqrt{2} + 4 \\ 4 \end{pmatrix}$$

(b)
$$Y(0) = \begin{pmatrix} 1 + \sqrt{2} \\ 1 \end{pmatrix}$$
$$Y(1) = \begin{pmatrix} \sqrt{2} + 2 \\ \sqrt{2} \end{pmatrix}$$
$$Y(2) = \begin{pmatrix} 2\sqrt{2} + 2 \\ 2 \end{pmatrix}$$
$$Y(3) = \begin{pmatrix} 2\sqrt{2} + 4 \\ 2\sqrt{2} \end{pmatrix}$$
$$Y(4) = \begin{pmatrix} 4\sqrt{2} + 4 \\ 4 \end{pmatrix}$$

(c)
$$Z(0) = \begin{pmatrix} 1 - \sqrt{2} \\ 1 \end{pmatrix}$$
$$Z(1) = \begin{pmatrix} 2 - \sqrt{2} \\ -\sqrt{2} \end{pmatrix}$$
$$Z(2) = \begin{pmatrix} 2 - 2\sqrt{2} \\ 2 \end{pmatrix}$$
$$Z(3) = \begin{pmatrix} 4 - 2\sqrt{2} \\ -2\sqrt{2} \end{pmatrix}$$
$$Z(4) = \begin{pmatrix} 4 - 4\sqrt{2} \\ 4 \end{pmatrix}$$

(d)
$$W(0) = \begin{pmatrix} 1 - \sqrt{2} \\ 1 \end{pmatrix}$$

$$W(1) = \begin{pmatrix} 2 - \sqrt{2} \\ -\sqrt{2} \end{pmatrix}$$

$$W(2) = \begin{pmatrix} 2 - 2\sqrt{2} \\ 2 \end{pmatrix}$$

$$W(3) = \begin{pmatrix} 4 - 2\sqrt{2} \\ -2\sqrt{2} \end{pmatrix}$$

$$W(4) = \begin{pmatrix} 4 - 4\sqrt{2} \\ 4 \end{pmatrix}$$

The X and Y sequences are the same; so are the Z and W sequences. In other words, X_0 is a vector such that $MX_0 = \sqrt{2}X_0$; M just scales X_0, and by an irrational scalar, which is sort of amazing given that all entries of M are integers. Similarly, $MZ_0 = -\sqrt{2}Z_0$. That $X_2 = 2X_0$ should not be surprising since, as shown in Exercise 1, $M^2 = 2I$.

15.

$$DP = \begin{pmatrix} \frac{\sqrt{2}}{2} \\ \frac{\sqrt{2}}{2} \end{pmatrix}$$

$$D^2 P = \begin{pmatrix} 0 \\ 1 \end{pmatrix}$$

$$D^3 P = \begin{pmatrix} -\frac{\sqrt{2}}{2} \\ \frac{\sqrt{2}}{2} \end{pmatrix}$$

$$D^4 P = \begin{pmatrix} -1 \\ 0 \end{pmatrix}$$

$$D^5 P = \begin{pmatrix} -\frac{\sqrt{2}}{2} \\ -\frac{\sqrt{2}}{2} \end{pmatrix}$$

$$DQ = \begin{pmatrix} \frac{\sqrt{2}}{2} \\ \frac{3\sqrt{2}}{2} \end{pmatrix}$$

$$D^2 Q = \begin{pmatrix} -1 \\ 2 \end{pmatrix}$$

$$D^3 Q = \begin{pmatrix} -3\frac{\sqrt{2}}{2} \\ \frac{\sqrt{2}}{2} \end{pmatrix}$$

$$D^4 Q = \begin{pmatrix} -2 \\ -1 \end{pmatrix}$$

$$D^5 Q = \begin{pmatrix} -\frac{\sqrt{2}}{2} \\ -3\frac{\sqrt{2}}{2} \end{pmatrix}$$

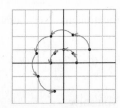

D rotates by 45° counterclockwise around the origin. So for instance, $D^4 = -I$ and $D^8 = I$.

16. (a) $\begin{pmatrix} 2 & 1 \\ 1 & 1 \end{pmatrix}$

(b) $\begin{pmatrix} 3 & 2 \\ 2 & 1 \end{pmatrix}$

(c) The entries are Fibonacci numbers. Specifically, if the Fibonacci numbers are indexed so that $F_1 = F_2 = 1$, then

$$B^n = \begin{pmatrix} F_{n+1} & F_n \\ F_n & F_{n-1} \end{pmatrix}$$

(d) The first few ordered pairs are

$$\begin{pmatrix} 2 \\ 1 \end{pmatrix}, \begin{pmatrix} 3 \\ 2 \end{pmatrix}, \begin{pmatrix} 5 \\ 3 \end{pmatrix}, \begin{pmatrix} 8 \\ 5 \end{pmatrix}$$

In general, $S_n = \begin{pmatrix} F_{n+3} \\ F_{n+2} \end{pmatrix}$.

(e)
$$s_0 = t_0 = 1$$
$$s_{n+1} = s_n + t_n$$
$$t_{n+1} = s_n$$

From the last equation above, $t_n = s_{n-1}$, so substituting in the middle equation you find $s_{n+1} = s_n + s_{n-1}$. This is precisely the Fibonacci recurrence.

4.11   Geometric Transformations

Check Your Understanding

1. (a) The mapping is $(x, y) \mapsto (-x, y)$, which means that points are reflected over the y-axis. This is a repeat of Exercise 4 in Lesson 4.10 (Getting Started).

(b) The mapping is $(x, y) \mapsto (y, x)$, which means that points are reflected over the 45° line through the origin, the line with equation $y = x$.

2. If A^{-1} undoes A on the matrix level, then $X \mapsto A^{-1}X$ ought to undo $X \mapsto AX$ from a geometric view. That is, $X \mapsto A^{-1}X$ ought to dilate all points by a factor of $\frac{1}{2}$. Indeed it does. Check by verifying that $A^{-1} = \begin{pmatrix} \frac{1}{2} & 0 \\ 0 & \frac{1}{2} \end{pmatrix}$

and so $A^{-1}\begin{pmatrix} x \\ y \end{pmatrix} = \frac{1}{2}\begin{pmatrix} x \\ y \end{pmatrix}$.

3. The mappings associated with A^2 and A^{-2} dilate by 4 and $\frac{1}{4}$ respectively. This makes sense, because if A dilates by a factor of 2, if you do it twice, the result should be a dilation by a factor of 4. Similarly, if you "undilate" by a factor of 2, you're dilating by a factor of $\frac{1}{2}$. If you do that twice, you're dilating by a factor of $\frac{1}{2} \times \frac{1}{2} = \frac{1}{4}$.

4.
$$\begin{pmatrix} c & -d \\ d & c \end{pmatrix}\begin{pmatrix} a \\ b \end{pmatrix} = \begin{pmatrix} ac - bd \\ ad + bc \end{pmatrix}$$

In other words, M maps the point $a + bi$ to $(ac - bd) + (ad + bc)i = (a + bi)(c + di)$. You know that multiplying by $z = c + di$ rotates by the argument (angle) of z and stretches by the magnitude of z.

5. Answers will vary, based on which points students choose, but the result of multiplying a point by this matrix is to locate its image after reflection over the line with equation $y = \frac{1}{2}x$. Here is a sample answer, showing the reflection of a square.

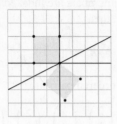

$$M\begin{pmatrix} 0 \\ 0 \end{pmatrix} = \begin{pmatrix} 0 \\ 0 \end{pmatrix}$$

$$M\begin{pmatrix} 0 \\ 2 \end{pmatrix} = \begin{pmatrix} \frac{8}{5} \\ \frac{-6}{5} \end{pmatrix}$$

$$M\begin{pmatrix} -2 \\ 2 \end{pmatrix} = \begin{pmatrix} \frac{2}{5} \\ \frac{-14}{5} \end{pmatrix}$$

$$M\begin{pmatrix} -2 \\ 0 \end{pmatrix} = \begin{pmatrix} \frac{-6}{5} \\ \frac{-8}{5} \end{pmatrix}$$

6. $X \mapsto M^{-1}X$ ought to undo $X \mapsto MX$ if you think geometrically. But $X \mapsto M^{-1}X$ reflects over the line with equation $y = \frac{1}{2}x$, and the only way to undo this reflection (or any reflection) is to do it again! Therefore, conjecture that $M^{-1} = M$. Computing M^{-1} with a calculator confirms that this is so.

7. (a) Solve $MX = -X$, which becomes

$$\begin{aligned} 3x + 4y &= -5x \\ 4x - 3y &= -5y \end{aligned} \implies \begin{aligned} 8x + 4y &= 0 \\ 4x + 2y &= 0 \end{aligned}$$

The two equations on the right are multiples of each other, both equivalent to the equation $y = -2x$. So any point on the line with equation $y = -2x$, and such points would be of the form $(x, -2x) = x(1, -2)$, is reflected to its negative. This means that the line with equation $y = -2x$ is mapped to itself, but that the points "switch sides" relative to the line of reflection.

(b) The angle between $\overrightarrow{OX}$ and $\overrightarrow{OY}$ is 90°. The line of reflection and the line determined in (a) are perpendicular. In general, for any point X (not necessarily on the line in (a)), and any point Y on the line of reflection, $\angle XOY = \angle X'OY$, where $X' = MX$. If $\angle XOY = 90°$ then (and only then) will X' be on the same line through the origin as X, so that $X' = kX$. Further, k has to be -1, since the lengths OX and OX' are the same.

(c) A typical point on the line of reflection is $t(2, 1)$. A typical point on this perpendicular line is $s(1, -2)$. The dot product is $(2t)s + t(-2s) = 0$. Hmm.

8. A reflection scales by 1 in the direction of the line of reflection (points on this line are not moved) and scales by -1 in the perpendicular direction identified in Exercise 7.

9. (a) It's rotated 180° counterclockwise around the origin to $(-x, -y)$.

(b) $R^2 = \begin{pmatrix} 0 & -1 \\ 1 & 0 \end{pmatrix}^2 = \begin{pmatrix} -1 & 0 \\ 0 & -1 \end{pmatrix}$ and so

$$R^2X = \begin{pmatrix} -x \\ -y \end{pmatrix}.$$

(c) It's rotated 270° counterclockwise around the origin to $(y, -x)$.

(d) $R^3 \begin{pmatrix} x \\ y \end{pmatrix} = \begin{pmatrix} 0 & 1 \\ -1 & 0 \end{pmatrix} \begin{pmatrix} x \\ y \end{pmatrix} = \begin{pmatrix} y \\ -x \end{pmatrix}.$

(e) It's rotated 360° counterclockwise around the origin, which has the same effect as doing nothing: $(x, y) \mapsto (x, y)$. Sure enough, $R^4 = \begin{pmatrix} 1 & 0 \\ 0 & 1 \end{pmatrix}$ so

$$R^4 \begin{pmatrix} x \\ y \end{pmatrix} = \begin{pmatrix} x \\ y \end{pmatrix}.$$

10. (a)

$$\begin{aligned} x + y &= kx \\ 2x &= ky \end{aligned} \implies \begin{aligned} (1 - k)x + y &= 0 \\ 2x - ky &= 0 \end{aligned}$$

(b) For both equations on the right to represent the same line, the slopes of the lines represented by the two equations must be the same. That is,

$$k - 1 = \frac{2}{k}$$

Cross multiplying yields $k^2 - k = 2 \implies k^2 - k - 2 = (k - 2)(k + 1) = 0$, so the solutions for k are 2 and -1.

(c) For $k = 2$:

$$\begin{aligned} x + y &= 2x \\ 2x &= 2y \end{aligned} \implies \begin{aligned} -x + y &= 0 \\ 2x - 2y &= 0 \end{aligned}$$

The solution is all points on the line with equation $y = x$.
For $k = -1$

$$\begin{aligned} x + y &= -x \\ 2x &= -y \end{aligned} \implies \begin{aligned} 2x + y &= 0 \\ 2x + y &= 0 \end{aligned}$$

The solution is all points on the line with equation $y = -2x$.

11. The linear equations that must represent the same line are

$$(-2.7 - k)x + 1.4y = 0$$
$$-2.1x + (2.2 - k)y = 0$$

So

$$\frac{-2.7 - k}{-1.4} = \frac{2.1}{2.2 - k}$$

After cross multiplication and considerable tidying up, this becomes

$$2k^2 + k - 6 = (2k - 3)(k + 2) = 0$$

so $k = -2, \frac{3}{2}$.
Now, for $k = -2$ you solve

$$-.7x + 1.4y = 0$$
$$-2.1x + 4.2y = 0$$

which has for its solutions all points on the line with equation $y = \frac{1}{2}x$. For $k = 1.5$ you solve

$$-4.2x + 1.4y = 0$$
$$-2.1x + .7y = 0$$

which has for its solutions all points on the line with equation $y = 3x$.

12. Two key points to look at are $\begin{pmatrix} 1 \\ 0 \end{pmatrix}$ and $\begin{pmatrix} 0 \\ 1 \end{pmatrix}$. That's because these points are easy to compute with and because they're the columns of the 2×2 identity matrix.

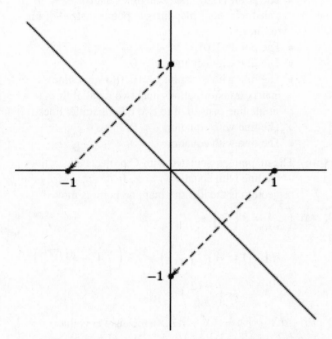

Whatever this matrix is, it has to send $\begin{pmatrix} 1 \\ 0 \end{pmatrix}$ to $\begin{pmatrix} 0 \\ -1 \end{pmatrix}$ and $\begin{pmatrix} 0 \\ 1 \end{pmatrix}$ to $\begin{pmatrix} -1 \\ 0 \end{pmatrix}$. Start with

$$M = \begin{pmatrix} a & b \\ c & d \end{pmatrix}$$

then you know that

$$\begin{pmatrix} a & b \\ c & d \end{pmatrix}\begin{pmatrix} 1 \\ 0 \end{pmatrix} = \begin{pmatrix} 0 \\ -1 \end{pmatrix}$$
$$\begin{pmatrix} a \\ c \end{pmatrix} = \begin{pmatrix} 0 \\ -1 \end{pmatrix}$$

So $a = 0, c = -1$

$$\begin{pmatrix} a & b \\ c & d \end{pmatrix}\begin{pmatrix} 0 \\ 1 \end{pmatrix} = \begin{pmatrix} -1 \\ 0 \end{pmatrix}$$
$$\begin{pmatrix} b \\ d \end{pmatrix} = \begin{pmatrix} -1 \\ 0 \end{pmatrix}$$

So $b = -1, d = 0$

Which gives you

$$M = \begin{pmatrix} 0 & -1 \\ -1 & 0 \end{pmatrix}$$

13. When you rotate the points $\begin{pmatrix} 1 \\ 0 \end{pmatrix}$ and $\begin{pmatrix} 0 \\ 1 \end{pmatrix}$, you'll create 45-45-90 triangles with the axes, and you can use that fact to figure out the coordinates of the rotation image points.

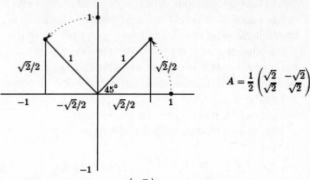

$A = \frac{1}{2}\begin{pmatrix} \sqrt{2} & -\sqrt{2} \\ \sqrt{2} & \sqrt{2} \end{pmatrix}$

$\begin{pmatrix} 1 \\ 0 \end{pmatrix}$ will be sent to $\begin{pmatrix} \frac{\sqrt{2}}{2} \\ \frac{\sqrt{2}}{2} \end{pmatrix}$, and $\begin{pmatrix} 0 \\ 1 \end{pmatrix}$ will be sent to $\begin{pmatrix} \frac{-\sqrt{2}}{2} \\ \frac{\sqrt{2}}{2} \end{pmatrix}$.

Start with

$$M = \begin{pmatrix} a & b \\ c & d \end{pmatrix}$$

then you know that

$$\begin{pmatrix} a & b \\ c & d \end{pmatrix}\begin{pmatrix} 1 \\ 0 \end{pmatrix} = \begin{pmatrix} \frac{\sqrt{2}}{2} \\ \frac{\sqrt{2}}{2} \end{pmatrix}$$
$$\begin{pmatrix} a \\ c \end{pmatrix} = \begin{pmatrix} \frac{\sqrt{2}}{2} \\ \frac{\sqrt{2}}{2} \end{pmatrix}$$

So $a = c = \dfrac{\sqrt{2}}{2}$

$$\begin{pmatrix} a & b \\ c & d \end{pmatrix}\begin{pmatrix} 0 \\ 1 \end{pmatrix} = \begin{pmatrix} \frac{-\sqrt{2}}{2} \\ \frac{\sqrt{2}}{2} \end{pmatrix}$$
$$\begin{pmatrix} b \\ d \end{pmatrix} = \begin{pmatrix} \frac{-\sqrt{2}}{2} \\ \frac{\sqrt{2}}{2} \end{pmatrix}$$

So $b = \dfrac{-\sqrt{2}}{2}, d = \dfrac{\sqrt{2}}{2}$

Which gives you

$$M = \begin{pmatrix} \frac{\sqrt{2}}{2} & \frac{-\sqrt{2}}{2} \\ \frac{\sqrt{2}}{2} & \frac{\sqrt{2}}{2} \end{pmatrix}$$

14. Substituting and rearranging yields

$$ax + by = c$$
$$a(px' + qy') + b(rx' + sy') = c$$
$$(ap + br)x' + (aq + bs)y' = c$$

So set

$$a' = ap + br, \quad b' = aq + bs, \quad c' = c$$

and you are done. All the steps are reversible, so you have shown that (x, y) satisfies $ax + by = c$ if and only if (x', y') satisfies $a'x' + b'y' = c'$. That is, the original set of points forms a line if and only if the image set under M forms a line (more than you were asked to show).

Well, you're not quite done. You haven't shown that not both of a', b' are 0. Here is a way, using proof by contradiction, to show they aren't without calculations. Suppose they were both 0. If $c \neq 0$, the $a'x' + b'y' = c'$ would have no solutions, which is impossible since every image under M of points on the original line has to be a solution. Suppose $c = 0$. Then every point (x', y') in the plane satisfies $a'x' + b'y' = c'$. But this is impossible because $X \mapsto MX$ is a 1-to-1 mapping (a consequence of M being invertible, as shown in Exercise 25), so points not on the original line must map to points not in the image, and the image is not the whole plane.

Here is a computational proof. Note that

$$\left(a' \ b' \right) = (a \ b) \begin{pmatrix} p & q \\ r & s \end{pmatrix} = (a \ b) M^{-1}$$

So

$$(a \ b) = (a' \ b') M$$

So if $(a' \ b')$ equalled $(0 \ 0)$, then also $(a \ b) = (0 \ 0)$, a contradiction. (This multiplication is written with a row on the left instead of a column on the right because this way you get to use the matrix M^{-1}, which you know all about.)

On Your Own

15. If A^{-1} undoes A on the matrix level, then $X \mapsto A^{-1}X$ ought to undo $X \mapsto AX$ geometrically. That is, $X \mapsto A^{-1}X$ ought to dilate the plane by a factor of $\frac{1}{3}$ in the x-direction and dilate by a factor of $\frac{1}{2}$ in the y-direction. Indeed it does.
$A^{-1} = \begin{pmatrix} \frac{1}{3} & 0 \\ 0 & \frac{1}{2} \end{pmatrix}$ and $A^{-1} \begin{pmatrix} x \\ y \end{pmatrix} = \begin{pmatrix} \frac{1}{3}x \\ \frac{1}{2}x \end{pmatrix}$.

16. You can use specific points if you like, or just a generic point $\begin{pmatrix} x \\ y \end{pmatrix}$.

$$\begin{pmatrix} 0 & -1 \\ 1 & 0 \end{pmatrix} \begin{pmatrix} x \\ y \end{pmatrix} = \begin{pmatrix} -y \\ x \end{pmatrix}$$

The distance from the origin to $\begin{pmatrix} x \\ y \end{pmatrix}$ is $\sqrt{x^2 + y^2}$. The distance from the origin to $\begin{pmatrix} -y \\ x \end{pmatrix}$ is $\sqrt{(-y)^2 + x^2}$ which is equal to $\sqrt{x^2 + y^2}$.

17. (a) The mapping is $(x, y) \mapsto (x, 0)$, so every point is *projected* vertically onto the x-axis

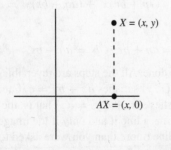

$X = (x, y)$

$AX = (x, 0)$

(b) The mapping is $(x, y) \mapsto \left(\frac{x+y}{2}, \frac{x+y}{2} \right)$, and it projects (x, y) perpendicularly onto the line with equation $y = x$. To see this, first note that

$$\left(\frac{x + y}{2}, \frac{x + y}{2} \right) = \frac{(x, y) + (y, x)}{2}$$

so the image is the midpoint of the line segment from (x, y) to its mirror image in the line with equation $y = x$. This line segment has slope -1, so it is perpendicular to $y = x$.

18. (a) The mapping $X \mapsto BX$ vertically projects the six lines to, respectively,
  - The point $(1, 0)$. (So sometimes matrix transformations map lines to points instead of lines to lines.)
  - The point $(2, 0)$.
  - The line with equation $y = 0$.
  - The line with equation $y = 0$. (So sometimes matrix transformations map two parallel lines to a single line instead of to two other parallel lines.)
  - The line with equation $y = 0$.
  - The line with equation $y = 0$.

  (b) The mapping associated with C projects all six lines to the line with equation $y = x$. In the case of L_5 the projection is the identity map; no point is moved.

19. (a) $\begin{pmatrix} 6 \\ 3 \end{pmatrix} = 3 \begin{pmatrix} 2 \\ 1 \end{pmatrix}$, so

$$A \begin{pmatrix} 6 \\ 3 \end{pmatrix} = A \left(3 \begin{pmatrix} 2 \\ 1 \end{pmatrix} \right) = 3A \begin{pmatrix} 2 \\ 1 \end{pmatrix} = 3 \begin{pmatrix} -4 \\ -2 \end{pmatrix}$$
$$= \begin{pmatrix} -12 \\ -6 \end{pmatrix}$$

  (b) $A(X + Y) = AX + AY$, so the answer is that $\big((2, 1) + (1, 3)\big) \mapsto \big((-4, -2) + (1.5, 4.5)\big) = (-2.5, 2.5)$.

  (c) $(-1, 2) = -(2, 1) + (1, 3)$, so it maps to $-(-4, -2) + (1.5, 4.5) = (5.5, 6.5)$.

  (d) Every point on the plain can be reached by some multiple of $(2, 1)$ added to some multiple of $(1, 3)$; draw a picture and see. That means that every (x, y) is of the form $a(2, 1) + b(1, 3)$ for some scalars a, b. But $A(aX + bY) = a(AX) + b(AY)$ by properties of matrix multiplication. So

$$a(2, 1) + b(1, 3) \mapsto a(-4, -2) + b(1.5, 4.5)$$

  So as soon as you determine a, b you can also determine what (x, y) maps to.

  (e) Sure enough, they check. For instance,

$$\begin{pmatrix} -2.7 & 1.4 \\ -2.1 & 2.2 \end{pmatrix} \begin{pmatrix} -1 \\ 2 \end{pmatrix} = \begin{pmatrix} 5.5 \\ 6.5 \end{pmatrix}$$

20. B has the same effect as A on the same two points. Since you were able to determine what matrix A did to any point (x, y) from the given information, the two matrices A and B must be the same.

21. If $X = \begin{pmatrix} x \\ y \end{pmatrix}$, the condition $RX = kX$ is equivalent to

$$\begin{aligned} -kx - y &= 0 \\ x - ky &= 0 \end{aligned} \quad \text{or} \quad \begin{aligned} y &= -kx \\ y &= (1/k)x \end{aligned}$$

You need to find values of k for which these two equations represent the same line. So $-k = 1/k$ or $k^2 = -1$. There are two solutions, the complex numbers $\pm i$. For $k = i$, setting $x = 1$ in $y = -kx$ gives the point $X = \begin{pmatrix} 1 \\ -i \end{pmatrix}$. For $k = -i$, setting $x = 1$ instead gives the point $X = \begin{pmatrix} 1 \\ i \end{pmatrix}$. And sure enough, you can check that, for instance

$$\begin{pmatrix} 0 & -1 \\ 1 & 0 \end{pmatrix} \begin{pmatrix} 1 \\ -i \end{pmatrix} = \begin{pmatrix} i \\ 1 \end{pmatrix} = i \begin{pmatrix} 1 \\ -i \end{pmatrix}$$

22. The $+3$ and $+4$ parts of the transformation are what causes it not to fix the origin. If you think of the transformation without those parts, you want something of the form $\begin{pmatrix} 1 & 2 \\ 3 & 0 \end{pmatrix}$, to match the coefficients of the linear terms. The final transformation will look like this:

$$\begin{pmatrix} x + 2y + 3 \\ 3x + 4 \end{pmatrix} = \begin{pmatrix} 1 & 2 \\ 3 & 0 \end{pmatrix} \begin{pmatrix} x \\ y \end{pmatrix} + \begin{pmatrix} 3 \\ 4 \end{pmatrix}$$

23.

$$A = \begin{pmatrix} 1 & 0 & a \\ 0 & 1 & b \\ 0 & 0 & 1 \end{pmatrix} \begin{pmatrix} x \\ y \\ 1 \end{pmatrix} = \begin{pmatrix} x + a \\ y + b \\ 1 \end{pmatrix}$$

Strip off the 1 on the bottom, and
$(x, y) \mapsto (x + a, y + b) = (x, y) + (a, b)$.

24. (a) $(1, 0) \mapsto (0, -1)$, $(0, 1) \mapsto (-1, 0)$, $(1, 1) \mapsto (-1, -1)$, $(-1, 1) \mapsto (-1, 1)$ (itself), and $(x, y) \mapsto (-y, -x)$. You can figure each of these out in two stages, first the rotation, then the reflection. For instances, $(x, y) \mapsto (-y, x) \mapsto (-y, -x)$.

(b) It suffices to find a matrix M such that

$$M \begin{pmatrix} x \\ y \end{pmatrix} = \begin{pmatrix} -y \\ -x \end{pmatrix}$$ because then M takes care of

every case. The only such matrix is $\begin{pmatrix} 0 & -1 \\ -1 & 0 \end{pmatrix}$.

(c) The rotation matrix is $R = \begin{pmatrix} 0 & -1 \\ 1 & 0 \end{pmatrix}$ as shown in the text. The reflection matrix is $R' = \begin{pmatrix} 1 & 0 \\ 0 & -1 \end{pmatrix}$.

(d) You do rotation first, so $X \mapsto R'(RX) = (R'R)X$. Computing $R'R$ by the rules of matrix multiplication gives

$$R'R = \begin{pmatrix} 0 & -1 \\ -1 & 0 \end{pmatrix} = M$$

as expected.

(e) Reflection over the line with equation $y = -x$.

25.

$$MX = MY$$
$$M^{-1}MX = M^{-1}MY$$
$$IX = IY$$
$$X = Y$$

In other words, if two points have the same image under M, then they are actually the same point.

26. Note that

$$M \begin{pmatrix} q \\ -p \end{pmatrix} = \begin{pmatrix} p & q \\ r & s \end{pmatrix} \begin{pmatrix} q \\ -p \end{pmatrix} = \begin{pmatrix} pq - pq \\ qr - ps \end{pmatrix} = \mathbf{0}$$

This shows that M is not one-to-one unless both p and q are 0. In that case

$$M \begin{pmatrix} s \\ -r \end{pmatrix} = \begin{pmatrix} 0 & 0 \\ r & s \end{pmatrix} \begin{pmatrix} s \\ -r \end{pmatrix} = \begin{pmatrix} 0 \\ rs - rs \end{pmatrix} = \mathbf{0}$$

Again, if M is one-to-one, then $r = s = 0$. However this makes M identically 0, so all vectors get mapped to $(0, 0)$. Thus, it is not one-to-one.

27. Given X', you want an X so that $MX = X'$. Since you know that M is invertible, you can multiply both sides on the left by M^{-1}, which gives you $X = M^{-1}X'$. So the point that maps to X' must be $M^{-1}X'$.
Check that it works:

$$M(M^{-1}X') = (MM^{-1})X' = X'$$

Here you have made use of the fact that the complete definition of inverses requires them to be two-sided: $M^{-1}M = MM^{-1} = I$.

28. Because MP is some point and MD is some nonzero ordered pair, so $MP + t(MD)$ is of the correct form to describe a line, as long as MD is a non-zero vector. $MD \neq \mathbf{0}$ because, if $MD = \mathbf{0}$, then multiplying both sides by M^{-1} yields $ID = D = M^{-1}\mathbf{0} = \mathbf{0}$, but $D \neq \mathbf{0}$.

29. A rotation preserves length. If $M = \begin{pmatrix} a & b \\ c & d \end{pmatrix}$ represents a rotation, then

$$\begin{pmatrix} a & b \\ c & d \end{pmatrix} \begin{pmatrix} 1 \\ 0 \end{pmatrix} = \begin{pmatrix} a \\ c \end{pmatrix}$$

has length 1, since $(1, 0)$ does. Thus $a^2 + c^2 = 1$ (likewise, $b^2 + d^2 = 1$), so A is true. If you reflect twice, you are back to where you started, so B is true.
If M is a matrix that rotates through $60°$, then M^6 rotates through $360°$. Thus $M^6 = I$ (and $6 = \frac{360°}{60°}$). A similar calculation holds for any angle that evenly divides $360°$, so C is true. If M rotates counterclockwise through θ, then M^{-1} rotates clockwise through θ. This is not the same thing (unless $\theta = 180°$). The correct answer choice is **D**.

Maintain Your Skills

30. (a) $180°$ rotation counterclockwise (which has the same effect as $180°$ clockwise).
(b) $270°$ rotation counterclockwise
(c) $360°$ rotation counterclockwise, which amounts to doing nothing: every point is mapped to itself. In mappings, it doesn't actually matter how you get to the result; only the result matters. Therefore, R^4 is the same mapping as the identity mapping corresponding to the matrix I. Indeed, if you do the matrix multiplication, you will find that $R^4 = I$.
(d) $450°$ rotation counterclockwise, that is $90°$ rotation counterclockwise
(e) scaling by 4

(f) scaling by -2

(g) Also scaling by -2. It doesn't matter which order you do these scaling operations in. This means the two matrices commute: $S_2 S_{-1} = S_{-1} S_2$.

(h) scaling by 1, that is, the identity map

(i) The identity map. Reflecting twice over the same line gets you back to where you started.

(j) $(x, y) \mapsto (-2y, 2x)$ There is no simple description of this in geometric terms, except to say everything is scaled by 2 after rotation.

(k) Again, $(x, y) \mapsto (-2y, 2x)$. It does not matter whether you scale first or rotate first.

(l) Reflection over the line with equation $y = -x$. The best way to see this is to slowly move around the unit circle from $(1, 0)$ to $(0, 1)$ and imagine the result of rotating and then reflecting. For instance, $(1, 0) \mapsto (0, -1)$ and then the images move clockwise to $(-1, 0)$, the image of $(0, 1)$.

(m) Reflection over the line with equation $y = x$. So $FR \neq RF$. The two mappings don't commute, and neither do their matrices.

31. (a) Dilates by 2, because $\begin{pmatrix} x \\ y \\ z \end{pmatrix} \mapsto 2 \begin{pmatrix} x \\ y \\ z \end{pmatrix}$.

(b) Dilates by 1 (i.e., does nothing) in the x-direction, Dilates by 2 in the y-direction, Dilates by 3 in the z-direction

(c) Reflects over the xy-plane. The z-coordinate of each point X is mapped to its negative, but the x- and y-coordinates are unchanged.

(d) Rotation of 90° counterclockwise around the z-axis. That is, the xy-plane is rotated. The z-coordinates of points are unchanged.

(e) 180° rotation around the y-axis, reversing the x and z coordinates of all points.

(f) Note that $(x, y, z) \mapsto (z, x, y)$. Points $(p, 0, 0)$ rotate to $(0, p, 0)$; that is, the x-axis rotates to the y-axis. Similarly, the y-axis rotates into the z-axis, and the z-axis rotates into the x-axis. The whole transformation amounts to a rotation 120° around the line with equation $x = y = z$, which is symmetrically placed to all 3 axes.

4.12   Transition Matrices

Check Your Understanding

1. The equation $MA = A$ expands to
$\begin{pmatrix} 0.8 & 0.5 \\ 0.2 & 0.5 \end{pmatrix} \begin{pmatrix} b \\ c \end{pmatrix} = \begin{pmatrix} b \\ c \end{pmatrix}$, that is,

$$0.8b + 0.5c = b \qquad -0.2b + 0.5c = 0$$
$$\text{or}$$
$$0.2b + 0.5c = c \qquad 0.2b - 0.5c = 0$$

Clearly the two equations on the right are for the same line, and can be written as $b = \frac{5}{2}c$. You also know that $b + c = 140$. So $\frac{7}{2}c = 140$, resulting in $(b, c) = (100, 40)$. This analysis confirms that $(100, 40)$ is a steady state, and also shows that there are no others.

2. Solutions will vary depending on the model of calculator you use. See the Technology Appendix in the Student Edition for advice on how you use your calculator to do this calculation efficiently.

In general, you will either store the initial matrix M in memory or copy it so that you can paste it into later equations. Multiply M on the right by $A(0)$. Then multiply the Ans by M on the left. (Another way to say this is "premultiply by M.") Then multiply the new Ans by M on the left. And so on.

Many calculators are set up expecting Ans to be the first thing on the left in the new computation, but others have a way to enter it at any point in a new computation. Remember that matrix multiplication doesn't commute, so M must be on the left in the multiplication. The two calculations:

$$\begin{pmatrix} a & b \\ c & d \end{pmatrix} \begin{pmatrix} x \\ y \end{pmatrix} \quad \text{and} \quad \begin{pmatrix} a & b \\ c & d \end{pmatrix} \begin{pmatrix} a & b \\ c & d \end{pmatrix}$$

require a total of 4 and 8 individual multiplications, respectively. $M^n(A(0))$ does one of the first and $n - 1$ of the second type, for a total of $4 + 8(n - 1) = 8n - 4$ multiplications. On the other hand, $M(M(\ldots MA(0))$ does n of the first type, for a total of $4n$ multiplications, which is far fewer in the long run.

3. (a) Each week, of the cars that begin at location A, 70% return to A at the end of the week, 20% are at B, and the remaining 10% end of at C. For those that start the week at B, 20% are at A, 50% are back at B, and 30% are at C by the end of the week. For those that start the week at C, 30% are at A, 10% are at B, and 60% are back at C by the end of the week.

(b) $M = \begin{pmatrix} 0.7 & 0.2 & 0.3 \\ 0.2 & 0.5 & 0.1 \\ 0.1 & 0.3 & 0.6 \end{pmatrix}$

(c) Define $P(n)$ to be the column vector $(a(n), b(n), c(n))$. Then $P(n) = M^n P(0)$ and $P(0) = (100, 100, 100)$. Matrix multiplication yields.

$$P(1) = \begin{pmatrix} 120 \\ 80 \\ 100 \end{pmatrix}, \quad P(2) = \begin{pmatrix} 130 \\ 74 \\ 96 \end{pmatrix},$$

$$P(3) = \begin{pmatrix} 134.6 \\ 72.6 \\ 92.8 \end{pmatrix}$$

Computing further suggests that the distribution settles down around $\begin{pmatrix} 137.84 \\ 72.97 \\ 89.19 \end{pmatrix}$

4. (a) You might start by computing the first few values of $X(n)$ and making sure the matrix equation works for them. Note that $X(n)$ is only defined for integer n, with $n > 0$. For example, $X(1) = \begin{pmatrix} 1 \\ 1 \end{pmatrix}$ and $X(2) = \begin{pmatrix} 2 \\ 1 \end{pmatrix}$. Then check to see that the following equation is true.

$$\begin{pmatrix} 1 & 1 \\ 1 & 0 \end{pmatrix} \begin{pmatrix} 1 \\ 1 \end{pmatrix} = \begin{pmatrix} 2 \\ 1 \end{pmatrix}$$

It is, so you can look more generally at the equation

$$X(n) = \begin{pmatrix} 1 & 1 \\ 1 & 0 \end{pmatrix} X(n-1)$$

Substitute from the definition of $X(n)$ to get

$$\begin{pmatrix} f(n) \\ f(n-1) \end{pmatrix} = \begin{pmatrix} 1 & 1 \\ 1 & 0 \end{pmatrix}\begin{pmatrix} f(n-1) \\ f(n-2) \end{pmatrix}$$

$$= \begin{pmatrix} f(n-1) + f(n-2) \\ f(n-1) \end{pmatrix}$$

This is true because $f(n) = f(n-1) + f(n-2)$ by definition and $f(n-1) = f(n-1)$.

(b) Let $M = \begin{pmatrix} 1 & 1 \\ 1 & 0 \end{pmatrix}$. Then

$$X_{10} = \begin{pmatrix} f_{10} \\ f_9 \end{pmatrix} = M^9 X_1 = \begin{pmatrix} 55 & 34 \\ 34 & 21 \end{pmatrix}\begin{pmatrix} 1 \\ 1 \end{pmatrix} = \begin{pmatrix} 89 \\ 55 \end{pmatrix}$$

So $f_{10} = 89$.

For Fibonacci numbers this method is *not* faster than just computing $f_2, f_2, \ldots, f_{10}$ by adding, but this is a general method which allows the full power of matrix theory to be applied to many recurrences.

5. For $n > 1$, $Y(n) = \begin{pmatrix} g(n) \\ g(n-1) \end{pmatrix}$. Then

$$Y(n) = \begin{pmatrix} a & b \\ c & d \end{pmatrix} Y(n-1)$$

$$\begin{pmatrix} 3g(n-1) - 4g(n-2) \\ g(n-1) \end{pmatrix} = \begin{pmatrix} ag(n-1) + bg(n-2) \\ cg(n-1) + dg(n-2) \end{pmatrix}$$

So $a = 3, b = -4, c = 1, d = 0$ and $Y_{n+1} = \begin{pmatrix} 3 & -4 \\ 1 & 0 \end{pmatrix} Y_n$

6. If you multiply the matrices in

$$\begin{pmatrix} h(n) \\ h(n-1) \\ h(n-2) \end{pmatrix} = \begin{pmatrix} 2 & -3 & 4 \\ 1 & 0 & 0 \\ 0 & 1 & 0 \end{pmatrix}\begin{pmatrix} h(n-1) \\ h(n-2) \\ h(n-3) \end{pmatrix}$$

you get

$$\begin{pmatrix} h(n) \\ h(n-1) \\ h(n-2) \end{pmatrix} = \begin{pmatrix} 2h(n-1) - 3h(n-2) + 4h(n-3) \\ h(n-1) \\ h(n-2) \end{pmatrix}$$

The first numerical equation in the matrix equation says $h(n) = 2h(n-1) - 3h(n-2) + 4h(n-3)$. The other two equations just say $h(n-1) = h(n-1)$ and $h(n-2) = h(n-2)$. Therefore, the first equation is the recurrence, a third-order recurrence.

On Your Own

7. $M = \begin{matrix} & \text{E W} \\ \begin{matrix} \text{E} \\ \text{W} \end{matrix} & \begin{pmatrix} 0.97 & 0.02 \\ 0.03 & 0.98 \end{pmatrix} \end{matrix}$, M^∞ (the limit of M^n) is $\begin{pmatrix} 0.4 & 0.4 \\ 0.6 & 0.6 \end{pmatrix}$ and $P(\infty)$ (the limit of $P(n) = M^n P(0)$) is $(120, 180)$. Which people are in which half changes, but the numbers are stable.

8. (a) $M = \begin{pmatrix} 0 & 0 & 15 \\ 0.7 & 0 & 0 \\ 0.02 & 0.2 & 0 \end{pmatrix}$

(b) There is no simple pattern, like M^3 being a diagonal matrix for the first beetle. Indeed, pretty soon all entries of the matrix are nonzero, because the generations get "mixed up." However, eventually the ratio of entries in each row becomes almost the same. In the limit the ratio is 1 to 0.515 to 0.091. That is, no matter what distribution you start with, eventually the ratio of eggs to larvae to adults is close to 1 to 0.515 to 0.091. Furthermore, eventually the population grows by about 1.359 in each category each period (that is, a rate of $1.359^3 \approx 2.510$ in each 3-year period, a little faster than for the first beetle).

9. (a) Answers will vary, but could be based on the examples used so far in this lesson.

(b) If the system is at a steady state, then

$$\begin{pmatrix} 0.6 & 0.25 \\ 0.4 & 0.75 \end{pmatrix}\begin{pmatrix} x \\ y \end{pmatrix} = \begin{pmatrix} x \\ y \end{pmatrix}$$

$$\begin{pmatrix} 0.6x + 0.25y \\ 0.4x + 0.75y \end{pmatrix} = \begin{pmatrix} x \\ y \end{pmatrix}$$

This gives you

$$0.6x + 0.25y = x$$
$$0.4x + 0.75y = y$$

Which simplifies to

$$-0.4x + 0.25y = 0$$
$$0.4x - 0.25y = 0$$

These two equations are the same, and since $x = 260 - y$, because you have a fixed population of 260, you get

$$-0.4(260 - y) + 0.25y = 0$$
$$-104 + 0.4y + 0.25y = 0$$
$$0.65y = 104$$
$$y = 160$$

$$x = 260 - 160$$
$$x = 100$$

So the steady state is $X = (100, 160)$.

10. (a) Add 1 ten times, so $x \mapsto x + 10$.

(b) The image of x will be the top entry of

$$\begin{pmatrix} 1 & 1 \\ 0 & 1 \end{pmatrix}^{10}\begin{pmatrix} x \\ 1 \end{pmatrix} = \begin{pmatrix} 1 & 10 \\ 0 & 1 \end{pmatrix}\begin{pmatrix} x \\ 1 \end{pmatrix} = \begin{pmatrix} x+10 \\ 1 \end{pmatrix}.$$

So $x \mapsto x + 10$.

11. The transition matrix is

$$\begin{matrix} & \text{B T} \\ \begin{matrix} \text{B} \\ \text{T} \end{matrix} & \begin{pmatrix} 0.85 & 0.65 \\ 0.15 & 0.35 \end{pmatrix} \end{matrix}$$

After 10 days, the situation is given by

$$\begin{pmatrix} 0.85 & 0.65 \\ 0.15 & 0.35 \end{pmatrix}^{10}\begin{pmatrix} 200 \\ 200 \end{pmatrix} = \begin{pmatrix} 325 \\ 75 \end{pmatrix} = \begin{pmatrix} B_{10} \\ T_{10} \end{pmatrix}$$

The correct answer choice is **D**.

Maintain Your Skills

12. (a) $\frac{1}{2} \cdot \frac{1}{2} = \frac{1}{4}$

(b) $\frac{1}{4}$. This was answered in a) because the only way for Bug 1 to make a move of 1 step counterclockwise in 2 minutes is to move clockwise each time.

(c) $\frac{1}{2} \cdot \frac{1}{2} + \frac{1}{2} \cdot \frac{1}{2} = \frac{1}{2}$. There are two ways for the bug to get back in two minutes: Go clockwise followed by counterclockwise, and vice versa.

13. (a) $\frac{1}{2} \cdot \frac{1}{3} = \frac{1}{6}$

(b) He must either go to R and reverse, or go to L and reverse. So the probability is $\frac{1}{2} \cdot \frac{2}{3} + \frac{1}{2} \cdot \frac{2}{3} = \frac{2}{3}$.

(c) $\frac{2}{3} \cdot \frac{1}{2} = \frac{1}{3}$.

(d) $\frac{2}{3} \cdot \frac{1}{2} + \frac{1}{3} \cdot \frac{1}{3} = \frac{4}{9}$.

14. (a) $\frac{1}{4} \cdot \frac{1}{4} = \frac{1}{16}$

(b) There are three ways for Bug 3 to do this. He could move clockwise both times; or he could move counterclockwise once and then stay put once; or he could stay put once and then move counterclockwise once. Adding the probabilities you get $\frac{1}{4} \cdot \frac{1}{4} + 2\frac{1}{2} \cdot \frac{1}{4} = \frac{5}{16}$.

(c) Again there are three ways: move either way and come back, or stay put both minutes. The probability is $2\left(\frac{1}{4}\right)^2 + \left(\frac{1}{2}\right)^2 = \frac{3}{8}$.

15. (a) $\frac{1}{2} \cdot \frac{1}{2} = \frac{1}{4}$

(b) Using C, S, and Cc for moving one vertex clockwise, staying put, and moving one vertex counterclockwise, Bug 4 can effect a move of one position counterclockwise in two minutes by either S-Cc, Cc-S, or C-C. The probability is

$$\frac{1}{3} \cdot \frac{1}{6} + \frac{1}{6} \cdot \frac{1}{3} + \frac{1}{2} \cdot \frac{1}{2} = \frac{13}{36}$$

(c) There are three ways to be where you started after two steps: S-S, C-Cc, and Cc-C. So the probability is

$$\frac{1}{3} \cdot \frac{1}{3} + \frac{1}{2} \cdot \frac{1}{6} + \frac{1}{6} \cdot \frac{1}{2} = \frac{10}{36}$$

4.13   Probability Models

Check Your Understanding

1. All parts can be solved by looking at

$$M^2 = \begin{pmatrix} \frac{1}{2} & \frac{1}{4} & \frac{1}{4} \\ \frac{1}{4} & \frac{1}{2} & \frac{1}{4} \\ \frac{1}{4} & \frac{1}{4} & \frac{1}{2} \end{pmatrix}$$

Parts (b) and (c) can be solved this way because they ask for the total probability of transitioning from one vertex to another in 2 steps. Part (a) can be solved this way because the only way Bug 1 can get one vertex counterclockwise in 2 steps is to move clockwise each time (since it won't stay put in any minute).

To read off the answers from the matrix, you can look at any column, as Bug 1 follows the same rules for each vertex. Part (c) can be answered by looking at the TT entry (top left). Parts (a) and (b) can be answered by

looking at the LT entry (second row, 1st column). These entries, $\frac{1}{2}$ and $\frac{1}{4}$, agree with the answers in the solution to Exercise 11.

2. If M is the transition matrix, then

$$M = \begin{pmatrix} \frac{1}{2} & \frac{1}{4} & \frac{1}{4} \\ \frac{1}{4} & \frac{1}{2} & \frac{1}{4} \\ \frac{1}{4} & \frac{1}{4} & \frac{1}{2} \end{pmatrix}, \quad M^2 = \begin{pmatrix} \frac{3}{8} & \frac{5}{16} & \frac{5}{16} \\ \frac{5}{16} & \frac{3}{8} & \frac{5}{16} \\ \frac{5}{16} & \frac{5}{16} & \frac{3}{8} \end{pmatrix}$$

Part (a) cannot be answered by M^2 for Bug 3 because (a) does not describe his only way to get one vertex counterclockwise in 2 steps. But (b) is answered by the LT entry and (c) is answered by the TT entry. (Again, each column contains the answers, because the rules Bug 3 follows are the same at every vertex.)

3. If M is the transition matrix, then

$$M = \begin{pmatrix} \frac{1}{3} & \frac{1}{2} & \frac{1}{6} \\ \frac{1}{6} & \frac{1}{3} & \frac{1}{2} \\ \frac{1}{2} & \frac{1}{6} & \frac{1}{3} \end{pmatrix}, \quad M^2 = \begin{pmatrix} \frac{5}{18} & \frac{13}{36} & \frac{13}{36} \\ \frac{13}{36} & \frac{5}{18} & \frac{13}{36} \\ \frac{13}{36} & \frac{13}{36} & \frac{5}{18} \end{pmatrix}$$

Part (a) cannot be answered by M^2 for Bug 4 because (a) does not describe her only way to get one vertex counterclockwise in 2 steps. But (b) is answered by the LT entry and (c) is answered by the TT entry. (Again, each column contains the answers, because the rules Bug 4 follows are the same at every vertex.)

4. First, probabilities can't be negative. Second, each column represents the probabilities of all possible one-step transitions from a particular state. When all possibilities are covered, the probability must add to 1.

5. The one-day weather transition matrix is

$$W = \begin{matrix} & \begin{matrix} S & R \end{matrix} \\ \begin{matrix} S \\ R \end{matrix} & \begin{pmatrix} 0.6 & 0.7 \\ 0.4 & 0.3 \end{pmatrix} \end{matrix}$$

and

$$W^2 = \begin{pmatrix} 0.64 & 0.63 \\ 0.36 & 0.37 \end{pmatrix}$$

and to three decimal places

$$W^5 = W^{10} = \begin{pmatrix} 0.636 & 0.636 \\ 0.364 & 0.364 \end{pmatrix}$$

So to three decimal places the long-run has already been reached after 5 days. By the way, $0.363636 = \frac{4}{11}$.

(a) The (1, 1) entry of W^2 gives the answer 0.64 for the probability of sun.

(b) The (1, 1) entry of W^5 gives the answer 0.636.

(c) The (1, 1) entry of W^{10} gives the answer 0.636.

(d) As noted, the long-run has already settled in, so the answer is 0.636 (actually $\frac{7}{11}$).

(e) The (1, 2) entry of W^5 and W^{10} says that the answer is also 0.636. In other words, by 5 days out the weather has "forgotten" its past; the probability no longer depends on what the weather is today.

6. (a) With G and B for good moods and bad, the transition

matrix is $M = \begin{matrix} & \begin{matrix} G & B \end{matrix} \\ \begin{matrix} G \\ B \end{matrix} & \begin{pmatrix} 0.8 & 0.1 \\ 0.2 & 0.9 \end{pmatrix} \end{matrix}$.

(b) Both (b) and (c) are answered by $M^{12} =$
$\begin{pmatrix} 0.343 & 0.329 \\ 0.657 & 0.671 \end{pmatrix}$. The top left entry says that if he
started in a good mood, the probability is 0.343 he
will be in a good mood 12 hours later. The bottom
left entry says that if he started in a bad mood, the
probability is 0.671 that he is in a bad mood 12 hours
later.

These probabilities are suspiciously close to $\frac{1}{3}$ and $\frac{2}{3}$.
Indeed, if you look at higher powers of M, you will see

that they converge to $\begin{pmatrix} \frac{1}{3} & \frac{1}{3} \\ \frac{2}{3} & \frac{2}{3} \end{pmatrix}$. So, in the long run, Bob is

in a bad mood $\frac{2}{3}$ the time. He needs to learn how to come
out of a funk!

7. Using the same 3×3 setup as in the Example, the
transition matrix is now

$$
G = \begin{array}{c} \\ A \\ B \\ E \end{array} \begin{array}{c} \begin{array}{ccc} A & B & E \end{array} \\ \begin{pmatrix} 0 & \frac{1}{2} & 0 \\ \frac{1}{2} & 0 & 0 \\ \frac{1}{2} & \frac{1}{2} & 1 \end{pmatrix} \end{array}
$$

and then

$$
G^3 = \begin{pmatrix} 0 & 0.125 & 0 \\ 0.125 & 0 & 0 \\ 0.875 & 0.875 & 1 \end{pmatrix}, \quad G^5 = \begin{pmatrix} 0 & 0.031 & 0 \\ 0.031 & 0 & 0 \\ 0.969 & 0.969 & 1 \end{pmatrix}
$$

(a) The probability that Alice loses right away is $\frac{1}{2}$, the
(3, 1) entry of G.

(b) Since Alice tosses first, the probability that the game
ends in 5 moves or less is the (3, 1) entry of G^5,
which is 0.969. Another way to think about this is to
realize that for the game not to end by the fifth move,
it would have to start with 5 tails in a row, which has
probability $\left(\frac{1}{2}\right)^5 = \frac{1}{32} = 0.031$.

(c) Multiply the probability that Bob gets the toss after
the third round (this is the (2, 1) entry of G^3) times
the probability he throws a head in the fourth $\left(\frac{1}{2}\right)$. So
the answer is $\frac{1}{8} \cdot \frac{1}{2} = \frac{1}{16}$. You could also figure this
out without matrices; from the start of the game there
must be 3 tails followed by a head.

On Your Own

8. Bug 3's transition matrix is

$$
M = \begin{array}{c} \\ T \\ L \\ R \end{array} \begin{array}{c} \begin{array}{ccc} T & L & R \end{array} \\ \begin{pmatrix} \frac{1}{2} & \frac{1}{4} & \frac{1}{4} \\ \frac{1}{4} & \frac{1}{2} & \frac{1}{4} \\ \frac{1}{4} & \frac{1}{4} & \frac{1}{2} \end{pmatrix} \end{array}
$$

and to 3 decimal places

$$
M^3 = \begin{pmatrix} 0.344 & 0.328 & 0.328 \\ 0.328 & 0.344 & 0.328 \\ 0.328 & 0.328 & 0.344 \end{pmatrix}, \quad M^4 = \begin{pmatrix} 0.336 & 0.332 & 0.332 \\ 0.332 & 0.336 & 0.332 \\ 0.332 & 0.332 & 0.336 \end{pmatrix}
$$

So for instance, the probability that it is at L after 4
moves if it starts at R is the row-L column R entry of M^4,
which is 0.332.

In particular, the probabilities of where the bug is do
depend on where it started, but very slightly, even after

only three moves. In fact, clearly all the entries are
heading towards $\frac{1}{3}$; further calculation shows that already
for M^6 all entries are $\frac{1}{3}$ to 3-decimal accuracy. So despite
Bug 3's preference for staying put, in the long-run (and it
doesn't take very long) it is equally likely to be
anywhere, no matter where it started.

9. Bug 4's transition matrix is

$$
M = \begin{array}{c} \\ T \\ L \\ R \end{array} \begin{array}{c} \begin{array}{ccc} T & L & R \end{array} \\ \begin{pmatrix} \frac{2}{6} & \frac{3}{6} & \frac{1}{6} \\ \frac{1}{6} & \frac{2}{6} & \frac{3}{6} \\ \frac{3}{6} & \frac{1}{6} & \frac{2}{6} \end{pmatrix} \end{array}
$$

and to 3 decimal places

$$
M^3 = \begin{pmatrix} 0.333 & 0.319 & 0.347 \\ 0.347 & 0.333 & 0.319 \\ 0.319 & 0.347 & 0.333 \end{pmatrix}, \quad M^4 = \begin{pmatrix} 0.338 & 0.331 & 0.331 \\ 0.331 & 0.338 & 0.331 \\ 0.331 & 0.331 & 0.338 \end{pmatrix}
$$

So for instance, the probability that it is at L after 4
moves if it starts at R is the row-L column R entry of M^4,
which is 0.331.

In particular, the probabilities of where the bug is do
depend on where it started, but very a little, even after
only three moves. In fact, clearly all the entries are
heading towards $\frac{1}{3}$; further calculation shows that already
for M^7 all entries are $\frac{1}{3}$ to 3-decimal accuracy. So despite
Bug 4's preference for moving clockwise, in the long-run
(and it doesn't take very long) it is equally likely to be
anywhere, no matter where it started.

10. The transition matrix is now

$$
M = \begin{array}{c} \\ A \\ B \\ AL \\ BL \\ EE \end{array} \begin{array}{c} \begin{array}{ccccc} A & B & AL & BL & EE \end{array} \\ \begin{pmatrix} 0 & \frac{5}{6} & 0 & 0 & 0 \\ \frac{5}{6} & 0 & 0 & 0 & 0 \\ \frac{1}{6} & 0 & 0 & 0 & 0 \\ 0 & \frac{1}{6} & 0 & 0 & 0 \\ 0 & 0 & 1 & 1 & 1 \end{pmatrix} \end{array}
$$

Now AL means Alice just lost in this round. EE means
the game ended earlier than this round. Notice that the
column for AL and BL has all its probability in the last
entry. This is because if a round begins with Alice having
just lost (in the previous round), the effect of the
(fictitious) next round is to move the lost to being
considered an earlier loss.

The probability Bob loses in the 4th round is now the
row-BL column-A entry of M^4. So he loses in the fourth
round with probability 0.096 and in the eighth round with
probability 0.047. He can't lose in the ninth round
because Alice tosses then (if the game reaches a ninth
round).

11. Almost all these questions are answered directly using
the 4×4 model, with states A (Alice about to toss), B
(Bob about to toss), AL (Alice has lost, just now or
earlier) and BL (same for Bob). The transition matrix is

$$
M = \begin{array}{c} \\ A \\ B \\ AL \\ BL \end{array} \begin{array}{c} \begin{array}{cccc} A & B & AL & BL \end{array} \\ \begin{pmatrix} \frac{1}{6} & \frac{2}{3} & 0 & 0 \\ \frac{2}{3} & \frac{1}{6} & 0 & 0 \\ \frac{1}{6} & 0 & 1 & 0 \\ 0 & \frac{1}{6} & 0 & 1 \end{pmatrix} \end{array}
$$

To answer the questions you mostly need M^5 but once M^4. To 3 decimal places they are

$$M^4 = \begin{pmatrix} 0.272 & 0.210 & 0 & 0 \\ 0.210 & 0.272 & 0 & 0 \\ 0.311 & 0.207 & 1 & 0 \\ 0.207 & 0.311 & 0 & 1 \end{pmatrix}, \quad M^5 = \begin{pmatrix} 0.185 & 0.217 & 0 & 0 \\ 0.217 & 0.185 & 0 & 0 \\ 0.356 & 0.242 & 1 & 0 \\ 0.242 & 0.356 & 0 & 1 \end{pmatrix}$$

(a) Add the AL-A and BL-A entries of M^5:
$0.356 + 0.242 = 0.598$.

(b) The AL-A entry of M^5: 0.356.

(c) The B-A entry of M^4: 0.311. This entry is the probability that, if Alice starts the game, at the *end* of the fourth round the toss passes to Bob. So Bob will make the fifth toss.

(d) $\frac{1}{6} \times 0.311 = 0.052$. You can't read this off directly from a power of M because there isn't a state for "just lost". But the answer is $\frac{1}{6}$ of the answer to (c).

(e) For this you have to look at higher powers of M until you see a limit for the AL-A entry. By M^{50} this entry appears to be 0.555 or $\frac{5}{9}$. (In fact, there are more sophisticated approaches that allow this answer to be obtained exactly by a bit of algebra.)

$$M^{50} = \begin{pmatrix} 0 & 0 & 0 & 0 \\ 0 & 0 & 0 & 0 \\ \frac{5}{9} & \frac{4}{9} & 1 & 0 \\ \frac{4}{9} & \frac{5}{9} & 0 & 1 \end{pmatrix}$$

12. Continue with the states A, B, AL, BL (although now that a player can win directly by a toss, maybe you could be more optimistic and name the states A, B, AW, BW; this would rearrange some entries in the matrices, since AW = BL). The transition matrix is

$$\begin{array}{c} \\ \\ M = \begin{array}{c} A \\ B \\ AL \\ BL \end{array} \end{array} \begin{array}{cccc} A & B & AL & BL \\ \end{array} \\ M = \begin{array}{c} A \\ B \\ AL \\ BL \end{array} \begin{pmatrix} \frac{1}{6} & \frac{1}{3} & 0 & 0 \\ \frac{1}{3} & \frac{1}{6} & 0 & 0 \\ \frac{1}{6} & \frac{1}{3} & 1 & 0 \\ \frac{1}{3} & \frac{1}{6} & 0 & 1 \end{pmatrix}$$

To answer the questions you mostly need M^5 but once M^4. To 3 decimal places they are

$$M^4 = \begin{pmatrix} 0.032 & 0.031 & 0 & 0 \\ 0.031 & 0.032 & 0 & 0 \\ 0.397 & 0.540 & 1 & 0 \\ 0.540 & 0.397 & 0 & 1 \end{pmatrix}, \quad M^5 = \begin{pmatrix} 0.016 & 0.016 & 0 & 0 \\ 0.016 & 0.016 & 0 & 0 \\ 0.413 & 0.556 & 1 & 0 \\ 0.556 & 0.413 & 0 & 1 \end{pmatrix}$$

(a) Add the AL-A and BL-A entries of M^5: $0.413 + 0.556 = 0.969$.

(b) The AL-A entry of M^5: 0.413.

(c) The B-A entry of M^4: 0.031. This entry is the probability that, if Alice starts the game, at the *end* of the fourth round the toss passes to Bob. So Bob will make the fifth toss.

(d) $\frac{1}{6} \times 0.031 = 0.005$. You can't read this off directly from a power of M because there isn't a state for "just lost". But the answer is $\frac{1}{6}$ of the answer to (c).

(e) For this you have to look at higher powers of M until you see a limit for the AL-A entry. By M^{10} (not very

far out) this entry appears to be 0.428 or $\frac{3}{7}$. (In fact, there are more sophisticated approaches that allow this answer to be obtained exactly by a bit of algebra.)

$$M^{10} \approx \begin{pmatrix} 0 & 0 & 0 & 0 \\ 0 & 0 & 0 & 0 \\ \frac{3}{7} & \frac{4}{7} & 1 & 0 \\ \frac{4}{7} & \frac{3}{7} & 0 & 1 \end{pmatrix}$$

13. Let the states be T (Alice about to toss), W (Alice has won), and L (Alice has lost). As usual, the matrix M models a round of the game, which consists of a toss if the game is still going on, and nothing if the game is already won or lost.

$$\begin{array}{c} \quad\quad T\ W\ L \\ M = \begin{array}{c} T \\ W \\ L \end{array} \begin{pmatrix} \frac{1}{2} & 0 & 0 \\ \frac{1}{3} & 1 & 0 \\ \frac{1}{6} & 0 & 1 \end{pmatrix}, \quad M^4 = \begin{pmatrix} 0.062 & 0 & 0 \\ 0.625 & 1 & 0 \\ 0.312 & 0 & 1 \end{pmatrix} \end{array}$$

(a) The W-T entry of M^4 is 0.625.

(b) The L-T entry of M^4 is 0.312.

(c) This cannot be determined by any one power of M, but look at

$$M^{10} = \begin{pmatrix} 0.001 & 0 & 0 \\ 0.666 & 1 & 0 \\ 0.333 & 0 & 1 \end{pmatrix}$$

The T-T entry is the probability that after 10 rounds it is still Alice's turn to toss, that is, the game has not ended. Clearly this entry is going to 0 as the power of M increases. So you can say that the probability of the game never ending is 0, even though it is theoretically possible that the die never rolls a 2, 3, or 6.

(d) From M^{10} you can conclude that the limit in M^n of the W-T entry is $\frac{2}{3}$. This makes sense, because on each toss she has twice as many ways to win (2 and 3 dots) as to lose (6 dots).

14. If $A = \begin{pmatrix} a & b \\ c & d \end{pmatrix}$, then $\det A = ad - bc$ and

$$A^{-1} = \frac{1}{ad - bc} \begin{pmatrix} d & -b \\ -c & a \end{pmatrix} = \begin{pmatrix} \frac{d}{ad-bc} & \frac{-b}{ad-bc} \\ \frac{-c}{ad-bc} & \frac{a}{ad-bc} \end{pmatrix}$$

Therefore, $\det A^{-1} = \frac{ad-bc}{(ad-bc)^2} = \frac{1}{ad-bc} = \frac{1}{\det A}$. This implies that choice B is true and choice A is false. It is easy to see that D is true. If matrix B is a reflection, then $B = B^{-1}$. So

$$1 = \det B \cdot \det B^{-1} = \det B \cdot \det B$$

Hence $\det B = \pm 1$. If $B = \begin{pmatrix} e & f \\ g & h \end{pmatrix}$ and $\det B = 1$, then $B^{-1} = \begin{pmatrix} h & -f \\ -g & e \end{pmatrix}$. So $e = h$ and $f = g = 0$. This implies $e^2 = eh = \det B = 1$. Therefore $B = \begin{pmatrix} 1 & 0 \\ 0 & 1 \end{pmatrix}$ or $\begin{pmatrix} -1 & 0 \\ 0 & -1 \end{pmatrix}$. Neither is a reflection, so it follows that $\det B = -1$. The correct answer choice is **A**.

15. (a) • $\det(A) = 1(4) - 2(3) = 4 - 6 = -2$

 • $\det(B) = 5(8) - 6(7) = 40 - 42 = -2$

 • $\det(AB) = \det \begin{pmatrix} 19 & 22 \\ 43 & 50 \end{pmatrix} = 19(50) - 22(43) = 4$

 (b) • $\det(A) = -2(-3) - 5(1) = 1$

 • $\det(B) = 7(-2) - 1(4) = -18$

 • $\det(AB) = \det \begin{pmatrix} -10 & -4 \\ 23 & 11 \end{pmatrix} =$
 $-10(11) - (-4)(23) = -18$

 (c) • $\det(A) = 6(1) - 2(3) = 0$

 • $\det(B) = 4(3) - 1(8) = 4$

 • $\det(AB) = \det \begin{pmatrix} 40 & 12 \\ 20 & 6 \end{pmatrix} = 40(6) - 20(12) = 0$

 (d) • $\det(A) = 1(4) - 2(2) = 0$

 • $\det(B) = xw - zy$

 • $\det(AB) = \det \begin{pmatrix} x + 2z & y + 2w \\ 2 + 4z & 2y + 4w \end{pmatrix} =$
 $(x + 2z)(2)(y + 2w) - (y + 2w)(2)(x + 2z) = 0$

16. (a) $\det A = 2,\ \det(A^{-1}) = \frac{1}{2}$

 (b) $\det A = 5,\ \det(A^{-1}) = \frac{1}{5}$

 (c) $\det A = 3,\ \det(A^{-1}) = \frac{1}{3}$

 (d) $\det A = x,\ \det(A^{-1}) = \frac{1}{x}$

4C MATHEMATICAL REFLECTIONS

1. (a)

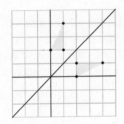

 (b) The transformation sends each point (x, y) to the point (y, x), which results in a reflection over the line with equation $y = x$.

2. A rotation of 90° clockwise around the origin will send the point $(1, 0)$ to $(0, -1)$ and the point $(0, 1)$ to the point $(1, 0)$. These two facts give you the columns of your transformation matrix: $\begin{pmatrix} 0 & 1 \\ -1 & 0 \end{pmatrix}$

This matrix sends any point (x, y) to the point $(y, -x)$. This graph shows the effect of this mapping on the three points from Exercise 1.

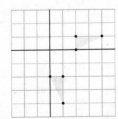

3. (a) $\begin{pmatrix} 0.6 & 0.9 \\ 0.4 & 0.1 \end{pmatrix}$ is a possible matrix.

 (b) To find the number of bikes at each station after 2 weeks, multiply the square of the transition matrix by $\begin{pmatrix} 50 \\ 50 \end{pmatrix}$ to get $\begin{pmatrix} 67.5 \\ 32.5 \end{pmatrix}$. Since you wouldn't predict a half-bike at either station, you could either answer 68 bikes at the north station and 32 at the south or 67 bikes at the north station and 33 at the south.

 (c) The product of the fourth power of the transition matrix with $\begin{pmatrix} 50 \\ 50 \end{pmatrix}$ gives you $\begin{pmatrix} 69.075 \\ 30.925 \end{pmatrix}$, or 69 bikes at the north station and 31 at the south.

 (d) Yes, the situation settles down in the long term. When you compute a large power of the transition matrix, both columns are the same, so you've reached a steady state. For example, the 20th power of the transition matrix is

$$\begin{pmatrix} 0.692307692 & 0.692307692 \\ 0.307692308 & 0.307692308 \end{pmatrix}$$

This would give you $\begin{pmatrix} 69.2307692 \\ 30.7692308 \end{pmatrix}$, or 69 bikes at the north station and 31 at the south in the steady state. (Note that you've already reached this condition at week four.)

4. (a) Here are the equations you will base your transition matrix on:

 • $e(n) = 100a(n - 1)$

 • $l(n) = .4e(n - 1)$

 • $a(n) = .1l(n - 1)$

 So the transition matrix is

$$\begin{pmatrix} 0 & 0 & 100 \\ .4 & 0 & 0 \\ 0 & .1 & 0 \end{pmatrix}$$

 (b) Find the sixth power of the transition matrix and multiply it by the column vector $\begin{pmatrix} 20 \\ 10 \\ 1 \end{pmatrix}$. This gives you $\begin{pmatrix} 320 \\ 160 \\ 16 \end{pmatrix}$. Derman sees 320 eggs, 160 larvae, and 16 adult beetles.

5. (a) The four states that can occur are:

 • F: Wrongway is at first base.

 • S: He is at second base.

 • T: He is at third base.

 • H: He has touched home plate and returned to the dugout.

 Set up your matrix so that, for example, in the S-column and the T-row you see the probability that Wrongway ran from second base to third base with a teammate's hit. (This is the correct direction, so the probability is .8.)

		F	S	T	H
	F	0	0.2	0	0
$M =$	S	0.8	0	0.2	0
	T	0	0.8	0	0
	H	0.2	0	0.8	1

(b) Square the transition matrix and multiply it by a column vector representing his starting place.

$$\begin{array}{c} \\ \begin{array}{c} F \\ S \\ T \\ H \end{array} \end{array} \begin{array}{cccc} F & S & T & H \\ \end{array}$$

$$\begin{array}{c} F \\ S \\ T \\ H \end{array} \begin{pmatrix} 0 & 0.2 & 0 & 0 \\ 0.8 & 0 & 0.2 & 0 \\ 0 & 0.8 & 0 & 0 \\ 0.2 & 0 & 0.8 & 1 \end{pmatrix}^2 \begin{pmatrix} 1 \\ 0 \\ 0 \\ 0 \end{pmatrix} = \begin{pmatrix} 0.16 \\ 0 \\ 0.64 \\ 0.2 \end{pmatrix}$$

He's at first base with probability 0.16, at third base with probability 0.64, and at home (and back in the dugout) with probability 0.2.

(c) Cube the transition matrix and multiply it by the same column vector.

$$\begin{array}{cccc} & F & S & T & H \end{array}$$

$$\begin{array}{c} F \\ S \\ T \\ H \end{array} \begin{pmatrix} 0 & 0.2 & 0 & 0 \\ 0.8 & 0 & 0.2 & 0 \\ 0 & 0.8 & 0 & 0 \\ 0.2 & 0 & 0.8 & 1 \end{pmatrix}^3 \begin{pmatrix} 1 \\ 0 \\ 0 \\ 0 \end{pmatrix} = \begin{pmatrix} 0 \\ 0.256 \\ 0 \\ 0.744 \end{pmatrix}$$

He has reached home base (one way or another) with probability 0.744.

(d) This time, you need the sixth power of your transition matrix. Then add together the probabilities that he's at first, second, or third base (or subtract the probability that he's made it to home plate from 1).

$$\begin{array}{cccc} & F & S & T & H \end{array}$$

$$\begin{array}{c} F \\ S \\ T \\ H \end{array} \begin{pmatrix} 0 & 0.2 & 0 & 0 \\ 0.8 & 0 & 0.2 & 0 \\ 0 & 0.8 & 0 & 0 \\ 0.2 & 0 & 0.8 & 1 \end{pmatrix}^6 \begin{pmatrix} 1 \\ 0 \\ 0 \\ 0 \end{pmatrix} = \begin{pmatrix} 0.016384 \\ 0 \\ 0.065536 \\ 0.91808 \end{pmatrix}$$

He's still running the base paths with probability 0.08192.

6. Yes, a matrix that represents a reflection must be its own inverse, because if you reflect the plane over any line and then reflect it back over that same line, the image of every point (x, y) after the double reflection is (x, y). This is the identity map, so $R \times R = I$, and R is its own inverse.

If $R \times R = I$, then there are a few things you can determine about the entries.

$$\begin{pmatrix} a & b \\ c & d \end{pmatrix} \begin{pmatrix} a & b \\ c & d \end{pmatrix} = \begin{pmatrix} 1 & 0 \\ 0 & 1 \end{pmatrix}$$

$$\begin{pmatrix} a^2 + bc & ab + bd \\ ac + cd & bc + d^2 \end{pmatrix} = \begin{pmatrix} 1 & 0 \\ 0 & 1 \end{pmatrix}$$

$$\begin{pmatrix} a^2 + bc & b(a + d) \\ c(a + d) & bc + d^2 \end{pmatrix} = \begin{pmatrix} 1 & 0 \\ 0 & 1 \end{pmatrix}$$

Since $b(a + d) = 0$, then either $b = 0$ or $a + d = 0$. If $a + d = 0$, then $c(a + d) = 0$ automatically, but if $b = 0$ and $a + d \neq 0$, then $c = 0$. This relationship could give you a quick way to see whether or not a particular 2×2 matrix could be a reflection matrix. However, you haven't proven that the fact that this relationship holds guarantees that a matrix *is* a reflection matrix, just that if it *doesn't* hold, it *isn't*.

You might also note that for a 2×2 reflection matrix, $a^2 + bc = bc + d^2 = 1$. This implies that $a^2 = d^2$, which

gives another quick way to check. If $a^2 \neq d^2$, the matrix cannot be a reflection matrix .

7. An absorbing state is a state which "ends the game." Maybe a player wins or a player loses, or a certain number of rounds have been played. In the baseball problem, when Wrongway reached home plate, he went to the dugout and stopped running the bases—this was an absorbing state. In a transition matrix, such a state will have all but one entry equal to zero in its corresponding column. The non-zero entry will be 1. It will look like a column from an identity matrix.

8. Yes, because as you take larger and larger powers of the matrix, the columns are becoming more and more similar, and the distribution approaches $\begin{pmatrix} 70 \\ 80 \end{pmatrix}$. You can show that this is the steady state by verifying that

$$\begin{pmatrix} 0.2 & 0.7 \\ 0.8 & 0.3 \end{pmatrix} \begin{pmatrix} 70 \\ 80 \end{pmatrix} = \begin{pmatrix} 70 \\ 80 \end{pmatrix}$$

CHAPTER REVIEW

1. You can solve the system by

$$x - y + 4z = 7 \qquad (1)$$
$$2x + 3y - 2z = 4 \qquad (2)$$
$$x + 2y + 8z = 6 \qquad (3)$$

Multiply equation (2) by 2 and add it to equation (1) to get $5x + 5y = 15$ or, dividing by 5, $x + y = 3$. Multiply equation (1) by 2 and subtract equation (3) to get $x - 4y = 8$. You now have the system

$$x + y = 3 \qquad (4)$$
$$x - 4y = 8 \qquad (5)$$

Subtract equation (5) from equation (4) to get $5y = -5 \longrightarrow y = -1$. Now substitute $y = -1$ into equation (4) to find x:

$$x + (-1) = 3 \longrightarrow x = 4$$

Substitute into equation (1) to find z:

$$4 - (-1) + 4z = 7$$
$$5 + 4z = 7$$
$$4z = 2$$
$$z = \frac{1}{2}$$

So, the solution is $\left(4, -1, \frac{1}{2}\right)$. You could also use Gaussian Elimination or your calculator to solve the system.

2. (a) $\begin{pmatrix} 2 & 3 & 1 & | & 5 \\ 1 & -1 & 0 & | & 7 \\ 1 & 0 & 2 & | & 16 \end{pmatrix}$

(b)

$$\begin{pmatrix} 2 & 3 & 1 & | & 5 \\ 1 & -1 & 0 & | & 7 \\ 1 & 0 & 2 & | & 16 \end{pmatrix} \xrightarrow{(1)-(2)} \begin{pmatrix} 1 & 4 & 1 & | & -2 \\ 1 & -1 & 0 & | & 7 \\ 1 & 0 & 2 & | & 16 \end{pmatrix} \xrightarrow{(2)-(3)}$$

$$\begin{pmatrix} 1 & 4 & 1 & | & -2 \\ 0 & -1 & -2 & | & -9 \\ 1 & 0 & 2 & | & 16 \end{pmatrix} \xrightarrow{(3)-(1)} \begin{pmatrix} 1 & 4 & 1 & | & -2 \\ 0 & -1 & -2 & | & -9 \\ 0 & -4 & 1 & | & 18 \end{pmatrix} \xrightarrow{-1\times(2)}$$

$$\begin{pmatrix} 1 & 4 & 1 & | & -2 \\ 0 & 1 & 2 & | & 9 \\ 0 & -4 & 1 & | & 18 \end{pmatrix} \xrightarrow{(3)+4\times(2)} \begin{pmatrix} 1 & 4 & 1 & | & -2 \\ 0 & 1 & 2 & | & 9 \\ 0 & 0 & 9 & | & 54 \end{pmatrix} \xrightarrow{(3)\div 9}$$

$$\begin{pmatrix} 1 & 4 & 1 & | & -2 \\ 0 & 1 & 2 & | & 9 \\ 0 & 0 & 1 & | & 6 \end{pmatrix} \xrightarrow{(2)-2\times(3)} \begin{pmatrix} 1 & 4 & 1 & | & -2 \\ 0 & 1 & 0 & | & -3 \\ 0 & 0 & 1 & | & 6 \end{pmatrix} \xrightarrow[(1)-(3)]{(1)-4\times(2)}$$

$$\begin{pmatrix} 1 & 0 & 0 & | & 4 \\ 0 & 1 & 0 & | & -3 \\ 0 & 0 & 1 & | & 6 \end{pmatrix}$$

So, the solution is $(4, -3, 6)$.

3. Enter the augmented matrix into your calculator and use the *rref* command.

$$\begin{pmatrix} 1 & 0 & 0 & | & 1 \\ 0 & 1 & 0 & | & -2 \\ 0 & 0 & 1 & | & 0 \end{pmatrix}$$

4. (a) Use matrix addition:

$$\begin{pmatrix} 10 & 12 & 5 \\ 8 & 8 & 3 \\ 15 & 12 & 10 \\ 14 & 8 & 9 \end{pmatrix} + \begin{pmatrix} 18 & 10 & 7 \\ 12 & 9 & 5 \\ 19 & 13 & 4 \\ 15 & 8 & 11 \end{pmatrix} = \begin{pmatrix} 28 & 22 & 12 \\ 20 & 17 & 8 \\ 34 & 25 & 14 \\ 29 & 16 & 20 \end{pmatrix}$$

So, completing the table:

		chocolate chip	sugar	oatmeal
	Art Club	28	22	12
Total	Spanish Club	20	17	8
	Math Club	34	25	14
	Science Club	29	16	20

(b) Use matrix multiplication:

$$\begin{pmatrix} 28 & 22 & 12 \\ 20 & 17 & 8 \\ 34 & 25 & 14 \\ 29 & 16 & 20 \end{pmatrix} \cdot \begin{pmatrix} 4 \\ 3 \\ 3.50 \end{pmatrix} =$$

$$\begin{pmatrix} 28(4) + 22(3) + 12(3.5) = 220 \\ 20(4) + 17(3) + 8(3.5) = 159 \\ 34(4) + 25(3) + 14(3.5) = 260 \\ 29(4) + 16(3) + 20(3.5) = 234 \end{pmatrix}$$

So, completing the table:

	Revenue
Art Club	220
Spanish Club	159
Math Club	260
Science Club	234

5. (a) $A = \begin{pmatrix} 1+1=2 & 1+2=3 \\ 2+1=3 & 2+2=4 \end{pmatrix}$

$B = \begin{pmatrix} 2(1)=2 & 2(2)=4 & 2(3)=6 \\ 2(1)=2 & 2(2)=4 & 2(3)=6 \end{pmatrix}$

$C = \begin{pmatrix} (2(1)-1)^2 = 1^2 = 1 \\ (2(2)-1)^2 = 3^2 = 9 \\ (2(3)-1)^2 = 5^2 = 25 \end{pmatrix}$

(b) $\begin{pmatrix} 2 & 3 \\ 3 & 4 \end{pmatrix} \begin{pmatrix} 2 & 4 & 6 \\ 2 & 4 & 6 \end{pmatrix} =$

$\begin{pmatrix} 2(2)+3(2)=10 & 2(4)+3(4)=20 & 2(6)+3(6)=30 \\ 3(2)+4(2)=14 & 3(4)+4(4)=28 & 3(6)+4(6)=42 \end{pmatrix}$

(c) $\begin{pmatrix} 2 & 4 & 6 \\ 2 & 4 & 6 \end{pmatrix} \begin{pmatrix} 1 \\ 9 \\ 25 \end{pmatrix} = \begin{pmatrix} 2(1)+4(9)+6(25)=188 \\ 2(1)+4(9)+6(25)=188 \end{pmatrix}$

(d) Not possible because the matrices are not the same size.

(e) $3B = 3 \cdot \begin{pmatrix} 2 & 4 & 6 \\ 2 & 4 & 6 \end{pmatrix} = \begin{pmatrix} 6 & 12 & 18 \\ 6 & 12 & 18 \end{pmatrix}$

(f) $A^{-1} = \frac{1}{2(4)-3(3)} \begin{pmatrix} 4 & -3 \\ -3 & 2 \end{pmatrix} = \begin{pmatrix} -4 & 3 \\ 3 & -2 \end{pmatrix}$

6. (a) First find the inverse of $\begin{pmatrix} 3 & 2 \\ 5 & 6 \end{pmatrix}$:

$$\begin{pmatrix} 3 & 2 \\ 5 & 6 \end{pmatrix}^{-1} = \frac{1}{18-10} \begin{pmatrix} 6 & -2 \\ -5 & 3 \end{pmatrix} = \begin{pmatrix} \frac{3}{4} & -\frac{1}{4} \\ -\frac{5}{8} & \frac{3}{8} \end{pmatrix}$$

Then,

$$\begin{pmatrix} x \\ y \end{pmatrix} = \begin{pmatrix} \frac{3}{4} & -\frac{1}{4} \\ -\frac{5}{8} & \frac{3}{8} \end{pmatrix} \begin{pmatrix} 4 \\ 20 \end{pmatrix}$$

$$\begin{pmatrix} x \\ y \end{pmatrix} = \begin{pmatrix} \frac{3}{4}(4) + -\frac{1}{4}(20) = 3 + -5 = -2 \\ -\frac{5}{8}(4) + \frac{3}{8}(20) = -\frac{5}{2} + \frac{15}{2} = \frac{10}{2} = 5 \end{pmatrix}$$

So, $x = -2$ and $y = 5$.

(b) $\begin{cases} 3x + 2y = 4 \\ 5x + 6y = 20 \end{cases}$

7. (a) $A \cdot \begin{bmatrix} 2 \\ -3 \end{bmatrix} = \begin{pmatrix} -1 & 0 \\ 0 & 1 \end{pmatrix} \cdot \begin{bmatrix} 2 \\ -3 \end{bmatrix} = \cdot \begin{bmatrix} -2 \\ -3 \end{bmatrix}$ This is a reflection in the y-axis.

(b) $B \cdot \begin{bmatrix} 2 \\ -3 \end{bmatrix} = \begin{pmatrix} 0 & -2 \\ 2 & 0 \end{pmatrix} \cdot \begin{bmatrix} 2 \\ -3 \end{bmatrix} = \begin{bmatrix} 6 \\ 4 \end{bmatrix}$ This is a rotation of 90° and a stretch by a factor of 2.

(c) $C \cdot \begin{bmatrix} 2 \\ -3 \end{bmatrix} = \begin{pmatrix} 0 & 1 \\ 1 & 0 \end{pmatrix} \cdot \begin{bmatrix} 2 \\ -3 \end{bmatrix} = \cdot \begin{bmatrix} -3 \\ 2 \end{bmatrix}$ This is a reflection in the line $y = x$.

8. $M^{\infty} = \begin{pmatrix} 0.5714 & 0.5714 \\ 0.4286 & 0.4286 \end{pmatrix}$ If $x + y = 700$,

$\begin{pmatrix} 0.5714 & 0.5714 \\ 0.4286 & 0.4286 \end{pmatrix} \cdot \begin{bmatrix} x \\ y \end{bmatrix}$ will be $\begin{bmatrix} 400 \\ 300 \end{bmatrix}$ no matter what your original choices are for x and y. So, $X = (400, 300)$.

9. (a) $\begin{array}{cc} & \text{H} \quad \text{U} \end{array}$
$\begin{array}{c} \text{H} \\ \text{U} \end{array} \begin{pmatrix} 0.6 & 0.1 \\ 0.4 & 0.9 \end{pmatrix}$

(b) Find

$$\begin{pmatrix} 0.6 & 0.1 \\ 0.4 & 0.9 \end{pmatrix}^4 = \begin{pmatrix} 0.25 & 0.1875 \\ 0.75 & 0.8125 \end{pmatrix}$$

The probability is 0.25 or 25%.

CHAPTER TEST

1. Use Gaussian Elimination:

$$\begin{pmatrix} 1 & 2 & | & 4 \\ 2 & -1 & | & 3 \end{pmatrix} \xrightarrow{(2)-2(1)} \begin{pmatrix} 1 & 2 & | & 4 \\ 0 & -5 & | & -5 \end{pmatrix} \xrightarrow{(2)\div-5} \begin{pmatrix} 1 & 2 & | & 4 \\ 0 & 1 & | & 1 \end{pmatrix}$$

$$\xrightarrow{(1)-2(2)} \begin{pmatrix} 1 & 0 & | & 2 \\ 0 & 1 & | & 1 \end{pmatrix}$$

Or, use your calculator and the *rref* command. The correct choice is **C**.

2. a_{12} is the element in the first row, second column, which is -9. The correct choice is **B**.

3. Find the dot product:

$$(2, 0, 0) \cdot (a, b, c) = 2 \cdot a + 0 \cdot b + 0 \cdot c$$
$$= 2a$$

The correct choice is **B**.

4. The correct choice is **C**

$$7x + 2y = a$$
$$-5x + 3y = b$$

5. To reflect across the y-axis, you want $(x, y) \mapsto (-x, y)$.

The correct choice is **A**, $\begin{pmatrix} -1 & 0 \\ 0 & 1 \end{pmatrix}$

6. $\begin{pmatrix} 1 & -1 & 1 & | & 8 \\ 0 & 2 & 1 & | & -12 \\ 1 & 0 & 4 & | & 12 \end{pmatrix} \xrightarrow{(3)-(1)}$

$\begin{pmatrix} 1 & -1 & 1 & | & 8 \\ 0 & 2 & 1 & | & -12 \\ 0 & 1 & 3 & | & 4 \end{pmatrix} \xrightarrow{switch(2)\&(3)}$

$\begin{pmatrix} 1 & -1 & 1 & | & 8 \\ 0 & 1 & 3 & | & 4 \\ 0 & 2 & 1 & | & -12 \end{pmatrix} \xrightarrow{(3)-2(2)} \begin{pmatrix} 1 & -1 & 1 & | & 8 \\ 0 & 1 & 3 & | & 4 \\ 0 & 0 & -5 & | & -20 \end{pmatrix} \xrightarrow{(3)\div-5}$

$\begin{pmatrix} 1 & -1 & 1 & | & 8 \\ 0 & 1 & 3 & | & 4 \\ 0 & 0 & 1 & | & 4 \end{pmatrix} \xrightarrow{(2)-3(3)} \begin{pmatrix} 1 & -1 & 1 & | & 8 \\ 0 & 1 & 0 & | & -8 \\ 0 & 0 & 1 & | & 4 \end{pmatrix} \xrightarrow[(1)-(3)]{(1)+(2)}$

$\begin{pmatrix} 1 & 0 & 0 & | & -4 \\ 0 & 1 & 0 & | & -8 \\ 0 & 0 & 1 & | & 4 \end{pmatrix}$ The solution is $(-4, -8, 4)$.

7. (a) 3×2

(b) $A + 2B = \begin{pmatrix} 4 & -1 \\ 0 & 3 \\ 6 & 5 \end{pmatrix} + 2 \cdot \begin{pmatrix} 10 & -4 \\ 3 & 2 \\ -5 & -20 \end{pmatrix} =$

$\begin{pmatrix} 4+2(10) = 24 & -1+2(-4) = -9 \\ 0+2(3) = 6 & 3+2(2) = 7 \\ 6+2(-5) = -4 & 5+2(-20) + -35 \end{pmatrix}$

(c) $B \cdot C = \begin{pmatrix} 10 & -4 \\ 3 & 2 \\ -5 & -20 \end{pmatrix} \cdot \begin{pmatrix} 1 & 4 \\ -5 & 6 \end{pmatrix} =$

$\begin{pmatrix} 10(1) + -4(-5) = 30 & 10(4) + -4(6) = 16 \\ 3(1) + 2(-5) = -7 & 3(4) + 2(6) = 24 \\ -5(1) + -20(-5) = 95 & -5(4) + -20(6) = -140 \end{pmatrix}$

(d) Not possible. The number of columns in the first matrix must be the same as the number of rows in the second matrix. The number of columns in C is 2 and

the number of rows in B is 3. So, the product CB does not exist.

(e) $C^2 = \begin{pmatrix} 1 & 4 \\ -5 & 6 \end{pmatrix} \cdot \begin{pmatrix} 1 & 4 \\ -5 & 6 \end{pmatrix} =$

$\begin{pmatrix} 1(1) + 4(-5) = -19 & 1(4) + 4(6) = 28 \\ -5(1) + 6(-5) = -35 & -5(4) + 6(6) = 16 \end{pmatrix}$

(f) $C^{-1} = \frac{1}{6-(-20)} \cdot \begin{pmatrix} 6 & -4 \\ 5 & 1 \end{pmatrix} = \begin{pmatrix} \frac{3}{13} & \frac{-2}{13} \\ \frac{5}{26} & \frac{1}{26} \end{pmatrix}$

8. The inverse of $\begin{pmatrix} 3 & -2 \\ 6 & 5 \end{pmatrix}$ is

$$\frac{1}{3(5) - 6(-2)} \begin{pmatrix} 5 & 2 \\ -6 & 3 \end{pmatrix} = \begin{pmatrix} \frac{5}{27} & \frac{2}{27} \\ -\frac{2}{9} & \frac{1}{9} \end{pmatrix}$$

Multiply both sides by the inverse:

$$\begin{pmatrix} x \\ y \end{pmatrix} = \begin{pmatrix} \frac{5}{27} & \frac{2}{27} \\ -\frac{2}{9} & \frac{1}{9} \end{pmatrix} \begin{pmatrix} 24 \\ 21 \end{pmatrix}$$

$$\begin{pmatrix} x \\ y \end{pmatrix} = \begin{pmatrix} \frac{5}{27} \cdot 24 + \frac{2}{27} \cdot 21 = 6 \\ -\frac{2}{9} \cdot 24 + \frac{1}{9} \cdot 21 = -3 \end{pmatrix}$$

So, $x = 6$ and $y = -3$.

9. (a)

$$A \cdot X = \begin{pmatrix} 0 & 1 \\ 1 & 0 \end{pmatrix} \cdot \begin{bmatrix} -2 \\ 5 \end{bmatrix} = \begin{bmatrix} 0(-2) + 1(5) = 5 \\ 1(-2) + 0(5) = -2 \end{bmatrix}$$

This is a reflection in the line $y = x$.

(b)

$$A \cdot X = \begin{pmatrix} 1 & 0 \\ 0 & -1 \end{pmatrix} \cdot \begin{bmatrix} -2 \\ 5 \end{bmatrix} = \begin{bmatrix} 1(-2) + 0(5) = -2 \\ 0(-2) + -1(5) = -5 \end{bmatrix}$$

This is a reflection in the x-axis.

(c)

$$A \cdot X = \begin{pmatrix} 2 & 0 \\ 0 & 2 \end{pmatrix} \cdot \begin{bmatrix} -2 \\ 5 \end{bmatrix} = \begin{bmatrix} 2(-2) + 0(5) = -4 \\ 0(-2) + 2(5) = 10 \end{bmatrix}$$

This matrix scales by a factor of 2.

(d)

$$A \cdot X = \begin{pmatrix} -\frac{1}{2} & 0 \\ 0 & \frac{1}{2} \end{pmatrix} \cdot \begin{bmatrix} -2 \\ 5 \end{bmatrix} = \begin{bmatrix} -\frac{1}{2}(-2) + 0(5) = 1 \\ 0(-2) + \frac{1}{2}(5) = \frac{5}{2} \end{bmatrix}$$

This matrix scales by a factor of $\frac{1}{2}$ and reflects over the y-axis.

10. (a) $M = \begin{pmatrix} 0.8 & 0.4 \\ 0.2 & 0.6 \end{pmatrix}$

(b) You want to know the probability of taking the second route in four days, so find M^4:

$$M^4 = \begin{array}{c} \\ \text{Rte 1} \\ \text{Rte 2} \end{array} \begin{pmatrix} \overset{\text{Rte 1}}{0.6752} & \overset{\text{Rte 2}}{0.6496} \\ 0.3248 & 0.3504 \end{pmatrix}$$

They took the first route Monday, so you want to look in the first column. You want to know the probability of taking the second route Friday, so look in the second row. So, the probability is $0.325 = 32.5\%$.

(c) Compute high powers of M:

$$M^{100} = \begin{array}{c} \\ \text{Rte 1} \\ \text{Rte 2} \end{array} \begin{array}{c} \text{Rte 1 \ Rte 2} \\ \begin{pmatrix} 0.6667 & 0.6667 \\ 0.3333 & 0.3333 \end{pmatrix} \end{array}$$

The matrix stabilizes. In the long run, the commuter will choose Route 1 66.7% of the time and Route 2 33.3% of the time.

11. In Gaussian Elimination, you begin by creating an augmented matrix to represent a system of linear equations. The coefficients are separated from the constants by a vertical line. Use any of the following three steps to change the form of this augmented matrix.

- Scaling
- Switching
- Subtracting

Through this process, an augmented matrix is transformed into a matrix where the entries to the left of the vertical line consist of rows in which each row has a leading 1 and a zero every where else (but there may be rows of all zeros at the bottom). The final result is called row-reduced echelon form.

CUMULATIVE REVIEW

1. $\sqrt{3} \cdot \sqrt{-27} = \sqrt{81} \cdot \sqrt{-1} = 9i$. The correct answer choice is **C**.
2. $z - \bar{z} = (-3 + 2i) - (-3 - 2i) = -3 + 2i + 3 + 2i = 4i$. The correct answer choice is B.
3. Simply by viewing the four labeled quadrants, you can see that I and III are opposites, while II and IV are opposites (signs of both coordinates are reversed). Alternately: being in quadrant II means that $a < 0$ and $b > 0$. Therefore, $-z = -a - bi$ has $-a > 0$ and $-b < 0$. It has a positive real part and a negative imaginary part, so it is in quadrant IV. The correct answer choice is **D**.
4. $|-5 + 4i| = \sqrt{(-5)^2 + 4^2} = \sqrt{25 + 16} = \sqrt{41}$. The correct answer choice is C.
5. If a quadratic equation has real coefficients, it will have a complex root if and only if the discriminant is negative. From the $\pm$ in the quadratic formula, these roots come in pairs that are complex conjugates. The correct answer choice is **A**.
6. (a) $0 = x^4 - 81 = (x^2 + 9)(x^2 - 9) = (x^2 + 9)(x + 3)(x - 3)$. The real roots are $x = -3, 3$.
   (b) The above also yields $x^2 + 9 = 0$. This in turn implies $x^2 = -9$, $x = \pm\sqrt{-9}$, $x = \pm 3i$.
7. (a) $z = (-9 + 2i) - (3 - 5i) = -9 + 2i - 3 + 5i = -12 + 7i$
   (b) If $z \cdot (6 - 4i) = 1$, then

$$z = \frac{1}{6 - 4i} \cdot \frac{6 + 4i}{6 + 4i} = \frac{6 + 4i}{36 - 16i^2}$$

$$= \frac{6 + 4i}{36 + 16} = \frac{6 + 4i}{52} = \frac{3}{26} + \frac{1}{13}i$$

8. (a) $z \cdot w = (\sqrt{3} + i)(4i) = 4\sqrt{3}i + 4i^2 = -4 + 4\sqrt{3}i$

(b)

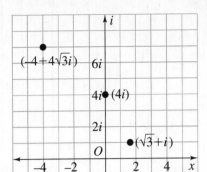

(c) $|z| = |\sqrt{3} + i| = \sqrt{\sqrt{3}^2 + 1^2} = \sqrt{3 + 1} = 2$, $|w| = |4i| = \sqrt{4^2} = 4$, and $|z \cdot w| = |z| \cdot |w| = 2 \cdot 4 = 8$ (or $\sqrt{(-4)^2 + (4\sqrt{3})^2} = \sqrt{16 + 48} = 8$). $\arg z = \tan^{-1}\left(\frac{1}{\sqrt{3}}\right) = 30°$, $\arg w = \arg(4i) = 90°$, and $\arg(z \cdot w) = 30° + 90° = 120°$. Alternately,

$$\arg(z \cdot w) = 180° - \tan^{-1}\left(\frac{4\sqrt{3}}{4}\right)$$
$$= 180° - \tan^{-1}\sqrt{3} = 180° - 60° = 120°$$

9. Given $|z| = 3$ and $\arg z = 120°$, it follows that
   (a) $|z^2| = |z|^2 = 3^2 = 9$ and $\arg(z^2) = 2 \cdot \arg z = 240°$
   (b) $|z^3| = |z|^3 = 3^3 = 27$ and $\arg(z^3) = 3 \cdot \arg z = 360°$ (or 0°)
   (c) $|z^4| = |z|^4 = 3^4 = 81$ and $\arg(z^4) = 4 \cdot \arg z = 480°$ (or 120°)

10. $0 = x^4 - 16 = (x^2 + 4)(x^2 - 4) = (x + 2i)(x - 2i)(x + 2)(x - 2)$. The solutions are: $x = 2, 2i, -2$, and $-2i$. They all have magnitude 2. Their directions are 0°, 90°, 180°, and 270°, respectively.

11. Using Gaussian elimination,

$$\begin{pmatrix} 2 & -1 & | & 5 \\ 1 & 3 & | & 8 \end{pmatrix} \sim \begin{pmatrix} 1 & 3 & | & 8 \\ 2 & -1 & | & 5 \end{pmatrix} \sim \begin{pmatrix} 1 & 3 & | & 8 \\ 0 & -7 & | & -11 \end{pmatrix}$$
$$\sim \begin{pmatrix} 1 & 3 & | & 8 \\ 0 & 1 & | & \frac{11}{7} \end{pmatrix} \sim \begin{pmatrix} 1 & 0 & | & \frac{23}{7} \\ 0 & 1 & | & \frac{11}{7} \end{pmatrix}$$

12. $a_{13} = 0$ and $a_{21} = -4$
13. $(5, 7, -1) \cdot (a, b, c) = 5a + 7b - c$
14. (a) $3a = 2x + 5y$ and $7b = -x + 4y$
    (b) $-a = 4x + 3y - z$, $2b = 2x + 8y + 5z$, and $5c = 6x - 3y + z$
15. $(x, y) \mapsto (-x, y)$ is represented by $\begin{pmatrix} -1 & 0 \\ 0 & 1 \end{pmatrix}$.
16. $(x, y) \mapsto (-y, x)$ is represented by $\begin{pmatrix} 0 & -1 \\ 1 & 0 \end{pmatrix}$.

17. The solution is $x = 4$, $y = 5$, $z = -2$, as can be seen by:

$$\begin{pmatrix} 4 & 0 & 8 & | & 0 \\ 3 & -2 & 1 & | & 0 \\ -2 & 1 & -1 & | & -1 \end{pmatrix} \sim \begin{pmatrix} 1 & 0 & 2 & | & 0 \\ 3 & -2 & 1 & | & 0 \\ -2 & 1 & -1 & | & -1 \end{pmatrix}$$

$$\sim \begin{pmatrix} 1 & 0 & 2 & | & 0 \\ 0 & -2 & -5 & | & 0 \\ 0 & 1 & 3 & | & -1 \end{pmatrix} \sim \begin{pmatrix} 1 & 0 & 2 & | & 0 \\ 0 & 1 & 3 & | & -1 \\ 0 & 0 & 1 & | & -2 \end{pmatrix} \sim \begin{pmatrix} 1 & 0 & 0 & | & 4 \\ 0 & 1 & 0 & | & 5 \\ 0 & 0 & 1 & | & -2 \end{pmatrix}$$

18. (a) $B + C = \begin{pmatrix} 1 & -4 \\ 9 & 5 \end{pmatrix}$

  (b) A has 3 columns and C has 2 rows: it's impossible.

  (c) $\begin{pmatrix} 5 & -6 \\ 9 & 2 \end{pmatrix} \begin{pmatrix} -4 & 2 \\ 0 & 3 \end{pmatrix} = \begin{pmatrix} -20 & -8 \\ -36 & 24 \end{pmatrix}$

  (d) Inverses exist only for (some) square matrices. Impossible.

  (e) $B^{-1} = \frac{1}{-12} \begin{pmatrix} 3 & -2 \\ 0 & -4 \end{pmatrix} = \begin{pmatrix} \frac{-1}{4} & \frac{1}{6} \\ 0 & \frac{1}{3} \end{pmatrix}$

19. $y = 4x$ and $y - 3 = 2x + 1$. Subtract the second equation from the first. $3 = 2x - 1$, so $2x = 4$, $x = 2$. Thus, $y = 8$.

20. (a) This is a reflection over the line $y = -x$.

$$AX = \begin{pmatrix} 0 & -1 \\ -1 & 0 \end{pmatrix} \begin{pmatrix} 5 \\ -2 \end{pmatrix} = \begin{pmatrix} 2 \\ -5 \end{pmatrix}$$

  (b) This is a reflection over the x-axis.

$$AX = \begin{pmatrix} 1 & 0 \\ 0 & -1 \end{pmatrix} \begin{pmatrix} 5 \\ -2 \end{pmatrix} = \begin{pmatrix} 5 \\ 2 \end{pmatrix}$$

  (c) This is a reflection over the y-axis, plus a dilation by a factor of 4.

$$AX = \begin{pmatrix} -4 & 0 \\ 0 & 4 \end{pmatrix} \begin{pmatrix} 5 \\ -2 \end{pmatrix} = \begin{pmatrix} -20 \\ -8 \end{pmatrix}$$

  (d) This a dilation by a factor of 3 in the x-direction, and by 5 in the y-direction.

$$AX = \begin{pmatrix} 3 & 0 \\ 0 & 5 \end{pmatrix} \begin{pmatrix} 5 \\ -2 \end{pmatrix} = \begin{pmatrix} 15 \\ -10 \end{pmatrix}$$

21. (a) $M = \begin{pmatrix} 0.3 & 0.6 \\ 0.7 & 0.4 \end{pmatrix}$, where the first row and column match the first exit.

  (b) After 3 days the probability is 0.447, since

$$M^3 = \begin{pmatrix} 0.447 & 0.474 \\ 0.553 & 0.526 \end{pmatrix}$$

  (c) In the long run the probabilities will stabilize at $\frac{6}{13} \approx 0.462$ for the first exit, and $\frac{7}{13} \approx 0.538$ for the second exit.

22.

Input, n	Output, $a(n)$	Δ	Δ^2
0	5	4	1
1	9	5	1
2	14	6	1
3	20	7	
4	27		

23. When the input increases by 5, the output decreases by 85. An increase of 50 yields a decrease of 850, so $a(50) = 83 - 850 = -767$. Likewise, $a(100) = 83 - 1700 = -1617$.

24. As the input increases by 1, the output increases by 5.

$$a(n) = \begin{cases} -1 & \text{if } n = 0 \\ a(n-1) + 5 & \text{if } n \geq 1 \end{cases}$$

25. The corresponding values on the line are: 5, 7, 9, 11, 13. The mean absolute error is

$$\frac{|5-4| + |7-5| + |9-6| + |11-7| + |13-8|}{5}$$

$$= \frac{1+2+3+4+5}{5} = 3$$

The mean squared error is

$$\frac{1^2 + 2^2 + 3^2 + 4^2 + 5^2}{5} = 11$$

The standard error is $\sqrt{11} \approx 3.3$.

26. (a) $f(-2) = 2(-2)^2 - 3 = 2 \cdot 4 - 3 = 8 - 3 = 5$

  (b) $f(g(3)) = f(-15 + 1) = f(-14) = 2(-14)^2 - 3 = 2 \cdot 196 - 3 = 389$

  (c) $g(f(x)) = g(2x^2 - 3) = -5(2x^2 - 3) + 1 = -10x^2 + 16$

  (d) The function g multiplies by -5, then adds 1. To undo this, you subtract 1, then divide by -5: $g^{-1}(x) = \frac{x-1}{-5} = -\frac{1}{5}x + \frac{1}{5}$.

27. (a) $81x^2 - 49y^2 = (9x)^2 - (7y)^2 = (9x + 7y)(9x - 7y)$

  (b) $64x^3 + 27y^3 = (4x)^3 + (3y)^3 = (4x + 3y)(16x^2 - 12xy + 9y^2)$

28. The function f multiplies by 4, then adds 1. The inverse subtracts 1, then divides by 4, so $f^{-1}(x) = \frac{x-1}{4} = \frac{1}{4}x - \frac{1}{4}$. Now $f(f^{-1}(x)) = f(\frac{1}{4}x - \frac{1}{4}) = 4(\frac{1}{4}x - \frac{1}{4}) + 1 = x - 1 + 1 = x$.

29. (a) The quotient is $2x^2 - 3x + 7$, and the remainder is -8:

$$\begin{array}{r} 2x^2 - 3x + 7 \\ x+1 \overline{) 2x^3 - x^2 + 4x - 1} \\ \underline{2x^3 + 2x^2} \\ -3x^2 + 4x - 1 \\ \underline{-3x^2 - 3x} \\ 7x - 1 \\ \underline{7x + 7} \\ -8 \end{array}$$

  (b) By the remainder theorem, $p(-1) = 8$.

30. (a) $5x^2 - 16x + 12 = (5x - 6)(x - 2)$

  (b) $6x^2 + 21x + 9 = 3(2x^2 + 7x + 3) = 2(2x + 1)(x + 3)$

  (c) $9x^4 - 35x^2 - 4 = (9x^2 + 1)(x^2 - 4) = (9x^2 + 1)(x + 2)(x - 2)$

Chapter 5

Exponential and Logarithmic Functions

INVESTIGATION 5A   WORKING WITH EXPONENTS

5.1 Getting Started

For You to Explore

1. Here is the completed table:

Input: n	Output: $f(n)$
6	64
5	32
4	16
3	8
2	4
1	2
0	1
−1	$\frac{1}{2}$
−2	$\frac{1}{4}$
−3	$\frac{1}{8}$

2. (a) $2^3 \cdot 2^5 = 2^{3+5} = 2^8$ so $2^a = 2^8$ and $a = 8$
   (b) $2^b \cdot 2^8 = 2^{b+8}$ so $2^{b+8} = 2^{14}$ and $b + 8 = 14$, $b = 6$
   (c) $3^c \cdot 3^c = 3^{c+c} = 3^{2c}$ so $3^{2c} = 3^{12}$ and $2c = 12$, $c = 6$
   (d) $(3^d)^2 = 3^{2d}$ so $3^{2d} = 3^8$ and $2d = 8$, $d = 4$
   (e) $\frac{5^7}{5^f} = 5^{7-f}$ so $5^{7-f} = 5^6$ and $7 - f = 6$, $f = 1$
   (f) $9^5 = (3^2)^5 = 3^{10}$ so $3^g = 3^{10}$ and $g = 10$
   (g) $5^{3h} = 5^7$ so $3h = 7$ and $h = \frac{7}{3}$
   (h) $(5^k)^3 = 5^{3k}$ so $5^{3k} = 5^4$ and $3k = 4$, $k = \frac{4}{3}$

3. The Laws of Exponents are

- $a^b \cdot a^c = a^{b+c}$
- $(a^b)^c = a^{bc}$
- $(ab)^c = a^c \cdot b^c$
- $\frac{a^b}{a^c} = a^{b-c}$, if $b > c$; $\frac{a^b}{a^c} = \frac{1}{a^{c-b}}$, if $c > b$; $\frac{a^b}{a^c} = 1$, if $c = b$
- $\left(\frac{a}{b}\right)^c = \frac{a^c}{b^c}$

4. (a) Multiply by 2: 4, 8, 16, <u>32</u>, <u>64</u>, <u>128</u>
   (b) Multiply by −2: 4, −8, 16, <u>−32</u>, <u>64</u>, <u>−128</u>
   (c) Multiply by $\sqrt{3}$: 2, $2\sqrt{3}$, <u>6</u>, <u>$6\sqrt{3}$</u>, <u>18</u>, <u>$18\sqrt{3}$</u>
   (d) Multiply by 2: a, $2a$, <u>$4a$</u>, <u>$8a$</u>, <u>$16a$</u>, <u>$32a$</u>
   (e) Multiply by 3: k, $3k$, <u>$9k$</u>, <u>$27k$</u>, <u>$81k$</u>, <u>$243k$</u>

5. (a) Multiply by 2: 1, <u>2</u>, <u>4</u>, 8, <u>16</u>, <u>32</u>
   (b) Multiply by $\frac{1}{2}$: <u>4</u>, <u>2</u>, 1, $\frac{1}{2}$, $\frac{1}{4}$, $\frac{1}{8}$
   (c) Multiply by 3: 2, <u>6</u>, 18, <u>54</u>, <u>162</u>, <u>486</u>
   (d) Multiply by $\sqrt{3}$: 1, <u>$\sqrt{3}$</u>, <u>3</u>, $3\sqrt{3}$, 9, <u>$27\sqrt{3}$</u>

On Your Own

6. (a) This is not always true. For example, let $a = 2$ and $b = 3$. Then you would get $2^3 = 3^2$ or $8 = 9$, which is, of course, false.
   (b) This is not always true. For example, let $a = 2$, $b = 3$, and $c = 4$. Then you would get $2^{3+4} = 2^3 + 2^4$ or $2^7 = 8 + 16$ or $128 = 24$ which is false.
   (c) This is one of the Laws of Exponents, and therefore true.
   (d) This is not always true. For example, let $a = 2, b = 3$ and $c = 4$. Then you would get $2^3 \cdot 2^4 = 2^{12}$ or $8 \cdot 16 = 4096$ or $128 = 4096$, which is false.
   (e) This is one of the Laws of Exponents, and therefore true.
   (f) This is not always true. For example, let $a = 2, b = 3$, and $c = 4$. Then you would get $(2^3)^4 = 2^{(3^4)}$ or $2^{12} = 2^{81}$, which is false.
   (g) This is true, as long as you allow $b - c$ to be 0 or negative.
   (h) This is not always true. For example, let $a = 2, b = 3$, and $c = 4$. Then you would get $(2 \cdot 3)^4 = 2 \cdot (3^4)$ or $6^4 = 2 \cdot 81$ or $1296 = 162$ which is false.

7. The value of $2^{10} + 2^2$ is *not* 2^{12}. Their product would be, but the sum doesn't work out. The same can be said about $2^9 + 2^3$, which also does not equal 2^{12}.

   The value of $2^6 2^6$ is 2^{12}. Add the exponents when multiplying. The same can be said about $(2^{10})(2^2)$ and $(2^4)(2^4)(2^4)$, and explains why $(2^4)(2^3)$ is *not* equal to 2^{12}.

   The value of $2^{11} + 2^{11}$ is 2^{12}. There are two 2^{11} terms added together, so the result is $2(2^{11})$. Since $2 = 2^1$, this is $2^1 \cdot 2^{11}$, which equals 2^{12}.

   The value of $4(2^{10})$ is 2^{12}. Since $4 = 2^2$, the expression can be rewritten as $2^2 \cdot 2^{10}$, and adding exponents gives 2^{12}.

8. Multiply the previous output by $\frac{1}{3}$ to get the new output.

Input: n	Output: $g(n)$
5	243
4	81
3	27
2	9
1	3
0	1
−1	$\frac{1}{3}$
−2	$\frac{1}{9}$
−3	$\frac{1}{27}$

9. (a) Since $h(x) = f(x) \cdot g(x)$, $h(x) = 2^x \cdot 3^x$ and
$h(3) = 2^3 \cdot 3^3 = 8 \cdot 27 = 216$

   (b) Similarly, $h(0) = 2^0 \cdot 3^0 = 1 \cdot 1 = 1$, and $h(1) = 2^1 \cdot 3^1 = 2 \cdot 3 = 6$, and $h(2) = 2^2 \cdot 3^2 = 4 \cdot 9 = 36$

   (c) Apply the Laws of Exponents to get $h(x) = 2^x \cdot 3^x = (2 \cdot 3)^x = 6^x$

10. (a) If a is a positive integer, 2^a will be a power of 2 and will be even. If b is a positive integer, 5^b will be a power of 5 and will be odd. So, 2^a (even) will never equal 5^b (odd).

    (b) You know that $2^2 = 4$ and $2^3 = 8$, so if $2^x = 5$ then x is between 2 and 3. Try $2^{2.5}$ and the result is $5.65685\ldots$. Try a number between 2 and 2.5. Continue to "zoom" in on x. Correct to 4 decimal places, $x = 2.3219$

    (c) Following the method for $2^x = 5$, begin with y is between 0 and 1, since $5^0 = 1$ and $5^1 = 5$. "Zoom" in on y. Correct to 4 decimal places, $y = 0.4307$.

    (d) Since $2^x = 5$ and $5^y = 2$, $(2^x)^y = 2$, $2^{x \cdot y} = 2^1$, $x \cdot y = 1$

Maintain Your Skills

11. (a) $3^x = 81$, $3^x = 3^4$, $x = 4$

    (b) $3^{x+1} = 81$, $3^{x+1} = 3^4$, $x + 1 = 4$, $x = 3$

    (c) $3^{2x} = 81$, $3^{2x} = 3^4$, $2x = 4$, $x = 2$

    (d) $3^{-x} = 81$, $3^{-x} = 3^4$, $-x = 4$, $x = -4$

    (e) $3^{4x-1} = 81$, $3^{4x-1} = 3^4$, $4x - 1 = 4$, $4x = 5$, $x = \frac{5}{4}$

    (f) $3^{x^2} = 81$, $3^{x^2} = 3^4$, $x^2 = 4$, $x = \pm 2$

5.2   Review: Laws of Exponents

Check Your Understanding

1. Here's a model to explain it:

$$(ab)^n = \underbrace{(ab) \cdot (ab) \cdot \cdots \cdot (ab)}_{n \text{ copies}}$$

$$= \underbrace{(a \cdot a \cdot \cdots \cdot a)}_{n \text{ copies}} \cdot \underbrace{(b \cdot b \cdot \cdots \cdot b)}_{n \text{ copies}} = a^n \cdot b^n$$

   The second step uses the commutative and associative laws to group the a and b terms together to form a^n and b^n.

2. A product model of this fraction will have 11 factors of 3 in the numerator and 5 factors of 3 in the denominator. Cancel 5 factors of 3, leaving 6 factors of 3 in the numerator and only 1 in the denominator.

$$\frac{3^{11}}{3^5} = \frac{3 \cdot 3 \cdot 3 \cdot 3 \cdot 3 \cdot 3 \cdot 3 \cdot 3 \cdot 3 \cdot 3 \cdot 3}{3 \cdot 3 \cdot 3 \cdot 3 \cdot 3\cdot}$$

$$= \frac{3 \cdot 3 \cdot 3 \cdot 3 \cdot 3}{3 \cdot 3 \cdot 3 \cdot 3 \cdot 3} \cdot 3 \cdot 3 \cdot 3 \cdot 3 \cdot 3 \cdot 3$$

$$= 3 \cdot 3 \cdot 3 \cdot 3 \cdot 3 \cdot 3$$

$$= 3^6$$

3. To prove Corollary 5.1.1, use the product model to expand a^b and a^c, then cancel out c copies from top and bottom.

$$\frac{a^b}{a^c} = \frac{\overbrace{a \cdot a \cdot a \cdots a \cdot a \cdot a}^{b \text{ copies}}}{\underbrace{a \cdot a \cdots a \cdot a}_{c \text{ copies}}} = \frac{\cancel{a} \cdots \cancel{a} \cdot \overbrace{a \cdots a}^{b-c \text{ copies}}}{\cancel{a} \cdots \cancel{a}}$$

$$= a^{b-c}$$

Similarly, to prove Corollary 5.1.2, expand a^b and write it c times, then count the total number of powers of a listed:

$$(a^b)^c = \underbrace{\underbrace{(a \cdot a \cdots a)}_{b \text{ copies}} \cdot \underbrace{(a \cdot a \cdots a)}_{b \text{ copies}} \cdots \underbrace{(a \cdot a \cdots a)}_{b \text{ copies}} \cdot}_{c \text{ copies of } a^b} = a^{b \cdot c} = a^{bc}$$

4. (a) Yes, this equals 3^{15}. There are 3 occurrences of 3^{14} added together, which is $3 \cdot 3^{14}$. Since $3 = 3^1$, this equals 3^{15} by adding exponents.

   (b) No, this equals 3^{54}. Multiply these exponents.

   (c) Yes, add the exponents to get 3^{15}.

   (d) No, add the exponents to get 3^8.

   (e) No, add the exponents to get 3^{16}.

   (f) Yes, add the exponents.

   (g) No, you cannot add these exponents. The result is not a power of 3.

   (h) Yes, multiply the exponents to get 3^{15}.

   (i) Yes, multiply the exponents.

   (j) Yes, since $9 = 3^2$, add the exponents to get 3^{15}.

   (k) No, this equals 3^{50}.

   (l) Yes, multiply the exponents. Or, recognize that $3^1 = 3$, and write it without the inner exponent.

5. For example, $c^{15} = c^{12} \cdot c^3 = (c^4)^3 \cdot c^3 = M^3 \cdot N$ or $c^{15} = \frac{c^{24}}{c^9} = \frac{(c^4)^6}{(c^3)^3} = \frac{M^6}{N^3}$

6. To multiply the two polynomials, you use the distributive property.

$(x^7 - 3x^2 + 6)(x^5 + 2x^3 + 3)$
$= x^5 \cdot (x^7 - 3x^2 + 6) + 2x^3 \cdot (x^7 - 3x^2 + 6) +$
$\quad 3 \cdot (x^7 - 3x^2 + 6)$
$= x^5 \cdot x^7 - x^5 \cdot 3x^2 + x^5 \cdot 6 + 2x^3 \cdot x^7 - 2x^3 \cdot 3x^2 +$
$\quad 2x^3 \cdot 6 + 3 \cdot x^7 - 3 \cdot 3x^2 + 3 \cdot 6$
$= x^{12} - 3x^7 + 6x^5 + 2x^{10} - 6x^5 + 12x^3 + 3x^7 - 9x^2 + 18$
$= x^{12} + 2x^{10} + 12x^3 - 9x^2 + 18$

You use the Laws of Exponents each time you multiply two powers of x together by adding the exponents.

7. $3 \cdot 3^2 \cdot 3^4 \cdot 3^8 \cdot 3^{16} = 3^{1+2+4+8+16} = 3^{31}$

8. (a) $2^3 = 8$, so $x = 3$.

   (b) $2^4 = 16$, so $y - 1$ must equal 4. Then $y = 5$.

   (c) $2^6 = 64$, so $5z$ must equal 6. Then $z = \frac{6}{5}$.

   (d) Since (2^w) is repeated twice, it is squared. What number squared makes 64? There are two, 8 and -8. Since powers of 2 are always positive, 2^w must be 8. Then $w = 3$ (see the first part of this problem).

9. To go from one output to the next, multiply by 5. Then the rule is $f(n) = a \cdot 5^n$ for some a. Use a particular input-output combination to find a: for example, $f(1) = 15$ gives $a \cdot 5 = 15$, so $a = 3$.

10. Find the mean by adding all five numbers, then dividing the sum by 5. You may want to convert the numbers from scientific notation to decimal form to do the calculation: $50,000 + 5000 + 500 + 50 + 5 = 55,555$, so the mean is 11,111.

    The numbers are already sorted from highest to lowest, so the middle number in the list is the median. The median is 500.

11. (a) $\frac{10^9}{10^8} = 10^{9-8} = 10^1 = 10$

  (b) $\frac{3^2 \cdot y^8}{(2y)^3} = \frac{9 \cdot y^8}{8 \cdot y^3} = \frac{9 \cdot y^{8-3}}{8} = \frac{9 \cdot y^5}{8}$

  (c) $\frac{6^3 \cdot x^9}{3^3 \cdot 2^2 \cdot x^5} = \frac{216 \cdot x^{9-5}}{27 \cdot 4} = \frac{216 \cdot x^4}{108} = 2 \cdot x^4$

  (d) $\frac{2^2}{2^5} = \frac{1}{2^{5-2}} = \frac{1}{2^3} = \frac{1}{8}$

12. (a) $(x-1)(x+1) = x^2 - 1 = 15$ so $x^2 = 16$ and $x = \pm 4$

  (b) $(2^x - 1)(2^x + 1) = 2^{2x} - 1 = 15$ so $2^{2x} = 16$, $2^{2x} = 2^4$ and $2x = 4$, $x = 2$

On Your Own

13. (a) $10^3 = 1000$

  (b) $100^6 = 1,000,000,000,000 \, (1 \; trillion)$

  (c) $1^{10} = 1$

  (d) $2^4 = 16$

  (e) $100^4 = 100,000,000$

  (f) $10^4 = 10,000$. In all of these expressions, there are two different bases raised to the same power. You can evaluate them more easily if you remember that $a^n b^n = (ab)^n$. In each case, the product of the bases is a simple number to calculate with.

14. (a) First you need to know how to think of a as an exponential expression. It does not have an exponent—at least, not one you can see. However, since $a \cdot a = a^2$, you can use Theorem 5.1 to realize that the "invisible exponent" has to be 1, because $a^1 \cdot a^1 = a^{1+1} = a^2$. Starting from $\frac{a^n}{a} = a^{n-1}$, multiply each side of the equation by $a^1 = a$. This is a basic move that is allowed since $a \neq 0$, and you get $a^n = a^{n-1} \cdot a^1$. Use Theorem 5.1 on the right side of the equation to get $a^n = a^{n-1+1} = a^n$. This equation is always true for n a positive integer greater than 1 and $a \neq 0$.

  (b) $\frac{a^n}{a} = \frac{\overbrace{(a \cdot a \cdot \dots \cdot a)}^{n \text{ copies}}}{a} = \frac{a \cdot \overbrace{(a \cdot a \cdot \dots \cdot a)}^{n-1 \text{ copies}}}{a} = \frac{a}{a} \cdot \underbrace{(a \cdot a \cdot \dots \cdot a)}_{n-1 \text{ copies}}$

    $= 1 \cdot a^{n-1} = a^{n-1}$

15. Each output is 3 times the previous output, so you will have the first term times a power of 3. For example, if $n = 1$, $g(1) = 5(the\ first\ term) \cdot 3^1$ and if $n = 2$, $g(2) = 5(the\ first\ term) \cdot 3^2$, so the rule is $g(n) = 5 \cdot 3^n$

16. Two ways are $A^2 \cdot B$ and B^4. See if you can find some others that use quotients.

17. Since 2^{10} is close to one thousand, 2^{20} will be close to one thousand times one thousand, which is one million. Then 2^{21} is twice 2^{20}, so it will be close to two million.

    The exact value of 2^{21} is 2,097,152.

18. (a) No, this equals 2^4. Subtract these exponents.

  (b) Yes, this equals 2^3 by subtracting exponents.

  (c) No, this is 2^2. The extra 1 exponent does nothing to change the number inside.

  (d) Yes, the numerator is 2^{10} and the denominator is 2^7. Subtract exponents to yield 2^3.

  (e) Yes, subtract these exponents.

  (f) No, this is 2^6.

  (g) No, this is 2^{10}. Add the exponents in the numerator, then subtract the exponent in the denominator.

19. (a) $2^9 = 2^8 \cdot 2^1$ so $2^9 = 256 \cdot 2 = 512$ The units digit is 2. We only needed the units digit, so it was only necessary to note that $2 \cdot 6 = 12$ to obtain the units digit of 2.

  (b) $2^{10} = 2^8 \cdot 2^2 = 256 \cdot 4 = 1024$. The units digit is 4. $(4 \cdot 6 = 24)$

  (c) $2^{16} = 2^8 \cdot 2^8 = 256 \cdot 256$ So, the units digit will be the units digit of $6 \cdot 6 = 36$ or 6.

  (d) $2^7 = \frac{2^8}{2^1} = \frac{256}{2} = 128$. So, the units digit is 8. You need to be careful here because you cannot just divide 6 by 2. It could be 16 divided by 2 or 8, which is the case here.

20. The units digit of 2^5 is 2, so the units digit of $(2^5)^2$ is 4. The units digit of 5^2 is 5, so the units digit of $(5^2)^2$ is 5. The units digit of the sum is $5 + 4 = 9$.

21. (a) Yes, this is the definition of 5^6, five multiplied by itself six times.

  (b) Yes, add the exponents.

  (c) No, the bases are not equal, so there is no reasonable result here.

  (d) Yes, subtract the exponents.

  (e) Yes, add the exponents in the numerator for 5^7, then subtract one (since $5 = 5^1$ in the denominator).

  (f) No, you cannot add exponents here. These would need to be multiplied.

  (g) Yes, subtract the exponents.

  (h) Yes, multiply the exponents.

  (i) Yes, multiply the exponents.

  (j) No, this is 5^9 by multiplying exponents.

  (k) Yes, the numerator is 5^9, then subtract exponents for the denominator.

  (l) No! This is 30, or $5 \cdot 6$. Definitely not the same as 5^6.

22. (a) x^{12}

  (b) x^{10}

  (c) x^{27}

  (d) x^{100}

  (e) x^6

  (f) x^2

  (g) x^8

23.

$$6^{x-1} = \frac{3}{2} \cdot 12^2 = \frac{3}{2} \cdot 2^2 \cdot 6^2 = 3 \cdot 2^1 \cdot 6^2 = 6^1 \cdot 6^2 = 6^3$$

Therefore, $x - 1 = 3$, so $x = 4$. The correct answer choice is **C**.

Maintain Your Skills

24. In general, the equation $(-x)^p = -x^p$ is an identity whenever p is an odd integer, and is not an identity whenever p is an even integer. This means that equations (a), (c), (e), and (f) are identities. For $(-x)^p = -x^p$ to be true for p an odd integer, the base x could only be equal to zero.

5.3 Extending to Zero and Negative Exponents

Check Your Understanding

1. (a) Yes, this comes from the definition of a negative exponent.
   (b) No, this is 7^{-7} by adding exponents.
   (c) No, this is 7^7 by adding exponents.
   (d) Yes, subtract the exponents in this quotient.
   (e) No, this is 7^{-9}. The denominator is 7^{11}.
   (f) No, this is 7^{10}. One way is to write 1 as 7^0, another is to use the Law of Exponents that $\frac{1}{b^x} = b^{-x}$. Then this is $7^{-(-10)} = 7^{10}$.
   (g) No, this is 7^3 by adding exponents.
   (h) Yes. The result inside the parentheses is 7^{-2}, then multiply the exponents.
   (i) No, this is 7^{-75} (a very, very small positive number) by multiplying the exponents.
   (j) Yes, multiply the exponents.
   (k) Yes, multiply the exponents.
   (l) Yes, since $\frac{1}{b^x} = b^{-x}$.

2. $10^{-2} \cdot 10^3 = \frac{1}{10^2} \cdot 10^3 = \frac{10^3}{10^2} = 10^{3-2} = 10^1$

3. • $a^b \cdot a^c = a^{b+c}$ If $b = 0$, then $a^0 \cdot a^c = 1 \cdot a^c = a^c$ and $a^{0+c} = a^c$, so both sides are equal.
   • $\frac{a^b}{a^c} = a^{b-c}$ (provided $b > c$) If $c = 0$ ($b > 0$) this becomes $\frac{a^b}{a^0} = a^{b-0} = a^b$ and $\frac{a^b}{a^0} = \frac{a^b}{1} = a^b$, so both sides are equal.
   • $(a^b)^c = a^{bc}$. If $b = 0$, then $(a^0)^c = (1)^c = 1$ and $a^{0 \cdot c} = a^0 = 1$, so both sides are equal.

4. (a) $3^{a+1} = 3^a \cdot 3^1 = 2 \cdot 3 = 6$
   (b) $3^{a-1} = 3^a \cdot 3^{-1} = 2 \cdot \frac{1}{3} = \frac{2}{3}$
   (c) $3^{2a} = (3^a)^2 = 2^2 = 4$
   (d) $3^{3a} = (3^a)^3 = 2^3 = 8$
   (e) $3^{0a} = 3^0 = 1$
   (f) $3^{\frac{a}{2}} = (3^a)^{\frac{1}{2}} = 2^{\frac{1}{2}} = \sqrt{2}$. Since $(2^{\frac{1}{2}})^2 = 2^1 = 2$, $2^{\frac{1}{2}}$ must be the square root of 2.

5. The first expression, $13^5 10^3$, is a multiple of 10 (specifically, a multiple of 1000). Any multiple of 10 ends in 0. The second expression is 1, since any number to the zero power is 1. The end result must have units digit $0 + 1 = 1$.

6. Find each travel time by dividing the number of miles by the number of miles per hour:

$$2.25 \cdot 10^5 \text{ miles} \cdot \frac{1 \text{ hour}}{3 \cdot 10^{-2} \text{ miles}} \approx 7.5 \cdot 10^6 \text{ hours}$$

Note the unit cancellation of "miles," which is why you end up dividing by the value $3 \cdot 10^{-2}$. Sometimes, keeping track of the units can tell you which direction a calculation should go. You can also remember that $distance = rate \times time$, so $time = distance \div rate$.

Here's a table with the number of hours for each destination:

Object	Travel time at snail pace (in hours)
Moon	$7.5 \cdot 10^6$
Mars	$1.15 \cdot 10^9$
Pluto	$8.87 \cdot 10^{10}$

7. (a) Each term is the previous term multiplied by $\frac{1}{2}$.
   $4 \cdot \frac{1}{2} = 2, 2 \cdot \frac{1}{2} = 1, 1 \cdot \frac{1}{2} = \frac{1}{2}$.
   (b) $2 \cdot 9 = 18$ or $2 \cdot 3 \cdot 3 = 18$. You want to multiply each term by 3 to get the next term in the sequence. $2 \cdot 3 = 6, 6 \cdot 3 = 18, 18 \cdot 3 = 54, 54 \cdot 3 = 162, 162 \cdot 3 = 486$
   (c) Each term is the previous term multiplied by a, so the next three terms are a^3, a^4, a^5
   (d) Each term is the previous term multiplied by b^{-3}, so the next three terms are b^{-3}, b^{-6}, b^{-9} or $\frac{1}{b^3}, \frac{1}{b^6}, \frac{1}{b^9}$
   (e) $c^{10} \cdot c^{-6} = c^4$ and $c^{-6} = c^{-2} \cdot c^{-2} \cdot c^{-2}$. Each term is the previous term multiplied by c^{-2}. $c^{10} \cdot c^{-2} = c^8$, $c^8 \cdot c^{-2} = c^6, c^6 \cdot c^{-2} = c^4, c^4 \cdot c^{-2} = c^2, c^2 \cdot c^{-2} = 1$

8. (a) Each term is the previous term multiplied by 5, so the rule will involve a power of 5. Since $h(0) = 2$, the power of 5 must be multiplied by 2. The rule is $h(x) = 2 \cdot 5^x$.
   (b)

x	$h(x)$
-3	$2 \cdot 5^{-3} = \frac{2}{5^3} = \frac{2}{125}$
-2	$2 \cdot 5^{-2} = \frac{2}{5^2} = \frac{2}{25}$
-1	$2 \cdot 5^{-1} = \frac{2}{5^1} = \frac{2}{5}$
0	2
1	10
2	50
3	250
4	1250

9. Using the Laws of Exponents, $(2^3)(2^{-3}) = 2^{3+-3} = 2^0$, and $2^0 = 1$ (by definition). So $(2^3)(2^{-3}) = 1$.

On Your Own

10. (a) $2^5 \cdot 2^{-3} = 2^{5+-3} = 2^2$ so $2^2 = 2^a$, and $a = 2$.
    (b) $2^5 \cdot 2^{-7} = 2^{5+-7} = 2^{-2}$ so $2^{-2} = 2^b$, and $b = -2$.
    (c) $\frac{2^5}{2^7} = 2^5 \cdot 2^{-7} = 2^{5+-7} = 2^{-2}$ so $2^{-2} = 2^c$, and $c = -2$.
    (d) $\frac{2^5}{2^{-7}} = \frac{2^5}{\frac{1}{2^7}} = 2^5 \cdot \frac{2^7}{1} = 2^{12}$ so $2^{12} = 2^d$, and $d = 12$.
    (e) $\frac{2^5}{2^7} = 2^5 \cdot 2^{-f} = 2^{5+-f}$ so $2^{5+-f} = 2^8, 5 + -f = 8$, and $f = -3$.

11. (a) $\left(\frac{1}{5}\right)^{-3} = \frac{1}{5^{-3}} = \frac{1}{\frac{1}{5^3}} = 5^3$ Yes
    (b) $5^{-3} \cdot 5^3 = 5^{-3+3} = 5^0 = 1$ No
    (c) $(5^8)(5^{-2}) = 5^{8+-2} = 5^6$ No
    (d) $\frac{5^6}{5^9} = 5^6 \cdot 5^{-9} = 5^{6+-9} = 5^{-3}$ No
    (e) $\frac{5^{10}}{5^2 \cdot 5^3 \cdot 5^2} = \frac{5^{10}}{5^{2+3+2}} = \frac{5^{10}}{5^7} = 5^{10-7} = 5^3$ Yes
    (f) $\left(\frac{1}{5^3}\right) = 5^{-3}$ No
    (g) $5^5 \cdot 5^{-2} = 5^{5+-2} = 5^3$ Yes
    (h) $\left(\frac{1}{5^3}\right)^{-1} = (5^{-3})^{-1} = 5^3$ Yes

(i) $(5^{15})^{\frac{1}{5}} = 5^{15 \cdot \frac{1}{5}} = 5^3$ Yes

(j) $(5^2)^1 = 5^{2 \cdot 1} = 5^2$ No

(k) $(5^4)^{-1} = 5^{4 \cdot -1} = 5^{-4}$ No

(l) $\left(\frac{1}{5^{-3}}\right) = \frac{1}{\frac{1}{5^3}} = 5^3$ Yes

12. On page 406, the rules are given for positive exponents only, and the second law applies only when $b > c$. On page 408 these restrictions have been removed. The laws apply to all integer exponents, and the second law can still be used when $b \le c$.

13. Anything raised to the zero power is 1. So, $(4x + 5y - 6z)^0$ is 1, and anything raised to the first power is unchanged, thus $(3xy^2 - 5z)^1 = 3xy^2 - 5z$. The result is $3xy^2 - 5z + 1$.

14. (a) $(3^x + 3^{-x})^2 = (3^x)^2 + 2 \cdot 3^x \cdot 3^{-x} + (3^{-x})^2 = 3^{2x} + 2 \cdot 3^0 + 3^{-2x} = 3^{2x} + 2 + 3^{-2x}$

(b) $(3^x - 3^{-x})^2 = (3^x)^2 - 2 \cdot 3^x \cdot 3^{-x} + (3^{-x})^2 = 3^{2x} - 2 \cdot 3^0 + 3^{-2x} = 3^{2x} - 2 + 3^{-2x}$

(c) $(3^x + 3^{-x})^2 - (3^x - 3^{-x})^2 = (3^{2x} + 2 + 3^{-2x}) - (3^{2x} - 2 + 3^{-2x}) = 2 - (-2) = 4$

15. (a) z^2 by adding exponents

(b) z^{-27}. The inner result $(z^3)^3$ is z^9 and then $(z^9)^{-3}$ is z^{-27}.

(c) z^{-4}. One way to do this is to cancel the z^2 from numerator and denominator.

(d) z^{-10}. The numerator is 1, since $z^0 = 1$.

(e) z^{-11}. The numerator is 1, as is the first factor in the denominator.

16. (a) $g \circ f(1) = g(f(1)) = g(3^1) = g(3) = 3^2 = 9$

(b) $g \circ f(-1) = g(f(-1)) = g(3^{-1}) = (3^{-1})^2 = 3^{-2} = \frac{1}{3^2} = \frac{1}{9}$

(c) $g \circ f(2) = g(f(2)) = g(3^2) = g(9) = 9^2 = 81$

(d) $g \circ f(x) = g(f(x)) = g(3^x) = (3^x)^2 = 3^{2x}$ or 9^x

(e) $f \circ g(1) = f(g(1)) = f(1^2) = f(1) = 3^1 = 3$

(f) $f \circ g(-1) = f(g(-1)) = f((-1)^2) = f(1) = 3^1 = 3$

(g) $f \circ g(2) = f(g(2)) = f(2^2) = f(4) = 3^4 = 81$

(h) $f \circ g(x) = f(g(x)) = f(x^2) = 3^{x^2}$

17.

Input	Output
-3	$\frac{1}{8}$
-2	$\frac{1}{4}$
-1	$\frac{1}{2}$
0	1
1	2
2	4
3	8

18.

Input	Output
-3	8
-2	4
-1	2
0	1
1	$\frac{1}{2}$
2	$\frac{1}{4}$
3	$\frac{1}{8}$

19. Since $\frac{1}{2} = 2^{-1}$, and $g(x) = (2^{-1})^x = 2^{-x}$, so $g(x) = f(-x)$. For example, the output for 3 in the first table will equal the output for -3 in the second table and the output for -3 in the first table will equal the output for 3 in the second table.

20.

Input	Output
-3	1
-2	$\frac{-1+i\sqrt{3}}{2}$
-1	$\frac{-1-i\sqrt{3}}{2}$
0	1
1	$\frac{-1+i\sqrt{3}}{2}$
2	$\frac{-1-i\sqrt{3}}{2}$
3	1
4	$\frac{-1+i\sqrt{3}}{2}$
5	$\frac{-1-i\sqrt{3}}{2}$

You know that $w(0) = 1$ and $w(1) = \frac{-1+i\sqrt{3}}{2}$ by the definitions for exponents 0 and 1. You also know that $w(3) = 1$. Use complex number multiplication to find $w(2) = \left(\frac{-1+i\sqrt{3}}{2}\right)^2 = \frac{1-2i\sqrt{3}+i^2 \cdot 3}{4} = \frac{1-2i\sqrt{3}+(-3)}{4} = \frac{-2-2i\sqrt{3}}{4} = \frac{-1-i\sqrt{3}}{2}$

Now you can write the rest of the entries in the table from these facts.

$w(-3) = \frac{1}{w(3)} = \frac{1}{1} = 1$. $w(-2) = w(-3) \cdot w(1) = 1 \cdot w(1) = w(1)$. $w(-1) = w(-2) \cdot w(1) = w(1) \cdot w(1) = w(2)$. $w(0) = 1$. $w(1) = \frac{-1+i\sqrt{3}}{2}$. $w(2) = \frac{-1-i\sqrt{3}}{2}$. $w(3) = 1$.

Now you can see that there is a repeating cycle of three outputs, which you can continue to fill in the table.

21.
$$\frac{5^2 \cdot (5^{-3})^0}{5^{-6}} = \frac{5^2 \cdot 5^0}{5^{-6}} = \frac{5^2}{5^{-6}} = 5^{2-(-6)} = 5^8$$

The correct answer choice is **D**.

Maintain Your Skills

22. In a geometric sequence, multiply each term by a constant value to get to the next term.

(a) $1 \cdot x \cdot x \cdot x = 125$ so $x^3 = 125$ and $x = 5$. The sequence will be $1, 1 \cdot 5, 1 \cdot 5 \cdot 5, 125$. So it is $1, \mathbf{5}, \mathbf{25}, 125$

(b) $x^3 = 27$, $x = 3$ Multiply each term by 3. $1, \mathbf{3}, \mathbf{9}, 27, \mathbf{81}$

(c) $x^2 = 64$, $x = \pm 8$ Multiply each term by ± 8. $1, \mathbf{8}, 64$ or $1, \mathbf{-8}, 64$

(d) $x^3 = 64$, $x = 4$ Multiply each term by 4. $1, \mathbf{4}, \mathbf{16}, 64$

(e) $x^6 = 64$, $x = \pm 2$ Multiply each term by ± 2. $1, \mathbf{2}, \mathbf{4}, \mathbf{8}, \mathbf{16}, \mathbf{32}, 64$ or $1, \mathbf{-2}, \mathbf{4}, \mathbf{-8}, \mathbf{16}, \mathbf{-32}, 64$

23. (a) $x = 5$

(b) $x = 3$

(c) $x = \pm 8$

(d) $x = 4$

(e) $x = \pm 2$

24. (a) 1.

  (b) $1\frac{1}{2}$.

  (c) $1\frac{3}{4}$.

  (d) $1\frac{7}{8}$.

  (e) $1\frac{15}{16}$.

  (f) The results are getting closer and closer to 2. Each result's numerator is one more than double the one before it. Each result's denominator is double the one before it. Comparing each result to 2 shows they are getting closer by powers of 2: each is $2 - \frac{1}{2^k}$ for increasing k. So, as the pattern continues, the results get ever closer to 2.

5.4 Sequences and Operations

Check Your Understanding

1. (a) Add 3 each time. 0, 3, 6, **9, 12, 15**

  (b) Add 6 each time. 0, **6, 12, 18, 24**, 30

  (c) Add 20 each time. 1, **21, 41, 61**, 81, **101**

  (d) Add -4 each time. 5, **1, -3, -7, -11, -15, -19**

2. Since you take five "steps" to get from 0 to 30, the third step in the sequence, 18, is $\frac{3}{5}$ of the way from 0 to 30. So,

$$30 \cdot \frac{3}{5} = 18$$

3. (a) $2 \cdot r = -6$, so $r = -3$. Keep multiplying by -3. 2, -6, 18, $\underline{-54}$, $\underline{162}$, $\underline{-486}$

  (b) $r = i$. Keep multiplying by i. 1, i, -1, $\underline{-i}$, $\underline{-i \cdot i = -i^2 = -(-1) = 1}$, $\underline{i}$

  (c) $r^2 = 5$, so $r = \pm\sqrt{5}$. Keep multiplying by $\pm\sqrt{5}$. 1, $\underline{\sqrt{5}}$, 5, $\underline{5 \cdot \sqrt{5}}$, $\underline{25}$, $25 \cdot \sqrt{5}$ or 1, $-\sqrt{5}$, 5, $-5\sqrt{5}$, 25, $-25\sqrt{5}$

  (d) $r^3 = 125$, so $r = 5$ Keep multiplying by 5. 1, $\underline{5}$, $\underline{25}$, 125, $\underline{625}$

  (e) $r^4 = 9$, so $r = \pm\sqrt[4]{9}$. Keep multiplying by $\pm\sqrt[4]{9}$. 1, $\sqrt[4]{9}$, $\sqrt[4]{81} = 3$, $3 \cdot \sqrt[4]{9}$, 9, $9 \cdot \sqrt[4]{9}$, 27 or 1, $-\sqrt[4]{9}$, 3, $-3\sqrt[4]{9}$, 9, $-9\sqrt[4]{9}$, 27

4. In the geometric sequence in Exercise 3d, you take three "steps" to get from 1 to 125. So, the second step, 25, should be $\frac{2}{3}$ of the way or $125^{\frac{2}{3}}$.

5. (a) An arithmetic sequence is in the form $a, a+d, a+2d, \ldots$ Therefore, $a + 2d = b$ and $d = \frac{b-a}{2}$. The second term is $a + d = a + \frac{b-a}{2} = \frac{a+b}{2}$

  (b) A geometric sequence is in the form $a, ar, ar^2, \ldots$ Therefore, $ar^2 = b$ and $r = \pm\sqrt{\frac{b}{a}} = \frac{\pm\sqrt{ab}}{a}$. The second term in the sequence will be $a \cdot r = a \cdot \frac{\pm\sqrt{ab}}{a} = \pm\sqrt{ab}$.

6. (a)

(a, b)	$\frac{a+b}{2}$	$\sqrt{ab}$
(1,2)	1.5	1.4142
(2,5)	3.5	3.1623
(4,1)	2.5	2
(3,3)	3	3
(6,9)	7.5	7.3485
(8,10)	9	8.9443
(7,7)	7	7

  (b) $\frac{a+b}{2} \geq \sqrt{ab}$ is the conclusion you can draw from the table, but you may also recognize this as the arithmetic-geometric mean inequality which was proven in both CME Project *Algebra 1* and *Geometry*. Here is a quick sketch of an algebraic proof:

$$\frac{a+b}{2} \geq \sqrt{ab}$$
$$\frac{a^2 + 2ab + b^2}{4} \geq ab$$
$$a^2 + 2ab + b^2 \geq 4ab$$
$$a^2 - 2ab + b^2 \geq 0$$
$$(a-b)^2 \geq 0$$

Each of these steps is only valid because you know that $a, b > 0$.

7. Since $r^4 = 16$, $r = \pm 2$ So, the missing terms could be 1, **2, 4, 8**, 16 or 1, **-2, 4, -8**, 16. In the first case, each term is multiplied by 2. In the second case, each term is multiplied by -2.

8. (a) First note that $64^{\frac{2}{3}} \cdot 64^{\frac{2}{3}} \cdot 64^{\frac{2}{3}} = 64^{\left(\frac{2}{3} + \frac{2}{3} + \frac{2}{3}\right)} = 64^{\frac{6}{3}} = 64^2$. So, $64^2 = x^3$ and $x = \sqrt[3]{64^2} = \sqrt[3]{4096} = 16$.

$$64^{\frac{2}{3}} = 16$$

  (b) $625^{\frac{1}{4}} \cdot 625^{\frac{1}{4}} \cdot 625^{\frac{1}{4}} \cdot 625^{\frac{1}{4}} = 625^{\frac{4}{4}} = 625$. So, $625 = x^4$, $x = \sqrt[4]{625} = 5$.

$$625^{\frac{1}{4}} = 5$$

9. (a) The value of $16^{\frac{1}{2}}$ is exactly 4, so this will be just a little more than 4.

  (b) The value of $27^{\frac{1}{3}}$ is exactly 3, so this will be just a little less than 3.

  (c) The value of $81^{\frac{1}{4}}$ is exactly 3, so this will be just a little more than 3.

  (d) Since 32 is an exact power of 2, this is $(2^5)^{\frac{4}{5}} = 2^4 = 16$ exactly.

On Your Own

10. Apply the Laws of Exponents to calculate each problem.

  (a) $81^{\frac{1}{2}} \cdot 81^{\frac{1}{2}} = 81^{\frac{1}{2} + \frac{1}{2}} = 81^1 = 81$ Add the exponents.

  (b) $(27^{\frac{1}{3}})^3 = 27^{\left(\frac{1}{3} \cdot 3\right)} = 27^1 = 27$ Multiply the exponents.

  (c) $16^{\frac{3}{4}} \cdot 16^{\frac{1}{4}} = 16^{\frac{4}{4}} = 16^1 = 16$ Add the exponents.

  (d) $(9^{\frac{1}{2}})^3 = 3^3 = 27$

11. (a) $25^{\frac{1}{2}}$ is exactly 5 and $36^{\frac{1}{2}}$ is exactly 6. 27 is closer to 25, so the nearest integer is 5.

  (b) $8^{\frac{1}{3}}$ is exactly 2. 7 is close to 8, so the nearest integer will be 2.

  (c) $64^{\frac{5}{6}} = (64^{\frac{1}{6}})^5 = 2^5 = 32$. This is exactly 32.

  (d) $125^{\frac{1}{3}}$ is exactly 5. So, this is close to 5.

12. (a)

Years	Balance
0	500
1	515
2	530.45
3	546.36
4	562.75
5	579.64
6	597.03

(b) Each time you *multiply* the previous output by 1.03, so the sequence is geometric.

13. (a) $f(25) = 25^{\frac{1}{2}} = 5$

(b) $f(100) = 100^{\frac{1}{2}} = 10$

(c) $f(49) = 49^{\frac{1}{2}} = 7$

(d) $f(1) = 1^{\frac{1}{2}} = 1$

(e) $f(f(256)) = f(256^{\frac{1}{2}}) = f(16) = 16^{\frac{1}{2}} = 4$

14. (a) $f(x) = \sqrt{x}$

(b) $f(f(x)) = (x^{\frac{1}{2}})^{\frac{1}{2}}$, and according to the Laws of Exponents, the exponents should be multiplied. The result is $f(f(x)) = x^{\frac{1}{4}}$. This is equivalent to $f(x) = \sqrt[4]{x}$.

15. The common ratio is $\frac{6}{4} = \frac{9}{6} = \frac{3}{2}$. The next term is $9 \cdot \frac{3}{2} = \frac{27}{2}$. The correct answer choice is **C**.

16. In order for an arithmetic sequence and a geometric sequence to be equal, corresponding terms would have to be equal. So, $a = a$, $ar = a + d$, $ar^2 = a + 2d$ and so on. Solving $ar = a + d$ for a, you get $a = \frac{d}{r-1}$. Solving $ar^2 = a + 2d$ for a, you get $a = \frac{2d}{r^2-1}$ and then

$$\frac{d}{r-1} = \frac{2d}{r^2-1}$$
$$d \cdot (r^2 - 1) = 2d \cdot (r - 1)$$
$$dr^2 - d = 2dr - 2d$$
$$dr^2 - 2dr + d = 0$$
$$d(r^2 - 2r + 1) = 0$$
$$d(r - 1)^2 = 0$$

So, $d = 0$ or $r = 1$. If $d = 0$, the sequence is $a, a + 0, a + 2 \cdot 0, \cdots = a, a, a, \ldots$. If $r = 1$, the sequence is $a, a \cdot 1, a \cdot 1^2, \cdots = a, a, a, \ldots$ Therefore, the only time a sequence is both arithmetic and geometric is if it is of the form $a, a, a, \ldots$

17. (a) Write both 8 and 4 as powers of 2. $(2^3)^x = 2^2$. So, $2^{3x} = 2^2$, $3x = 2$, $x = \frac{2}{3}$

(b) Write both 5 and 25 as powers of 5. $5^x = (5^2)^{x-3}$, $5^x = 5^{2x-6}$, $x = 2x - 6$, $x = 6$

(c) Write both 3 and 9 as powers of 3. $3^{2x-1} = (3^2)^{x+1}$, $3^{2x-1} = 3^{2x+2}$, $2x - 1 = 2x + 2$, $-1 = 2$ No solution.

(d) Write both 8 and 4 as powers of 2. $(2^3)^{2x} = (2^2)^{x-1}$, $2^{6x} = 2^{2x-2}$, $6x = 2x - 2$, $4x = -2$, $x = \frac{-1}{2}$

(e) If $x = 0$, $8^0 = 3^0 = 1$. Since $8 > 3$, if $x > 0$, then $8^x > 3^x$. If $x < 0$, then $-x > 0$, so $8^{-x} > 3^{-x}$; taking reciprocals, $8^x < 3^x$. Thus, there are no other solutions.

18. First write each equation in quadratic form. Then solve by factoring, or use the quadratic formula.

(a) $2^{2x} + 2^x - 6 = 0$ or $(2^x)^2 + 2^x - 6 = 0$. $(2^x + 3)(2^x - 2) = 0$ so $2^x + 3 = 0$ or $2^x - 2 = 0$. $2^x = -3$ gives no solution (2 raised to a power will never be negative). $2^x = 2$ gives $x = 1$ as a solution.

(b) $3^{2x} - 12 \cdot 3^x + 27 = 0$ or $(3^x)^2 - 12 \cdot 3^x + 27 = 0$, $(3^x - 9)(3^x - 3) = 0$, $3^x = 9 = 3^2$ or $3^x = 3$. Therefore, $x = 2$ or $x = 1$

(c) $4^{2x} - 6 \cdot 4^x + 8 = 0$ or $(4^x)^2 - 6 \cdot 4^x + 8 = 0$, So, $(4^x - 2)(4^x - 4) = 0$, $4^x = 2$ or $4^x = 4$. If $4^x = 2$ then $2^{2x} = 2$ so $2x = 1$ and $x = \frac{1}{2}$. If $4^x = 4$ then $x = 1$.

Maintain Your Skills

19. Apply the quotient rule for exponents.

(a) $\frac{8^{\frac{4}{3}}}{8^{\frac{1}{3}}} = 8^{\left(\frac{4}{3} - \frac{1}{3}\right)} = 8^{\frac{3}{3}} = 8^1 = 8$

(b) $\frac{27}{27^{\frac{2}{3}}} = 27^{\left(1 - \frac{2}{3}\right)} = 27^{\frac{1}{3}} = 3$

(c) $\frac{125^{\frac{1}{3}}}{125^{\frac{2}{3}}} = 125^{\left(\frac{1}{3} - \frac{2}{3}\right)} = 125^{-\frac{1}{3}} = \frac{1}{5}$

(d) $\frac{49^{\frac{1}{2}}}{49^{\frac{3}{2}}} = 49^{\left(\frac{1}{2} - \frac{3}{2}\right)} = 49^{-1} = \frac{1}{49}$

(e) $\frac{17^{\frac{7}{5}}}{17^{\frac{2}{5}}} = 17^{\frac{5}{5}} = 17^1 = 17$

20. (a) 1, because the function $y = x^3$ is one-to-one.

(b) 2, because there will be both a positive and a negative real solution.

(c) 1, because the function $y = x^3$ is one-to-one.

(d) 1, because the function $y = x^5$ is one-to-one.

(e) 0, because you can't raise a real number to an even power and get a negative result.

(f) 1, because the function $y = x^3$ is one-to-one.

21. It depends on whether n is even or odd. If n is odd, there will always be one real solution, and a can be either positive or negative. This is because functions of the form $y = x^n$ with n an odd integer are all one-to-one.

If, however, n is even, then there are two solutions if a is positive, and no solutions if a is negative. This is because functions of the form $y = x^n$ with n an even integer are not one-to-one. Their range is $y \geq 0$, and for each non-zero y, there are two values of x which solve the equation—a positive and a negative real number.

5.5 Defining Rational Exponents

Check Your Understanding

1. For the second, use $37^{\frac{3}{2}} = 37 \cdot 37^{\frac{1}{2}}$.

(a) Since $36^{\frac{1}{2}} = 6$, $37^{\frac{1}{2}}$ is a little more than 6.

(b) Since $37^{\frac{3}{2}} = 37 \cdot 37^{\frac{1}{2}}$, the product will be a little more than $37 \cdot 6$ or a little more than 222. You could also answer that it was a little more than $216 = 6^3$, because you are cubing a number that is a little more than 6.

2. (a) Rewrite $3^{\frac{1}{3}} \cdot 9^{\frac{1}{3}}$ as $(3 \cdot 9)^{\frac{1}{3}} = 27^{\frac{1}{3}} = 3$

(b) $64^{\frac{5}{6}} = (64^{\frac{1}{6}})^5 = 2^5 = 32$

(c) $(7^{\frac{1}{3}})^6 = 7^{\frac{6}{3}} = 7^2 = 49$

(d) $81^{\frac{1}{3}} \cdot 81^{\frac{1}{6}} = 81^{\left(\frac{1}{3}+\frac{1}{6}\right)} = 81^{\frac{1}{2}} = 9$

3. (a) One possible solution is $a = 32$ and $b = 4$, since
$32^{\frac{2}{5}} = (32^{\frac{1}{5}})^2 = 2^2 = 4$

(b) Yes, if a and b satisfy the relationship $a^{\frac{2}{5}} = b$. Raise each side of the equation to the fifth power.
$(a^{\frac{2}{5}})^5 = b^5$ and $a^2 = b^5$

4.
$$1^{\frac{p}{q}} = (1^p)^{\frac{1}{q}}$$
$$= (1)^{\frac{1}{q}}$$
$$= \sqrt[q]{1}$$
$$= 1$$

5. The graph will contain points on the horizontal lines $y = 1$ and $y = -1$. Whenever x is an even integer, the output will be 1. When x is an odd integer the output will be -1. When x is not an integer, the output may or may not be defined. For example, $(-1)^{\frac{1}{2}}$ is not real, but $(-1)^{\frac{1}{3}} = -1$. The graph will have "holes" where the output is not defined.

6. (a) $a(b(9)) = a(3) = 9$, $b(a(7)) = b(49) = 7$

(b) These are *not* inverse functions! Consider
$b(a(-7)) = b(49) = 7$

7. If $a, b, c, d, \ldots$ is an *arithmetic* sequence, then $b = a + k, c = a + 2k, d = a + 3k$, for some number k. The sequence, $10^a, 10^b, 10^c, 10^d, \ldots$ becomes 10^a, $10^{a+k}, 10^{a+2k}, 10^{a+3k}, \ldots$ Using the Laws of Exponents, we can write this as $10^a, 10^a \cdot 10^k, 10^a \cdot 10^{2k}$, $10^a \cdot 10^{3k}, \ldots$ This is a *geometric* sequence where the first term is 10^a and the common ratio is 10^k.

On Your Own

8. $(-25)^{\frac{1}{2}}$ is defined to be the *real* square root of -25. Since there is no real number whose square is -25, this is undefined.

9. (a) $7^{\frac{1}{3}} \cdot 7^{-\frac{1}{3}} = 7^{(\frac{1}{3}+-\frac{1}{3})} = 7^0 = 1$

(b) $27^{-\frac{2}{3}} = (27^{\frac{1}{3}})^{-2} = 3^{-2} = \frac{1}{9}$

(c) $(9^{\frac{2}{3}})^{\frac{3}{4}} = 9^{\frac{1}{2}} = 3$

(d) $(62^{\frac{a}{3}})^{\frac{3}{a}} = 62^{\frac{3a}{3a}} = 62^1 = 62 \ (a \neq 0)$

10. You can solve this equation by factoring.
$$x^4 = 81$$
$$x^4 - 81 = 0$$
$$(x^2 - 9)(x^2 + 9) = 0$$
$$(x + 3)(x - 3)(x + 3i)(x - 3i) = 0$$
$$x = \pm 3 \text{ or } x = \pm 3i$$

11. (a) $81^{\frac{1}{4}} = \sqrt[4]{81} = 3$

(b) $81^{-\frac{1}{4}} = \frac{1}{81^{\frac{1}{4}}} = \frac{1}{\sqrt[4]{81}} = \frac{1}{3}$

12. (a) Let $a = 0$ and $b = 1$. Then $E(1) = E(1) \cdot E(0)$, and since $E(1) = 3$ this means $3 = 3 \cdot E(0)$. Then $E(0) = 1$.

(b) Find $E(2)$ first: $E(2) = E(1) \cdot E(1)$, so $E(2) = 9$. Then $E(4) = E(2) \cdot E(2)$, so $E(4) = 81$. Alternately, find and use $E(3) = 27$.

(c) Let $a = 1$ and $b = n - 1$. Then
$E(n) = E(1) \cdot E(n - 1) = 3 \cdot E(n - 1)$.

(d) Part (c) gives $E(n)$ defined by a recursive rule that multiplies by 3, so it is an exponential function. Specifically, $E(n) = 3^n$ is the only exponential function with $E(0) = 1$ and $E(1) = 3$.

13. $8^{\frac{1}{6}} = (2^3)^{\frac{1}{6}} = 2^{\frac{3}{6}} = 2^{\frac{1}{2}} = \sqrt{2}$

14. Since this is a geometric sequence, you need to find the common ratio, r. $1 \cdot r^3 = a^2$ Raise each side of the equation to the power of $\frac{1}{3}$. This gives you $(r^3)^{\frac{1}{3}} = (a^2)^{\frac{1}{3}}$ or $r = a^{\frac{2}{3}}$. Now you can complete the sequence. Remember that the Laws of Exponents say that to multiply two powers (with the same base), you add the exponents. $1, \mathbf{a^{\frac{2}{3}}}, \mathbf{a^{\frac{4}{3}}}, a^2, \mathbf{a^{\frac{8}{3}}}, \mathbf{a^{\frac{10}{3}}}, \mathbf{a^4}, \mathbf{a^{\frac{14}{3}}}$

15. (a) Here is the completed table:

x	$f(x) = x^3$	$g(x) = x^{1/3}$
-8	-512	-2
-2	-8	-1.2599
-1	-1	-1
$-\frac{1}{2}$	$-\frac{1}{8}$	-0.794
$-\frac{1}{8}$	$-\frac{1}{512}$	$-\frac{1}{2}$
0	0	0
$\frac{1}{8}$	$\frac{1}{512}$	$\frac{1}{2}$
$\frac{1}{2}$	$\frac{1}{8}$	0.794
1	1	1
2	8	1.2599
8	512	2

(b) Here are the two graphs:

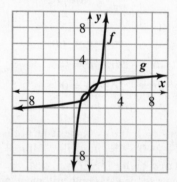

(c) The two graphs are reflections of each other. The reflection is over the line $y = x$. This happens because $f(x)$ and $g(x)$ are inverse functions.

(d) There are 3 intersections, so $f(x) = g(x)$ three times.

16. $x^{\frac{2}{3}} = (x^2)^{\frac{1}{3}} = \sqrt[3]{x^2}$. The correct answer choice is **D**.

Maintain Your Skills

17. Experiment with your calculator, and "zoom" in on the solution. To begin, you might recognize that $10^0 = 1$ and $10^1 = 10$, so a must be between 0 and 1.

(a) $a = 0.301$

(b) $b = 0.602$

(c) $c = 0.903$

(d) $d = 1.204$

18. (a) $a = 0.301$

(b) $b = 0.477$

(c) $c = 0.778$

(d) $d = 1.079$

(e) $f = 1.556$

5A MATHEMATICAL REFLECTIONS

1.

$$\frac{b^6}{b^2} = \frac{b \cdot b \cdot b \cdot b \cdot b \cdot b}{b \cdot b}$$

$$= \frac{b \cdot b}{b \cdot b} \cdot b \cdot b \cdot b \cdot b$$

$$= 1 \cdot b^4$$

$$= b^{6-2}$$

2. (a) $p^6 \cdot p^{-6} = p^{6+-6} = p^0 = 1$

(b) $q^8 \cdot q^{\frac{1}{8}} = q^{8+\frac{1}{8}} = q^{\frac{65}{8}}$

(c) $(r^2)^{-2} = r^{2(-2)} = r^{-4}$ or $\frac{1}{r^4}$

(d) $(s^4)^{\frac{1}{4}} = s^{4\left(\frac{1}{4}\right)} = s^1 = s$

(e) $\frac{t^5}{t^{-2}} = t^{5--2} = t^7$

(f) $\frac{u^6}{u^{\frac{1}{3}}} = u^{6-\frac{1}{3}} = u^{\frac{17}{3}}$

3. (a) $2^{m+1} = 2^m \cdot 2^1 = 3 \cdot 2 = 6$

(b) $2^{3m} = 2^m \cdot 2^m \cdot 2^m = 3 \cdot 3 \cdot 3 = 27$

(c) $2^{m-1} = 2^m \cdot 2^{-1} = 3 \cdot \frac{1}{2} = \frac{3}{2}$

(d) $(2^2)^m = 2^{2m} = (2^m)^2 = 2^m \cdot 2^m = 3 \cdot 3 = 9$

4. (a) 1, 4, 16, 64, 256, 1024

(b) The ratio between successive terms in the sequence is 4, because you need to get to 64 in three steps in order to evaluate $64^{\frac{2}{3}}$. That would mean that the sequence is $1, r, r^2, r^3 = 64, \ldots$, and if $r^3 = 64, r = 4$.

(c) $64^{\frac{4}{3}} = 256$ because each step in the sequence multiplies by a factor of $64^{\frac{1}{3}} = 4$. You want to take four such steps from 1 in this sequence of thirds to find $64^{\frac{4}{3}}$ which gets you to 256 in the sequence.

5. (a) $81^{\frac{3}{4}} = (3^4)^{\frac{3}{4}} = 3^{4 \cdot \frac{3}{4}} = 3^3 = 27$

(b) $32^{\frac{4}{5}} = (2^5)^{\frac{4}{5}} = 2^{5 \cdot \frac{4}{5}} = 2^4 = 16$

(c) $(11^4)^{\frac{1}{2}} = 11^{4 \cdot \frac{1}{2}} = 11^2 = 121$

(d) $(\sqrt[3]{64})^2 = (\sqrt[3]{4^3})^2 = 4^2 = 16$

6. The Fundamental Law of Exponents says, "Let $a \neq 0$ and let b and c be rational numbers, then $a^b \cdot a^c = a^{b+c}$." In other words, when you multiply two expressions where the same base is raised to a power, the product will be the same base raised to the sum of the two powers.

Corollaries include the following.

- $\frac{a^b}{a^c} = a^{b-c}$
- $(a^b)^c = a^{bc}$
- $a^0 = 1$
- $a^{-b} = \frac{1}{a^b}$

7. To extend the definition of exponent to include zero, negative, and rational exponents, you make choices so that the Laws of Exponents will still hold.

If you want to evaluate b^0 for $b > 0$, you could think about $b^0 \cdot b^m$ where $m \neq 0$. If you assume that the

Fundamental Law of Exponents holds for 0 exponents, $b^0 \cdot b^m = b^{0+m} = b^m$. This means that b^0 has to be a number that can be multiplied by b^m to give a product of b^m. The only value that would work for b^0 would be 1.

To think about b^{-m} with $b, m > 0$, assume that the Fundamental Law of Exponents holds for negative exponents. Then $b^{-m} \cdot b^m = b^{-m+m} = b^0 = 1$. So, b^{-m} is a number that can be multiplied by b^m to give a product of 1. It must be the reciprocal of b^m, which is $\frac{1}{b^m}$.

Then, to think about rational exponents, start with the expression $b^{\frac{1}{q}}$ with $b > 0$, and q an integer. Again assume that the Fundamental Law of Exponents applies to rational exponents. A corollary to that law says that $(b^m)^n = b^{mn}$, so $\left(b^{\frac{1}{q}}\right)^q = b^{\frac{1}{q}(q)} = b^1 = b$. This means that when you raise $b^{\frac{1}{q}}$ to the q power, you get b. This is how the q-th root of b behaves, so that's how you define $b^{\frac{1}{q}} = \sqrt[q]{b}$.

8. $4^0 = 1, 7^{-2} = \frac{1}{7^2} = \frac{1}{49}, 5^{\frac{2}{3}} = \sqrt[3]{25} \approx 2.92$

INVESTIGATION 5B EXPONENTIAL FUNCTIONS

5.6 Getting Started

For You to Explore

1.

Input	Output	Δ
0	1	3
1	4	3
2	7	3
3	10	3
4	13	3
5	16	3

2.

Input	Output	Δ
0	1	0
1	1	2
2	3	4
3	7	6
4	13	8
5	21	10

3.

Input	Output	Δ
0	1	2
1	3	6
2	9	18
3	27	54
4	81	162
5	243	486

4.

Input	Output	Δ
0	3	12
1	15	60
2	75	300
3	375	1500
4	1875	7500
5	9375	37,500

5.

Input	Output	Δ
0	1	$-\frac{1}{2}$
1	$\frac{1}{2}$	$-\frac{1}{4}$
2	$\frac{1}{4}$	$-\frac{1}{8}$
3	$\frac{1}{8}$	$-\frac{1}{16}$
4	$\frac{1}{16}$	$-\frac{1}{32}$
5	$\frac{1}{32}$	$-\frac{1}{64}$

6. In the last problem, $f(x) = \left(\frac{1}{2}\right)^x = 2^{-x}$, the outputs are the negatives of the inputs. So, a good guess might be $g(x) = 2^x$. The table for $g(x)$ is:

Input	Output	Δ
0	1	1
1	2	2
2	4	4
3	8	8
4	16	16
5	32	32

The output column equals the difference column. $g(x) = 0$ also works.

7. (a)

Input	Output	÷
0	1	4
1	4	**1.75**
2	7	**1.43**
3	10	1.3
4	13	**1.23**
5	16	**1.19**

(b) The numbers in the ratio column appear to be approaching 1. This makes sense because as the outputs get larger and larger, adding three to the previous output doesn't change it as much as when the outputs are small.

8. (a) $b(x) = x^2 - x + 1$

Input	Output	÷
0	1	1
1	1	3
2	3	2.33
3	7	1.86
4	13	1.62
5	21	1.48

(b) $c(x) = 3^x$

Input	Output	÷
0	1	3
1	3	3
2	9	3
3	27	3
4	81	3
5	243	3

(c) $d(x) = 3 \cdot 5^x$

Input	Output	÷
0	3	5
1	15	5
2	75	5
3	375	5
4	1875	5
5	9375	5

(d) $f(x) = \left(\frac{1}{2}\right)^x$

Input	Output	÷
0	1	$\frac{1}{2}$
1	$\frac{1}{2}$	$\frac{1}{2}$
2	$\frac{1}{4}$	$\frac{1}{2}$
3	$\frac{1}{8}$	$\frac{1}{2}$
4	$\frac{1}{16}$	$\frac{1}{2}$
5	$\frac{1}{32}$	$\frac{1}{2}$

9. (a) If a table has constant differences, the function is linear and the rule will be in the form $f(x) =$ (constant difference) $\cdot x +$ (a constant). To find the constant, look at the output for an input of 0. So, the function will be $f(x) = ($ constant difference $) \cdot x + (f(0))$.

(b) If the table has constant ratios, then the function is exponential and the rule will be in the form $f(x) = ($ a constant $) \cdot ($ constant ratio $)^x$. To find the constant, look at the output for an input of 0. So, the function will be $f(x) = f(0) \cdot ($ common ratio $)^x$.

10. If the common ratio is going to equal the output, your table will look like this:

Input	Output	÷
0	$f(0)$	$f(0)$
1	$f(1)$	$f(1)$
2	$f(2)$	$f(2)$
3	$f(3)$	$f(3)$
4	$f(4)$	$f(4)$
5	$f(5)$	$f(5)$

If the common ratios = the outputs, $\frac{f(2)}{f(1)} = f(1)$, $\frac{f(3)}{f(2)} = f(2)$, and $\frac{f(4)}{f(3)} = f(3)$. So, $f(2) = (f(1))^2$, $f(3) = (f(2))^2$, and $f(4) = (f(3))^2$. Now your table looks like this:

Input	Output	÷
0	$f(0)$	$f(0)$
1	$f(0)^2$	$f(0)^2$
2	$f(1)^2 = f(0)^4$	$f(0)^4$
3	$f(2)^2 = f(0)^8$	$f(0)^8$
4	$f(3)^2 = f(0)^{16}$	$f(0)^{16}$
5	$f(0)^{32}$	$f(0)^{32}$

You can let $f(0)$ be some number, say 3, the exponents for the function are powers of 2. One possible solution is $f(x) = 3^{(2^x)}$

On Your Own

11. (a) For $x^2 = 5$, take the square root of both sides. Remember that the solution could be the positive or negative square root. $x = \pm\sqrt{5}$
    (b) Estimate the solution using your calculator. Since $2^2 = 4$ and $2^3 = 8$, a good guess to start would be a little more than 2. $x \approx 2.322$. Many students will choose this equation as the most difficult for them to solve.
    (c) $x = 5^2 = 25$
    (d) Since 8 is a power of 2, rewrite the equation as $2^3 = 2^x$ and $x = 3$.

12.

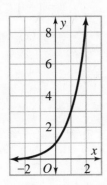

13. $\sqrt{2} \approx 1.414$, and $x = 1.414$ is between $x = 1$ and $x = 2$. Since the graph of $y = 3^x$ is continuous, which means (informally) that you can trace it without picking up your pencil, and increasing, you can say that $3^{\sqrt{2}}$ must be between 3^1 and 3^2, or between 3 and 9.

14. One way you could make a more accurate estimate of $3^{\sqrt{2}}$ is by "zooming" in on the graph to find a point whose x-coordinate is close to $1.414\ldots$ You could also use your calculator to evaluate $3^{\sqrt{2}}$, either in the home screen or in the graph screen. See the Technology Appendix for some ideas about how to do this.

15. (a) $f(a) = 3 \cdot 2^a$

Input: a	Output: $f(a)$
-2	$\frac{3}{4}$
-1	$\frac{3}{2}$
0	3
1	6
2	12

(b) $g(a) = 30 \cdot 2^a$

Input: a	Output: $g(a)$
-2	$\frac{30}{4} = \frac{15}{2}$
-1	$\frac{30}{2} = 15$
0	30
1	60
2	120

(c) $h(a) = \frac{1}{5} \cdot 5^a$

Input: a	Output: $h(a)$
0	$\frac{1}{5}$
1	1
2	5
3	25
4	125

(d) $j(a) = 27 \cdot \left(\frac{1}{3}\right)^a$

Input: a	Output: $j(a)$
-1	81
0	27
1	9
2	3
3	1

16. (a) $k(a) = 4 \cdot 3^a$
    (b) $L(h) = 100 \cdot \left(\frac{1}{2}\right)^h$
    (c) $p(x) = 2 \cdot \left(\frac{1}{4}\right)^x$
    (d) $Q(n) = 8 \cdot \left(\frac{3}{2}\right)^n$

17.

x	$f(x) = 2^x$
0	1
1	2
1.4	2.639
1.41	2.657
1.414	2.665
1.4142	2.665
1.41421	2.665
1.414213	2.665

18. (a) For an integer $a > 0$, $5^b = 2^a > 1$, so $b > 0$. However, 2^a is even and 5^b is odd in this case, so they cannot be equal. For an integer $a < 0$, $5^b = 2^a < 1$, so $b < 0$. Now $2^a = 5^b$ implies that $2^{-a} = 5^{-b}$ (by taking reciprocals). Here the exponents are again positive integers, and you get the same contradiction as in the first case. Therefore, you must have $a = 0$, so $5^b = 2^0 = 1$. Hence $b = 0$.

(b) Since $4 = 2^2$ and $8 = 2^3$, you can write

$$4^c = 8^d$$
$$(2^2)^c = (2^3)^d$$
$$2^{2c} = 2^{3d}$$
$$2c = 3d$$

There are many possible solutions. For example, $c = 3$ and $d = 2$, or $c = 6$ and $d = 4$. You can write $c = \frac{3}{2} \cdot d$. If you choose even integers for d, you will get an integer value for c.

Maintain Your Skills

19. a, b, d, and e can all be found directly. There is no solution for g. To answer c and f, you can estimate or use a calculator.

(a) $f(0) = 2^0 = 1$

(b) $f\left(\frac{1}{2}\right) = 2^{\frac{1}{2}} = \sqrt{2}$

(c) $f(\pi) = 2^\pi \approx 8.825$ (using a calculator)

(d) $f(f(2)) = f(2^2) = f(4) = 2^4 = 16$

(e)

$$f(a) = \frac{1}{8}$$
$$2^a = 2^{-3}$$
$$a = -3$$

(f)

$$f(a) = 7$$
$$2^a = 7$$
$$a \approx 2.807$$

This is found using a calculator.

(g) 2^a will never be a negative number, so there is no solution.

5.7 Graphs of Exponential Functions

Check Your Understanding

1. In the first graph, the y values are negative, so $a < 0$. Therefore, $f(x) = -3 \cdot 2^x$ describes this graph. The second graph is decreasing, so $0 < b < 1$. $f(x) = 3 \cdot \left(\frac{1}{2}\right)^x$ describes this graph. The third graph passes through $(1, 6)$. $f(x) = 3 \cdot 2^x$ describes this graph. The last graph passes through $(1, 15)$. $f(x) = 3 \cdot 5^x$ describes this graph.

2. (a) Given $f(x) = a \cdot b^x$ and the points $(0, 12)$ and $(2, 3)$, you can write the equations $12 = a \cdot b^0$, so $a = 12$ and $3 = 12 \cdot b^2$, $\frac{1}{4} = b^2$, so $b = \pm\frac{1}{2}$. $b \not< 0$, so $b = \frac{1}{2}$. The function you are looking for is $f(x) = 12 \cdot \left(\frac{1}{2}\right)^x$

(b) Write the equations $12 = a \cdot b^2$ and $3 = a \cdot b^4$. Solve each equation for a, and you get $a = \frac{12}{b^2}$ and $a = \frac{3}{b^4}$. Therefore,

$$\frac{12}{b^2} = \frac{3}{b^4}$$
$$12b^4 = 3b^2$$
$$12b^4 - 3b^2 = 0$$
$$3b^2(4b^2 - 1) = 0$$
$$3b^2(2b + 1)(2b - 1) = 0$$

$b = 0$ or $b = \pm\frac{1}{2}$ Since $b > 0$, $b = \frac{1}{2}$. Substitute to find a: $3 = a \cdot \left(\frac{1}{2}\right)^4$, $3 = a \cdot \frac{1}{16}$, and $a = 3 \cdot 16 = 48$. The function you are looking for is $f(x) = 48 \cdot \left(\frac{1}{2}\right)^x$

3. (a) To find a possible solution, choose a convenient value for a. A good choice would be 2 because $72 \div 2 = 36$

(a perfect square) or 8 because $72 \div 8 = 9$ (a perfect square). In the first case, $72 = 2 \cdot b^2$ and $b = \pm 6$, $b \neq -6$, $b = 6$. One equation is $f(x) = 2 \cdot 6^x$. Then, let $a = 8$ so $72 = 8 \cdot b^2$ and $b = \pm 3$, $b \neq -3$, $b = 3$. Another equation is $f(x) = 8 \cdot 3^x$.

(b) To find the general form, solve the equation $72 = a \cdot b^2$ for a in terms of b, or for b in terms of a. $a = \frac{72}{b^2}$ or $b = \sqrt{\frac{72}{a}}$. The two resulting equations are

$$f(x) = \left(\frac{72}{b^2}\right) \cdot b^x \text{ and } f(x) = a \cdot \left(\sqrt{\frac{72}{a}}\right)^x.$$

4. The proof of Lemma 5.2 is precisely the same as that of Lemma 5.1 with all the $>$ signs reversed. Alternately, if $0 < b < 1$, then $b = \frac{1}{c}$ with $c > 1$. Lemma 5.1 implies that $c^x > 1$. Now $c^x = \left(\frac{1}{b}\right)^x = \frac{1}{b^x}$, so $\frac{1}{b^x} > 1$. Therefore, $1 > b^x$. The proof of Theorem 5.3 mimics that of Theorem 5.2 with the signs reversed, or again you can use $b = \frac{1}{c}$ with $c > 1$. Then $f(x) = b^x = \left(\frac{1}{c}\right)^x = \frac{1}{c^x}$. Since the denominator is strictly increasing, the fraction is strictly decreasing.

5. If two graphs are reflections over the y-axis, a point (x, y) on one graph will have an image $(-x, y)$ on the other graph. We need to show that $f(-x) = g(x)$.

$$f(-x) = 2^{-x}$$
$$= \frac{1}{2^x}$$
$$= \left(\frac{1}{2}\right)^x$$
$$= g(x)$$

6. $x \approx 2.807$

7.

$$2^x = \frac{1}{7} \cdot 4^x$$
$$7 \cdot 2^x = 4^x$$
$$7 = \frac{4^x}{2^x}$$
$$7 = \left(\frac{4}{2}\right)^x$$
$$7 = 2^x$$

This equation is the same as the one for which you approximated a solution in Exercise 6, so $x \approx 2.807$.

8. (a)

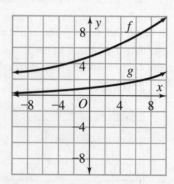

The graphs do not intersect in this window.

(b) The graphs intersect once. The intersection is at roughly $x = 35.24$ and $y = 54.26$. You can find this point by "zooming out" on your calculator and then using the "intersect" function. See the Technology Appendix for more about how to do this.

9. (a) $2.66514^{\sqrt{2}} \approx 3.999991207 \cdots \approx 4$

   (b) Yes, $\left(2^{\sqrt{2}}\right)^{\sqrt{2}} = 2^{\sqrt{2} \cdot \sqrt{2}} = 2^2 = 4$

10. When you try decimal values to approximate $(-2)^{\sqrt{2}}$ with a calculator, you get an error: Non-real result. If you evaluate $(-2)^{\sqrt{2}}$, the result is $2^{\sqrt{2}} \cdot (-1)^{\sqrt{2}}$. Exponential functions b^x are restricted to $b > 0$, because $(-1)^x$ cannot be calculated for many fractional values. For example, $(-1)^{\frac{1}{2}}$ would be $\sqrt{-1}$, which is undefined.

On Your Own

11. The y-intercept is $(0, a)$ because
$f(0) = a \cdot b^0 = a \cdot 1 = a$

12. Test each point to see if it is on the graph.

   A. $f(0) = -3 \cdot 2^0 = -3 \cdot 1 = -3 \neq 1$. $(0, 1)$ is NOT on the graph.

   B. $f(-1) = -3 \cdot 2^{-1} = -3 \cdot \frac{1}{2} = -\frac{3}{2} \neq 6$. $(-1, 6)$ is NOT on the graph.

   C. $f(-2) = -3 \cdot 2^{-2} = -3 \cdot \frac{1}{2^2} = -3 \cdot \frac{1}{4} = -\frac{3}{4} = -.75$. $(-2, -.75)$ IS on the graph.

   D. $f(2) = -3 \cdot 2^2 = -3 \cdot 4 = -12 \neq 36$. $(2, 36)$ is NOT on the graph.

   The correct choice is **C**.

13. (a) Next year the cost will increase by 3 percent, so the price will be $3.99 + .03 \cdot 3.99$ or

   $$3.99 \cdot (1 + .03) = 3.99 \cdot 1.03 = \$4.11.$$

   The following year, the cost will increase by 3 percent again $4.11 \cdot 1.03 = \$4.23$. Notice that this is

   $$4.11 \cdot 1.03 = (3.99 \cdot 1.03) \cdot 1.03 = 3.99 \cdot 1.03^2 = \$4.23$$

   (b) Multiply $3.99 by 1.03 ten times or by 1.03^{10}. $3.99 \cdot 1.03^{10} = \$5.36$

   (c) Use your calculator. After 55 years the price, will be $20.28.

   (d) $C(n) = 3.99 \cdot 1.03^n$. The cost will be the original price multiplied by $(1 + \text{percent increase}/100)$ raised to the power (number of years)

14. By evaluating 2^x for some negative integer values, you can find that $2^{-20} = \frac{1}{1048576} < \frac{1}{1000000}$. Any value less than -20 will also work.

15. Since $\sqrt{6} \approx 2.449$, $\sqrt{6}$ is between 2 and 3. Therefore, $3^{\sqrt{6}}$ must be between $3^2 = 9$ and $3^3 = 27$. You can reason this because we see that $y = 3^x$ is continuous and increasing.

16. It is not possible for $2^p = 7^q$ if p and q are nonzero integers. First consider positive integers p and q. If p is a positive integer, 2^p is a power of 2, and therefore is an even integer. If q is a positive integer, 7^q is a power of 7, and is an odd integer. Since 2^p is even and 7^q is odd, they cannot be equal. If p and q are negative integers,

consider $2^p = \frac{1}{2^{-p}}$ and $7^q = \frac{1}{7^{-q}}$. Following the same argument, the denominator of the first fraction is always even and the denominator of the second fraction is always odd, so they are never equal.

17. Since 8 is a multiple of 2, the expressions on each side of the equation will both be even numbers, so they could be equal. In particular, $2^{\frac{p}{q}} = 8 = 2^3$, so $\frac{p}{q} = 3$, and $p = 3q$. There are many integers that satisfy this equation.

18. (a)

Input	Output
-2	$\frac{1}{4}$
-1	$-\frac{1}{2}$
0	1
1	-2
2	4
3	-8

   (b) The points are alternately positive and negative, so you cannot connect them with a smooth curve without crossing the x-axis. It is not possible for $f(x)$ to equal zero, so the curve cannot cross the x-axis.

19. Suppose first that b and d are positive.
   - If $b \neq d$, there will be exactly one solution as long as a and c have the same sign.
   - If a and c have opposite signs, there is no solution. Also, if $b = d$ and $a \neq c$, there are no solutions.
   - If $b = d$ and $a = c$, there will be infinitely many solutions, because the two sides of the equation will be identical.
   Other possibilities arise if you allow any of the parameters to be 0, or if you allow b and d to be negative.

20. (a) By definition, if x is a positive integer, then b^x is just $\underbrace{b \cdot b \cdot b \cdots}_{x \text{ copies}}$. If $b > 0$, then $b \cdot b \cdot b \cdot b \cdots$ will be the product of positive numbers and therefore positive. If $x = 0$, then $b^x = 1 > 0$. If $x < 0$, then b^x is the reciprocal of a positive number, so it is positive.

   (b) If x is rational, then $b^x = b^{\frac{p}{q}} = \sqrt[q]{b^p}$ where p and q are integers. If $b > 0$, you just showed that $b^p > 0$ and the $\sqrt[q]{\text{positive number}}$ will be positive.

Maintain Your Skills

21. (a) $\left(3^{\sqrt{2}}\right)^{\sqrt{2}} = 3^{\sqrt{4}} = 3^2 = 9$

   (b) $\left(3^{\sqrt{2}}\right)^2 = 3^{2 \cdot \sqrt{2}}$

   (c) $\left(3^{-\sqrt{2}}\right)^{-1} = 3^{\sqrt{2}}$

   (d) $\left(3^{\sqrt{8}}\right)^{\sqrt{2}} = 3^{\sqrt{16}} = 3^4 = 81$

   (e) $3^{\sqrt{2}} \cdot 3^{-\sqrt{2}} = 3^{\sqrt{2} + (-\sqrt{2})} = 3^0 = 1$

   (f) $\left(3^{-\sqrt{2}}\right)^{-\sqrt{2}} = 3^{\sqrt{4}} = 3^2 = 9$

   (g) $3^{\sqrt{2}} \cdot 5^{\sqrt{2}} = (3 \cdot 5)^{\sqrt{2}} = 15^{\sqrt{2}}$

   (h) $\left(3^{\sqrt[3]{2}}\right)^{\sqrt[3]{2}} = 3^{\sqrt[3]{4}}$

   (i) $\left(3^{\sqrt[3]{2}}\right)^{\sqrt[3]{4}} = 3^{\sqrt[3]{8}} = 3^2 = 9$

22.

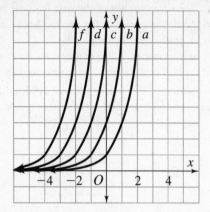

These graphs are all translations of each other. For example, $a(x) = 9$ when $x = 2$, but $b(x) = 9$ when $x = 1$. The graph of $b(x)$ is the image of $a(x)$ after a translation of 1 unit to the left.

5.8 Tables of Exponential Functions

Check Your Understanding

1. (a) $A(n) = 18 \cdot \left(\frac{1}{3}\right)^n$

(b) $B(x) = -2 \cdot 4^x$

(c) This is not an exponential function, because there is not a constant ratio between successive terms. $\frac{6}{4} \neq \frac{12}{9}$

(d) $D(z) = \frac{1}{3} \cdot 6^z$

2. (a)

$$A(n) = \begin{cases} 18 & \text{if } n = 0 \\ \frac{1}{3} \cdot A(n-1) & \text{if } n > 0 \end{cases}$$

(b)

$$B(x) = \begin{cases} -2 & \text{if } x = 0 \\ 4 \cdot B(x-1) & \text{if } x > 0 \end{cases}$$

(c) Not an exponential function.

(d)

$$D(z) = \begin{cases} \frac{1}{3} & \text{if } z = 0 \\ 6 \cdot D(z-1) & \text{if } z > 0 \end{cases}$$

3. $q(x) = a \cdot b^x$ So you can set up two equations with the given points:

$$100 = a \cdot b^3$$
$$4 = a \cdot b^5$$

Then divide one equation by the other to get an equation in b alone, and solve for b:

$$\frac{100}{4} = \frac{a \cdot b^3}{a \cdot b^5}$$
$$25 = b^{-2}$$
$$b^2 = \frac{1}{25}$$
$$b = \frac{1}{5}$$

To find a, just substitute your value for b into either of your original equations:

$$100 = a \cdot \left(\frac{1}{5}\right)^3$$
$$100 = a \cdot \left(\frac{1}{125}\right)$$
$$12,500 = a$$

The equation is $q(x) = 12,500 \cdot \left(\frac{1}{5}\right)^x$. If you like, you can check this equation with your second point.

4. $b = \frac{-1}{5}$ is not a solution because negative bases are not allowed in the definition of an exponential function. Exercise 4 begins by telling you that $q(x)$ is an exponential function.

5. You can find a linear function that solves the problem: $f(x) = 2x + 16$. Another polynomial function that solves the problem is $f(x) = 2x + 16 + (x+3)(x-2) \ldots$ You can also find an exponential function that solves the problem:

$$10 = a \cdot b^{-3}$$
$$20 = a \cdot b^2$$

Divide:

$$\frac{1}{2} = b^{-5}$$
$$\frac{1}{2} = \frac{1}{b^5}$$
$$2 = b^5$$
$$2^{\frac{1}{5}} = b$$

Find a:

$$10 = a \cdot \left(2^{\frac{1}{5}}\right)^{-3}$$
$$10 = a \cdot 2^{-\frac{3}{5}}$$
$$10 \cdot 2^{\frac{3}{5}} = a$$

The exponential equation we are looking for is

$$f(x) = 10 \cdot 2^{\frac{3}{5}} \cdot \left(2^{\frac{1}{5}}\right)^x \approx 15.157 \cdot 1.149^x$$

6. (a) You want to go from 100 to 300 in 5 steps, so $b^5 = 3$ and $b = 3^{\frac{1}{5}}$. Since $T(0) = 100 = a \cdot b^0 = a \cdot 1$, you know that $a = 100$. The function is

$$T(x) = 100 \cdot \left(3^{\frac{1}{5}}\right)^x$$

(b)

x	$T(x)$	$\div$
0	100	$3^{\frac{1}{5}} \approx 1.246$
1	$100 \cdot 3^{\frac{1}{5}} \approx 124.57$	$3^{\frac{1}{5}} \approx 1.246$
2	$100 \cdot 3^{\frac{2}{5}} \approx 155.18$	$3^{\frac{1}{5}} \approx 1.246$
3	$100 \cdot 3^{\frac{3}{5}} \approx 193.32$	$3^{\frac{1}{5}} \approx 1.246$
4	$100 \cdot 3^{\frac{4}{5}} \approx 240.82$	$3^{\frac{1}{5}} \approx 1.246$
5	300	$3^{\frac{1}{5}} \approx 1.246$

7. (a) Since the car depreciates 20%, it retains 80% of its value. Multiply by 80% or 0.8. After 1 year the value is $20{,}000 \cdot 0.8 = \$16{,}000$. After 2 years the value is $\$16{,}000 \cdot 0.8 = \$12{,}800$. After 3 years the value is $\$12{,}800 \cdot 0.8 = \$10{,}240$.

(b) This is an exponential function with $a = 20{,}000$ and $b = 0.8$.

$$V(n) = 20{,}000 \cdot (0.8)^n$$

(c) Since the function is decreasing, it will eventually be worth less than $1000. Using your calculator, you can find that $V(14) \approx \$880$ which is less than $1000.

8.

$$y_1 = a \cdot b^{x_1}$$
$$y_2 = a \cdot b^{x_2}$$

Divide:

$$\frac{y_1}{y_2} = b^{x_1 - x_2}$$

$$\left(\frac{y_1}{y_2}\right)^{\frac{1}{x_1 - x_2}} = b$$

Substitute to find a:

$$y_1 = a \cdot \left(\left(\frac{y_1}{y_2}\right)^{\frac{1}{x_1 - x_2}}\right)^{x_1}$$

$$\frac{y_1}{\left(\frac{y_1}{y_2}\right)^{\frac{x_1}{x_1 - x_2}}} = a$$

Simplify the expression for a:

$$a = y_1^{\frac{-x_2}{x_1 - x_2}} \cdot y_2^{\frac{x_1}{x_1 - x_2}}$$

The exponential function that passes through (x_1, y_1) and (x_2, y_2) is

$$y = y_1^{\frac{-x_2}{x_1 - x_2}} \cdot y_2^{\frac{x_1}{x_1 - x_2}} \cdot \left(\left(\frac{y_1}{y_2}\right)^{\frac{1}{x_1 - x_2}}\right)^{x}$$

On Your Own

9. Substituting the given values into the function yields

$$a \cdot b^0 = 4$$
$$a \cdot b^2 = 25$$

Divide the second equation by the first to get $b^2 = \frac{25}{4}$, so $b = \frac{5}{2}$. The first equation simplifies to $a = 4$. The correct answer choice is **C**.

10.

n	$M(n)$	$\div$
0	16	1.5
1	24	1.5
2	36	1.5
3	54	1.5
4	81	

A closed-form rule would be $M(n) = 16 \cdot \left(\frac{3}{2}\right)^n$, since $M(0) = 16 = a$ and each term is multiplied by $\frac{3}{2} = b$. To find a recursive rule, use the fact that you multiply by 1.5 to get from one term to the next.

$$M(n) \begin{cases} 16 & \text{if } n = 0 \\ \frac{3}{2} \cdot M(n-1) & \text{if } n > 0 \end{cases}$$

11. (a)

n	$F(n)$	$\div$
0	1	1
1	1	2
2	2	3
3	6	4
4	24	5
5	120	6
6	720	7

(b) This is not an exponential function because the ratio is not constant.

(c) Since $F(1) = 1$, $F(2) = 2 = 2 \cdot 1$, $F(3) = 6 = 3 \cdot 2 \cdot 1$, and $F(4) = 24 = 4 \cdot 3 \cdot 2 \cdot 1$, you can calculate
$F(10) = 10 \cdot 9 \cdot 8 \cdot 7 \cdots 3 \cdot 2 \cdot 1 = 3{,}628{,}800$

12. (a) $y = 3 \cdot 2^x$

(b) $y = -5^{\frac{1}{4}} \cdot \left(5^{\frac{1}{4}}\right)^x$

(c) $y = 3 \cdot 2^{\frac{1}{3}} \cdot \left(\frac{1}{2}\right)^{\frac{x}{6}}$

13. (a) Since the interest is added to Kara's account, she will have $\$1000 + 0.03 \cdot \$1000 = \$1000 \cdot (1 + 0.03) = \$1000 \cdot (1.03) = \$1030$ in 1 year. Each year you multiply by 1.03 to get the new amount.
$\$1030 \cdot 1.03 = \$1060.90$ in 2 years.
$\$1060.90 \cdot 1.03 = \$1092.73$ in 3 years.

(b) To calculate the amount of money in the account after 20 years, you would multiply $1000 by 1.03 twenty times. $\$1000 \cdot 1.03^{20} = \$1806.11$

14. (a) Multiply by 0.98 each time because if you pay 2%, there will be $100\% - 2\% = 98\%$ remaining. $B(1) = \$2000 \cdot 0.98 = \$1960$; $B(2) = \$1960 \cdot 0.98 = \$1920.80$; $B(3) = \$1920.80 \cdot 0.98 = \$1882.38$

(b) $B(n) = 2000 \cdot (0.98)^n$

(c) The domain is $0, 1, 2 \ldots 12$ since payment is made each month for 12 months.

15. Use the equation $1000 = 2000 \cdot b^{12}$ so $b = \left(\frac{1}{2}\right)^{\frac{1}{12}}$, $b = 0.944$. The payment should be $100\% - 94.4\% = 5.6\%$ each month.

16. The functions would not look the same because they have different domains. $f(x)$ is defined for all real numbers, and its graph would be a smooth, connected curve. $g(x)$ is only defined for nonnegative integers. There would be no points to the left of the y-axis, and points to the right of the y-axis would only take on integer values of x and would not be connected to each other.

Maintain Your Skills

17. (a) $b(5) = 3^5 = 243$

(b) $b(3) \cdot b(2) = 3^3 \cdot 3^2 = 27 \cdot 9 = 243$

(c) $b(1) = 3^1 = 3$

(d) $\frac{b(3)}{b(2)} = \frac{3^3}{3^2} = 3^{3-2} = 3^1 = 3$

(e) $b(6) = 3^6 = 729$

(f) $(b(2))^3 = (3^2)^3 = 9^3 = 729$

18. (a) $f(0) = b^0 = 1$

(b) $f(-3) = b^{-3} = \frac{1}{b^3} = \frac{1}{f(3)} = \frac{1}{p}$

(c) $f(8) = b^8 = b^3 \cdot b^5 = f(3) \cdot f(5) = pq$

(d) $f(6) = b^6 = (b^3)^2 = (f(3))^2 = p^2$

(e) $f(15) = b^{15} = (b^3)^5 = (f(3))^5 = p^5$ or
$f(15) = b^{15} = (b^5)^3 = (f(5))^3 = q^3$. This last equation gives you a way to write p in terms of q.

5.9 Properties of Exponential Functions

Check Your Understanding

1. To find C, raise b to the power of x and multiply the result by a.
2. To find a, raise b to the power of x. Then divide C by this number.
3. To find b, divide C by a and raise the result to the power $\frac{1}{x}$.
4. To find x, first divide C by a. This gives you $\frac{C}{a} = b^x$. In order to find x, you can approximate the solution by taking successive guesses at x and use the fact that the function b^x is increasing if $b > 1$ and decreasing if $b < 1$. (If $b = 1$ then $\frac{C}{a}$ had better equal 1, too, or there is no solution.)
5.

x	$f(x) = 2^x$
0	1
1	2
1.5850	3
2	4
2.3219	5
2.5850	6
2.8074	7
3	8
3.1700	9
3.3219	10

(a) Since $2^2 = 4$ and $2^3 = 8$, you can fill in those entries immediately. To find x if $f(x) = 6$, write

$$f(x) = 6$$
$$2^x = 2 \cdot 3$$
$$2^x = 2^1 \cdot 2^{1.5850}$$
$$2^x = 2^{2.5850}$$
$$x = 2.5850$$

To find x if $f(x) = 9$, write

$$f(x) = 9$$
$$2^x = 3^2$$
$$2^x = (2^{1.5850})^2 = 2^{1.5850 \cdot 2}$$

$$2^x = 2^{3.1700}$$
$$x = 3.1700$$

To find x if $f(x) = 10$, write

$$f(x) = 10$$
$$2^x = 2 \cdot 5$$
$$2^x = 2^1 \cdot 2^{2.3219}$$
$$2^x = 2^{3.3219}$$
$$x = 3.3219$$

(b) Since $2^{2.5850} = 6$ and $2^3 = 8$, the solution to $2^x = 7$ must be between 2.5850 and 3. By taking successive guesses at x, you can find $x \approx 2.8074$

6. Each of the three rules will change. Let $f(x) = a \cdot b^x$:

(a) $f(x+y) = a \cdot b^{x+y} = a \cdot b^x \cdot b^y = f(x) \cdot b^y$ Since you need $a \cdot b^y = f(y)$, multiply by $\frac{a}{a}$. The result is

$$f(x+y) = f(x) \cdot \left(\frac{a}{a}\right) \cdot b^y = \frac{f(x) \cdot a \cdot b^y}{a}$$
$$= \frac{f(x) \cdot f(y)}{a}$$

(b) $f(x-y) = a \cdot b^{x-y} = a \cdot b^x \cdot b^{-y} = f(x) \cdot \frac{1}{b^y}$ Multiply by $\frac{a}{a}$ to get $a \cdot b^y$ in the denominator. The result is

$$f(x-y) = f(x) \cdot \left(\frac{a}{a}\right) \cdot \frac{1}{b^y} = f(x) \cdot \frac{a}{a \cdot b^y} = a \cdot \frac{f(x)}{f(y)}$$

(c) $f(xy) = a \cdot b^{xy} = a \cdot (b^x)^y$ You need to multiply by $\frac{a^y}{a^y}$ to get $a \cdot b^x$ in parentheses. The result is

$$(xy) = a \cdot \frac{a^y}{a^y} \cdot (b^x)^y = \frac{a}{a^y} \cdot (a \cdot b^x)^y = a^{1-y} \cdot (f(x))^y$$

7. (a) Since the ratio column is constant, the entries in the Earnings column are a geometric sequence. To go from 1 to 10 in two steps, the middle step must be $10^{\frac{1}{2}} \approx 3.162$

(b) $k = \frac{10^{\frac{1}{2}}}{1} = 10^{\frac{1}{2}}$ or $\sqrt{10}$

(c) Multiply \$1500 by $\sqrt{10}$ to get \$4743.42.

8. (a) Since the ratio column is constant, the entries in the Earnings column are a geometric sequence. You want to go from 1 to 10 in 3 steps, so you multiply by $10^{\frac{1}{3}}$ and $j = \frac{10^{\frac{1}{3}}}{1} = 10^{\frac{1}{3}} \approx 2.154$

(b) $j = \frac{10^{\frac{1}{3}}}{1} = 10^{\frac{1}{3}}$ or $\sqrt[3]{10}$

(c) Multiply \$1500 by $10^{\frac{2}{3}}$ to get \$6962.38

9. If $x = 1$, $1^y = 1$ for any real number y. If $y = 0$, $x^0 = 1$, provided that $x \neq 0$. If $x = -1$, $(-1)^y = 1$ if y is an even integer or if y can be written in the form $\frac{p}{q}$ where p and q are relatively prime integers and p is even.

On Your Own

10. (a) $5^x = 25 = 5^2$, so $x = 2$

(b) $5^x = 5^{-11}$, so $x = -11$

(c) $5^x = 25^3 = (5^2)^3 = 5^6$, so $x = 6$

(d) $5^x \neq 0$, so there is no solution.

11. Examples will vary.

(a) Let $x = 2$ and $y = 3$, then $f(x + y) = f(2 + 3) = f(5) = 10^5$ and $f(x) \cdot f(y) = f(2) \cdot f(3) = 10^2 \cdot 10^3 = 10^{2+3} = 10^5$. Therefore, $f(x + y) = f(x) \cdot f(y)$.

(b) Let $x = 4$ and $y = 3$, then $f(x - y) = f(4 - 3) = f(1) = 10^1 = 10$ and $\frac{f(x)}{f(y)} = \frac{f(4)}{f(3)} = \frac{10^4}{10^3} = 10^{4-3} = 10^1 = 10$. Therefore, $f(x - y) = \frac{f(x)}{f(y)}$.

(c) Let $x = 3$ and $y = 2$, then $f(xy) = f(3 \cdot 2) = f(6) = 10^6$ and $(f(x))^y = (f(3))^2 = (10^3)^2 = 10^6$. Therefore, $f(xy) = (f(x))^y$.

12. (a) Solve $200 = 100 \cdot 1.06^x$ or $2 = 1.06^x$ Estimate the value of x on your calculator. Since $1.06^{12} \approx 2.0122$, x must be a little less than 12. You can find $x \approx 11.90$

(b) Solve $300 = 100 \cdot 1.06^x$ or $3 = 1.06^x$. Using your calculator, $x \approx 18.85$ years.

(c) Solve $600 = 100 \cdot 1.06^x$ or $6 = 1.06^x$. Using your calculator, $x \approx 30.75$ years.

13.

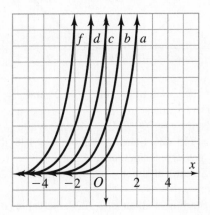

The graphs are translation images of each other. That is because, for each point (x, y) that is on the graph of $a(x)$, there is a corresponding point with the same y-value on the graph of each of the other functions. For example, the point $(3, 27)$ is on the graph of $a(x)$, but the point $(1, 27)$ is on the graph of $c(x)$, since $c(x) = 9 \cdot 3^x = 3^2 \cdot 3^x = 3^{x+2}$. $c(x)$ is the image of $a(x)$ after a translation of two units to the left.

14. One possible answer is if $N = 15$. If $f(x) = 2^x = 15$, then $2^x = 15 = 3 \cdot 5 = 2^{1.5850} \cdot 2^{2.3219} = 2^{1.5850+2.3219} = 2^{3.9069}$ then $x = 3.9069$.

Another possible answer is if $N = 12 = 4 \cdot 3$. If $f(x) = 2^x = 4 \cdot 3 = 2^2 \cdot 2^{1.5850} = 2^{2+1.5850} = 2^{3.5850}$ then $x = 3.5850$.

15. (a) $f(2) = i^2 = -1$, $f(3) = i^3 = -i$, $f(5) = i^5 = i$ Since $(-1) \cdot (-i) = i$, it is true that $f(2) \cdot f(3) = f(5)$.

(b) The other rules also hold.

$$f(x - y) = i^{x-y} = i^x \cdot i^{-y} = \frac{i^x}{i^y} = \frac{f(x)}{f(y)}$$

$$f(xy) = i^{xy} = (i^x)^y = (f(x))^y$$

16. (a) Plan1: 2 years because $25{,}000 + 3000 \cdot 2 = 31{,}000$
Plan 2: 3 years because $25{,}000 \cdot 1.08^3 = 31{,}492.80$

(b) Plan 1: 5 years because $25{,}000 + 3000 \cdot 5 = 40{,}000$
Plan 2: 7 years because $25{,}000 \cdot 1.08^7 = 42{,}845.60$

(c) Plan 1: 9 years because $25{,}000 + 3000 \cdot 9 = 52{,}000$
Plan 2: 10 years because $25{,}000 \cdot 1.08^{10} = 53{,}973.10$

(d) Plan 1: 25 years because $25{,}000 + 3000 \cdot 25 = 100{,}000$
Plan 2: 19 years because $25{,}000 \cdot 1.08^{19} = 107{,}893$

17. $f(x) = x^3$ is not an exponential function, it is a polynomial. In an exponential function, the variable is an exponent.

18. (a)

$$L(1) + L(2) = L(1 \cdot 2)$$
$$L(1) + L(2) = L(2)$$
$$L(1) + L(2) - L(2) = L(2) - L(2)$$
$$L(1) = 0$$

$$L(2) + L(2) = L(2 \cdot 2)$$
$$1 + 1 = L(4)$$
$$2 = L(4)$$

(b) $L(x) = 6 = 2 + 2 + 2 = L(4) + L(4) + L(4) = L(4 \cdot 4) + L(4) = L(16) + L(4) = L(16 \cdot 4) = L(64)$, so, $x = 64$

(c) (i) $n > 0$

$$L(a^n) = L(\underbrace{a \cdot a \cdot a \cdots a}_{n \text{ copies}})$$
$$= \underbrace{L(a) + L(a) + \cdots + L(a)}_{n \text{ copies}}$$
$$= n \cdot L(a)$$

(ii) $n = 0$

$$L(a^n) = L(a^0)$$
$$= L(1)$$
$$= 0$$

$$n \cdot L(a) = 0 \cdot L(a)$$
$$= 0$$

So, $L(a^n) = n \cdot L(a)$

(iii) $n < 0$

Let $n = -m$ where $m > 0$:

$$L(a^m \cdot a^{-m}) = L(a^m) + L(a^{-m})$$
$$L(a^0) = m \cdot L(a) + L(a^{-m})$$
$$L(1) = m \cdot L(a) + L(a^{-m})$$
$$0 = m \cdot L(a) + L(a^{-m})$$
$$-m \cdot L(a) = L(a^{-m})$$
$$n \cdot L(a) = L(a^n)$$

(d) For $x > 0$, we have $L(x^2) = 2 \cdot L(x) = 1 = L(2)$. Since L is one-to-one, $x^2 = 2$. Since $x > 0$, $x = \sqrt{2}$.

19. Every year the sales is 1.15 times the previous year's. If S is the sales for the first year, then 5 years later (the sixth year), the sales will be $(1.15)^5 \cdot S$. The desired ratio is

$$(1.15)^5 = \frac{(1.15)^8}{(1.15)^3} \approx \frac{3.059}{1.521}$$

which is barely over 2. The correct answer choice is **B**.

Maintain Your Skills

20. (a) $x = 2.807$ You can find this on your calculator by "zooming" in. Since $2^3 = 8$, start with values for x that are a little less than 3.

(b) Since $4 = 2^2$, think of this as $2^{2x} = 7$. $2^{2x} = 2^{2.807}$, $2x = 2.807$, $x = 1.404$

(c) Since $8 = 2^3$, $2^{3x} = 2^{2.807}$, $3x = 2.807$, $x = .936$

(d) Since $16 = 2^4$, $2^{4x} = 2^{2.807}$, $4x = 2.807$, $x = .702$

(e) Since $1024 = 2^{10}$, $2^{10x} = 2^{2.807}$, $10x = 2.807$, $x = 0.281$

21. (a) $x = 1.984$

(b) $x = 0.504$

(c) $x = 3.033$

(d) $x = 0.330$

(e) $x = 1.517$

(f) $x = 0.659$

5.10 Exponential Functions are One-to-One

Check Your Understanding

1. We know that the domain of $f(x)$ is the set of real numbers and the range of $f(x)$ is the set of positive real numbers. Since $L_2(x) = f^{-1}(x)$, the domain of $L_2(x) = $ range of f(x) = {positive real numbers} and the range of $L_2(x) = $ domain of f(x) = {all real numbers}.

2. (a) $L_5(25) = 2$ because $5^2 = 25$

(b) $L_7(1) = 0$ because $7^0 = 1$

(c) $L_{11}(11^6) = 6$ because $11^6 = 11^6$

(d) $L_{0.1}(0.001) = 3$ because $0.1^3 = 0.001$

(e) $L_3\left(\frac{1}{9}\right) = -2$ because $3^{-2} = \frac{1}{3^2} = \frac{1}{9}$

3. (a) 1.1610

(b) $\frac{3}{2}$

(c) 2.6610

(d) 0.3390

4.

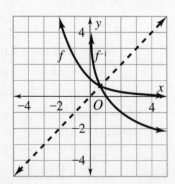

5. (a) The mean of $f(3)$ and $f(5)$ is 20 and $f(4) = 16$, so the mean is greater.

(b) The mean of $f(5)$ and $f(7)$ is 80 and $f(6) = 64$, so the mean is greater.

(c) The mean of $f(-4)$ and $f(-2)$ is $\frac{5}{32}$. $f(-3) = \frac{1}{8} = \frac{4}{32}$, so the mean is greater.

(d) The mean of $f(x)$ and $f(y)$ is greater than $f\left(\frac{x+y}{2}\right)$, because if you draw a line segment between any two points on the graph of 2^x, the segment will lie *above* the curve. The mean is the midpoint of the segment, so it will be above (have a greater y-value) than the point on the curve with the same x-coordinate.

6. (a)

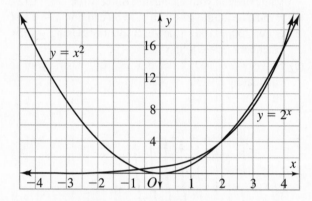

(b) There are 3 solutions, since $y = 2^x$ and $y = x^2$ intersect 3 times.

7. No. Consider $x = 200$. $200^2 = 40,000$ while $1.06^{200} = 115,126$. Starting at about $x = 178$, the values of 1.06^x get larger than the values of x^2.

8. (a) No. Starting at about $x = 59$, the values of 2^x will be larger.

(b) No. Starting at about $x = 1220$, the values of 1.06^x will be larger.

(c) Yes.

9. The value of b is approximately 1.4, and the coordinates of the point are approximately (2.7, 2.7).

On Your Own

10. $L_2(x)$ is the inverse of $f(x) = 2^x$ and $f(x)$ is one-to-one. So $L_2(x)$ must also be one-to-one.

11. $L_3(28) = x$ means that $3^x = 28$. $3^3 = 27$ and $3^4 = 81$, so $L_3(28)$ is between 3 and 4. The correct answer choice is **C**.

12.

x	$L_2(x)$
1	0
2	1
3	1.5850
4	2
5	2.3219
6	2.5850
7	2.8074
8	3
9	3.170

13. (a) $L_8(8) = 1$ because $8^1 = 8$.

(b) $L_8(2) = \frac{1}{3}$ because $8^{\frac{1}{3}} = \sqrt[3]{8} = 2$.

(c)

x	$L_4(x)$
1	0
2	0.3333
3	0.5283
4	$\frac{2}{3}$
5	0.7740
6	0.8617
7	0.9358
8	1
9	1.0566

14. $L_2(x) = a$ means $x = 2^a$

$3 \cdot L_8(x) = b$ means $L_8(x) = \frac{b}{3}$ and

$x = 8^{\frac{b}{3}} = (2^3)^{\frac{b}{3}} = 2^b$

$$2^a = 2^b$$

$$a = b$$

$$L_2(x) = 3 \cdot L_8(x)$$

15. To find the amount in her account after t years, use the exponential equation $A(t) = \$500 \cdot 1.09^t$. When $t = 8$, the amount is $\$500 \cdot 1.09^8 = \$996.28$. When $t = 9$, the amount is $\$500 \cdot 1.09^9 = \$1085.95$. After 8 years, she is closest to doubling her money.

16.

Doubling Time	
APR	# Years to Double
3%	23
4%	18
5%	14
6%	12
7%	10
8%	9
9%	8
10%	7
12%	6

17. (a) The Rule of 72 will gives the same number of years for doubling the investment in all cases, except 3%, when it gives 24 years instead of 23 years.

(b) $72 \div 18 = 4$, so the balance will double in 4 years.

(c) Her money will double every 8 years, because $72 \div 9 = 8$. In 40 years it will double 5 times. After 8 years, she will have $\$500 \cdot 2 = \$1000$. After 16 years, she will have $\$1000 \cdot 2 = \$2000$. After 24 years, she will have $\$2000 \cdot 2 = \$4000$. After 32 years, she will have $\$4000 \cdot 2 = \$8000$. So, after 40 years she will have $\$8000 \cdot 2 = \$16,000$. Since her money has been multiplied by 2 five times, you can multiply $500 \cdot 2^5 = 16,000$.

Maintain Your Skills

18. (a) 0.6826

(b) 1.3652

(c) 2.0478

(d) 2.7304

19. (a) 2.8073

(b) 1.4037

(c) 0.9358

(d) 0.7018

(e) 0.2807

5B MATHEMATICAL REFLECTIONS

1. An exponential function is a function of the form $y = a \cdot b^x$ where a and b are real numbers, $a \neq 0$, $b > 0$, and $b \neq 1$. Examples will vary, but will have the real numbers as the domain and if a is positive, the real numbers $y > 0$ as the range. (If a is negative, the range is the real numbers $y < 0$.) If the base is $0 < b < 1$ and a is positive, then the function is decreasing for all x. This is also the case if a is negative and $b > 1$. If $b > 1$ and a is positive, the function is increasing for all x. This is also the case if a is negative and $0 < b < 1$.

2. (a) The ratio between successive terms is 2, so to get from one term to the next, you multiply by 2. To make a complete recursive definition, though, you also need to establish the first input-output pair.

$$g(x) = \begin{cases} -5 & \text{if } x = 0 \\ 2 \cdot g(x-1) & \text{if } x > 0 \end{cases}$$

(b) $g(x) = -5 \cdot 2^x$

(c) No, because the recursive function has only the integers $0, 1, 2, \dots$ as its domain, and the domain of the closed-form function is the real numbers.

3. (a)

x	$h(x)$	$\div$
0	9	$\frac{2}{3}$
1	6	$\frac{2}{3}$
2	4	$\frac{2}{3}$
3	$\frac{8}{3}$	$\frac{2}{3}$
4	$\frac{16}{9}$	

(b) $h(23) = 9 \cdot \left(\frac{2}{3}\right)^{23} \approx 0.0008$.

(c) $h(x)$ could be an exponential function because the entries in the table show a constant ratio between successive terms. It does not have to be an exponential function, though, because through Lagrange Interpolation you could find a polynomial function that matches this table completely.

4. (a) $12 = 3x^2$, so $x^2 = 4$ and $x \pm 2$.

(b) $x = 5 \cdot 4^{-\frac{1}{2}} = 5 \cdot (2^2)^{-\frac{1}{2}} = 5 \cdot 2^{2 \cdot -\frac{1}{2}} = 5 \cdot 2^{-1} = \frac{5}{2}$

(c) $16 = 4 \cdot 32^x$ so $4 = 32^x$ and $2^2 = (2^5)^x$ or $2^2 = 2^{5x}$. Because exponential functions are one-to-one, you know that $2 = 5x$ and $x = \frac{2}{5}$.

(d) $-5 = x \cdot 27^{\frac{2}{3}}$, so $-5 = x \cdot (3^3)^{\frac{2}{3}} = x \cdot 3^{3 \cdot \frac{2}{3}} = x \cdot 9$. Since $-5 = 9x$, $x = -\frac{5}{9}$.

5. (a) If $L_3(1) = x$, then $3^x = 1$ and $x = 0$.

(b) If $L_3(81) = x$, then $3^x = 81 = 3^4$, so $x = 4$.

(c) If $L_3(2) \approx 0.6309$, then $3^{0.6309} = 2$. To find $L_3(4)$, you are looking for the solution to the equation $3^x = 4$ and you can find this by squaring both sides of the equation $3^{0.6309} = 2$. This gives you $3^{2(0.6309)} = 4$, so $L_3(4) = 2(0.6309) = 1.2618$. Similarly, cube both sides of the equation $3^{0.6309} = 2$ to get $3^{3(0.6309)} = 8$. This means that $L_3(8) = 3(0.6309) = 1.8928$.

(d) You know that $L_3(5)$ must be between 1 and 2, because 5 is between 3^1 and 3^2. Try different guesses for $L_3(5)$, zeroing in on the correct value.

x	3^x	What next?
1.5	5.1961	smaller
1.4	4.6555	bigger
1.45	4.9184	bigger
1.46	4.9728	bigger
1.47	5.0277	smaller
1.465	5.0001	a little too big
1.464	4.9947	too small
1.4649	4.9996	1.4650 is better

6. Use the definition of the function to write an expression for the left side of the equation.

$$f(m) \cdot f(n) = b^m \cdot b^n$$

Then use the Laws of Exponents.

$$b^m \cdot b^n = b^{m+n}$$

Use the definition of the function.

$$b^{m+n} = f(m+n)$$

This gives you the expression on the right side of the equation.

7. Exponential functions are strictly increasing or strictly decreasing. This implies that every exponential function is one-to-one, and all one-to-one functions have inverses.

8. You get 6% of the amount in the account as interest at the end of the year, so in effect, each year you have 1.06 times as much as the year before. If you start with $1,000, you'll have $1000 \cdot (1.06)^n$ after n years. After 30 years, you have $1000 \cdot (1.06)^{30} \approx 5743.49$ or $5743.49.

MID-CHAPTER TEST

1. Since $(5^3)(5^4) = 5^{3+4} = 5^7$, the correct choice is **B**.
2. Use the Laws of Exponents: $((x^{-2})^2)^2 = (x^{-2 \cdot 2})^2 = (x^{-4})^2 = x^{-4 \cdot 2} = x^{-8}$. The correct choice is **A**.
3. Use the Laws of Exponents: $64^{\frac{3}{2}} = \left(64^{\frac{1}{2}}\right)^3 = (\sqrt{64})^3 = 8^3 = 512$. The correct choice is **C**.
4. Only **C** is not on the graph: $f(1) = 4 \cdot \left(\frac{1}{2}\right)^1 = 4 \cdot \frac{1}{2} = 2 \neq \frac{1}{2}$.
5. $L_4(16) = 2$ because $4^2 = 16$. The correct choice is **C**.
6. (a) Since $h(x) = c \cdot a^x$, $h(0) = 3$, and $h(1) = 6$, you know that

$$h(0) = c \cdot a^0 = 3 \longrightarrow c \cdot 1 = 3 \longrightarrow c = 3$$

and

$$h(1) = 3 \cdot a^1 = 6 \longrightarrow a = 2$$

So,

$$h(x) = 3 \cdot 2^x$$

(b)

x	$h(x)$	$\div$
0	3	2
1	6	2
2	12	2
3	24	2
4	48	2
5	96	

(c) The recursive definition is

$$h(x) = \begin{cases} 3 & \text{if } x = 0 \\ 2 \cdot h(x-1) & \text{if } x > 0 \end{cases}$$

7. (a) If the sequence is arithmetic, there is a common difference between consecutive terms. Since the first two terms are 3 and 6, the common difference is $6 - 3 = 3$. To find new terms, just add 3: $6 + 3 = 9$, $9 + 3 = 12$, $12 + 3 = 15$. So, the next three terms are 9, 12, 15.

(b) If the sequence is geometric, there is a common ratio of consecutive terms. Since the first two terms are 3 and 6, the common ratio is $\frac{6}{3} = 2$. To find new terms, just multiply by 2: $6 \cdot 2 = 12$, $12 \cdot 2 = 24$, $24 \cdot 2 = 48$. So, the next three terms are 12, 24, 48.

8. (a) $x^{-4} \cdot x^6 = x^{(-4+6)} = x^2$

(b) $\left(y^{\frac{1}{3}}\right)^3 = y^{\left(\frac{1}{3} \cdot 3\right)} = y^1 = y$

(c) $\frac{x^{-2}}{x^6} = x^{(-2-6)} = x^{-8} = \frac{1}{x^8}$

(d) $z^{-7} \cdot z^7 = z^{(-7+7)} = z^0 = 1$

(e) $x^{\frac{1}{2}} \cdot x^2 = x^{\left(\frac{1}{2}+2\right)} = x^{\frac{5}{2}}$

(f) $(x^{-6})^{-5} = x^{(-6 \cdot -5)} = x^{30}$

9. (a) Write the equations $9 = a \cdot b^2$ and $27 = a \cdot b^3$. Solve each equation for a, and you get $a = \frac{9}{b^2}$ and $a = \frac{27}{b^3}$. Therefore,

$$\frac{9}{b^2} = \frac{27}{b^3}$$

$$9b^3 = 27b^2$$

$$9b^3 - 27b^2 = 0$$

$$9b^2(b - 3) = 0$$

$b = 0$ or $b = 3$. Since $b > 0$, $b = 3$. Substitute to find a:

$$9 = a \cdot 3^2 \longrightarrow 9 = 9a \longrightarrow a = 1$$

The function you are looking for is

$$q(x) = 3^x$$

(b)

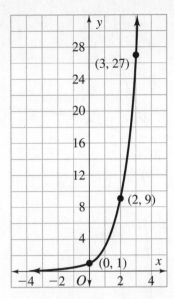

(c)

$$t(x) = -2 \cdot q(x) = -2 \cdot 3^x$$
$$t(2) = -2 \cdot 3^2 = -2 \cdot 9 = -18$$
$$t(3) = -2 \cdot 3^3 = -2 \cdot 27 = -54$$

s
(d)

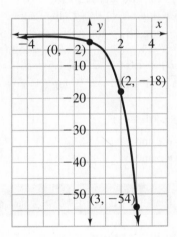

10. (a)

$$16 = 4x^2$$
$$4 = x^2$$
$$\pm\sqrt{4} = x$$
$$\pm 2 = x$$

(b)

$$16 = 4 \cdot 2^x$$
$$4 = 2^x$$
$$2^2 = 2^x$$
$$2 = x$$

(c) $x = 4 \cdot 16^{-\frac{1}{2}} = 4 \cdot \frac{1}{16^{\frac{1}{2}}} = 4 \cdot \frac{1}{\sqrt{16}} = 4 \cdot \frac{1}{4} = 1$

11. $4^0 = 1, 7^{-2} = \frac{1}{7^2} = \frac{1}{49}, 5^{\frac{2}{3}} = \sqrt[3]{25} \approx 2.92$

INVESTIGATION 5C   LOGARITHMIC FUNCTIONS

5.11   Getting Started

For You to Explore

1.

x	$\log (x)$
0	undefined
1	0
2	0.3010
3	0.4771
4	0.6021
5	0.6990
6	0.7782
7	0.8451
8	0.9031
9	0.9542
10	1

2. Using the table, $\log (2) + \log (3) = 0.3010 + 0.4771 = 0.7781$. Using your calculator and rounding to four decimal places, $\log (2) + \log (3) = 0.7782$.

3. (a) 1.0792
(b) 1.0792
(c) 1.0792
(d) $x = 12$

4. (a) You might estimate that $\log (15) = \log (3) + \log (5) = 0.4771 + 0.6990 = 1.1761$
(b) $\log (24) = \log (3) + \log (8) = 0.4771 + 0.9031 = 1.3802$
(c) $\log (36) = \log (6) + \log (6) = 2 \cdot \log (6) = 2 \cdot 0.7782 = 1.5564$. On the calculator, $\log (36) = 1.5563$
(d) $\log (63) = \log (7) + \log (9) = 0.8451 + 0.9542 = 1.7993$

5. $\log (MN) = \log (M) + \log (N)$

6. (a) $\log (16) = \log (2) + \log (2) + \log (2) + \log (2) = 4 \cdot \log (2) = 4 \cdot 0.3010 = 1.2040$. Using the calculator, the result is 1.2041.
(b) $\log (32) = \log (16) + \log (2) = 4 \cdot \log (2) + \log (2) = 5 \cdot \log (2) = 5 \cdot 0.3010 = 1.5050$. Using the calculator, the result is 1.5051
(c) $\log (64) = \log (32) + \log (2) = 5 \cdot \log (2) + \log (2) = 6 \cdot \log (2) = 6 \cdot 0.3010 = 1.8060$. Using the calculator, the result is 1.8062.
(d) $\log (2^{10}) = 10 \cdot \log (2) = 10 \cdot 0.3010 = 3.010$. Using the calculator, the result is 3.0103.
(e) $\log (3^5) = 5 \cdot \log (3) = 5 \cdot 0.4771 = 2.3855$. Using the calculator, the result is 2.3856.

7. $\log (M^p) = p \cdot \log (M)$

8. Since $\frac{1}{8} = 2^{-3}$, $\log \left(\frac{1}{8}\right) = \log (2^{-3}) = -3 \cdot \log (2) = -3 \cdot 0.3010 = -0.9030$.

9. The domain is the set of positive real numbers. The range is the set of real numbers.

10. Take the log of both sides.

$$2^x = 5$$
$$\log(2^x) = \log(5)$$
$$x \log(2) = \log(5)$$
$$x = \frac{\log(5)}{\log(2)}$$
$$x = \frac{0.69897}{0.30103}$$
$$x = 2.3219$$

On Your Own

11. (a) 2
  (b) 3
  (c) 6
  (d) 10
  (e) −3

12. (a) 2
  (b) 3
  (c) 6
  (d) 10
  (e) This is undefined because −3 is not in the domain of $\log(x)$.

13. $f(x) = \log(x)$ and $g(x) = 10^x$ are inverse functions because $f(g(x)) = g(f(x)) = x$. For example, $f(g(2)) = f(10^2) = \log(10^2) = 2$ and $g(f(2)) = g(\log(2)) = 10^{\log(2)} = 2$.

14. (a) $\log\left(\frac{5}{4}\right) + \log(4) = \log\left(\frac{5}{4} \cdot 4\right) = \log(5) = \log(x)$, so $x = 5$

  (b) $\log\left(\frac{7}{3}\right) + \log(3) = \log\left(\frac{7}{3} \cdot 3\right) = \log(7) = \log(x)$, so $x = 7$

  (c) $\log\left(\frac{6}{17}\right) + \log(17) = \log\left(\frac{6}{17} \cdot 17\right) = \log(6) = \log(x)$, so $x = 6$

  (d)
$$\log(x) + \log(2) = \log(5)$$
$$\log(2 \cdot x) = \log(5)$$
$$2 \cdot x = 5$$
$$x = \frac{5}{2}$$

  (e)
$$\log(x) + \log(7) = \log(3)$$
$$\log(7 \cdot x) = \log(3)$$
$$7 \cdot x = 3$$
$$x = \frac{3}{7}$$

  (f)
$$\log(x) = \log(11) - \log(4)$$
$$\log(x) + \log(4) = \log(11)$$
$$\log(4 \cdot x) = \log(11)$$
$$4 \cdot x = 11$$
$$x = \frac{11}{4}$$

15. $\log\left(\frac{M}{N}\right) = \log(M) - \log(N)$

16.

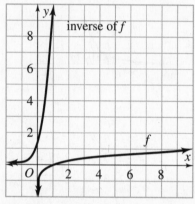

17.

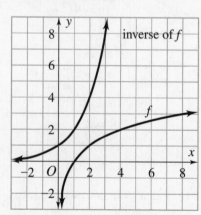

18. (a) $\log(AB) = \log(A) + \log(B) = 1.6 + 2.7 = 4.3$
  (b) $\log(A^2) = 2 \cdot \log(A) = 2 \cdot 1.6 = 3.2$
  (c) $\log\left(\frac{1}{A}\right) = \log(A^{-1}) = -1 \cdot \log(A) = -1.6$
  (d) $\log\left(\frac{B}{A}\right) = \log(B) - \log(A) = 2.7 - 1.6 = 1.1$
  (e) $\log(AB^2) = \log(A) + \log(B^2) = \log(A) + 2 \cdot \log(B) = 1.6 + 2 \cdot 2.7 = 1.6 + 5.4 = 7$
  (f) $\log(\sqrt{A}) = \log(A^{\frac{1}{2}}) = \frac{1}{2} \cdot \log(A) = \frac{1}{2} \cdot 1.6 = 0.8$

Maintain Your Skills

19. • 0 and 1   • 1 and 2
   • 3 and 4   • 5 and 6

5.12 Defining Logarithms

Check Your Understanding

1. (a)

(b) $f^{-1}(x) = 2^x$

2. (a) FALSE; $2^3 \neq 9$
   (b) FALSE; $16^2 \neq 4$
   (c) TRUE. Let the left side equal x. Then $5^x = 10$. Let the right side equal y. Then $5^y = 9$. Since $10 > 9$, $5^x > 5^y$ and $x > y$ and the statement is true.
   (d) FALSE; $4^1 \neq 0$

3. (a) $\frac{1}{2}$
   (b) $\frac{1}{2} + \frac{5}{2} = 3$
   (c) 3
   (d) $\frac{3}{2}$
   (e) $\frac{3}{2} + \frac{1}{2} = 2$
   (f) 2

4. $\log_b (0) = x \Leftrightarrow b^x = 0$. $b^x = 0$ only if $b = 0$, but $b \neq 0$, so $\log_b (0)$ does not exist.

5. $\log_2 (0.1) \approx -3.322$, but you really just need to conclude that it is less than zero for this exercise.
   $\log_5 \left(\frac{1}{5}\right) = -1$, because $5^{-1} = \frac{1}{5}$.
   $\log_{73} (1) = 0$, because $73^0 = 1$.
   $\log_{100} (10) = \frac{1}{2}$, because $100^{\frac{1}{2}} = 10$.
   $\log (99)$ has to be almost 2, because $\log (100) = 2$.
   $\log_4 (18)$ has to be more than 2, because $\log_4 (16) = 2$.
   $\log_2 (18)$ has to be more than 4, because $\log_2 16 = 4$.
   This makes the correct order $\log_2 (0.1)$, $\log_5 \left(\frac{1}{5}\right)$, $\log_{73} (1)$, $\log_{100} (10)$, $\log (99)$, $\log_4 (18)$, $\log_2 (18)$.

6. (a) $b^4 = 9$
   (b) $b = \sqrt[4]{9} = \sqrt{3}$ or $b \approx 1.7321$

7. Let $x = 3^{\log_3 (75)}$. Then use the definition of $\log_b (M)$:
$$x = 3^{\log_3 (75)}$$
$$\log_3 (x) = \log_3 (75) \text{ Definition of logarithm}$$
$$x = 75$$

8. (a) $\log_b (2) = 1.35 \Leftrightarrow b^{1.35} = 2$
   (b) $\log_b (3) = 2.14 \Leftrightarrow b^{2.14} = 3$
   (c) $b^{3.49} = b^{1.35+2.14} = b^{1.35} \cdot b^{2.14} = 2 \cdot 3 = 6$
   (d) $b^{6.42} = b^{2.14 \cdot 3} = (b^{2.14})^3 = 3^3 = 27$
   (e) $\log_b (6) = x \Leftrightarrow b^x = 6$ But, we just showed that $b^{3.49} = 6$. So, $x = 3.49$.
   (f) $\log_b (27) = x \Leftrightarrow b^x = 27$ But, $b^{6.42} = 27$. So, $x = 6.42$.

9.
$$4^x = 25$$
$$\log (4^x) = \log (25)$$
$$x \log (4) = \log (25)$$
$$x = \frac{\log (25)}{\log (4)}$$
$$x = \frac{1.3979}{.6021}$$
$$x = 2.322$$

10. You might start by looking at a series of logarithms such as $\log (2000)$, $\log (200)$, $\log (20)$, and $\log (2)$. You will find that
$$\log (2) = 0.3010$$
$$\log (20) = 1.3010$$
$$\log (200) = 2.3010$$
$$\log (2000) = 3.3010$$

All of these logarithms have the same mantissa, so the mantissa tells you about the 2 that is part of each input. $10^{0.3010} \approx 2$. The ordinate (characteristic) in each case is the power of 10 which is multiplied by the 2 to get the input for the logarithm.

So if you know $\log (X)$ you can find X using the ordinate and mantissa: $X = (10^{\text{mantissa}}) \cdot (10^{\text{ordinate}})$ That's fairly obvious, though, because $10^{\log (X)} = 10^{\text{ordinate}+\text{mantissa}} = X$.

The ordinate, however, is a good indicator of the size of the number. If $\log (X)$ is positive and has ordinate O, then X has $O + 1$ digits to the left of the decimal. (If the logarithm is negative, $X < 1$, and there are $|O|$ zeroes to the right of the decimal.) The mantissa, however, is really only useful if you have to look up logarithms in a table. That means you can figure out the logarithm of any number X from a table that only lists the logarithms for numbers from 0.0000 to 0.9999.

On Your Own

11. By definition $\log_b (b) = 1 \Leftrightarrow b^1 = b$, which is true for any base b.

12. By definition, $\log_b (1) = 0 \Leftrightarrow b^0 = 1$, which is true.

13. (a)
$$b^y = M^2$$
$$b^y = (b^x)^2$$
$$b^y = b^{2x}$$
$$y = 2x$$

   (b) $M^{10} = (b^x)^{10} = b^{10x}$ or $M^{10} = (M^2)^5 = (b^y)^5 = b^{5y}$ The missing exponent is $10x$ or $5y$.
   (c) By definition of logarithm, $\log_b (M^2) = y$ and $\log_b (M) = x$. We found that $y = 2x$, so $\log_b (M^2) = 2 \cdot \log_b (M)$

14. Only $(100, 2)$ is on the graph because $f (100) = \log (100) = 2$. The correct answer choice is **B**.

15. (a) (b)

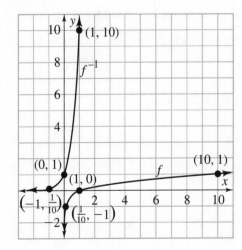

   (c) The domain of f is $\mathbb{R}^+$ and the range is $\mathbb{R}$. The domain of f^{-1} is $\mathbb{R}$ and the range is $\mathbb{R}^+$.
   (d) $f^{-1}(x) = 10^x$

16. (a) $\log_4 (18) = \frac{\log (18)}{\log (4)} = 2.085$

(b) $\log_2 (0.1) = \frac{\log (0.1)}{\log (2)} = -3.322$

(c) $\log_{73} (1) = \frac{\log (1)}{\log (73)} = 0$

(d) $\log_1 (9) = \frac{\log (9)}{\log (1)} = \frac{\log (9)}{0} =$ undefined

(e) $\log_3 (7) = \frac{\log (7)}{\log (3)} = 1.771$

(f) $\log_9 (49) = \frac{\log (49)}{\log (9)} = 1.771$

17. (a) $\log_2 \left(\frac{1}{8}\right) = -3$, because $2^{-3} = \frac{1}{8}$.

(b) $\log_2 (8) = 3$, because $2^3 = 8$.

(c) $\log_4 (16) = 2$, because $4^2 = 16$.

(d) $\log_4 \left(\frac{1}{16}\right) = -2$, because $4^{-2} = \frac{1}{16}$.

(e) $\log_{1/2} (8) = -3$, because $\left(\frac{1}{2}\right)^{-3} = 8$.

(f) $\log_{1/4} \left(\frac{1}{16}\right) = 2$, because $\left(\frac{1}{4}\right)^2 = \frac{1}{16}$.

18. (a)

$$\log_b (M) = k$$
$$b^k = M \quad \text{Definition of logarithm}$$
$$(b^k)^{-1} = (M)^{-1} \quad \text{Raise each side to the } -1 \text{ power.}$$
$$b^{-k} = \frac{1}{M}$$
$$\log_b \left(\frac{1}{M}\right) = -k \quad \text{Definition of logarithm}$$

(b) Let $\log_b M = k$. Then $b^k = M$. Taking reciprocals, $\frac{1}{b^k} = \frac{1}{M}$, or $\left(\frac{1}{b}\right)^k = \frac{1}{M}$. By the definition of logarithm, $\log_{\frac{1}{b}} \left(\frac{1}{M}\right) = k = \log_b M$.

19. The generalization would be $\log_b (a) = \log_{b^2} (a^2)$ You can prove this. First, let $\log_b (a) = x$. Then

$$\log_b (a) = x$$
$$b^x = a$$
$$(b^x)^2 = a^2$$
$$b^{2x} = a^2$$
$$(b^2)^x = a^2$$
$$\log_{b^2} (a^2) = x$$
$$\log_{b^2} (a^2) = \log_b (a)$$

20. The base of a logarithm must be a positive number and not 1. Therefore, $\sqrt{3}$ is the only solution.

Maintain Your Skills

21. (a) $\frac{1}{2}$

(b) 2

(c) $\frac{3}{2}$

(d) $\frac{2}{3}$

(e) 5

(f) $\frac{1}{5}$

(g) $\frac{1}{0.3010} \approx 3.3$

22. (a) 0.863

(b) 1.863

(c) 2.863

(d) 6.863

(e) 5.4771

5.13 Laws of Logarithms

Check Your Understanding

1. (a) $\log_b (M^2) = 2 \cdot \log_b (M) = 2 \cdot 2 = 4$

(b) $\log_b (MN) = \log_b M + \log_b N = 2 + 5 = 7$

(c) $\log_b \frac{M^3}{N} = \log_b M^3 - \log_b N = 3 \log_b M - \log_b N = 3 \cdot 2 - 5 = 6 - 5 = 1$

(d) $\log_b (MN)^3 = 3 \log_b MN = 3(\log_b M + \log_b N) = 3(2 + 5) = 3 \cdot 7 = 21$

(e) $\log_b \sqrt{MN} = \log_b (MN)^{\frac{1}{2}} = \frac{1}{2} \cdot \log_b MN = \frac{1}{2}(\log_b M + \log_b N) = \frac{1}{2}(2 + 5) = \frac{1}{2} \cdot 7 = \frac{7}{2}$

2. $\log_2 3 \cdot \log_3 4 \cdot \log_5 6 \cdot \log_6 25 = \frac{\log 3}{\log 2} \cdot \frac{\log 4}{\log 3} \cdot \frac{\log 6}{\log 5} \cdot \frac{\log 25}{\log 6} = \frac{\log 4}{\log 2} \cdot \frac{\log 25}{\log 5} = \log_2 4 \cdot \log_5 25 = 2 \cdot 2 = 4$

3. $\frac{\log_2 32}{\log_2 8}$ is not in the form $\log_b \frac{M}{N}$, so you cannot apply the rule $\log_b \frac{M}{N} = \log_b M - \log_b N$. In fact, $\frac{\log_2 32}{\log_2 8} = \frac{5}{3} \neq 2$

4. (a) Let $b^x = M$ and $b^y = N$ so $\log_b M = x$ and $\log_b N = y$.
Then,

$$\frac{b^x}{b^y} = \frac{M}{N}$$
$$b^{x-y} = \frac{M}{N}$$
$$\log_b \left(\frac{M}{N}\right) = x - y$$
$$\log_b \left(\frac{M}{N}\right) = \log_b M - \log_b N$$

(b) Think of $\frac{M}{N}$ as $(M) \cdot \left(\frac{1}{N}\right)$.

$$\log_b \frac{M}{N} = \log_b M - \log_b N$$
$$\log_b (M) \cdot \left(\frac{1}{N}\right) = \log_b M - \log_b N$$
$$\log_b M + \log_b \left(\frac{1}{N}\right) = \log_b M - \log_b N$$
$$\log_b M + \log_b N^{-1} = \log_b M - \log_b N$$
$$\log_b M - \log_b N = \log_b M - \log_b N$$

5. (a) Look at the Fundamental Law of Logarithms with $N = 1$.

$$\log_b M \cdot 1 = \log_b M + \log_b 1$$
$$\log_b M = \log_b M + \log_b 1$$

This means that $\log_b 1$ must be a number that when added to $\log_b M$ leaves it unchanged. So $\log_b 1 = 0$.

(b) Say that $\log_b b = z$. Convert this equation to exponential form. $b^z = b$. By the Laws of Exponents, $z = \log_b b = 1$.

(c) Look at the Fundamental Law of Logarithms with $M = \frac{1}{N}$.

$$\log_b \left(\frac{1}{N} \right) \cdot N = \log_b \frac{1}{N} + \log_b N$$

$$\log_b 1 = \log_b \frac{1}{N} + \log_b N$$

$$0 = \log_b \frac{1}{N} + \log_b N$$

$$-\log_b N = \log_b \frac{1}{N}$$

6. (a) Since the cost grows by $3\% = 0.03$ each year, you want to multiply by $1 + 0.03 = 1.03$ each year. The function is $C(n) = 3.99(1.03)^n$

(b) $C(n) = 20$, so your equation is

$$20 = 3.99(1.03)^n$$

$$\log 20 = \log (3.99(1.03)^n)$$

$$\log 20 = \log 3.99 + \log 1.03^n$$

$$\log 20 = \log 3.99 + n \cdot \log 1.03$$

$$\log 20 - \log 3.99 = n \cdot \log 1.03$$

$$\frac{\log 20 - \log 3.99}{\log 1.03} = n$$

$$n = 54.533 \approx 55 \text{ years}$$

7.

$$2 \cdot 5^x = 7$$

$$\log (2 \cdot 5^x) = \log 7$$

$$\log 2 + \log 5^x = \log 7$$

$$\log 2 + x \cdot \log 5 = \log 7$$

$$x \cdot \log 5 = \log 7 - \log 2$$

$$x = \frac{\log 7 - \log 2}{\log 5}$$

$$x = \frac{\log 3.5}{\log 5}$$

$$x \approx 0.778$$

8. Just follow the same steps as in the last problem.

$$a \cdot b^x = c$$

$$\log (a \cdot b^x) = \log c$$

$$\log a + \log b^x = \log c$$

$$\log a + x \cdot \log b = \log c$$

$$x \log b = \log c - \log a$$

$$x = \frac{\log c - \log a}{\log b}$$

OR

$$x = \frac{\log \frac{c}{a}}{\log b}$$

9.

$$2 \cdot 5^x = 7 \cdot 3^x$$

$$\log (2 \cdot 5^x) = \log (7 \cdot 3^x)$$

$$\log 2 + \log 5^x = \log 7 + \log 3^x$$

$$\log 2 + x \log 5 = \log 7 + x \log 3$$

$$x \log 5 - x \log 3 = \log 7 - \log 2$$

$$x(\log 5 - \log 3) = \log 7 - \log 2$$

$$x = \frac{\log 7 - \log 2}{\log 5 - \log 3}$$

$$x = \frac{\log \frac{7}{2}}{\log \frac{5}{3}}$$

$$x \approx 2.452$$

10. Follow the same sequence of steps as in the last exercise.

$$a \cdot b^x = c \cdot d^x$$

$$\log (a \cdot b^x) = \log (c \cdot d^x)$$

$$\log a + \log b^x = \log c + \log d^x$$

$$\log a + x \log b = \log c + x \log d$$

$$x \log b - x \log d = \log c - \log a$$

$$x(\log b - \log d) = \log c - \log a$$

$$x = \frac{\log c - \log a}{\log b - \log d}$$

OR

$$x = \frac{\log \frac{c}{a}}{\log \frac{b}{d}}$$

11. Solve each equation for x.

$$6^x = 35$$

$$\log 6^x = \log 35$$

$$x \log 6 = \log 35$$

$$x = \frac{\log 35}{\log 6}$$

$$35^x = 6$$

$$\log 35^x = \log 6$$

$$x \log 35 = \log 6$$

$$x = \frac{\log 6}{\log 35}$$

Since $\frac{\log 35}{\log 6} \cdot \frac{\log 6}{\log 35} = 1$, the two results are reciprocals.

12. (a)

$$\log x + \log (x + 1) = \log 6$$

$$\log (x(x + 1)) = \log 6$$

$$\log (x^2 + x) = \log 6$$

$$x^2 + x = 6$$

$$x^2 + x - 6 = 0$$

$$(x + 3)(x - 2) = 0$$

$$x = -3 \text{ or } x = 2$$

The solution $x = -3$ is not in the domain of x ($\log -3$ is not defined), so the only solution is $x = 2$.

(b)

$$\log (x^2 + x) = \log 6$$

$$x^2 + x = 6$$

$$x^2 + x - 6 = 0$$

$$(x + 3)(x - 2) = 0$$

$$x = -3 \text{ or } x = 2$$

This time both solutions work because neither makes $x^2 + x$ negative or zero.

(c)
$$\log 2x - \log x = \log 2$$
$$\log \frac{2x}{x} = \log 2$$
$$\log 2 = \log 2$$

This equation will be true for all values in the domain. The solution is $x > 0$.

(d)
$$\log_2 (x - 3) + \log_2 (x + 3) = 4$$
$$\log_2 (x - 3)(x + 3) = 4$$
$$\log_2 (x - 3)(x + 3) = \log_2 16$$
$$(x - 3)(x + 3) = 16$$
$$x^2 - 9 = 16$$
$$x^2 = 25$$
$$x = \pm 5$$

But, $x \neq -5$, so the solution is $x = 5$.

(e)
$$\log_2 (x - 3) - \log_2 (x + 3) = 4$$
$$\log_2 \frac{x - 3}{x + 3} = 4$$
$$\log_2 \frac{x - 3}{x + 3} = \log_2 16$$
$$\frac{x - 3}{x + 3} = 16$$
$$x - 3 = 16x + 48$$
$$-15x = 51$$
$$x = -\frac{51}{15} = -\frac{17}{5}$$

This is not in the domain, $x > 3$, so there is no solution.

13. You can set up an equation between two logarithms if you can find two expressions that are equal to the same number. If $\log 2 = 0.3$, then $5 \log 2 = 5 \cdot 0.3 = 1.5$.
If $\log 3 = 0.5$, then $3 \log 3 = 3 \cdot 0.5 = 1.5$.
Since both log expressions are equal to 1.5, you can set them equal to each other. Use the rules of logarithms and algebra to prove that $0 = 1$.

$$5 \log 2 = 3 \log 3$$
$$\log 2^5 = \log 3^3$$
$$\log 32 = \log 27$$
$$32 = 27$$
$$32 - 32 = 27 - 32$$
$$0 = -5$$
$$\frac{0}{-5} = \frac{-5}{-5}$$
$$0 = 1$$

14. To find the number of years it takes an investment to double, solve the equation $2A = A \left(1 + \frac{r}{100}\right)^y$ for y. (r is the interest rate, and A is the initial investment amount.)

$$2A = A \left(1 + \frac{r}{100}\right)^y$$
$$2 = \left(1 + \frac{r}{100}\right)^y$$
$$\log 2 = \log \left(1 + \frac{r}{100}\right)^y$$
$$\log 2 = y \cdot \log \left(1 + \frac{r}{100}\right)$$
$$y = \frac{\log 2}{\log \left(1 + \frac{r}{100}\right)}$$

Now you can make a table comparing the value of $\frac{72}{r}$ to $\frac{\log 2}{\log(1+\frac{r}{100})}$ for interest rates from 6% to 12%.

r	$\frac{72}{r}$	$\frac{\log 2}{\log(1+\frac{r}{100})}$
6	12	11.8957
7	10.2857	10.2448
8	9	9.0065
9	8	8.0432
10	7.2	7.2725
11	6.5455	6.6419
12	6	6.1163

The results are pretty close!

On Your Own

15. $\log_5 135$ is the power of 5 that gives you 135. That is, $5^{\log_5 135} = 135$. Since $5^3 = 125$ and $5^4 = 625$, $3 < \log_5 135 < 4$. Similarly, $\log_7 300$ is the power of 7 that gives you 300. Since $7^2 = 49$ and $7^3 = 343$, $2 < \log_7 300 < 3$. Therefore, $\log_5 135$ is larger.

16.

x	$\log_3 x$
1	0
2	0.6309
3	1
4	1.2619
5	1.4650
6	1.6309
7	1.7712
8	1.8928
9	2

17. Since the $\log_3 7$ is the power of 3 that gives 7, $\log_3 7$ is less than 2 ($3^2 = 9$) but greater than 1($3^1 = 4$). $\log_9 81 = 2$. Therefore, $\log_3 7 + \log_9 81$ is between 3 and 4 (choice **D**).

18. You're given that $\log_b 297736 = 7$ so you know that $b^7 = 297736$, or $b = \sqrt[7]{297736} \approx 6.0531$.

19. (a) $\log 6 = \log (2 \cdot 3) = \log 2 + \log 3 = a + b$
    (b) $\log 1.5 = \log \frac{3}{2} = \log 3 - \log 2 = b - a$
    (c) $\log 27 = \log 3^3 = 3 \log 3 = 3b$
    (d) $\log 200 = \log (2 \cdot 100) = \log 2 + \log 100 = a + 2$
    (e) $\log \sqrt{3} = \log 3^{\frac{1}{2}} = \frac{1}{2} \log 3 = \frac{b}{2}$

20. From smallest to largest they are
    $\log_3 7 = 1.77124$
    $\log_8 40 = 1.77398$
    $\log 60 = 1.77815$

$\log_{12} 83 = 1.77827$

$\log_9 50 = 1.78044$

$\log_2 3.44 = 1.78241$

21. Since the bases are different, you cannot apply the rule $\log_b a + \log_b c = \log_b (ac)$. To find the correct value, evaluate each log separately. $\log 100 = 2$ and $\log_2 8 = 3$, so the correct value is $2 + 3 = 5$.

22.
$$2^x = \frac{1}{1,000,000}$$
$$2^x = 10^{-6}$$
$$\log 2^x = \log 10^{-6}$$
$$x \log 2 = -6$$
$$x = \frac{-6}{\log 2}$$
$$x \approx -19.932$$

23. (a)
$$50 = 100 \cdot 0.5^h$$
$$\frac{1}{2} = 0.5^h \quad \text{Divide both sides by 100.}$$
$$\log\left(\frac{1}{2}\right) = \log 0.5^h \quad \text{Take the log of both sides.}$$
$$\log 0.5 = h \log 0.5$$
$$1 = h$$

(b)
$$20 = 100 \cdot 0.5^h$$
$$\frac{1}{5} = 0.5^h \quad \text{Divide both sides by 100.}$$
$$\log\left(\frac{1}{5}\right) = \log (0.5^h) \quad \text{Take the log of both sides.}$$
$$\log\left(\frac{1}{5}\right) = h \log \frac{1}{2}$$
$$\log 5^{-1} = h \log 2^{-1}$$
$$-\log 5 = -h \log 2$$
$$\frac{\log 5}{\log 2} = h$$
$$2.322 \approx h$$

(c)
$$10 = 100 \cdot 0.5^h$$
$$\frac{1}{10} = 0.5^h \quad \text{Divide both sides by 100.}$$
$$\log\left(\frac{1}{10}\right) = \log 0.5^h \quad \text{Take the log of both sides.}$$
$$\log 10^{-1} = h \log 2^{-1}$$
$$-\log 10 = -h \log 2$$
$$-1 = -h \log 2$$
$$\frac{1}{\log 2} = h$$
$$3.322 \approx h$$

Notice that this answer is the sum of the previous two answers.

(d)
$$c = 100 \cdot 0.5^h$$
$$\frac{c}{100} = 0.5^h \quad \text{Divide both sides by 100.}$$
$$\log\left(\frac{c}{100}\right) = \log 0.5^h \quad \text{Take the log of both sides.}$$
$$\log c - \log 100 = h \cdot \log 0.5$$
$$h = \frac{\log c - 2}{\log 0.5}$$

(e) You can use the previous result:
$$h = \frac{\log 1 - 2}{\log 0.5}$$
or, since $\log 1 = 0$,
$$h = \frac{-2}{\log 0.5} \approx 6.6439$$

24. They are NOT the same. $(\log x)^2 = \log x \cdot \log x$ and $\log x^2 = \log (x \cdot x) = \log x + \log x$.
However, there are values for which $(\log x)^2 = \log x^2$.
$$(\log x)^2 = \log x^2$$
$$(\log x)^2 - 2 \log x = 0$$
$$(\log x)(\log x - 2) = 0$$
So these two expressions will be equal if $\log x = 0$, which means that $x = 1$, or when $\log x = 2$, which means that $x = 100$.

25. (a)
$$\log_2 x^2 - 5 \log_2 x + 6 = 0$$
$$2 \log_2 x - 5 \log_2 x + 6 = 0$$
$$-3 \log_2 x = -6$$
$$\log_2 x = 2$$
$$x = 2^2 = 4$$

(b)
$$(\log_2 x)^2 - 5 \log_2 x + 6 = 0$$
$$(\log_2 x - 3)(\log_2 x - 2) = 0 \quad \text{Factor.}$$
$$\log_2 x - 3 = 0 \text{ or } \log_2 x - 2 = 0 \quad \text{Set each factor to 0.}$$
$$\log_2 x = 3 \text{ or } \log_2 x = 2 \quad \text{Solve for } \log_2 x.$$
$$x = 2^3 = 8 \text{ or } x = 2^2 = 4$$

(c)
$$\log x = 1 + \frac{6}{\log x}$$
$$(\log x)^2 = \log x + 6 \quad \text{Multiply by } \log x.$$
$$(\log x)^2 - \log x - 6 = 0$$
$$(\log x - 3)(\log x + 2) = 0 \quad \text{Factor.}$$
$$\log x - 3 = 0 \text{ or } \log x + 2 = 0 \quad \text{Set each factor equal to 0.}$$
$$\log x = 3 \text{ or } \log x = -2$$
$$x = 10^3 = 1000 \text{ or } x = 10^{-2} = \frac{1}{100}$$

26. Special case: let $M = 1$ in the original.
$$\log_b \left(\frac{1}{N}\right) = \log_b 1 - \log_b N = 0 - \log_b N = -\log_b N$$

27. It is true if $M = N$, because then both $\frac{\log M}{\log N}$ and $\frac{M}{N}$ are equal to 1. Furthermore, their equality can be rewritten as $N \cdot \log M = M \cdot \log N$, which implies $\log (M^N) = \log (N^M)$. Therefore, $M^N = N^M$. See the solution to Lesson 5.15, Exercise 13, for additional solutions with $M \neq N$.

Maintain Your Skills

28. Using the laws of logarithms,

$$\log \left(\frac{xy^2}{z}\right) = \log (xy^2) - \log z$$
$$= \log x + \log (y^2) - \log z$$
$$= \log x + 2 \cdot \log y - \log z$$

The correct answer choice is **B**.

29. Since the population is increasing at 2.5%, you want to multiply by $1 + 0.025 = 1.025$ each year. The function is $P(n) = 10 \cdot 1.025^n$ where n is the number of years and $P(n)$ is the population in millions after n years.

(a)
$$20 = 10 \cdot 1.025^n$$
$$2 = 1.025^n$$
$$\log 2 = \log 1.025^n$$
$$\log 2 = n \log 1.025$$
$$n = \frac{\log 2}{\log 1.025}$$
$$n \approx 28.07$$

(b)
$$30 = 10 \cdot 1.025^n$$
$$3 = 1.025^n$$
$$\log 3 = \log 1.025^n$$
$$\log 3 = n \log 1.025$$
$$n = \frac{\log 3}{\log 1.025}$$
$$n \approx 44.49$$

(c)
$$40 = 10 \cdot 1.025^n$$
$$4 = 1.025^n$$
$$\log 4 = \log 1.025^n$$
$$\log 4 = n \log 1.025$$
$$n = \frac{\log 4}{\log 1.025}$$
$$n \approx 56.14$$

(d)
$$60 = 10 \cdot 1.025^n$$
$$6 = 1.025^n$$
$$\log 6 = \log 1.025^n$$
$$\log 6 = n \log 1.025$$
$$n = \frac{\log 6}{\log 1.025}$$
$$n \approx 72.56$$

(e)
$$120 = 10 \cdot 1.025^n$$
$$12 = 1.025^n$$
$$\log 12 = \log 1.025^n$$
$$\log 12 = n \log 1.025$$
$$n = \frac{\log 12}{\log 1.025}$$
$$n \approx 100.63$$

(f)
$$240 = 10 \cdot 1.025^n$$
$$24 = 1.025^n$$
$$\log 24 = \log 1.025^n$$
$$\log 24 = n \log 1.025$$
$$n = \frac{\log 24}{\log 1.025}$$
$$n \approx 128.70$$

5.14 Graphing Logarithmic Functions

Check Your Understanding

1. Using algebra,

$$\log_2 (3x + 1) - \log_2 (2x - 3) = 2$$
$$\log_2 \frac{(3x + 1)}{(2x - 3)} = \log_2 4$$
$$\frac{(3x + 1)}{(2x - 3)} = 4$$
$$\frac{(3x + 1)}{(2x - 3)} \cdot (2x - 3) = 4 \cdot (2x - 3)$$
$$3x + 1 = 8x - 12$$
$$-5x = -13$$
$$x = \frac{13}{5} = 2.6$$

Using the graphing calculator,
In $y1$, enter

$$\frac{\log \frac{3x+1}{2x-3}}{\log 2}$$

In $y2$, enter

$$2$$

The point of intersection is $(2.6, 2)$, so $x = 2.6$.

2. (a) $\ln(0)$ is undefined. $\ln(1) = 0$
   (b) One way to find b is to use your calculator. You can determine that $\ln 2 \approx 0.693147$. Use the change-of-base formula to get

$$\ln 2 = \log_b 2 = \frac{\log 2}{\log b} \approx 0.693147$$

   Try different values for b to eventually get that $b \approx 2.71828\ldots$
   You can use a similar approximation technique, inputting different numbers into the **LN** function until you find a number a so that $\mathbf{LN}a = 1$.

3. (a)

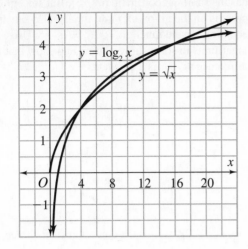

(b) There are 2 solutions. They are $x = 16$ and $x = 4$.

4. No, after $x \approx 31622$, $\sqrt{x} > \log_{1.06}(x)$.

5. You can experiment with these functions as graphs or as tables on your calculator to answer the questions:

(a) no

(b) no

(c) yes

6. You should graph each side of the equation separately, and look for the number of intersections.

(a) 2

(b) 1

(c) 2

(d) 0

(e) 2

7. Use your calculator and experiment with different values of b between 1.4 and 2, since when $b = 1.4$ there are two intersections, and when $b = 2$ there are no intersections. In fact, there is still no point of intersection when $b = 1.45$. If $b = 1.4447$, the two points of intersection are VERY close together. The actual value of b is approximately 1.4447. The point of intersection is about $(2.7183, 2.7183)$.

On Your Own

8. (a) Find 1.383 on the horizontal axis. Go up to the graph of $f(x) = \log_2 x$ and across to the y-axis to read the solution. $\log_2 1.383 \approx 0.468$.

(b) Here you find 0.4 on the y-axis. Read across and down to find the solution. $\log_2 1.32 \approx 0.4$

9. The Laws of Logarithms say that $\log_b a^c = c \log_b a$, so you can say that $\log x^2 = 2 \log x$. However, the graphs are not identical because the two functions have different domains. The domain of $f(x) = \log x^2$ is all real numbers except zero. The domain of $g(x) = 2 \log x$ is only positive real numbers. So, the graphs are not the same.

10. (a)

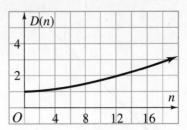

(b) $D^{-1}(n) = \log_{1.06} n$

(c)

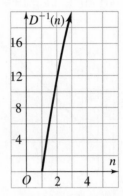

(d) Solve $1.06^n = 10$. Then $n = \log_{1.06} 10$, which is about 40 years.

11. (a)

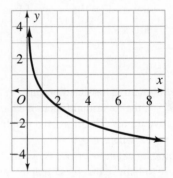

(b) Since $y = \log_b x \Leftrightarrow b^y = x$, as y gets bigger x gets smaller and closer to 0. For example, if $b = \frac{1}{2}$, $\left(\frac{1}{2}\right)^2 = \frac{1}{4}$ and $\left(\frac{1}{2}\right)^3 = \frac{1}{8}$. This also means that as y gets smaller, x gets bigger. For example, $\left(\frac{1}{2}\right)^{-1} = 2$ and $\left(\frac{1}{2}\right)^{-2} = 4$. If y gets smaller as x gets bigger, the function is decreasing.

12. Let $y = g(x)$. Then

$$y = \log_8 x$$
$$8^y = x \quad \text{Definition of } \log_b x$$
$$(2^3)^y = x$$
$$2^{3y} = x$$
$$3y = \log_2 x \quad \text{Definition of } \log_b x$$
$$3g(x) = f(x) \quad \text{Substitute } g(x) = y$$
$$\text{and } f(x) = \log_2 x.$$

Therefore, $f(x)$ is three times as large as $g(x)$.

13. (a)

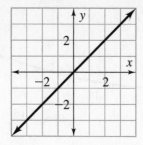

The graph is just the line with equation $y = x$, because $y = \log 10^x = x \log 10 = x \cdot 1 = x$.

(b)

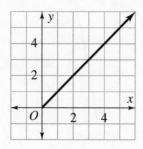

$$y = 10^{\log x}$$

$\log y = \log 10^{\log x}$ Take the log of both sides.

$\log y = \log x \cdot \log 10$ Law of Logarithms

$\log y = \log x \cdot 1$

$\log x = \log y$

$x = y$

But, the domain is restricted because in the original $y = 10^{\log x}$, the logarithm function cannot accept nonpositive inputs. Therefore, the graph is only the part of $y = x$ where $x > 0$.

14. After graphing an example or two on your calculator, you may be ready to believe that these graphs are horizontal translations of each other. In that case, there is some number t so that a point (x, y) on one of the graphs maps to a point $(x + t, y)$ on the other graph. That is what you want to show in each of these cases.

(a) The graph of $g(x) = 3^x$ contains the point $(m, 3^m)$. There is a point on the graph of $f(x) = a \cdot 3^x$ that has the same y-coordinate $(n, 3^m)$. But since this point is on the graph of $f(x)$, it must also satisfy the equation for the function, so $3^m = a \cdot 3^n$. Use logarithms to solve this equation and show that the difference $m - n$ is a constant.

$$3^m = a \cdot 3^n$$

$$m \log 3 = \log a + n \log 3$$

$$m = \frac{\log a}{\log 3} + n$$

$$m - n = \frac{\log a}{\log 3}$$

(b) The graph of $g(x) = b^x$ contains the point $(m, 3^m)$. There is a point on the graph of $f(x) = a \cdot b^x$ that has the same y-coordinate (n, b^m). But since this point is on the graph of $f(x)$, it must also satisfy the equation for the function, so $b^m = a \cdot b^n$. Use logarithms to solve this equation and show that the difference $m - n$ is a constant.

$$b^m = a \cdot b^n$$

$$m \log b = \log a + n \log b$$

$$m = \frac{\log a}{\log b} + n$$

$$m - n = \frac{\log a}{\log b}$$

15. $g(x) = f(x + 2) - 1$, so the correct answer choice is **C**.

Maintain Your Skills

16.

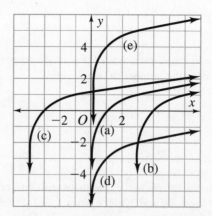

The graphs of $y = \log_3 (x - 3)$ and $y = \log_3 (x) - 3$ are not the same. In the first, you subtract 3 from x and then take the logarithm. This results in a horizontal translation of $y = \log_3 x$ three units to the right. In the second, you take the log of x and then subtract 3. This results in a vertical translation of $y = \log_3 x$ three units down.

5.15   The Logarithmic Scale

Check Your Understanding

1. The primes are less frequent among larger numbers because the values in the $\frac{x}{\pi(x)}$ are getting larger. You are told that out of all the numbers from 1 to x, about one in every $\frac{x}{\pi(x)}$ will be prime. If something occurs 1 in 22 times, that is less frequent than 1 in 8 times.

2. Here is a graph showing the first several points.

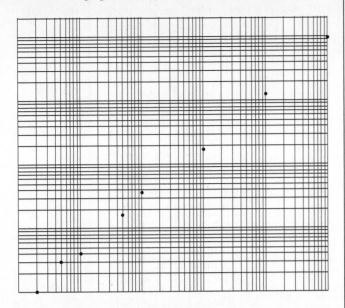

The graph appears to be a straight line.

3. The graph appears to be a straight line, especially as the values of x get larger.

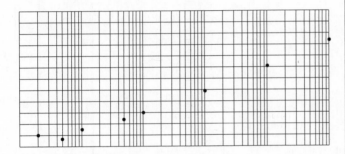

With a logarithmic x-axis and a linear y-axis, this indicates a logarithm function.

4. This scale is logarithmic because the values on the vertical axes that differ by the same amount are not represented by equal lengths. That is, the distance between 50 and 60 is greater than the distance between 100 and 110.

5. (a) Consider any logarithmic function $y = \log_b x$ with $b > 0$ and $b \neq 1$. Graphed with a logarithmic scale on the x-axis, the base-10 logarithm outputs of the x-values are displayed. So you want to calculate $\log x$ in terms of b and y, using the Laws of Logarithms.

$$y = \log_b x$$
$$b^y = x$$
$$\log b^y = \log x$$
$$y \log b = \log x$$
$$y = \frac{1}{\log b} \cdot \log x$$

Since $\frac{1}{\log b}$ is just some number, say B, the equation becomes $y = B \log x$, which is in linear form.

(b) The slope of that line is $\frac{1}{\log b}$.

6. (a)
$$y = a \cdot x^b$$
$$\log y = \log (a \cdot x^b)$$
$$\log y = \log a + b \log x$$

Let $A = \log a$ and $b = B$. The form of the equation is $\log y = A + B \cdot \log x$, which is in linear form.

(b) The slope of the line is b.

7. There are no negative numbers or zero on the logarithmic axes. Therefore, the intersection point (0,0) does not appear. What the graph does show is that for any value of x, $10x^2$ is 10 times x^2, so the graphs are always the same distance apart.

On Your Own

8. A function is one-to-one if it has an inverse, and $f(f^{-1}(x)) = f^{-1}(f(x)) = x$. In this case, you know that the inverse of $f(x) = \log_2 x$ is $f^{-1}(x) = 2^x$. You can show that $f(f^{-1}(x)) = \log_2 (2^x) = x \log_2 2 = x \cdot 1 = x$ and $f^{-1}(f(x)) = 2^{\log_2 x} = x$. Therefore, the function is one-to-one.

9. (a) (b)

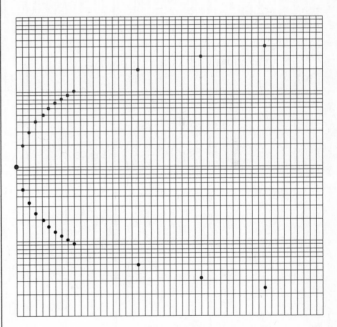

The graph of $y = x$, shown in lighter points, looks like a logarithmic graph would look on standard axes. This makes sense because $\log y = \log x$ is what is being displayed. The graph of $y = \frac{1}{x}$ also looks like a logarithmic graph, but since it's displaying $\log \left(\frac{1}{x}\right)$, as x gets larger, the y-values are decreasing.

(c) Let $v = \log y$. If $y = x$, then $\log y = \log x$ or $v = \log x$. If $y = \frac{1}{x}$, then $\log y = \log \left(\frac{1}{x}\right) = -\log x$ or $v = -\log x$. In the x-v plane, these graphs are reflections of each other over the x-axis ($v = 0$, which corresponds to $y = 1$).

10. (a) The bases are the same. $\log_3 x = \log_3 7 \Rightarrow x = 7$

(b)

$$\log_3 x + \log_3 (x+1) = \log_3 12$$
$$\log_3 x(x+1) = \log_3 12$$
$$x(x+1) = 12$$
$$x^2 + x - 12 = 0$$
$$(x+4)(x-3) = 0$$
$$x = -4 \text{ or } x = 3$$

But $x \neq -4$ because you cannot take the logarithm of a negative number. So, $x = 3$.

(c)

$$\log(x^2) = 4$$
$$x^2 = 10^4$$
$$x^2 = 10000$$
$$x = \pm 100$$

Both solutions work since x^2 is positive.

(d)

$$\log_5 (x+1) - \log_5 x = 1$$
$$\log_5 \left(\frac{x+1}{x}\right) = \log_5 5$$
$$\frac{x+1}{x} = 5$$
$$x + 1 = 5x$$
$$1 = 4x$$
$$\frac{1}{4} = x$$

11. (a) $\log_4 17$ is the power of 4 that gives 17, so it is a little more than 2 because $4^2 = 16$.

(b) $\log_3 27$ is exactly 3.

(c) $\log_5 117$ is the power of 5 that gives 117, so it is less than 3 because $5^3 = 125$.

(d) $\log_2 9$ is the power of 2 that gives 9, so it is a little more than 3 because $2^3 = 8$.

Therefore, choice **D** is the largest.

12. (a) $F(n)$ is exponential because you multiply by 2 to get from one output to the next. The constant ratio between successive terms tells you that the function must be exponential.

(b) Exponential functions appear as straight lines when you plot them with a logarithmic scale on the y-axis.

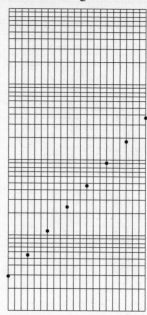

13. Let $y = kx$. Then

$$x^y = y^x$$
$$x^{kx} = (kx)^x$$
$$(x^k)^x = (kx)^x$$
$$x^k = kx$$
$$x^{k-1} = k$$
$$x = k^{\frac{1}{k-1}} \ (k \neq 1)$$

Then to find y,

$$y = kx$$
$$y = k \cdot k^{\frac{1}{k-1}}$$
$$y = k^{\frac{k}{k-1}}$$

Some ordered pairs that work:

Let $k = 2$. Then $x = 2^{\frac{1}{2-1}} = 2$ and $y = kx = 2 \cdot 2 = 4$. The ordered pair is $(2, 4)$.

Let $k = 3$. Then $x = 3^{\frac{1}{3-1}} = 3^{\frac{1}{2}} = \sqrt{3}$ and $y = kx = 3\sqrt{3}$. The ordered pair is $(\sqrt{3}, 3\sqrt{3})$.

Maintain Your Skills

14. (a)

x	$\log_2 (x)$	$\log_8 (x)$
0	undef.	undef.
1	0	0
2	1	$\frac{1}{3}$
3	1.5850	0.5283
4	2	$\frac{2}{3}$
5	2.3219	0.7740
6	2.5850	0.8617
7	2.8074	0.9358
8	3	1
9	3.1699	1.0566
10	3.3219	1.1073

(b) If $\log_8 (23) = 1.5079$, then $\log_2 (23) = 3(1.5079) = 4.5237$.

15.

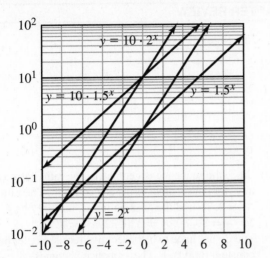

16.

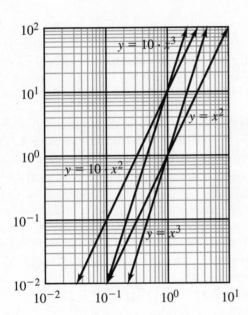

5C   MATHEMATICAL REFLECTIONS

1. (a)
$$\log \frac{5}{6} + \log 6 = \log x$$

Apply the Fundamental Law of Logarithms.
$$\log \left(\frac{5}{6} \cdot 6 \right) = \log x$$

Simplify.
$$\log (5) = \log x$$

Logarithmic functions are one-to-one.
$$x = 5$$

(b)
$$\log_3 2 + \log_3 \frac{1}{2} = \log_3 x$$

Apply the Fundamental Law of Logarithms.
$$\log_3 \left(2 \cdot \frac{1}{2} \right) = \log_3 x$$

Simplify.
$$\log_3 (1) = \log_3 x$$

Logarithmic functions are one-to-one.
$$x = 1$$

(c)
$$\log (10) \cdot \log (x) = \log (30)$$
$$\log_b b = 1$$
$$1 \cdot \log (x) = \log (30)$$
$$\log (x) = \log (30)$$

Logarithmic functions are one-to-one.
$$x = 30$$

(d)
$$\log_2 (4) \cdot \log_2 \left(\frac{1}{2} \right) = \log_2 (x)$$
$$2^2 = 4 \text{ and } 2^{-1} = \frac{1}{2}$$
$$2 \cdot (-1) = \log_2 (x)$$
$$-2 = \log_2 (x)$$

Convert the form.
$$2^{-2} = x$$
$$x = \frac{1}{4}$$

2. $\log_4 (2) < \log_4 \left(\frac{5}{2} \right) < \log_4 (4)$, because $2 < \frac{5}{2} < 4$, so $\frac{1}{2} < \log_4 \left(\frac{5}{2} \right) < 1$.
$\log_2 \left(\frac{1}{8} \right) = -3$, because $2^{-3} = \frac{1}{8}$.
$\log (0.1) < \log (0.3) < \log (1)$, because $0.1 < 0.3 < 1$, so $-1 < \log (0.3) < 0$.
$\log_7 (1) = 0$, because $7^0 = 1$.
$\log_{\frac{1}{2}} (4) = -2$, because $\left(\frac{1}{2} \right)^{-2} = 4$.
So, the correct order is

$$\log_2 \left(\frac{1}{8} \right), \log_{\frac{1}{2}} (4), \log (0.3), \log_7 (1), \log_4 \left(\frac{5}{2} \right)$$

3. (a) Find two consecutive powers of three, a and b, so that $a < 17 < b$. $a = 9 = 3^2$ and $b = 27 = 3^3$ work, because $9 < 17 < 27$. This means that $j = 2$ and $k = 3$, and $2 < N < 3$.
(b) $N = \log_3 17 = \frac{\log 17}{\log 3}$
(c) $\log_3 (3 \cdot 17^2) = \log_3 3 + 2 \cdot \log_3 17 = 1 + 2N$

4.
$$\log (x - 20) + \log (x - 50) = 3$$
Apply the Fundamental Law of Logarithms.
$$\log (x - 20)(x - 50) = 3$$
$$10^3 = 1000, \text{ so } \log 1000 = 3$$
$$\log (x - 20)(x - 50) = \log 1000$$

Logarithmic functions are one-to-one.

$$(x - 20)(x - 50) = 1000$$

Multiply

$$x^2 - 70x + 1000 = 1000$$

Simplify

$$x^2 - 70x = 0$$

Factor

$$x(x - 70) = 0$$

,Use the Zero Product Property.

$$x = 0 \text{ or } 70$$

Check each potential solution in the original equation. $x = 0$ results in negative inputs to a logarithmic function, so it is not a true solution to the equation. $x = 70$ is the only solution.

5. (a) If the graph of $f(x)$ is increasing, you know that its base, b, is greater than 1. If the graph is decreasing, $0 < b < 1$.

   (b) $f(x) = 0$ says that $\log_b x = 0$. This implies $x = b^0 = 1$.

   (c) $f(x)$ must pass through $(1, 0)$, because $b^0 = 1$ and therefore $\log_b (1) = 0$ for any base.

   (d) The point $(b, 1)$ must be on the graph because $b^1 = b$ and therefore $\log_b b = 1$. Find an intersection between the graph of $f(x)$ and the line with equation $y = 1$. The x-coordinate of the intersection point is the base of the logarithm.

6. Answers will vary, but should include the idea that you can solve an equation of the form $b^x = c$ without using trial and error. Some students may also say that logarithms allow you to change a multiplication problem to an addition problem, or an expression involving an exponent to a product.

7. A logarithmic scale is structured so that any two numbers a and b on the scale that are a distance d apart from each other have the same ratio. (In a linear scale, any two numbers a and b on the scale that are a distance d apart from each other have the same difference.) As you take equal steps along a logarithmic scale, instead of adding you multiply. Most logarithmic scales for graph paper are built using base-10 logarithms. Only positive numbers can be shown on a logarithmic scale, and you might see values like $\ldots$, 10^{-2}, 10^{-1}, 1, 10, 100, $\ldots$ labeling the axes. It is convenient to use for graphing certain functions involving logarithms or exponentials, "turning" the graphs into ones that are linear, or close to it.

8. You want to solve the equation $10{,}000 = 1000\left(1 + \frac{6}{100}\right)^n$ for n.

$$10{,}000 = 1000\left(1 + \frac{6}{100}\right)^n$$

$$10 = (1.06)^n$$

$$\log 10 = n \log 1.06$$

$$n = \frac{1}{\log 1.06}$$

$$n \approx 39.5165$$

It will take 40 years for the investment to be worth more than \$10,000.

CHAPTER REVIEW

1. Use the Rules of Exponents:

   (a) $x^{-2} \cdot x^{-1} = x^{-2+-1} = x^{-3}$

   (b) $\left(\frac{1}{x}\right)^{-2} = \left(\frac{1}{x^{-2}}\right) = x^2$

   (c) $((x^3)^{-2})^{-5} = x^{3 \cdot -2 \cdot -5} = x^{30}$

   (d) $\frac{x^4}{x^{-4}} = x^{4-(-4)} = x^8$

   (e) $(x^6)^0 \cdot x^3 = 1 \cdot x^3 = x^3$

   (f) $\frac{(x^5)(x^{-2})}{x^{10}} = \frac{x^{5+-2}}{x^{10}} = \frac{x^3}{x^{10}} = x^{3-10} = x^{-7}$

2. (a) Since the sequence is geometric, the ratio between any two consecutive terms is a constant. The ratio is $\frac{20}{5} = 4$. To find the missing terms, multiply by 4: $20 \cdot 4 = 80$, $80 \cdot 4 = 320$, $320 \cdot 4 = 1280$.

   (b) You do not have two consecutive terms. So, let the constant ratio be r. The sequence becomes $6, 6r, 6r^2, 6r^3, 6r^4$.

   $$6r^2 = 24$$
   $$r^2 = 4$$
   $$r = \pm 2$$

   If $r = 2$, the sequence is $6, 6 \cdot 2 = 12, 12 \cdot 2 = 24$, $24 \cdot 2 = 48, 48 \cdot 2 = 96$.

   If $r = -2$, the sequence would be $6, 6 \cdot -2 = -12$, $-12 \cdot -2 = 24, 24 \cdot -2 = -48, -48 \cdot -2 = 96$.

   (c) If the common ratio is r, the sequence is $1, r, r^2, r^3$. So, $r^2 = 6$ and $r = \pm\sqrt{6}$. The sequence is $1, \sqrt{6}, 6, 6\sqrt{6}$ or $1, -\sqrt{6}, 6, -6\sqrt{6}$. Since $\sqrt{6} = 6^{\frac{1}{2}}$, you can write the two solutions as $1, 6^{\frac{1}{2}}, 6, 6^{\frac{3}{2}}$ or $1, -6^{\frac{1}{2}}$, $6, -6^{\frac{3}{2}}$.

   (d) The sequence is $1, r, r^2, r^3$ So, $r^3 = 125 \longrightarrow r = 5$. The terms are $1, 1 \cdot 5 = 5, 5 \cdot 5 = 25, 25 \cdot 5 = 125$.

   (e) The sequence is $1, 5, 25, 125$. Counting by one-third terms, $1, 125^{\frac{1}{3}}, 125^{\frac{2}{3}}, 125^{\frac{3}{3}}$. So, $125^{\frac{2}{3}} = 25$.

3. (a) $49^{\frac{1}{2}} = \sqrt{49} = 7$

   (b) $81^{\frac{3}{4}} = (81^{\frac{1}{4}})^3 = (\sqrt[4]{81})^3 = 3^3 = 27$

   (c) $8^{-\frac{4}{3}} = \frac{1}{8^{\frac{4}{3}}} = \frac{1}{\left(8^{\frac{1}{3}}\right)^4} = \frac{1}{2^4} = \frac{1}{16}$

   (d) $(\sqrt[4]{16})^5 = 2^5 = 32$

4. (a) You are looking for an equation in the form $f(x) = a \cdot b^x$. Write $f(2) = a \cdot b^2 = \frac{9}{2}$ and $f(3) = a \cdot b^3 = \frac{27}{2}$. Solve each equation for a:

   $$a = \frac{\frac{9}{2}}{b^2}$$

   $$a = \frac{\frac{27}{2}}{b^3}$$

   So,

   $$\frac{\frac{9}{2}}{b^2} = \frac{\frac{27}{2}}{b^3}$$

   $$\frac{9}{2} \cdot b^3 = \frac{27}{2} \cdot b^2$$

$$9b^3 = 27b^2$$
$$9b^3 - 27b^2 = 0$$
$$9b^2(b - 3) = 0$$

So $b = 0$ or $b = 3$. But $b > 0$, so $b = 3$. Substitute to find a:

$$f(2) = a \cdot 3^2 = \frac{9}{2} \longrightarrow 9a = \frac{9}{2} \longrightarrow a = \frac{1}{2}$$

Therefore $f(x) = \frac{1}{2}(3)^x$.

(b)

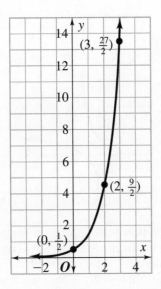

5. (a)

x	$g(x)$	$\div$
0	-2	$\frac{-20}{-2} = 10$
1	-20	$\frac{-200}{-20} = 10$
2	-200	$\frac{-2000}{-200} = 10$
3	-2000	10

To find the next term, you multiply by 10. So,

$$g(x) = \begin{cases} -2 & \text{if } x = 0 \\ 10 \cdot g(x - 1) & \text{if } x > 0 \end{cases}$$

(b) A closed-form definition will be in the form $g(x) = a \cdot b^x$. $g(0) = -2 = a \cdot b^0$. So, $a = -2$. Substitute to find b: $g(1) = -20 = -2 \cdot b^1 \longrightarrow b = 10$. The closed-form definition is

$$g(x) = -2(10)^x$$

(c) $g(4) = -2(10)^4 = -2(10{,}000) = -20{,}000$ and $g(6) = -2(10)^6 = -2(1{,}000{,}000) = -2{,}000{,}000$.

6. (a) If $L_4(1) = x$, then $4^x = 1$ and $x = 0$.
(b) If $L_4(64) = x$, then $4^x = 64 = 4^3$, so $x = 3$.
(c) If $L_4\left(\frac{1}{16}\right) = x$, then $4^x = \frac{1}{16} = \frac{1}{4^2} = 4^{-2}$, so $x = -2$.

7. You can find the exact or approximate value of each number by using your calculator and the change-of-base formula or by using the definition of $\log_b (x)$.

$$\log_2 (16) = 4$$
$$\log 5 \approx 0.699$$
$$\log_3 (8) = \frac{\log 8}{\log 3} \approx 1.893$$
$$\log_4 \left(\frac{1}{8}\right) = -\frac{3}{2}$$
$$\log_{\frac{1}{2}} (16) = -4$$

Arrange the numbers from smallest to largest:

$$\log_{\frac{1}{2}} (16), \log_4 \left(\frac{1}{8}\right), \log 5, \log_3 (8), \log_2 (16)$$

8. (a)
$$\log x - \log 5 = \log 15$$
$$\log \left(\frac{x}{5}\right) = \log 15$$
$$\frac{x}{5} = 15$$
$$x = 15 \cdot 5 = 75$$

(b)
$$\log_2 (x - 1) + \log_2 (x + 1) = 3$$
$$\log_2 ((x - 1)(x + 1)) = 3$$
$$\log_2 (x^2 - 1) = 3$$
$$x^2 - 1 = 2^3$$
$$x^2 - 1 = 8$$
$$x^2 = 9$$
$$x = \pm 3$$

-3 cannot be a solution because you cannot take the log of a negative number and $x - 1 < 0$ if $x = -3$. The only solution is $x = 3$.

(c)
$$5^x = 7$$
$$\log (5^x) = \log 7$$
$$x \log 5 = \log 7$$
$$x = \frac{\log 7}{\log 5}$$
$$x \approx 1.209$$

(d)
$$3 \cdot 2^x = 20$$
$$2^x = \frac{20}{3}$$
$$\log 2^x = \log \left(\frac{20}{3}\right)$$
$$x \log 2 = \log \left(\frac{20}{3}\right)$$
$$x = \frac{\log \left(\frac{20}{3}\right)}{\log 2}$$
$$= \frac{\log 20 - \log 3}{\log 2}$$
$$x \approx 2.737$$

9. (a)

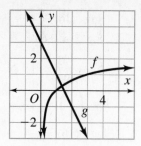

(b) The graphs intersect in one point. There is one solution.

(c) Find the point of intersection: $x \approx 1.36$

CHAPTER TEST

1. $(2^3)^{\frac{1}{3}} = 2^{3 \cdot \frac{1}{3}} = 2^1 = 2 \neq 1$. The correct choice is **A**.

2. Use the Laws of Exponents: $3^{m+1} = 3^m \cdot 3^1 = 2 \cdot 3 = 6$. The correct choice is **D**.

3. A. $25^{\frac{1}{2}} = \sqrt{25} = 5$

B. $4^{-2} = \frac{1}{4^2} = \frac{1}{16}$

C. $\log_2 (8) = 3$ because $2^3 = 8$

D. $\log_{\frac{1}{2}} (8) = -3$ because $\left(\frac{1}{2}\right)^{-3} = 2^3 = 8$

So, **D** is the smallest.

4. Use the Laws of Logarithms. The only choice that does not work is **C** because $\log (a \cdot b) = \log (a) + \log (b)$ not $\log (a) \cdot \log (b)$.

5. By definition, $y = \log_3 (x)$ means $3^y = x$. The only choice that solves this equation is (9,2) because $3^2 = 9$. The correct choice is **C**.

6. (a)

x	$h(x)$	$\div$
0	6	$\frac{3}{6} = \frac{1}{2}$
1	3	$\frac{\frac{3}{2}}{3} = \frac{1}{2}$
2	$\frac{3}{2}$	$\frac{\frac{3}{4}}{\frac{3}{2}} = \frac{1}{2}$
3	$\frac{3}{4}$	$\frac{\frac{3}{8}}{\frac{3}{4}} = \frac{1}{2}$
4	$\frac{3}{8}$	

(b)

$$h(x) = \begin{cases} 6 & \text{if } x = 0 \\ \frac{1}{2} \cdot h(x-1) & \text{if } x > 0 \end{cases}$$

(c) Write a function in the form $h(x) = a \cdot b^x$. Since $h(0) = 6$, $a \cdot b^0 = 6$ and $a = 6$. Since $h(1) = 3$ and $h(1) = 6 \cdot b^1$, $b = \frac{3}{6} = \frac{1}{2}$. The closed-form definition is

$$h(x) = 6\left(\frac{1}{2}\right)^x$$

(d) $h(8) = 6\left(\frac{1}{2}\right)^8 = 6 \cdot \frac{1}{256} = \frac{3}{128}$

7. (a)(i)

x	$f(x)$
-1	$\frac{1}{4}$
0	1
$\frac{1}{2}$	2
1	4
2	16

(ii)

x	$g(x)$
$\frac{1}{4}$	-1
1	0
2	$\frac{1}{2}$
4	1

(b)

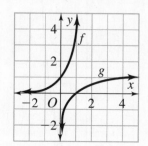

(c) The graph is increasing from left to right.

(d) The graph is increasing from left to right.

8. (a) By definition, $N = \log_2 (28)$ if $2^N = 28$. Since $16 < 28 < 32 \longrightarrow 2^4 < 2^N < 2^5$, N must be between $j = 4$ and $k = 5$.

(b) $\log_2 (7) = \log_2 \left(\frac{28}{4}\right) = \log_2 (28) - \log_2 (4) = N - 2$

(c) $\log_2 (28) = \frac{\log (28)}{\log (2)} \approx 4.807$

9. (a)

$$x \cdot 16^{\frac{1}{2}} = 64^{\frac{4}{3}}$$
$$x \cdot 4 = (64^{\frac{1}{3}})^4$$
$$4x = 4^4$$
$$x = 4^3$$
$$= 64$$

(b)

$$45 = 5 \cdot 27^x$$
$$9 = 27^x$$
$$3^2 = (3^3)^x$$
$$3^2 = 3^{3x}$$
$$2 = 3x$$
$$\frac{2}{3} = x$$

(c)

$$2 \cdot 7^x = 24$$
$$7^x = 12$$
$$\log (7^x) = \log (12)$$
$$x \log (7) = \log (12)$$
$$x = \frac{\log (12)}{\log (7)}$$
$$\approx 1.277$$

(d)
$$\log(x) + \log(x-2) = \log(8)$$
$$\log(x(x-2)) = \log(8)$$
$$\log(x^2 - 2x) = \log(8)$$
$$x^2 - 2x = 8$$
$$x^2 - 2x - 8 = 0$$
$$(x-4)(x+2) = 0$$
$$x = 4 \text{ or } x = -2$$

But, $x \neq -2$ because you cannot take the log of a negative number. So, $x = 4$.

10. Write an exponential equation:

$$M = 10{,}000(1.055)^n$$

where M is the amount of money in the account after n years. You want to know when $M = 15{,}000$. Use logarithms to solve the equation:

$$10{,}000(1.055)^n = 15{,}000$$
$$1.055^n = 1.5$$
$$\log(1.055^n) = \log(1.5)$$
$$n\log(1.055) = \log(1.5)$$
$$n = \frac{\log(1.5)}{\log(1.055)}$$
$$\approx 7.573$$

So, it will take 8 years for the money to reach $15,000 because the interest is applied annually.

11. Use the definition of the function to write an expression for the left side of the equation:

$$f(m) \cdot f(n) = b^m \cdot b^n$$

Then use the Laws of Exponents:

$$b^m \cdot b^n = b^{m+n}$$

Use the definition of the function:

$$b^{m+n} = f(m+n)$$

This gives the expression on the right side of the equation, so $f(m) \cdot f(n) = f(m+n)$.

INVESTIGATION 6A   BASIC GRAPHS, TRANSLATIONS, AND DILATIONS

6.1   Getting Started

For You to Explore

1.

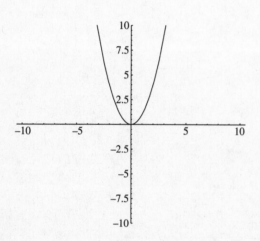

2. (a) This is the graph of $y = x^2$ shifted 5 units down.

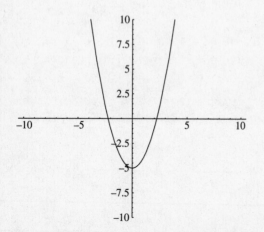

(b) This is the graph of $y = x^2$ shifted 5 units to the left.

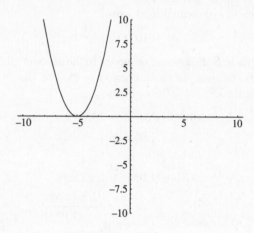

(c) This is the graph of $y = x^2$ shifted 5 units up.

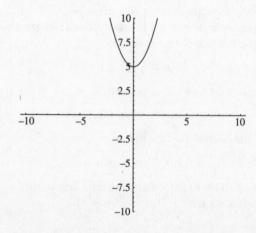

(d) This is the graph of $y = x^2$ shifted 3 units up and 2 units to the left.

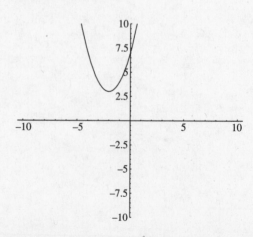

3.

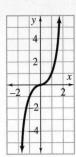

4. (a) This is the same as the graph of $y = x^3$ shifted 5 units down.

(b) This is the same as the graph of $y = x^3$ shifted 5 units left.

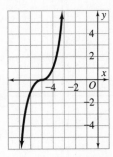

(c) This is the same as the graph of $y = x^3$ shifted 5 units up.

(d) This is the same as the graph of $y = x^3$ shifted left 2 units and up 3 units.

5. The graph of $y = x^2$ has the y-axis as a line of symmetry, so if you were to fold the graph along the y-axis, the two halves of the graph would match up. The graph of $y = x^3$ has rotational symmetry. If you rotate the graph of $y = x^3$ 180° around the origin, the rotated image will coincide with the original graph.

The graph of $y = x^2$ passes through quadrants I and II, and the graph of $y = x^3$ passes through quadrants I and III.

When you zoom in near the origin, the two graphs both begin to look the same for positive x-values. Away from the origin, it's evident that the y-values of the graph of $y = x^3$ are negative for negative x-values, but that the graph of $y = x^2$ only has positive y-values. In quadrant I, you can see that the graph of $y = x^3$ is steeper than the graph of $y = x^2$ away from the origin.

6.

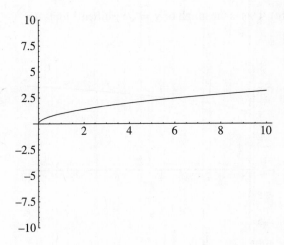

7. (a) This is the graph of $y = \sqrt{x}$ shifted 5 units down.

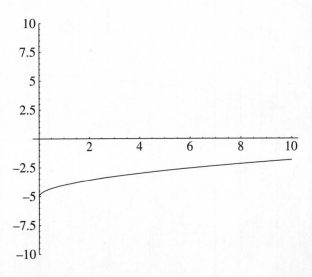

(b) This is the graph of $y = \sqrt{x}$ shifted 5 units to the left.

8.

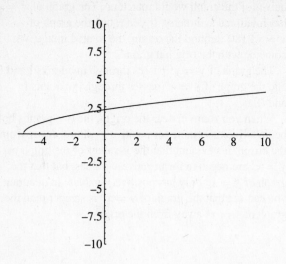

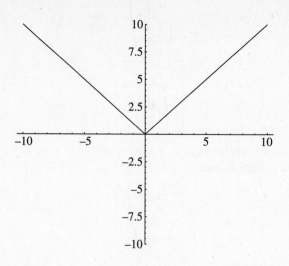

(c) This is the graph of $y = \sqrt{x}$ shifted 5 units up.

9. (a) This is the graph of $y = |x|$ shifted 5 units down.

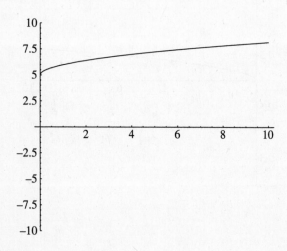

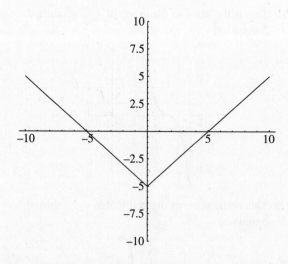

(d) This is the graph of $y = \sqrt{x}$ shifted 3 units up and 2 units to the left.

(b) This is the graph of $y = |x|$ shifted 5 units to the left.

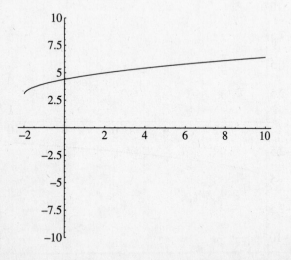

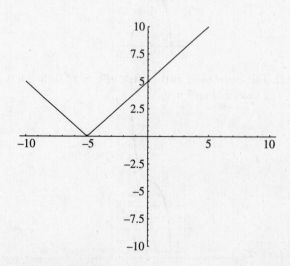

(c) This is the graph of $y = |x|$ shifted 5 units up.

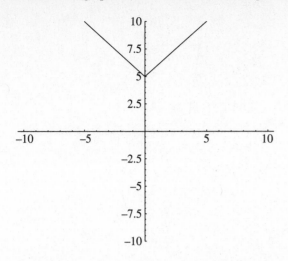

(d) This is the graph of $y = |x|$ shifted 3 units up and 2 units to the left.

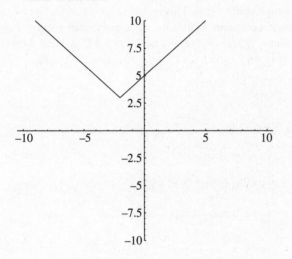

10. (a)

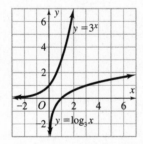

(b) The graphs are reflections of each other over the line with equation $y = x$. If you were to fold the paper along the line with equation $y = x$, the graph of $y = 3^x$ would match up with the graph of $y = \log_3 x$. This property is characteristic of functions that are inverses of each other.

11. Only one linear equation passes through two points. In this example, the linear equation is $y = 0$. However, infinitely many quadratic equations, cubic equations and other polynomials are possible. One quadratic equation is $y = (x + 3)(x - 6)$ and one cubic equation is

$y = x(x + 3)(x - 6)$. You can multiply the right side of either equation by any polynomial and it will still pass through these two points. For example, $y = 2(x + 3)(x - 6)$ and $y = (x^4 + x)(x + 3)(x - 6)$ still pass through these points.

On Your Own

12. (a), (c)

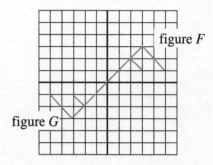

(b) • Connect endpoints $(0, 0)$ and $(-3, -3)$.
   • Connect endpoints $(-2, -2)$ and $(-3, -1)$.
   • Connect endpoints $(-3, -3)$ and $(-5, -1)$.

(d) If you were to rotate F $180°$ around the origin, you'd get G. Or you might also see that if you were to reflect F over the y-axis and G over the x-axis, the two reflected images would coincide.

13. It has $180°$ rotational symmetry. If you were to turn the paper upside down, the graph of O would look the same as it does when the paper is right side up.

14. (a), (c)

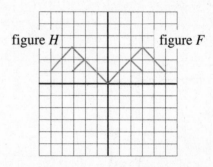

(b) • Connect endpoints $(0, 0)$ and $(-3, 3)$.
   • Connect endpoints $(-2, 2)$ and $(-3, 1)$.
   • Connect endpoints $(-3, 3)$ and $(-5, 1)$.

(d) If you were to reflect F over the y-axis, you'd get H.

15. It has the y-axis as a line of symmetry. If you were to fold the paper along the y-axis, the two halves of figure E would coincide.

16. (a)

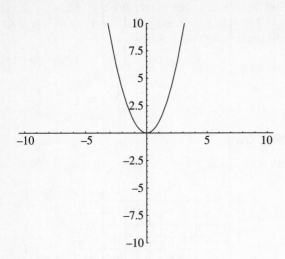

(b)

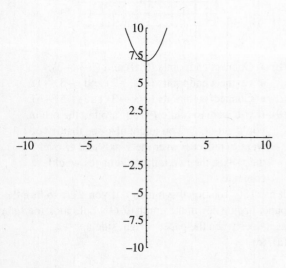

(c)

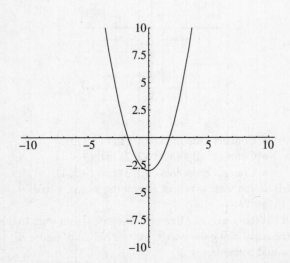

(d)

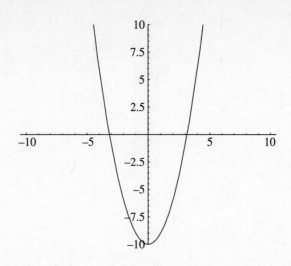

17. The value of C shifts the graph vertically. When C is positive, the graph shifts up; when C is negative, the graph shifts down. This makes sense because, since C is just a constant, it adds the same number to every y-value. Thus, every y-value will be 3 more if C is 3 and 4 less if C is -4.

18. (a)

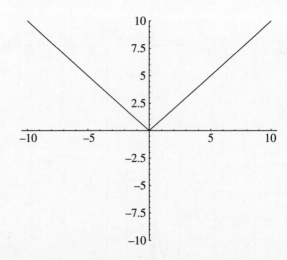

(b)

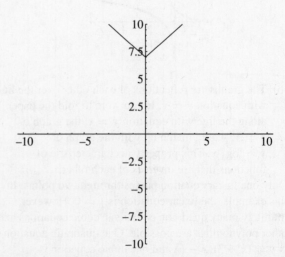

(c)

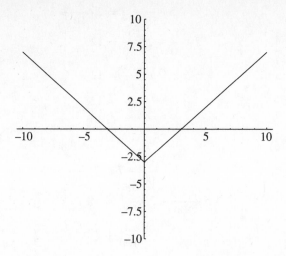

(d)

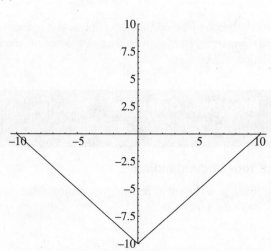

19. The parameter C has the same effect on the graph of $y = |x|$ as on the graph of $y = x^2$. C simply shifts the graph vertically. When C is positive, the graph shifts up. When C is negative, the graph shifts down.

20. (a) This is the graph of $y = 3^x$ shifted 5 units down.

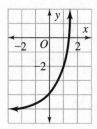

(b) This is the graph of $y = 3^x$ shifted 5 units left.

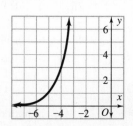

(c) This is the graph of $y = 3^x$ shifted 5 units up.

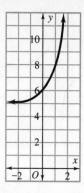

(d) This is the graph of $y = 3^x$ shifted 2 units left and 3 units up.

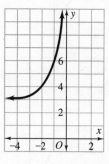

21. (a)

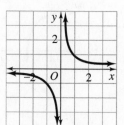

(b) The graph of $y = \frac{1}{x}$ can never intersect the y-axis, because division by 0 is undefined. To see why it can never intersect the x-axis, assume that it does and see what happens. If the graph does intersect the x-axis, then $\frac{1}{x}$ is equal to 0 for some value of x, say $x = a$. This a cannot be equal to 0, because division by zero is undefined. That means you can multiply both sides of the equation by a in order to try to solve it. That would give you $1 = 0$, which is impossible. So the graph cannot intersect the x-axis either.

22. (a) This is the graph of $y = \frac{1}{x}$ shifted 5 units down.

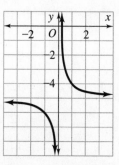

(b) This is the graph of $y = \frac{1}{x}$ shifted 5 units left.

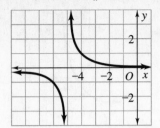

(c) This is the graph of $y = \frac{1}{x}$ shifted 5 units up.

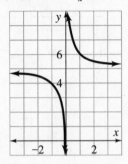

(d) This is the graph of $y = \frac{1}{x}$ shifted 2 units left and 3 units up.

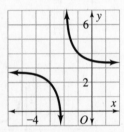

23.

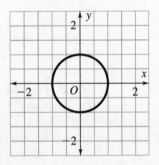

Maintain Your Skills

24. (a)
$$5x - 7 = 2x + 5$$
$$3x = 12$$
$$x = 4$$

(b)
$$5 \cdot \frac{x}{3} - 7 = 2 \cdot \frac{x}{3} + 5$$
$$5 \cdot \frac{x}{3} - 2 \cdot \frac{x}{3} = 12$$
$$\frac{3x}{3} = 12$$
$$x = 12$$

(c)
$$5 \cdot \frac{x}{10} - 7 = 2 \cdot \frac{x}{10} + 5$$
$$5 \cdot \frac{x}{10} - 2 \cdot \frac{x}{10} = 12$$
$$\frac{3x}{10} = 12$$
$$3x = 120$$
$$x = 40$$

(d)
$$5 \cdot \frac{x}{100} - 7 = 2 \cdot \frac{x}{100} + 5$$
$$5 \cdot \frac{x}{100} - 2 \cdot \frac{x}{100} = 12$$
$$\frac{3x}{100} = 12$$
$$3x = 1200$$
$$x = 400$$

25. If the solution to the original equation is $x = s$, then when x is replaced by $\frac{x}{C}$ to make a new equation, the new solution will be $x = Cs$.

6.2 More Basic Graphs: $x^2 + y^2 = 1$, $y = x^3 \pm x$

Check Your Understanding

1. (a) First, you'll want to find the y-coordinate that goes with the x-coordinate $\frac{4}{5}$.

$$\left(\frac{4}{5}\right)^2 + y^2 = 1$$
$$\frac{16}{25} + y^2 = \frac{25}{25}$$
$$y^2 = \frac{9}{25}$$
$$y = \pm\frac{3}{5}$$

This means that the points $\left(\frac{4}{5}, \frac{3}{5}\right)$ and $\left(\frac{4}{5}, -\frac{3}{5}\right)$ are both on the unit circle.

(b) $\left(-\frac{4}{5}, \frac{3}{5}\right)$, $\left(-\frac{4}{5}, -\frac{3}{5}\right)$, $\left(\frac{3}{5}, \frac{4}{5}\right)$, $\left(\frac{3}{5}, -\frac{4}{5}\right)$, $\left(-\frac{3}{5}, \frac{4}{5}\right)$, and $\left(-\frac{3}{5}, -\frac{4}{5}\right)$ are all on the unit circle.

2. (a) Use the equation to find the x-coordinate that goes with this y-coordinate.

$$\left(\frac{5}{13}\right)^2 + x^2 = 1$$
$$\frac{25}{169} + x^2 = \frac{169}{169}$$
$$x^2 = \frac{144}{169}$$
$$x = \pm\frac{12}{13}$$

So $\left(\frac{12}{13}, \frac{5}{13}\right)$ and $\left(-\frac{12}{13}, \frac{5}{13}\right)$ are both on the unit circle.

(b) Use the equation to find the y-coordinate that goes with this x-coordinate.

$$\left(\frac{8}{17}\right)^2 + y^2 = 1$$

$$\frac{64}{289} + y^2 = \frac{289}{289}$$

$$y^2 = \frac{225}{289}$$

$$y = \pm\frac{15}{17}$$

So $\left(\frac{8}{17}, \frac{15}{17}\right)$ and $\left(\frac{8}{17}, -\frac{15}{17}\right)$ are both on the unit circle.

3. Mariko noticed several patterns in the points she found for the unit circle. All the coordinates were fractions, and the x and y-coordinates for any point had the same denominator. That denominator was the largest of the three numbers in a Pythagorean triple, and the numerators were the other two numbers in the triple. The reason this is a sensible way to find coordinates for the unit circle is that Pythagorean triples are numbers a, b, and c such that $a^2 + b^2 = c^2$. If you divide each side of that equation by c^2, you get

$$\frac{a^2}{c^2} + \frac{b^2}{c^2} = 1.$$

That equation can be rewritten as

$$\left(\frac{a}{c}\right)^2 + \left(\frac{b}{c}\right)^2 = 1.$$

That result shows you that the point $\left(\frac{a}{c}, \frac{b}{c}\right)$ satisfies the equation for the unit circle, $x^2 + y^2 = 1$.

4. (a) $f(-x) = (-x)^2 = x^2 = f(x)$.
   (b) The graph of $y = x^2$ has the y-axis as a line of symmetry, so it is an even function.

5. (a)

$$f(-x) = (-x)^3 + (-x)$$

$$= -x^3 - x$$

$$= -(x^3 + x)$$

$$= -f(x)$$

   (b) The graph of f has $180°$ rotational symmetry. That means that if you were to replace each point (x, y) by the point $(-x, -y)$, you'd get the same graph.

6. The following functions are even.

   • $y = x^2$—See Exercise 4.
   • $y = |x|$—If $f(x) = |x|$, then $f(-x) = |-x| = |x| = f(x)$.

   The following functions are odd.

   • $y = x$—If $f(x) = x$, then $f(-x) = -x = -f(x)$
   • $y = \frac{1}{x}$—If $f(x) = \frac{1}{x}$, then $f(-x) = \frac{1}{-x} = -\frac{1}{x} = -f(x)$
   • $y = x^3$—If $f(x) = x^3$, then $f(-x) = (-x)^3 = -x^3 = -f(x)$
   • $y = x^3 - x$—If $f(x) = x^3 - x$, then $f(-x) = (-x)^3 - (-x) = -x^3 + x = -(x^3 - x) = -f(x)$
   • $y = x^3 + x$—See Exercise 5.

The following functions are neither even nor odd.

   • $y = \sqrt{x}$—If $f(x) = \sqrt{x}$, then $f(-x) = \sqrt{-x}$ is only defined for $x \le 0$. It isn't equal to $f(x)$ or $-f(x)$.
   • $y = b^x (b > 0, b \ne 1)$—If $f(x) = b^x$, then $f(-x) = b^{-x} = \frac{1}{b^x}$. It isn't equal to $f(x)$ or $-f(x)$.
   • $y = \log_b x (b > 0, b \ne 1)$—If $f(x) = \log_b x$, then $f(-x) = \log_b(-x)$ is only defined for $x < 0$. It isn't equal to $f(x)$ or $-f(x)$.

The graph of $x^2 + y^2 = 1$ is not the graph of a function, so it is neither even nor odd.

7. To find the x-intercepts for the graph, set $y = 0$. That's because you want to find all of the points on the x-axis (which has equation $y = 0$) that satisfy the graph's equation. You'll get an equation that you can solve by factoring.

$$0 = x^3 + x$$

$$0 = x(x^2 + 1)$$

$x = 0$ is the only real-number solution to the equation. (i and $-i$ are two complex solutions.)

8. (a)

x	$x - 3$	$(x - 3)^2$
-1	-4	16
0	-3	9
1	-2	4
2	-1	1
3	0	0
4	1	1
5	2	4
6	3	9
7	4	16

   (b)

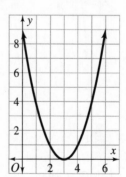

   (c) The graph of $y = (x - 3)^2$ is the same as the graph of $y = x^2$ shifted 3 units to the right

On Your Own

9. (a)

$$g(-x) = (-x)^3 - (-x)$$

$$= -x^3 + x$$

$$= -(x^3 - x)$$

$$= -g(x)$$

(b) The graph of $y = x^3 - x$ has $180°$ rotational symmetry. That means that if you were to replace each point (x, y) by the point $(-x, -y)$, you'd get the same graph.

10. (a) Near the origin, the x^3-term in the equation $y = x^3 - x$ is much smaller (in absolute value) than the $-x$-term, so it's negligible in comparison. It has much less effect on the size of the y-coordinate. Look at $x = 0.001$. In that case, $y = 0.000000001 - 0.001 = -0.000999999 \approx -0.001$.

(b) Away from the origin, the x^3-term in the equation $y = x^3 - x$ is much larger (in absolute value) than the $-x$-term, so the $-x$-term is negligible in comparison to the x^3 term. Look at $x = 1000$. In that case, $y = 1,000,000,000 - 1000 = 999,999,000 \approx 1,000,000,000$

11. To find the x-intercepts, set $y = 0$ and solve for x by factoring.

$$0 = x^3 - x$$
$$0 = x(x^2 - 1)$$
$$0 = x(x - 1)(x + 1)$$
$$x = 0, 1, -1$$

There are three x-intercepts: $(-1, 0)$, $(0, 0)$, and $(1, 0)$.

12. (a)

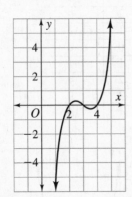

(b)

$$0 = (x - 3)^3 - (x - 3)$$
$$= (x - 3)[(x - 3)^2 - 1]$$
$$= (x - 3)[(x - 3) - 1][(x - 3) + 1]$$
$$= (x - 3)(x - 4)(x - 2)$$
$$x = 3, 4, 2$$

The x-intercepts are $(2, 0)$, $(3, 0)$, and $(4, 0)$.

(c) The graph of $y = (x - 3)^3 - (x - 3)$ is the same as the graph of $y = x^3 - x$ shifted 3 units to the right.

13. Start with the distance formula,

$$\sqrt{(x - 0)^2 + (y - 0)^2} = 5$$

Square both sides to get an equation for the circle.

$$x^2 + y^2 = 25$$

14. Start with the distance formula,

$$\sqrt{(x - 3)^2 + (y - 0)^2} = 5$$

Square both sides to get an equation for the circle.

$$(x - 3)^2 + y^2 = 25$$

15. (a) $(x - 6)^2 + y^2 = 25$
(b) $(x + 3)^2 + y^2 = 16$
(c) $x^2 + (y + 4)^2 = 1$
(d) $(x - 3)^2 + (y + 4)^2 = 1$
(e) $(x + 2)^2 + (y - 3)^2 = 9$
(f) $(x - a)^2 + (y - b)^2 = r^2$

16.

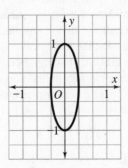

This is the same as the graph of $x^2 + y^2 = 1$ after dilating by a factor of $\frac{1}{3}$ in the x-direction. This kind of graph is called an *ellipse*.

17. Whenever you replace x by $x - c$, where c is a positive constant, the graph shifts to the right by c units. The correct answer choice is **D**.

Maintain Your Skills

18. (a) You can solve $x^2 + 5x - 14 = 0$ by factoring.

$$x^2 + 5x - 14 = 0$$
$$(x + 7)(x - 2) = 0$$
$$x = -7, 2$$

(b) If you substitute $M = x - 3$ into the equation $(x - 3)^2 + 5(x - 3) - 14 = 0$, you will get $M^2 + 5M - 14 = 0$. From the previous part, you know then that $M = -7, 2$. This means that $x - 3 = -7, 2$ and $x = -4, 5$.

(c) If you substitute $N = x - 5$ into the equation $(x - 5)^2 + 5(x - 5) - 14 = 0$, you will get $N^2 + 5N - 14 = 0$. From part (a), you know then that $N = -7, 2$. This means that $x - 5 = -7, 2$ and $x = -2, 7$.

(d) If you substitute $P = x + 2$ into the equation $(x + 2)^2 + 5(x + 2) - 14 = 0$, you will get $P^2 + 5P - 14 = 0$. From part (a), you know then that $P = -7, 2$. This means that $x + 2 = -7, 2$ and $x = -9, 0$.

19. If the solutions to the original equation are $a, b, c, \ldots$, the solutions to the equation where the variable x has been replaced by $x - C$ will be $a + C, b + C, c + C, \ldots$.

Check Your Understanding

1. (a)

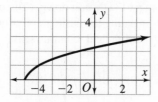

$x = M - 5$	M	$y = \sqrt{M}$
-5	0	0
-4	1	1
-1	4	2
4	9	3
11	16	4
20	25	5

(b) The graph of $y = \sqrt{x + 5}$ is the same as the graph of $y = \sqrt{x}$ shifted 5 units to the left.

(c) The domain is $x \geq -5$ and the range is $y \geq 0$.

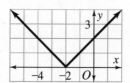

2. (a)

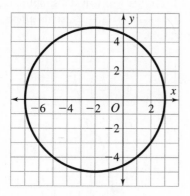

(b)

(c)

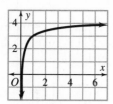

(d)

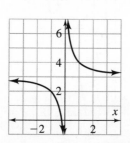

3. (a)

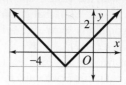

(b)

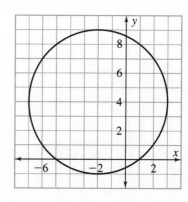

(c)

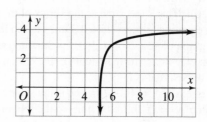

(d)

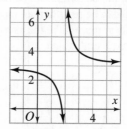

4. You should disagree with Walter. He did not replace every instance of x in the equation of the basic graph with $x - 2$. If he were to graph his equation, his graph would be shifted two units below the graph he actually wanted.

5. (a) The graph of $y = (x - 2)^3 + 6(x - 2)^2 + 11(x - 2) + 7$ will be the same as the graph of $y = x^3 + 6x^2 + 11x + 7$ shifted two units to the right.

(b)

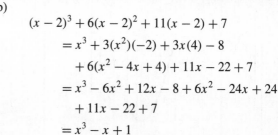

$$(x - 2)^3 + 6(x - 2)^2 + 11(x - 2) + 7$$
$$= x^3 + 3(x^2)(-2) + 3x(4) - 8$$
$$\quad + 6(x^2 - 4x + 4) + 11x - 22 + 7$$
$$= x^3 - 6x^2 + 12x - 8 + 6x^2 - 24x + 24$$
$$\quad + 11x - 22 + 7$$
$$= x^3 - x + 1$$

(c) Start with the basic graph for the equation $y = x^3 - x$. Shift that graph up 1 unit, and you have the graph of $y = x^3 - x + 1$ which is also the graph of $y = (x-2)^3 + 6(x-2)^2 + 11(x-2) + 7$. The graph of $y = x^3 + 6x^2 + 11x + 7$ is the same as this one, but shifted two units to the left. Here's what your graph should look like.

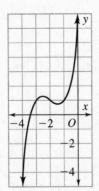

6. (a) The graph of $y = (x+3)^2$ is the same as the graph of $y = x^2$ shifted 3 units to the left, so its vertex is $(-3, 0)$. (That's the same as the vertex of the parabola with equation $y = x^2$ shifted 3 units to the left.)
   (b) The graph of $y - 2 = (x+3)^2$ is the same as the graph of $y = x^2$ shifted 3 units to the left and 2 units up, so its vertex is $(-3, 2)$.
   (c) The graph of $y = (x+h)^2 + k$ is the same as the graph of $y = x^2$ shifted h units to the left and k units up, so its vertex is $(-h, k)$.

7. (a) To sketch the graph of $y = x^2 + 6x + 9$, it will help to notice that the quadratic can be factored, and that this equation can be rewritten as $y = (x+3)^2$. That means that its graph will be the same as the graph of $y = x^2$ shifted 3 units to the left.

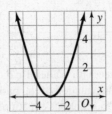

   (b) The graph of $y = x^2 + 6x + 7$ must be the same as the graph of $y = x^2 + 6x + 9$ shifted 2 units down.

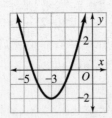

On Your Own

8. (a) To graph $y = (x-2)^3 + (x-2)$, translate the basic graph of $y = x^3 + x$ 2 units to the right.

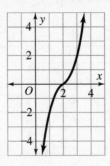

   (b) To graph $y + 1 = (x-2)^3 + (x-2)$, translate the graph from part (a) 1 unit down. (You could also think of translating the basic graph of $y = x^3 + x$ 2 units to the right and 1 unit down.)

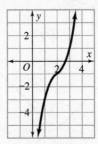

   (c) $y = (x-2)^3 + x - 3$ is just a simplified form of $y + 1 = (x-2)^3 + (x-2)$, so its graph is the same as in part (b).

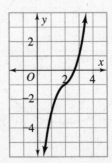

   (d) $y = x^3 - 6x^2 + 13x - 11$ is the expanded form of $y = (x-2)^3 + x - 3$, so its graph is the same as in parts (b) and (c).

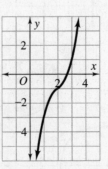

9. (a) The slope is 3.

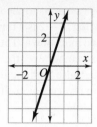

(b) The slope is 3.

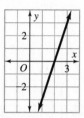

(c) The slope is 3.

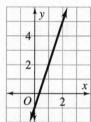

(d) All of the graphs are lines, and they're all parallel to each other with slope 3. The graph in part (b) is the same as the graph in part (a) shifted 2 units to the right. The graph in part (c) is the same as the graph in part (b) shifted 5 units up or the graph in part (a) shifted 2 units to the right and 5 units up.

10. (a)

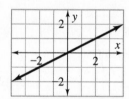

(b) $y = \frac{1}{2}(x - 3)$

(c) $y = \frac{1}{2}(x - 3) + 1$

11. (a) The line through the origin of slope 4 has equation $y = 4x$. If you translate that line 3 units to the right and 1 unit up, it will pass through the point $(3, 1)$. That means its equation must be $y = 4(x - 3) + 1$ or $y = 4x - 11$.

(b) The line through the origin of slope $\frac{2}{3}$ has equation $y = \frac{2}{3}x$. If you translate that line 2 units to the left and 1 unit down, it will pass through the point $(-2, -1)$. That means its equation must be $y = \frac{2}{3}(x + 2) - 1$ or $y = \frac{2}{3}x + \frac{1}{3}$ (or even $3y - 2x = 1$).

(c) The line through the origin of slope m has equation $y = mx$. If you translate that line h units to the right and k units up, it will pass through the point (h, k). That means its equation must be $y = m(x - h) + k$.

12. (a) The graph of $y = (x - 3)^2 + 6(x - 3) + 7$ will be the same as the graph of $y = x^2 + 6x + 7$ shifted 3 units to the right. That's because every instance of x in the equation $y = x^2 + 6x + 7$ has been replaced by $M = x - 3$. So if you're looking at a graph of $y = M^2 + 6M + 7$ and want to use it to graph $y = (x - 3)^2 + 6(x - 3) + 7$, you'll end up shifting each point 3 units to the right because $x = M + 3$.

(b) The graph of $y - 2 = (x - 3)^2 + 6(x - 3) + 7$ will be the same as the graph of $y = (x - 3)^2 + 6(x - 3) + 7$ shifted 2 units up. The effect of replacing y in the equation $y = (x - 3)^2 + 6(x - 3) + 7$ by $N = y - 2$ means that if you're looking at a graph of $N = (x - 3)^2 + 6(x - 3) + 7$ and want to use it to graph $y - 2 = (x - 3)^2 + 6(x - 3) + 7$, you'll end up shifting each point 2 units up because $y = N + 2$.

(c)

$$y - 2 = (x - 3)^2 + 6(x - 3) + 7$$
$$y = x^2 - 6x + 9 + 6x - 18 + 7 + 2$$
$$y = x^2$$

13. The two equations $y - 1 = 4(x - 3)$ and $y + 3 = 4(x - 2)$ are really the same. To see this, solve each equation for y. They both simplify to $y = 4x - 11$, so they are the same, and Susan is incorrect in thinking that there are two different lines that meet the requirements.

14. In Derman's way of thinking, the original basic graph of the parabola, in the picture below, is the graph of $y = M^2$. The horizontal axis is the M-axis, and the line with equation $M = 0$ is the y-axis *with respect to* that M-axis.

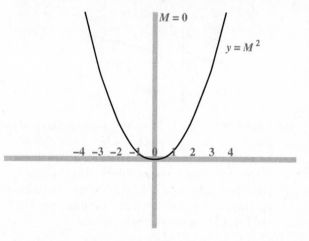

When he thinks about moving the coordinate axes, he's picturing the relationship $M = x - 3$ in this way:

−4	−3	−2	−1	0	1	2	3	4
−1	0	1	2	3	4	5	6	7

By looking at the corresponding values of M (above the number line) and x (below the number line), you can see that the M-value is always 3 less than the x-value, so $M = x - 3$. You can see that the x-axis is the image of the M-axis after a translation of three units left.

Now the y-axis with respect to the x-axis is in a different place. The y-axis should now be the line with equation $x = 0$. The old y-axis (with respect to the M-axis) now has equation $x = 3$. It's still useful to know the equation of this line, because it's the line of symmetry for the parabola in the new coordinate system.

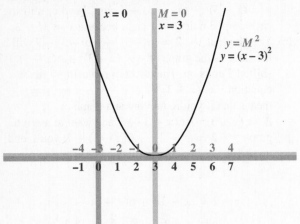

15. Start with $y = x^2$ and translate this 1 unit to the left and 2 units down. The new equation corresponding to this is $y + 2 = (x + 1)^2$. The correct answer choice is **D**.

Maintain Your Skills

16. (a) The two graphs are reflections of each other over the line with equation $y = x$. This is because the functions 3^x and $\log_3 x$ are inverses of each other.

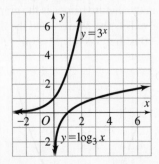

(b) The graph of $y = 3 \cdot 3^x = 3^{x+1}$ is a translation of the graph of $y = 3^x$ one unit to the left. The graph of $y = \log_3\left(\frac{x}{3}\right) = \log_3 x - 1$ is a translation of the graph of $y = \log_3 x$ one unit down. The two new graphs are reflections of each other over the line with equation $y = x$. This is because the functions $3 \cdot 3^x$ and $\log_3\left(\frac{x}{3}\right)$ are inverses of each other.

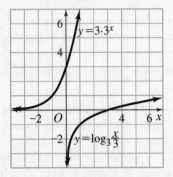

(c) The graph of $y = 9 \cdot 3^x = 3^{x+2}$ is a translation of the graph of $y = 3^x$ two units to the left. The graph of $y = \log_3\left(\frac{x}{9}\right) = \log_3 x - 2$ is a translation of the graph of $y = \log_3 x$ two units down. The two new graphs are reflections of each other over the line with equation $y = x$. This is because the functions $y = 9 \cdot 3^x$ and $y = \log_3\left(\frac{x}{9}\right)$ are inverses of each other.

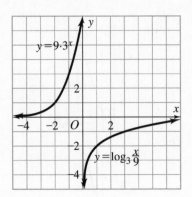

(d) The graph of $y = 27 \cdot 3^x = 3^{x+3}$ is a translation of the graph of $y = 3^x$ three units to the left. The graph of $y = \log_3\left(\frac{x}{27}\right) = \log_3 x - 3$ is a translation of the graph of $y = \log_3 x$ three units down. The two new graphs are reflections of each other over the line with equation $y = x$. This is because the functions $y = 27 \cdot 3^x$ and $y = \log_3\left(\frac{x}{27}\right)$ are inverses of each other.

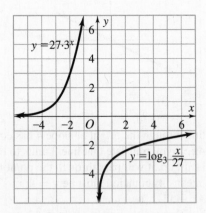

(e) The graph of $y = 3^n \cdot 3^x = 3^{x+n}$ is a translation of the graph of $y = 3^x$ n units to the left. The graph of $y = \log_3\left(\frac{x}{3^n}\right) = \log_3 x - n$ is a translation of the graph of $y = \log_3 x$ n units down. The two new graphs are reflections of each other over the line with equation $y = x$. This is because the functions $y = 3^n \cdot 3^x$ and $y = \log_3\left(\frac{x}{3^n}\right)$ are inverses of each other.

Check Your Understanding

1. (a) Complete the following table.

x	$N = x^2 + 1$	$y = \frac{N}{5}$
-2	5	1
-1	2	$\frac{2}{5}$
0	1	$\frac{1}{5}$
1	2	$\frac{2}{5}$
2	5	1
3	10	2

(b) The y-values for the graph of $5y = x^2 + 1$ are smaller by a factor of 5 when compared to the corresponding y-values for the graph of $y = x^2 + 1$. This means that the graph of $5y = x^2 + 1$ is the same as the graph of $y = x^2 + 1$ after that graph has been dilated vertically by a factor of $\frac{1}{5}$. Both of the graphs will be parabolas, and they'll have the y-axis as their line of symmetry.

(c)

2. (a)

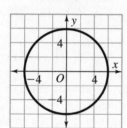

(b)

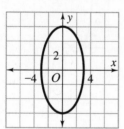

(c)

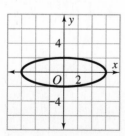

(d)

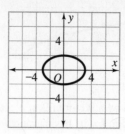

(e)

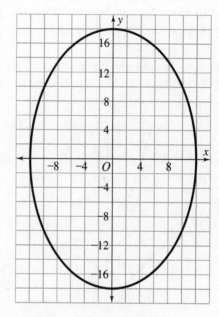

3. (a) The domain is $x \geq 0$, the range is $y \leq 0$.

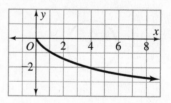

(b) The domain is $x \geq 0$, the range is $y \leq 0$.

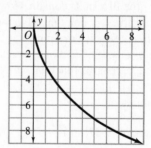

(c) The domain is $x \leq 0$, the range is $y \geq 0$.

(d) The domain is $x \le 1$, the range is $y \ge 0$.

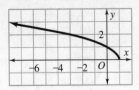

4. To dilate a graph by a factor of 2, replace every instance of x in the equation for its basic graph with $\frac{1}{2}x$. In this case, that would give you $y = \left(\frac{1}{2}x\right)^2$.

   Then to translate a graph 3 units up, replace every instance of y in the equation by $y - 3$. This gives you $y - 3 = \left(\frac{1}{2}x\right)^2$, or (to graph it more easily on a graphing calculator) $y = \left(\frac{1}{2}x\right)^2 + 3$.

   To translate a graph 4 units to the right, replace every instance of x in the equation by $x - 4$. This gives you $y = \left(\frac{1}{2}(x - 4)\right)^2 + 3$, or $y = \left(\frac{1}{2}x - 2\right)^2 + 3$.

5. (a)

   (b)

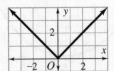

   (c)

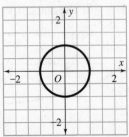

6. Both Tony and Sasha are right. A function is **even** if $f(-x) = f(x)$ for all x in its domain. However, it's also true that if you map every point (x, y) to the point $(-x, y)$, the effect of such a mapping is to reflect the figure over the y-axis. If a function is even, that reflection would map the graph of the function onto itself.

7. A function is even if $f(-x) = f(x)$ for all x in the domain of the function.

$$y = (-x)^8 + 37(-x)^6 - 71(-x)^2 + 4$$
$$= x^8 + 37x^6 - 71x^2 + 4$$

8. Reflecting a function over the y-axis is the same as mapping each point (x, y) in a graph to the point $(-x, y)$. If you do that mapping on the function $g(x)$, you'll get the same graph because $g(-x) = f(-x) + f(--x) = f(x) + f(-x) = g(x)$. In other words, $g(x)$ is an even function.

9. (a) (b)

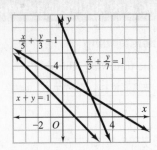

   (c) One way to find points is to set one of the variables equal to 0 and solve for the other. If $x = 0$, then $0 + \frac{y}{12} = 1$, and you have the point $(0, 12)$. If $y = 0$, then $\frac{x}{-17} + 0 = 1$, and you have the point $(-17, 0)$.

   (d) Because you can read the coordinates of the x-intercept and the y-intercept directly from the equation, $(a, 0)$ is the x-intercept and $(0, b)$ is the y-intercept.

On Your Own

10. (a) Notice that this is the basic graph of $y = x^3 + x$ after the mapping $(x, y) \mapsto (-x, y)$. The effect of such a mapping is to reflect the graph over the y-axis.

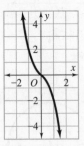

   (b) Notice that this is the basic graph of $y = x^3 - x$ after the mapping $(x, y) \mapsto (-x, y)$. The effect of such a mapping is to reflect the graph over the y-axis.

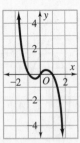

   (c) This is the same as the graph in part (a).

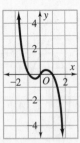

(d) This is the same as the graph in part (b).

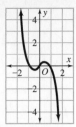

(e) This is the basic graph of $y = x^3 + x$ after the mapping $(x, y) \mapsto (-x, -y)$. The effect of such a mapping is to reflect the graph over the y-axis *and then* over the x-axis. These two reflections, when composed, are equivalent to a rotation of $180°$ around the origin. If you look at this graph upside down, it will look the same as the basic graph does right side up.

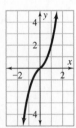

(f) This is the basic graph of $y = x^3 - x$ after the mapping $(x, y) \mapsto (-x, -y)$. As in part (e), the effect of such a mapping is to reflect the graph over the y-axis *and then* over the x-axis. These two reflections, when composed, are equivalent to a rotation of $180°$ around the origin. If you look at this graph upside down, it will look the same as the basic graph does right side up.

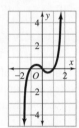

11. (a) The graph of $y = \frac{1}{-x}$ is the same as the graph of $y = \frac{1}{x}$ after it's reflected over the y-axis.

(b) The graph of $y = \frac{1}{-4x}$ is the same as the graph of $y = \frac{1}{x}$ after it's reflected over the y-axis and has been dilated horizontally by a factor of $\frac{1}{4}$.

(c) The graph of $y = \frac{4}{-x}$ is the same as the graph of $y = \frac{1}{x}$ after it's reflected over the y-axis and has been dilated vertically by a factor of 4.

(d) The graph of $-y = \frac{1}{x}$ is the same as the graph of $y = \frac{1}{x}$ after it's reflected over the x-axis. It looks the same as the graph in part (a), because for this function, $f(-x) = -f(x)$. (It's an *odd* function.)

(e) The graph of $-4y = \frac{1}{x}$ is the same as the graph of $y = \frac{1}{x}$ after it's reflected over the y-axis and has been dilated horizontally by a factor of $\frac{1}{4}$. It's the same as the graph in part (b).

(f) The graph of $-\frac{y}{4} = \frac{1}{x}$ is the same as the graph of $y = \frac{1}{x}$ after it's reflected over the y-axis and has been dilated vertically by a factor of 4. It's the same as the graph in part (c).

(g) The graph of $-y = \frac{1}{-x}$ is the same as the graph of $y = \frac{1}{x}$. Since the two reflections, shown separately in parts (a) and (d) had the same effect, when you compose the two reflections, they will undo each other. (A reflection is its own inverse.)

(h) The graph of $-\frac{y}{4} = \frac{1}{-4x}$ is the same as the graph of $y = \frac{1}{x}$. The transformations in parts (b) and (f) are inverses of each other. The shrinking in part (b) is undone by the stretching in part (f), and reflection over the y-axis is its own inverse.

12. All three of them are right. the mapping $(x, y) \mapsto (-x, -y)$ is what Tony describes. This is the mapping that results from the composition of a reflection over the y-axis (which maps x to $-x$) and a reflection over the x-axis (which maps y to $-y$). This composition of two reflections is equivalent to a $180°$ rotation around the origin.

13. The graph of $(x + 3)^2 + (y - 4)^2 = 1$ is a circle of radius 1 with center $(-3, 4)$. The graph of $(-x + 3)^2 + (-y - 4)^2 = 1$ is a circle of radius 1 with center $(3, -4)$. It's also the same as the equation $(x + 3)^2 + (y - 4)^2 = 1$ under the mapping $(x, y) \mapsto (-x, -y)$, which is equivalent to a reflection over the x-axis and then over the y-axis (or vice versa) or a rotation of $180°$ around the origin. These interpretations are both equivalent, because the mapping $(x, y) \mapsto (-x, -y)$ sends the center of the first circle to the center of the second, and doesn't have an effect on the radius.

14. (a) This is an ellipse. You can think of it as a circle of radius 6, centered at the origin, that has been dilated by a factor of $\frac{1}{3}$ horizontally and by a factor of $\frac{1}{2}$ vertically.

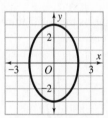

(b) This is the graph from part (a) after a translation of 1 unit to the left and 4 units up. (The ellipse is now centered at $(-1, 4)$.)

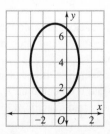

(c) This is the same as the graph from part (b). You can use the algebraic simplification to transform one of these equations into the other.

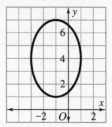

15. Reflecting over the y-axis corresponds to replacing x by $-x$. The correct answer choice is **C**.

16. Yes, the two ways of visualizing the situation are consistent. If you think of the line as "more steep," you're saying that for every one-unit increase in an x-coordinate you get a larger increase in the corresponding y-coordinates. Successive y-values in a table are farther apart. This is exactly what happens in a vertical stretch—y-values are farther apart.

17. (a) The graph of $y = (x-1)^3 + 3(x-1)^2 + 7(x-1) + 13$ is the same as the graph of $y = x^3 + 3x^2 + 7x + 13$ translated one unit to the right.

(b)
$$(x-1)^3 + 3(x-1)^2 + 7(x-1) + 13$$
$$= x^3 - 3x^2 + 3x - 1 + 3x^2$$
$$- 6x + 3 + 7x - 7 + 13$$
$$= x^3 + 4x + 8$$

(c) The graph of $\frac{1}{8}y = \left(\frac{1}{2}x\right)^3 + \left(\frac{1}{2}x\right) + 1$ is the same as the graph of $y = x^3 + x + 1$ after it has been dilated vertically by a factor of 8 and dilated horizontally by a factor of 2.

(d) This is the same as the basic graph of $y = x^3 + x$ translated up one unit.

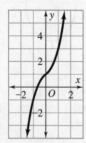

(e) Think of going backwards along the trail established in parts (a) through (d) and undoing each transformation.

Start with a sketch of the basic graph of $y = x^3 + x$. Translate it up one unit. Dilate it by a factor of $\frac{1}{2}$ horizontally and a factor of 8 vertically. Then

translate it one unit to the left, and what you'll have is the graph of $y = x^3 + 3x^2 + 7x + 13$.

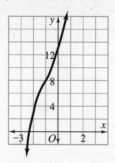

18. In Derman's way of thinking, the original basic graph of the parabola, drawn using the axes in the picture below, is the graph of $y = M^2$. The horizontal axis is the M-axis, and the line with equation $M = 0$ is the y-axis *with respect to* that M-axis.

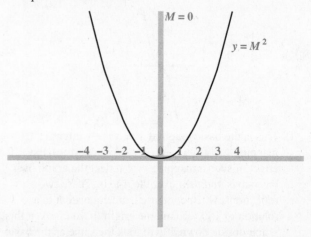

When he thinks about moving the coordinate axes, he's picturing the relationship $M = \frac{x}{3}$ in this way:

-4	-3	-2	-1	0	1	2	3	4
-12	-9	-6	-3	0	3	6	9	12

By looking at the corresponding values of M (above the number line) and x (below the number line), you can see that the M-value is always one-third of the x-value, so $M = \frac{x}{3}$.

The strange thing here is that the parabola does not look any different, even though it is been dilated horizontally by a factor of 3.

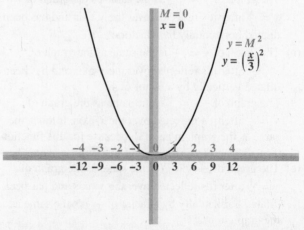

That is because in the new coordinate system, the x and y-axes are not on the same scale. This really affects the picture. If you rescale the x-axis so that one unit in x is equal to one unit in y, the graph does look different.

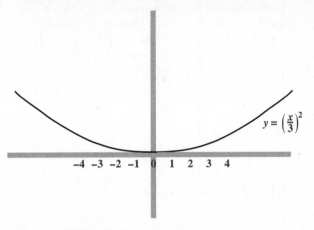

$$y = \left(\tfrac{x}{3}\right)^2$$

Maintain Your Skills

19. (a) Even
  (b) Odd
  (c) Even
  (d) Odd
  (e) Even
  (f) Odd
  (g) $f(x) = x^n$ is even if $n = 2k$ for some integer k and odd if $n = 2k + 1$ for some integer k.

6A   MATHEMATICAL REFLECTIONS

1. (a) A function is even if $f(-x) = f(x)$ for all x in its domain. $y = x^2$ and $y = |x|$ are both even functions.
  The graphs of even functions have the y-axis as a line of symmetry (left and right halves are reflections of each other).
  (b) A function is odd if $f(-x) = -f(x)$ for all x in its domain. $y = x$ and $y = x^3$ are both odd functions.
  The graphs of odd functions have "rotational symmetry". If you rotate it $180°$, you obtain the same graph.

2. This graph is the same as the graph of $y = |x|$ after a translation of 2 units to the right and 3 units up.

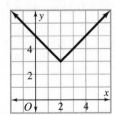

3. $y = (x + 3)^3 + 1$

4. The graph of $x^2 + y^2 = 25$ is a circle of radius 5 centered at the origin. The graph of $\left(\tfrac{x}{2}\right)^2 + (3y)^2 = 25$ is the same as the graph of $x^2 + y^2 = 25$ after it has been dilated

horizontally by a factor of 2 and dilated vertically by a factor of $\tfrac{1}{3}$.

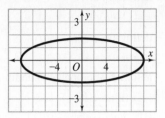

5. $y = \tfrac{6}{x}$

6. The graph of $y = (x - 3)^2$ is the same as the graph of $y = x^2$ after its been translated 3 units to the right.

7. The graph of $(x + 1)^2 + (y - 4)^2 = 36$ is a circle of radius 6 centered at the point $(-1, 4)$.

8. The graph of $-2y = x^3 - x$ is the same as the graph of $y = x^3 - x$ after it has been reflected over the x-axis and dilated vertically by a factor of $\tfrac{1}{2}$.

INVESTIGATION 6B   AFFINE TRANSFORMATIONS

6.5   Getting Started

For You to Explore

1. (a) • $T_3(2) = 2 + 3 = 5$
  • $T_3(5) = 5 + 3 = 8$
  • $T_3(-1) = -1 + 3 = 2$
  • $T_3(-7) = -7 + 3 = -4$
  • $T_3(0) = 0 + 3 = 3$
  (b) T_a is called a *translation by a*, because if you think of each input you're operating on as a point on the number line, the output is a point on the number line that is a units to the right of the input if $a > 0$ or a units to the left if $a < 0$ (or equal to the input if $a = 0$). It is the image of the input after a translation of a units.

2. (a) • $T_0(2) = 2 + 0 = 2$
  • $T_0(5) = 5 + 0 = 5$
  • $T_0(-1) = -1 + 0 = -1$
  • $T_0(-7) = -7 + 0 = -7$
  • $T_0(0) = 0 + 0 = 0$
  (b) T_0 is called the *identity* transformation because it outputs the same value that's input. It leaves the input unchanged.

3. (a) • $(T_3 \circ T_2)(4) = T_3(4 + 2) = (4 + 2) + 3 = 9$
  • $(T_3 \circ T_2)(-1) = T_3(-1 + 2) = (-1 + 2) + 3 = 4$
  • $(T_3 \circ T_2)(179) = T_3(179 + 2) = (179 + 2) + 3 = 184$
  • $(T_3 \circ T_2)(\pi) = T_3(\pi + 2) = (\pi + 2) + 3 = \pi + 5$
  • $(T_3 \circ T_2)(x) = T_3(x + 2) = (x + 2) + 3 = x + 5$
  (b) In the previous part of this exercise, you showed that $(T_3 \circ T_2)(x) = x + 5$, so you can rewrite that as $T_5(x)$.

4.

$T_a \circ T_b(x) = T_a(x + b)$

    definition of T_b

$= (x + b) + a$

    definition of T_a

$= x + (b + a)$

    associative property of addition

$= x + (a + b)$

    commutative property of addition

$= (x + a) + b$

    associative property of addition

$= T_b(x + a)$

    definition of T_b

$= T_b \circ T_a(x)$

    definition of T_a

5. (a) $(T_{-4} \circ T_4)(3) = T_{-4}(3 + 4) = (3 + 4) + -4 = 3$

(b) $(T_{-4} \circ T_4)(-2) = T_{-4}(-2 + 4) = (-2 + 4) + -4 = -2$

(c) $(T_{-4} \circ T_4)(7) = T_{-4}(7 + 4) = (7 + 4) + -4 = 7$

(d) $(T_{-4} \circ T_4)(-1) = T_{-4}(-1 + 4) = (-1 + 4) + -4 = -1$

(e) $(T_{-4} \circ T_4)(x) = T_{-4}(x + 4) = (x + 4) + -4 = x$ for any real number x.

(f) $(T_4 \circ T_{-4})(x) = T_4(x + -4) = (x + -4) + 4 = x$ for any real number x.

6.

$T_a \circ T_{-a}(x) = T_a(x + -a)$

$= x + -a + a$

$= x$

$T_{-a} \circ T_a(x) = T_{-a}(x + a)$

$= x + a + -a$

$= x$

T_a and T_{-a} are inverses, because $T_a \circ T_{-a}(x) = T_{-a} \circ T_a(x) = x$ for any real number x.

On Your Own

7. (a) • $D_3(2) = 3 \cdot 2 = 6$

    • $D_3(5) = 3 \cdot 5 = 15$

    • $D_3(-1) = 3 \cdot (-1) = -3$

    • $D_3(-7) = 3 \cdot (-7) = -21$

    • $D_3(0) = 3 \cdot 0 = 0$

(b) D_s is called a *dilation by s* because you can think of it as scaling points on the number line, each by a factor of s, using the origin of the number line as the center of dilation.

8. (a) • $D_1(2) = 1 \cdot 2 = 2$

    • $D_1(5) = 1 \cdot 5 = 5$

    • $D_1(-1) = 1 \cdot (-1) = -1$

    • $D_1(-7) = 1 \cdot (-7) = -7$

    • $D_1(x) = 1 \cdot x = x$

(b) No matter what you input to the function D_1, the output will be equal to the input, so D_1 is the identity transformation.

9. • $D_{-1}(2) = -1 \cdot 2 = -2$

    • $D_{-1}(5) = -1 \cdot 5 = -5$

• $D_{-1}(-1) = -1 \cdot (-1) = 1$

• $D_{-1}(-7) = -1 \cdot (-7) = 7$

• $D_{-1}(0) = -1 \cdot 0 = 0$

The output for D_{-1} is always equal to the image after reflection over the y-axis of any input x, which is $-x$.

10. (a) • $(D_3 \circ D_2)(4) = D_3(2 \cdot 4) = 3 \cdot (2 \cdot 4) = 24$

    • $(D_3 \circ D_2)(-1) = D_3(2 \cdot -1) = 3 \cdot (2 \cdot -1) = -6$

    • $(D_3 \circ D_2)(0) = D_3(2 \cdot 0) = 3 \cdot (2 \cdot 0) = 0$

    • $(D_3 \circ D_2)(7) = D_3(2 \cdot 7) = 3 \cdot (2 \cdot 7) = 42$

    • $(D_3 \circ D_2)(8) = D_3(2 \cdot 8) = 3 \cdot (2 \cdot 8) = 48$

(b) $D_3 \circ D_2(x) = 3 \cdot 2 \cdot x = 6 \cdot x = D_6$, so $k = 6$.

11.

$D_s \circ D_t(x) = D_s(tx)$

    definition of D_t

$= s(tx)$

    definition of D_s

$= (st)x$

    associative property of multiplication

$= (ts)x$

    commutative property of multiplication

$= t(sx)$

    associative property of multiplication

$= t \cdot D_s(x)$

    definition of D_s

$= D_t \circ D_s$

    definition of D_t

12. (a) $(D_{\frac{1}{4}} \circ D_4)(3) = D_{\frac{1}{4}}(4 \cdot 3) = \frac{1}{4} \cdot 4 \cdot 3 = 3$

(b) $(D_{\frac{1}{4}} \circ D_4)(-2) = D_{\frac{1}{4}}(4 \cdot -2) = \frac{1}{4} \cdot 4 \cdot -2 = -2$

(c) $(D_3 \circ D_{\frac{1}{3}})(7) = D_3(\frac{1}{3} \cdot 7) = 3 \cdot \frac{1}{3} 7 = 7$

(d) $(D_{\frac{1}{3}} \circ D_3)(-1) = D_{\frac{1}{2}}(3 \cdot -1) = \frac{1}{3} \cdot 3 \cdot -1 = -1$

(e) $(D_{\frac{1}{4}} \circ D_4)(x) = D_{\frac{1}{4}}(4 \cdot x) = \frac{1}{4} \cdot 4 \cdot x = x$ for any real number x.

(f) $(D_4 \circ D_{\frac{1}{4}})(x) = D_4(\frac{1}{4} \cdot x) = 4 \cdot \frac{1}{4}x = x$ for any real number x.

13.

$$D_s \circ D_{\frac{1}{s}}(x) = D_s\left(\frac{x}{s}\right)$$
$$= s\frac{x}{s}$$
$$= x$$
$$D_{\frac{1}{s}} \circ D_s(x) = D_{\frac{1}{s}}(sx)$$
$$= \frac{1}{s} \cdot sx$$
$$= x$$

D_s and $D_{\frac{1}{s}}$ are inverse functions.

14. (a) $T_5 \circ D_2(x) = T_5(2x) = 2x + 5$, so $x \mapsto 2x + 5$.

(b) $D_2 \circ T_5(x) = D_2(x + 5) = 2(x + 5) = 2x + 10$, so $x \mapsto 2x + 10$.

15. (a) $T_r \circ D_s(x) = T_r(sx) = sx + r$

(b) $D_s \circ T_r(x) = D_s(x + r) = s(x + r) = sx + rs$

Maintain Your Skills

16. (a)

n	$f(n)$
0	2
1	5
2	8
3	11
4	14
5	17
6	20

(b) There is a constant difference of 3 between successive outputs, and an initial output of 2, so $f(n) = 3n + 2$

17. (a) $f \circ f = 2(2x + 3) + 3 = 4x + 9$

(b) $f \circ f \circ f = 2(4x + 9) + 3 = 8x + 21$

(c) $f \circ f \circ f \circ f = 2(8x + 21) + 3 = 16x + 45$

(d) $\underbrace{f \circ f \circ \cdots \circ f}_{7 f\text{'s}} = 128x + 381$

6.6 Introducing Affine Transformations

Check Your Understanding

1. $\mathcal{A}_{(1,b)} = T_b \circ D_1$, but D_1 is the identity transformation, so this is just T_b.

2. $\mathcal{A}_{(a,b)} = T_b \circ D_a$, so if $b = 0$, T_b is the identity transformation, and if $a \neq 0$ the result is a dilation. (If $a = 1$ and $b = 0$, then this is the identity transformation.)

3. Theorem 6.2 says:

Let s and t be nonzero real numbers. Then

$$D_s \circ D_t = D_{st}.$$

Here is a proof:

$D_s \circ D_t(x) = D_s(D_t(x))$

    definition of composition

$= D_s(tx)$

    definition of D_n

$= s(tx)$

    definition of D_n

$= (st)x$

    associative property of multiplication

$= D_{st}x$

    definition of D_n

4. (a) $(T_3 \circ D_2)(x) = T_3(2x) = 2x + 3$

(b) $(D_2 \circ T_3)(x) = D_2(x + 3) = 2x + 6$

(c) $(T_{-5} \circ D_7)(x) = T_{-5}(7x) = 7x - 5$

(d) $(D_7 \circ T_{-5})(x) = D_7(x - 5) = 7x - 35$

(e) $(T_b \circ D_a)(x) = T_b(ax) = ax + b$

(f) $(D_a \circ T_b)(x) = D_a(x + b) = ax + ab$

5. In Exercise 4, you can see that in most cases

$$T_b \circ D_a \neq D_a \circ T_b,$$

but you can also see where the difference occurs. Look at parts (e) and (f) of the exercise. The two expressions would be the same as long as $b = ab$. That will happen if $b = 0$ or if $a = 1$, or both. What happens when $a = 1$ is that the composition (in either order) is really just a translation because the dilation it is composed with is the identity transformation. Similarly, if $b = 0$, the composition (in either order) is a dilation.

6. (a) $\mathcal{A}_{(2,-1)} \circ \mathcal{A}_{(3,5)}(x) = \mathcal{A}_{(2,-1)}(3x + 5)$

$= 2(3x + 5) - 1$

$= 6x + 9$

$\mathcal{A}_{(6,9)}$

(b) $\mathcal{A}_{(3,5)} \circ \mathcal{A}_{(2,-1)}(x) = \mathcal{A}_{(3,5)}(2x - 1)$

$= 3(2x - 1) + 5$

$= 6x + 2$

$\mathcal{A}_{(6,2)}$

(c) $\mathcal{A}_{(1,4)} \circ \mathcal{A}_{(-1,3)}(x) = \mathcal{A}_{(1,4)}(-x + 3)$

$= -x + 3 + 4$

$= -x + 7$

$\mathcal{A}_{(-1,7)}$

(d) $\mathcal{A}_{(-1,3)} \circ \mathcal{A}_{(1,4)}(x) = \mathcal{A}_{(-1,3)}(x + 4)$

$= -(x + 4) + 3$

$= -x - 1$

$\mathcal{A}_{(-1,-1)}$

(e) $\mathcal{A}_{\left(\frac{1}{2},-3\right)} \circ \mathcal{A}_{(2,6)}(x) = \mathcal{A}_{\left(\frac{1}{2},-3\right)}(2x + 6)$

$= \dfrac{1}{2}(2x + 6) - 3$

$= x$

$\mathcal{A}_{(1,0)}$

(f) $\mathcal{A}_{(2,6)} \circ \mathcal{A}_{\left(\frac{1}{2},-3\right)}(x) = \mathcal{A}_{(2,6)}\left(\dfrac{1}{2}x - 3\right)$

$= 2\left(\dfrac{1}{2}x - 3\right) + 6$

$= x$

$\mathcal{A}_{(1,0)}$

7. $\mathcal{A}_{(a,b)} \circ \mathcal{A}_{(c,d)}(x) = \mathcal{A}_{(a,b)}(cx + d)$

$= a(cx + d) + b$

$= (ac)x + (ad + b)$

$\mathcal{A}_{(ac,ad+b)}$

8. (a) $\mathcal{A}_{(a,b)} \circ \mathcal{A}_{(4,1)}(x) = \mathcal{A}_{(12,11)}(x)$

$\mathcal{A}_{(a,b)}(4x + 1) = 12x + 11$

$a(4x + 1) + b = 12x + 11$

$4ax + a + b = 12x + 11$

So, $4a = 12$ and $a = 3$. $a + b = 11$, so $3 + b = 11$ and $b = 8$.

(b) $\quad A_{(4,3)} \circ A_{(a,b)}(x) = A_{(20,11)}(x)$

$\quad\quad A_{(4,3)}(ax + b) = 20x + 11$

$\quad\quad 4(ax + b) + 3 = 20x + 11$

$\quad\quad 4ax + 4b + 3 = 20x + 11$

So, $4a = 20$ and $a = 5$. $4b + 3 = 11$, so $4b = 8$ and $b = 2$.

(c) $\quad A_{(a,b)} \circ A_{(2,3)}(x) = \mathrm{id}(x)$

$\quad\quad A_{(a,b)}(2x + 3) = x$

$\quad\quad a(2x + 3) + b = x$

$\quad\quad 2ax + 3a + b = x$

So, $2a = 1$ and $a = \frac{1}{2}$. $3a + b = 0$, so $b = -\frac{3}{2}$.

(d) $\quad A_{(2,3)} \circ A_{(a,b)}(x) = \mathrm{id}(x)$

$\quad\quad A_{(2,3)}(ax + b) = x$

$\quad\quad 2(ax + b) + 3 = x$

$\quad\quad 2ax + 2b + 3 = x$

So, $2a = 1$ and $a = \frac{1}{2}$. $2b + 3 = 0$, so $b = -\frac{3}{2}$

On Your Own

9. (a) $\quad A_{(1,m)} \circ A_{(1,n)}(x) = A_{(1,m)}(x + n)$

$\quad\quad\quad\quad = 1(x + n) + m$

$\quad\quad\quad\quad = x + n + m$

$\quad\quad\quad\quad = A_{(1,n+m)}(x)$

(b) $\quad A_{(s,0)} \circ A_{(t,0)}(x) = A_{(s,0)}(tx + 0)$

$\quad\quad\quad\quad = s(tx) + 0$

$\quad\quad\quad\quad = stx$

$\quad\quad\quad\quad = A_{(st,0)}(x)$

(c) $\quad A_{(1,b)} \circ A_{(a,0)}(x) = A_{(1,b)}(ax + 0)$

$\quad\quad\quad\quad = 1(ax) + b$

$\quad\quad\quad\quad = ax + b$

$\quad\quad\quad\quad = A_{(a,b)}(x)$

(d) $\quad A_{(a,0)} \circ A_{(1,b)}(x) = A_{(a,0)}(x + b)$

$\quad\quad\quad\quad = a(x + b) + 0$

$\quad\quad\quad\quad = ax + ab$

$\quad\quad\quad\quad = A_{(a,ab)}(x)$

10. (a) $\quad 4x + 8 = y$

$\quad\quad\quad 4x = y - 8$

$\quad\quad\quad x = \frac{1}{4}y - 2$

(b) To show that two affine transformations are inverses, you want to compose them and show that the result is the identity transformation. You should still compose them in both orders, because you have not yet proven that the order doesn't matter when composing an inverse pair.

$A_{(4,8)} \circ A_{\left(\frac{1}{4},-2\right)} = A_{(4,8)}\left(\frac{1}{4}x - 2\right)$

$\quad\quad\quad\quad = 4\left(\frac{1}{4}x - 2\right) + 8$

$\quad\quad\quad\quad = x - 8 + 8$

$\quad\quad\quad\quad = x$

$A_{\left(\frac{1}{4},-2\right)} \circ A_{(4,8)} = A_{\left(\frac{1}{4},-2\right)}(4x + 8)$

$\quad\quad\quad\quad = \frac{1}{4}(4x + 8) - 2$

$\quad\quad\quad\quad = x + 2 - 2$

$\quad\quad\quad\quad = x$

Since both compositions are equivalent to the identity transformation, these two affine transformations are inverses.

11. (a) $(A_{(2,-1)})^{-1} = A_{(c,d)}$ means that $A_{(2,-1)} \circ A_{(c,d)} = A_{(1,0)}$ and $A_{(c,d)} \circ A_{(2,-1)} = A_{(1,0)}$.

$\quad\quad A_{(2,-1)} \circ A_{(c,d)}(x) = A_{(1,0)}(x)$

$\quad\quad\quad A_{(2,-1)}(cx + d) = x$

$\quad\quad\quad 2(cx + d) - 1 = x$

$\quad\quad\quad 2cx + 2d - 1 = x$

So $2c = 1$ and $c = \frac{1}{2}$. $2d - 1 = 0$, so $d = \frac{1}{2}$. Now, to be sure that $(A_{(2,-1)})^{-1} = A_{\left(\frac{1}{2},\frac{1}{2}\right)}$, you need to check the composition in the other order.

$A_{\left(\frac{1}{2},\frac{1}{2}\right)} \circ A_{(2,-1)}(x) = A_{\left(\frac{1}{2},\frac{1}{2}\right)}(2x - 1)$

$\quad\quad\quad\quad = \frac{1}{2}(2x - 1) + \frac{1}{2}$

$\quad\quad\quad\quad = x - \frac{1}{2} + \frac{1}{2}$

$\quad\quad\quad\quad = x$

(b) $\quad A_{(3,5)} \circ A_{(c,d)}(x) = A_{(1,0)}(x)$

$\quad\quad\quad A_{(3,5)}(cx + d) = x$

$\quad\quad\quad 3(cx + d) + 5 = x$

$\quad\quad\quad 3cx + 3d + 5 = x$

So $3c = 1$ and $c = \frac{1}{3}$. $3d + 5 = 0$, so $d = -\frac{5}{3}$. Now, to be sure that $(A_{(3,5)})^{-1} = A_{\left(\frac{1}{3},-\frac{5}{3}\right)}$, you need to check the composition in the other order.

$A_{\left(\frac{1}{3},-\frac{5}{3}\right)} \circ A_{(3,5)}(x) = A_{\left(\frac{1}{3},-\frac{5}{3}\right)}(3x + 5)$

$\quad\quad\quad\quad = \frac{1}{3}(3x + 5) - \frac{5}{3}$

$\quad\quad\quad\quad = x + \frac{5}{3} - \frac{5}{3}$

$\quad\quad\quad\quad = x$

(c) $\quad A_{\left(\frac{1}{2},-3\right)} \circ A_{(c,d)}(x) = A_{(1,0)}(x)$

$\quad\quad\quad A_{\left(\frac{1}{2},-3\right)}(cx + d) = x$

$\quad\quad\quad \frac{1}{2}(cx + d) - 3 = x$

$\quad\quad\quad \frac{c}{2}x + \frac{d}{2} - \frac{6}{2} = x$

So $\frac{c}{2} = 1$ and $c = 2$. $\frac{d-6}{2} = 0$, so $d = 6$. Now, to be sure that $(A_{\left(\frac{1}{2},-3\right)})^{-1} = A_{(2,6)}$, you need to check the composition in the other order.

$$A_{(2,6)} \circ A_{\left(\frac{1}{2},-3\right)}(x) = A_{(2,6)}\left(\frac{1}{2}x - 3\right)$$

$$= 2\left(\frac{1}{2}x - 3\right) + 6$$

$$= x + -6 + 6$$

$$= x$$

(d) In part (c) of this exercise, you found that $A_{(2,6)}$ is the inverse of $A_{\left(\frac{1}{2},-3\right)}$, so $A_{\left(\frac{1}{2},-3\right)}$ is the inverse of $A_{(2,6)}$.

(e) $A_{(a,b)} \circ A_{(c,d)}(x) = A_{(1,0)}(x)$

$A_{(a,b)}(cx + d) = x$

$a(cx + d) + b = x$

$acx + ad + b = x$

So $ac = 1$, and $c = \frac{1}{a}$. $ad + b = 0$, so $d = -\frac{b}{a}$. $(A_{(a,b)})^{-1} = A_{\left(\frac{1}{a},-\frac{b}{a}\right)}$. Now, to check the composition in the other order.

$$A_{\left(\frac{1}{a},-\frac{b}{a}\right)} \circ A_{(a,b)}(x) = A_{\left(\frac{1}{a},-\frac{b}{a}\right)}(ax + b)$$

$$= \frac{1}{a}(ax + b) - \frac{b}{a}$$

$$= x + \frac{b}{a} - \frac{b}{a}$$

$$= x$$

12. (a) $2x - 1 = y$

$2x = y + 1$

$x = \frac{1}{2}y + \frac{1}{2}$

(b) $3x + 5 = y$

$3x = y - 5$

$x = \frac{1}{3}y - \frac{5}{3}$

(c) $\frac{x}{2} - 3 = y$

$\frac{x}{2} = y + 3$

$x = 2y + 6$

(d) $2x + 6 = y$

$2x = y - 6$

$x = \frac{1}{2}y - 3$

(e) $ax + b = y$

$ax = y - b$

$x = \frac{1}{a}y - \frac{b}{a}$

13. (a) $(A_{(3,4)})^{-1}(x) = (T_4 \circ D_3)^{-1}(x)$

$$= (D_3)^{-1} \circ (T_4)^{-1}(x)$$

$$= D_{\frac{1}{3}} \circ T_{-4}(x)$$

$$= D_{\frac{1}{3}}(x - 4)$$

$$= \frac{1}{3}(x - 4)$$

$$= \frac{1}{3}x - \frac{4}{3}$$

$$= A_{\left(\frac{1}{3},-\frac{4}{3}\right)}(x)$$

So the inverse of $A_{(3,4)}$ is $A_{\left(\frac{1}{3},-\frac{4}{3}\right)}$.

(b) $(A_{(5,1)})^{-1}(x) = (T_1 \circ D_5)^{-1}(x)$

$$= (D_5)^{-1} \circ (T_1)^{-1}(x)$$

$$= D_{\frac{1}{5}} \circ T_{-1}(x)$$

$$= D_{\frac{1}{5}}(x - 1)$$

$$= \frac{1}{5}(x - 1)$$

$$= \frac{1}{5}x - \frac{1}{5}$$

$$= A_{\left(\frac{1}{5},-\frac{1}{5}\right)}(x)$$

So the inverse of $A_{(5,1)}$ is $A_{\left(\frac{1}{5},-\frac{1}{5}\right)}$.

(c) $(A_{(3,2)})^{-1}(x) = (T_2 \circ D_3)^{-1}(x)$

$$= (D_3)^{-1} \circ (T_2)^{-1}(x)$$

$$= D_{\frac{1}{3}} \circ T_{-2}(x)$$

$$= D_{\frac{1}{3}}(x - 2)$$

$$= \frac{1}{3}(x - 2)$$

$$= \frac{1}{3}x - \frac{2}{3}$$

$$= A_{\left(\frac{1}{3},-\frac{2}{3}\right)}(x)$$

So the inverse of $A_{(3,2)}$ is $A_{\left(\frac{1}{3},-\frac{2}{3}\right)}$.

14. (a) You have already found $(A_{(3,4)})^{-1} = A_{\left(\frac{1}{3},-\frac{4}{3}\right)}$ in Exercise 13a.

$$A_{(a,b)} \circ A_{(3,4)}(x) = A_{(9,6)}(x)$$

$$A_{(a,b)} \circ A_{(3,4)} \circ (A_{(3,4)})^{-1}(x) = A_{(9,6)} \circ (A_{(3,4)})^{-1}(x)$$

$$A_{(a,b)}(x) = A_{(9,6)} \circ A_{\left(\frac{1}{3},-\frac{4}{3}\right)}(x)$$

$$= A_{(9,6)}\left(\frac{1}{3}x - \frac{4}{3}\right)$$

$$= 9\left(\frac{1}{3}x - \frac{4}{3}\right) + 6$$

$$= 3x - 12 + 6$$

$$= 3x - 6$$

$$= A_{(3,-6)}$$

So $a = 3, b = -6$.

(b) You have already found $(\mathcal{A}_{(3,4)})^{-1} = \mathcal{A}_{\left(\frac{1}{3}, -\frac{4}{3}\right)}$ in Exercise 13a.

$$\mathcal{A}_{(3,4)} \circ \mathcal{A}_{(a,b)}(x) = \mathcal{A}_{(13,6)}(x)$$
$$(\mathcal{A}_{(3,4)})^{-1} \circ \mathcal{A}_{(3,4)} \circ \mathcal{A}_{(a,b)}(x) = (\mathcal{A}_{(3,4)})^{-1} \circ \mathcal{A}_{(13,6)}(x)$$
$$\mathcal{A}_{(a,b)}(x) = \mathcal{A}_{\left(\frac{1}{3}, -\frac{4}{3}\right)} \circ \mathcal{A}_{(13,6)}(x)$$
$$= \mathcal{A}_{\left(\frac{1}{3}, -\frac{4}{3}\right)}(13x + 6)$$
$$= \frac{1}{3}(13x + 6) - \frac{4}{3}$$
$$= \frac{13}{3}x + 2 - \frac{4}{3}$$
$$= \frac{13}{3}x + \frac{2}{3}$$
$$= \mathcal{A}_{\left(\frac{13}{3}, \frac{2}{3}\right)}$$

So $a = \frac{13}{3}$, $b = \frac{2}{3}$.

(c) You have already found $(\mathcal{A}_{(5,1)})^{-1} = \mathcal{A}_{\left(\frac{1}{5}, -\frac{1}{5}\right)}$ in Exercise 13b.

$$\mathcal{A}_{(a,b)} \circ \mathcal{A}_{(5,1)}(x) = \mathrm{id}(x)$$
$$\mathcal{A}_{(a,b)} \circ \mathcal{A}_{(5,1)} \circ (\mathcal{A}_{(5,1)})^{-1}(x) = \mathcal{A}_{(1,0)} \circ (\mathcal{A}_{(5,1)})^{-1}(x)$$
$$\mathcal{A}_{(a,b)} = \mathcal{A}_{(1,0)} \circ \mathcal{A}_{\left(\frac{1}{5}, -\frac{1}{5}\right)}$$
$$= \mathcal{A}_{\left(\frac{1}{5}, -\frac{1}{5}\right)}$$

So $a = \frac{1}{5}$, $b = -\frac{1}{5}$.

(d) You have already found $(\mathcal{A}_{(3,2)})^{-1} = \mathcal{A}_{\left(\frac{1}{3}, -\frac{2}{3}\right)}$ in Exercise 13c.

$$\mathcal{A}_{(3,2)} \circ \mathcal{A}_{(a,b)}(x) = \mathrm{id}(x)$$
$$(\mathcal{A}_{(3,2)})^{-1} \circ \mathcal{A}_{(3,2)} \circ \mathcal{A}_{(a,b)}(x) = (\mathcal{A}_{(3,2)})^{-1} \circ \mathrm{id}(x)$$
$$\mathcal{A}_{(a,b)}(x) = \mathcal{A}_{\left(\frac{1}{3}, -\frac{2}{3}\right)}(x)$$

So $a = \frac{1}{3}$, $b = -\frac{2}{3}$.

15. (a) Look back at your solution to Exercise 6. In part (a), you simplified $\mathcal{A}_{(2,-1)} \circ \mathcal{A}_{(3,5)}$ to $\mathcal{A}_{(6,9)}$

$$(\mathcal{A}_{(6,9)})^{-1}(x) = (T_9 \circ D_6)^{-1}(x)$$
$$= (D_6)^{-1} \circ (T_9)^{-1}(x)$$
$$= D_{\frac{1}{6}} \circ T_{-9}(x)$$
$$= D_{\frac{1}{6}}(x - 9)$$
$$= \frac{1}{6}x - \frac{3}{2}$$
$$= \mathcal{A}_{\left(\frac{1}{6}, -\frac{3}{2}\right)}$$

(b) Look back at your solution to Exercise 11. In parts (a) and (b), you found $(\mathcal{A}_{(2,-1)})^{-1} = \mathcal{A}_{\left(\frac{1}{2}, \frac{1}{2}\right)}$ and $(\mathcal{A}_{(3,5)})^{-1} = \mathcal{A}_{\left(\frac{1}{3}, -\frac{5}{3}\right)}$.

$$(\mathcal{A}_{(3,5)})^{-1} \circ (\mathcal{A}_{(2,-1)})^{-1}(x) = \mathcal{A}_{\left(\frac{1}{3}, -\frac{5}{3}\right)} \circ \mathcal{A}_{\left(\frac{1}{2}, \frac{1}{2}\right)}$$
$$= \mathcal{A}_{\left(\frac{1}{3}, -\frac{5}{3}\right)}\left(\frac{1}{2}x + \frac{1}{2}\right)$$
$$= \frac{1}{3}\left(\frac{1}{2}x + \frac{1}{2}\right) - \frac{5}{3}$$
$$= \frac{1}{6}x + \frac{1}{6} - \frac{10}{6}$$
$$= \frac{1}{6}x - \frac{9}{6}$$
$$= \frac{1}{6}x - \frac{3}{2}$$
$$= \mathcal{A}_{\left(\frac{1}{6}, -\frac{3}{2}\right)}$$

(c) Look back at your solution to Exercise 6. In part (e), you simplified $(\mathcal{A}_{\left(\frac{1}{2}, -3\right)} \circ \mathcal{A}_{(2,6)})^{-1}$ to $\mathcal{A}_{(1,0)}$. (The two affine transformations being composed are inverses.) The identity transformation is its own inverse, so $(\mathcal{A}_{\left(\frac{1}{2}, -3\right)} \circ \mathcal{A}_{(2,6)})^{-1} = \mathcal{A}_{(1,0)}$.

(d) Look back at your solution to Exercise 11. In parts (c) and (d), you found $(\mathcal{A}_{\left(\frac{1}{2}, -3\right)})^{-1} = \mathcal{A}_{(2,6)}$ and $(\mathcal{A}_{(2,6)})^{-1} = \mathcal{A}_{\left(\frac{1}{2}, -3\right)}$. So, $(\mathcal{A}_{(2,6)})^{-1} \circ (\mathcal{A}_{\left(\frac{1}{2}, -3\right)})^{-1} = \mathcal{A}_{\left(\frac{1}{2}, -3\right)} \circ \mathcal{A}_{(2,6)}$, which is equal to the identity transformation because these two affine transformations are inverses.

16. (a) You can start by simplifying several expressions. Simplify $\mathcal{A}_{(a,b)} \circ \mathcal{A}_{(c,d)}$.

$$\mathcal{A}_{(a,b)} \circ \mathcal{A}_{(c,d)}(x) = \mathcal{A}_{(a,b)}(cx + d)$$
$$= a(cx + d) + b$$
$$= acx + ad + b$$
$$= \mathcal{A}_{(ac, ad+b)}$$

Use the results to simplify $(\mathcal{A}_{(a,b)} \circ \mathcal{A}_{(c,d)})^{-1}$.

$$(\mathcal{A}_{(a,b)} \circ \mathcal{A}_{(c,d)})^{-1}(x) = (\mathcal{A}_{(ac, ad+b)})^{-1}(x)$$
$$= (T_{ad+b} \circ D_{ac})^{-1}(x)$$
$$= (D_{ac})^{-1} \circ (T_{ad+b})^{-1}(x)$$
$$= D_{\frac{1}{ac}} \circ T_{-ad-b}(x)$$
$$= D_{\frac{1}{ac}}(x - ad - b)$$
$$= \frac{1}{ac}(x - ad - b)$$
$$= \frac{1}{ac}x - \frac{ad + b}{ac}$$
$$= \mathcal{A}_{\left(\frac{1}{ac}, -\frac{ad+b}{ac}\right)}$$

Find $(A_{(c,d)})^{-1}$.

$$(A_{(c,d)})^{-1}(x) = (T_d \circ D_c)^{-1}(x)$$
$$= (D_c)^{-1} \circ (T_d)^{-1}(x)$$
$$= D_{\frac{1}{c}} \circ T_{-d}(x)$$
$$= D_{\frac{1}{c}}(x - d)$$
$$= \frac{1}{c}(x - d)$$
$$= \frac{1}{c}x - \frac{d}{c}$$
$$= A_{\left(\frac{1}{c}, -\frac{d}{c}\right)}$$

Similarly, $(A_{(a,b)})^{-1} = A_{\left(\frac{1}{a}, -\frac{b}{a}\right)}$

Now the equation

$$(A_{(a,b)} \circ A_{(c,d)})^{-1} = (A_{(c,d)})^{-1} \circ (A_{(a,b)})^{-1}$$

becomes

$$A_{\left(\frac{1}{ac}, -\frac{ad+b}{ac}\right)}(x) = A_{\left(\frac{1}{c}, -\frac{d}{c}\right)} \circ A_{\left(\frac{1}{a}, -\frac{b}{a}\right)}(x)$$
$$= A_{\left(\frac{1}{c}, -\frac{d}{c}\right)}\left(\frac{1}{a}x - \frac{b}{a}\right)$$
$$= \frac{1}{c}\left(\frac{1}{a}x - \frac{b}{a}\right) - \frac{d}{c}$$
$$= \frac{1}{ac}x - \frac{b}{ac} - \frac{ad}{ac}$$
$$= \frac{1}{ac}x - \frac{ad+b}{ac}$$
$$= A_{\left(\frac{1}{ac}, -\frac{ad+b}{ac}\right)}(x)$$

Since the two expressions are equal for any variables a, b, c, d as long as $a, c \neq 0$, this proves the "socks and shoes" method of taking inverses for compositions of affine transformations.

(b) $A_{(a,b)} \circ A_{(c,d)}$ is the process you are taking the inverse of—the process of putting on your socks and shoes. Although some people put on a sock and a shoe and a sock and a shoe, and others put on a sock and a sock and then a shoe and a shoe, think of this as applying to one foot, in which case you have to put the sock on before the shoe. $A_{(c,d)}$ represents the first thing you do, which is putting on a sock. $A_{(a,b)}$ represents the second step in the process, which is putting on a shoe. The equation

$$(A_{(a,b)} \circ A_{(c,d)})^{-1} = (A_{(c,d)})^{-1} \circ (A_{(a,b)})^{-1}$$

says, in effect, "To take off your socks and shoes, first take off your shoes, and then take off your socks." This is because in the inverse—described by the right hand side of the equation—the first step to be undone is $A_{(a,b)}$. To undo this, you take off a shoe. Then the second step to be undone is $A_{(c,d)}$, which means to take off a sock.

Basically, to undo a multi-step process you undo each step in reverse order.

17. This is equivalent to

$$a(2x + 4) + b = 6x + 6$$
$$2ax + (4a + b) = 6x + 6$$

This is an identity, so $2a = 6$, $a = 3$. Now $4a + b = 6$, so $12 + b = 6$, $b = -6$. The correct answer choice is **C**.

18. (a) $(A_{(a,b)})^{(2)}(x) = A_{(a,b)}(ax + b) = a(ax + b) + b = a^2x + ab + b = A_{(a^2, ab+b)}(x)$

(b) $(A_{(a,b)})^{(3)}(x) = A_{(a,b)}(a^2x + ab + b) = a(a^2x + ab + b) + b = a^3x + a^2b + ab + b = A_{(a^3, a^2b+ab+b)}(x)$

(c) $(A_{(a,b)})^{(4)}(x) = A_{(a,b)}(a^3x + a^2b + ab + b) = a(a^3x + a^2b + ab + b) + b = a^4x + a^3b + a^2b + ab + b = A_{(a^4, a^3b+a^2b+ab+b)}(x)$

(d) $(A_{(a,b)})^{(5)}(x) = A_{(a,b)}(a^4x + a^3b + a^2b + ab + b) = a(a^4x + a^3b + a^2b + ab + b) + b = a^5x + a^4b + a^3b + a^2b + ab + b = A_{(a^5, a^4b+a^3b+a^2b+ab+b)}(x)$

19. (a) Following the pattern established in Exercise 17,
$$(A_{(a,b)})^{(n)}(x) = A_{(a^n, a^{n-1}b+a^{n-2}b+\cdots+a^2b+ab+b)}(x)$$

(b) When $a = 1$ the formula becomes $(A_{(1,b)})^{(n)}(x) = A_{(1,nb)}(x)$. This makes sense because $A_{(1,b)}$ is just T_b, and if you iterate a translation of b units n times, it is equivalent to a translation of nb units.

(c) When $b = 0$ the formula becomes $(A_{(a,0)})^{(n)}(x) = A_{(a^n, 0)}(x)$. This makes sense because $A_{(a,0)}$ is just D_a, and if you iterate a dilation by a factor of a n times, it is equivalent to a dilation by a factor of a^n.

(d) You can factor a b out of every term in the translation part of the affine transformation.

$$(A_{(a,b)})^{(n)}(x) = A_{(a^n, a^{n-1}b+a^{n-2}b+\cdots+a^2b+ab+b)}(x)$$
$$= A_{(a^n, b(a^{n-1}+a^{n-2}+\cdots+a^2+a+1))}(x)$$

Now you can use the identity

$$(a - 1)(a^{n-1} + a^{n-2} + \cdots + a + 1) = a^n - 1$$

To find a closed form expression for the sum $a^{n-1} + a^{n-2} + \cdots + a^2 + a + 1$.

$$(a^{n-1} + a^{n-2} + \cdots + a + 1) = \frac{a^n - 1}{a - 1}$$

So

$$(A_{(a,b)})^{(n)}(x) = A_{\left(a^n, b \cdot \frac{a^n-1}{a-1}\right)}(x)$$
$$= a^n x + b \cdot \frac{a^n - 1}{a - 1}$$

20. (a) $(A_{(a,b)})^{(0)}(x) = a^0 x + b \cdot \frac{a^0-1}{a-1} = x$. This makes sense because if you apply the affine transformation 0 times to an input x, it ought to be unchanged.

(b) $(A_{(a,b)})^{(-1)}(x) = a^{-1}x + b \cdot \frac{a^{-1}-1}{a-1} = \frac{1}{a}x - \frac{b}{a}$. The result is the inverse of the original affine transformation $A_{(a,b)}$. This makes sense, because applying the affine transformation -1 times ought to mean "un-applying" it once, or in other words, applying the inverse once.

(c) $(\mathcal{A}_{(a,b)})^{\frac{1}{2}}(x) = a^{\frac{1}{2}}x + b \cdot \frac{a^{\frac{1}{2}}-1}{a-1}$ If you compose this function with itself, you get

$$(\mathcal{A}_{(a,b)})^{(\frac{1}{2})} \circ (\mathcal{A}_{(a,b)})^{(\frac{1}{2})}$$

$$= a^{\frac{1}{2}}\left(a^{\frac{1}{2}}x + b \cdot \frac{a^{\frac{1}{2}}-1}{a-1}\right) + b \cdot \frac{a^{\frac{1}{2}}-1}{a-1}$$

$$= \sqrt{a}\left(\sqrt{a}x + b \cdot \frac{\sqrt{a}-1}{a-1}\right) + b \cdot \frac{\sqrt{a}-1}{a-1}$$

$$= ax + b \cdot \frac{a-\sqrt{a}}{a-1} + b \cdot \frac{\sqrt{a}-1}{a-1}$$

$$= ax + \frac{b}{a-1}(a - \sqrt{a} + \sqrt{a} - 1)$$

$$= ax + \frac{b}{a-1}(a-1)$$

$$= ax + b$$

This makes sense, because if you apply "half" the transformation twice, you will get one whole transformation.

21. (a) $\mathcal{A}_{(3,12)} = T_{12} \circ D_3 = T_a \circ D_b$, so $a = 12$ and $b = 3$.

(b) $D_a \circ T_b(x) = a(x+b) = ax + ab = \mathcal{A}_{(a,ab)}(x) = \mathcal{A}_{(3,12)}(x)$. This means that $a = 3$ and $3b = 12$, so $b = 4$.

22. (a)

$$D_a \circ T_{\frac{b}{a}}(x) = a\left(x + \frac{b}{a}\right)$$

$$= ax + b$$

$$= T_b \circ D_a(x)$$

(b)

$$T_b \circ D_a \circ T_{-\frac{b}{a}}(x) = D_a(x)$$

$$T_b \circ D_a\left(x - \frac{b}{a}\right) = ax$$

$$T_b\left(a\left(x - \frac{b}{a}\right)\right) = ax$$

$$T_b(ax - b) = ax$$

$$(ax - b) + b = ax$$

$$ax = ax$$

Maintain Your Skills

23. (a)

n	$f(n)$
0	2
1	6
2	18
3	54
4	162
5	486
6	1458

(b) $f(n) = 2 \cdot 3^n$

6.7 Transforming Equations

Check Your Understanding

1.

$$N = M^2$$

$$8y + 121 = (8x - 1)^2$$

$$8y + 121 = 64x^2 - 16x + 1$$

$$8y = 64x^2 - 16x - 120$$

$$y = 8x^2 - 2x - 15$$

2. (a) First, make the equation monic by multiplying each side of the equation by 9.

$$9y = (9x)^2 + 12(9x) - 45$$

Substitute $P = D_9x = 9x$ and $Q = D_9y = 9y$ to get the monic equation

$$Q = P^2 + 12P - 45$$

Now complete the square by adding and subtracting 36. $(P^2 + 12P + 36 = (P+6)^2)$

$$Q = (P^2 + 12P + 36) - 36 - 45$$

$$Q = (P+6)^2 - 81$$

$$Q + 81 = (P+6)^2$$

Substitute

$$M = T_6P = T_6 \circ D_9x = \mathcal{A}_{(9,6)}x$$

and

$$N = T_{81}Q = T_{81} \circ D_9y = \mathcal{A}_{(9,81)}y$$

to get

$$N = M^2$$

So $a = 9$, $b = 6$, $c = 9$, and $d = 81$.

(b) If $y = 0$, then $N = \mathcal{A}_{(9,81)}(0) = 9(0) + 81 = 81$
$N = M^2$, so $81 = M^2$ and $M = \pm 9$
Since $M = \mathcal{A}_{(9,6)}x = 9x + 6$, you get

$9 = 9x + 6$	or	$-9 = 9x + 6$
$3 = 9x$		$-15 = 9x$
$x = \dfrac{1}{3}$		$x = -\dfrac{5}{3}$

(c) The roots of $9x^2 + 12x - 5 = 0$ are $x = \frac{1}{3}$ or $-\frac{5}{3}$.

3. (a) First, make the equation monic by multiplying each side by 2.

$$2y = (2x)^2 + 4(2x) + 10$$

Substitute $P = D_2x = 2x$ and $Q = D_2y = 2y$ to get the monic equation

$$Q = P^2 + 4P + 10$$

Now complete the square by adding and subtracting 4. ($P^2 + 4P + 4 = (P+2)^2$)

$$Q = (P^2 + 4P + 4) - 4 + 10$$
$$Q = (P+2)^2 + 6$$
$$Q - 6 = (P+2)^2$$

Substitute

$$M = T_2 P = T_2 \circ D_2 x = \mathcal{A}_{(2,2)} x$$

and

$$N = T_{-6} Q = T_{-6} \circ D_2 y = \mathcal{A}_{(2,-6)} y$$

to get

$$N = M^2$$

So $a = 2$, $b = 2$, $c = 2$, and $d = -6$

(b) If $y = 0$, then $N = \mathcal{A}_{(2,-6)}(0) = 2(0) - 6 = -6$
$N = M^2$, so $-6 = M^2$ and there are no real solutions for M or for x. This equation has no real roots.

(c) The equation $2x^2 + 4x + 5 = 0$ has no real roots

4. (a) Since $x^2 + 6x + 9 = (x+3)^2$

$$y = x^2 + 6x + 5$$
$$y = (x^2 + 6x + 9) - 9 + 5$$
$$y = (x+3)^2 - 4$$

$k = 3$, $D = -4$

(b) Since $x^2 - 4x + 4 = (x-2)^2$

$$y = x^2 - 4x + 1$$
$$y = (x^2 - 4x + 4) - 4 + 1$$
$$y = (x-2)^2 - 3$$

$k = -2$, $D = -3$

(c) Since $x^2 + 5x + \frac{25}{4} = \left(x + \frac{5}{2}\right)^2$

$$y = x^2 + 5x + 7$$
$$y = \left(x^2 + 5x + \frac{25}{4}\right) - \frac{25}{4} + \frac{28}{4}$$
$$y = \left(x + \frac{5}{2}\right)^2 + \frac{3}{4}$$

$k = \frac{5}{2}$, $D = \frac{3}{4}$

5. (a)

$$y = (M - k)^2 + b(M - k) + c$$
$$y = M^2 - 2kM + k^2 + bM - bk + c$$
$$y = M^2 + (-2k + b)M + k^2 - bk + c$$

If $-2k + b = 0$, then $k = \frac{b}{2}$

(b)

$$y = M^2 + (-2k + b)M + k^2 - bk + c$$
$$y = M^2 + \left(-2\frac{b}{2} + b\right)M + \left(\frac{b}{2}\right)^2 - b\left(\frac{b}{2}\right) + c$$
$$y = M^2 + \frac{b^2}{4} - \frac{b^2}{2} + c$$
$$y = M^2 - \frac{b^2}{4} + c$$

(c) $y = \left(x + \frac{b}{2}\right)^2 + \left(-\frac{b^2}{4} + c\right)$, so $D = -\frac{b^2}{4} + c$

6. (a) The equation $y = x^3 + 6x^2 + 11x + 7$ is already monic, so now you want to find the translation that gets rid of the quadratic term. If $P = T_k x = x + k$, then $x = P - k$.

$$y = (P - k)^3 + 6(P - k)^2 + 11(P - k) + 7$$
$$= P^3 - 3kP^2 + 3k^2 P - k^3 + 6P^2 + \dots$$

So you want $-3k + 6 = 0$, and $k = 2$. $P = T_2 x = x + 2$, then $x = P - 2$

$$y = (P - 2)^3 + 6(P - 2)^2 + 11(P - 2) + 7$$
$$y = P^3 - P + 1$$
$$y - 1 = P^3 - P$$

So $Q = T_{-1} y$ and $Q = P^3 - P$. You already have the form you wanted! That means that the substitutions

$$M = \mathcal{A}_{(1,2)} x$$
$$N = \mathcal{A}_{(1,-1)} y$$

are the ones you want to get $N = M^3 - M$, and $a = 1$, $b = 2$, $c = 1$, and $d = -1$.

(b) Again, the equation $y = x^3 + 3x^2 + 7x + 13$ is already monic, so now you want to find the translation that gets rid of the quadratic term. If $P = T_k x = x + k$, then $x = P - k$.

$$y = (P - k)^3 + 3(P - k)^2 + 7(P - k) + 13$$
$$= P^3 - 3kP^2 + 3k^2 P - k^3 + 3P^2 + \dots$$

So you want $-3k + 3 = 0$, and $k = 1$. $P = T_1 x = x + 1$, then $x = P - 1$

$$y = (P - 1)^3 + 3(P - 1)^2 + 7(P - 1) + 13$$
$$y = P^3 + 4P + 8$$
$$y - 8 = P^3 + 4P$$

So $Q = T_{-8} y$ and $Q = P^3 + 4P$.

Now you need to find a dilation that will make the coefficient of the P-term 1. Multiply each side of the equation by a cube.

$$\alpha^3 Q = (\alpha P)^3 + 4\alpha^2 (\alpha P)$$

You want $4\alpha^2 = 1$, so $\alpha = \frac{1}{2}$. This gives you

$$\frac{1}{8} Q = \left(\frac{1}{2} P\right)^3 + \left(\frac{1}{2} P\right)$$

Substitute

$$M = D_{\frac{1}{2}} P = D_{\frac{1}{2}} \circ T_1 x = \frac{1}{2}(x + 1)$$
$$= \frac{1}{2} x + \frac{1}{2} = \mathcal{A}_{\left(\frac{1}{2},\frac{1}{2}\right)} x$$
$$N = D_{\frac{1}{8}} Q = D_{\frac{1}{8}} \circ T_{-8} y = \frac{1}{8}(y - 8)$$
$$= \frac{1}{8} y - 1 = \mathcal{A}_{\left(\frac{1}{8},-1\right)} y$$

to get $N = M^3 + M$. and $a = \frac{1}{2}$, $b = \frac{1}{2}$, $c = \frac{1}{8}$, and $d = -1$.

On Your Own

7. (a) First you want to make the equation monic, so multiply each side by 5.

$$5y = (5x)^2 + 6(5x) - 35$$

Substitute $P = D_5x$ and $Q = D_5y$ to get

$$Q = P^2 + 6P - 35$$

Now complete the square by adding and subtracting 9. ($P^2 + 6P + 9 = (P + 3)^2$)

$$Q = (P^2 + 6P + 9) - 9 - 35$$

$$Q = (P + 3)^2 - 44$$

$$Q + 44 = (P + 3)^2$$

Substitute

$$M = T_3 P = T_3 \circ D_5x = \mathcal{A}_{(5,3)}x$$
$$N = T_{44} Q = T_{44} \circ D_5y = \mathcal{A}_{(5,44)}y$$

and you have $N = M^2$ with $a = 5, b = 3, c = 5$, and $d = 44$

(b) If $y = 0$, then $N = \mathcal{A}_{(5,44)}(0) = 5(0) + 44 = 44.$
If $N = 44$, then since $N = M^2$, $M = \pm\sqrt{44} = \pm 2\sqrt{11}$
Now $M = \mathcal{A}_{(5,3)}x = 5x + 3$, so

$$5x + 3 = 2\sqrt{11}$$

$$x = \frac{2\sqrt{11} - 3}{5}$$

or

$$5x + 3 = -2\sqrt{11}$$

$$x = \frac{-2\sqrt{11} - 3}{5}$$

(c) $x = \dfrac{2\sqrt{11} - 3}{5}$ or $\dfrac{-2\sqrt{11} - 3}{5}$

8. (a) First you want to make the equation monic, so multiply each side by 9.

$$9y = (9x)^2 - 12(9x) + 36$$

Substitute $P = D_9x$ and $Q = D_9y$ to get

$$Q = P^2 - 12P + 36$$

The right hand side is already a perfect square!
$Q = (P - 6)^2$ so substitute

$$M = T_{-6}P = T_{-6} \circ D_9x = \mathcal{A}_{(9,-6)}x$$
$$N = T_0 Q = T_0 \circ D_9y = \mathcal{A}_{(9,0)}y$$

and you have $N = M^2$ with $a = 9, b = -6, c = 9$, and $d = 0$

(b) If $y = 0$, then $N = \mathcal{A}_{(9,0)}(0) = 9(0) + 0 = 0.$
If $N = 0$, then since $N = M^2$, $M = 0$
Now $M = \mathcal{A}_{(9,-6)}x = 9x - 6$, so

$$9x - 6 = 0$$

$$x = \frac{2}{3}$$

(c) There is only one root to the equation $9x^2 - 12x + 4 = 0$, and that is $x = \frac{2}{3}$.

9. (a) First you want to make the equation monic, so multiply each side by a.

$$ay = (ax)^2 + b(ax) + ac$$

Substitute $P = D_ax$ and $Q = D_ay$ to get

$$Q = P^2 + bP + ac$$

Now complete the square by adding and subtracting $\frac{b^2}{4}$. ($P^2 + bP + \frac{b^2}{4} = (P + \frac{b}{2})^2$)

$$Q = \left(P^2 + bP + \frac{b^2}{4}\right) - \frac{b^2}{4} + ac$$

$$Q = \left(P + \frac{b}{2}\right)^2 + \left(-\frac{b^2}{4} + ac\right)$$

$$Q + \frac{b^2 - 4ac}{4} = \left(P + \frac{b}{2}\right)^2$$

Substitute

$$M = T_{\frac{b}{2}} P = T_{\frac{b}{2}} \circ D_ax = \mathcal{A}_{\left(a, \frac{b}{2}\right)}(x)$$
$$N = T_{\frac{b^2-4ac}{4}} Q = T_{\frac{b^2-4ac}{4}} \circ D_ay = \mathcal{A}_{\left(a, \frac{b^2-4ac}{4}\right)}(y)$$

to get the transformed equation $N = M^2$.
That gives you $e = a$, $f = \frac{b}{2}$, $g = a$, and $h = \frac{b^2}{4} - ac.$

(b) If $y = 0$, then $N = \mathcal{A}_{\left(a, \frac{b^2}{4} - ac\right)}(0) = a(0) + \frac{b^2}{4} - ac = \frac{b^2}{4} - ac.$
If $N = \frac{b^2 - 4ac}{4}$, then since $N = M^2$,

$$M = \pm\sqrt{\frac{b^2 - 4ac}{4}} = \pm\frac{\sqrt{b^2 - 4ac}}{2}$$

$M = \mathcal{A}_{\left(a, \frac{b}{2}\right)}(x) = ax + \frac{b}{2}$, so

$$ax + \frac{b}{2} = \pm\frac{\sqrt{b^2 - 4ac}}{2}$$

$$ax = \frac{-b \pm \sqrt{b^2 - 4ac}}{2}$$

$$x = \frac{-b \pm \sqrt{b^2 - 4ac}}{2a}$$

Hey! What do you know? It's the quadratic formula!

(c) $x = \dfrac{-b \pm \sqrt{b^2 - 4ac}}{2a}$

10. $0 = 2x^2 + 7x + 5 = (2x + 5)(x + 1)$

$2x + 5 = 0$ or $x + 1 = 0$

$x = -\dfrac{5}{2}$ or $x = -1$

The correct answer choice is **C**.

11. $y = x^3 + bx^2 + cx + d$

$$= (M - k)^3 + b(M - k)^2 + c(M - k) + d$$

$$= M^3 - 3kM^2 + 3k^2M - k^3 + bM^2 - \dots$$

(It is okay to stop multiplying here because there will not be any other M^2 terms after this one.)
If $-3k + b = 0$, then $k = \frac{b}{3}$.

12. (a) In Exercise 11, you found the value of k that, in the substitution $x = M - k$, would make the quadratic term vanish, and it was $k = \frac{b}{3}$. That's the substitution here, so the quadratic term should vanish. Here is what that calculation would look like:

$$y = \left(M - \frac{b}{3}\right)^3 + b\left(M - \frac{b}{3}\right)^2 + c\left(M - \frac{b}{3}\right) + d$$

$$= M^3 - bM^2 + \frac{b^2}{3}M - \frac{b^3}{27} + bM^2 - \frac{2b^2}{3}M +$$

$$\frac{b^3}{9} + cM - \frac{bc}{3} + d$$

$$= M^3 + \left(\frac{3c - b^2}{3}\right)M + \left(\frac{2b^2 - 9bc + 27d}{27}\right)$$

And that pesky quadratic is gone.

(b) Look at the simplified form of the substitution equation that you found in part (a). The coefficient of the M-term is $\frac{3c-b^2}{3}$. If that is positive, you will get $N = M^3 + M$. If it is zero, you'll get $N = M^3$, and if it is negative, you'll get $N = M^3 - M$.

(c) First, think about how you would transform the equation $y = ax^3 + bx^2 + cx + d$ into a monic equation. You would multiply through by a^2 to get

$$a^2 y = (ax)^3 + b(ax)^2 + ac(ax) + a^2 d$$

Then you would make the substitutions $P = D_a x$ and $Q = D_{a^2} y$ to get

$$Q = P^3 + bP^2 + acP + a^2 d$$

Now you have a monic equation, so you can use your previous result. After the translation, the coefficient of the M-term will be $\frac{3(ac)-b^2}{3}$, so if that is positive, you will get $N = M^3 + M$. If it is zero, you will get $N = M^3$, and if it is negative, you will get $N = M^3 - M$.

13. First make the equation monic by multiplying each side by 64 to get

$$64y = (8x)^3 - 6(8x)^2 + 16(8x) - 64$$

Substitute $P = D_8 x$ and $Q = D_{64} y$ to get

$$Q = P^3 - 6P^2 + 16P - 64$$

If $M = T_k P$, then $P = M - k$ and

$$Q = (M - k)^3 - 6(M - k)^2 + 16(M - k) - 64$$

$$= M^3 - 3kM^2 + 3k^2 M - k^3 - 6M^2 - \dots$$

You want $-3k - 6 = 0$, so $k = -2$.

$$Q = (M + 2)^3 - 6(M + 2)^2 + 16(M + 2) - 64$$

$$Q = M^3 + 4M - 48$$

$$Q + 48 = M^3 + 4M$$

With the substitutions $M = T_{-2}P$ and $N = T_{48}Q$, you get

$$N = M^3 + 4M$$

Multiply each side of this equation by α^3 to get

$$\alpha^3 N = (\alpha M)^3 + 4\alpha^2 (\alpha M)$$

You want $4\alpha^2 = 1$, so $\alpha = \frac{1}{2}$ and $\alpha^3 = \frac{1}{8}$
So the final substitutions you want to make are

$$R = D_{\frac{1}{2}} \circ T_{-2} \circ D_8(x) = 4x - 1 = \mathcal{A}_{(4,-1)}$$

$$S = D_{\frac{1}{8}} \circ T_{48} \circ D_{64}(y) = 8y + 6 = \mathcal{A}_{(8,6)}$$

to get $S = R^3 + R$.

14. First make the equation monic by multiplying each side by a^2.

$$a^2 y = (ax)^3 + b(ax)^2 + ac(ax) + a^2 d$$

Substitute $P = D_a x$ and $Q = D_{a^2} y$ to get

$$Q = P^3 + bP^2 + acP + a^2 d.$$

If $M = T_k P$, then $P = M - k$

$$Q = (M - k)^3 + b(M - k)^2 + ac(M - k) + a^2 d$$

$$= M^3 - 3kM^2 + 3k^2 M - k^3 + bM^2 - \dots$$

You want $-3k + b = 0$, so $k = \frac{b}{3}$.

$$Q = \left(M - \frac{b}{3}\right)^3 + b\left(M - \frac{b}{3}\right)^2 + ac\left(M - \frac{b}{3}\right) + a^2 d$$

$$Q = M^3 + \frac{3ac - b^2}{3}M + \frac{2b^3 - 9abc + 27a^2 d}{27}$$

$$Q + \frac{9abc - 2b^3 - 27a^2 d}{27} = M^3 + \frac{3ac - b^2}{3}M$$

So the substitutions

$$M = T_{\frac{b}{3}}P$$

$$N = T_{\frac{9abc - 2b^3 - 27a^2 d}{27}}Q$$

give you $N = M^3 + \dfrac{3ac - b^2}{3}M$.

Notice that if $3ac = b^2$, this equation simplifies to $N = M^3$ and you're done. However, if $3ac \neq b^2$, you get to continue!
Multiply each side of that equation by α^3 to get

$$\alpha^3 N = (\alpha M)^3 + \frac{(3ac - b^2)\alpha^2}{3}(\alpha M)$$

You want $\dfrac{(3ac - b^2)\alpha^2}{3} = \pm 1$, which gives you

$$\alpha = \sqrt{\frac{3}{|3ac - b^2|}}$$

Using that value of α, your final substitutions, which will give you either $S = R^3 - R$ or $S = R^3 + R$, are

$$R = D_\alpha \circ T_{\frac{b}{3}} \circ D_a(x)$$

$$S = D_{\alpha^3} \circ T_{\frac{9abc - 2b^3 - 27a^2 d}{27}} \circ D_{a^2}(y)$$

Maintain Your Skills

15. (a) $(\mathcal{A}_{(2,3)})^{-1}$ undoes $\mathcal{A}_{(2,3)}(x) = 2x + 3$. To undo this function subtract three and divide by 2. In symbols, $D_{\frac{1}{2}} \circ T_{-3}(x) = \frac{1}{2}x - \frac{3}{2}x = \mathcal{A}_{\left(\frac{1}{2}, -\frac{3}{2}\right)}$.

$$\mathcal{A}_{(2,3)} \circ T_4 \circ (\mathcal{A}_{(2,3)})^{-1}(x) = \mathcal{A}_{(2,3)} \circ T_4 \left(\frac{1}{2}x - \frac{3}{2}\right)$$
$$= \mathcal{A}_{(2,3)} \left(\frac{1}{2}x + \frac{5}{2}\right)$$
$$= 2\left(\frac{1}{2}x + \frac{5}{2}\right) + 3$$
$$= x + 8$$
$$= T_8(x)$$

(b) $(\mathcal{A}_{(3,-7)})^{-1} = \mathcal{A}_{\left(\frac{1}{3}, \frac{7}{3}\right)}$.

$$\mathcal{A}_{(3,-7)} \circ T_{-3} \circ (\mathcal{A}_{(3,-7)})^{-1} = \mathcal{A}_{(3,-7)} \circ T_{-3}\left(\frac{1}{3}x + \frac{7}{3}\right)$$
$$= \mathcal{A}_{(3,-7)} \left(\frac{1}{3}x - \frac{2}{3}\right)$$
$$= 3\left(\frac{1}{3}x - \frac{2}{3}\right) - 7$$
$$= x - 9$$
$$= T_{-9}(x)$$

(c) $(\mathcal{A}_{(-1,8)})^{-1} = \mathcal{A}_{(-1,8)}$.

$$\mathcal{A}_{(-1,8)} \circ T_5 \circ (\mathcal{A}_{(-1,8)})^{-1} = \mathcal{A}_{(-1,8)} \circ T_5(-x + 8)$$
$$= \mathcal{A}_{(-1,8)}(-x + 13)$$
$$= -(-x + 13) + 8$$
$$= x - 5$$
$$= T_{-5}(x)$$

(d) $(\mathcal{A}_{(-5,12)})^{-1} = \mathcal{A}_{\left(-\frac{1}{5}, \frac{12}{5}\right)}$.

$$\mathcal{A}_{(-5,12)} \circ T_{-2} \circ (\mathcal{A}_{(-5,12)})^{-1} = \mathcal{A}_{(-5,12)} \circ T_{-2}\left(-\frac{1}{5}x + \frac{12}{5}\right)$$
$$= \mathcal{A}_{(-5,12)} \left(-\frac{1}{5}x + \frac{2}{5}\right)$$
$$= -5\left(-\frac{1}{5}x + \frac{2}{5}\right) + 12$$
$$= x + 10$$
$$= T_{10}(x)$$

16.

$$(\mathcal{A}_{(a,b)})^{-1}(x) = (T_b \circ D_a)^{-1}(x)$$
$$= (D_a)^{-1} \circ (T_b)^{-1}(x)$$
$$= D_{\frac{1}{a}} \circ T_{-b}(x)$$
$$= D_{\frac{1}{a}}(x - b)$$
$$= \frac{1}{a}x - \frac{b}{a}$$
$$= \mathcal{A}_{\left(\frac{1}{a}, -\frac{b}{a}\right)}$$

$$\mathcal{A}_{(a,b)} \circ T_r \circ (\mathcal{A}_{(a,b)})^{-1}(x) = \mathcal{A}_{(a,b)} \circ T_r\left(\frac{1}{a}x - \frac{b}{a}\right)$$
$$= \mathcal{A}_{(a,b)} \left(\frac{1}{a}x + \frac{ar - b}{a}\right)$$
$$= a\left(\frac{1}{a}x + \frac{ar - b}{a}\right) + b$$
$$= x + (ar - b) + b$$
$$= x + ar$$
$$= T_{ar}(x)$$

6B MATHEMATICAL REFLECTIONS

1. (a) $T_3 \circ T_{-1} \circ T_5 = T_{3-1+5} = T_7 = \mathcal{A}_{(1,7)}$

(b) $D_{-4} \circ D_2 \circ D_{-3} = D_{(-4)(2)(-3)} = D_{24} = \mathcal{A}_{(24,0)}$

(c) $D_{-4} \circ T_3(x) = D_{-4}(x + 3) = -4x - 12 = \mathcal{A}_{(-4,-12)}(x)$

(d) $T_3 \circ D_{-4} = \mathcal{A}_{(-4,3)}$

(e) $T_3 \circ D_{-3} \circ (T_3)^{-1}(x) = T_3 \circ D_{-3} \circ T_{-3}(x)$
$$= T_3 \circ D_{-3}(x - 3)$$
$$= T_3(-3x + 9)$$
$$= -3x + 12$$
$$= \mathcal{A}_{(-3,12)}$$

(f) $(D_{-4})^{-1} \circ T_5 \circ D_{-4}(x) = D_{-\frac{1}{4}} \circ T_5 \circ D_{-4}(x)$
$$= D_{-\frac{1}{4}} \circ T_5(-4x)$$
$$= D_{-\frac{1}{4}}(-4x + 5)$$
$$= x - \frac{5}{4}$$
$$= \mathcal{A}_{\left(1, -\frac{5}{4}\right)}$$

2. (a) $(\mathcal{A}_{(2,5)})^{-1} = \mathcal{A}_{\left(\frac{1}{2}, -\frac{5}{2}\right)}$

(b) $(\mathcal{A}_{(-3,4)})^{-1} = \mathcal{A}_{\left(-\frac{1}{3}, \frac{4}{3}\right)}$

(c) $\mathcal{A}_{(-3,4)} \circ \mathcal{A}_{(2,5)}(x) = \mathcal{A}_{(-3,4)}(2x + 5)$
$$= -3(2x + 5) + 4$$
$$= -6x - 11$$
$$= \mathcal{A}_{(-6,-11)}$$

(d) $\mathcal{A}_{(2,5)} \circ \mathcal{A}_{(-3,4)}(x) = \mathcal{A}_{(2,5)}(-3x + 4)$
$$= 2(-3x + 4) + 5$$
$$= -6x + 13$$
$$= \mathcal{A}_{(-6,13)}$$

(e) $\left(\mathcal{A}_{(2,5)} \circ \mathcal{A}_{(-3,4)}\right)^{-1}(x) = \left(\mathcal{A}_{(-3,4)}\right)^{-1} \circ \left(\mathcal{A}_{(2,5)}\right)^{-1}(x)$
$$= \mathcal{A}_{\left(-\frac{1}{3}, \frac{4}{3}\right)} \circ \mathcal{A}_{\left(\frac{1}{2}, -\frac{5}{2}\right)}(x)$$
$$= \mathcal{A}_{\left(-\frac{1}{3}, \frac{4}{3}\right)}\left(\frac{1}{2}x - \frac{5}{2}\right)$$
$$= -\frac{1}{3}\left(\frac{1}{2}x - \frac{5}{2}\right) + \frac{4}{3}$$
$$= -\frac{1}{6}x + \frac{13}{6}$$
$$= \mathcal{A}_{\left(-\frac{1}{6}, \frac{13}{6}\right)}(x)$$

(f) $(\mathcal{A}_{(2,5)} \circ \mathcal{A}_{(-3,4)})^{-1} = (\mathcal{A}_{(-3,4)})^{-1} \circ (\mathcal{A}_{(2,5)})^{-1}$

3. Make the equation $y = 3x^2 + 10x + 7$ monic by multiplying each side by 3 to get

$$3y = (3x)^2 + 10(3x) + 21$$

Substitute $P = D_3 x$ and $Q = D_3 y$, and you have

$$Q = P^2 + 10P + 21$$

Complete the square by adding and subtracting 25. $(P^2 + 10P + 25 = (P + 5)^2)$

$$Q = (P^2 + 10P + 25) - 25 + 21$$
$$Q = (P + 5)^2 - 4$$
$$Q + 4 = (P + 5)^2$$

Make these substitutions:

$$M = T_5 P = T_5 \circ D_3 x = \mathcal{A}_{(3,5)} x$$
$$N = T_4 Q = T_4 \circ D_3 y = \mathcal{A}_{(3,4)} y$$

Now you have $N = M^2$, and $a = 3, b = 5, c = 3$, and $d = 4$.

4. (a) $M = \mathcal{A}_{(6,-5)}(x) = 6x - 5$, $N = \mathcal{A}_{(4,1)}(y) = 4y + 1$, so

$$4y + 1 = (6x - 5)^2$$
$$4y + 1 = 36x^2 - 60x + 25$$
$$4y = 36x^2 - 60x + 24$$
$$y = 9x^2 - 15x + 6$$

(b) If $y = 0$, then $N = \mathcal{A}_{(4,1)}(0) = 4(0) + 1 = 1$
Since $N = M^2$, $M = \pm 1$
If $M = 1$, then $6x - 5 = 1$ and $x = 1$. If $M = -1$, then $6x - 5 = -1$ and $x = \frac{2}{3}$

5. $y = x^3 - 3x^2 + 12x + 17$ is already monic, so find the translation that will eliminate the quadratic term.
If $P = T_k x$, then $x = P - k$

$$y = (P - k)^3 - 3(P - k)^2 + 12(P - k) + 17$$
$$= P^3 - 3kP^2 + 3k^2 P - k^3 - 3P^2 + \dots$$

You want $-3k - 3 = 0$, so $k = -1$

$$y = (P + 1)^3 - 3(P + 1)^2 + 12(P + 1) + 17$$
$$y = P^3 + 3P^2 + 3P + 1 - 3P^2 - 6P - 3$$
$$\quad + 12P + 12 + 17$$
$$y = P^3 + 9P + 27$$
$$y - 27 = P^3 + 9P$$

So with the substitutions $P = T_{-1} x$ and $Q = T_{-27} y$, you have

$$Q = P^3 + 9P$$

Multiply each side by α^3 to get

$$\alpha^3 Q = (\alpha P)^3 + 9\alpha^2 (\alpha P)$$

You want $9\alpha^2 = 1$, so $\alpha = \frac{1}{3}$
Substitute

$$R = D_{\frac{1}{3}} P = D_{\frac{1}{3}} \circ T_{-1} x = \mathcal{A}_{\left(\frac{1}{3}, -\frac{1}{3}\right)}$$

and

$$S = D_{\frac{1}{27}} Q = D_{\frac{1}{27}} \circ T_{-27} x = \mathcal{A}_{\left(\frac{1}{27}, -1\right)}$$

to get $S = R^3 + R$. This gives you $a = \frac{1}{3}$, $b = -\frac{1}{3}$, $c = \frac{1}{27}$, and $d = -1$

6. You know that $D_a \circ D_b = D_{ab}$. If you reverse the order of the composition, you'll still have the same product ab in the resulting dilation. Because multiplication is commutative for the real numbers, dilations are commutative under function composition.

7. An affine transformation $\mathcal{A}_{(a,b)}$ is equal to $T_b \circ D_a$, so to find the inverse of this multi-step process, you undo each step in reverse order. This means that $(\mathcal{A}_{(a,b)})^{-1} = (T_b \circ D_a)^{-1} = (D_a)^{-1} \circ (T_b)^{-1} = D_{\frac{1}{a}} \circ T_{-b}$. To express this as a single affine transformation, use $D_{\frac{1}{a}} \circ T_{-b}(x) = D_{\frac{1}{a}}(x - b) = \frac{1}{a}(x - b) = \frac{1}{a}x - \frac{b}{a}$. This shows that $(\mathcal{A}_{(a,b)})^{-1} = \mathcal{A}_{\left(\frac{1}{a}, -\frac{b}{a}\right)}$.

8. First make the equation monic with appropriate dilations. You usually do this by multiplying through by the coefficient of the x^3-term and finding out what the corresponding dilations are from the resulting equation. Then find a transformation that eliminates the quadratic term. You usually do this by trying a general translation by k and then figuring out which k gets rid of the quadratic term. Then, if the equation is in the form $R^3 + aR$ where $a \neq \pm 1$, you find another dilation that keeps the equation monic but makes this coefficient equal to 1. This is done by multiplying each side of the equation by α^3. Then you get a coefficient equal to the old a multiplied by α^2, which you can set equal to 1. This tells you the value of α, which gives you your final dilations.

MID-CHAPTER TEST

Multiple Choice

1. The correct choice is **C**, 4 units left.

2. This is a translation of the graph of $y = x^2$ 1 unit left and 4 units up. Since the vertex of $y = x^2$ is $(0, 0)$, the vertex of $y - 4 = (x + 1)^2$ is $(0 - 1, 0 + 4) = (-1, 4)$. The correct choice is **B**.

3. Since $f(-x) = (-x)^2 + 4(-x) = x^2 - 4x$ which is not $f(x)$ or $-f(x)$, f is neither odd nor even. But, $g(-x) = (-x)^3 + 4(-x) = -x^3 - 4x = -(x^3 + 4x) = -g(x)$. So, g is an odd function. The correct choice is **D**.

4. $(D_2 \circ D_{-3})(5) = D_2(D_{-3}(5)) = D_2(-3 \cdot 5) = D_2(-15) = 2(-15) = -30$ The correct choice is **A**.

5. For a real number x, you have

$$\mathcal{A}_{(2,4)} \circ \mathcal{A}_{(-1,3)}(x) = \mathcal{A}_{(2,4)}(-x + 3)$$
$$= 2(-x + 3) + 4$$
$$= -2x + 6 + 4$$
$$= -2x + 10$$

So, the correct choice is **C**, $\mathcal{A}_{(-2,10)}$.

Open Response

6. (a)

$$x^2 + y^2 = 1$$
$$y^2 = 1 - x^2$$
$$y^2 = 1 - \left(\frac{7}{25}\right)^2$$
$$= 1 - \frac{49}{625}$$
$$= \frac{576}{625}$$
$$y = \pm\sqrt{\frac{576}{625}}$$
$$= \pm\frac{24}{25}$$

So, the two points you are looking for are $\left(\frac{7}{25}, \frac{24}{25}\right)$, $\left(\frac{7}{25}, -\frac{24}{25}\right)$. You could have recognized that 7, 24, 25 is a Pythagorean Triple and used that to find the points.

(b) Find the other points by using the symmetry of the unit circle: $\left(-\frac{7}{25}, \frac{24}{25}\right)$, $\left(-\frac{7}{25}, -\frac{24}{25}\right)$, $\left(\frac{24}{25}, \frac{7}{25}\right)$, $\left(\frac{24}{25}, -\frac{7}{25}\right)$, $\left(-\frac{24}{25}, \frac{7}{25}\right)$, $\left(-\frac{24}{25}, -\frac{7}{25}\right)$

7. (a)

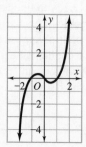

(b) The equation will be $y + 2 = (x - 5)^3 - (x - 5)$.

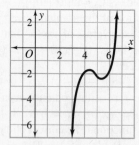

(c) The equation will be $y = \left(\frac{x}{3}\right)^3 - \left(\frac{x}{3}\right)$.

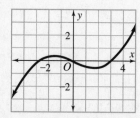

8. (a)

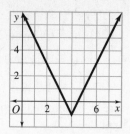

The graph of $y + 1 = 2|x - 4|$ is the graph of $y = |x|$ scaled vertically by a factor of 2 and translated 4 units right and 1 unit down.

(b)

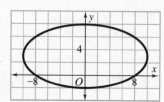

The graph of $\left(\frac{x}{2}\right)^2 + (y - 3)^2 = 25$ is the graph of $x^2 + y^2 = 25$ stretched horizontally by a factor of 2 and translated 3 units up.

9. (a) For a real number x, you have

$$D_3 \circ T_1(x) = D_3(x+1) = 3(x+1) = 3x + 3 = A_{(3,3)}(x)$$

Therefore,

$$D_3 \circ T_1 = A_{(3,3)}$$

(b) For a real number x, you have

$$T_1 \circ D_3(x) = T_1(3x) = 3x + 1 = A_{(3,1)}(x)$$

Therefore, $T_1 \circ D_3 = A_{(3,1)}$

(c) For a real number x, you have

$$D_2 \circ D_{-2} \circ T_6(x) = D_2 \circ D_{-2}(x+6) = D_2(-2(x+6))$$
$$= D_2(-2x - 12)$$
$$= 2(-2x - 12)$$
$$= -4x - 24$$
$$= A_{(-4,-24)}(x)$$

Therefore, $D_2 \circ D_{-2} \circ T_6 = A_{(-4,-24)}$

(d) For a real number x, you have

$$T_4 \circ (D_2)^{-1}(x) = T_4\left(\frac{1}{2}x\right) = \frac{1}{2}x + 4 = A_{\left(\frac{1}{2}, 4\right)}(x)$$

Therefore, $T_4 \circ (D_2)^{-1} = A_{\left(\frac{1}{2}, 4\right)}$

(e) For a real number x, you have: $\left(A_{(2,6)}\right)^{-1} = A_{(c,d)}$ means $A_{(2,6)} \circ A_{(c,d)} = A_{(1,0)}$ and $A_{(c,d)} \circ A_{(2,6)} = A_{(1,0)}$

$$A_{(2,6)} \circ A_{(c,d)}(x) = A_{(1,0)}(x)$$
$$A_{(2,6)}(cx + d) = x + 0$$
$$2(cx + d) + 6 = x$$
$$2cx + 2d + 6 = x$$

So,

$$2c = 1 \longrightarrow c = \frac{1}{2}$$

and

$$2d + 6 = 0 \longrightarrow d = -3$$

And,

$$(\mathcal{A}_{(2,6)})^{-1} = \mathcal{A}_{\left(\frac{1}{2}, -3\right)}$$

Now, to be sure that $(\mathcal{A}_{(2,6)})^{-1} = \mathcal{A}_{\left(\frac{1}{2}, -3\right)}$, you need to check the composition in the other order:

$$\mathcal{A}_{\left(\frac{1}{2}, -3\right)} \circ \mathcal{A}_{(2,6)}(x) = \mathcal{A}_{\left(\frac{1}{2}, -3\right)}(2x + 6)$$

$$= \frac{1}{2}(2x + 6) - 3$$

$$= x + 3 - 3$$

$$= x$$

(f) For a real number x, you have

$$\mathcal{A}_{(2,-4)} \circ \mathcal{A}_{(-3,5)}(x) = \mathcal{A}_{(2,-4)}(-3x + 5)$$

$$= 2(-3x + 5) - 4$$

$$= -6x + 10 - 4$$

$$= -6x + 6$$

$$= \mathcal{A}_{(-6,6)}(x)$$

Therefore, $\mathcal{A}_{(2,-4)} \circ \mathcal{A}_{(-3,5)} = \mathcal{A}_{(-6,6)}$

10. Make the equation $y = 2x^2 + 6x - 3$ monic by multiplying each side by 2 to get

$$2y = (2x)^2 + 6(2x) - 6$$

Substitute $P = D_2x$ and $Q = D_2y$, and you have

$$Q = P^2 + 6P - 6$$

Complete the square by adding and subtracting 9. $(P^2 + 6P + 9 = (P + 3)^2)$

$$Q = (P^2 + 6P + 9) - 9 - 6$$

$$Q = (P + 3)^2 - 15$$

$$Q + 15 = (P + 3)^2$$

Make these substitutions:

$$M = T_3P = T_3 \circ D_2x = \mathcal{A}_{(2,3)}$$
$$N = T_{15}Q = T_{15} \circ D_2y = \mathcal{A}_{(2,15)}$$

Now you have $N = M^2$, and $a = 2, b = 3, c = 2$, and $d = 15$.

11. The graph of $-2y = x^3 - x$ is the same as the graph of $y = x^3 - x$ after it has been reflected over the x-axis and shrunk vertically by a factor of 2.

INVESTIGATION 6C   GRAPHING USING AFFINE TRANSFORMATIONS

6.8   Getting Started

For You to Explore

1. (a) Make the equation $y = 2x^2 - 12x + 17$ monic by multiplying each side by 2.

$$2y = (2x)^2 - 12(2x) + 34$$

Then the substitutions

- $P = D_2x$
- $Q = D_2y$

give you $Q = P^2 - 12P + 34$. Add and subtract 36 to complete the square.

$$Q = (P^2 - 12P + 36) - 36 + 34$$
$$Q + 2 = (P - 6)^2$$

Then the substitutions

- $M = T_{-6}P = T_{-6} \circ D_2x = \mathcal{A}_{(2,-6)}x$
- $N = T_2Q = T_2 \circ D_2y = \mathcal{A}_{(2,2)}y$

give you $N = M^2$. So $a = 2, b = -6, c = 2$, and $d = 2$.

(b) Make the equation $y = -x^2 + 2x + 3$ monic by multiplying each side by -1.

$$-y = (-x)^2 + 2(-x) - 3$$

Then the substitutions

- $P = D_{-1}x$
- $Q = D_{-1}y$

give you $Q = P^2 + 2P - 3$. Add and subtract 1 to complete the square.

$$Q = (P^2 + 2P + 1) - 1 - 3$$
$$Q + 4 = (P + 1)^2$$

Then the substitutions

- $M = T_1P = T_1 \circ D_{-1}x = \mathcal{A}_{(-1,1)}x$
- $N = T_4Q = T_4 \circ D_{-1}y = \mathcal{A}_{(-1,4)}y$

give you $N = M^2$. So $a = -1, b = 1, c = -1$, and $d = 4$.

2. (a) Make the equation $y = 3x^2 - 14x + 10$ monic by multiplying each side by 3.

$$3y = (3x)^2 - 14(3x) + 30$$

Then the substitutions

- $P = D_3x$
- $Q = D_3y$

give you $Q = P^2 - 14P + 30$. Add and subtract 49 to complete the square.

$$Q = (P^2 - 14P + 49) - 49 + 30$$
$$Q + 19 = (P - 7)^2$$

Then the substitutions

- $M = T_{-7}P = T_{-7} \circ D_3 x = \mathcal{A}_{(3,-7)}x$
- $N = T_{19}Q = T_{19} \circ D_3 y = \mathcal{A}_{(3,19)}y$

give you $N = M^2$. So $a = 3$, $b = -7$, $c = 3$, and $d = 19$.

(b) Make the equation $y = -\frac{1}{4}x^2 + 6x + 8$ monic by multiplying each side by $-\frac{1}{4}$.

$$-\frac{1}{4}y = \left(-\frac{1}{4}x\right)^2 + 6\left(-\frac{1}{4}x\right) - 2$$

Then the substitutions

- $P = D_{-\frac{1}{4}}x$
- $Q = D_{-\frac{1}{4}}y$

give you $Q = P^2 + 6P - 2$. Add and subtract 9 to complete the square.

$$Q = (P^2 + 6P + 9) - 9 - 2$$

$$Q + 11 = (P + 3)^2$$

Then the substitutions

- $M = T_3 P = T_3 \circ D_{-\frac{1}{4}}x = \mathcal{A}_{\left(-\frac{1}{4},3\right)}x$
- $N = T_{11}Q = T_{11} \circ D_{-\frac{1}{4}}y = \mathcal{A}_{\left(-\frac{1}{4},11\right)}y$

give you $N = M^2$. So $a = -\frac{1}{4}$, $b = 3$, $c = -\frac{1}{4}$, and $d = 11$.

3. (a) $(x^2 + 4x + 4) - 4 = (x + 2)^2 - 4$, so $h = -2$ and $k = -4$.

(b) $(x^2 - 6x + 9) - 9 = (x - 3)^2 - 9$, so $h = 3$ and $k = -9$.

(c) $\left(x^2 + 5x + \frac{25}{4}\right) - \frac{25}{4} = \left(x + \frac{5}{2}\right)^2 - \frac{25}{4}$, so $h = -\frac{5}{2}$ and $k = -\frac{25}{4}$.

(d) $\left(x^2 + 3x + \frac{9}{4}\right) - \frac{9}{4} = \left(x + \frac{3}{2}\right)^2 - \frac{9}{4}$, so $h = -\frac{3}{2}$ and $k = -\frac{9}{4}$.

4. (a)
$$x^2 + y^2 + 4x = 0$$
$$(x^2 + 4x +) + y^2 = 0$$
$$(x^2 + 4x + 4) - 4 + y^2 = 0$$
$$(x + 2)^2 + y^2 = 4$$
So $h = -2$, $k = 0$, and $r = 2$.

(b)
$$x^2 + y^2 - 6x + 4y - 12 = 0$$
$$(x^2 - 6x +) + (y^2 + 4y +) = 12$$
$$(x^2 - 6x + 9) - 9 + (y^2 + 4y + 4) - 4 = 12$$
$$(x - 3)^2 + (y + 2)^2 = 25$$
So $h = 3$, $k = -2$, and $r = 5$.

(c)
$$x^2 + y^2 + 5x = 0$$
$$(x^2 + 5x +) + y^2 = 0$$
$$\left(x^2 + 5x + \frac{25}{4}\right) - \frac{25}{4} + y^2 = 0$$
$$\left(x + \frac{5}{2}\right)^2 + y^2 = \frac{25}{4}$$
So $h = -\frac{5}{2}$, $k = 0$, and $r = \frac{5}{2}$.

(d)
$$x^2 + y^2 + 3x + 5y - \frac{1}{2} = 0$$
$$(x^2 + 3x +) + (y^2 + 5y +) - \frac{1}{2} = 0$$
$$\left(x^2 + 3x + \frac{9}{4}\right) - \frac{9}{4} + \left(y^2 + 5y + \frac{25}{4}\right) - \frac{25}{4} - \frac{2}{4} = 0$$
$$\left(x + \frac{3}{2}\right)^2 + \left(y + \frac{5}{2}\right)^2 = 9$$

So $h = -\frac{3}{2}$, $k = -\frac{5}{2}$, and $r = 3$.

5. For each value of M, the corresponding value of x is 3 more, so $x = M + 3$. The M-axis is the image of the x-axis after it has been translated three units to the right. ($M = T_{-3}x$) You can also see the x-axis as the image of the M-axis after it has been translated three units to the left.

6. (a) $M = x + 4$, $x = M - 4$

(b) $M = x - 2$, $x = M + 2$

(c) $M = x + \frac{3}{2}$, $x = M - \frac{3}{2}$

(d) $M = x$

(e) If $M = T_a(x)$ then the M-axis is the image of the x-axis after a translation of $|a|$ units to the left if $a > 0$, or $|a|$ units to the right if $a < 0$. You can also think of the x-axis as the image of the M-axis after a translation of $|a|$ units to the right if $a > 0$ or $|a|$ units to the left if $a < 0$.

On Your Own

7. For each value of M, the corresponding value of x is half as large, so $x = \frac{M}{2}$. The M-axis is the image of the x-axis after it has been dilated by a factor of $\frac{1}{2}$. ($M = D_2 x$) You can also see the x-axis as the image of the M-axis after it has been dilated by a factor of 2. The unit on the x-axis is twice as big as the unit on the M-axis.

8. (a) $M = 3x$, so $x = \frac{M}{3}$.

(b) $M = \frac{1}{2}x$, so $x = 2M$.

-4	-3	-2	-1	0	1	2	3	4	M
-8 -7 -6 -5 -4 -3 -2 -1				0 1	2	3 4	5 6	7 8	x

(c) $M = -x$, so $x = -M$

-4	-3	-2	-1	0	1	2	3	4	M
4	3	2	1	0	-1	-2	-3	-4	x

(d) $M = -\frac{1}{2}x$, so $x = -2M$.

-4	-3	-2	-1	0	1	2	3	4	M
8 7 6 5 4 3 2 1				0 -1	-2	-3 -4	-5 -6	-7 -8	x

(e) If $M = D_s(x)$, then the x-axis is the image of the M-axis after it has been dilated by a factor of s. You can also think of the M-axis as the image of the x-axis after it has been dilated by a factor of $\frac{1}{s}$.

9. For each value of M, the corresponding value of x is $\frac{1}{2}M + \frac{3}{2}$, and for each value of x, the corresponding value of M is $2x - 3$. The M-axis is the image of the x-axis after it has been dilated by a factor of $\frac{1}{2}$ and then translated 3 units to the right. The x-axis is the image of the M-axis after it has been dilated by a factor of 2 and then translated $\frac{3}{2}$ units to the left.

10. (a) $M = \mathcal{A}_{(3,-1)}(x) = 3x - 1$, so $x = \frac{1}{3}M + \frac{1}{3}$.

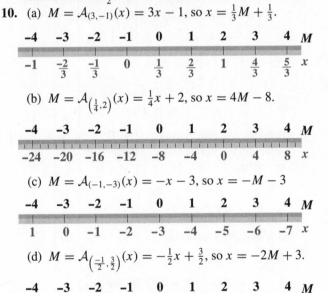

-4	-3	-2	-1	0	1	2	3	4	M
-1	$-\frac{2}{3}$	$-\frac{1}{3}$	0	$\frac{1}{3}$	$\frac{2}{3}$	1	$\frac{4}{3}$	$\frac{5}{3}$	x

(b) $M = \mathcal{A}_{\left(\frac{1}{4},2\right)}(x) = \frac{1}{4}x + 2$, so $x = 4M - 8$.

-4	-3	-2	-1	0	1	2	3	4	M
-24	-20	-16	-12	-8	-4	0	4	8	x

(c) $M = \mathcal{A}_{(-1,-3)}(x) = -x - 3$, so $x = -M - 3$

-4	-3	-2	-1	0	1	2	3	4	M
1	0	-1	-2	-3	-4	-5	-6	-7	x

(d) $M = \mathcal{A}_{\left(\frac{-1}{2},\frac{3}{2}\right)}(x) = -\frac{1}{2}x + \frac{3}{2}$, so $x = -2M + 3$.

-4	-3	-2	-1	0	1	2	3	4	M
11 10 9	8	7 6	5	4 3	2	1 0	-1 -2	-3 -4 -5	x

11. (a) $M = (\mathcal{A}_{(3,-1)})^{-1}(x) = \mathcal{A}_{\left(\frac{1}{3},\frac{1}{3}\right)}x = \frac{1}{3}x + \frac{1}{3}$, so $x = 3M - 1$.

-4	-3	-2	-1	0	1	2	3	4	M
-13	-10	-7	-4	-1 0	2	5	8	11	x

(b) $M = (\mathcal{A}_{\left(\frac{1}{4},2\right)})^{-1}(x) = \mathcal{A}_{(4,-8)}x = 4x - 8$, so $x = \frac{1}{4}M + 2$.

-4	-3	-2	-1	0	1	2	3	4	M
1	$\frac{5}{4}$	$\frac{3}{2}$	$\frac{7}{4}$	2	$\frac{9}{4}$	$\frac{5}{2}$	$\frac{11}{4}$	3	x

(c) $M = (\mathcal{A}_{(-1,-3)})^{-1}(x) = \mathcal{A}_{(-1,-3)} = -x - 3$, so $x = -M - 3$.

-4	-3	-2	-1	0	1	2	3	4	M
1	0	-1	-2	-3	-4	-5	-6	-7	x

(d) $M = (\mathcal{A}_{\left(\frac{-1}{2},\frac{3}{2}\right)})^{-1}(x) = \mathcal{A}_{(-2,3)} = -2x + 3$, so $x = -\frac{1}{2}M + \frac{3}{2}$.

-4	-3	-2	-1	0	1	2	3	4	M
$\frac{7}{2}$	3	$\frac{5}{2}$	2	$\frac{3}{2}$	1	$\frac{1}{2}$	0	$\frac{-1}{2}$	x

12. (a)
$$(T_3 \circ D_2)^{-1}x = (D_2)^{-1} \circ (T_3)^{-1}x$$
$$= D_{\frac{1}{2}} \circ T_{-3}x$$
$$= D_{\frac{1}{2}}(x - 3)$$
$$= \frac{1}{2}x - \frac{3}{2}$$
$$= \mathcal{A}_{\left(\frac{1}{2},-\frac{3}{2}\right)}x$$

(b)
$$(D_2 \circ T_3)^{-1}x = (T_3)^{-1} \circ (D_2)^{-1}x$$
$$= T_{-3} \circ D_{\frac{1}{2}}x$$
$$= T_{-3}\left(\frac{1}{2}x\right)$$
$$= \frac{1}{2}x - 3$$
$$= \mathcal{A}_{\left(\frac{1}{2},-3\right)}x$$

(c)
$$(T_{-3} \circ D_{\frac{1}{2}})^{-1}x = (D_{\frac{1}{2}})^{-1} \circ (T_{-3})^{-1}x$$
$$= D_2 \circ T_3x$$
$$= D_2(x + 3)$$
$$= 2x + 6$$
$$= \mathcal{A}_{(2,6)}x$$

(d)
$$(D_{\frac{1}{2}} \circ T_{-3})^{-1}x = (T_{-3})^{-1} \circ (D_{\frac{1}{2}})^{-1}x$$
$$= T_3 \circ D_2x$$
$$= T_3(2x)$$
$$= 2x + 3$$
$$= \mathcal{A}_{(2,3)}$$

Maintain Your Skills

13. (a)
$$y = (x - 1)^3 + 3(x - 1)^2 - (x - 1) + 4$$
$$= x^3 - 3x^2 + 3x - 1 + 3x^2 - 6x + 3 - x + 1 + 4$$
$$= x^3 - 4x + 7$$

(b)
$$y = (x + 2)^3 - 6(x + 2)^2 - 4(x + 2) + 1$$
$$= x^3 + 6x^2 + 12x + 8 - 6x^2 - 24x - 24$$
$$- 4x - 8 + 1$$
$$= x^3 - 16x - 23$$

(c)
$$y = (x - 2)^3 + 6(x - 2)^2 + 4(x - 2) + 1$$
$$= x^3 - 6x^2 + 12x - 8 + 6x^2 - 24x + 24$$
$$+ 4x - 8 + 1$$
$$= x^3 - 8x + 9$$

(d)
$$y = (x + 1)^3 - 3(x + 1)^2 + 2(x + 1) + 4$$
$$= x^3 + 3x^2 + 3x + 1 - 3x^2 - 6x - 3 +$$
$$2x + 2 + 4$$
$$= x^3 - x + 4$$

14. The $\left(x - \frac{b}{3}\right)^3$ term will contribute $-bx^2$, and the $b\left(x - \frac{b}{3}\right)^2$ term will contribute bx^2, so the coefficient in the final expansion will be 0.

6.9 Replacing the Axes

Check Your Understanding

1. (a)
$$M = -2x + 1$$
$$M - 1 = -2x$$
$$-\frac{1}{2}M + \frac{1}{2} = x$$
$$T_{\frac{1}{2}}\left(-\frac{1}{2}M\right) = x$$
$$\left(T_{\frac{1}{2}} \circ D_{-\frac{1}{2}}\right)(M) = x$$

(b)

-4 -3 -2 -1 0 1 2 3 4 M

2 $\frac{3}{2}$ 1 $\frac{1}{2}$ 0 $\frac{-1}{2}$ -1 $\frac{-3}{2}$ -2 $D_{-\frac{1}{2}}(M)$

$\frac{5}{2}$ 2 $\frac{3}{2}$ 1 $\frac{1}{2}$ 0 $\frac{-1}{2}$ -1 $\frac{-3}{2}$ x

(c) • The $D_{-\frac{1}{2}}(M)$-axis is the image of the M-axis after it has been reflected over a vertical line through 0 and dilated by a factor of 2.
• The x-axis is the image of the $D_{-\frac{1}{2}}(M)$-axis after it has been translated $\frac{1}{2}$ unit to the right.
• The x-axis is the image of the M-axis after it has been reflected over a vertical line through 0, dilated by a factor of 2, and then translated $\frac{1}{2}$ unit to the right. There are other correct descriptions of these relationships.

2. (a)
$$M = -2x + 1$$
$$M = T_1(-2x)$$
$$M = T_1 \circ D_{-2}x$$
$$(T_1 \circ D_{-2})^{-1}M = x$$
$$(D_{-2})^{-1} \circ (T_1)^{-1}M = x$$
$$\left(D_{-\frac{1}{2}} \circ T_{-1}\right)(M) = x$$

(b)

-4 -3 -2 -1 0 1 2 3 4 M

-5 -4 -3 -2 -1 0 1 2 3 $T_{-1}(M)$

$\frac{5}{2}$ 2 $\frac{3}{2}$ 1 $\frac{1}{2}$ 0 $\frac{-1}{2}$ -1 $\frac{-3}{2}$ x

(c) • The $T_{-1}(M)$-axis is the image of the M-axis after a translation of 1 unit to the right.
• The x-axis is the image of the $T_{-1}(M)$-axis after it has been reflected over a vertical line through 0 and dilated by a factor of 2.
• The x-axis is the image of the M-axis after it has been translated 1 unit to the right, reflected over a vertical line through 0 and dilated by a factor of 2. However, you could also just repeat your answer to Exercise 1(c), because this different series of transformations has produced the same result and the earlier description of the relationship between the number lines for M and x also holds.

3. (a) First make the equation $y = 3x^2 + 2x - 1$ monic by multiplying each side by 3. This gives you

$$3y = (3x)^2 + 2(3x) - 3.$$

Then make the substitutions

$$P = D_3 x$$
$$Q = D_3 y$$

transform the equation into $Q = P^2 + 2P - 3$. Complete the square in this equation by adding and subtracting 1.

$$Q = (P^2 + 2P + 1) - 1 - 3$$
$$Q + 4 = (P + 1)^2$$

Now make the substitutions

$$M = T_1 P = T_1 \circ D_3 x = \mathcal{A}_{(3,1)}x$$
$$N = T_4 Q = T_4 \circ D_3 y = \mathcal{A}_{(3,4)}y$$

transform the equation into $N = M^2$.

(b) Use the substitutions above, but solve for $x = \mathcal{A}_{\left(\frac{1}{3}, -\frac{1}{3}\right)}M$ and $y = \mathcal{A}_{\left(\frac{1}{3}, -\frac{4}{3}\right)}N$.

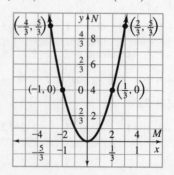

4. Yes, but you would have to use more than two transformations. An example is

$$D_{\frac{1}{2}} \circ T_1 \circ D_{-1}x = D_{\frac{1}{2}} \circ T_1(-x)$$
$$= D_{\frac{1}{2}}(-x + 1)$$
$$= -\frac{1}{2}x + \frac{1}{2}$$
$$= \mathcal{A}_{\left(-\frac{1}{2}, \frac{1}{2}\right)}$$

5. (a) $M = \mathcal{A}_{(2,3)}(x) = 2x + 3$ and
$N = \mathcal{A}_{(2,-1)}(y) = 2y - 1$.

$$N = M^2$$
$$2y - 17 = (2x + 3)^2$$
$$2y - 1 = 4x^2 + 12x + 9$$
$$2y = 4x^2 + 12x + 10$$
$$y = 2x^2 + 6x + 5$$

(b)

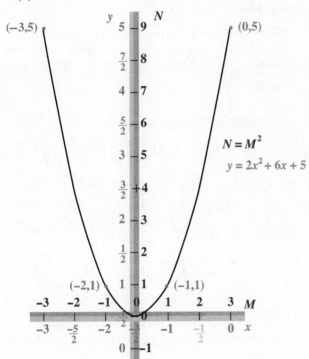

6. $M = \mathcal{A}_{(9,6)}x$, so $x = \dfrac{M - 6}{9}$. $N = \mathcal{A}_{(9,81)}y$, so
$y = \dfrac{N - 81}{9}$.

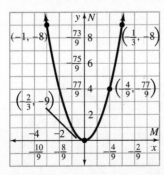

7. $M = \mathcal{A}_{\left(-\frac{1}{4},3\right)}x$, so $x = -4M + 12$. $N = \mathcal{A}_{\left(-\frac{1}{4},11\right)}y$, so
$y = -4N + 44$.

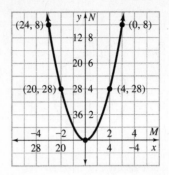

8. (a) $(x + 5)^2 + y^2 = 9$ is transformed to $M^2 + N^2 = 9$ with the substitutions $M = x + 5$ (so $x = M - 5$) and $N = y$.

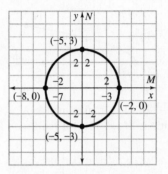

(b) $(-2x + 1)^2 + y^2 = 9$ is transformed to $M^2 + N^2 = 9$ with the substitutions $M = -2x + 1$ (so $x = -\frac{1}{2}M + \frac{1}{2}$) and $N = y$.

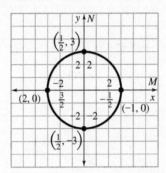

(c) $(x - 1)^2 + (-y + 4)^2 = 9$ is transformed to $M^2 + N^2 = 9$ with the substitutions $M = x - 1$ (so $x = M + 1$) and $N = -y + 4$ (so $y = -N + 4$).

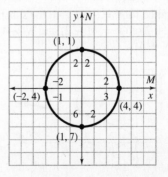

(d) $(x + 2)^2 + (4y - 16)^2 = 9$ is transformed to $M^2 + N^2 = 9$ with the substitutions $M = x + 2$ (so $x = M - 2$) and $N = 4y - 16$ (so $y = \frac{1}{4}N + 4$).

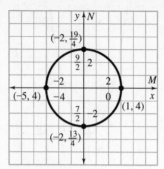

9. (a) $y = \sqrt{x + 5}$ is transformed to $N = \sqrt{M}$ with the substitutions $M = x + 5$ (so $x = M - 5$) and $N = y$.

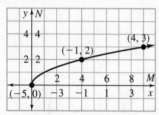

(b) $y = \sqrt{-2x + 1}$ is transformed to $N = \sqrt{M}$ with the substitutions $M = -2x + 1$ (so $x = -\frac{1}{2}M + \frac{1}{2}$) and $N = y$.

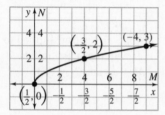

(c) $y = -\sqrt{x - 1} + 4$, or $-y + 4 = \sqrt{x - 1}$, is transformed to $N = \sqrt{M}$ with the substitutions $M = x - 1$ (so $x = M + 1$) and $N = -y + 4$ (so $y = -N + 4$).

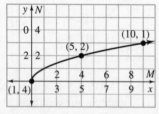

(d) $y = \frac{1}{4}\sqrt{x + 2} + 4$, or $4y - 16 = \sqrt{x + 2}$, is transformed to $N = \sqrt{M}$ with the substitutions $M = x + 2$ (so $x = M - 2$) and $N = 4y - 16$ (so $y = \frac{1}{4}N + 4$).

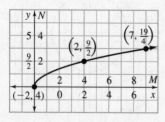

10. The graphs in parts (a) and (c) of Exercise 8 are circles, because the units on the x- and y-axes for those graphs have units that are the same size. However, in the "replacing the axes" sketches, the graphs in parts (b) and (d) have different scales on their x- and y-axes.

In the graph of $(-2x + 1)^2 + y^2 = 9$, the distance between the two (x, y) points that correspond to the M-intercepts—$(-1, 0)$ and $(2, 0)$—is 3 units, but the distance between the points that correspond to the N-intercepts—$(\frac{1}{2}, 3)$ and $(\frac{1}{2}, -3)$—is 6 units. If the x, y graph were a circle, these two segments would be diameters and would have the same length. Since these two distances are different, this is not the graph of a circle, but of an ellipse.

Similarly, in part (d) the two points that correspond to the M-intercepts are $(1, 4)$ and $(-5, 4)$. The distance between them is 6 units. The two points that correspond to the N-intercepts are $(-2, \frac{19}{4})$ and $(-2, \frac{13}{4})$. The distance between them is $\frac{3}{2}$ units.

On Your Own

11. (a) The substitutions that transformed the equation $y = x^3 + 6x^2 + 11x + 7$ into the form $N = M^3 - M$ were

- $M = \mathcal{A}_{(1,2)}x$
- $N = \mathcal{A}_{(1,-1)}y$

This leads to the following graph:

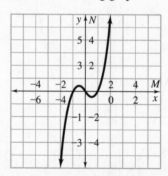

(b) The substitutions that transformed the equation $y = x^3 + 3x^2 + 7x + 13$ into the form $N = M^3 + M$ were

- $M = \mathcal{A}_{\left(\frac{1}{2}, \frac{1}{2}\right)}x$
- $N = \mathcal{A}_{\left(\frac{1}{8}, -1\right)}y$

This leads to the following graph:

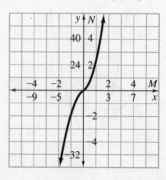

12. The substitutions that transformed the equation $y = 8x^3 - 6x^2 + 2x - 1$ into the form $S = R^3 + R$ were

- $R = D_{\frac{1}{2}} \circ T_{-2} \circ D_8(x) = 4x - 1 = \mathcal{A}_{(4,-1)}$
- $S = D_{\frac{1}{8}} \circ T_{48} \circ D_{64}(y) = 8y + 6 = \mathcal{A}_{(8,6)}$

to get $S = R^3 - R$. This leads to the following graph:

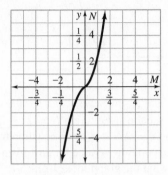

13. (a)

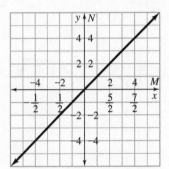

(b)

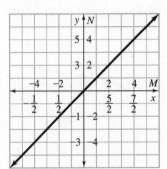

(c)

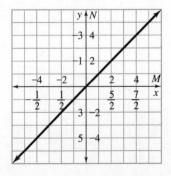

(d)

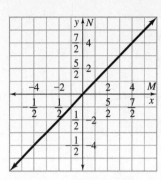

14. (a) This is a transformation of the basic graph $y = \frac{1}{x}$. You can use the substitution $M = 2x - 3$, which gives you $x = \frac{1}{2}M + \frac{3}{2}$ as an equation to use to find the corresponding x-value for any given value of M. Here is what the graph looks like:

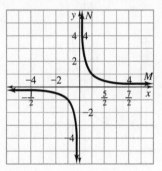

(b)

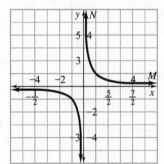

(c)

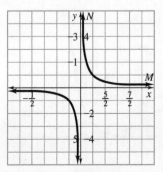

(d)

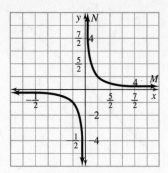

(d)

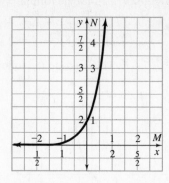

15. (a) You can use the substitution $M = 2x - 3$, which gives you $x = \frac{1}{2}M + \frac{3}{2}$ as an equation to use to find the corresponding x-value for any given value of M. Here is what the graph looks like:

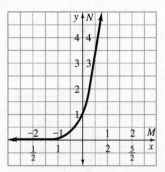

(b)

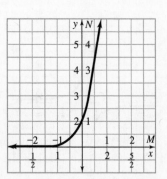

(c)

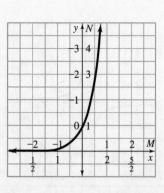

16. (a) You can use the substitution $N = 2y - 3$, which gives you $y = \frac{1}{2}N + \frac{3}{2}$ as an equation to use to find the corresponding y-value for any given value of N. Here is what the graph looks like:

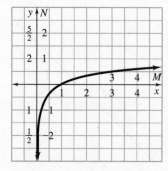

(b)

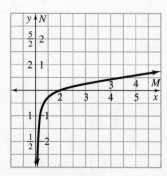

(c)

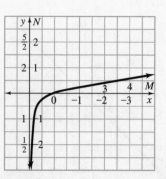

(d)

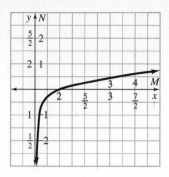

17. The corresponding functions (part (a) in one exercise to part (a) in the other, for example) are inverses of each other.

   Therefore, their graphs are mirror-images of each other over the line $y = x$.

18. (a)

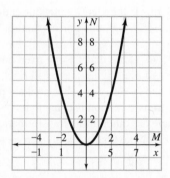

(b) $M = x - 3$, so $x = M + 3$. The x-axis is the image of the M-axis after a translation of three units to the left.

(c) Since the x-axis is 3 units left when compared to the M-axis, you are now "standing" 3 units farther to the left when you look at the graph. Its vertex and axis of symmetry are now 3 units to your right instead of passing through the point where you are standing. The graph of $y = x^2$ has its vertex at the origin $(0, 0)$, but the parabola which is the graph of the equation $y = (x - 3)^2$ has its vertex at the point $(3, 0)$ according to the (x, y) coordinates you can read off of your "replacing the axes" graph.

19. (a)

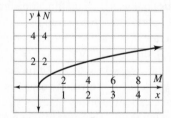

(b) The x-axis is the image of the M-axis after a dilation by a factor of 2. In other words, a unit on the x-axis is twice as big as a unit on the M-axis.

(c) In the "replacing the axes" picture from part (a), the units on the x-axis are twice as big as the units on the y-axis. If you re-draw the graph on a grid where these units are the same size, you will appear to be squishing the graph horizontally, because to make the

units the same size, you have to shrink the x-distances.

20. (a)

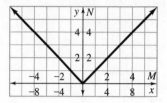

(b) The x-axis is the image of the M-axis after a dilation by a factor of $\frac{1}{2}$. In other words, a unit on the x-axis is half as big as a unit on the M-axis.

(c) In the "replacing the axes" picture from part (a), the units on the x-axis are half as big as the units on the y-axis. If you re-draw the graph on a grid where these units are the same size, you will appear to be stretching the graph horizontally, because to make the units the same size, you have to stretch the x-distances.

21. (a)

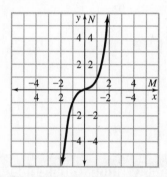

(b) The x-axis is the image of the M-axis after a reflection over the line $M = 0$. Corresponding points have opposite sign.

(c) In the "replacing the axes" picture, the x-axis is backwards as compared to the usual x-axis. Numbers are *decreasing* as you move along the line from left to right. When you transfer this graph to the usual set of coordinate axes, you have to reflect the whole thing over the y-axis so that the x-coordinates *increase* as you move along the line from left to right.

22. This can be rewritten as

$$(x + 3)^2 + (y - 7)^2 = 5^2$$

This is a circle centered at $(-3, 7)$ with radius 5. The correct answer choice is **B**.

Maintain Your Skills

23. (a)
$$\mathcal{A}_{(2, -1)}x = 0$$
$$2x - 1 = 0$$
$$2x = 1$$
$$x = \frac{1}{2}$$

(b) $\mathcal{A}_{(4,-2)}x = 0$

$4x - 2 = 0$

$4x = 2$

$x = \dfrac{1}{2}$

(c) $\mathcal{A}_{(6,-3)}x = 0$

$6x - 3 = 0$

$6x = 3$

$x = \dfrac{1}{2}$

(d) $\mathcal{A}_{\left(-1,\frac{1}{2}\right)}x = 0$

$-x + \dfrac{1}{2} = 0$

$-x = -\dfrac{1}{2}$

$x = \dfrac{1}{2}$

(e) $\mathcal{A}_{\left(-3,\frac{3}{2}\right)}x = 0$

$-3x + \dfrac{3}{2} = 0$

$-3x = -\dfrac{3}{2}$

$x = \dfrac{1}{2}$

6.10   Advanced Affine Transformations

Check Your Understanding

1. (a) $\mathcal{A}_{(4,-2)}x = x$

$4x - 2 = x$

$3x = 2$

$x = \dfrac{2}{3}$

(b) $\mathcal{A}_{(-2,4)}x = x$

$-2x + 4 = x$

$4 = 3x$

$x = \dfrac{4}{3}$

(c) $\mathcal{A}_{(-10,22)}x = x$

$-10x + 22 = x$

$22 = 11x$

$x = 2$

(d) $\mathcal{A}_{(a,0)}x = x$

$ax = x$

$(a - 1)x = 0$

If $a = 1$, this is fixed for all x, but if $a \neq 1$, this is fixed for $x = 0$.

(e) $\mathcal{A}_{(1,-3)}x = x$

$x - 3 = x$

This is not true for *any* value of x, so this transformation has no fixed points.

(f) For $a \neq 1$ you can calculate as follows.

$$\mathcal{A}_{(a,b)}x = x$$
$$ax + b = x$$
$$(a - 1)x = -b$$
$$x = \dfrac{-b}{a - 1}$$

However if $a = 1$ this calculation would be undefined. You can treat that as a separate case.

$$\mathcal{A}_{(1,b)}x = x$$
$$x + b = x$$

If $b = 0$, this is the identity transformation and it fixes all x. If $b \neq 0$, this transformation has no fixed points.

2.
- If $a \neq 1$, $\mathcal{A}_{(a,b)}$ has exactly one fixed point.
- If $a = 1$ and $b = 0$, $\mathcal{A}_{(a,b)}$ fixes all points.
- If $a = 1$ and $b \neq 0$, $\mathcal{A}_{(a,b)}$ has no fixed point.

3. The identity transformation is equal to its own inverse. However, there are other affine transformations for which this is also true. Note that if $a = 0$, then there is no inverse for $\mathcal{A}_{(a,b)}$, so $a \neq 0$.

$$(\mathcal{A}_{(a,b)})^{-1}x = \mathcal{A}_{(a,b)}x$$
$$\mathcal{A}_{\left(\frac{1}{a},-\frac{b}{a}\right)}x = ax + b$$
$$\dfrac{1}{a}x - \dfrac{b}{a} = ax + b$$
$$x - b = a^2x + ab$$
$$(1 - a^2)x - b(1 + a) = 0$$
$$(1 + a)((1 - a)x - b) = 0$$

By the Zero Product Property, this expression equals 0 only if one (or both) of its factors equal 0. If $1 + a = 0$, then $a = -1$. Therefore, $(\mathcal{A}_{(-1,b)})^{-1} = \mathcal{A}_{(-1,b)}$.

(If you set the other factor equal to zero, you will get a particular value for x, $x = \dfrac{b}{1-a}$, for which the product is zero, but your goal was to find affine transformations for which this property was *always* true.)

4. If the n-th iterate of the affine transformation $\mathcal{A}_{(a,b)}$ is equal to $\mathcal{A}_{(a,b)}$, then certainly $(\mathcal{A}_{(a,b)})^2 = \mathcal{A}_{(a,b)}$. In fact, if you show that $(\mathcal{A}_{(a,b)})^2 = \mathcal{A}_{(a,b)}$, it means that applying $\mathcal{A}_{(a,b)}$ to $ax + b$ gives the result $ax + b$, and therefore you can do it as many times as you like and still get $ax + b$ as the result. However, if you just look at $(\mathcal{A}_{(a,b)})^2 = \mathcal{A}_{(a,b)}$, you get the following.

$$a(ax + b) + b = ax + b$$
$$a^2x + ab + b - ax - b = 0$$
$$a[(a - 1)x + b] = 0$$

If $a = 0$, this is true for all x, also if $a = 1$ and $b = 0$, this is true for all x.

5. Larry started with the equation $3x + 7 = 3x - 2$, which has no solutions. Using the basic rules, he came up with another equation that also has no solutions. If you start with an equation that is not true for any value of x, you are making a false assumption, and you can prove anything from a false assumption. However, once he realizes that $A_{(1,-3)}$ has no fixed point, he could use that fact to show that the original equation had no solutions, because he knows there are no solutions to the equation he has got now.

6.

$$A_{(a,b)}(5) = 5$$
$$5a + b = 5$$
$$b = 5 - 5a$$

So $S_5 = A_{(a,5-5a)}$.

On Your Own

7. We want the solution to

$$3x + 34 = x$$
$$2x = -34$$
$$x = -17$$

The correct answer choice is **A**.

8. (a) $A_{(3,-4)}(2) = 3(2) - 4 = 6 - 4 = 2$
$A_{(-5,12)}(2) = -5(2) + 12 = -10 + 12 = 2$

(b) $A_{(3,-4)} \circ A_{(-5,12)}(2) = A_{(3,-4)}(2)$, because $A_{(-5,12)}$ is in S_2. And since $A_{(3,-4)}$ is also in S_2, $A_{(3,-4)} \circ A_{(-5,12)}(2) = 2$ and the composition is in the stabilizer. Similarly $A_{(-5,12)} \circ A_{(3,-4)}(2) = 2$ because each step in the composition returns an output of 2.

(c) You know that $A_{(3,-4)}(2) = 2$. Apply $(A_{(3,-4)})^{-1}$ to each side of the equation. This gives you $2 = (A_{(3,-4)})^{-1}(2)$, so $(A_{(3,-4)})^{-1}$ is in the stabilizer. Similarly, since $A_{(-5,12)}(2) = 2$, you can apply $(A_{(-5,12)})^{-1}$ to both sides and you'll get $2 = (A_{(-5,12)})^{-1}(2)$ so $(A_{(-5,12)})^{-1}$ is in the stabilizer.

(d) $A_{(3,-4)} \circ A_{(-5,12)}(x) = 3(-5x + 12) - 4 = -15x + 32 = A_{(-15,32)}$
$A_{(-5,12)} \circ A_{(3,-4)}(x) = -5(3x - 4) + 12 = -15x + 32 = A_{(-15,32)}$

The result of the composition was the same even though the affine transformations were in a different order the second time. Normally, affine transformations do not commute under composition, but this exercise leads to the conjecture that affine transformations that both fix the same point may commute under composition.

9. (a) $A_{(a,b)} \circ A_{(c,d)}(x) = A_{(a,b)}(x) = x$. Each step in the composition returns x, so $A_{(a,b)} \circ A_{(c,d)}$ is in S_x.

(b) You know that $A_{(a,b)}(x) = x$. Apply $(A_{(a,b)})^{-1}$ to each side, to get $x = (A_{(a,b)})^{-1}(x)$, so $(A_{(a,b)})^{-1}$ is in S_x.

(c) There is an x such that $(A_{(a,b)} \circ A_{(c,d)})(x) = x = (A_{(c,d)} \circ A_{(a,b)})(x)$. This implies that $acx + ad + b = cax + cb + d$. Therefore, $ad + b = cb + d$. It follows that, for any

real number u, $acu + ad + b = cau + cb + d$. That is, $A_{(a,b)} \circ A_{(c,d)} = A_{(c,d)} \circ A_{(a,b)}$.

10. If $A_{(a,b)}$ is in S_0, then

$$A_{(a,b)}(0) = 0$$
$$a(0) + b = 0$$

This equation is true as long as $b = 0$, and if $b = 0$, $A_{(a,0)} = D_a$ is a dilation.

11. (a) $T_3 \circ D_4 \circ (T_3)^{-1}(3) = T_3 \circ D_4(0)$
$= T_3(4(0)) \quad = T_3(0)$
$= 3$

(b) $T_3 \circ D_{-1} \circ (T_3)^{-1}(3) = T_3 \circ D_{-1}(0)$
$= T_3(0)$
$= 3$

(c) $T_3 \circ D_2 \circ (T_3)^{-1}(3) = T_3 \circ D_2(0)$
$= T_3(0)$
$= 3$

(d) $T_3 \circ D_a \circ (T_3)^{-1}(3) = T_3 \circ D_a(0)$
$= T_3(0)$
$= 3$

(e) $T_x \circ D_a \circ (T_x)^{-1}$ is in S_x because $(T_x)^{-1}(x) = 0$, then $D_a(0) = 0$ and $T_x(0) = x$.

12. (a) $(A_{(2,3)})^{(5)}(x) = A_{\left(2^5, 3 \cdot \frac{2^5-1}{2-1}\right)} = A_{(32,93)}$

(b) $f(5) = (A_{(2,3)})^{(5)} f(0)$ because the recursion step is to apply $A_{(2,3)}$. To compute $f(5)$, you would start with $f(0)$ and then apply $A_{(2,3)}$ five times.

(c) $f(5) = A_{(32,93)}(1) = 32(1) + 93 = 125$.

13. (a)

$$3\sigma(n-1) \overset{?}{=} g(1) + g(2) + \cdots + g(n)$$
$$3[g(0) + g(1) + g(2) + \cdots + g(n-1)]$$
$$\overset{?}{=} g(1) + g(2) + \cdots + g(n)$$
$$3[2 + 2 \cdot 3 + 2 \cdot 3^2 + \cdots + 2 \cdot 3^{(n-1)}]$$
$$\overset{?}{=} g(1) + g(2) + \cdots + g(n)$$
$$2 \cdot 3 + 2 \cdot 3^2 + 2 \cdot 3^3 + \cdots + 2 \cdot 3^n]$$
$$\overset{?}{=} g(1) + g(2) + \cdots + g(n)$$
$$g(1) + g(2) + \cdots + g(n)$$
$$= g(1) + g(2) + \cdots + g(n)$$

(b) From part (a), you have
$$3\sigma(n-1) = g(1) + g(2) + \cdots + g(n) = \sigma(n) - g(0).$$

$$3\sigma(n-1) = \sigma(n) - 2$$
$$3\sigma(n-1) + 2 = \sigma(n)$$
$$A_{(3,2)}(\sigma(n-1)) = \sigma(n)$$

(c) From part (b), $\sigma(10) = (A_{(3,2)})^{10}(g(0))$ From the formula for iteration of an affine transformation, $\sigma(10) = 3^{10}(2) + 2 \cdot \frac{3^{10}-1}{3-1}$. This simplifies to

$\sigma(10) = 177146.$

$$\sigma(10) = g(0) + g(1) + g(2) + \cdots + g(10)$$
$$= 2 + 6 + 18 + 54 + 162 + 486 + 1458 +$$
$$4374 + 13122 + 39366 + 118098$$
$$= 177146$$

(d)

$$\sigma(n) = 3^n(2) + 2 \cdot \frac{3^n - 1}{3 - 1}$$
$$= 2 \cdot 3^n + 3^n - 1$$
$$= 3 \cdot 3^n - 1$$
$$= 3^{n+1} - 1$$

Maintain Your Skills

14.

$$\mathcal{A}_{(a,b)}(-4) = -4$$
$$-4a + b = -4$$
$$b = 4a - 4$$

6C MATHEMATICAL REFLECTIONS

1. (a) You know that $M = T_4 x = x + 4$, so $x = M - 4$.

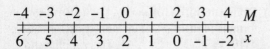

| -4 | -3 | -2 | -1 | 0 | 1 | 2 | 3 | 4 | M |
| -8 | -7 | -6 | -5 | -4 | -3 | -2 | -1 | 0 | x |

(b) You know that $M = D_{\frac{1}{3}} x = \frac{x}{3}$, so $x = 3M$.

| -4 | -3 | -2 | -1 | 0 | 1 | 2 | 3 | 4 | M |
| -12 | -9 | -6 | -3 | 0 | 3 | 6 | 9 | 12 | x |

(c) You know that $M = \mathcal{A}_{(-1,2)} x = -x + 2$, so $x = -M + 2.$

| -4 | -3 | -2 | -1 | 0 | 1 | 2 | 3 | 4 | M |
| 6 | 5 | 4 | 3 | 2 | 1 | 0 | -1 | -2 | x |

2. (a) For $M = T_4 x$, the number line for x is the image of the number line for M after a translation of 4 units to the right.

(b) For $M = D_{\frac{1}{3}} x$, the number line for x is the image of the number line for M after a dilation by a factor of $\frac{1}{3}$.

(c) For $M = \mathcal{A}_{(-1,2)} x$, the number line for x is the image of the number line for M after reflection over a vertical line through 0 and a translation of 2 units to the right.

3. Using the substitutions

- $M = \mathcal{A}_{(2,-1)} x$
- $N = \mathcal{A}_{(1,3)} y$

you can transform the equation $(2x - 1)^2 + (y + 3)^2 = 16$ into the form $M^2 + N^2 = 16$. Then you can make the following sketch.

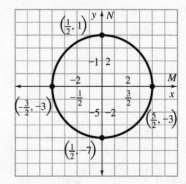

This is the image of the graph of $x^2 + y^2 = 16$ after a horizontal dilation by a factor of $\frac{1}{2}$ and a translation of $\frac{1}{2}$ units to the right and 3 units down.

4. (a)

$$S = R^2$$
$$-y + 2 = (x - 3)^2$$
$$-y + 2 = x^2 - 6x + 9$$
$$-y = x^2 - 6x + 7$$
$$y = -x^2 + 6x - 7$$

(b) Since $R = \mathcal{A}_{(1,-3)} x = x - 3$, you know that $x = R + 3$. Since $S = \mathcal{A}_{(-1,2)} y = -y + 2$, you know that $y = -S + 2$.

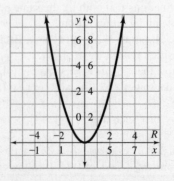

(c) The graph of $y = -x^2 + 6x - 7$ is an image of the basic graph of $y = x^2$ after a reflection over the x-axis and a translation of 2 units up and 3 units to the right.

5. If $\mathcal{A}_{(a,b)}$ has 6 as a fixed point, then

$$\mathcal{A}_{(a,b)}6 = 6$$
$$6a + b = 6$$
$$b = 6 - 6a$$

Any affine transformation of the form $\mathcal{A}_{(a,6-6a)}$ has 6 as a fixed point. Some examples include $\mathcal{A}_{(-1,12)}$, $\mathcal{A}_{(0,6)}$, $\mathcal{A}_{(1,0)}$, and $\mathcal{A}_{(2,-6)}$.

6. First you want to transform this equation into one of the basic graph forms—$S = R^3$, $S = R^3 + R$, or $S = R^3 - R$. It is already monic, so now you want to find a translation $M = T_k(x)$ that will get rid of the x^2 term.

$$y = (M - k)^3 + 3(M - k)^2 - (M - k) + 4$$
$$= M^3 - 3kM^2 + 3k^2M - k^3 + 3M^2 - \ldots$$

The translation you want satisfies the equation $-3k + 3 = 0$, so $k = 1$.

$$y = (M - 1)^3 + 3(M - 1)^2 - (M - 1) + 4$$
$$y = M^3 - 3M^2 + 3M - 1 + 3M^2 -$$
$$6M + 3 - M + 1 + 4$$
$$y = M^3 - 4M + 7$$
$$y - 7 = M^3 - 4M$$

So the substitutions

- $M = T_1(x)$
- $N = T_{-7}(y)$

transform the equation into $N = M^3 - 4M$.
Now you want to get the equation into the form $S = R^3 - R$.

$$\alpha^3 N = (\alpha M)^3 - 4\alpha^2(\alpha M)$$

You want $4\alpha^2 = 1$, so $\alpha = \frac{1}{2}$ and $\alpha^3 = \frac{1}{8}$.
The substitutions

- $R = D_{\frac{1}{2}}(M) = D_{\frac{1}{2}} \circ T_1(x) = \frac{1}{2}x + \frac{1}{2} = \mathcal{A}_{\left(\frac{1}{2},\frac{1}{2}\right)}$
- $S = D_{\frac{1}{8}}(N) = D_{\frac{1}{8}} \circ T_{-7}(y) = \frac{1}{8}x - \frac{7}{8} = \mathcal{A}_{\left(\frac{1}{8},-\frac{7}{8}\right)}$

transform the equation into $S = R^3 - R$.
To graph the equation, use the equations for each of the transformations to label x and y axes appropriately

You can use the relationships between the R, S axes and the x, y axes to find the (x, y) coordinates of as many points as you'd like. Then you can use those points to sketch the graph on a standard set of x, y axes to see its true shape.

7. The vertex of the parabola has (x, y) coordinates $(3, 0)$ and the line with equation $x = 3$ is the line of symmetry for the parabola. This means that the graph of $y = (x - 3)^2$ is the image of the graph of $y = x^2$ after it has been translated 3 units to the right.

8.

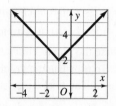

$$\mathcal{A}_{(5,3)}(x) = x$$
$$5x + 3 = x$$
$$4x = -3$$
$$x = -\frac{3}{4}$$

CHAPTER REVIEW

1. (a)

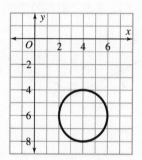

The graph of $y - 2 = |x + 1|$ is the same as the graph of $y = |x|$ after a translation 1 unit to the left and 2 units up.

(b)

The graph of $(x - 4)^2 + (y + 6)^2 = 4$ is the same as the graph of $x^2 + y^2 = 4$ after a translation 4 units to the right and 6 units down.

2. (a)

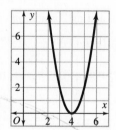

The graph of $\dfrac{y}{2} = (x - 4)^2$ is the same as the graph of $y = x^2$ after a vertical stretch by a factor of 2 and a translation 4 units to the right.

(b)

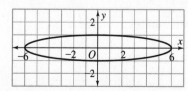

The graph of $\left(\dfrac{x}{3}\right)^2 + (2y)^2 = 4$ is the same as the graph of $x^2 + y^2 = 4$ after a vertical shrink by a factor of 2 and a horizontal stretch by a factor of 3.

(c)

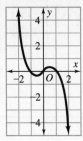

The graph of $y = (-x)^3 - (-x)$ is the same as the graph of $y = x^3 - x$ after a reflection over the y axis.

3. Replace x with $\frac{x}{2}$ for a horizontal stretch of factor 2: $y = |\frac{x}{2}|$. To translate the graph 3 units left, replace x with $x + 3$: $y = |\frac{x+3}{2}|$. To translate the graph 7 units down, replace y with $y + 7$. The final equation is

$$y + 7 = |\frac{x+3}{2}|$$

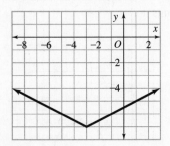

4. (a) For a real number x,

$$T_4 \circ D_3(x) = T_4(3x) = 3x + 4 = \mathcal{A}_{(3,4)}$$

(b) For a real number x,

$$D_{-1} \circ T_6 \circ T_{-2}(x) = D_{-1} \circ T_6(x - 2) = D_{-1}(x - 2 + 6)$$
$$= -1(x + 4) = -x - 4 = \mathcal{A}_{(-1,-4)}$$

(c) The inverse of adding 7 is adding -7. So,

$$(T_7)^{-1} = T_{-7}$$

(d) The inverse of multiplying by 7 is multiplying by $\frac{1}{7}$. So,

$$(D_7)^{-1} = D_{\frac{1}{7}}$$

(e) For a real number x,

$$\mathcal{A}_{(2,-1)} \circ \mathcal{A}_{(-3,-5)}(x) = \mathcal{A}_{(2,-1)}(-3x - 5)$$

$$= 2(-3x - 5) - 1 = -6x - 10 - 1 = -6x - 11 = \mathcal{A}_{(-6,-11)}$$

(f) For a real number x, you have $\left(\mathcal{A}_{(-2,8)}\right)^{-1} = \mathcal{A}_{(c,d)}$ means $\mathcal{A}_{(-2,8)} \circ \mathcal{A}_{(c,d)} = \mathcal{A}_{(1,0)}$ and $\mathcal{A}_{(c,d)} \circ \mathcal{A}_{(-2,8)} = \mathcal{A}_{(1,0)}$

$$\mathcal{A}_{(-2,8)} \circ \mathcal{A}_{(c,d)}(x) = \mathcal{A}_{(1,0)}(x)$$
$$\mathcal{A}_{(-2,8)}(cx + d) = x + 0$$
$$-2(cx + d) + 8 = x + 0$$
$$-2cx + -2d + 8 = x + 0$$

So,

$$-2c = 1 \longrightarrow c = -\frac{1}{2}$$

and

$$-2d + 8 = 0 \longrightarrow d = 4$$

And,

$$(\mathcal{A}_{(-2,8)})^{-1} = \mathcal{A}_{\left(-\frac{1}{2},4\right)}$$

Now, to be sure that $(\mathcal{A}_{(-2,8)})^{-1} = \mathcal{A}_{\left(-\frac{1}{2},4\right)}$, you need to check the composition in the other order:

$$\mathcal{A}_{\left(-\frac{1}{2},4\right)} \circ \mathcal{A}_{(-2,8)}(x) = \mathcal{A}_{\left(-\frac{1}{2},4\right)}(-2x + 8)$$
$$= -\frac{1}{2}(-2x + 8) + 4$$
$$= x - 4 + 4$$
$$= x$$

5. (a) For some number x,

$$\mathcal{A}_{(a,b)} \circ \mathcal{A}_{(3,9)}(x) = \mathcal{A}_{(15,8)}(x)$$
$$\mathcal{A}_{(a,b)} = \mathcal{A}_{(15,8)} \circ (\mathcal{A}_{(3,9)})^{-1}(x)$$
$$= \mathcal{A}_{(15,8)} \circ \mathcal{A}_{\left(\frac{1}{3},-3\right)}(x)$$
$$= \mathcal{A}_{(15,8)}(\frac{1}{3}x - 3)$$
$$= 15(\frac{1}{3}x - 3) + 8$$
$$= 5x - 45 + 8$$
$$= 5x - 37$$
$$= \mathcal{A}_{(5,-37)}(x)$$

So, $a = 5$ and $b = -37$.

(b) For some number x,

$$\mathcal{A}_{(4,-1)} \circ \mathcal{A}_{(a,b)}(x) = \mathcal{A}_{(16,7)}(x)$$
$$(\mathcal{A}_{(4,-1)})^{-1} \circ \mathcal{A}_{(4,-1)} \circ \mathcal{A}_{(a,b)}(x) = (\mathcal{A}_{(4,-1)})^{-1} \circ \mathcal{A}_{(16,7)}(x)$$
$$\mathcal{A}_{(a,b)}(x) = (\mathcal{A}_{(4,-1)})^{-1} \circ \mathcal{A}_{(16,7)}(x)$$
$$= \mathcal{A}_{\left(\frac{1}{4},\frac{1}{4}\right)} \circ \mathcal{A}_{(16,7)}(x)$$
$$= \mathcal{A}_{\left(\frac{1}{4},\frac{1}{4}\right)}(16x + 7)$$
$$= \frac{1}{4}(16x + 7) + \frac{1}{4}$$
$$= 4x + \frac{7}{4} + \frac{1}{4}$$
$$= 4x + \frac{8}{4}$$
$$= 4x + 2$$
$$= \mathcal{A}_{(4,2)}(x)$$

So, $a = 4$ and $b = 2$.

6. Make the equation $y = 5x^2 - 4x + 6$ monic by multiplying each side by 5 to get

$$5y = (5x)^2 - 4(5x) + 30$$

Substitute $P = D_5 x$ and $Q = D_5 y$, and you have

$$Q = P^2 - 4P + 30$$

Complete the square by adding and subtracting 4.
$(P^2 - 4P + 4 = (P - 2)^2)$

$$Q = (P^2 - 4P + 4) - 4 + 30$$
$$Q = (P - 2)^2 + 26$$
$$Q - 26 = (P - 2)^2$$

Make these substitutions:

$$M = T_{-2}P = T_{-2} \circ D_5 x = \mathcal{A}_{(5,-2)}$$
$$N = T_{-26}Q = T_{-26} \circ D_5 y = \mathcal{A}_{(5,-26)}$$

Now you have $N = M^2$, and $a = 5$, $b = -2$, $c = 5$, and $d = -26$.

7. (a)

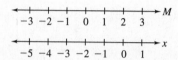

The number line for x is the image of the number line for M after a translation of 2 units to the right.

(b)

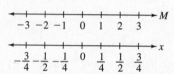

The number line for x is the image of the number line for M after a dilation by a factor of 4.

(c)

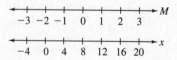

The number line for x is the image of the number line for M after a translation of 2 units to the left followed by a dilation by a factor of $\frac{1}{4}$.

8. Using the substitutions

$$M = \mathcal{A}_{(3,-4)}(x)$$
$$N = \mathcal{A}_{(2,1)}(y)$$

you can transform the equation $2y + 1 = \sqrt{3x - 4}$ into the form $N = \sqrt{M}$. Then you can make the following sketch:

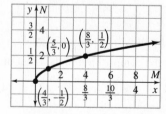

This is the image of the graph of $y = \sqrt{x}$ after a horizontal dilation by a factor of $\frac{1}{3}$, a vertical dilation by a factor of $\frac{1}{2}$, and a translation $\frac{4}{3}$ units right and $\frac{1}{2}$ unit down.

9. (a) $\mathcal{A}_{(2,-3)}(x) = 2x - 3$ To find the fixed points, solve $2x - 3 = x$ for x:

$$2x - 3 = x$$
$$2x - x - 3 = 0$$
$$x - 3 = 0$$
$$x = 3$$

(b) $\mathcal{A}_{(-3,2)}(x) = -3x + 2$ To find the fixed points, solve $-3x + 2 = x$ for x:

$$-3x + 2 = x$$
$$-3x - x + 2 = 0$$
$$-4x = -2$$
$$x = \frac{1}{2}$$

(c) $\mathcal{A}_{\left(\frac{2}{3},4\right)}(x) = \frac{2}{3}x + 4$ To find the fixed points, solve $\frac{2}{3}x + 4 = x$ for x:

$$\frac{2}{3}x + 4 = x$$
$$\frac{2}{3}x - x + 4 = 0$$
$$-\frac{1}{3}x = -4$$
$$x = 12$$

(d) $\mathcal{A}_{(1,6)}(x) = x + 6$ To find the fixed points, solve $x + 6 = x$ for x:

$$x + 6 = x$$
$$x - x + 6 = 0$$
$$0x = -6$$
$$0 = -6$$

There are no fixed points.

CHAPTER TEST

Multiple Choice

1. For a translation of the graph 2 units to the right, replace x with $x - 2$. For a translation of the graph 7 units down, replace y with $y + 7$. The result is $(x - 2)^2 + (y + 7)^2 = 4$. The correct choice is **C**.

2. For a horizontal stretch by a factor of 4, replace x with $\frac{x}{4}$:

$$y = \frac{1}{\frac{x}{4}} = \frac{4}{x}$$

The correct choice is **A**.

3.
$$D_3 \circ T_{-2} \circ D_{\frac{1}{2}}(8) = D_3 \circ T_{-2}(\frac{1}{2} \cdot 8)$$
$$= D_3 \circ T_{-2}(4)$$
$$= D_3(4 - 2)$$
$$= D_3(2)$$
$$= 3(2)$$
$$= 6$$

The correct choice is **B**.

4.

$$A_{(-4,1)} \circ A_{\left(\frac{1}{4},-1\right)}(x) = A_{(-4,1)}\left(\frac{1}{4}x - 1\right)$$

$$= -4\left(\frac{1}{4}x - 1\right) + 1$$

$$= -x + 4 + 1$$

$$= -x + 5$$

$$= A_{(-1,5)}(x)$$

So, the correct choice is **D**, $A_{(-1,5)}$.

5. $A_{(2,3)}(3) = 2(3) + 3 = 6 + 3 = 9 \neq 3$ The correct choice is **C**.

Open Response

6. (a)

The graph of $y - 1 = (2x)^2$ is the same as the graph of $y = x^2$ after a horizontal shrink by a factor of 2, and a translation 1 unit up.

(b)

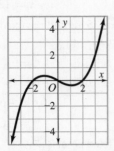

The graph of $y = \left(\frac{x}{2}\right)^3 - \frac{x}{2}$ is the same as the graph of $y = x^3 - x$ after a horizontal stretch by a factor of 2.

(c)

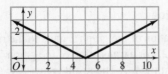

The graph of $2y = |x - 5|$ is the same as the graph of $y = |x|$ after a vertical shrink by a factor of 2, and a translation 5 units right.

(d)

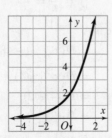

The graph of $y = 2^{x+1}$ is the same as the graph of $y = 2^x$ after a translation 1 unit left.

7. (a) For some number x,

$$D_5 \circ (D_2)^{-1} \circ T_{-4}(x) = D_5 \circ (D_2)^{-1}(x - 4)$$

$$= D_5 \circ D_{\frac{1}{2}}(x - 4)$$

$$= D_5\left(\frac{1}{2}(x - 4)\right)$$

$$= D_5\left(\frac{1}{2}x - 2\right)$$

$$= 5\left(\frac{1}{2}x - 2\right)$$

$$= \frac{5}{2}x - 10$$

$$= A_{\left(\frac{5}{2},-10\right)}(x)$$

(b) For some number x,

$$A_{\left(\frac{2}{3},-8\right)} \circ A_{(6,-2)}(x) = A_{\left(\frac{2}{3},-8\right)}(6x - 2)$$

$$= \frac{2}{3}(6x - 2) - 8$$

$$= 4x - \frac{4}{3} - 8$$

$$= 4x - \frac{28}{3}$$

$$= A_{\left(4,-\frac{28}{3}\right)}(x)$$

(c) For a real number x, you have: $\left(A_{(4,8)}\right)^{-1} = A_{(c,d)}$ means $A_{(4,8)} \circ A_{(c,d)} = A_{(1,0)}$ and $A_{(c,d)} \circ A_{(4,8)} = A_{(1,0)}$

$$A_{(4,8)} \circ A_{(c,d)}(x) = A_{(1,0)}(x)$$

$$A_{(4,8)}(cx + d) = x + 0$$

$$4(cx + d) + 8 = x + 0$$

$$4cx + 4d + 8 = x + 0$$

So,

$$4c = 1 \longrightarrow c = \frac{1}{4}$$

and

$$4d + 8 = 0 \longrightarrow d = -2$$

And,

$$\left(A_{(4,8)}\right)^{-1} = A_{\left(\frac{1}{4},-2\right)}$$

Now, to be sure that $\left(A_{(4,8)}\right)^{-1} = A_{\left(\frac{1}{4},-2\right)}$, you need to check the composition in the other order:

$$A_{\left(\frac{1}{4},-2\right)} \circ A_{(4,8)}(x) = A_{\left(\frac{1}{4},-2\right)}(4x + 8)$$

$$= \frac{1}{4}(4x + 8) - 2$$

$$= x + 2 - 2$$

$$= x$$

8. (a) For some number x,

$$\mathcal{A}_{(a,b)} \circ \mathcal{A}_{(-1,3)}(x) = \mathcal{A}_{(-2,-4)}(x)$$
$$\mathcal{A}_{(a,b)} = \mathcal{A}_{(-2,-4)} \circ (\mathcal{A}_{(-1,3)})^{-1}(x)$$
$$= \mathcal{A}_{(-2,-4)} \circ \mathcal{A}_{(-1,3)}(x)$$
$$= \mathcal{A}_{(-2,-4)}(-x + 3)$$
$$= -2(-x + 3) - 4$$
$$= 2x - 6 - 4$$
$$= 2x - 10$$
$$= \mathcal{A}_{(2,-10)}(x)$$

So, $a = 2$ and $b = -10$.

(b) For some number x,

$$\mathcal{A}_{(4,-6)} \circ \mathcal{A}_{(a,b)}(x) = \mathcal{A}_{(12,3)}(x)$$
$$\mathcal{A}_{(a,b)} = (\mathcal{A}_{(4,-6)})^{-1} \circ \mathcal{A}_{(12,3)}(x)$$
$$= \mathcal{A}_{\left(\frac{1}{4},\frac{3}{2}\right)} \circ \mathcal{A}_{(12,3)}(x)$$
$$= \mathcal{A}_{\left(\frac{1}{4},\frac{3}{2}\right)}(12x + 3)$$
$$= \frac{1}{4}(12x + 3) + \frac{3}{2}$$
$$= 3x + \frac{3}{4} + \frac{3}{2}$$
$$= 3x + \frac{9}{4}$$
$$= \mathcal{A}_{\left(3,\frac{9}{4}\right)}(x)$$

So, $a = 3$ and $b = \dfrac{9}{4}$.

9. (a)

$$M = T_{-5}x$$
$$M = x - 5$$
$$M + 5 = x$$

So, $x = M + 5 = T_5 M$.

(b)

$$M = D_{10}x$$
$$M = 10x$$
$$\frac{1}{10}M = x$$

So, $x = \dfrac{1}{10}M = D_{\frac{1}{10}}M$.

(c)

$$M = \mathcal{A}_{(2,-6)}x$$
$$M = 2x - 6$$
$$M + 6 = 2x$$
$$\frac{1}{2}M + 3 = x$$

So, $x = \dfrac{1}{2}M + 3 = \mathcal{A}_{\left(\frac{1}{2},3\right)}M$.

10. Using the transformations

$$M = \mathcal{A}_{(3,2)}x$$
$$N = \mathcal{A}_{\left(\frac{1}{2},0\right)}y$$

you can transform the equation
$\dfrac{y}{2} = (3x + 2)^3 + (3x + 2)$ into $N = M^3 + M$

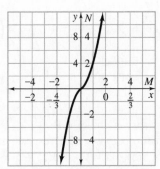

This is the image of the graph of $y = x^3 + x$ after a vertical dilation by a factor of 2, a horizontal dilation by a factor of $\dfrac{1}{3}$ and a translation of $\dfrac{2}{3}$ units to the left.

11. The graph of $(x + 1)^2 + (y - 4)^2 = 36$ is a circle of radius 6 centered at the point $(-1, 4)$.

CUMULATIVE REVIEW

1. Use the basic rule $\dfrac{x^a}{x^b} = x^{a-b}$.

$$\frac{x^{-5}y^{-9}}{x^{-11}y^{-7}} = x^{-5+11} \cdot y^{-9+7} = x^6 y^{-2} = \frac{x^6}{y^2}$$

The correct answer choice is **C**.

2. $4^x = 32$ implies

$$4^{4x} = (4^x)^4 = 32^4 = (2^5)^4 = 2^{20} = (2^2)^{10} = 4^{10}$$

The correct answer choice is **B**.

3. We have $12^{-1} = \frac{1}{12}$, $9^{\frac{3}{2}} = \sqrt{9}^3 = 3^3 = 27$, $(\frac{2}{3})^{-1} = \frac{3}{2}$, and $\log_2 8 = \log_2 (2^3) = 3$. The correct answer choice is **B**.

4. $\log 45 = \log (9 \cdot 5) = \log 9 + \log 5$. The correct answer choice is **A**.

5. $f(4) = \log_4 (4^1) = 1$, so $(4, 1)$ is on the graph. Choices B and C have the input and output reversed, while

$$f(8) = \log_4 8 = \log_4 4 + \log_4 2 = 1 + \frac{1}{2} \neq 2$$

The correct answer choice is **A**.

6. $x \mapsto x + 4$ translates 4 units to the left, while $y \mapsto y + 5$ translates 5 units down. This can be written as $y + 5 = (x + 4)^3$. The correct answer choice is **D**.

7. $x \mapsto 3x$ yields a horizontal scaling by $\frac{1}{3}$, and $y \mapsto -y$ yields a reflection over the x-axis. The equation can be written as $-y = |3x|$. The correct answer choice is **B**.

8. Applying the definitions,

$$(T_2 \circ D_4 \circ D_{\frac{1}{2}})(6) = (T_2 \circ D_4)\left(\frac{1}{2} \cdot 6\right) = (T_2 \circ D_4)(3)$$

$$= T_2(4 \cdot 3)$$
$$= T_2(12)$$
$$= 12 + 2 = 14$$

The correct answer choice is **D**.

9. For any x

$$A_{(4,-6)} \circ A_{\left(\frac{1}{2}, 3\right)}(x) = A_{(4,-6)}\left(\frac{1}{2}x + 3\right) = 4\left(\frac{1}{2}x + 3\right) - 6$$

$$= 2x + 12 - 6$$
$$= 2x + 6$$
$$= A_{(2,6)}(x)$$

The correct answer choice is **B**.

10. The four transformations send 5, respectively, to $2(5) - 5 = 5, 5(5) - 1 = 24, -3(5) + 5 = -10, -1(5) + 2 = -3$. The correct answer choice is **A**.

11. (a)

x	$g(x)$	$\div$
0	-3	-2
1	6	-2
2	-12	-2
3	24	

(b) $g(x) = \begin{cases} -3 & \text{if } x = 0 \\ -2 \cdot g(x - 1) & \text{if } x \geq 1 \end{cases}$

(c) Since the common ratio is -2, and the initial value is -3, the function is $g(x) = -3(-2)^x$.

(d) $g(5) = -3(-2)^5 = -3(-32) = 96$

12. (a)

x	$f(x)$
-2	$\frac{1}{36}$
-1	$\frac{1}{6}$
0	1
1	6
2	36

x	$g(x)$
$\frac{1}{36}$	-2
$\frac{1}{6}$	-1
1	0
6	1
36	2

(b)

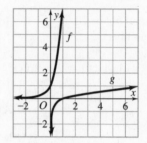

(c) Increasing: going from left to right the curve goes up.

(d) Increasing: going from left to right the curve goes up.

13. (a) Since $3^2 = 9 < 15 < 27 = 3^3$, it follows that $2 < \log_3 15 < 3$.

(b) $\log_3 45 = \log_3 (15 \cdot 3) = \log_3 15 + \log_3 3 = N + 1$

(c) $\log_3 15 = \dfrac{\log 15}{\log 3} \approx \dfrac{1.1761}{0.4771} \approx 2.465$

14. (a) If $3^x = 48$, then by definition

$$x = \log_3 48 = \frac{\log 48}{\log 3} \approx 3.524$$

(b) If $x \cdot 8^3 = 16^2$, then

$$x = \frac{16^2}{8^3} = \frac{2^2 \cdot 8^2}{8 \cdot 8^2} = \frac{4}{8} = \frac{1}{2}$$

(c) We have

$$3 = \log 2x + \log 8 = \log 16x$$

so by definition

$$16x = 10^3 = 1000$$
$$x = \frac{1000}{16} = \frac{125}{2} = 62.5$$

15. After t years, you will have $\$3000(1.06)^t$. You wish to find t when

$$\$3000(1.06)^t = \$9000$$
$$(1.06)^t = 3$$
$$\log\left[(1.06)^t\right] = \log 3$$
$$t\log (1.06) = \log 3$$
$$t = \frac{\log 3}{\log (1.06)} \approx 18.85$$

It will take 19 years (since the interest is paid at the end of the year).

16. (a)

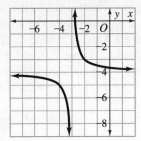

Translate the hyperbola $y = \frac{1}{x}$ 3 units to the left and 4 units down.

(b)

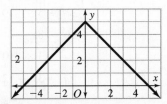

Reflect $y = |x|$ over the x-axis and then translate it 5 units up.

(c)

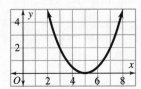

Dilate the parabola $y = x^2$ vertically by the factor $\frac{1}{2}$ and then translate it 5 units to the right.

(d)

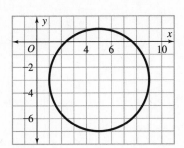

Translate the circle $x^2 + y^2 = 16$ 5 units to the right and 3 units down.

17. (a) For any x,

$$(T_{-4})^{-1} \circ D_8 \circ D_7(x) = T_4 \circ D_8 \circ D_7(x)$$
$$= T_4 \circ D_8(7x)$$
$$= T_4(56x) = 56x + 4$$

The answer is $\mathcal{A}_{(56,4)}$.

(b) For any x,

$$\mathcal{A}_{(-2,3)} \circ \mathcal{A}_{(4,-7)}(x) = \mathcal{A}_{(-2,3)}(4x - 7)$$
$$= -2(4x - 7) + 3$$
$$= -8x + 14 + 3$$
$$= -8x + 17$$

The answer is $\mathcal{A}_{(-8,17)}$.

(c) The opposite of multiplying by 4 and adding 5 is subtracting 5, then dividing by 4. This would send x to $x - \frac{5}{4} = \frac{1}{4}x - \frac{5}{4}$. The answer is $\mathcal{A}_{(\frac{1}{4}, -\frac{5}{4})}$.

18. (a) For any number x

$$\mathcal{A}_{(a,b)}(x) = \mathcal{A}_{(-4,9)} \circ \left(\mathcal{A}_{(2,1)}\right)^{-1}(x)$$
$$= \mathcal{A}_{(-4,9)} \circ \mathcal{A}_{(\frac{1}{2}, -\frac{1}{2})}(x)$$
$$= \mathcal{A}_{(-4,9)}\left(\frac{1}{2}x - \frac{1}{2}\right)$$
$$= -4\left(\frac{1}{2}x - \frac{1}{2}\right) + 9$$
$$= -2x + 11$$

Therefore, $a = -2$, $b = 11$.

(b) For any number x

$$\mathcal{A}_{(a,b)}(x) = (\mathcal{A}_{(2,-3)})^{-1} \circ \mathcal{A}_{(7,1)}(x)$$
$$= \mathcal{A}_{(\frac{1}{2}, \frac{3}{2})} \circ \mathcal{A}_{(7,1)}(x)$$
$$= \mathcal{A}_{(\frac{1}{2}, \frac{3}{2})}(7x + 1)$$
$$= \frac{1}{2}(7x + 1) + \frac{3}{2}$$
$$= \frac{7}{2}x + 2$$

Therefore, $a = \frac{7}{2}$, $b = 2$.

19. (a) $M = x + 6$, so $x = M - 6$.

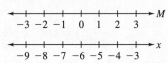

(b) $M = \frac{1}{2}x$, so $x = 2M$.

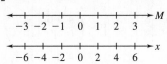

(c) $M = -3x + 5$, so $x = -\frac{1}{3}M + \frac{5}{3}$.

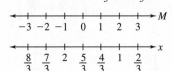

20. (a)

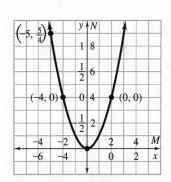

(b) It is a vertical dilation by a factor of $\frac{1}{4}$, with a shift 2 units to the left and 1 unit down.

21. We wish to find all x such that

$$\mathcal{A}_{(4,7)}(x) = x$$
$$4x + 7 = x$$
$$3x = -7$$
$$x = -\frac{7}{3}$$

22. $\sqrt{5} \cdot \sqrt{-20} = \sqrt{-100} = \sqrt{100} \cdot \sqrt{-1} = 10i$

23. $-z + \bar{z} = -(5 - 4i) + (5 + 4i) = -5 + 4i + 5 + 4i = 8i$

24. (a) $zw = (3\sqrt{3} + 3i)(-2i) = -6\sqrt{3}i - 6i^2 = 6 - 6\sqrt{3}i$

(b)

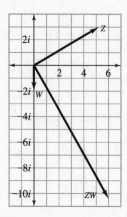

(c) $|z| = \sqrt{(3\sqrt{3})^2 + 3^2} = \sqrt{27 + 9} = \sqrt{36} = 6$,

$|w| = \sqrt{(-2)^2} = \sqrt{4} = 2$, $|zw| = 6 \cdot 2 = 12$;

$$\arg z = \tan^{-1}\left(\frac{3}{3\sqrt{3}}\right) = \tan^{-1}\left(\frac{1}{\sqrt{3}}\right) = 30°$$

$\arg w = 270°$, $\arg(zw) = 30° + 270° = 300°$.

25.

$$\begin{pmatrix} 4 & -6 & \bigm| & -3 \\ 0 & -8 & \bigm| & 5 \end{pmatrix} \sim \begin{pmatrix} 4 & -6 & \bigm| & -3 \\ 0 & 1 & \bigm| & -\frac{5}{8} \end{pmatrix}$$

$$\sim \begin{pmatrix} 4 & 0 & \bigm| & -\frac{27}{4} \\ 0 & 1 & \bigm| & -\frac{5}{8} \end{pmatrix}$$

$$\sim \begin{pmatrix} 1 & 0 & \bigm| & -\frac{27}{16} \\ 0 & 1 & \bigm| & -\frac{5}{8} \end{pmatrix}$$

26. (a) $\begin{pmatrix} 7 & 4 \\ -7 & -2 \end{pmatrix}$

(b) Impossible, since A has 3 columns, while C has 2 rows.

(c)

$$\begin{pmatrix} 3 & 6 \\ -9 & -2 \end{pmatrix}\begin{pmatrix} 4 & -2 \\ 2 & 0 \end{pmatrix} = \begin{pmatrix} 12 + 12 & -6 + 0 \\ -36 - 4 & 18 + 0 \end{pmatrix}$$

$$= \begin{pmatrix} 24 & -6 \\ -40 & 18 \end{pmatrix}$$

(d) Impossible, since only (certain) square matrices have inverses.

(e)

$$B^{-1} = \frac{1}{0 - (-4)}\begin{pmatrix} 0 & 2 \\ -2 & 4 \end{pmatrix} = \begin{pmatrix} 0 & \frac{1}{2} \\ -\frac{1}{2} & 1 \end{pmatrix}$$

27. This could be done by Lagrange interpolation. Alternatively, a quadratic could be used to fit three points, and the second differences would be 4 (the first differences here are 4 and 8). So the coefficient of x^2 is 2. The values of $f(x) - 2x^2$ are 5, 7, and 9. These have a common difference of 2 and can be described by the function $2x + 5$. So $f(x) - 2x^2 = 2x + 5$, or $f(x) = 2x^2 + 2x + 5$.

28. (a) The quotient is $x^2 - 2x + 3$, and the remainder is 2:

$$\require{enclose}
\begin{array}{r}
x^2 - 2x + 3 \\
x + 4 \enclose{longdiv}{x^3 + 2x^2 - 5x + 10} \\
\underline{x^3 + 4x^2} \\
-2x^2 - 5x + 10 \\
\underline{-2x^2 - 8x} \\
3x + 10 \\
\underline{3x + 12} \\
-2
\end{array}$$

(b) By the remainder theorem, $p(-4) = -2$.

29. There is a common difference of 3.

$$a(n) = \begin{cases} -5 & \text{if } n = 0 \\ a(n-1) + 3 & \text{if } n \geq 1 \end{cases}$$

INVESTIGATION 7A THE NEED TO SUM

7.1 Getting Started

For You to Explore

1. (a) $f(n) = 10,000 + 1,000n$, $g(n) = 2^n(.01)$
   (b) In year 22, Emile gets \$32,000 from Option 1, but \$41,943.04 from Option 2. $f(n) < g(n)$ for $n \geq 22$
   (c) $f(n) > g(n)$ for $n \leq 21$

2. (a)

End of year	Amount received (\$)	Total received (\$)
0	10,000	10,000
1	11,000	21,000
2	12,000	33,000
3	13,000	46,000
4	14,000	60,000
5	15,000	75,000

   (b)

End of year	Amount received (\$)	Total received (\$)
0	.01	.01
1	.02	.03
2	.04	.07
3	.08	.15
4	.16	.31
5	.32	.63

   (c) In year 25, Emile would have received a total of \$585,000 from Option 1, but would have gotten \$671,088.63 from Option 2. $F(n) < G(n)$ for $n \geq 25$
   (d) $F(n) > G(n)$ for $n \leq 24$

3. (a) The original function is the difference column for the sum. Since that column has a constant difference of 1,000, you can conclude that the coefficient of the n^2 term in the closed-form rule will be 500. Make a new column for $F(n) - 500n^2$ for the first few entries. You'll see that this column has a constant difference of 10,500 with a first term of 10,000. That means that $F(n) - 500n^2 = 10,500n + 10,000$ and $F(n) = 500n^2 + 10,500n + 10,000$.
   (b) To find a closed-form rule for this function, you can use the fact that the entries are *almost* doubling each time. This means that it may be useful to compare $G(n)$ to 2^n. This will eventually lead you to the rule $G(n) = 0.01(2^{n+1} - 1)$.

4. Answers may vary. For many people, their first instinct is that Option 1 is clearly a better deal. After you work it

out, you see that Option 2 actually gives you much more total money by the end of the 26 years. There might still be good reasons to pick Option 1, though: Perhaps Emile is in desperate need of money right now. He might be better off choosing Option 1 and getting more money now, when he needs it. Also, if Emile knows a good way to invest his money at a high interest rate, he could make the money in Option 1 grow so that he might in fact end up with more total, counting interest.

5. (a)

n	$h(n)$	$\sum$
0	0	0
1	2	2
2	4	6
3	6	12
4	8	20
5	10	30

   (b) One way to find a rule for the $\sum$ column is to create a difference table for it.

n	$\sum$	Δ	Δ^2
0	0	2	2
1	2	4	2
2	6	6	2
3	12	8	2
4	20	10	
5	30		

The second difference is constant, so you can find a quadratic function to match this table. Because that constant difference is 2, the coefficient of the n^2 term in the rule will be 1. Add a column for $\sum -n^2$ to the table. (You may also have noticed that the difference column is the same as the output column from the original table.)

n	$\sum$	Δ	Δ^2	$\sum -n^2$
0	0	2	2	0
1	2	4	2	1
2	6	6	2	2
3	12	8	2	3
4	20	10		4
5	30			5

Now you can see that $\sum -n^2 = n$, so $\sum = n^2 + n$.

On Your Own

6. (a)

Move	Gain	Total
1	5	55
2	−2	53
3	−4	49
4	3	52
5	−6	46
6	1	47
7	−6	41

(b) It's not a fair game. You can pair up rolls for Ken and Maggie from lowest to highest; they can each get

Ken	Maggie
2	1
4	3
6	5

On average, Ken will do better than Maggie, since each of his rolls is one higher than each of her comparable rolls. He will tend to take more chips and lose fewer of them.

7.

n	$t(n)$	$\sum$
0	1	1
1	9	10
2	90	100
3	900	1,000
4	9,000	10,000

$$n \mapsto 10^n$$

8.

n	$h(n)$	$\sum$
0	5	5
1	5	10
2	5	15
3	5	20
4	5	25

$$n \mapsto 5(n+1)$$

9.

n	$g(n)$	$\sum$
0	−1	−1
1	1	0
2	3	3
3	5	8
4	7	15
5	9	24

The $g(n)$ column would be the Δ column in a difference table for $\sum$. It shows a constant difference of 2, which means that $\sum$ can be modeled by a quadratic rule with 1 as the coefficient for the n^2 term. If you look at a column for $\sum -n^2$, you see the following.

$\sum -n^2$
−1
−1
−1
−1
−1
−1

This tells you that $\sum -n^2 = -1$ and $\sum = n^2 - 1$.

10. 16

11. Here is the completed sum table:

time	baked or bought	amount	$\sum$
6:00 A.M.	baked	144	144
6:10 A.M.	bought	12	132
6:25 A.M.	bought	2	130
6:45 A.M.	bought	24	106
7:00 A.M.	bought	5	101
7:15 A.M.	baked	24	125
7:30 A.M.	bought	36	89
8:15 A.M.	baked	12	101
8:25 A.M.	bought	6	95
8:30 A.M.	bought	24	71

(a) 71

(b) Yes, at 8:30 there were 71 muffins, but 6 dozen would be 72.

12. (a) $h(n) = 100n^2$

(b) (i) $h(n) < f(n)$ when $n < 17$.

(ii) $h(n) > f(n)$ when $n > 16$.

(iii) $h(n) < g(n)$ when $n > 22$.

(iv) $h(n) > g(n)$ when $n < 23$ (except for $n = 0$).

Here's a table comparing the year-by-year earnings for each plan:

Year	Option 1 $f(n) = 10{,}000 + 1000n$	Option 2 $g(n) = (.01)2^n$	Option 3 $h(n) = 100n^2$
0	10,000	0.01	0
1	11,000	0.02	100
2	12,000	0.04	400
3	13,000	0.08	900
4	14,000	0.16	1600
5	15,000	0.32	2500
6	16,000	0.64	3600
7	17,000	1.28	4900
8	18,000	2.56	6400
9	19,000	5.12	8100
10	20,000	10.24	10,000
11	21,000	20.48	12,100
12	22,000	40.96	14,400
13	23,000	81.92	16,900
14	24,000	163.84	19,600
15	25,000	327.68	22,500
16	26,000	655.36	25,600
17	27,000	1310.72	28,900
18	28,000	2621.44	32,400
19	29,000	5242.88	36,100
20	30,000	10,485.76	40,000

Year	Option 1 $f(n) = 10,000 + 1000n$	Option 2 $g(n) = (.01)2^n$	Option 3 $h(n) = 100n^2$
21	31,000	20,971.52	44,100
22	32,000	41,943.04	48,400
23	33,000	83,886.08	52,900
24	34,000	167,772.16	57,600
25	35,000	335,544.32	62,500
26	36,000	671,088.64	67,600

Notice that after year 22, Emile would receive more each year with Option 3 than with Option 1. (That is $h(n) > f(n)$ when $n > 22$.) But, in the next exercise, you see that the total Emile has received under Option 1 is always greater than the total he has received under Option 3. ($F(n)$ is always greater than $H(n)$, at least for the 26 years we care about.)

13. (a) $H(n) < F(n)$ for all 26 years.
(b) It's never true in the first 26 years that $H(n) > F(n)$.
(c) $H(n) < G(n)$ when $n > 24$.
(d) $H(n) > G(n)$ when $n < 25$.

Year	Option 1 $F(n)$	Option 2 $G(n)$	Option 3 $H(n)$
0	10,000	0.01	0
1	21,000	0.03	100
2	33,000	0.07	500
3	46,000	0.15	1400
4	60,000	0.31	3000
5	75,000	0.63	5500
6	91,000	1.27	9100
7	108,000	2.55	14,000
8	126,000	5.11	20,400
9	145,000	10.23	28,500
10	165,000	20.47	38,500
11	186,000	40.95	50,600
12	208,000	81.91	65,000
13	231,000	163.83	81,900
14	255,000	327.67	101,500
15	280,000	655.35	124,000
16	306,000	1310.71	149,600
17	333,000	2621.43	178,500
18	361,000	5242.87	210,900
19	390,000	10,485.75	247,000
20	420,000	20,971.51	287,000
21	451,000	41,943.03	331,100
22	483,000	83,886.07	379,500
23	516,000	167,772.15	432,400
24	550,000	335,544.31	490,000
25	585,000	671,088.63	552,500
26	621,000	1,342,177.27	620,100

Maintain Your Skills

14.

n	$F(n)$	Δ
0	1	3
1	4	5
2	9	7
3	16	9
4	25	11
5	36	

$F(n) = (n + 1)^2$

n	$T(n)$	Δ
0	1	9
1	10	90
2	100	900
3	1000	9000
4	10000	90000
5	100000	

$T(n) = 10^n$

n	$H(n)$	Δ
0	5	5
1	10	5
2	15	5
3	20	5
4	25	5
5	30	

$H(n) = 5n + 5$

7.2 Gauss' Method and Euclid's Method

Check Your Understanding

1. (a)
$$\begin{aligned} S &= 0 + 1 + 2 + \cdots + n \\ + S &= n + (n-1) + (n-2) + \cdots + 0 \\ \hline 2S &= n + n + n + \cdots + n \end{aligned}$$
You have $(n + 1)$ terms, each equal to n, and their sum is twice the sum you want. The sum of the integers from 0 to n is $\frac{(n+1)n}{2}$.

(b) You could do this part in exactly the same way, getting n terms, each equal to $n + 1$. However, you might also notice that this is the same sum as in part (a), $\frac{(n+1)n}{2}$. Both sums are adding the same set of numbers, except that part (a) includes 0 and part (b) does not. Adding 0 does not change the sum.

(c)
$$\begin{aligned} S &= 0 + 1 + 2 + \cdots + (n-1) \\ + S &= (n-1) + (n-2) + (n-3) + \cdots + 0 \\ \hline 2S &= (n-1) + (n-1) + (n-1) + \cdots + (n-1) \end{aligned}$$
You have n terms, each equal to $(n - 1)$, and their sum is twice the sum you want. The sum of the integers from 0 to $n - 1$ is $\frac{n(n-1)}{2}$.

You could also subtract n from either of the previous sums, because it's the only term missing.
$$\frac{(n+1)n}{2} - n = \frac{n^2+n-2n}{2} = \frac{n^2-n}{2} = \frac{(n-1)n}{2}$$

2. (a)
$$\begin{aligned} S &= 0 + 2 + 4 \\ + S &= 4 + 2 + 0 \\ \hline 2S &= 4 + 4 + 4 \end{aligned}$$
You have three terms, each equal to 4.

$$\frac{3 \cdot 4}{2} = 6$$

(b)
$$\begin{aligned}
S &= 0 + 2 + 4 + 6 + 8 + 10 \\
+\ S &= 10 + 8 + 6 + 4 + 2 + 0 \\
\hline
2S &= 10 + 10 + 10 + 10 + 10 + 10
\end{aligned}$$
You have six terms, each equal to 10.
$$\frac{6 \cdot 10}{2} = 30$$

(c) The method is exactly the same as above. In this case, you would have 501 terms, each summing to 1000. So, $2S = 501 \cdot 1000$, $S = \frac{501 \cdot 1,000}{2} = 250,500$

3. (a)
$$\begin{aligned}
S &= 1 + 3 + 5 + 7 \\
+\ S &= 7 + 5 + 3 + 1 \\
\hline
2S &= 8 + 8 + 8 + 8
\end{aligned}$$
You have 4 terms, each equal to 8.
$$\frac{4 \cdot 8}{2} = 16$$

(b) The method is the same as above. In this case, you would have 7 terms, each equal to 14.
$$\frac{7 \cdot 14}{2} = 49$$

(c) In this case, using the same method, you would have 500 terms, each equal to 1000.
$$\frac{500 \cdot 1,000}{2} = 250,000$$

4. The key in this exercise is to count the number of terms you're summing. For even numbers from 0 to $2n$, you have $(n + 1)$ terms. For odd numbers from 1 to $(2n + 1)$, you have $(n + 1)$ terms.

(a)
$$\begin{aligned}
S &= 0 + 2 + 4 + \cdots + 2n \\
+\ S &= 2n + (2n-2) + (2n-4) + \cdots + 0 \\
\hline
2S &= 2n + 2n + 2n + \cdots + 2n
\end{aligned}$$
$$S = \frac{(n+1) \cdot 2n}{2} = n(n+1)$$

(b)
$$\begin{aligned}
S &= 1 + 3 + 5 + \cdots + 2n+1 \\
+\ S &= (2n+1) + (2n-1) + (2n-3) + \cdots + 1 \\
\hline
2S &= (2n+2) + (2n+2) + (2n+2) + \cdots + (2n+2)
\end{aligned}$$
$$S = \frac{(n+1) \cdot (2n+2)}{2} = (n+1)^2$$

5. (a) The ratio between successive terms is 2.
$$\begin{aligned}
2S &= 2^6 + 2^7 + \ldots + 2^{15} + 2^{16} \\
-S &= 2^5 + 2^6 + 2^7 + \ldots + 2^{15} \\
\hline
S &= -2^5 \phantom{+ 2^6 + 2^7 + \ldots + 2^{15}} + 2^{16}
\end{aligned}$$
So $S = 2^{16} - 2^5 = 65504$.

(b) The ratio between successive terms is 2.
$$\begin{aligned}
2S &= 3 \cdot 2^6 + 3 \cdot 2^7 + \ldots + 3 \cdot 2^{15} + 3 \cdot 2^{16} \\
-S &= 3 \cdot 2^5 + 3 \cdot 2^6 + 3 \cdot 2^7 + \ldots + 3 \cdot 2^{15} \\
\hline
S &= -3 \cdot 2^5 + 3 \cdot 2^{16}
\end{aligned}$$
So $S = 3 \cdot 2^{16} - 3 \cdot 2^5 = 196,512$. You might also have noticed that since each term in this sum is three times the corresponding term in the previous sum, this sum is just three times the previous one.
$3 \cdot 65,504 = 196,512$.

(c) The ratio between successive terms is $\frac{9}{10}$.
$$\begin{aligned}
S &= \tfrac{9}{10} + \left(\tfrac{9}{10}\right)^2 + \left(\tfrac{9}{10}\right)^3 + \cdots + \left(\tfrac{9}{10}\right)^{10} \\
-\tfrac{9}{10}S &= \phantom{\tfrac{9}{10} +} \left(\tfrac{9}{10}\right)^2 + \left(\tfrac{9}{10}\right)^3 + \cdots + \left(\tfrac{9}{10}\right)^{10} + \left(\tfrac{9}{10}\right)^{11} \\
\hline
\tfrac{1}{10}S &= \tfrac{9}{10} \phantom{+ \left(\tfrac{9}{10}\right)^2 + \cdots} - \left(\tfrac{9}{10}\right)^{11}
\end{aligned}$$
So $S = 10\left(\tfrac{9}{10} - \left(\tfrac{9}{10}\right)^{11}\right) \approx 5.862$.

(d) The ratio between successive terms is $\frac{1}{10}$.
$$\begin{aligned}
S &= \tfrac{9}{10} + \tfrac{9}{10^2} + \tfrac{9}{10^3} + \cdots + \tfrac{9}{10^{10}} \\
-\tfrac{1}{10}S &= \phantom{\tfrac{9}{10} +} \tfrac{9}{10^2} + \tfrac{9}{10^3} + \cdots + \tfrac{9}{10^{10}} + \tfrac{9}{10^{11}} \\
\hline
\tfrac{9}{10}S &= \tfrac{9}{10} \phantom{+ \tfrac{9}{10^2} + \cdots} - \tfrac{9}{10^{11}}
\end{aligned}$$
So $S = \tfrac{10}{9}\left(\tfrac{9}{10} - \tfrac{9}{10^{11}}\right) = 1 - \tfrac{1}{10^{10}} \approx 1$.

(e) The ratio between successive terms is $-\frac{1}{2}$. (You can tell that the ratio is negative because the terms alternate in sign.)
$$\begin{aligned}
S &= 1 - \tfrac{1}{2} + \left(\tfrac{1}{2}\right)^2 - \left(\tfrac{1}{2}\right)^3 + \cdots - \left(\tfrac{1}{2}\right)^7 \\
-\tfrac{1}{2}S &= - \tfrac{1}{2} + \left(\tfrac{1}{2}\right)^2 - \left(\tfrac{1}{2}\right)^3 + \cdots - \left(\tfrac{1}{2}\right)^7 + \left(\tfrac{1}{2}\right)^8 \\
\hline
\tfrac{3}{2}S &= 1 \phantom{- \tfrac{1}{2} + \left(\tfrac{1}{2}\right)^2 \cdots} - \left(\tfrac{1}{2}\right)^8
\end{aligned}$$
So $S = \tfrac{2}{3}\left(1 - \left(\tfrac{1}{2}\right)^8\right) \approx 0.664$.

6. Examples will vary.

(a) Gauss's method works when there's a constant difference between the terms. For example:
$$4 + 7 + 10 + 13 + \cdots + 304$$

(b) Euclid's method works when there's a constant ratio between the terms. For example,
$$4 + 12 + 36 + 108 + \cdots + 4 \cdot 3^{100}$$

7. (a)
$$\begin{aligned}
S &= 1 + r + r^2 + r^3 + \cdots + r^n \\
rS &= r + r^2 + r^3 + \cdots + r^n + r^{(n+1)}
\end{aligned}$$
Subtracting S from rS, you get
$$\begin{aligned}
rS &= r + r^2 + \cdots + r^n + r^{(n+1)} \\
-S &= -1 - r - r^2 - \cdots - r^n \\
\hline
(r-1)S &= -1 + r^{(n+1)}
\end{aligned}$$
Dividing both sides by $(r - 1)$ tells you that
$$S = \frac{r^{n+1} - 1}{r - 1}$$

(b) You can use the same method as part (a), multiplying by r to get rS. Or you can factor an a out of the entire sum, and then use the result from part (a):
$$\begin{aligned}
S_{(b)} &= a + ar + ar^2 + \cdots + ar^n \\
&= a(1 + r + r^2 + \cdots + r^n) \\
&= a(S_{(a)}) \\
&= a \cdot \frac{r^{n+1} - 1}{r - 1}
\end{aligned}$$

On Your Own

8. (a)

$$
\begin{aligned}
S &= -4 + -3 + -2 + -1 + 0 \\
+S &= 0 + -1 + -2 + -3 + -4 \\
\hline
2S &= -4 + -4 + -4 + -4 + -4 \\
2S &= -20 \\
S &= -10
\end{aligned}
$$

(b)

$$
\begin{aligned}
S &= -10 + -9 + \cdots + -1 + 0 \\
+S &= 0 + -1 + \cdots + -9 + -10 \\
\hline
2S &= -10 + -10 + \cdots + -10 + -10 \\
2S &= -110 \\
S &= -55
\end{aligned}
$$

(c)

$$
\begin{aligned}
S &= -1000 + -999 + \cdots + -1 + 0 \\
+S &= 0 + -1 + \cdots + -999 + -1000 \\
\hline
2S &= -1000 + -1000 + \cdots + -1000 + -1000 \\
2S &= -1{,}001{,}000 \\
S &= -500{,}500
\end{aligned}
$$

9.

$$
\begin{aligned}
S &= -n + -n+1 + \cdots + -1 + 0 \\
+S &= 0 + -1 + \cdots + -n+1 + -n \\
\hline
2S &= -n + -n + \cdots + -n + -n \\
2S &= -n(n+1) \\
S &= \frac{-n(n+1)}{2}
\end{aligned}
$$

10. Split the sum into two parts—the sum from -10 to 0 and the part from 1 to 8. Use $\frac{-n(n+1)}{2}$ with $n = 10$ for the first part, getting $\frac{-10(11)}{2} = -55$. Then use $\frac{n(n+1)}{2}$ with $n = 8$ for the second part, getting $\frac{8(9)}{2} = 36$. Then the sum you want is $-55 + 36 = -19$.

11. (a) Here's the expanded version of the sum: $0 + 3 + 6 + 9 + \cdots + 3(n-1) + 3n$. This sum has $n + 1$ terms, and if you reverse the order of the terms and add the two sums, you'll end up with $n + 1$ copies of $3n$ added together equal to twice the sum you want. So, the sum you want is $S = \frac{3n(n+1)}{2}$.

(b) Expand the sum: $0 + 5 + 10 + 15 + \cdots + 5(n-1) + 5n$. This sum has $n + 1$ terms, and if you reverse the order of the terms and add the two sums, you'll end up with $n + 1$ copies of $5n$ added together equal to twice the sum you want. So, the sum you want is $S = \frac{5n(n+1)}{2}$.

(c) Similarly, $S = \frac{7n(n+1)}{2}$.

(d) By the same logic, $S = \frac{kn(n+1)}{2}$.

12.

n	$f(n)$
1	$\frac{1}{2}$
2	$\frac{1}{2} + \frac{1}{4} = \frac{3}{4}$
3	$\frac{1}{2} + \frac{1}{4} + \frac{1}{8} = \frac{7}{8}$
4	$\frac{1}{2} + \frac{1}{4} + \frac{1}{8} + \frac{1}{16} = \frac{15}{16}$
5	$\frac{31}{32}$

You can write the closed form for f in many ways. Here are a few possibilities:

$$f(n) = 1 - \frac{1}{2^n}$$

$$f(n) = 1 - \left(\frac{1}{2}\right)^n$$

$$f(n) = \frac{2^n - 1}{2^n}$$

13.

n	$g(n)$
0	$\left(\frac{1}{2}\right)^0 = 1$
1	$\left(\frac{1}{2}\right)^0 + \left(\frac{1}{2}\right)^1 = \frac{3}{2}$
2	$1 + \frac{1}{2} + \frac{1}{4} = \frac{7}{4}$
3	$\frac{15}{8}$
4	$\frac{31}{16}$
5	$\frac{63}{32}$

You can write the closed form for g in many ways. Here are a few possibilities:

$$g(n) = 2 - \frac{1}{2^n}$$

$$g(n) = 2 - \left(\frac{1}{2}\right)^n$$

$$g(n) = \frac{2^{n+1} - 1}{2^n}$$

14. If there were n people at the party, then one person shook $n - 1$ hands, a second shook an additional $n - 2$ hands (because the first person was counted already), a third shook an additional $n - 3$, and so on. The total equals

$$(n - 1) + (n - 2) + \ldots + 1 = \frac{n(n - 1)}{2} = 78$$

Therefore,

$$n^2 - n = 156$$
$$n^2 - n - 156 = 0$$
$$(n - 13)(n + 12) = 0$$

Since n must be positive, $n = 13$. The correct answer choice is **D**.

Maintain Your Skills

15. (a)

$$
\begin{aligned}
S &= 3 + 4 + 5 \\
+ \ S &= 5 + 4 + 3 \\
\hline
2S &= 8 + 8 + 8
\end{aligned}
$$

You have 3 terms, each equal to 8.

$$\frac{3 \cdot 8}{2} = 12$$

(b)

$$
\begin{aligned}
S &= 55 + 56 + 57 + 58 + 59 + 60 \\
+ \ S &= 60 + 59 + 58 + 57 + 56 + 55 \\
\hline
2S &= 115 + 115 + 115 + 115 + 115 + 115
\end{aligned}
$$

You have 6 terms, each equal to 115.

$$\frac{6 \cdot 115}{2} = 345$$

(c)

$$\begin{array}{rcl}
S &=& 5 + 6 + 7 + \cdots + 80 \\
+\ S &=& 80 + 79 + 78 + \cdots + 5 \\
\hline
2S &=& 85 + 85 + 85 + \cdots + 85
\end{array}$$

You have 76 terms, each equal to 85.

$$\frac{76 \cdot 85}{2} = 3{,}230$$

(d) After cancelling:

$$\begin{array}{rcl}
S &=& 8 + 9 + 10 + \cdots + 150 \\
+\ S &=& 150 + 149 + 148 + \cdots + 8 \\
\hline
2S &=& 158 + 158 + 158 + \cdots + 158
\end{array}$$

You have 143 terms, each equal to 158.

$$\frac{143 \cdot 158}{2} = 11{,}297$$

(e) After cancelling:

$$\begin{array}{rcl}
S &=& 32 + 33 + 34 + \cdots + 131 \\
+\ S &=& 131 + 130 + 129 + \cdots + 32 \\
\hline
2S &=& 163 + 163 + 163 + \cdots + 163
\end{array}$$

You have 100 terms, each equal to 163.

$$\frac{100 \cdot 163}{2} = 8{,}150$$

(f)

$$\begin{array}{rcl}
S &=& n + n+1 + \cdots + m-1 + m \\
+\ S &=& m + m-1 + \cdots + n+1 + n \\
\hline
2S &=& (n+m) + (n+m) + \cdots + (n+m) + (n+m)
\end{array}$$

You have $m - n + 1$ terms, each equal to $n + m$.

$$\frac{(m - n + 1) \cdot (m + n)}{2}$$

7.3 Ways to Visualize Sums

Check Your Understanding

1. Cori is right, because you never add any paper to the process. David is also partly right, because the total area of the paper on the desk does grow at each step, just by a smaller and smaller amount.

   The piece of paper in your hand is getting smaller and smaller. It will never disappear because you always leave some in your hand, but it's pretty small just after doing the steps 4 or 5 times. The stack on the desk is getting bigger and bigger. It's getting close to being the same as the original paper, because the only thing missing is the tiny piece in your hand.

   You could calculate the area of the paper on the desk either by adding up the individual pieces, or by subtracting what's in your hand from 1 (the starting area of the paper).

2. At each step in the process, Emma is closer to having all of the paper on the desk. The piece in her hand gets smaller and smaller. If she were to continue "forever," she could never have more than area 1 on the desk. You could argue that she always has something left in her hand, and that's true *until* it's been "forever." That's the trick— Emma is always holding some paper, but Emma is never "finished." The question asks you to think about what it would look like if she were.

3. (a) The rectangle measures 24 units by 25 units, and has area 600 square units. The original staircase had 300 blocks.

   (b) The rectangle measures 56 units by 57 units, and has area 3192 square units. The original staircase had 1596 blocks.

   (c) The rectangle measures 80 units by 81 units, and has area 6480 square units. The original staircase had 3240 blocks.

   (d) The rectangle measures 123 units by 124 units, and has area 15,252 square units. The original staircase had 7626 blocks.

   (e) The rectangle measures n units by $n + 1$ units, and has area $n(n + 1)$ square units. The original staircase had $\frac{n(n+1)}{2}$ blocks.

4. (a) $(1 - r)(1 + r) = 1 + r - r - r^2 = 1 - r^2$

   (b) $(1 - r)(1 + r + r^2) = 1 + r + r^2 - r - r^2 - r^3 = 1 - r^3$

   (c) $(1 - r)(1 + r + r^2 + r^3) = 1 + r + r^2 + r^3 - r - r^2 - r^3 - r^4 = 1 - r^4$

   (d) $(1 - r)(1 + r + r^2 + r^3 + \cdots + r^n) = 1 + r + r^2 + r^3 + \cdots + r^n - r - r^2 - \cdots - r^n - r^{n+1} = 1 - r^{n+1}$

5. (a) $\frac{1 - \left(\frac{2}{3}\right)^9}{1 - \frac{2}{3}} = \frac{19{,}171}{6561} \approx 2.92$

   (b) $\frac{1 - \left(\frac{1}{4}\right)^9}{1 - \frac{1}{4}} = \frac{87{,}381}{65{,}536} \approx 1.33$

   (c) $\frac{10^{11} - 1}{10 - 1} = \frac{99{,}999{,}999{,}999}{9} = 11{,}111{,}111{,}111$

6. One way to do this is to factor (-1) out of the numerator and denominator, and then cancel the (-1)'s.

$$\frac{r^{n+1} - 1}{r - 1} = \frac{(-1)(1 - r^{n+1})}{(-1)(1 - r)} = \frac{1 - r^{n+1}}{1 - r}$$

On Your Own

7. The sum equals

$$\frac{1 - \left(\frac{3}{4}\right)^5}{1 - \frac{3}{4}} = \frac{781}{256} \approx 3.05$$

The correct answer choice is **C**.

8. (a)

n	$s(n)$	$\sum$
0	2	2
1	5	7
2	8	15
3	11	26

   (b) The entries in the $s(n)$ column have a constant difference of 3 and a first term equal to 2. This pattern points to the linear rule $s(n) = 3n + 2$.

(c) Call the function in the $\sum$ column $S(n)$. Here are the first few staircases:

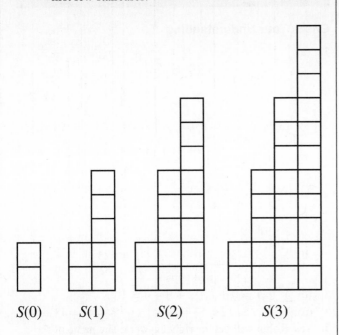

$S(0)$ $S(1)$ $S(2)$ $S(3)$

Here's one rectangle you can make with two copies of a staircase.

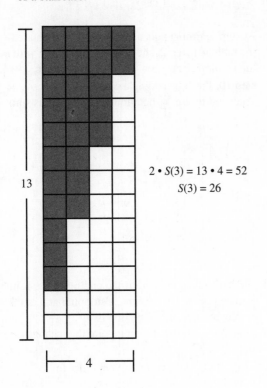

$2 \cdot S(3) = 13 \cdot 4 = 52$
$S(3) = 26$

$$\text{height} = s(n) + 2 = 3n + 4$$
$$\text{width} = n + 1$$
$$\text{area of rectangle} = (n + 1)(3n + 4)$$
$$S(n) = \frac{(n + 1)(3n + 4)}{2}$$

Here's a second approach. Instead of making a single rectangle, you can make a rectangle with two extra

squares sticking out of it:

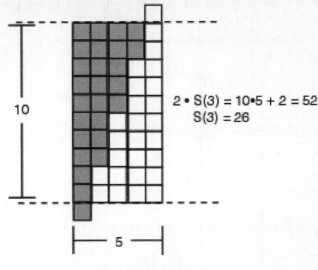

$2 \cdot S(3) = 10 \cdot 5 + 2 = 52$
$S(3) = 26$

$$\text{height} = s(n) - 1 = 3n + 1$$
$$\text{width} = n + 2$$
$$\text{two extra squares} = 2$$
$$\text{area of rectangle} = (n + 2)(3n + 1) + 2$$
$$S(n) = \frac{(n + 2)(3n + 2)}{2} + 1$$

9. At each stage, what's on the table is

$$1 - (\text{what's in your hand})$$

Each stack has half of what's on the table, so that's

$$\frac{1}{2}(1 - (\text{what's in your hand})) = \frac{1}{2}\left(1 - \frac{1}{3^n}\right)$$

(a) In your hand: $\frac{1}{3^2} = \frac{1}{9}$
    In each pile: $\frac{1}{3} + \frac{1}{9} = \frac{4}{9}$
(b) In your hand: $\frac{1}{3^3} = \frac{1}{27}$
    In each pile: $\frac{1}{3} + \frac{1}{9} + \frac{1}{27} = \frac{13}{27}$
(c) In your hand: $\frac{1}{3^n}$
    In each pile: $\frac{1}{2}\left(1 - \frac{1}{3^n}\right)$
(d) If you were to continue this process forever, the piece of paper left in your hand would be smaller and smaller and would eventually be microscopic. The two piles on the table would each be the same size, and together they'd include virtually all of the original sheet of paper, so the area of all the pieces of paper in each pile would approach $\frac{1}{2}$.

10. One way to come up with this answer is to think about the paper ripping in Exercise 8. Consider one of the stacks on the table after going through the steps n times. The first piece is $\frac{1}{3}$. The second piece is $\frac{1}{3}\left(\frac{1}{3}\right) = \left(\frac{1}{3}\right)^2$, and in general the nth piece is $\left(\frac{1}{3}\right)^n$. So the total in the stack can be found by adding up all these pieces:

$$\left(\frac{1}{3}\right) + \left(\frac{1}{3}\right)^2 + \left(\frac{1}{3}\right)^3 + \cdots + \left(\frac{1}{3}\right)^n$$

In the solution for Exercise 8, you argued that amount in each stack is $\frac{1}{2}\left(1 - \frac{1}{3^n}\right)$. Putting these two ways of looking at the stack together, you can see that

$$\left(\frac{1}{3}\right) + \left(\frac{1}{3}\right)^2 + \left(\frac{1}{3}\right)^3 + \cdots + \left(\frac{1}{3}\right)^n = \frac{1}{2}\left(1 - \frac{1}{3^n}\right)$$

Another way to solve this problem is to use Euclid's method.

$$S = \tfrac{1}{3} + \left(\tfrac{1}{3}\right)^2 + \left(\tfrac{1}{3}\right)^3 + \cdots + \left(\tfrac{1}{3}\right)^n$$
$$\tfrac{1}{3}S = \qquad \left(\tfrac{1}{3}\right)^2 + \left(\tfrac{1}{3}\right)^3 + \cdots + \left(\tfrac{1}{3}\right)^n + \left(\tfrac{1}{3}\right)^{n+1}$$

Subtracting $\tfrac{1}{3}S$ from S, you get:

$$S = \tfrac{1}{3} + \left(\tfrac{1}{3}\right)^2 + \left(\tfrac{1}{3}\right)^3 + \cdots + \left(\tfrac{1}{3}\right)^n$$
$$-\tfrac{1}{3}S = \quad - \left(\tfrac{1}{3}\right)^2 - \left(\tfrac{1}{3}\right)^3 - \cdots - \left(\tfrac{1}{3}\right)^n - \left(\tfrac{1}{3}\right)^{n+1}$$
$$\overline{\tfrac{2}{3}S = \tfrac{1}{3} \qquad\qquad\qquad\qquad\qquad - \left(\tfrac{1}{3}\right)^{n+1}}$$

Solving this last equation for S, you have

$$S = \frac{3}{2}\left(\frac{1}{3} - \left(\frac{1}{3}\right)^{n+1}\right)$$
$$= \frac{1}{2}\left(1 - \left(\frac{1}{3}\right)^n\right)$$

Maintain Your Skills

11. (a) 4
    (b) 9
    (c) 16
    (d) 25
    (e) 625
    (f) n^2

There are many ways to solve this problem in general. For example, you might see how to cut out the "descending" steps of the staircase, rotate them, and fit them into the "ascending" steps.

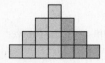

You could also visualize each sum as a tilted square.

 $1 + 2 + 1$

 $1 + 2 + 3 + 2 + 1$

 $1 + 2 + 3 + 4 + 3 + 2 + 1$

Check Your Understanding

1. (a)

$$\sum_{j=0}^{6}(3j + 4) = (3\cdot 0 + 4) + (3\cdot 1 + 4) + (3\cdot 2 + 4) +$$
$$(3\cdot 3 + 4) + (3\cdot 4 + 4) + (3\cdot 5 + 4) +$$
$$(3\cdot 6 + 4)$$
$$= 91$$

   (b) $\displaystyle\sum_{i=1}^{324} 1 = \underbrace{1 + 1 + \cdots + 1 + 1}_{\text{324 copies}} = 324$

   (c) $\displaystyle\sum_{i=0}^{4} i = 0 + 1 + 2 + 3 + 4 = 10$

   (d) $\displaystyle\sum_{i=12}^{45} i = 12 + 13 + 14 + 15 + \cdots + 44 + 45 = 969$

2. Yes, Robin will get the right answers. The name of the index variable doesn't matter—it's just a placeholder.

3. (a) $\displaystyle\sum_{i=1}^{n} i^2$

   (b) $\displaystyle\sum_{i=1}^{6} 1$ or $\displaystyle\sum_{i=0}^{5} 1$ or $\displaystyle\sum_{i=10}^{15} 1 \ldots$

   (c) $\displaystyle\sum_{i=1}^{10} i$

4. (a) At step 1, Emma puts a piece of paper with area $\tfrac{1}{2}$ on the table. At step 2, she adds another piece with half the *remaining* area, or $\tfrac{1}{4}$, so now the sum is $\tfrac{1}{2} + \tfrac{1}{4}$. At step 10, she'll be adding a piece with area $\tfrac{1}{1024} = \tfrac{1}{2^{10}}$. You want to use $\sum$ notation to describe this sum:

$$\frac{1}{2} + \frac{1}{4} + \frac{1}{8} + \cdots + \frac{1}{1024}$$
$$= \sum_{j=1}^{10} \frac{1}{2^j}$$

   (b) All that's changing here is the ending value. Rather than stopping at 10, Emma is stopping at n, so the correct answer in $\sum$ notation is $\displaystyle\sum_{j=1}^{n} \frac{1}{2^j}$.

   (c) Again, it's just the stopping point that changes, so the answer is $\displaystyle\sum_{j=1}^{\infty} \frac{1}{2^j}$

5. $\tfrac{1023}{1024} = 0.999023438$, which is very close to 1.

On Your Own

6. (a) At step 1, you create two piles, each with a piece of paper with area $\tfrac{1}{3}$. At step 2, you adds another piece to each pile with one-third of the *remaining* area, or $\tfrac{1}{9}$, so now the sum is $\tfrac{1}{3} + \tfrac{1}{9}$. At step 10, you'll be adding a piece with area $\tfrac{1}{59049} = \tfrac{1}{3^{10}}$.

You want to use $\sum$ notation to describe this sum:

$$\frac{1}{3} + \frac{1}{9} + \frac{1}{27} + \cdots + \frac{1}{59,049}$$

$$= \sum_{j=1}^{10} \frac{1}{3^j}$$

(b) All that's changing here is the ending value. Rather than stopping at 10, you are stopping at n, so the correct answer in $\sum$ notation is $\sum_{j=1}^{n} \frac{1}{3^j}$.

(c) Again, it's just the stopping point that changes, so the answer is $\sum_{j=1}^{\infty} \frac{1}{3^j}$

7. $\frac{29,524}{59,049} \approx 0.499991532$

8. There are 9 terms, and they are all odd numbers. The expressions $2i \pm 1$ describe odd numbers, while $2i$ describes a general even number. The correct answer choice is **A**.

Maintain Your Skills

9. (a) $\sum_{j=1}^{4}(5j - 1) = (5 \cdot 1 - 1) + (5 \cdot 2 - 1) + (5 \cdot 3 - 1) + (5 \cdot 4 - 1) = 46$

(b) $\sum_{j=4}^{10}(5j - 1) = (5 \cdot 4 - 1) + (5 \cdot 5 - 1) +$
$\quad (5 \cdot 6 - 1) + (5 \cdot 7 - 1) +$
$\quad (5 \cdot 8 - 1) + (5 \cdot 9 - 1) +$
$\quad (5 \cdot 10 - 1)$
$\quad = 238$

(c) This is exactly the same as part (a), but a different variable is being used for the index. That change has no effect on the sum, which is still 46.

(d) $\sum_{i=0}^{6} 2i = 2 \cdot 0 + 2 \cdot 1 + 2 \cdot 2 + 2 \cdot 3 + 2 \cdot 4 + 2 \cdot 5 + 2 \cdot 6 = 42$

(e) $\sum_{k=1}^{6} k(k+1) = 1 \cdot 2 + 2 \cdot 3 + 3 \cdot 4 + 4 \cdot 5 + 5 \cdot 6 + 6 \cdot 7 = 112$

(f) $\sum_{i=0}^{15} 1 = \underbrace{1 + 1 + \cdots + 1 + 1}_{16 \text{ copies}} = 16$

(g) This is the same as part (f), but the index has an ending value that is one more, so you add another 1 to the sequence, giving a sum of 17.

(h) Again, this is the same as part (f), but this time the index starts at 1 instead of 0, meaning that there will be one fewer 1 in the sequence, giving a sum of 15.

7A   MATHEMATICAL REFLECTIONS

1.

n	$g(n)$	$\sum$
0	−3	−3
1	1	−2
2	5	3
3	9	12
4	13	25
5	17	42

To find a closed-form rule for the $\sum$ column, first note that the $g(n)$ is the Δ column for $\sum$. By looking at the entries in the $g(n)$ column, you can see that $\sum$ has a constant *second* difference of 4, which means that the coefficient of the n^2 term in a closed-form rule for $\sum$ should be 2. Add a new column to the table computing $\sum -2n^2$.

n	$g(n)$	$\sum$	$\sum -2n^2$
0	−3	−3	−3
1	1	−2	−4
2	5	3	−5
3	9	12	−6
4	13	25	−7
5	17	42	−8

Now you can see that $\sum -2n^2$ is equal to $-3 - n$, so $\sum = 2n^2 - n - 3$.

2. (a) Euclid's Method works to find the sum of any sequence of numbers that has a constant ratio between successive terms. In this sequence, there is a common ratio of 2 between each term and the next in the sequence.

(b)

$2S =$		$\frac{2}{3}+$	$\frac{4}{3}+$	$\cdots+$	$\frac{256}{3}+$	$\frac{512}{3}$
$-S =$	$\frac{1}{3}+$	$\frac{2}{3}+$	$\frac{4}{3}+$	$\cdots+$	$\frac{256}{3}$	
$S =$	$-\frac{1}{3}$					$+\frac{512}{3}$

So $S = \frac{512}{3} - \frac{1}{3} = \frac{511}{3} \approx 170.333$.

3. The constant ratio of 2 indicates that the terms in this sequence are being generated by an exponential function with base 2. The first term is $\frac{2^0}{3}$ and the last term is $\frac{2^8}{3}$, so you can write this sum in $\sum$ notation as $\sum_{j=0}^{8} \frac{2^j}{3}$.

4. (a) You can use Gauss' Method to find this sum because there is a common difference of 2 between successive terms in the sequence.

$S =$	$3+$	$5+$	$7+$	$\cdots+$	$29+$	$31+$	33
$+S =$	$33+$	$31+$	$29+$	$\cdots+$	$7+$	$5+$	3
$2S =$	$36+$	$36+$	$36+$	$\cdots+$	$36+$	$36+$	36

So twice the sum is equal to 36 added to itself some number of times. To figure out the number of terms in the sequence, realize that $33 - 3 = 30$, but you're only counting odd numbers. $\frac{1}{2} \cdot 30 = 15$, so there are 15 odd numbers from 3 to 33 *not including 3*. Since you want to include 3, you'll have 16 terms in your sequence.

Therefore $2S = 16 \cdot 36 = 576$ and $S = 288$.

(b) You can use Euclid's Method to find this sum because there is a common ratio of 4 between successive terms in the sequence.

$4S =$	$4 + 16 + \cdots + 4,194,304 +$	$16,777,216$
$-S =$	$1 + 4 + 16 + \cdots + 4,194,304$	
$3S = -1$		$16,777,216$

So $3S = 16{,}777{,}216 - 1 = 16{,}777{,}215$, and
$S = \frac{16{,}777{,}215}{3} = 5{,}592{,}405$

5. (a) $\sum_{i=1}^{8} \left(\frac{1}{2}\right)^i = \frac{1}{2} + \frac{1}{4} + \cdots + \frac{1}{128} + \frac{1}{256}$. Since this sequence has a common ratio of $\frac{1}{2}$ between successive terms, you can use Euclid's Method.

$$S = \frac{1}{2} + \frac{1}{4} + \cdots + \frac{1}{128} + \frac{1}{256}$$

$$-\frac{1}{2}S = \quad\;\; \frac{1}{4} + \cdots + \frac{1}{128} + \frac{1}{256} + \frac{1}{512}$$

$$\frac{1}{2}S = \frac{1}{2} \qquad\qquad\qquad\qquad\quad -\frac{1}{512}$$

Since $\frac{1}{2}S = \frac{1}{2} - \frac{1}{512}$, $S = 1 - \frac{1}{256} = \frac{255}{256} \approx 0.9961$.

(b) $\sum_{k=0}^{8}(9 - 3k) = (9 - 0) + (9 - 3) + \cdots + (9 - 21) + (9 - 24)$. Since this sequence has a common difference of -3 between successive terms, you can use Gauss' Method.

$$S = \quad 9 + \quad 6 + \cdots + -12 + -15$$
$$+S = -15 + -12 + \cdots + \quad 6 + \quad 9$$
$$\overline{2S = \;-6 + \;-6 + \cdots + \;-6 + \;-6}$$

So twice the sum you want is equal to -6 added to itself 9 times. $2S = (-6)(9) = -54$ and $S = -27$.

6. The story is that Gauss first wrote the sum with the addends in increasing order.

$$S = 1 + 2 + 3 + \cdots + (n - 2) + (n - 1) + n$$

Then he wrote the same sum, but this time with the addends in decreasing order.

$$S = n + (n - 1) + (n - 2) + \cdots + 3 + 2 + 1$$

Then he added the two equations together to get a new equation.

$$2S = (n+1)+(n+1)+(n+1)+\cdots+(n+1)+(n+1)+(n+1)$$

This is a sequence of $n + 1$ added to itself n times, so

$$2S = n(n + 1)$$

and

$$S = \frac{n(n + 1)}{2}$$

7.

$$\sum_{j=0}^{n} 2^j = 1 + 2 + 4 + \cdots + 2^n$$

Since successive terms in this sequence have a constant ratio of 2, you can use Euclid's method.

$$2S = \qquad\;\; 2 + 4 + \cdots + 2^n + 2^{n+1}$$
$$-S = \;\; 1 + 2 + 4 + \cdots + 2^n$$
$$\overline{S = -1 \qquad\qquad\qquad\qquad + 2^{n+1}}$$

So $\sum_{j=0}^{n} 2^j = -1 + 2^{n+1}$

8. $\sum_{j=1}^{5} 4j = 4 + 8 + 12 + 16 + 20 = 60$

7.5 Getting Started

For You to Explore

1. (a)

n	$f(n)$	$\sum$
0	−2	−2
1	3	1
2	8	9
3	13	22
4	18	40
5	23	63

(b)

n	$g(n)$	$\sum$
0	0	0
1	2	2
2	4	6
3	6	12
4	8	20
5	10	30

(c)

n	$f(n) + g(n)$	$\sum$
0	−2	−2
1	5	3
2	12	15
3	19	34
4	26	60
5	33	93

(d)

n	$2f(n)$	$\sum$
0	−4	−4
1	6	2
2	16	18
3	26	44
4	36	80
5	46	126

(e)

n	$3g(n)$	$\sum$
0	0	0
1	6	6
2	12	18
3	18	36
4	24	60
5	30	90

(f)

n	$f(n) \cdot g(n)$	$\sum$
0	0	0
1	6	6
2	32	38
3	78	116
4	144	260
5	230	490

2. (a) $\sum_{j=1}^{5} 1$ is just the sum of five ones, so it's 5.

(b) $\sum_{j=1}^{5} j$ can be computed with Gauss's Method as $\frac{5(6)}{2} = 15$.

(c) $\sum_{j=1}^{5} 2j$ can also be computed with Gauss's Method. If you set up the sum and the reverse sum, you'll get a total double sum composed of five terms, each equal to 12. So this sum is equal to $\frac{5(12)}{2} = 30$. (You could also think of factoring a 2 out of each term in the sum, and then using the result from part (b).)

(d) $\sum_{j=1}^{5} 3j = 3 \cdot 15 = 45$. As in the previous part, you can factor out a 3 from each term, or use Gauss's Method to get a double sum composed of 5 terms, each equal to 18.

(e) $2\sum_{j=1}^{5} j = 30$. Use your result from part (b).

(f) $3\sum_{j=1}^{5} j = 45$. Use your result from part (b).

(g) $\sum_{j=1}^{5}(j+1) = 15 + 5 = 20$. If you rearrange the terms in this sum, collecting all the j's and all the 1's, you can split it into two sums—the sum from part (a) and the one from part (b).

(h) $\sum_{j=1}^{5} j^2 = 1 + 4 + 9 + 16 + 25 = 55$. (Neither Gauss's Method nor Euclid's Method is helpful with this sum. Luckily, it only has a few terms.)

(i) $\left(\sum_{j=1}^{5} j\right)^2 = 15^2 = 225$. Use your result from part (b).

(j) $\sum_{j=6}^{10} j = 40$ Use Gauss's Method to get a double sum with 5 terms each equal to 16. That means this sum is $\frac{5(16)}{2} = 40$. Another way to think about it is to realize that if you take your result from part (k) and subtract the result from part (b), this is what's left.

(k) $\sum_{j=1}^{10} j = 55$. Use Gauss's Method to get $\frac{10(11)}{2} = 55$.

On Your Own

3. (a) Using techniques from Chapter 1:

n	$q(n)$	Δ
0	5	3
1	8	3
2	11	3
3	14	3
4	17	3
5	20	3

Because there is a constant difference between successive terms, $q(n)$ is linear, with closed form $q(n) = 3n + 5$

(b) In a difference table where $\sum$ is the function, the Δ column will just be the $q(n)$ column from the table in the exercise. In part (a), you showed that $q(n)$ has a constant difference, which means that $\sum$ has a constant second difference. This means that $\sum$ is quadratic as a function of the inputs.

(c) Yes, because the differences of the function column are the second differences of the $\sum$ column. Since the differences of the function column are constant, $\sum$ has a constant second difference, and it's quadratic.

Maintain Your Skills

4. (a) Complete the following tables, where the numbers in the $\sum$ column are just the running totals of the outputs in the Δ column.

n	$f(n)$	Δ	$\sum$
0	0	1	1
1	1	3	4
2	4	5	9
3	9	7	16
4	16	9	25
5	25		

n	$g(n)$	Δ	$\sum$
0	1	1	1
1	2	3	4
2	5	5	9
3	10	7	16
4	17	9	25
5	26		

n	$h(n)$	Δ	$\sum$
0	5	1	1
1	6	3	4
2	9	5	9
3	14	7	16
4	21	9	25
5	30		

(b) For each of the three different functions, the difference column can be matched by the function $\Delta(n) = 2n + 1$. The functions aren't identical because they have different starting points, but they do have identical "difference functions." This means that when that difference function is summed, the results will all be the same.

Check Your Understanding

1. (a) Yes

$$\sum_{k=1}^{n} 2k = 2\cdot 1 + 2\cdot 2 + 2\cdot 3 + \cdots + 2\cdot n$$

$$= 2\cdot(1+2+3+\cdots+n)$$

$$= 2\left(\sum_{k=1}^{n} k\right)$$

(b) Yes (You multiply every term of the sum by 2, so you can factor a 2 out of the whole sum.)

$$\sum_{k=1}^{n} 2f(k) = 2f(1) + 2f(2) + 2f(3) + \cdots + 2f(n)$$

$$= 2\cdot(f(1) + f(2) + f(3) + \cdots + f(n))$$

$$= 2\left(\sum_{k=1}^{n} f(k)\right)$$

(c) No

$$\sum_{k=1}^{n} k^2 = 1^2 + 2^2 + 3^2 + \cdots + n^2$$

$$\left(\sum_{k=1}^{n} k\right)^2 = (1 + 2 + 3 + \cdots + n)^2$$

If you let $n = 3$ for example, you see that $\sum_{k=1}^{3} k^2 = 14$ and $\left(\sum_{k=1}^{3} k\right)^2 = 36$.

(d) Yes (Use Gauss's method to find the sum.)
(e) Yes (Use Gauss's method to find the sum.)
(f) Yes (You are adding up $n+1$ ones.)
(g) Yes (You are adding up n ones.)
(h) No. The left side amounts to the same sum as in (g) (since $1^2 = 1$), so it equals n. The right side equals $(n)^2$.
(i) No

$$\sum_{k=0}^{n} g(k)f(k)$$

$$= g(0)f(0) + g(1)f(1) + \cdots + g(n)f(n) \times$$

$$\left(\sum_{k=0}^{n} g(k)\right) \times \left(\sum_{k=0}^{n} f(k)\right)$$

$$= (g(0) + g(1) + g(2) + \cdots + g(n)) \times$$
$$(f(0) + f(1) + f(2) + \cdots + f(n))$$

$$= g(0)f(0) + g(0)f(1) + \cdots + g(0)f(n) +$$
$$g(1)f(0) + g(1)f(1) + \cdots + g(1)f(n)$$

$$\vdots$$

$$+ g(n)f(0) + g(n)f(1) + \cdots + g(n)f(n)$$

You get many extra terms with the second sum than with the first. You've already seen one specific

example where it does not hold: $f(k) = k$ and $g(k) = k$. (See part (c).)

(j) Yes (Use Euclid's method to find the sum.)
(k) Yes (You are just regrouping the $f(k)$ terms to be together and the $g(k)$ terms to be together.)

$$\sum_{k=0}^{n} (f(k) + g(k))$$

$$= (f(0) + g(0)) + (f(1) + g(1)) +$$
$$\cdots + (f(n) + g(n))$$

$$= (f(0) + f(1) + \cdots + f(n)) +$$
$$(g(0) + g(1) + \cdots + g(n))$$

$$= \left(\sum_{k=0}^{n} f(k)\right) + \left(\sum_{k=0}^{n} g(k)\right)$$

2. (a) (i) $\sum_{k=1}^{16}(3k+2) = 3(1+2+\cdots+16) + 2\cdot 16 = 3\frac{16(17)}{2} + 32 = 408 + 32 = 440$

(ii) This is the same as the previous sum, but it starts at 0 instead of 1. This means that there will be a new term $3(0) + 2$ at the beginning of the sum, so it will be two more or 442. You could also just use the same method to get $\sum_{k=0}^{16}(3k+2) = 3(0+1+2+\cdots+16) + 2\cdot 17 = 3\frac{16(17)}{2} + 34 = 408 + 34 = 442$

(b) (i) Use Euclid's Method to evaluate $\sum_{k=1}^{13} 2\cdot 3^k$.

$3S$	$=$		$2\cdot 3^1$	$+\cdots$	$+2\cdot 3^{13}$	$+2\cdot 3^{14}$
$-S$	$= 2\cdot 3^0$		$+2\cdot 3^1$	$+\cdots$	$+2\cdot 3^{13}$	
$2S$	$= -2\cdot 3^0$					$+2\cdot 3^{14}$

So $S = -1 + 3^{14} = 4{,}782{,}968$.

(ii) This is the same as the previous sum, but it has a different stopping point. Since the method will work exactly the same, you can tell that $S = -1 + 3^7 = 2186$. If you don't see this relationship, you can just go through the standard Euclid's Method calculations from the beginning.

(c) Suppose, as in the For You to Do on page 610, that $f(n) = 5n - 1$ and $g(n) = 2n + 3$.

(i) $\sum_{k=0}^{12}(f(k) - g(k)) = \sum_{k=0}^{12}(3k - 4)$ When you use Sasha's method on this sum, you'll get $3(0 + 1 + 2 + \cdots + 12) - 4(13) = 3\frac{13(12)}{2} - 52 = 234 - 52 = 182$.

(ii) $\sum_{j=5}^{12} f(j) = 5(5 + 6 + \cdots + 12) - 8(1)$. To find the sum $5 + 6 + \cdots + 12$, you can either use Gauss' Method, or you can use the formula to find $1 + 2 + \cdots + 12 = 78$ and subtract $1 + 2 + 3 + 4 = 10$ Finally, the sum is $5(68) - 8(1) = 332$.

3. (a)
$$\sum_{k=1}^{5}(2k-1)$$
$$= (2\cdot 1 - 1) + (2\cdot 2 - 1) + (2\cdot 3 - 1) +$$
$$(2\cdot 4 - 1) + (2\cdot 5 - 1)$$
$$= (2\cdot 1 + 2\cdot 2 + 2\cdot 3 + 2\cdot 4 + 2\cdot 5) +$$
$$(-1-1-1-1-1)$$
$$= 2(1+2+3+4+5) + 5(-1)$$
$$= \frac{2\cdot 5\cdot 6}{2} - 5$$
$$= 25$$

(b)
$$\sum_{k=1}^{10}(2k-1)$$
$$= (2\cdot 1 - 1) + (2\cdot 2 - 1) + (2\cdot 3 - 1) + \cdots +$$
$$(2\cdot 10 - 1)$$
$$= (2\cdot 1 + 2\cdot 2 + 2\cdot 3 + \cdots + 2\cdot 10)$$
$$+ \underbrace{(-1-1-\cdots-1-1-1)}_{10 \text{ copies}}$$
$$= 2(1+2+3+\cdots+10) + 10(-1)$$
$$= \frac{2\cdot 10\cdot 11}{2} - 10$$
$$= 100$$

(c)
$$\sum_{k=6}^{10}(2k-1)$$
$$= (2\cdot 6 - 1) + (2\cdot 7 - 1) + (2\cdot 8 - 1) +$$
$$(2\cdot 9 - 1) + (2\cdot 10 - 1)$$
$$= (2\cdot 6 + 2\cdot 7 + 2\cdot 8 + 2\cdot 9 + 2\cdot 10) +$$
$$(-1-1-1-1-1)$$
$$= 2(6+7+8+9+10) + 5(-1)$$
$$= \frac{2\cdot 5\cdot 16}{2} - 5$$
$$= 75$$

Remember that the sum of the numbers from m–n (in this case from 6–10) is $\frac{(n+m)(n-m+1)}{2}$. That is, it's half this product:

(first term + last term)(number of terms)

(d)
$$\sum_{k=1}^{n}(2k-1)$$
$$= (2\cdot 1 - 1) + (2\cdot 2 - 1) + (2\cdot 3 - 1) + \cdots +$$
$$(2n - 1)$$
$$= (2\cdot 1 + 2\cdot 2 + 2\cdot 3 + \cdots + 2n) +$$
$$\underbrace{(-1-1-\cdots-1-1-1)}_{n \text{ copies}}$$
$$= 2(1+2+3+\cdots+n) + n(-1)$$
$$= \frac{2n(n+1)}{2} - n$$
$$= n^2 + n - n$$
$$= n^2$$

(e) $\sum_{k=1}^{1000}(2k-1) = 1000^2 = 1{,}000{,}000$

On Your Own

4.
$$\sum_{k=0}^{n}(5k-1)$$
$$= (5\cdot 0 - 1) + (5\cdot 1 - 1) + (5\cdot 2 - 1) + \cdots +$$
$$(5\cdot n - 1)$$
$$= (5\cdot 0 + 5\cdot 1 + 5\cdot 2 + \cdots + 5\cdot n) +$$
$$\underbrace{(-1-1-1\cdots-1)}_{(n+1) \text{ copies}}$$
$$= 5\cdot (0+1+2+\cdots+n) + \underbrace{(-1-1-1\cdots-1)}_{(n+1) \text{ copies}}$$
$$= 5\cdot \frac{n(n+1)}{2} + (n+1)\cdot(-1)$$

(Use Gauss's method to find this sum.)
$$= \frac{5n^2 + 5n}{2} - \frac{2n+2}{2}$$
$$= \frac{5n^2 + 3n - 2}{2}$$
$$= \frac{(n+1)(5n-2)}{2}$$

5. (a) $\frac{(23+1)(5\cdot 23 - 2)}{2} = 1356$

(b) $\frac{(7+1)(5\cdot 7 - 2)}{2} = 132$

6.
$$\left(\sum_{k=0}^{n} 5k\right) - 1 = (5\cdot 0 + 5\cdot 1 + 5\cdot 2 + \cdots + 5\cdot n) - 1$$
$$= 5\cdot (0+1+2+\cdots+n) - 1$$
$$= 5\cdot \frac{n(n+1)}{2} - 1$$

7. (a) $\sum_{k=0}^{5} 7$ will have 6 terms, each equal to 7. The total sum is then $6 \times 7 = 42$.

(b) $\sum_{k=1}^{6} 7$ will have 6 terms, each equal to 7. The total sum is then $6 \times 7 = 42$.

(c) $\sum_{k=1}^{n} 7$ will have n terms, each equal to 7. The total sum is then $7n$.

(d) $\sum_{k=0}^{n-1} 7$ will have n terms, each equal to 7. The total sum is then $7n$.

8. If you collect the terms as in Sasha's method, $\sum_{k=1}^{n}(ak+b) = a(1+2+\cdots+n) + bn$. Then, using the formula for the sum of the first n integers, you get
$$\frac{an(n+1)}{2} + bn$$

9. (a)
$$\sum_{k=0}^{4} 9\cdot 10^k = 9\cdot 1 + 9\cdot 10 + 9\cdot 10^2 +$$
$$9\cdot 10^3 + 9\cdot 10^4$$
$$= 9(1 + 10 + 10^2 + 10^3 + 10^4)$$
$$= 9\left(\frac{10^5 - 1}{10 - 1}\right)$$
$$= 10^5 - 1$$
$$= 99{,}999$$

(b)

$$\sum_{k=0}^{12} 9 \cdot 10^k = 9 \cdot 1 + 9 \cdot 10 +$$
$$9 \cdot 10^2 + \cdots + 9 \cdot 10^{12}$$
$$= 9(1 + 10 + 10^2 + \cdots + 10^{12})$$
$$= 9\left(\frac{10^{13} - 1}{10 - 1}\right)$$
$$= 10^{13} - 1$$
$$= 9,999,999,999,999$$

(c)

$$\sum_{k=5}^{12} 9 \cdot 10^k = 9 \cdot 10^5 + 9 \cdot 10^6 + 9 \cdot 10^7 +$$
$$\cdots + 9 \cdot 10^{12}$$
$$= 9 \cdot 10^5(1 + 10 + 10^2 + \cdots + 10^7)$$
$$= 9 \cdot 10^5\left(\frac{10^8 - 1}{10 - 1}\right)$$
$$= 10^5(10^8 - 1)$$
$$= 9,999,999,900,000$$

(d)

$$\sum_{k=0}^{n} 9 \cdot 10^k = 9 \cdot 1 + 9 \cdot 10 + 9 \cdot 10^2 +$$
$$\cdots + 9 \cdot 10^n$$
$$= 9(1 + 10 + 10^2 + \cdots + 10^n)$$
$$= 9\left(\frac{10^{n+1} - 1}{10 - 1}\right)$$
$$= (10^{n+1} - 1)$$
$$10^{n+1} - 1 = \underbrace{9999 \cdots 999}_{n+1 \text{ nines}}$$

10. Each term is $r = \frac{2}{3}$ times the previous. The sum is

$$\frac{1 - \left(\frac{2}{3}\right)^{n+1}}{1 - \frac{2}{3}} = \frac{1 - \left(\frac{2}{3}\right)^{n+1}}{\frac{1}{3}} = \left(1 - \left(\frac{2}{3}\right)^{n+1}\right) \cdot \frac{3}{1}$$

The correct answer choice is **B**.

Maintain Your Skills

11. (a) Yes (You are just splitting up the sum into two parts.)

$$\sum_{k=1}^{n} f(k) = f(1) + f(2) + \cdots + f(m) + f(m+1) +$$
$$\cdots + f(n)$$
$$= (f(1) + f(2) + \cdots + f(m)) +$$
$$(f(m+1) + f(m+2) + \cdots + f(n))$$
$$= \left(\sum_{k=1}^{m} f(k)\right) + \left(\sum_{k=m+1}^{n} f(k)\right)$$

(b) Yes

$$\sum_{k=1}^{n} ck^2 = c \cdot 1^2 + c \cdot 2^2 + c \cdot 3^2 + \cdots + c \cdot n^2$$
$$= c(1^2 + 2^2 + 3^2 + \cdots + n^2)$$
$$= c\sum_{k=1}^{n} k^2$$

(c) Yes

$$\sum_{k=1}^{n} k(k+1) = \sum_{k=1}^{n} (k^2 + k)$$
$$= (1^2 + 1) + (2^2 + 2) + (3^2 + 3) +$$
$$\cdots + (n^2 + n)$$
$$= (1^2 + 2^2 + 3^2 + \cdots + n^2) +$$
$$(1 + 2 + 3 + \cdots + n)$$
$$= \sum_{k=1}^{n} k^2 + \sum_{k=1}^{n} k$$

(d) No

$$\sum_{k=1}^{n} k(k+1) = 1 \cdot 2 + 2 \cdot 3 + 3 \cdot 4 + \cdots + n(n+1)$$

$$\left(\sum_{k=1}^{n} k\right) \times \left(\sum_{k=1}^{n} (k+1)\right)$$
$$= (1 + 2 + 3 + \cdots + n)(2 + 3 + 4 + \cdots + (n+1))$$
$$= 1 \cdot 2 + 1 \cdot 3 + 1 \cdot 4 + \cdots + 1 \cdot (n+1) +$$
$$2 \cdot 2 + 2 \cdot 3 + 2 \cdot 4 + \cdots + 2 \cdot (n+1) +$$
$$\vdots$$
$$+ 2n + 3n + 4n + \cdots + n(n+1)$$

Notice you get many extra terms with the second summation than with the first. They can't possibly be equal. For a specific counterexample, let $n = 3$. You have

$$\sum_{k=1}^{3} k(k+1) = 1 \cdot 2 + 2 \cdot 3 + 3 \cdot 4 = 20$$

$$\left(\sum_{k=1}^{3} k\right) \times \left(\sum_{k=1}^{3} (k+1)\right) = (1 + 2 + 3)(2 + 3 + 4)$$
$$= 54$$

7.7 $\sum$ Identities

Check Your Understanding

1.

$$\sum_{k=1}^{50} (5(k+1)) = 5\left(\sum_{k=1}^{50} (k+1)\right) \quad \text{(Factors come out.)}$$
$$= 5\left(\sum_{k=1}^{50} k + \sum_{k=1}^{50} 1\right)$$

(The sigma of the sum is the sum of the sigmas.)

$$= 5\left(\frac{50 \cdot 51}{2} + 50\right)$$

(Gauss and add a bunch of ones.)

$$= 6{,}625$$

You could also do this by first simplifying inside the sum:

$$\sum_{k=1}^{50}(5(k+1)) = \sum_{k=1}^{50}(5k+5) = 5\sum_{k=1}^{50}k + 5\sum_{k=1}^{50}1$$

You would get the same answer.

2. (a)

$$\sum_{k=0}^{16}(3k-2) = \sum_{k=0}^{16}3k + \sum_{k=0}^{16}-2$$

$$= 3\sum_{k=0}^{16}k - 2\sum_{k=0}^{16}1$$

$$= 3\frac{17(16)}{2} - 2(17)$$

$$= 408 - 34$$

$$= 374$$

(b)

$$\sum_{k=0}^{13}\left(\frac{1}{2}\right)^k = \frac{\left(\frac{1}{2}\right)^{14} - 1}{\left(\frac{1}{2}\right) - 1}$$

$$= \frac{\left(\frac{1}{16{,}384}\right) - 1}{\left(\frac{1}{2}\right) - 1}$$

$$= \frac{1 - 16{,}384}{8192 - 16{,}384}$$

$$= \frac{16{,}383}{8192}$$

$$\approx 1.99987793$$

(c) $\sum_{k=1}^{13}\left(\frac{1}{2}\right)^k$ is the same as the sum in part (b), except it's missing the first term—$\left(\frac{1}{2}\right)^0 = 1$. This gives you a sum of $\frac{8191}{8192} \approx 0.99987793$.

3. (a)

$$\sum_{k=0}^{12}(5k-1) = \sum_{k=0}^{12}5k - \sum_{k=0}^{12}1$$

$$= 5\sum_{k=0}^{12}k - \sum_{k=0}^{12}1$$

$$= 5\frac{12 \cdot 13}{2} - 13$$

$$= 377$$

(b) $\sum_{k=0}^{12}(f(k) + g(k)) = \sum_{k=0}^{12}f(k) + \sum_{k=0}^{12}g(k)$
(The sigma of the sum is the sum of the sigmas.)
Since you know the value of $\sum_{k=0}^{12}f(k)$ from part (a), you can just figure out $\sum_{k=0}^{12}g(k)$ and then add them together.

$$\sum_{k=0}^{12}(2k+3) = \sum_{k=0}^{12}2k + \sum_{k=0}^{12}3$$

$$= 2\sum_{k=0}^{12}k + 3\sum_{k=0}^{12}1$$

$$= 2\frac{12 \cdot 13}{2} + 3 \cdot 13$$

$$= 195$$

So the total is $377 + 195 = 572$.

(c)

$$\sum_{k=0}^{12}(3f(k) + g(k)) = \sum_{k=0}^{12}3f(k) + \sum_{k=0}^{12}g(k)$$

$$= 3\sum_{k=0}^{12}f(k) + \sum_{k=0}^{12}g(k)$$

Since you know $\sum_{k=0}^{12}f(k) = 377$ from part (a) and $\sum_{k=0}^{12}g(k) = 195$ from part (b), you can just compute the total:

$$3\sum_{k=0}^{12}f(k) + \sum_{k=0}^{12}g(k) = 3 \cdot 377 + 195 = 1326$$

(d)

$$\sum_{j=0}^{12}f(j) = \sum_{j=0}^{4}f(j) + \sum_{j=5}^{12}f(j) \quad \text{(splitting up a sum)}$$

$$\sum_{j=5}^{12}f(j) = \sum_{j=0}^{12}f(j) - \sum_{j=0}^{4}f(j)$$

Since you know $\sum_{j=0}^{12}f(j) = 377$ from part (a), you can just compute $\sum_{j=0}^{4}f(j)$ and then subtract.

$$\sum_{j=0}^{4}(5j-1) = \sum_{j=0}^{4}5j - \sum_{j=0}^{4}1$$

$$= 5\sum_{j=0}^{4}j - \sum_{k=0}^{4}1$$

$$= 5\frac{4 \cdot 5}{2} - 5$$

$$= 45$$

$$\sum_{j=5}^{12}f(j) = \sum_{j=0}^{12}f(j) - \sum_{j=0}^{4}f(j) = 377 - 45 = 332$$

On Your Own

4. (a)

$$\sum_{j=1}^{12}(5j-1) = 5 \cdot \sum_{j=1}^{12}j - \sum_{j=1}^{12}1$$

$$= 5 \cdot \frac{12(13)}{2} - 12$$

$$= 378$$

(b)

$$\sum_{j=7}^{12}(5j-1) = \sum_{j=1}^{12}(5j-1) - \sum_{j=1}^{6}(5j-1)$$

$$= 378 - \left(5\cdot\sum_{j=1}^{6}j - \sum_{j=1}^{6}1\right)$$

$$= 378 - \left(5\cdot\frac{6(7)}{2} - 6\right)$$

$$= 378 - 99$$

$$= 279$$

(c)

$$\sum_{j=1}^{n}(5j-1) = 5\cdot\sum_{j=1}^{n}j - \sum_{j=1}^{n}1$$

$$= 5\cdot\frac{n(n+1)}{2} - n$$

$$= \frac{5n^2+5n}{2} - \frac{2n}{2}$$

$$= \frac{5n^2+3n}{2}$$

(d) $\sum_{j=0}^{7}2^j = \frac{2^{7+1}-1}{2-1} = 2^8 - 1 = 255$

(e) $\sum_{j=0}^{7}3\cdot2^j = 3\cdot\sum_{j=0}^{7}2^j = 3\cdot255 = 765$

(f)

$$\sum_{j=0}^{n}3\cdot2^j = 3\cdot\sum_{j=0}^{n}2^j = 3\cdot\frac{2^{n+1}-1}{2-1} = 3(2^{n+1}-1)$$

5. (a) $\sum_{k=0}^{10}f(k) = 10^2 - 3(10) = 100 - 30 = 70$

(b) You can find $\sum_{k=5}^{10}f(k)$ by subtracting $\sum_{k=0}^{4}f(k) = 4^2 - 3(4) = 4$ from the previous answer. $70 - 4 = 66$

(c) $\sum_{k=1}^{11}f(k-1) = \sum_{j=0}^{10}f(j) = 70$

(d)

$$\sum_{k=0}^{10}(3f(k)+5^k) = 3\sum_{k=0}^{10}f(k) + \sum_{k=0}^{10}5^k$$

$$= 3(70) + \frac{5^{11}-1}{5-1}$$

$$= 210 + \frac{48,828,124}{4}$$

$$= 210 + 12,207,031$$

$$= 12,207,241$$

6. (a) All you know is the series associated with f, which tells you the running total of the outputs of f. Call the function that generates the series $t(n) = n^2 - 3n$, and then work backwards to figure out what outputs for f would give you that total.

• $f(0)$ has to be the same as $t(0) = 0^2 - 3(0) = 0$.
• $f(n)$ for $n > 0$ has to satisfy this equation. $t(n) = t(n-1) + f(n)$. In other words, the new total is the old total plus the latest output for f.

Using these ideas you can make a table.

n	$t(n) = n^2 - 3n$	$f(n)$
0	0	0
1	-2	-2
2	-2	0
3	0	2
4	4	4
5	10	6

A function that agrees with $f(n)$ for $n > 0$ (notice that it doesn't agree with the table at $n = 0$) is $g(n) = 2n - 4$.

(b) No, because there's only one way to get that set of running totals with a polynomial function. This isn't like the situations in Chapter 1 where you could find infinitely many polynomials to agree with a table, because you want this polynomial to agree with f for all values $n > 0$, not just for the ones you choose to include in your table.

7. (a) $\sum_{k=0}^{10}g(k) = 2(10)^2 - 5(10) = 200 - 50 = 150$

(b) You can find $\sum_{k=5}^{10}g(k)$ by subtracting $\sum_{k=0}^{4}g(k) = 2(4)^2 - 5(4) = 32 - 20 = 12$ from the previous answer. $150 - 12 = 138$

(c) $\sum_{k=1}^{11}g(k-1) = \sum_{j=0}^{10}g(j) = 150$

(d)

$$\sum_{k=0}^{10}(3g(k)+7^k) = 3\sum_{k=0}^{10}g(k) + \sum_{k=0}^{10}7^k$$

$$= 3(150) + \frac{7^{11}-1}{7-1}$$

$$= 450 + \frac{1,977,326,742}{6}$$

$$= 450 + 329,554,457$$

$$= 329,554,907$$

8. (a) All you know is the series associated with g, which tells you the running total of the outputs of g. Call the function that generates the series $t(n) = 2n^2 - 5n$, and then work backwards to figure out what outputs for g would give you that total.

• $g(0)$ has to be the same as $t(0) = 2(0)^2 - 5(0) = 0$.
• $g(n)$ for $n > 0$ has to satisfy this equation $t(n) = t(n-1) + g(n)$. In other words, the new total is the old total plus the latest output for g.

Using these ideas you can make a table.

n	$t(n) = 2n^2 - 5n$	$g(n)$
0	0	0
1	-3	-3
2	-2	1
3	3	5
4	12	9
5	25	13

A function that agrees with $g(n)$ for $n > 0$ (notice that it doesn't agree with the table at $n = 0$) is
$h(n) = 4n - 7$.

(b) No, because there's only one way to get that set of running totals with a polynomial function. This isn't like the situations in Chapter 1 where you could find infinitely many polynomials to agree with a table, because you want this polynomial to agree with g for all values $n > 0$, not just for the ones you choose to include in your table.

9. One way to approach this problem is to write out the sum you want to find, and then see if you can put that sum into $\sum$ notation and apply Bernoulli's formulas or any of the identities. $3 + 6 + 9 + 12 + \cdots + 999 = \sum_{k=1}^{333} 3k = 3\sum_{k=1}^{333} k$.
You can apply the formula to find

$$3\sum_{k=1}^{333} k = \frac{3 \cdot 333 \cdot 334}{2} = 166{,}833$$

10. (a)
$$\sum_{k=1}^{30} k(k+1)(k+2) = \sum_{k=1}^{30}(k^3 + 3k^2 + 2k)$$
$$= \sum_{k=1}^{30} k^3 + 3\sum_{k=1}^{30} k^2 + 2\sum_{k=1}^{30} k$$
$$= \frac{30^2 \cdot 31^2}{4} + \frac{3 \cdot 30 \cdot 31 \cdot 61}{6} +$$
$$\frac{2 \cdot 30 \cdot 31}{2}$$
$$= 245{,}520$$

(b)
$$\sum_{k=1}^{100}(3k^2 + 5k - 7) = 3\sum_{k=1}^{100} k^2 + 5\sum_{k=1}^{100} k - 7\sum_{k=1}^{100} 1$$
$$= \frac{3 \cdot 100 \cdot 101 \cdot 201}{6} +$$
$$\frac{5 \cdot 100 \cdot 101}{2} - 7 \cdot 100$$
$$= 1{,}039{,}600$$

11. (a)
$$\sum_{k=0}^{n} k(k+1) = \sum_{k=0}^{n}(k^2 + k)$$
$$= \sum_{k=0}^{n} k^2 + \sum_{k=0}^{n} k$$
$$= \frac{n(n+1)(2n+1)}{6} + \frac{n(n+1)}{2}$$

$$= \frac{n(n+1)(2n+1) + 3n(n+1)}{6}$$
$$= \frac{n(n+1)(2n+4)}{6}$$
$$= \frac{n(n+1)(n+2)}{3}$$

(b)
$$\sum_{k=0}^{n} k(k+1)(k+2)$$
$$= \sum_{k=0}^{n}(k^3 + 3k^2 + 2k)$$
$$= \sum_{k=0}^{n} k^3 + 3 \cdot \sum_{k=0}^{n} k^2 + 2 \cdot \sum_{k=0}^{n} k$$
$$= \frac{n^2(n+1)^2}{4} + 3 \cdot \frac{n(n+1)(2n+1)}{6} + 2 \cdot \frac{n(n+1)}{2}$$
$$= \frac{n^2(n+1)^2}{4} + \frac{n(n+1)(2n+1)}{2} + n(n+1)$$
$$= \frac{n(n+1)(n+2)(n+3)}{4}$$

(c)
$$\sum_{k=0}^{n} k(k+1)(k+2)(k+3)$$
$$= \sum_{k=0}^{n}(k^4 + 6k^3 + 11k^2 + 6k)$$
$$= \sum_{k=0}^{n} k^4 + 6 \cdot \sum_{k=0}^{n} k^3 + 11 \cdot \sum_{k=0}^{n} k^2 + 6 \cdot \sum_{k=0}^{n} k$$
$$= \frac{n(n+1)(2n+1)(3n^2 + 3n - 1)}{30} + 6 \cdot \frac{n^2(n+1)^2}{4} +$$
$$11 \cdot \frac{n(n+1)(2n+1)}{6} + 6 \cdot \frac{n(n+1)}{2}$$
$$= \frac{n(n+1)(2n+1)(3n^2 + 3n - 1)}{30} + \frac{3n^2(n+1)^2}{2} +$$
$$\frac{11n(n+1)(2n+1)}{6} + 3n(n+1)$$
$$= \frac{n(n+1)(n+2)(n+3)(n+4)}{5}$$

12. (a) You can use the formula from For You to Do problem 8:
$$\sum_{j=0}^{n}(4j+3) = (2n+3)(n+1)$$
$$\sum_{j=12}^{45}(4j+3) = \sum_{j=0}^{45}(4j+3) - \sum_{j=0}^{11}(4j+3)$$
$$= (2 \cdot 45 + 3)(46) - (2 \cdot 11 + 3)(12)$$
$$= 3978$$

(b) One approach is to rewrite the sum using $\sum$ notation and then apply Bernoulli's formulas. Each term of the sum is one more than a multiple of 4, so you could use the expression $(4k + 1)$ to describe the terms you're adding. You then need to figure out the starting and ending values of k that will give you 5 and 201—they are $k = 1$ and $k = 50$.

$$5 + 9 + 13 + \cdots + 201 = \sum_{k=1}^{50}(4k + 1)$$

$$= 4\sum_{k=1}^{50}k + \sum_{k=1}^{50}1$$

$$= \frac{4 \cdot 50 \cdot 51}{2} + 50$$

$$= 5,150$$

(c) From Exercise 11, you know that

$$\sum_{k=1}^{n}k(k+1) = \frac{n(n+1)(n+2)}{3}.$$

You can just evaluate this expression at $n = 36$:
$\frac{36(37)(38)}{3} = 16,872.$

(d) One approach is to pair up the terms, and see that you have 500 pairs, each equal to -1:

$$\underbrace{1-2}_{-1} + \underbrace{3-4}_{-1} + \underbrace{5-6}_{-1} + \cdots + \underbrace{999-1000}_{-1} = 500 \cdot (-1)$$

(e) One approach is to rewrite the sum using $\sum$ notation and apply the identities, in particular, to "Think Euclid":

$$1 - 2 + 4 - 8 + 16 - \cdots + 1024$$
$$= (-2)^0 + (-2)^1 + (-2)^2 + (-2)^3 + \cdots + (-2)^{10}$$

$$= \sum_{k=0}^{10}(-2)^k$$

$$= \frac{1 - (-2)^{11}}{1 - (-2)}$$

$$= \frac{2049}{3}$$

$$= 683$$

You could also apply Euclid's method from earlier in the chapter:

$$S = 1 - 2 + 4 - 8 + \cdots + 1024$$
$$2S = \quad\; 2 - 4 + 8 - \cdots - 1024 + 2048$$

Since the signs already alternate, terms will cancel if you *add* S and $2S$:

$$\begin{array}{r} 2S = \quad\; 2 - 4 + 8 - \cdots - 1024 + 2048 \\ + \quad S = 1 - 2 + 4 - 8 + \cdots + 1024 \qquad\quad \\ \hline 3S = 1 \qquad\qquad\qquad\qquad\qquad\;\; + 2048 \end{array}$$

$$S = \frac{2049}{3} = 683$$

13. (a)

$$\sum_{k=1}^{5}2k^3 = 2 \cdot \sum_{k=1}^{5}k^3$$

$$= 2 \cdot \frac{5^2(5+1)^2}{4} \quad \left(\text{Note that } \sum_{k=0}^{5}k^3 = \sum_{k=1}^{5}k^3\right)$$

$$= \frac{25(36)}{2} = 450$$

(b)

$$\sum_{k=1}^{30}(k-1)^3 = 0^3 + 1^3 + \cdots + 28^3 + 29^3$$

$$= \sum_{k=0}^{29}k^3$$

$$= \frac{29^2 \cdot 30^2}{4}$$

$$= 189,225$$

You could also multiply out $(k-1)^3$ and find this sum using the identities:

$$\sum_{k=1}^{30}(k-1)^3 = \sum_{k=1}^{30}(k^3 - 3k^2 + 3k - 1).$$

But noticing the terms you're actually summing and changing the bounds of the summation requires much less computation.

(c)

$$\sum_{k=1}^{30}(k+1)^3 = 2^3 + 3^3 + \cdots + 30^3 + 31^3$$

$$= \sum_{k=0}^{31}k^3 - 1^3$$

$$= \frac{31^2(31+1)^2}{4} - 1$$

$$= \frac{31^2 \cdot 32^2}{4} - 1 = 246,015$$

You could also multiply out $(k+1)^3$ and find this sum using the identities:

$$\sum_{k=1}^{30}(k+1)^3 = \sum_{k=1}^{30}(k^3 + 3k^2 + 3k + 1)$$

(d) First note that

$$\sum_{k=7}^{30}(k+2)^3 = 9^3 + 10^3 + \ldots + 32^3$$

$$= \sum_{k=0}^{32}k^3 - \sum_{k=0}^{8}k^3$$

$$= \frac{32^2 \cdot 33^2}{4} - \frac{8^2 \cdot 9^2}{4}$$

$$= 277,488$$

14. You wish to find

$$1^2 + 2^2 + 3^2 + \ldots + 10^2 = \sum_{k=1}^{10}k^2$$

The correct answer choice is **C**.

15. (a)

n	$f(n)$	Δ	Σ
0	0	2	2
1	2	4	6
2	6	6	12
3	12	8	20
4	20	10	30
5	30		

n	$g(n)$	Δ	Σ
0	1	2	2
1	3	4	6
2	7	6	12
3	13	8	20
4	21	10	30
5	31		

n	$h(n)$	Δ	Σ
0	5	2	2
1	7	4	6
2	11	6	12
3	17	8	20
4	25	10	30
5	35		

(b) For each of the three different functions, the difference column can be matched by the function $\Delta(n) = 2n + 2$. The functions aren't identical because they have different starting points, but they do have identical "difference functions." This means that when that difference function is summed, the results will all be the same.

7.8 Tables and Figurate Numbers

Check Your Understanding

1. One technique for finding a closed form function to match a recursively defined function is to write out the first several terms as a computer would calculate them.

```
3
3+      1
3+      1+      2
3+      1+      2+      3
3+      1+      2+      3+      4
```

After doing this a few times, you can see that $H(n) = 3 + \frac{n(n+1)}{2}$, which is just 3 plus the formula for the sum of the first n integers. If you like, you can simplify this to $\frac{n^2+n+6}{2}$.

2. (a) Start by completing the difference table.

n	$q(n)$	Δ
0	32	2
1	34	4
2	38	6
3	44	

In each case, you want to add $2n$ to $q(n-1)$ to get $q(n)$, which leads to the following recursive definition.

$$q(n) = \begin{cases} 32 & \text{if } n = 0 \\ q(n-1) + 2n & \text{if } n > 0 \end{cases}$$

(b) $q(n) = 32 + 2 + 4 + 6 + \cdots + 2n$, so $Q(n) = 32 + 2\frac{n(n+1)}{2} = 32 + n(n+1)$

3.

$$S(n) = 1 + 3 + 5 + \cdots + (2n - 1)$$

$$= \sum_{j=1}^{n}(2j - 1)$$

$$= 2\sum_{j=1}^{n} j - \sum_{j=1}^{n} 1$$

$$= \frac{2n(n+1)}{2} - n$$

$$= n^2 + n - n$$

$$= n^2$$

On Your Own

4. $m(n) = 28 + (1 + 3 + 5 + \cdots + 2n - 1)$, which is 28 plus the sum of the first n odd numbers, which you've just shown to be n^2. This gives you $M(n) = 28 + n^2$.

5. (a)

n	$s(n)$	Δ
0	7	1
1	8	4
2	12	9
3	21	

In each case, you add n^2 to $s(n-1)$ to get $s(n)$, which leads to the following recursive definition.

$$s(n) = \begin{cases} 7 & \text{if } n = 0 \\ s(n-1) + n^2 & \text{if } n > 0 \end{cases}$$

(b) As shown below, each value of $s(n)$ is equal to 7 plus the sum of the first n squares. You can use Bernoulli's formula to find a closed form for that sum.

$$S(n) = 7 + \sum_{k=1}^{n} k^2$$

$$= 7 + \frac{n(n+1)(2n+1)}{6}$$

$$= \frac{2n^3 + 3n^2 + n + 42}{6}$$

$$S(n) = \frac{2n^3 + 3n^2 + n + 42}{6}$$

6. (a) $t(n) = 1 + 2^1 + 2^2 + \cdots + 2^n = \sum_{k=0}^{n} 2^k$

(b) From Euclid's Method,

$$\sum_{k=0}^{n} 2^k = \frac{2^{n+1} - 1}{2 - 1} = 2^{n+1} - 1$$

7. (a) 38

(b) Here's one way to find the answer: Adding up the Δ, you see that $g(5) = 12 + 5 + 6 + 7 + 8 = 38$.

(c) In each case, you're adding $n + 3$ to $g(n - 1)$ to get $g(n)$, which leads to the following recursive definition.

$$g(n) \begin{cases} 12 & \text{if } n = 1 \\ g(n - 1) + n + 3 & \text{if } n > 1 \end{cases}$$

(d)

$$G(n) = 12 + \sum_{k=2}^{n} k + 3 \cdot \sum_{k=2}^{n} 1$$

(from unstacking and rearranging)

$$= 12 + \left(\frac{n(n + 1)}{2} - 1 \right) + 3 \cdot (n - 1)$$

(remember the sums start at $k = 2$)

$$= \frac{n^2 + 7n + 16}{2}$$

8. In general, if the differences are linear, the function is quadratic. If quadratic, the function is cubic (third degree). If they are cubic, the function will be quartic (fourth degree).

Here, the differences are cubic ($8n^3$), and the four choices have degrees 5, 2, 8, and 4, so only the last could possibly be correct.

A precise calculation is

$$f(n) = 5 + \sum_{k=1}^{n} 8k^3 = 5 + 8 \sum_{k=1}^{n} k^3$$

$$= 5 + 8 \cdot \frac{n^2(n + 1)^2}{4} = 5 + 2n^2(n + 1)^2$$

(using Bernoulli's formula). The correct answer choice is **D**.

9. (a) 1 and 36

(b) Yes, the next one is 1,225.

10. (a) Here are the first four pentagonal numbers: 1, 5, 12, 22. Here's what a difference table would look like for the pentagonal numbers:

n	$p(n)$	Δ
1	1	4
2	5	7
3	12	10
4	22	

In each case, you're adding $3n - 2$ to $p(n - 1)$ to get $p(n)$, which leads to the following recursive definition.

$$p(n) = \begin{cases} 1 & \text{if } n = 1 \\ p(n - 1) + (3n - 2) & \text{if } n > 1 \end{cases}$$

(b)

$$P(n) = 1 + 4 + 7 + \cdots + (3n - 2)$$

$$= \sum_{j=1}^{n} (3j - 2)$$

$$= 3 \sum_{j=1}^{n} j - 2 \sum_{j=1}^{n} 1$$

$$= \frac{3n(n + 1)}{2} - 2n$$

$$= \frac{3n^2 + 3n - 4n}{2}$$

$$= \frac{3n^2 - n}{2}$$

11. (a)

n	$h(n)$	Δ
1	1	
		$\rightarrow$ 5
2	6	
		$\rightarrow$ 9
3	15	
		$\rightarrow$ 13
4	28	

In each case you're adding $4n - 3$ to $h(n - 1)$ to get $h(n)$, which leads to the following recursive definition.

$$h(n) = \begin{cases} 1 & \text{if } n = 1 \\ h(n - 1) + (4n - 3) & \text{if } n > 1 \end{cases}$$

(b)

$$H(n) = 1 + 5 + 9 + 13 + \cdots + (4n - 3)$$

$$= \sum_{j=1}^{n} (4j - 3)$$

$$= 4 \sum_{j=1}^{n} j - 3 \sum_{j=1}^{n} 1$$

$$= \frac{4n(n + 1)}{2} - 3n$$

$$= 2n^2 + 2n - 3n$$

$$= 2n^2 - n$$

Maintain Your Skills

12. $T(n - 1) = \frac{(n-1)n}{2}$. $T(n) = \frac{n(n+1)}{2}$. So add them together:

$$T(n - 1) + T(n) = \frac{(n - 1)n}{2} + \frac{n(n + 1)}{2}$$

$$= \frac{n^2 - n + n^2 + n}{2}$$

$$= \frac{2n^2}{2}$$

$$= n^2$$

You can also think about this pictorially. You can redraw the triangular numbers as right triangles rather than equilateral triangles:

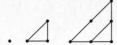

And here's what happens when you put a triangular number together with the previous one. (You have to rotate one of them.)

13. (a)

$$a(n) = \begin{cases} 1 & \text{if } n = 1 \\ a(n-1) + \frac{n(n+1)}{2} & \text{if } n > 1 \end{cases}$$

(b)

$$A(n) = 1 + 3 + 6 + 10 + \cdots + \frac{n(n+1)}{2}$$

$$= \sum_{j=1}^{n} \frac{j(j+1)}{2}$$

$$= \frac{1}{2} \sum_{j=1}^{n} (j^2 + j)$$

$$= \frac{1}{2} \sum_{j=1}^{n} j^2 + \frac{1}{2} \sum_{j=1}^{n} j$$

$$= \frac{1}{2} \left(\frac{n(n+1)(2n+1)}{6} \right) + \frac{1}{2} \left(\frac{n(n+1)}{2} \right)$$

$$= \frac{2n^3 + 3n^2 + n}{12} + \frac{3n^2 + 3n}{12}$$

$$= \frac{2n^3 + 6n^2 + 4n}{12}$$

$$= \frac{n(n+1)(n+2)}{6}$$

7B   MATHEMATICAL REFLECTIONS

1. (a)

$$\sum_{k=2}^{21} (2k-4) = \sum_{k=0}^{21} (2k-4) - \sum_{k=0}^{1} (2k-4)$$

$$= \sum_{k=0}^{21} 2k + \sum_{k=0}^{21} -4 - (-4 - 2)$$

$$= 2 \cdot \sum_{k=0}^{21} k - 4 \cdot \sum_{k=0}^{21} 1 + 6$$

$$= 2 \cdot \frac{21(22)}{2} - 4(22) + 6$$

$$= 462 - 88 + 6$$

$$= 380$$

(b)

$$\sum_{k=3}^{10} 2 \cdot 5^k = \sum_{k=0}^{10} 2 \cdot 5^k - \sum_{k=0}^{2} 2 \cdot 5^k$$

$$= 2 \cdot \sum_{k=0}^{10} 5^k - (2 + 10 + 50)$$

$$= 2 \cdot \frac{5^{11} - 1}{5 - 1} - 62$$

$$= 2 \cdot \frac{48,828,125 - 1}{4} - 62$$

$$= 24,414,062 - 62$$

$$= 24,414,000$$

2. (a)

$$\sum_{k=0}^{n} (2k-4) = \sum_{k=0}^{n} 2k + \sum_{k=0}^{n} -4$$

$$= 2 \cdot \sum_{k=0}^{n} k - 4 \cdot \sum_{k=0}^{n} 1$$

$$= 2 \cdot \frac{n(n+1)}{2} - 4(n+1)$$

$$= n(n+1) - 4(n+1)$$

$$= (n+1)(n-4) \text{ or } n^2 - 3n - 4$$

(b)

$$\sum_{k=0}^{n} 2 \cdot 5^k = 2 \cdot \sum_{k=0}^{n} 5^k$$

$$= 2 \cdot \frac{5^{n+1} - 1}{5 - 1}$$

$$= \frac{5^{n+1} - 1}{2}$$

3. (a) The closed form for the indefinite sum can be used to generate the entries in the $\sum$ column of the table. Then you can use a little logic to figure out the entries for the $f(n)$ column. If the total is 4 after one output, that output was 4. Then the next total is 7, so you had to have added 3 to get there. And the process continues in the same way to finish the column.

n	$f(n)$	$\sum$
0	4	4
1	3	7
2	9	16
3	15	31
4	21	52
5	27	79

(b) If you just look at the entries for $n > 0$, you see a constant difference of 6, so g has to be of the form $6n + b$. You also know that $g(1) = 3$, so $3 = 6(1) + b$, and $b = -3$. That gives you $g(n) = 6n - 3$, which you can check to be sure that it matches the rest of the entries for f in the table.

4. A recursive rule for the series is

$$F(n) = \begin{cases} 3 & \text{if } n = 0 \\ F(n-1) + 3 - 8n & \text{if } n > 0 \end{cases}$$

This means that $F(n) = 3 + (3 - 8 \cdot 1) + (3 - 8 \cdot 2) + \cdots + (3 - 8 \cdot n)$, or

$$F(n) = \sum_{j=0}^{n} 3 - 8 \cdot \sum_{j=0}^{n} j$$

$$= 3(n + 1) - 8 \cdot \frac{n(n + 1)}{2}$$

$$= 3n + 3 - 4n^2 - 4n$$

$$= -4n^2 - n + 3$$

5. (a) $\sum_{k=0}^{n} r^k = \frac{r^{n+1}-1}{r-1} \cdot \frac{-1}{-1} = \frac{1-r^{n+1}}{1-r}$ Or, in words, multiply both the numerator and denominator in the original expression by -1, you'll leave its value unchanged and get the second expression.

(b)

$$\sum_{k=2}^{n} r^k = \sum_{k=0}^{n} r^k - \sum_{k=0}^{1} r^k$$

$$= \frac{r^{n+1} - 1}{r - 1} - (1 + r)$$

$$= \frac{(r^{n+1} - 1) - (r^2 - 1)}{r - 1}$$

$$= \frac{r^{n+1} - r^2}{r - 1}$$

6.

$$\sum_{k=0}^{25} (k + 6^k) = \sum_{k=0}^{25} k + \sum_{k=0}^{25} 6^k$$

$$= \frac{25(26)}{2} + \frac{6^{26} - 1}{6 - 1}$$

$$= 325 + 34,116,345,635,915,641,651$$

$$= 34,116,345,635,915,641,976$$

7.

$$F(n) = \begin{cases} 6 & \text{if } n = 0 \\ F(n - 1) + 3n + 6 & \text{if } n > 0 \end{cases}$$

8.

$$F(n) = 5 + \sum_{k=1}^{n} (2k^2 + 3k + 2)$$

$$= 5 + \sum_{k=0}^{n} (2k^2 + 3k + 2) - (2)$$

$$= 3 + 2 \cdot \sum_{k=0}^{n} k^2 + 3 \cdot \sum_{k=0}^{n} k + \sum_{k=0}^{n} 2$$

$$= 3 + 2\frac{n(n + 1)(2n + 1)}{6} + 3 \cdot \frac{n(n + 1)}{2} + 2(n + 1)$$

$$= \frac{3 \cdot 6 + 2n(n + 1)(2n + 1) + 9n(n + 1) + 12(n + 1)}{6}$$

$$= \frac{18 + 4n^3 + 6n^2 + 2n + 9n^2 + 9n + 12n + 12}{6}$$

$$= \frac{4n^3 + 15n^2 + 23n + 30}{6}$$

Multiple Choice

1. Use the formula

$$1 + r + r^2 + r^3 + \cdots + r^n = \frac{1 - r^{n+1}}{1 - r}$$

$$1 + \frac{1}{10} + \left(\frac{1}{10}\right)^2 + \left(\frac{1}{10}\right)^3 + \cdots + \left(\frac{1}{10}\right)^6$$

$$= \frac{1 - \left(\frac{1}{10}\right)^7}{1 - \left(\frac{1}{10}\right)} = 1.111111$$

You might recognize that this is just $1 + 0.1 + 0.01 + 0.001 + \cdots + 0.000001$. The correct choice is **B**.

2. Since $1 + 2 + 4 + 8 + \cdots + 128 = 2^0 + 2^1 + 2^2 + 2^3 + \cdots 2^7$, the correct choice is **A**.

3. $\sum_{j=3}^{5}(2j - 1) = (2(3) - 1) + (2(4) - 1) + (2(5) - 1) = 5 + 7 + 9 = 21$. The correct choice is **C**.

4.

$$\sum_{k=1}^{n} 3 = 3 \sum_{k=1}^{n} 1 \quad \text{Factors come out.}$$

$$= 3(n) \quad \text{Add a bunch of ones.}$$

$$= 3n$$

The correct choice is **C**.

5. Fill in the table:

n	$h(n)$	$\sum$
0	5	5
1	8	$5 + 8 = 13$
2		$13 + h(2) = 30$

Since $13 + h(2) = 30$, $h(2) = 30 - 13 = 17$. The correct choice is **D**.

Open Response

6. (a) Let

$$S = -5 + -4 + -3 + \cdots + 73 + 74 + 75.$$

Write

$$S = 75 + 74 + 73 \cdots + -3 + -4 + -5$$

and add to get

$$2S = 70 + 70 + 70 + \cdots + 70 + 70$$

$$2S = 81(70)$$

$$S = \frac{81(70)}{2}$$

$$= 2835$$

(b) Let

$$S = 5^0 + 5^1 + 5^2 + \cdots + 5^{12}$$

Multiply S by 5 to get

$$5S = 5^1 + 5^2 + 5^3 \cdots + 5^{13}$$

Subtract:

$$5S - S = 5^{13} - 5^0$$

$$4S = 5^{13} - 1$$

$$S = \frac{5^{13} - 1}{4}$$

$$= 305,175,781$$

7.

n	$f(n)$	$\sum$
0	3	3
1	5	$3 + 5 = 8$
2	7	$8 + 7 = 15$
3	9	$15 + 9 = 24$
4	11	$24 + 11 = 35$
5	13	$35 + 13 = 48$

To find a closed-form rule for the $\sum$ column, first note that $f(n)$ is the Δ column for $\sum$. By looking at the entries in the $f(n)$ column, you can see that $\sum$ has a constant *second* difference of 2, which means that the coefficient of the n^2 term in a closed-form rule for $\sum$ should be $\frac{2}{2} = 1$. Add a new column to the table computing $\sum -n^2$.

n	$f(n)$	$\sum$	$\sum -n^2$
0	3	3	3
1	5	8	7
2	7	15	11
3	9	24	15
4	11	35	19
5	13	48	23

Now you can see that $\sum -n^2$ is equal to $4n + 3$, so $\sum = n^2 + 4n + 3$

8. (a) $\sum_{k=6}^{8}(10k + 4) = (10(6) + 4) + (10(7) + 4) + (10(8) + 4) = 64 + 74 + 84 = 222$

(b) $\sum_{k=0}^{10}(3k - 1) = 3\sum_{k=0}^{10} k - \sum_{k=0}^{10} 1 =$

$3 \cdot \frac{(10)(11)}{2} - 1(10+1) = 3(55) - 11 = 165 - 11 = 154$

(c) $\sum_{k=0}^{20}(k^2 + 2) = \sum_{k=0}^{20}(k^2) + \sum_{k=0}^{20}(2) =$

$\frac{20(20+1)(2(20)+1)}{6} + 2(20 + 1) = \frac{20(21)(41)}{6} + 2(21) =$

$2870 + 42 = 2912$

(d) $\sum_{k=5}^{18}(k^3) = \sum_{k=0}^{18}(k^3) - \sum_{k=0}^{4}(k^3) =$

$\frac{18^2(18+1)^2}{4} - \frac{4^2(4+1)^2}{4} = \frac{324(361)}{4} - \frac{16(25)}{4} =$

$81(361) - 4(25) = 29241 - 100 = 29141$

9. (a) $\sum_{k=0}^{n}(5k+3) = 5\sum_{k=0}^{n}(k) + 3\sum_{k=0}^{n}(1) = 5 \cdot \frac{n(n+1)}{2} +$

$3(n + 1) = 5 \cdot \frac{n^2+n}{2} + \frac{6n+6}{2} = \frac{5n^2+5n+6n+6}{2} = \frac{n^2+11n+6}{2}$

(b) $\sum_{k=0}^{n}(3k^2 + k) = 3 \cdot \sum_{k=0}^{n}(k^2) + \sum_{k=0}^{n}(k) =$

$3 \cdot \frac{n(n+1)(2n+1)}{6} + \frac{n(n+1)}{2} = \frac{n(n+1)(2n+1)}{2} + \frac{n(n+1)}{2} =$

$\frac{n(n+1)(2n+1+1)}{2} = \frac{n(n+1)(2n+2)}{2} = n(n + 1)(n + 1) =$

$n(n + 1)^2$

10.

$$G(n) = 3 + (1^2 + 4) + (2^2 + 4) + (3^2 + 4) + \cdots$$
$$+ (n^2 + 4)$$

$$= 3 + \sum_{j=1}^{n} j^2 + \sum_{j=1}^{n} 4$$

$$= 3 + \frac{n(n + 1)(2n + 1)}{6} + 4n$$

$$= \frac{18}{6} + \frac{(n^2 + n)(2n + 1)}{6} + \frac{24n}{6}$$

$$= \frac{18}{6} + \frac{(2n^3 + 3n^2 + n)}{6} + \frac{24n}{6}$$

$$= \frac{2n^3 + 3n^2 + 25n + 18}{6}$$

$$= \frac{n^3}{3} + \frac{n^2}{2} + \frac{25n}{6} + 3$$

11.

$$F(n) = \begin{cases} 6 & \text{if } n = 0 \\ F(n - 1) + 3n + 6 & \text{if } n > 0 \end{cases}$$

INVESTIGATION 7C   ARITHMETIC AND GEOMETRIC SEQUENCES AND SERIES

7.9   Getting Started

For You to Explore

1. (a)

Table K		
n	$K(n)$	Δ
0	3	5
1	8	5
2	13	5
3	18	5
4	23	

Table L		
m	$L(m)$	Δ
0	3	6
1	9	6
2	15	6
3	21	6
4	27	

(b) The functions that match tables K and L are both linear functions, because each has a constant difference. $K(n) = 5n + 3$ and $L(n) = 6n + 3$. The graphs of the two functions both pass through the point $(0, 3)$, but L has a steeper slope than K.

2. (a)

Bounces	Height (meters)	Ratio ÷
0	2.00	0.84
1	1.68	0.84
2	1.41	0.84
3	1.19	0.84
4	1.00	0.84
5	0.84	0.84
6	0.71	

Since there is a nearly constant ratio between successive terms, you can use the ratio to write a recursive rule to match the data.

$$h(n) = \begin{cases} 2 & \text{if } n = 0 \\ h(n-1) \cdot 0.84 & \text{if } n > 0 \end{cases}$$

(b) Your calculator may not be able to compute the height of the 100th bounce using the recursive rule, so you will want to write a closed form rule. Exponential functions model data with constant ratios between successive terms, and this data matches the exponential function $h(n) = 2 \cdot 0.84^n$. $h(100) = 2 \cdot 0.84^{100}$ m ≈ 0.000000054 m, which is too small for Pandora to measure without really sophisticated tools.

3. This exercise is asking for the sum of the integers from 1 to 75, which is $\frac{75(76)}{2} = 2,850$.

4. (a) $1, 2, 4, 8, 16, 32, 64, \ldots$ $(r = 2)$

(b) $1, -2, 4, -8, 16, -32, 64 \ldots$ $(r = -2)$

(c) $1, -1, 1, -1, 1, -1, \ldots$ $(r = -1)$

(d) $2, 6, 18, 54, 162, \ldots$ $(r = 3)$

(e) $4, 1, \frac{1}{4}, \frac{1}{16}, \frac{1}{64}, \ldots$ $\left(r = \frac{1}{4}\right)$

(f) $-1, \frac{2}{3}, -\frac{4}{9}, \frac{8}{27} \ldots$ $\left(r = -\frac{2}{3}\right)$

On Your Own

5. (a) Making a table is helpful:

day number	height in the morning	height in the evening
0	0	5
1	3	8
2	6	11
3	9	14

The height in the morning is given by $m(n) = 3n$, and the height in the evening is given by $e(n) = 3n + 5$.

(b) Both columns in the table above have constant differences between outputs.

(c) Notice that for every n, $m(n) < e(n)$. So the snail will never reach the top in the morning; he'll do it sometime between the morning and evening. So we want to find the first value of n so that $e(n) > 40$:

$$e(n) > 40$$
$$3n + 5 > 40$$
$$3n > 35$$
$$n > 11\frac{2}{3}$$

The first n that is bigger than $11\frac{2}{3}$ is $n = 12$, so the snail reaches the top on day 12, sometime between morning and evening.

6.

n	$F(n)$	Δ = constant
0	8	1
1	9	1
2	10	1
3	11	1
4	12	

7. Let $g(n)$ be the amount of the fee for the nth month. Let $n = 0$ correspond with the first month. Then, $g(n) = 70 - 2n$. So the associated series is $G(n) = 70(n + 1) - \frac{2n(n+1)}{2} = -n^2 + 69n + 70$ and it corresponds to the total amount of money paid to the health club up to and including month n. You want to know the total cost of membership for one year, so compute $G(11) = 708$.

Maintain Your Skills

8. (a) The first is 9 and the last is 18, so there are 2 multiples of 9 that meet the requirements.

(b) The first is 9 and the last is 54, so there are 6 multiples.

(c) The first is 9 and the last is 999, so there are 111 multiples.

(d) The trick is to find the largest multiple of 9 that is smaller than n. To do that, divide n by 9 and take the integer part, q, of the quotient (in other words, disregard anything after the decimal point in the division). Because the first multiple in the list would have to be 9 and the last would be $9q$, there would be q multiples. That's because you're counting from 9×1 up to $9 \times q$.

9. (a) The first is 3 and the last is 21, so there are 7 multiples of 3 that meet the requirements.

(b) The first is 48, which is 3×16, and the last is 60, which is 3×20, so there are 5 multiples. $(20 - 16 + 1 = 5)$

(c) The first is 48, which is 3×16, and the last is 999, which is 3×111, so there are 96 multiples. $(111 - 16 + 1 = 96)$

(d) Find the largest multiple of 3 less than or equal to m, and call it $3a$, and the largest multiple of 3 less than n, call it $3b$. Then there will be $b - a$ multiples of 3 strictly between m and n.

7.10 Arithmetic Sequences and Series

Check Your Understanding

1. Call the sequence f. Then, the nth term is $f(n - 1) = 12 = 8 + (n - 1) \cdot d$. So, $d = \frac{4}{n-1}$.

2. Yes, let $d = \frac{1}{6}$ with first term $\frac{1}{6}$. The corresponding sequence is $\frac{1}{6}, \frac{1}{3}, \frac{1}{2}, \frac{2}{3}, \frac{5}{6}, 1 \ldots$

3. Yes. 1, 3, π. That's because to go from 1 to 3 in any positive integer number of steps m with a constant "step length" d each time, you'd have to use a rational number for d, because $1 + md = 3$, so $d = \frac{2}{m}$. Since both 2 and m are integers, d is rational. But you can't get to π using only rational number step lengths, because that would imply that $1 + md = \pi$ and therefore that π is rational.

4. (a)

n	$q(n)$	$\sum$
0	9	9
1	15	24
2	21	45
3	27	72
4	33	105

$q(n) = 6n + 9$ and the associated series is
$n \mapsto 9(n + 1) + \frac{6n(n+1)}{2} = 3n^2 + 12n + 9$.

(b)

n	$p(n)$	$\sum$
0	12	12
1	7	19
2	2	21
3	−3	18
4	−8	10

$p(n) = 12 - 5n$ and the associated series is
$n \mapsto 12(n + 1) - \frac{5n(n+1)}{2} = -\frac{5}{2}n^2 + \frac{19}{2}n + 12$.

5. 8, 10, 12, 14, 16, 18, 20, …
There is no other such sequence, because knowing that it took 2 steps to get from 8 to 12 tells you that the constant difference must be $\frac{12-8}{2} = 2$. Once you know the initial term and the constant difference, the arithmetic sequence is completely determined.

6. (a) The first four terms of g are 2, 5, 8, and 11.
   (b) The first four terms of G are 2, 7, 15, and 26.
   (c) $g(n) = 3n + 2$ and $G(n) = 2(n + 1) + \frac{3n(n+1)}{2} = \frac{3}{2}n^2 + \frac{7}{2}n + 2$

7. (a) $t(n) = 9n + 5$ and $T(n) = 5(n + 1) + \frac{9n(n+1)}{2} = \frac{9}{2}n^2 + \frac{19}{2}n + 5$

n	$t(n)$	$\sum$
0	5	5
1	14	19
2	23	42
3	32	74
4	41	115

   (b) $h(n) = 7 - 4n$ and
   $H(n) = 7(n + 1) - \frac{4n(n+1)}{2} = -2n^2 + 5n + 7$

n	$h(n)$	$\sum$
0	7	7
1	3	10
2	−1	9
3	−5	4
4	−9	−5

   (c) $t(n) = \frac{1}{2}n + 6$ and
   $T(n) = 6(n + 1) + \frac{1}{2} \cdot \frac{n(n+1)}{2} = \frac{1}{4}n^2 + \frac{25}{4}n + 6$

n	$t(n)$	$\sum$
0	6	6
1	$\frac{13}{2}$	$\frac{25}{2}$
2	7	$\frac{39}{2}$
3	$\frac{15}{2}$	27
4	8	35

8. (a)

n	$f(n)$	$\sum$
0	a	a
1	$a + d$	$2a + d$
2	$a + 2d$	$3a + 3d$
3	$a + 3d$	$4a + 6d$
4	$a + 4d$	$5a + 10d$
5	$a + 5d$	$6a + 15d$

   (b) $n \mapsto a(n + 1) + d \cdot \frac{n(n+1)}{2} = \frac{d}{2}n^2 + \left(a + \frac{d}{2}\right)n + a = \frac{1}{2}(n + 1)(2a + nd)$

On Your Own

9. (a) $f(8) = 51$
   (b) The closed form for $f(n)$ is $6n + 3$.
   (c) No. This question really asks you to decide whether or not $78,209,756 = 6n + 3$ for some natural number n. The answer, then, is no because $(78,209,756 - 3)$ is not divisible by 6.

10. $f(1) = 1$
   $f(2) = 1 + 1 = 2$
   $f(3) = 2 + 1 = 3$
   $\vdots$

   The sequence whose first term is one and whose common difference is also one is called the positive integers, the natural numbers, or the counting numbers.

11. Three consecutive integers are of the form $n - 1, n, n + 1$. The average is $\frac{(n-1)+n+(n+1)}{3} = \frac{3n}{3} = n$.

12. $t(n - 1) = t(n) - d$ and $t(n + 1) = t(n) + d$. Using these, we see

$$\frac{t(n - 1) + t(n + 1)}{2} = \frac{(t(n) - d) + (t(n) + d)}{2}$$
$$= \frac{2 \cdot t(n)}{2}$$
$$= t(n)$$

13. (a) 1, 5, 14, 30, 55
   (b) $1^2 + 2^2 + \cdots + n^2 = \sum_{k=1}^{n} k^2$ This is not an arithmetic series because the differences are not constant.
   (c) $\sum_{k=1}^{n} k^2 = \frac{n(n+1)(2n+1)}{6}$
   (d) $\sum_{k=1}^{10} k^2 = \frac{10(11)(21)}{6} = 385$

14. First, notice that

$$a_1 + a_3 + a_5 = -12$$
$$a_1 + (a_1 + 2d) + (a_1 + 4d) = -12$$
$$3a_1 + 6d = -12$$
$$a_1 + 2d = -4$$
$$a_3 = -4$$

Substituting $a_3 = -4$ into $a_1 + a_3 + a_5 = -12$ and $a_1 a_3 a_5 = 80$, you find $a_1 + a_5 = -8$ and $a_1 a_5 = -20$. Now solve $a_1 a_5 = -20$ for a_5 to get $a_5 = \frac{-20}{a_1}$. Plugging this into $a_1 + a_5 = -8$, yields

$$a_1 + \frac{-20}{a_1} = -8$$
$$(a_1)^2 + 8a_1 - 20 = 0 \qquad \text{(by multiplying through by } a_1)$$
$$(a_1 - 2)(a_1 + 10) = 0$$

So, $a_1 = 2$ or $a_1 = -10$.
  If $a_1 = 2$, you know that $a_3 = -4$, which makes $a_5 = -10$. In this case, $d = -3$, so the sequence is $2, -1, -4, -7, -10$.
  If $a_1 = -10$, you know that $a_3 = -4$, which makes $a_5 = 2$. In this case, $d = 3$, so the sequence is $-10, -7, -4, -1, 2$.

15. Call the first term of the sequence a_0. Then, you are given that $a_1 \cdot d = 30$ and $a_2 + a_4 = 32$.

$$a_2 + a_4 = 32$$
$$(a_1 + d) + (a_1 + 3d) = 32$$
$$2a_1 + 4d = 32$$
$$a_1 + 2d = 16$$
$$(a_1)^2 + 2d \cdot a_1 = 16a_1$$
$$\text{(multiplying through by } a_1)$$
$$(a_1)^2 + 2 \cdot 30 = 16a_1 \qquad \text{(because } d \cdot a_1 = 30)$$
$$(a_1)^2 - 16a_1 + 60 = 0$$
$$(a_1 - 10)(a_1 - 6) = 0$$

So, $a_1 = 6$ or $a_1 = 10$.
  If $a_1 = 6$, then $d = 5$ which forces $a_0 = 1$ and $a_2 = 11$.
  If $a_1 = 10$, then $d = 3$ which forces $a_0 = 7$ and $a_2 = 13$.

16. Consider the sequence $0, 1, 4, 9, 16, 25, \ldots$ The Δ is $1, 3, 5, 7, 9, \ldots$ which is an arithmetic sequence ($a_0 = 1$ and $d = 2$). The closed formula for the original sequence is $f(n) = n^2$.

17. Consider the sequence $3, 3, 3, 3, \ldots$ The $\sum$ is $3, 6, 9, 12, \cdots$ which is an arithmetic sequence ($a_0 = 3$ and $d = 3$). The closed formula for the original sequence is $f(n) = 3$.

18. Yes, constant sequences are arithmetic ($d = 0$) and their sums are also arithmetic.

19. First, notice that

$$a_0 + a_4 = \frac{5}{3}$$
$$a_0 + (a_0 + 4d) = \frac{5}{3}$$
$$a_0 + 2d = \frac{5}{6}$$

Now, observe that

$$a_2 \cdot a_3 = \frac{65}{72}$$
$$(a_0 + 2d)(a_0 + 3d) = \frac{65}{72}$$
$$\frac{5}{6} \cdot (a_0 + 3d) = \frac{65}{72} \qquad \text{since } \left(a_0 + 2d = \tfrac{5}{6}\right)$$
$$a_0 + 3d = \frac{13}{12}$$

So, we have that $a_0 + 2d = \frac{5}{6}$ and $a_0 + 3d = \frac{13}{12}$. Solving for d, we see that $d = \frac{1}{4}$. Substituting $d = \frac{1}{4}$ into $a_0 + 2d = \frac{5}{6}$, we get $a_0 = \frac{1}{3}$. $a_n = \frac{1}{3} + \frac{1}{4}n$. $\sum_{k=0}^{n} a_n = \frac{1}{3}(n + 1) + \frac{1}{4} \cdot \frac{n(n+1)}{2}$.
  Using this formula tells us that the sum of the first 17 terms (which is $\sum_{k=0}^{16} a_n$) is $\frac{119}{3}$.

20. We have

$$G(3) = g(0) + g(1) + g(2) + g(3)$$
$$= 5 + 2 + (-1) + (-4) = 2$$

The correct answer choice is **D**.

21. (a) $S(n) = 1 + 3 + 5 + \cdots + (2n - 1)$. The sequence is $s(n) = 2n - 1$. It is arithmetic; the common difference is 2.

  (b) $S(n) = n^2$.

22. (a) $G(n) = 1 \cdot 1 + 3 \cdot 2 + 5 \cdot 3 + \cdots + (2n - 1) \cdot n$. The sequence is $g(n) = (2n - 1)n$. It is not arithmetic; the differences between terms of the sequence increases.
  You could reason out the sequence using the results of Exercise 21. You know that at each stage you add $2n - 1$ new terms, and they are all equal to n. So you add $(2n - 1)n$ at each stage.

  (b)

$$G(n) = \sum_{k=1}^{n} (2k^2 - k)$$
$$= 2 \cdot \sum_{k=1}^{n} k^2 - \sum_{k=1}^{n} k$$
$$= \frac{2n(n + 1)(2n + 1)}{6} - \frac{n(n + 1)}{2}$$
$$= \frac{2n(n + 1)(2n + 1) - 3n(n + 1)}{6}$$
$$= \frac{n(n + 1)(4n + 2 - 3)}{6}$$
$$= \frac{n(n + 1)(4n - 1)}{6}$$

23. (a), (b)

n	$t(n)$	$\frac{t(n)}{t(n-1)}$
0	$1 \cdot 2^0 = 1$	4
1	$2 \cdot 2^1 = 4$	3
2	$3 \cdot 2^2 = 12$	2.7
3	$4 \cdot 2^3 = 32$	2.5
4	$5 \cdot 2^4 = 80$	2.4
5	$6 \cdot 2^5 = 192$	

(c) No, and you could have determined that by looking at the definition. For a sequence to be arithmetic, it would have to have a constant difference between successive terms. You can use the formula to calculate the difference.
$t(n+1) - t(n) = (n+2)2^{n+1} - (n+1)2^n = 2^n(2n + 4 - n - 1) = 2^n(n+3)$ The differences between successive terms are not constant, so this is not an arithmetic sequence.

(d) Using the identities developed this far, you wouldn't be able to directly evaluate the sum $\sum_{k=0}^{n}(k+1)2^k$. The problem is that you don't have a way to deal with terms of the form $k \cdot 2^k$, because they don't have a constant difference between terms (for "Think Gauss") or a constant ratio between terms (for "Think Euclid"). So you could use your CAS to get $2n \cdot 2^n + 1$.

Alternately, you could rewrite this series as follows:

$$\sum_{k=0}^{n}(k+1)2^k = 1 \cdot 2^0 + 2 \cdot 2^1 + 3 \cdot 2^2 + \ldots + (n+1) \cdot 2^n$$

$$= (2^0 + 2^1 + 2^2 + \ldots + 2^n) +$$
$$(2^1 + 2^2 + \ldots + 2^n) +$$
$$(2^2 + \ldots + 2^n) +$$
$$\ldots$$
$$+ (2^n)$$

Now you have the sum of $n + 1$ geometric series. Each one can be summed using the formula $a\left(\frac{r^m - 1}{r-1}\right)$, where a = the first term, m = the number of terms, and $r = 2$. Therefore, this equals

$$2^0(2^{n+1} - 1) + 2^1(2^n - 1) + 2^2(2^{n-1} - 1)$$
$$+ \ldots + 2^n(2^1 - 1)$$
$$= (2^{n+1} - 2^0) + (2^{n+1} - 2^1) + (2^{n+1} - 2^2)$$
$$+ \ldots + (2^{n+1} - 2^n)$$
$$= (n+1) \cdot 2^{n+1} - (2^0 + 2^1 + \ldots + 2^n)$$
$$= (n+1) \cdot 2^{n+1} - (2^{n+1} - 1)$$
$$= n \cdot 2^{n+1} + 1 = 2n \cdot 2^n + 1$$

Check Your Understanding

1. (a) $g(n) = 5 \cdot 2^{n-1}$ for $n \geq 1$. So, $g(7) = 5 \cdot 2^6 = 320$.
   (b) $g(n) = 5 \cdot (-2)^{n-1}$ for $n \geq 1$. So, $g(7) = 5 \cdot (-2)^6 = 320$.
   (c) $g(n) = 5$ for $n \geq 1$. So, $g(7) = 5$.
   (d) $g(n) = 5 \cdot \left(\frac{1}{2}\right)^{n-1}$ for $n \geq 1$. So, $g(7) = 5 \cdot \left(\frac{1}{2}\right)^6 = \frac{5}{64}$.
   (e) $r = \frac{g(6)}{g(5)} = \frac{1}{2}$. So, $g(7) = r \cdot g(6) = \frac{1}{2} \cdot 9 = \frac{9}{2}$.
   (f) $r^2 = \frac{g(5)}{g(3)} = \frac{5}{2}$. So, $g(7) = r^2 \cdot g(5) = \frac{5}{2} \cdot 30 = 75$.
   (g) $r^2 = \frac{g(8)}{g(6)} = 9$. Therefore, $r = \pm 3$. So, $g(7) = r \cdot g(6) = \pm 3 \cdot 6 = \pm 18$.
   (h) $r^4 = \frac{g(9)}{g(5)} = 9$. Therefore, $r^2 = 3$. So, $g(7) = r^2 \cdot g(5) = 3 \cdot 6 = 18$.

2. Yes. Consider a constant sequence (e.g. $-2, -2, -2, -2, \ldots$). It is arithmetic ($d = 0$) and geometric ($r = 1$).

3. Answers will vary depending on the examples students choose. For an arithmetic sequence a,
   - a will increase if the common difference is greater than than zero.
   - a will stay constant if the common difference is equal to zero.
   - a will decrease if the common difference is less than zero.

   For a geometric sequence g,
   - A negative ratio makes the signs alternate.
   - If the ratio is between -1 and 1 ($|r| < 1$), then g approaches 0.
   - If the ratio is greater than 1 in absolute value ($|r| > 1$), g gets arbitrarily large in absolute value.
   - If the ratio is one, then g is constant.
   - If the ratio is zero, then g is a constant zero after for all but the first term.

4. (a)

$$\sum_{i=0}^{n} s(i) = \sum_{i=0}^{n}\left(5 \cdot \left(\frac{1}{2}\right)^i\right)$$
$$= 5 \cdot \sum_{i=0}^{n}\left(\frac{1}{2}\right)^i$$
$$= 5 \cdot \frac{1 - \left(\frac{1}{2}\right)^{n+1}}{1 - \frac{1}{2}}$$
$$= 10\left(1 - \left(\frac{1}{2}\right)^{n+1}\right)$$

   (b) $\sum_{i=0}^{15} s(i) = 10\left(1 - \left(\frac{1}{2}\right)^{16}\right) = \frac{327{,}675}{32{,}768} \approx 9.99985$

5. (a) Set up the balance function like this:

$$b(n, m) = \begin{cases} 10{,}000 & \text{if } n = 0 \\ \left(1 + \frac{.04}{12}\right)b(n-1, m) - m & \text{if } n > 0 \end{cases}$$

   Solve $b(36, m) = 0$ for m, to get \$295.24.

   (b) Use the same balance function, but with $m = 500$, and find the n which gives you a balance under \$500.

At $n = 20$, the balance remaining is $365.12, and Rosita will pay that amount in month 21 to pay off her car.

On Your Own

6. (a) $g(n) = 5 \cdot 2^{n-1}$

(b) $g(n) = 5 \cdot (-2)^{n-1}$

(c) $g(n) = 5$

(d) You need to find the initial term, $g(0)$. You know that $g(0) \cdot \frac{1}{2} = 5$, so $g(0) = 10$. Now you have $g(n) = 10 \left(\frac{1}{2}\right)^n$.

(e) You need to find the initial term again. You know that the ratio r is $\frac{1}{2}$ and since $g(5) = 18$, $18 = a \left(\frac{1}{2}\right)^5$ and $a = 576$. This means that $g(n) = 576 \left(\frac{1}{2}\right)^n$.

(f) Since $g(3) = 12$ and $g(5) = 30$, $r = \pm\sqrt{\frac{5}{2}}$. There are two possible functions. If $r = \sqrt{\frac{5}{2}}$, then

$g(3) = 12 = a \left(\sqrt{\frac{5}{2}}\right)^3$ and $a = 0.96\sqrt{10}$. This gives you $g(n) = 0.96\sqrt{10} \cdot \left(\sqrt{\frac{5}{2}}\right)^n$.

If $r = -\sqrt{\frac{5}{2}}$, then $g(3) = 12 = a \left(-\sqrt{\frac{5}{2}}\right)^3$ and $a = -0.96\sqrt{10}$. This gives you $g(n) = -0.96\sqrt{10} \cdot \left(-\sqrt{\frac{5}{2}}\right)^n$.

(g) There are two possibilities, because $r = \pm 3$.
If $r = 3$, $g(6) = 6 = a \cdot 3^6$, and $a = \frac{2}{243}$. This gives you $g(n) = \frac{2}{243} \cdot 3^n$.
If $r = -3$, $g(6) = 6 = a \cdot (-3)^6$, and $a = \frac{2}{243}$. This gives you $g(n) = \frac{2}{243} \cdot (-3)^n$.

(h) There are two possibilities, because $r = \pm\sqrt{3}$.
If $r = \sqrt{3}$, then $g(5) = 6 = a \cdot (\sqrt{3})^5$ and $a = \frac{2\sqrt{3}}{9}$. So $g(n) = \frac{2\sqrt{3}}{9} \cdot (\sqrt{3})^n$.
If $r = -\sqrt{3}$, then $g(5) = 6 = a \cdot (-\sqrt{3})^5$ and $a = -\frac{2\sqrt{3}}{9}$. So $g(n) = -\frac{2\sqrt{3}}{9} \cdot (-\sqrt{3})^n$.

7. $a(5) = 6 \cdot \left(\frac{3}{2}\right)^5 = \frac{729}{16}$.
The correct answer choice is **D**.

8. (a) The length of a side from the second square is $\frac{\sqrt{2}}{2}$. The length of a side from the third square is $\frac{1}{2}$.
In this picture, each side of the second square is the hypotenuse of a right triangle like the one shaded.

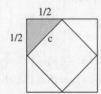

In a right triangle, the sides are related by the Pythagorean Theorem: $a^2 + b^2 = c^2$ where c is the hypotenuse. In this case, $\left(\frac{1}{2}\right)^2 + \left(\frac{1}{2}\right)^2 = c^2$, so $c = \frac{\sqrt{2}}{2}$. Now in this picture, the side of the third square is now the hypotenuse of a right triangle.

The other two sides are $\frac{\sqrt{2}}{4}$ (half the side of the second square). Apply the Pythagorean Theorem again to find d: $\left(\frac{\sqrt{2}}{4}\right)^2 + \left(\frac{\sqrt{2}}{4}\right)^2 = d^2$, so $d = \sqrt{\frac{1}{4}} = \frac{1}{2}$.

(b) Yes. The first term is 1 and the ratio is $\frac{1}{\sqrt{2}}$ or $\frac{\sqrt{2}}{2}$.

(c) The area of the second square is $\frac{\sqrt{2}}{2} \cdot \frac{\sqrt{2}}{2} = \frac{1}{2}$. The area of the third square is $\frac{1}{2} \cdot \frac{1}{2} = \frac{1}{4}$

(d) Yes. The first term is 1 and the constant ratio is $\frac{1}{2}$

(e) A square has four equal sides and four right angles. We must show both conditions are met.
   First, all sides are congruent because of SAS triangle congruence. The triangle shaded in the first picture in part (a) is identical to the triangles in the other three corners of the square. They each have two sides that measure $\frac{1}{2}$ and a right angle between those sides. So all four of the the other sides (the sides of the internal figure) will be congruent.
   Each of the right triangles has two congruent legs, so the non-right angles must be equal. Since the sum of the angle measures in a triangle is $180°$, each of the other two must measure $45°$. A straight line also measures $180°$. You can see that along a straight segment (the side of the original square) three angles meet: two $45°$ angles and an angle from the internal figure. This third angle must be $90°$ because $45 + 45 + 90 = 180$.
   The inside figure has four congruent sides and four right angles, so it is indeed a square.

9. In the picture below, s is the length of the side of the first square: $\frac{1}{2}$ in.

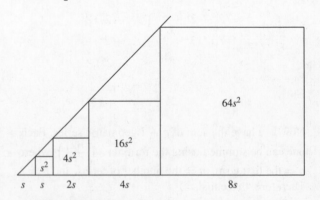

The lengths of the other sides of the squares are 1, 2, and 4 inches. Two geometric sequences: Sides of squares, $a = \frac{1}{2}$ and $r = 2$; areas of squares, $a = \frac{1}{4}$ and $r = 4$.

10. (a) There are $2^{63} = 9{,}223{,}372{,}036{,}854{,}775{,}808$ grains of rice on the 64th square.

(b) $\sum_{i=0}^{63} 2^i = \frac{2^{64}-1}{2-1} = 2^{64} - 1$. This is about 1.84×10^{19} grains of rice.

(c) $\frac{2^{64}-1 \text{ grains}}{8{,}000 \text{ grains/lb}} = 2.305843 \times 10^{15}$ lb of rice.

11. (a) Let $g(n)$ be the number of people who hear the joke (for the first time) on day n where n starts with 0. $g(n) = 2^n$. The number of people who hear the joke (for the first time) on the 8th day is $g(8) = 2^8 = 256$.

(b) The total number of people who have heard the joke by the end of the 8th day is $\sum_{i=1}^{8} g(i) = \sum_{i=0}^{8} 2^i = \frac{2^9 - 1}{2 - 1} = 511$.

(c), (d) Answers will vary depending on population of the school and city. Here's a solution strategy:

Suppose the school has 1000 students. You're looking for the number n so that $\sum_{i=0}^{n} g(i) \geq 1000$.

You know that $\sum_{i=0}^{n} g(i) = 2^{n+1} - 1$, so you need to find the first power of 2 that is greater than 1000.

Since $2^{10} = 1024$, $2^{10} - 1 = 1023 \geq 1000$. Now, $\sum_{i=0}^{9} g(i) = 2^{10} - 1$, so on the 9th day the whole school would have heard the joke.

(e) $\sum_{i=0}^{n} g(i) = 2^{n+1} - 1$. So, the question reduces to: For which n is $2^{n+1} - 1 \geq 6$ billion? Since $2^{32} - 1 < 6$ billion and $2^{33} - 1 > 6$ billion, it will take 32 days for the joke to reach everyone in the world. $\sum_{i=0}^{32} g(i) = 2^{33} - 1 > 6$ billion.

12. (a) Set up a balance function like this:

$$b(n, m, r) = \begin{cases} 9000 & \text{if } n = 0 \\ \left(1 + \frac{r}{12}\right) \cdot b(n - 1, m, r) - m & \text{if } n > 0 \end{cases}$$

Now, to find the entry in the table for 1%, for example, you can solve $b(36, m, 0.01) = 0$ for m.

r	m
0%	$250
1%	$253,87
2%	$257.78
3%	$261.73
4%	$265.72
5%	$269.74

(b) Solve $b(36, 300, r) = 0$ for r, and you'll see that Jaden can afford to take a 12% loan.

13. Set up a balance function like this:

$$b(n, c) = \begin{cases} c & \text{if } n = 0 \\ \left(1 + \frac{.04}{12}\right) \cdot b(n - 1, c) - 500 & \text{if } n > 0 \end{cases}$$

Then solve $b(60, c) = 0$ for c, and you'll see that Hector can afford a loan of $27,149.53, so he can buy a car for $28,649.53.

14. (a) $5 + 5(0.1) = 5.5$

(b) $5.5 + 5.5(0.1) = 6.05$

(c) Let $g(n)$ be the number of miles run in week n (starting with 5 miles in week 0). Then the closed formula for $g(n)$ is $5 \cdot (1.1)^n$. Now, Michelle is planning on running a marathon during the 33rd week, which corresponds with $n = 32$. Therefore, the number of miles run the week before the marathon is $g(31) = 5 \cdot (1.1)^{31} = 96$.

(d) The total mileage she will log before the marathon is

$$\sum_{i=0}^{31} g(i) = \sum_{i=0}^{31} 5 \cdot (1.1)^i = 5 \cdot \frac{(1.1)^{32} - 1}{1.1 - 1}$$
$$= 1005.7$$

15. (a) The last term that is added to the first series is $10{,}000 + 1000{\cdot}26 = 36{,}000$.

The last term that is added to the second series is $(0.01) \cdot 2^{26}$, which corresponds with $n = 26$.

(b) Emile gets

$$\sum_{i=0}^{26}(10{,}000 + 1000i) = \sum_{i=0}^{26} 10{,}000 + 1000 \sum_{i=0}^{26} i$$
$$= 10{,}000(26 + 1)$$
$$+ 1000\left(\frac{26 \cdot 27}{2}\right)$$
$$= 621{,}000$$

(c) Emile gets

$$\sum_{i=0}^{26}(0.01) \cdot 2^i = (0.01) \cdot \frac{2^{27} - 1}{2 - 1} = 1{,}342{,}177.27$$

16. After the first bounce, the ball falls 1.68 meters. After the second bounce, the ball falls 1.41 meters. After the third bounce, the ball falls 1.19 meters.

17. x is approximately 0.84.

18.

$$2 + 2x + 2x^2 + \cdots + 2x^{100} = 2\sum_{j=0}^{100} x^j$$
$$= 2\sum_{j=0}^{100}(0.84)^j$$
$$= 2 \cdot \frac{1 - 0.84^{101}}{1 - 0.84}$$
$$= 12.5$$

19. The distance the ball bounces up is the same as what it falls, except for the original 2 meter fall. So it is 12.5 meters $-$ 2 meters $= 10.5$ meters.

20. The total is 23 meters. The total for 1000 bounces would not be significantly different. We have rounded up a bit in these calculations, so with enough decimal places of accuracy you could tell a difference between 100 and 1000 bounces. The total for 1000 bounces would be even closer to 23 meters.

Maintain Your Skills

21. (a) After three jumps, Zeno has traveled $12 + 6 + 3 = 21$. He still has $24 - 21 = 3$. left to reach the wall.

(b) After six jumps, Zeno has traveled $12 + 6 + 3 + \frac{3}{2} + \frac{3}{4} + \frac{3}{8} = 23\frac{5}{8}$. He still has $24 - 23\frac{5}{8} = \frac{3}{8}$. left to reach the wall.

(c) After n jumps, Zeno has traveled

$$\sum_{i=0}^{n-1} 12\left(\frac{1}{2}\right)^i = \frac{12}{1-\frac{1}{2}}\left(1-\left(\frac{1}{2}\right)^n\right)$$
$$= 24\left(1-\left(\frac{1}{2}\right)^n\right) \text{ ft.}$$

He still has $24 - 24\left(1-\left(\frac{1}{2}\right)^n\right) = 24\left(\frac{1}{2}\right)^n = \frac{24}{2^n}$ left to reach the wall.

(d) He will not reach the wall if he keeps up this "jumping half-way" scheme. Except, of course, he will eventually be closer than, say, the length of his nose. Closer than the thickness of a piece of paper. Closer than the diameter of an atom …

7.12 Limits

Check Your Understanding

1. (a) Sequence: $7, 1.56, 0.346, 0.077, \ldots$; series: $7, 8.56, 8.9, 8.97, \ldots$; yes, it seems to have a limit of 9
   (b) Sequence: $100, 50, 25, 12.5, \ldots$; series: $100, 150, 175, 187.5, \ldots$; it's not obvious if this series has a limit. The differences between terms is getting smaller, so it seems likely that there is a limit. One way to decide is think about a familiar series: $S(n) = 1 + \frac{1}{2} + \frac{1}{4} + \cdots$. $S(n)$ has a limit of 2, and the series in question is really $100 \cdot S(n)$, so it likely has a limit as well, and the limit is probably 200.
   (c) Sequence: $0.75, 1.5, 3, 6, \ldots$; series: $0.75, 2.25, 5.25, 11.25, \ldots$; the series does not have a limit. $S(n) = \frac{\frac{3}{4}}{1-2}\cdot(1-2^{n+1}) = \frac{-3}{4}\cdot(1-2^{n+1})$. $(1-2^{n+1})$ does not approach any real number as n gets larger and larger.
   (d) Sequence: $1, 1, 1, 1, \ldots$; series: $1, 2, 3, 4, \ldots$; this series has no limit. $S(n) = n + 1$ (where n starts with 0), which does not approach a real number as n gets larger and larger.

2. First, Pat runs a mile (Sam is at the half mile). Since Pat runs twice as fast, he will cover $\frac{2}{3}$ of the distance between them as he runs back, while Sam will only cover $\frac{1}{3}$ of that distance. Since there is $\frac{1}{2}$ mile between them, Pat runs $\frac{2}{3}\cdot\frac{1}{2} = \frac{1}{3}$ mile. Then he turns around and runs that same $\frac{1}{3}$ mile again. So he has run $1 + \frac{1}{3} + \frac{1}{3}$ miles so far.

   Remember that Pat and Sam were together $\frac{1}{3}$ mile from the end. While Pat ran that $\frac{1}{3}$ mile, Sam walked half of it, or $\frac{1}{6}$ mile. When Pat turns around, he will cover $\frac{2}{3}$ of that remaining $\frac{1}{6}$ of the mile, so he runs another $\frac{1}{9}$ of a mile before meeting up with Sam, turning around and running that $\frac{1}{9}$ of a mile back.

   As this continues, Pat runs $1 + \frac{1}{3} + \frac{1}{3} + \frac{1}{9} + \frac{1}{9} + \cdots + \frac{1}{3^n} + \frac{1}{3^n}$. You want to find the limit of this series. Here is a series that's easier to sum:

$$S(n) = 1 + 1 + \frac{1}{3} + \frac{1}{3} + \frac{1}{9} + \frac{1}{9} + \cdots + \frac{1}{3^n} + \frac{1}{3^n}$$
$$= 2 + \frac{2}{3} + \frac{2}{9} + \cdots + \frac{2}{3^n}$$
$$S(n) = \sum_{k=0}^{n} \frac{2}{3^k} = 2\left(\frac{1-\frac{1}{3^{n+1}}}{1-\frac{1}{3}}\right) = 3\left(1-\frac{1}{3^{n+1}}\right)$$

The limit of this series is 3. This is one mile more than the limit of Pat's series, so Pat runs 2 miles.

Here's another approach: If you think of it in terms of their "meeting" times, the first time they meet

$$S + P = S + 2S = 2$$
$$3S = 2$$
$$S = \frac{2}{3}$$

So, Sam has walked $\frac{2}{3}$ mile and Pat has run twice as far: $1\frac{1}{3}$ mile.

Now there is only $\frac{1}{3}$ mile left. By the same reasoning, Sam walks $\frac{2}{3}$ of it, or $\frac{2}{9}$ mile. Pat runs twice as far, or $\frac{4}{9}$ mile.

In the next step, there is $\frac{1}{9}$ mile left. Sam walks $\frac{2}{3}$, or $\frac{2}{27}$ mile, and Pat runs twice as far, or $\frac{4}{27}$ mile. All together, Pat runs:

$$\frac{4}{3} + \frac{4}{9} + \frac{4}{27} + \cdots = \frac{4}{3}\sum_{k=0}^{n}\left(\frac{1}{3}\right)^k$$

This geometric series has a limit, and it is $\frac{\frac{4}{3}}{1-\frac{1}{3}} = 2$.

On Your Own

3. (a)

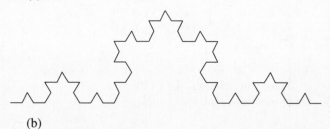

(b)

Stage 0	length $= 1$	
Stage 1	length $= \frac{4}{3}$	(4 segments, each length $\frac{1}{3}$)
Stage 2	length $= \frac{16}{9}$	(16 segments, each length $\frac{1}{9}$)
Stage 3	length $= \frac{64}{27}$	(64 segments, each length $\frac{1}{27}$)

(c) At Stage n, the length is $\left(\frac{4}{3}\right)^n$. Going from Stage $(n-1)$ to Stage n, each segment in the curve is replaced by 4 more segments, each $\frac{1}{3}$ as long as the segment they replace.

(d) There is no limit. As n increases, $\left(\frac{4}{3}\right)^n$ gets bigger and bigger without bound.

4. (a) Stage 2: Note that the area of Stage 1 is still there. In addition, you add 4 triangles similar to the Stage 1 triangle. The sides are $\frac{1}{3}$ as long, so the area is $\frac{1}{9}$ the area of the Stage 1 triangle. This gives a total of $1 + \frac{4}{9} = \frac{13}{9}$.

Stage 3: Note that the area of Stage 2 is still there. In addition, you add 16 triangles similar to the Stage 1 triangle. The sides are $\frac{1}{9}$ as long, so the area is $\frac{1}{81}$ the area of the Stage 1 triangle. This gives a total of $1 + \frac{4}{9} + \frac{16}{81} = \frac{133}{81}$.

Stage 4: Note that the area of Stage 3 is still there. In addition, you add 64 triangles similar to the Stage 1 triangle. The sides are $\frac{1}{27}$ as long, so the area is $\frac{1}{27^2}$ the area of the Stage 1 triangle. This gives a total of $1 + \frac{4}{9} + \frac{4^2}{9^2} + \frac{4^3}{9^3} = \frac{1261}{729}$.

(b) Going from Stage $(n-1)$ to Stage n, you add 4^{n-1} new triangles, each with area $\frac{1}{9^{n-1}}$ the area of the original triangle. So the total at Stage n is

$$1 + \left(\frac{4}{9}\right) + \left(\frac{4}{9}\right)^2 + \cdots + \left(\frac{4}{9}\right)^{n-1} = \sum_{i=1}^{n} \left(\frac{4}{9}\right)^{i-1}$$

$$= \sum_{i=0}^{n-1} \left(\frac{4}{9}\right)^i = \frac{1 - \left(\frac{4}{9}\right)^n}{1 - \frac{4}{9}} = \frac{9}{5}\left(1 - \left(\frac{4}{9}\right)^n\right)$$

(c) Yes. It is a geometric series with $r = \frac{4}{9}$. Since $|r| < 1$, the series has a limit. That limit is $\frac{1}{1 - \frac{4}{9}} = \frac{9}{5}$.

5. (a) You might start by looking at the first several terms of the series:

$$1 + \left(\frac{2}{3}\right)^2 + \left(\frac{2}{3}\right)^4 + \left(\frac{2}{3}\right)^6 + \cdots$$

This is a geometric series with initial term 1 and ratio $\frac{4}{9}$. So you want to look at the sum

$$\sum_{j=0}^{n} \left(\frac{4}{9}\right)^j = \frac{1 - \left(\frac{4}{9}\right)^{n+1}}{1 - \frac{4}{9}}$$

as n gets larger and larger.

$$\frac{1 - \left(\frac{4}{9}\right)^{n+1}}{1 - \frac{4}{9}} = \frac{1}{1 - \frac{4}{9}} \cdot \left(1 - \left(\frac{4}{9}\right)^{n+1}\right)$$

$$= \frac{9}{9 - 4} \cdot \left(1 - \left(\frac{4}{9}\right)^{n+1}\right)$$

$$= \frac{9}{5} \cdot \left(1 - \left(\frac{4}{9}\right)^{n+1}\right)$$

As n gets larger and larger, the factor in parentheses approaches 1, because it's equal to one minus a very small number. That means the entire sum approaches $A = \frac{9}{5}$.

(b) To find the perimeter of the infinite staircase, look at it in parts. The bottom boundary of the shape has length 1. The left and right boundaries have the same length, and each square contributes one sidelength to both the top and bottom boundary. The top boundary is a little more complicated to think about, but here are the first several terms.

$$\left(1 - \frac{2}{3}\right) + \left(\frac{2}{3} - \frac{4}{9}\right) + \left(\frac{4}{9} - \frac{8}{27}\right) + \cdots$$

$$= \left(\frac{1}{3}\right) + \left(\frac{2}{9}\right) + \left(\frac{4}{27}\right) + \cdots$$

$$= \sum_{j=0}^{n} \frac{2^k}{3^{k+1}}$$

$$= \frac{1}{3} \cdot \sum_{j=0}^{n} \left(\frac{2}{3}\right)^k$$

(Or you can simply observe that this is a "telescoping sum" — all the terms cancel except the first and last. The last one approaches 0, and the total is 1. Or even simpler — the top pieces add up to the same length as the bottom, which is 1!)

Now the perimeter can be written as a sum of these parts.

$$P = \text{bottom} + \text{top} + \text{left} + \text{right}$$

$$= 1 + \frac{1}{3} \cdot \sum_{j=0}^{n} \left(\frac{2}{3}\right)^k + \sum_{j=0}^{n} \left(\frac{2}{3}\right)^k + \sum_{j=0}^{n} \left(\frac{2}{3}\right)^k$$

$$= 1 + \frac{7}{3} \cdot \sum_{j=0}^{n} \left(\frac{2}{3}\right)^k$$

$$= 1 + \frac{7}{3} \cdot \frac{1 - \left(\frac{2}{3}\right)^{n+1}}{1 - \frac{2}{3}}$$

$$= 1 + \frac{7}{3} \cdot \frac{1}{1 - \frac{2}{3}} \cdot \left(1 - \left(\frac{2}{3}\right)^{n+1}\right)$$

$$= 1 + \frac{7}{3} \cdot 3 \cdot \left(1 - \left(\frac{2}{3}\right)^{n+1}\right)$$

$$= 1 + 7 \cdot \left(1 - \left(\frac{2}{3}\right)^{n+1}\right)$$

As n gets larger and larger, the factor in parentheses approaches 1, because it's equal to one minus a very small number. That means the entire sum approaches $P = 8$.

6. In the first stage, if you were to cut the entire square into triangles with the same size as the one's you're shading, it would be easier to see that the area of each triangle is $\frac{1}{8}$ of the total area of the square, and that the midpoint square has exactly half the area of the original square. So, in the first stage, you shade $\frac{1}{4}$ of the total area. In the second stage, you shade $\frac{1}{4}$ of the midpoint square, which is $\frac{1}{4}$ of area $\frac{1}{2}$ or $\frac{1}{8}$ of the original square. The new midpoint square has half the area of the old midpoint square, and you shade $\frac{1}{4}$ of that, and so on.

$$\text{Area} = \frac{1}{4} + \frac{1}{8} + \frac{1}{16} + \cdots$$

This is a geometric series with first term $\frac{1}{4}$ and ratio $\frac{1}{2}$. So you want to find the limit of the following sum as n gets larger and larger.

$$\text{area} = \frac{1}{4} \cdot \sum_{j=0}^{n} \left(\frac{1}{2}\right)^j$$

$$= \frac{1}{4} \cdot \frac{1 - \left(\frac{1}{2}\right)^{n+1}}{1 - \left(\frac{1}{2}\right)}$$

$$= \frac{1}{4} \cdot \frac{1}{1 - \left(\frac{1}{2}\right)} \cdot \left(1 - \left(\frac{1}{2}\right)^{n+1}\right)$$

$$= \frac{1}{4} \cdot 2 \cdot \left(1 - \left(\frac{1}{2}\right)^{n+1}\right)$$

The limit of the factor in parentheses as n gets larger and larger is 1, so the limit of the total shaded area is $\frac{1}{2}$.

7. The first term is 1, and the common ratio $r = \frac{3}{5}$ (which is < 1), so the sum is $\frac{1}{1 - \frac{3}{5}} = \frac{1}{\frac{2}{5}} = \frac{5}{2}$. The correct answer choice is **C**.

Maintain Your Skills

8. No, because in each of the stages above, the time interval is shorter and shorter. Call the time it takes Achilles to run 10 meters t. After Achilles has run for $2t$, he's gone 20 meters. During that time the Tortoise has only traveled 2 meters, and even with his 10-meter head start, he's 8 meters behind Achilles.

9. In the first step, you shade the center block which has area 1 in.^{2}. There are 8 blocks remaining.

In the second step, you shade in $\frac{1}{9}$ of each of the remaining 8 blocks, adding $\frac{8}{9}$ in.^{2} of shaded area. There are 64 blocks, each with area $\frac{1}{9}$, remaining.

In the third step, you shade in $\frac{1}{9}$ of each of the remaining 64 blocks (and each of these has area $\frac{1}{9}$), adding $\frac{64}{81}$ in.^{2} of shaded area. There are 512 blocks, each with area $\frac{1}{81}$, remaining.

$$\text{Shaded Area} = 1 + \frac{8}{9} + \frac{64}{81} + \cdots$$

$$= \sum_{j=0}^{n} \left(\frac{8}{9}\right)^j$$

$$= \frac{1 - \left(\frac{8}{9}\right)^{n+1}}{1 - \left(\frac{8}{9}\right)}$$

$$= \frac{1}{1 - \left(\frac{8}{9}\right)} \cdot \left(1 - \left(\frac{8}{9}\right)^{n+1}\right)$$

$$= 9 \cdot \left(1 - \left(\frac{8}{9}\right)^{n+1}\right)$$

So the total shaded area as n gets larger and larger approaches 9 in.^{2}—the entire area of the original square!

Check Your Understanding

1. (a) $a = \frac{123}{1000}$

   (b) $r = \frac{1}{1000}$

   (c)

$$0.123123123\ldots = \frac{123}{1000} \cdot \left(\frac{1}{1 - \frac{1}{1000}}\right)$$

$$= \frac{123}{1000} \cdot \frac{1000}{999}$$

$$= \frac{123}{999}$$

2. (a)

$$0.121212\ldots = \frac{12}{100} + \frac{12}{100} \cdot \frac{1}{100} +$$

$$\frac{12}{100} \cdot \left(\frac{1}{100}\right)^2 + \ldots$$

$$= \frac{12}{100} \cdot \left(\frac{1}{1 - \frac{1}{100}}\right)$$

$$= \frac{12}{100} \cdot \frac{100}{99}$$

$$= \frac{12}{99}$$

(b)

$$0.807807807\ldots = \frac{807}{1000} + \frac{807}{1000} \cdot \frac{1}{1000} +$$

$$\frac{807}{1000} \cdot \left(\frac{1}{1000}\right)^2 + \ldots$$

$$= \frac{807}{1000} \cdot \left(\frac{1}{1 - \frac{1}{1000}}\right)$$

$$= \frac{807}{1000} \cdot \frac{1000}{999}$$

$$= \frac{807}{999}$$

(c)

$$0.0123123123\ldots = \frac{123}{10,000} + \frac{123}{10,000} \cdot \frac{1}{1000} +$$

$$\frac{123}{10,000} \cdot \left(\frac{1}{1000}\right)^2 + \ldots$$

$$= \frac{123}{10,000} \cdot \left(\frac{1}{1 - \frac{1}{1000}}\right)$$

$$= \frac{123}{10,000} \cdot \frac{1000}{999}$$

$$= \frac{123}{9990}$$

(d)

$$0.075123123123\ldots = \frac{75}{1000} + \frac{123}{1{,}000{,}000} +$$

$$\frac{123}{1{,}000{,}000} \cdot \frac{1}{1000} +$$

$$\frac{123}{1{,}000{,}000} \cdot \left(\frac{1}{1000}\right)^2 + \ldots$$

$$= \frac{75}{1000} + \frac{123}{1{,}000{,}000} \cdot \left(\frac{1}{1 - \frac{1}{1000}}\right)$$

$$= \frac{75}{1000} + \frac{123}{1{,}000{,}000} \cdot \frac{1000}{999}$$

$$= \frac{75}{1000} \cdot \frac{999}{999} + \frac{123}{999{,}000}$$

$$= \frac{74{,}925}{999{,}000} + \frac{123}{999{,}000}$$

$$= \frac{75{,}048}{999{,}000}$$

On Your Own

3. (a) $0.090909\ldots = \frac{9}{100} + \frac{9}{100}\left(\frac{1}{100}\right) + \frac{9}{100}\left(\frac{1}{100}\right)^2 + \cdots$
The limit will be

$$\frac{\frac{9}{100}}{1 - \frac{1}{100}} = \frac{\frac{9}{100}}{\frac{99}{100}} = \frac{1}{11}$$

(b) $0.037037\ldots = \frac{37}{1000} + \frac{37}{1000}\left(\frac{1}{1000}\right) + \frac{37}{1000}\left(\frac{1}{1000}\right)^2 + \cdots$
The limit will be

$$\frac{\frac{37}{1000}}{1 - \frac{1}{1000}} = \frac{37}{999} = \frac{1}{27}$$

(c) $0.052222\ldots = \frac{5}{100} + \frac{2}{1000} + \frac{2}{1000} \cdot \frac{1}{10} + \frac{2}{1000} \cdot \left(\frac{1}{10}\right)^2 + \cdots$
The limit will be

$$0.052222\ldots = \frac{5}{100} + \frac{2}{1000} \cdot \left(\frac{1}{1 - \frac{1}{10}}\right)$$

$$= \frac{5}{100} + \frac{2}{1000} \cdot \frac{10}{9}$$

$$= \frac{5}{100} \cdot \frac{9}{9} + \frac{2}{900}$$

$$= \frac{45}{900} + \frac{2}{900}$$

$$= \frac{47}{900}$$

4. Shannon needs to realize that her mistake was in "calling it x." By calling this series x, she's assuming that a real number limit exists for the series, but since the terms are increasing, this series is growing without bound and has no limit. Her x is not a real number, and so it's not valid to calculate with it. You could prove to Shannon that the series diverges by showing her that you can find a single term in her series that's larger than any very large number she can name.

Alternatively, look at what happens when you stop after a finite number of terms:

$$\begin{array}{rl} 2x = & 2 + 4 + 8 + 16 + 32 + 64 + 128 \\ x = & 1 + 2 + 4 + 8 + 16 + 32 + 64 \\ \hline x = & -1 \qquad\qquad\qquad\qquad\quad + 128 \end{array}$$

The "leftover part" (128) is big, not small. The further out you go, the bigger it will get (in other examples you looked at, the leftover part got smaller as you went out further).

5. This equals

$$\frac{25}{100} + \frac{714}{100{,}000} + \frac{714}{100{,}000} \cdot \frac{1}{1000} + \cdots$$

$$= \frac{25}{100} + \frac{714}{100{,}000}\left(\frac{1}{1 - \frac{1}{1000}}\right)$$

$$= \frac{25}{100} \cdot \frac{999}{999} + \frac{714}{100{,}000} \cdot \frac{1000}{999}$$

$$= \frac{24{,}975}{99{,}900} + \frac{714}{99{,}900}$$

$$= \frac{25{,}689}{99{,}900} = \frac{8563}{33{,}300}$$

Maintain Your Skills

6. (a)

$$0.111\ldots = \frac{1}{10} + \frac{1}{10} \cdot \frac{1}{10} + \frac{1}{10} \cdot \left(\frac{1}{10}\right)^2 + \cdots$$

$$= \frac{1}{10} \cdot \frac{1}{1 - \frac{1}{10}}$$

$$= \frac{1}{10} \cdot \frac{10}{9}$$

$$= \frac{1}{9}$$

(b) This series is 2 times the previous series, so it's equal to $\frac{2}{9}$.

(c) This series is 3 times the series in part (a), so it's equal to $\frac{3}{9}$.

(d) This series is 4 times the series in part (a), so it's equal to $\frac{4}{9}$.

(e) This series is 5 times the series in part (a), so it's equal to $\frac{5}{9}$.

(f) This series is 6 times the series in part (a), so it's equal to $\frac{6}{9}$.

(g) This series is 7 times the series in part (a), so it's equal to $\frac{7}{9}$.

(h) This series is 8 times the series in part (a), so it's equal to $\frac{8}{9}$.

(i) This series is 9 times the series in part (a), so it's equal to $\frac{9}{9} = 1$.

7C MATHEMATICAL REFLECTIONS

1. (a) The information in the problem statement tells you that $8 + 3d = 1$, where d is the common difference between successive terms of the sequence. There is only one value of d that satisfies the equation, and once you know any term and the common difference, an arithmetic sequence is completely determined.

(b)
$$8 + 3d = 1$$
$$3d = -7$$
$$d = -\frac{7}{3}$$

(c) The fifth term of the sequence is 1, and if you add the common difference to the fifth term 23 times, you'll get the 28th term. $1 + 23\left(-\frac{7}{3}\right) = -\frac{158}{3}$

(d) In the closed form for a sequence, $s(0)$ is conventionally the first term, so $s(1) = 8$ is the second term and $s(4) = 1$ is the fifth term. This would mean that $s(0) = 8 + \frac{7}{3} = \frac{31}{3}$ and $s(n) = \frac{1}{3} \cdot (31 - 7n)$.

You could also answer $\frac{1}{3} \cdot (38 - 7n)$, where you begin the sequence with $s(1)$ rather than $s(0)$. Since this is contrary to convention, however, you'd need to explain what you were doing.

2. (a)

n	$g(n)$	Σ
0	-10	-10
1	-6	-16
2	-2	-18
3	2	-16
4	6	-10
5	10	0

(b) $g(n) = -10 + 4n$, because it's an arithmetic sequence with initial term -10 and common difference 4.

(c)
$$G(n) = \begin{cases} -10 & \text{if } n = 0 \\ G(n-1) + 4n - 10 & \text{if } n > 0 \end{cases}$$

$$G(n) = \sum_{j=0}^{n}(4j - 10)$$

$$= 4 \cdot \sum_{j=0}^{n} j - \sum_{j=0}^{n} 10$$

$$= 4\frac{n(n+1)}{2} - 10(n+1)$$

$$= 2n^2 + 2n - 10n - 10$$

$$= 2n^2 - 8n - 10$$

3. A geometric sequence s has second term 8 and fifth term 1.

(a) From the given information, you know that $8 \cdot r^3 = 1$, where r is the common ratio for the sequence. There is only one solution to the equation, $r = \frac{1}{2}$, so there is only one geometric sequence that meets the requirements, because once you know one of the terms and the common ratio, a geometric sequence is completely determined.

(b) $\frac{1}{2}$

(c) The fifth term is 1, so if you multiply that by r 23 times, you'll get the 28th term. $1 \cdot \left(\frac{1}{2}\right)^{23} = \frac{1}{8,388,608}$

(d) Again, convention says that the first term of the sequence is $s(0)$, so the second term is $s(1)$. Since $s(1) = 8$, $s(0)$ must be 16. A closed form for the sequence would be $s(n) = 16 \cdot \left(\frac{1}{2}\right)^n$.

4. (a)

n	$h(n)$	Σ
0	-10	-10
1	-40	-50
2	-160	-210
3	-640	-850
4	-2560	-3410
5	$-10,240$	$-13,650$

(b) $h(n) = -10 \cdot 4^n$, because it is a geometric sequence with initial term -10 and common ratio 4.

(c)
$$H(n) = \sum_{j=0}^{n} -10 \cdot 4^j$$

$$= -10 \cdot \left(\frac{4^{n+1} - 1}{4 - 1}\right)$$

$$= -\frac{10}{3}\left(4^{n+1} - 1\right)$$

5. (a)
$$\sum_{k=0}^{19} 50,000 \left(\frac{1}{1.06}\right)^k = 50,000 \sum_{k=0}^{19} \left(\frac{1}{1.06}\right)^k$$

$$= 50,000 \cdot \frac{\left(\frac{1}{1.06}\right)^{19+1} - 1}{\frac{1}{1.06} - 1}$$

$$= 607,906$$

The present value of Derman's winnings is \$607,906.

(b) If Derman had a guaranteed interest rate of 8%, the present value of his winnings would be less, because he'd be losing out on more interest income by not receiving all the money up front. You would calculate the new present value with this sum:

$$\sum_{k=0}^{19} 50,000 \left(\frac{1}{1.08}\right)^k$$

The present value for this interest rate is \$530,180.

The better investor you are, the more you'd rather have the money up front and in your control, because you could make a bigger profit. If you were the kind of investor who was likely to lose money, you'd rather have the lottery authority hold onto it for you, so there would be some left for the future.

6. An arithmetic sequence is a function whose domain is the set of non-negative integers and for which there is a number d such that $f(n) = f(n-1) + d$ for all $n > 0$.

7. If a sequence g is a geometric sequence (a function whose domain is the set of non-negative integers and for which there is a number $r \neq 0$ such that $g(n) = r \cdot g(n-1)$ for all integers $n > 0$) with initial term $g(0)$, the associated series $G(n) = \sum_{j=0}^{n} g(k)$ is a geometric series.

8.

$$0.121212121\cdots = \frac{12}{100} + \frac{12}{100}\cdot\left(\frac{1}{100}\right) + \frac{12}{100}\cdot\left(\frac{1}{100}\right)^2 + \cdots$$

So you can find the equivalent fraction by finding the limit of the following sum as n gets arbitrarily large.

$$\sum_{j=0}^{n}\frac{12}{100}\cdot\left(\frac{1}{100}\right)^j = \frac{12}{100}\left(\frac{1-\left(\frac{1}{100}\right)^{n+1}}{1-\frac{1}{100}}\right)$$

$$= \frac{12}{100}\cdot\left(\frac{1}{1-\frac{1}{100}}\right)\cdot\left(1-\left(\frac{1}{100}\right)^{n+1}\right)$$

$$= \frac{12}{100}\cdot\left(\frac{100}{100-1}\right)\cdot\left(1-\left(\frac{1}{100}\right)^{n+1}\right)$$

As n gets larger and larger, the last factor in the expression above gets closer and closer to 1, so the limit of this sum as n gets arbitrarily large is $\frac{12}{99}$.

INVESTIGATION 7D PASCAL'S TRIANGLE AND THE BINOMIAL THEOREM

7.14 Getting Started

For You to Explore

1.

n	$f(n)$	$\sum$	$\sum\sum$	$\sum\sum\sum$	$\sum\sum\sum\sum$
1	1	1	1	1	1
2	2	3	4	5	6
3	3	6	10	15	21
4	4	10	20	35	56
5	5	15	35	70	126
6	6	21	56	126	252
7	7	28	84	210	462
8	8	36	120	330	792
9	9	45	165	495	1287
10	10	55	220	715	2002

2. Answers will vary. Students may say that $f(n)$ is the natural numbers. Some students may notice symmetry in the table—row 2 is the same as the $f(n)$ column, row 3 starts out the same as $\sum f(n)$, and so on. A few students may recognize the triangular numbers in the $\sum$ column. Others will point out properties of sum tables that are also present here, like the "hockey stick" property or the "up and over" property.

3. $f(n) = n$

4. (a) Read off the row 7 entry from the $\sum$ column, 28
  (b) $\sum_{k=1}^{1000} f(k)$ is the sum of the integers from 1 to 1000, so you can use Gauss' Method or the closed form that you've memorized. $\frac{1000\cdot 1001}{2} = 500{,}500$.
  (c) $\sum_{k=1}^{n} f(k) = \frac{n(n+1)}{2}$, which is the closed form for the sum of the integers from 1 to n.

5. (a) $\frac{n(n+1)(n+2)}{6}$
  (b) $\frac{n(n+1)(n+2)(n+3)}{24}$
  (c) Answers will vary, but you might notice that the numerators are products of consecutive integers. This could make you think of the factorial function, $n! = n(n-1)(n-2)\cdots(3)(2)(1)$. You could then recognize the denominator of the first expression as 3!, and the second as 4!. You could predict (and check) that a closed form for the $\sum\sum\sum\sum$ column is $\frac{n(n+1)(n+2)(n+3)(n+4)}{120}$. You might also recognize these as related to problems from Lesson 7.7 Exercise 11.

On Your Own

6. (a) $(a+b)^2 = a^2 + 2ab + b^2$
  (b)

$$(a+b)^3 = (a+b)(a^2 + 2ab + b^2)$$
$$= a^3 + 2a^2b + ab^2 + a^2b + 2ab^2 + b^3$$
$$= a^3 + 3a^2b + 3ab^2 + b^3$$

  (c)

$$(a+b)^4 = (a+b)(a^3 + 3a^2b + 3ab^2 + b^3)$$
$$= a^4 + 3a^3b + 3a^2b^2 + ab^3 + a^3b +$$
$$3a^2b^2 + 3ab^3 + b^4$$
$$= a^4 + 4a^3b + 6a^2b^2 + 4ab^3 + b^4$$

  (d)

$$(a+b)^5 = (a+b)(a^4 + 4a^3b + 6a^2b^2 + 4ab^3 + b^4)$$
$$= a^5 + 4a^4b + 6a^3b^2 + 4a^2b^3 + ab^4 + a^4b +$$
$$4a^3b^2 + 6a^2b^3 + 4ab^4 + b^5$$
$$= a^5 + 5a^4b + 10a^3b^2 + 10a^2b^3 +$$
$$5ab^4 + b^5$$

  (e)

$$(a+b)^6 = (a+b)(a^5 + 5a^4b + 10a^3b^2 +$$
$$10a^2b^3 + 5ab^4 + b^5)$$
$$= a^6 + 5a^5b + 10a^4b^2 + 10a^3b^3 + 5a^2b^4 + ab^5 +$$
$$a^5b + 5a^4b^2 + 10a^3b^3 + 10a^2b^4 + 5ab^5 + b^6$$
$$= a^6 + 6a^5b + 15a^4b^2 + 20a^3b^3 + 15a^2b^4 +$$
$$6ab^5 + b^6$$

  (f) One pattern you might notice is that the coefficients are symmetrical. For example, the coefficients of $(a+b)^4$ are 1, 4, 6, 4, 1. Also, the second and second to last coefficient are always equal to the power that you raised $(a+b)$ to. The first and last coefficient are always 1.

7.

$$(M + N)^4 = M^4 + 4M^3N + 6M^2N^2 + 4MN^3 + N^4$$
$$= (2d)^4 + 4(2d)^3(7) + 6(2d)^2(7)^2 +$$
$$\quad 4(2d)(7)^3 + (7)^4$$
$$= 16d^4 + 4(8)(7)d^3 + 6(4)(49)d^2 +$$
$$\quad 4(2)(343)d + 2401$$
$$= 16d^4 + 224d^3 + 1176d^2 + 2744d + 2401$$

8. (a) You know that $(a + b)^2 = a^2 + 2ab + b^2$.

$$\left(\frac{1}{4}r + \frac{3}{4}s\right)^2 = \left(\frac{1}{4}r\right)^2 + 2\left(\frac{1}{4}r\right)\left(\frac{3}{4}s\right) + \left(\frac{3}{4}s\right)^2$$
$$= \frac{1}{16}r^2 + \frac{6}{16}rs + \frac{9}{16}s^2$$

(b) You know that $(a + b)^3 = a^3 + 3a^2b + 3ab^2 + b^3$.

$$\left(\frac{1}{4}r + \frac{3}{4}s\right)^3 = \left(\frac{1}{4}r\right)^3 + 3\left(\frac{1}{4}r\right)^2\left(\frac{3}{4}s\right) +$$
$$\quad 3\left(\frac{1}{4}r\right)\left(\frac{3}{4}s\right)^2 + \left(\frac{3}{4}s\right)^3$$
$$= \frac{1}{64}r^3 + \frac{9}{64}r^2s + \frac{27}{64}rs^2 + \frac{27}{64}s^3$$

(c) You know that $(a + b)^4 = a^4 + 4a^3b + 6a^2b^2 + 4ab^3 + b^4$.

$$\left(\frac{1}{4}r + \frac{3}{4}s\right)^4 = \left(\frac{1}{4}r\right)^4 + 4\left(\frac{1}{4}r\right)^3\left(\frac{3}{4}s\right) +$$
$$\quad 6\left(\frac{1}{4}r\right)^2\left(\frac{3}{4}s\right)^2 +$$
$$\quad 4\left(\frac{1}{4}r\right)\left(\frac{3}{4}s\right)^3 + \left(\frac{3}{4}s\right)^4$$
$$= \frac{1}{256}r^4 + \frac{12}{256}r^3s + \frac{54}{256}r^2s^2 +$$
$$\quad \frac{108}{256}rs^3 + \frac{81}{256}s^4$$

(d) You know that $(a + b)^5 = a^5 + 5a^4b + 10a^3b^2 + 10a^2b^3 + 5ab^4 + b^5$.

$$\left(\frac{1}{4}r + \frac{3}{4}s\right)^5 = \left(\frac{1}{4}r\right)^5 + 5\left(\frac{1}{4}r\right)^4\left(\frac{3}{4}s\right) +$$
$$\quad 10\left(\frac{1}{4}r\right)^3\left(\frac{3}{4}s\right)^2 + 10\left(\frac{1}{4}r\right)^2\left(\frac{3}{4}s\right)^3 +$$
$$\quad 5\left(\frac{1}{4}r\right)\left(\frac{3}{4}s\right)^4 + \left(\frac{3}{4}s\right)^5$$
$$= \frac{1}{1024}r^5 + \frac{15}{1024}r^4s + \frac{90}{1024}r^3s^2 +$$
$$\quad \frac{270}{1024}r^2s^3 + \frac{405}{1024}rs^4 + \frac{243}{1024}s^5$$

Maintain Your Skills

9. (a) $99^1 = 99, 99^2 = 9801, 99^3 = 970,299, 99^4 = 96,059,601, 99^5 = 9,509,900,499$

(b) Answers will vary. Possible responses include

- The first digit is always 9
- The second digit decreases by 1 each time (9, 8, 7, 6, 5)
- The third digit (if there is one) is always 0
- The last digit alternates between 9 and 1 (It's 9 for an odd power and 1 for an even)

10.

n	$(n + 1)^3 - n^3$	$\sum$
0	1	1
1	7	8
2	19	27
3	37	64
4	61	125
4	91	216
6	127	343
7	169	512
8	217	729
9	271	1000
10	331	1331
11	397	1728
12	469	2197
13	547	2744
14	631	3375
15	721	4096
16	817	4913
17	919	5832
18	1027	6859
19	1141	8000

A closed form for the $\sum$ column is $(n + 1)^3$.

7.15 Pascal's Triangle

Check Your Understanding

1. (a) $\sum_{k=0}^{5}\binom{5}{k} = 1 + 5 + 10 + 10 + 5 + 1 = 32 = 2^5$

(b) $\sum_{k=0}^{6}\binom{6}{k} = 1 + 6 + 15 + 20 + 15 + 6 + 1 = 64 = 2^6$

(c) $\sum_{k=0}^{7}\binom{7}{k} = 1 + 7 + 21 + 35 + 35 + 21 + 7 + 1 = 128 = 2^7$

(d) $\sum_{k=0}^{n}\binom{n}{k} = 2^n$

2. One way to think about the sum: It starts at 1 in row 0, and then doubles at each row. Each number in row $(n - 1)$ contributes twice to a number in row n, so the sum of row n will be exactly double the sum of row $(n - 1)$:

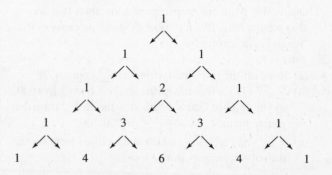

Another way to think about this sum uses the Binomial Theorem, which will be covered in the next lesson.

Given a positive integer, say n, and a pair of real numbers, say x and y, then the Binomial Theorem states that

$$(x + y)^n = \binom{n}{0}x^n + \binom{n}{1}x^{n-1}y +$$

$$\binom{n}{2}x^{n-2}y^2 + \cdots + \binom{n}{n-1}xy^{n-1} + \binom{n}{n}y^n$$

$$= \sum_{k=0}^{n} \binom{n}{k}x^{n-k}y^k$$

Now, choose $x = 1$ and $y = 1$. The left side of the equation above gives $(1 + 1)^n = 2^n$. The right side gives

$$\sum_{k=0}^{n} \binom{n}{k}1^{n-k}1^k = \sum_{k=0}^{n} \binom{n}{k}$$

which is the sum of the entries in row n of Pascal's Triangle.

On Your Own

3. There are a couple of ways to come up with the answer. One way is to make a table of the row number and the number of odd entries and to look for a pattern. In looking for the number of odds in row 64, you might notice that there are always only two odd numbers in any row whose number is a power of 2, so in row 64 there will be two odd numbers.

Another surprising pattern emerges:

row number	number of odd entries
0	1 ⟩double
1	2
2	2
3	4
4	2
5	4
6	4
7	8

row number	number of odd entries
0	1
1	2
2	2
3	4
4	2
5	4
6	4
7	8

double each entry

row number	number of odd entries
0	1
1	2
2	2
3	4
4	2
5	4
6	4
7	8

double each entry

So the number of odds in rows 8–15 would be 2, 4, 4, 8, 4, 8, 8, 16—twice the number of odds in the corresponding rows 0 through 7. If you continue this pattern, you would find that the number of odds in rows 64 through 127 will each be twice the number of odds in the corresponding rows 0 through 63, so the number of odds in row 100 is twice the number of odds in row 36. Similarly, the number of odds in rows 32 through 63 are each twice the number of odds in the corresponding rows 0 through 31, so the number of odds in row 36 is twice the number of odds in row 4. There are 2 odds in row 4, so there are 4 odds in row 36, and eight odds in row 100.

4. **(a)** The pattern looks something like this (odds are shaded, evens are blank):

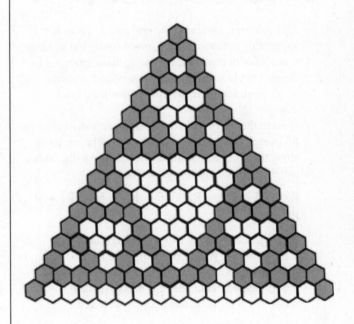

There is a repeating pattern of downward-pointing triangles of blanks (evens). This pattern continues, with upside-down blank triangles in the middle of upward-pointing shaded triangles.

To color in the cells, it helps to think a bit about evens and odds. You don't actually have to fill in the actual entries. Instead, you know that there are odd numbers all along the outside edges (the ones), and then you can follow these rules:

$$\text{even} + \text{even} = \text{even}$$
$$\text{even} + \text{odd} = \text{odd}$$
$$\text{odd} + \text{odd} = \text{even}$$

(b) The pattern looks something like this (remainder 1 is light, remainder 2 is black, remainder 0 is blank):

This pattern is similar to the one above. There is still a repeating pattern of large, upward-pointing shaded triangles with downward-pointing blank triangles in the middle. In addition to the downward-pointing blank triangles, there are upward-pointing black triangles mixed in.

As in the previous part, you don't actually have to fill in each number. Instead, you know the entries along the outer edges all have remainder 1 (the ones), and then you can follow these rules:

R1 + R1 = R2; R1 + R2 = R0; R2 + R2 = R1;
R0 + n = n

You're just adding the two remainders and subtracting 3 if your sum is larger than 2.

(c) The pattern looks something like this (remainder 1 is lightly shaded, remainder 2 is darkly shaded, remainder 3 is black, remainder 0 is blank):

As in the previous part, you don't actually have to fill in the entries. You can just calculate with the

remainders, using the numbers 0–3. If the sum you get when adding two remainders is bigger than 3, just subtract 4 to find the remainder. For example, R3 + R2 = 5 = R1.

5. Using the definition of Pascal's triangle:

$$\binom{17}{6} = \binom{16}{5} + \binom{16}{6}$$

$$= \binom{15}{4} + 2 \cdot \binom{15}{5} + \binom{15}{6}$$

$$= 1365 + 2 \cdot 3003 + 5005 = 12{,}376$$

The correct answer choice is **C**.

6. To reiterate: here are the results you found in Lesson 7.14, together with their "Pascal" interpretation.

$$k = 0: \quad f(n) = n = \binom{n}{1}$$

$$k = 1: \quad \sum_{j=1}^{n} f(j) = \frac{(n+1)n}{2} = \binom{n+1}{2}$$

$$k = 2: \quad \sum\sum f = \frac{(n+2)(n+1)n}{3!} = \binom{n+2}{3}$$

$$k = 3: \quad \sum\sum\sum f = \frac{(n+3)(n+2)(n+1)n}{4!}$$

$$= \binom{n+3}{4}$$

Following this pattern, in general you have

$$\underbrace{\sum\sum\sum\sum \cdots \sum f}_{k \text{ copies}} = \binom{n+k}{k+1}$$

Maintain Your Skills

7. (a) m must be 3 or 5.
   (b) m must be 1.
   (c) m must be 6 or 7.
   (d) m must be 99 and n must be 14 or 85. (Using the fact that $\binom{n}{k} = \binom{n}{n-k}$—the symmetry about the vertical line through the center of the triangle.)

7.16 The Binomial Theorem

Check Your Understanding

1. (a) $(x + y)^7 = x^7 + 7x^6y + 21x^5y^2 + 35x^4y^3 + 35x^3y^4 + 21x^2y^5 + 7xy^6 + y^7$
   (b)

   $$(x + 2y)^5 = x^5 + 5x^4(2y) + 10x^3(2y)^2 + 10x^2(2y)^3 + 5x(2y)^4 + (2y)^5$$

   $$= x^5 + 10x^4y + 40x^3y^2 + 80x^2y^3 + 80xy^4 + 32y^5$$

2. (a) The coefficient of the term a^3b^5 is in column 5 (count across, a^8 is column 0, a^7 is column 1, a^6 is column 2, and so on) of row 8 in Pascal's Triangle $\left(\binom{8}{5}\right)$, so this term has coefficient 56.

(b) Pascal's Triangle is symmetric about a vertical line through the center, so $\binom{n}{k} = \binom{n}{n-k}$. That means that $\binom{8}{5} = \binom{8}{3}$, and the a^5b^3-term will also have coefficient 56.

(c) The center entry, $\binom{8}{4}$, is unique in row 8, and it gives the coefficient for the a^4b^4 term. That term is the only one in the expansion with coefficient 70.

3. (a) Count over to column 7 in row 10 of Pascal's Triangle. (The column number always matches the exponent of the second term in the binomial you're expanding.) $\binom{10}{7} = 120$

(b) This is the term just before y^{10}, so it has to have coefficient 10. You could also find $\binom{10}{9} = 10$ on Pascal's Triangle.

(c) x^5y^5 is the center term, so it's the unique term in row 10—252.

On Your Own

4. • $\binom{5}{0} - \binom{5}{1} + \binom{5}{2} - \binom{5}{3} + \binom{5}{4} - \binom{5}{5} = 1 - 5 + 10 - 10 + 5 - 1 = 0$

• $\binom{6}{0} - \binom{6}{1} + \binom{6}{2} - \binom{6}{3} + \binom{6}{4} - \binom{6}{5} + \binom{6}{6}$
$= 1 - 6 + 15 - 20 + 15 - 6 + 1 = 0$

• $\binom{11}{0} - \binom{11}{1} + \binom{11}{2} - \binom{11}{3} + \binom{11}{4} - \binom{11}{5} + \binom{11}{6} - \binom{11}{7} +$
$\binom{11}{8} - \binom{11}{9} + \binom{11}{10} - \binom{11}{11} = 1 - 11 + 55 - 165 + 330 -$
$462 + 462 - 330 + 165 - 55 + 11 - 1 = 0$

5. Answers will vary. An example is $(x-2)^4 = x^4 - 8x^3 + 24x^2 - 32x + 16$.

6.

$$(\sqrt{3} - \sqrt{2})(\sqrt{3} + \sqrt{2}) = (\sqrt{3})^2 - (\sqrt{2})^2 = 3 - 2 = 1$$

You can rewrite $(\sqrt{3} + \sqrt{2})^{100}(\sqrt{3} - \sqrt{2})^{100}$ as $[(\sqrt{3} + \sqrt{2})(\sqrt{3} - \sqrt{2})]^{100}$, so it's 1.

7. The x^3 term in $(2x - 1)^4$ is given by

$$\binom{4}{1}(2x)^3(-1)^1 = 4 \cdot 8x^3(-1) = -32x^3$$

The correct answer choice is **A**.

Maintain Your Skills

8. Look at the following multiplication. In the product, the place value of each number is written below it.

$$\begin{array}{ccccccc}
 & 1 & 4 & 6 & 4 & 1 \\
\times & & & & 1 & 1 \\
\hline
1 & 5 & 10 & 10 & 5 & 1 \\
(10^5) & (10^4) & (10^3) & (10^2) & (10^1) & (10^0)
\end{array}$$

So the expanded product is

$$1 \times 10^5 + 5 \times 10^4 + 10 \times 10^3 + 10 \times 10^2 + 5 \times 10^1 + 1 \times 10^0$$

which is, in fact, equal to 161,051.

You cannot have a "two-digit" digit, so when the Pascal's Triangle entry has two digits, you have to regroup it into the next place value. For example, $10 \times 10^3 = 1 \times 10^4$.

---

9. (a) 101, 10201, 1030301, 104060401, 10510100501, 1061520150601, 107213535210701

(b) 1001, 1002001, 1003003001, 1004006004001, 1005010010005001, 1006015020015006001, 1007021035035021007001

7D MATHEMATICAL REFLECTIONS

1.

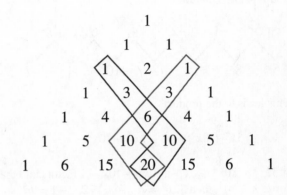

$1 + 3 + 6 + 10 = 20$

2. (a) To solve $\binom{m}{1} = 27$, you want to find the row number in Pascal's Triangle where there's a 27 in column 1. The number in column 1 for any row is always equal to the row number, so you want $m = 27$.

(b) $\binom{24}{m} = 1$ asks you to figure out which columns in row 24 have entry 1. There is always a 1 in the first and last entry of any row, so $m = 0, 24$.

(c) In this equation, $\binom{m}{31} = 32$, the entry in the triangle is one more than the column number. That's a property of the second-to-last column in any row. If 31 is the second-to-last column, the last column is column 32, and that's equal to the row number. $m = 32$.

(d) $\binom{m}{4} + \binom{m}{5} = \binom{19}{5}$ is an instance of the addition property that generates Pascal's Triangle. When you add the entries from columns 4 and 5 in row 18, you get the entry for column 5 of row 19. $m = 18$.

3. Here is an input-output table for $b(n)$ which also shows enough differences to arrive at a constant difference:

n	$b(n) = \binom{n}{2}$	Δ	Δ
2	1	2	1
3	3	3	1
4	6	4	1
5	10	5	1
6	15		

Since these entries have a constant second difference, this table can be matched by a quadratic polynomial. Since the constant second difference is 1, the coefficient of the x^2-term in the polynomial rule is $\frac{1}{2}$. Make a new column in your table showing $b(n) - \frac{1}{2}n^2$.

n	$b(n) = \binom{n}{2}$	$b(n) - \frac{1}{2}n^2$
2	1	-1
3	3	-1.5
4	6	-2
5	10	-2.5
6	15	-3

From this table, you can conclude that $b(n) - \frac{1}{2}n^2 = -\frac{1}{2}n$ or that $b(n) = \frac{1}{2}n^2 - \frac{1}{2}n$ will match the table.

4. If you use the shorthand method shown in the lesson, you'll get this picture:

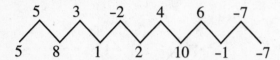

This leads to the product

$$5x^6 + 8x^5 + x^4 + 2x^3 + 10x^2 - x - 7$$

5. If $32x^5 - 80x^4 + cx^3 - 40x^2 + 10x - 1$ factors into the form $(a + b)^5$, then $32x^5 = a^5$, so $a = 2x$. $-1 = b^5$, so $b = -1$. Then $cx^3 = 10a^3b^2 = 10(2x)^3(-1)^2 = 80x^3$ and $c = 80$.

6. The sum of the entries in row n of Pascal's Triangle is 2^n. So the sum of the entries in row 10 is $2^{10} = 1024$.

7.

$$(2d + 7)^8 = (2d)^8 + 8(2d)^7(7) + 28(2d)^6(7)^2 +$$
$$56(2d)^5(7)^3 + 70(2d)^4(7)^4 + 56(2d)^3(7)^5 +$$
$$28(2d)^2(7)^6 + 8(2d)(7)^7 + (7)^8$$
$$= 256d^8 + 7168d^7 + 87,808d^6 + 614,656d^5 +$$
$$2,689,120d^4 + 7,529,536d^3 + 13,176,688d^2 +$$
$$13,176,688d + 5,764,801$$

8. $\binom{10}{3} = 120$

CHAPTER REVIEW

1.

n	$g(n)$	Σ
0	1	1
1	2	$1 + 2 = 3$
2	6	$3 + 6 = 9$
3	18	$9 + 18 = 27$
4	54	$27 + 54 = 81$
5	162	$81 + 162 = 243$

The Σ column consists of powers of 3, so the closed form is

$$n \mapsto 3^n$$

2. (a) The constant difference is $6 - 3 = 3$.

$$S = 3 + 6 + \cdots + 93 + 96$$
$$\underline{S = 96 + 93 + \cdots + 6 + 3}$$
$$2S = 99 + 99 + \cdots + 99 + 99$$
$$2S = (32)(99)$$
$$S = \frac{(32)(99)}{2}$$
$$S = 1584$$

(b) The constant ratio is $\frac{6}{3} = 2$.

$$S = 3 + 6 + 12 + \cdots + 48 + 96 = 3 + 3 \cdot 2$$
$$+ 3 \cdot 2^2 + \cdots 3 \cdot 2^5$$
$$2S = 3 \cdot 2 + 3 \cdot 2^2 + \cdots + 3 \cdot 2^5 + 3 \cdot 2^6$$

Subtract:

$$2S = \qquad 3 \cdot 2 + 3 \cdot 2^2 + \cdots + 3 \cdot 2^5 + 3 \cdot 2^6$$
$$\underline{S = 3 + 3 \cdot 2 + 3 \cdot 2^2 + \cdots + 3 \cdot 2^5}$$
$$S = -3 + 3 \cdot 2^6$$
$$= 189$$

3. (a) $\sum_{j=0}^{3}(3^j) = 3^0 + 3^1 + 3^2 + 3^3 = 1 + 3 + 9 + 27 = 40$

(b) $\sum_{k=1}^{5}(k + 2) = (1 + 2) + (2 + 2) + (3 + 2) + (4 + 2) + (5 + 2) = 3 + 4 + 5 + 6 + 7 = 25$

(c) $S = \frac{1}{2} + 1 + \frac{3}{2} + 2 + \cdots + 6 =$

$\frac{1}{2} + \frac{2}{2} + \frac{3}{2} + \cdots + \frac{12}{2} = \sum_{j=1}^{12}\left(\frac{j}{2}\right)$

4. (a)

$$S(n) = \sum_{k=0}^{n}(4 - 3k)$$
$$= \sum_{k=0}^{n}4 - 3\sum_{k=0}^{n}k$$
$$= 4(n + 1) - 3\frac{n(n + 1)}{2}$$
$$= \frac{8(n + 1)}{2} - 3\frac{n(n + 1)}{2}$$
$$= \frac{8n + 8 - 3n^2 - 3n}{2}$$
$$= \frac{8 + 5n - 3n^2}{2}$$

(b) Use "Think Euclid":

$$T(n) = \frac{\left(\frac{1}{2}\right)^{n+1} - 1}{\frac{1}{2} - 1}$$
$$= \frac{\left(\frac{1}{2}\right)^{n+1} - 1}{-\frac{1}{2}}$$
$$= -2 \cdot \left(\left(\frac{1}{2}\right)^{n+1} - 1\right)$$
$$= -2 \cdot \frac{1}{2} \cdot \left(\frac{1}{2}\right)^n - (-2)(1)$$

$$= -1 \cdot \left(\frac{1}{2}\right)^n + 2$$

$$= 2 - \left(\frac{1}{2}\right)^n$$

(c) $S(100) = \frac{8 + 5(100) - 3(100)^2}{2} = -14{,}746$

(d) $T(4) = 2 - \left(\frac{1}{2}\right)^4 = 2 - \frac{1}{16} = \frac{31}{16}$

5. The series associated with g is the function defined on nonnegative integers by

$$G(n) = \sum_{k=0}^{n} g(k) = g(0) + g(1) + g(2) = \cdots + g(n)$$

A recursive rule for the series is

$$G(n) = \begin{cases} 4 & \text{if } n = 0 \\ G(n-1) + 4 - 5n & \text{if } n > 0 \end{cases}$$

This means that $G(n) = 4 + (4 - 5 \cdot 1) + (4 - 5 \cdot 2) + \cdots + (4 - 5 \cdot n)$, or

$$G(n) = \sum_{j=0}^{n} 4 - 5 \sum_{j=0}^{n} j$$

$$= 4(n+1) - 5 \cdot \frac{n(n+1)}{2}$$

$$= 4n + 4 - \frac{5n^2 + 5n}{2}$$

$$= \frac{8n + 8}{2} - \frac{5n^2 + 5n}{2}$$

$$= \frac{-5n^2 + 3n + 8}{2}$$

6. (a)

n	$f(n)$	$\sum$
0	5	5
1	$5 + 2 = 7$	$5 + 7 = 12$
2	$7 + 2 = 9$	$12 + 9 = 21$
3	$9 + 2 = 11$	$21 + 11 = 32$
4	$11 + 2 = 13$	$32 + 13 = 45$
5	$13 + 2 = 15$	$45 + 15 = 60$

- The function is linear. Since there is a constant difference of 2 and $f(0) = 5$, the function is defined by $f(n) = 2n + 5$

$$F(n) = \sum_{k=0}^{n} (2k + 5)$$

$$= 2 \sum_{k=0}^{n} k + \sum_{k=0}^{n} 5$$

$$= 2 \frac{n(n+1)}{2} + 5(n+1)$$

$$= n^2 + n + 5n + 5$$

$$= n^2 + 6n + 5$$

- $f(10) = 2(10) + 5 = 25$, $F(10) = 10^2 + 6(10) + 5 = 165$

(b)

n	$f(n)$	$\sum$
0	5	5
1	$5 \cdot 2 = 10$	$5 + 10 = 15$
2	$10 \cdot 2 = 20$	$15 + 20 = 35$
3	$20 \cdot 2 = 40$	$35 + 40 = 75$
4	$40 \cdot 2 = 80$	$75 + 80 = 155$
5	$80 \cdot 2 = 160$	$155 + 160 = 315$

- The sequence is geometric. There is a constant ratio of 2 with initial term 5. So, $f(n) = 5 \cdot 2^n$.
- "Think Euclid": $F(n) = \frac{5}{2-1}(2^{n+1} - 1) = 5(2^{n+1} - 1)$
- $f(10) = 5 \cdot 2^{10} = 5 \cdot 1024 = 5120$, $F(10) = 5(2^{11} - 1) = 5(2048 - 1) = 5(2047) = 10{,}235$

7. (a)
- $10, 1, \frac{1}{10}, \frac{1}{100}$
- $10, 11, 11\frac{1}{10}, 11\frac{11}{100}$
- Yes, the series will have a limit because $-1 < r = \frac{1}{10} < 1$
- The limit will be $\frac{a}{1-r} = \frac{10}{1 - \frac{1}{10}} = \frac{10}{\frac{9}{10}} = \frac{100}{9} = 11.1111\ldots$

(b)
- $2, 3, \frac{9}{2}, \frac{27}{4}$
- $2, 5, \frac{19}{2}, \frac{65}{4}$
- The series does not have a limit because $r = \frac{3}{2} > 1$.
- The series does not have a limit.

8. (a) First write $0.151515\ldots$ as a sum of fractions:

$$\frac{15}{100} + \frac{15}{10{,}000} + \frac{15}{1{,}000{,}000} + \cdots$$

This is a geometric series with $a = \frac{15}{100}$ and $r = \frac{1}{100}$. So,

$$0.151515\ldots = \frac{15}{100} + \frac{15}{10{,}000} + \frac{15}{1{,}000{,}000} + \cdots$$

$$= \frac{15}{100} \cdot \frac{1}{1 - \frac{1}{100}}$$

$$= \frac{15}{100} \cdot \frac{100}{99}$$

$$= \frac{5}{33}$$

(b) First write $0.100100100\ldots$ as a sum of fractions:

$$\frac{100}{1000} + \frac{100}{1{,}000{,}000} + \frac{100}{1{,}000{,}000{,}000} + \cdots$$

This is a geometric series with $a = \frac{100}{1000}$ and $r = \frac{1}{1000}$. So,

$$0.100100100\ldots = \frac{100}{1000} + \frac{100}{1{,}000{,}000}$$

$$+ \frac{100}{1{,}000{,}000{,}000} + \cdots$$

$$= \frac{100}{1000} \cdot \frac{1}{1 - \frac{1}{1000}}$$

$$= \frac{100}{1000} \cdot \frac{1000}{999}$$

$$= \frac{100}{999}$$

9. (a) (b)

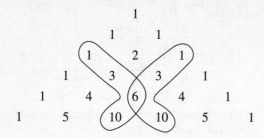

(c) Use Pascal's Triangle. $\binom{4}{2} = 6$ (4th row, 2nd column) and $\binom{5}{4} = 5$ (5th row, 4th column). So, $6 + 5 = 11$.

10. (a) Use the 5th row of Pascal's Triangle:

$$1 \quad 5 \quad 10 \quad 10 \quad 5 \quad 1$$

$$(3x + 2)^5 = 1(3x)^5(2)^0 + 5(3x)^4(2)^1 + 10(3x)^3(2)^2 +$$
$$10(3x)^2(2)^3 + 5(3x)^1(2)^4 + 1(3x)^0(2)^5$$
$$= 243x^5 + 810x^4 + 1080x^3 +$$
$$720x^2 + 240x + 32$$

(b) Use the 6th row, 4th column of Pascal's Triangle: $15 \cdot 2^4 = 240$

CHAPTER TEST

1. Use Gauss' Method:

$$\begin{aligned} S &= 7 + 9 + 11 + \cdots + 51 + 53 + 55 \\ S &= 55 + 53 + 51 + \cdots + 11 + 9 + 7 \\ \hline 2S &= 62 + 62 + 62 + \cdots + 62 + 62 + 62 \end{aligned}$$
$$2S = (25)(62)$$
$$2S = 1550$$
$$S = 775$$

The correct choice is **B**.

2. Use Pascal's Triangle. To solve $\binom{j}{1} = 5$, you want to find the row number where there is a 5 in column 1. The number in column 1 for any row is always equal to the row number, so you want $j = 5$. The correct choice is **C**.

3. Write the repeating decimal as a geometric series with first term $\frac{9}{10}$ and common ratio $\frac{1}{10}$. Then find the sum:

$$0.999\ldots = \frac{9}{10} + \frac{9}{100} + \frac{9}{1000}\cdots$$
$$= \frac{\frac{9}{10}}{1 - \frac{1}{10}}$$
$$= \frac{\frac{9}{10}}{\frac{9}{10}}$$
$$= 1$$

The correct choice is **D**.

4. The information in the problem tells you that $9 + 6d = 33$.

$$9 + 6d = 33$$
$$6d = 24$$
$$d = 4$$

Since the common difference is 4, the third term will be $9 + 4 = 13$. The correct choice is **C**.

5. In the expansion of $(x + y)^9$, you use the 9th row of Pascal's Triangle. To find the coefficient of x^4y^5, you want the 5th column, starting the count at 0. So, the coefficient is $\binom{9}{5}$ or 126. The correct choice is **D**.

6. (a)

$$\sum_{k=0}^{10}(7 - 4k) = \sum_{k=0}^{10}7 - 4\sum_{k=0}^{10}k$$
$$= 7(10 + 1) - 4\frac{10(10 + 1)}{2}$$
$$= 77 - 2(110)$$
$$= 77 - 220$$
$$= -143$$

(b)

$$\sum_{j=0}^{8}\left(\frac{1}{3}\right)^j = \frac{1}{1 - \frac{1}{3}}\left(1 - \left(\frac{1}{3}\right)^{8+1}\right)$$
$$= \frac{3}{2}\left(1 - \frac{1}{19{,}683}\right)$$
$$= \frac{3}{2} \cdot \frac{19{,}682}{19{,}683}$$
$$= \frac{9841}{6561}$$
$$\approx 1.49992$$

(c)

$$\sum_{k=3}^{12}4k = \sum_{k=0}^{12}4k - \sum_{k=0}^{2}4k$$
$$= 4\sum_{k=0}^{12}k - 4\sum_{k=0}^{2}k$$
$$= 4 \cdot \frac{12(12 + 1)}{2} - 4 \cdot \frac{2(2 + 1)}{2}$$
$$= 2(12)(13) - 2(2)(3)$$
$$= 312 - 12$$
$$= 300$$

7. (a)

$$\sum_{k=0}^{n}(6k + 2) = 6\sum_{k=0}^{n}k + \sum_{k=0}^{n}2$$
$$= 6 \cdot \frac{n(n + 1)}{2} + 2(n + 1)$$
$$= 3n(n + 1) + 2n + 2$$
$$= 3n^2 + 3n + 2n + 2$$
$$= 3n^2 + 5n + 2$$

(b)

$$\sum_{k=0}^{n}(k^2+1) = \sum_{k=0}^{n}k^2 + \sum_{k=0}^{n}1$$

$$= \frac{n(n+1)(2n+1)}{6} + 1(n+1)$$

$$= \frac{n(n+1)(2n+1)+6(n+1)}{6}$$

$$= \frac{(n+1)(2n^2+n+6)}{6}$$

$$= \frac{2n^3+3n^2+7n+6}{6}$$

8. The recursive rule is

$$H(n) = \begin{cases} 4 & \text{if } n = 0 \\ H(n-1)+4-6n & \text{if } n > 0 \end{cases}$$

The closed-form rule is

$$H(n) = \sum_{k=0}^{n}4-6k$$

$$= \sum_{k=0}^{n}4 - 6\sum_{k=0}^{n}k$$

$$= 4(n+1) - 6 \cdot \frac{n(n+1)}{2}$$

$$= 4n+4 - 3n(n+1)$$

$$= 4n+4 - 3n^2 - 3n$$

$$= -3n^2 + n + 4$$

9. (a)

n	$h(n)$	$\sum$
0	18	18
1	$18 \cdot \frac{1}{3} = 6$	$18+6 = 24$
2	$6 \cdot \frac{1}{3} = 2$	$24+2 = 26$
3	$2 \cdot \frac{1}{3} = \frac{2}{3}$	$26 + \frac{2}{3} = 26\frac{2}{3}$
4	$\frac{2}{3} \cdot \frac{1}{3} = \frac{2}{9}$	$26\frac{2}{3} + \frac{2}{9} = 26\frac{8}{9}$

(b) $h(n) = 18\left(\frac{1}{3}\right)^n$

(c) The sequence is geometric, with $a = 18$ and $r = \frac{1}{3}$.
So,

$$H(n) = \frac{18}{1-\frac{1}{3}}\left(1 - \left(\frac{1}{3}\right)^{n+1}\right)$$

$$= 27\left(1 - \left(\frac{1}{3}\right)^{n+1}\right)$$

$$= 27 - 27(3^{-n-1})$$

$$= 27 - 3^3(3^{-n-1})$$

$$= 27 - 3^{2-n}$$

10. Since $a^7 = x^7$ and $b^7 = -128 = (-2)^7$, $a = x$ and $b = -2$. To find the value of c, use the 7th row and 3rd

entry of Pascal's Triangle, $\binom{7}{3} = 35$.

$$cx^4 = 35 \cdot x^4(-2)^3$$

$$= 35(-8)x^4$$

$$= -280x^4$$

$$c = -280$$

11. If a sequence g is a geometric sequence (a function whose domain is the set of non-negative integers and for which there is a number $r \neq 0$ such that $f(n) = r \cdot f(n-1)$ for all integers $n > 0$) with initial term $g(0)$, the associated series $G(n) = \sum_{k=0}^{n} g(k)$ is a geometric series.

INVESTIGATION 8A   TRIGONOMETRIC FUNCTIONS

8.0   Right Triangle Trigonometry

Check Your Understanding

1. Use the trigonometric functions to find the two missing sides. Let $a = $ side opposite 40° and $b = $ side adjacent to 40°.

$$\sin(40°) = \frac{\text{side opposite}}{\text{hypotenuse}} = \frac{a}{10}$$

$$a = 10 \cdot \sin(40°) = 10 \cdot 0.643 = 6.43$$

$$\cos(40°) = \frac{\text{adjacent}}{\text{hypotenuse}} = \frac{b}{10}$$

$$b = 10 \cdot \cos(40°) = 10 \cdot 0.766 = 7.66$$

The perimeter will be the sum of the three sides: $10 + 6.43 + 7.66 = 24.09$.

2. (a) One leg of the triangle is the base and the other leg is the height relative to that base. The area is
$\frac{1}{2} \cdot$ base $\cdot$ height $= \frac{1}{2} \cdot 20 \cdot 21 = 210$.

   (b) Use the Pythagorean Theorem: $c^2 = a^2 + b^2$.

$$c^2 = 20^2 + 21^2 = 400 + 441 = 841$$

$$c = \sqrt{841} = 29$$

   (c)

Since the legs are close in length, the estimates of the angles should be close to 45°.

   (d) Let θ be the angle opposite the side of length 21. Then, $\sin(\theta) = \frac{21}{29} = 0.724138$ and $\theta = \sin^{-1}$ $(0.724138 = 46.4°)$. The other angle is $90° - 46.4° = 43.6°$.

3. Since the $\cos(\theta) = \frac{\text{opposite}}{\text{hypotenuse}}$, you can set up a right triangle where the hypotenuse is 17 and the side adjacent to θ is 8. The opposite side will be 15 ($8 - 15 - 17$ is a Pythagorean triple). You can also use the Pythagorean

Theorem to find the missing side.

$$\sin(\theta) = \frac{\text{opposite}}{\text{hypotenuse}} = \frac{15}{17}$$

$$\tan(\theta) = \frac{\text{opposite}}{\text{adjacent}} = \frac{15}{8}$$

4. $\tan(\theta) = \frac{\text{opposite}}{\text{adjacent}} = \frac{\frac{\text{opposite}}{\text{hypotenuse}}}{\frac{\text{adjacent}}{\text{hypotenuse}}} = \frac{\sin(\theta)}{\cos(\theta)}$

5. Draw a right triangle with a hypotenuse of length 4 and with the side opposite θ of length 1. The side adjacent to θ can be found using the Pythagorean Theorem: $c^2 = a^2 + b^2$.

$$4^2 = a^2 + 1^2$$

$$16 = a^2 + 1$$

$$15 = a^2$$

$$\sqrt{15} = a$$

So, $\cos(\theta) = \frac{\text{adjacent}}{\text{hypotenuse}} = \frac{\sqrt{15}}{4}$.

6. There are three possible areas, depending on which side is 12. In all cases, you are working with a 30-60-90 triangle so the sides are in the ratio $2 : 1 : \sqrt{3}$.

   (a) *12 is the side opposite 30°.*
   The adjacent side is $12\sqrt{3}$.

$$\text{area} = \frac{1}{2} \cdot \text{base} \cdot \text{height} = \frac{1}{2} \cdot 12 \cdot 12\sqrt{3}$$

$$= 72\sqrt{3} \approx 124.7$$

   (b) *12 is the side adjacent to 30°.*
   The opposite side is $\frac{12}{\sqrt{3}} = 4\sqrt{3}$.

$$\text{area} = \frac{1}{2} \cdot 12 \cdot 4\sqrt{3} = 24\sqrt{3} \approx 41.6$$

   (c) *12 is the hypotenuse.*
   Then the two legs are 6 and $6\sqrt{3}$.

$$\text{area} = \frac{1}{2} \cdot 6 \cdot 6\sqrt{3} = 18\sqrt{3} \approx 31.2$$

On Your Own

7. Call the side opposite θ, a, and the side adjacent to θ, b. Then, $\sin(\theta) = \frac{a}{1} = a$ and $\cos(\theta) = \frac{b}{1} = b$ The lengths of the two sides of the triangle are $\sin(\theta)$ and $\cos(\theta)$.

8. In a right triangle, the two acute angles have a sum of $90°$. If one of the acute angles is θ, the other acute angle is $90° - \theta$. Also, the side opposite θ is the side adjacent to $90° - \theta$. Then,

$$\sin(\theta) = \frac{\text{side opposite } \theta}{\text{hypotenuse}} = \frac{\text{side adjacent to } 90° - \theta}{\text{hypotenuse}}$$
$$= \cos(90° - \theta)$$

9.

angle θ	$\sin(\theta)$	$\cos(\theta)$	$\tan(\theta)$
30°	$\frac{1}{2}$	$\frac{\sqrt{3}}{2}$	$\frac{1}{\sqrt{3}} = \frac{\sqrt{3}}{3}$
60°	$\frac{\sqrt{3}}{2}$	$\frac{1}{2}$	$\frac{\sqrt{3}}{1} = \sqrt{3}$

10.

angle θ	$\sin(\theta)$	$\cos(\theta)$	$\tan(\theta)$
45°	$\frac{1}{\sqrt{2}} = \frac{\sqrt{2}}{2}$	$\frac{1}{\sqrt{2}} = \frac{\sqrt{2}}{2}$	$\frac{1}{1} = 1$

11. Derman sees that the $\sin(\theta)$ is getting bigger and closer to 1 as θ gets closer to $90°$. So, he should pick $\sin(90°) = 1$. The $\cos(\theta)$ is getting smaller and closer to 0 as θ gets closer to $90°$. So, he should pick $\cos(90°) = 0$.

12. (a) The largest value is 1 and the smallest is 0. As θ gets close to $90°$, the $\sin(\theta)$ is getting close to 1, and as θ gets close to 0, the $\sin(\theta)$ gets close to 0.

(b) The largest value is 1 and the smallest is 0. As θ gets close to $90°$, the $\cos(\theta)$ is getting close to 0, and as θ gets close to 0, the $\cos(\theta)$ gets close to 1.

(c) The smallest value is 0 and there is no largest value. Since $\tan(\theta) = \frac{\sin(\theta)}{\cos(\theta)}$, this value would be 0 when $\sin(\theta) = 0$. The value of the $\tan(\theta)$ would get very large as the value of the denominator ($\cos(\theta)$) gets close to 0.

13. (a)

$$\sin(\theta) = \frac{8}{10} = \frac{4}{5}$$
$$\cos(\theta) = \frac{6}{10} = \frac{3}{5}$$
$$\tan(\theta) = \frac{8}{6} = \frac{4}{3}$$

(b)

$$\sin(\theta) = \frac{6}{10} = \frac{3}{5}$$
$$\cos(\theta) = \frac{8}{10} = \frac{4}{5}$$
$$\tan(\theta) = \frac{6}{8} = \frac{3}{4}$$

(c)

$$\sin(\theta) = \frac{1}{\sqrt{2}} = \frac{\sqrt{2}}{2}$$
$$\cos(\theta) = \frac{1}{\sqrt{2}} = \frac{\sqrt{2}}{2}$$
$$\tan(\theta) = \frac{1}{1} = 1$$

(d)

$$\sin(\theta) = \frac{12}{13}$$
$$\cos(\theta) = \frac{5}{13}$$
$$\tan(\theta) = \frac{12}{5}$$

14. Trig relationships only work in right triangles ... for now. You are not told that the triangle is a right triangle.

15. In a right triangle, the side opposite θ is the side adjacent to $90° - \theta$ and the side adjacent to θ is the side opposite $90° - \theta$.

$$\tan(\theta) = \frac{\text{side opposite } \theta}{\text{side adjacent to } \theta} = \frac{\text{side adjacent to } 90° - \theta}{\text{side opposite } 90° - \theta}$$
$$= \frac{1}{\dfrac{\text{side opposite } 90° - \theta}{\text{side adjacent to } 90° - \theta}} = \frac{1}{\tan(90° - \theta)}$$

Maintain Your Skills

16.

Angle θ	$\sin(\theta)$	$\cos(\theta)$	$\tan(\theta)$
10°	0.174	0.985	0.176
20°	0.342	0.940	0.364
30°	0.500	0.866	0.577
40°	0.643	0.766	0.839
50°	0.766	0.643	1.192
60°	0.866	0.500	1.732
70°	0.940	0.342	2.747
80°	0.985	0.174	5.671

17. They are equal because $10 + 80 = 90$, so they would be the acute angles of the same right triangle. The side adjacent to $80°$ would be the side opposite $10°$ and so $\cos(80°) = \sin(10°)$.

8.1 Getting Started

For You to Explore

1. (a) The distance between Olivia and Paul is always the length of the radius, which is 1.

(b) You can use the distance formula. The distance between (x, y) and $(0, 0)$ is 1.

$$\sqrt{(x - 0)^2 + (y - 0)^2} = 1$$
$$\sqrt{x^2 + y^2} = 1$$
$$x^2 + y^2 = 1$$

2. Drop an altitude from the point (x, y) to make a right triangle with sides x, y, and 1 (hypotenuse). Then, $\cos(70°) = \frac{x}{1}$ and $\sin(70°) = \frac{y}{1}$. $x = \cos 70° \approx 0.342$ and $y = \sin 70° \approx 0.940$. So the point is $(0.342, 0.940)$

3. This is an isosceles right triangle, so $x = y$.

$$x^2 + y^2 = 1 \qquad \text{Pythagorean Theorem}$$
$$x^2 + x^2 = 1 \qquad \quad \text{Substitute } x = y.$$
$$2x^2 = 1$$
$$x^2 = \frac{1}{2}$$
$$x = \sqrt{\frac{1}{2}} = \frac{\sqrt{2}}{2}$$

Since x and y are equal, $x = y = \frac{\sqrt{2}}{2}$.

4. If you drop an altitude from the point (x, y), you will get the $45 - 45 - 90$ triangle that you just found the sides of in exercise 3. So, the coordinates are $\left(\frac{\sqrt{2}}{2}, \frac{\sqrt{2}}{2}\right)$.

5. Paul will be standing on the positive y-axis, 1 unit from the origin. The coordinates are $(0, 1)$.

6. (a) Since Paul's path is the unit circle, you check to see if the point $\left(\frac{3}{5}, \frac{4}{5}\right)$ is on the unit circle: $x^2 + y^2 = 1$.

$$\left(\frac{3}{5}\right)^2 + \left(\frac{4}{5}\right)^2 = \frac{9}{25} + \frac{16}{25} = \frac{25}{25} = 1$$

$\left(\frac{3}{5}, \frac{4}{5}\right)$ is on the unit circle and Paul will pass through the point.

(b) Drop an altitude from the point $\left(\frac{3}{5}, \frac{4}{5}\right)$ to find the angle, you can use $\sin \theta = \dfrac{\frac{4}{5}}{1} = \frac{4}{5}$.

$$\theta = \sin^{-1} \frac{4}{5} \approx 53°$$

(You could also have used cos or tan here.)

7. The y-coordinate begins at 0 and increases to 1 as the angle Olivia turns goes from $0°$ to $90°$. Then, the y-coordinate decreases from 1 to 0 as the angle goes from $90°$ to $180°$. The y-coordinate continues to decrease from 0 to -1 as the angle goes from $180°$ to $270°$. The y-coordinate increases from -1 to 0 as the angle goes from $270°$ to $360°$. Paul is now back at his starting point. The pattern will repeat from $360°$ to $720°$ and again from $720°$ to $1080°$ and so on.

8. You can use the special 45-45-90 triangle to find the coordinates when you are not on an axis. Remember to make x and y positive or negative depending on the quadrant.

Angle	Coordinates
0°	$(1, 0)$
45°	$\left(\frac{\sqrt{2}}{2}, \frac{\sqrt{2}}{2}\right)$
90°	$(0, 1)$
135°	$\left(-\frac{\sqrt{2}}{2}, \frac{\sqrt{2}}{2}\right)$
180°	$(-1, 0)$
225°	$\left(-\frac{\sqrt{2}}{2}, -\frac{\sqrt{2}}{2}\right)$
270°	$(0, -1)$
315°	$\left(\frac{\sqrt{2}}{2}, -\frac{\sqrt{2}}{2}\right)$
360°	$(1, 0)$
405°	$\left(\frac{\sqrt{2}}{2}, \frac{\sqrt{2}}{2}\right)$
450°	$(0, 1)$

9.

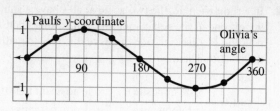

10. First divide 10,000 by 360 to see how many times Paul has walked around the circle. $\frac{10,000}{360} = 27\frac{280}{360}$. Paul has walked around the circle 27 times plus another $280°$. Drop an altitude from that point to the x-axis. The angle of your triangle is $360° - 280° = 80°$. Next find x and y.

$$\cos 80° = \frac{x}{1}$$

so

$$x = \cos 80° \approx 0.174$$
$$\sin 80° = \frac{y}{1}$$

so

$$y = \sin 80° \approx 0.985$$

Paul is in Quadrant IV, so the point is $(0.174, -0.985)$.

On Your Own

11. For each ordered pair, drop an altitude to the x-axis and use trigonometry to find the coordinates.

Angle	Coordinates
0°	$(1, 0)$
10°	$(0.985, 0.174)$
20°	$(0.940, 0.342)$
30°	$\left(\frac{\sqrt{3}}{2}, \frac{1}{2}\right)$
40°	$(0.766, 0.643)$
50°	$(0.643, 0.766)$
60°	$\left(\frac{1}{2}, \frac{\sqrt{3}}{2}\right)$
70°	$(0.342, 0.940)$
80°	$(0.174, 0.985)$
90°	$(0, 1)$

12. (a)

$$\text{magnitude} = \sqrt{3^2 + 4^2} = \sqrt{9 + 16} = \sqrt{25} = 5$$
$$\text{direction} = \tan^{-1} \frac{4}{3} \approx 53°$$

(b)

$$\text{magnitude} = \sqrt{\left(\frac{3}{5}\right)^2 + \left(\frac{4}{5}\right)^2} = \sqrt{\frac{9}{25} + \frac{16}{25}} = \sqrt{\frac{25}{25}} = 1$$
$$\text{direction} = \tan^{-1}\left(\frac{\frac{4}{5}}{\frac{3}{5}}\right) = \tan^{-1} \frac{4}{3} \approx 53°$$

(c) Drop an altitude to the x-axis to find the direction. You will have to subtract the angle from $180°$.

$$\text{magnitude} = \sqrt{(-5)^2 + (12)^2} = \sqrt{25 + 144}$$
$$= \sqrt{169} = 13$$
$$\text{direction} = 180° - \tan\frac{12}{5} \approx 180° - 67° = 113°$$

(d) Drop an altitude to the x-axis to find the direction. You will have to subtract the angle from $180°$.

$$\text{magnitude} = \sqrt{\left(\frac{-5}{13}\right)^2 + \left(\frac{12}{13}\right)^2} = \sqrt{\frac{25}{169} + \frac{144}{169}}$$
$$= \sqrt{\frac{169}{169}} = 1$$
$$\text{direction} = 180° - \tan^{-1}\frac{\frac{12}{13}}{\frac{5}{13}} = 180° - \tan^{-1}\frac{12}{5}$$
$$\approx 180° - 67° = 113°$$

13. To determine if the point is on the unit circle, see if the ordered pair solves $x^2 + y^2 = 1$.

(a) $\left(\frac{1}{2}\right)^2 + \left(-\frac{1}{2}\right)^2 = \frac{1}{4} + \frac{1}{4} = \frac{2}{4} = \frac{1}{2} \neq 1$ no

(b) $1^2 + (-1)^2 = 1 + 1 = 2 \neq 1$ no

(c) $\left(\frac{-5}{13}\right)^2 + \left(\frac{12}{13}\right)^2 = \frac{25}{169} + \frac{144}{169} = \frac{169}{169} = 1$ yes

(d) $\left(\frac{2}{3}\right)^2 + \left(-\frac{4}{5}\right)^2 = \frac{4}{9} + \frac{16}{25} = \frac{100}{225} + \frac{144}{225} = \frac{244}{225} \neq 1$ no

14. In both cases, drop an altitude to the x-axis and the angle made with the x-axis is $50°$. $x = \cos 50° \approx 0.643$ and $y = \sin 50° \approx 0.766$ Then make x and y positive or negative depending upon the quadrant.

(a) $(-0.643, 0.766)$ Quadrant II

(b) $(-0.643, -0.766)$ Quadrant III

15. The x-coordinate begins at 1 and decreases to 0 as the angle Olivia turns goes from $0°$ to $90°$. Then, the x-coordinate decreases from 0 to -1 as the angle goes from $90°$ to $180°$. The x-coordinate increases from -1 to 0 as the angle goes from $180°$ to $270°$. The x-coordinate continues to increase from 0 to 1 as the angle goes from $270°$ to $360°$. Paul is now back at his starting point. The pattern will repeat from $360°$ to $720°$ and again from $720°$ to $1080°$ and so on.

16.

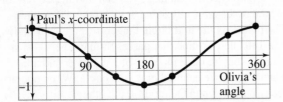

17. Since $430° > 360°$, Olivia has turned more than one complete revolution. To find out how much more, subtract 360 from 430. $430° - 360° = 70°$. To find the

coordinates, drop an altitude from Paul's location point. The angle of the right triangle is $70°$. Use trigonometry to find the sides, x and y.

$$x = \cos 70° \approx 0.342$$
$$y = \sin 70° \approx 0.940$$

The coordinates of Paul's location are $(0.342, 0.940)$.

18. If the direction of $a + bi$ is $120°$, the acute angle $a + bi$ makes with the real axis is $60°$, and the right triangle formed when you drop an altitude is a 30-60-90 triangle. The magnitude of $a + bi$, 2, is the length of the hypotenuse. The other two sides are $\sqrt{3}$ (opposite the $60°$ angle) and 1 (opposite the $30°$ angle). $a + bi$ is in Quadrant II, so $a = -1$ and $b = \sqrt{3}$.

Maintain Your Skills

19. (a) 2 intersections

$$x^2 + y^2 = 1$$
$$x = 0.5$$

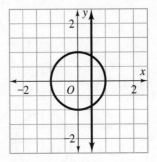

(b) 2 intersections

$$x^2 + y^2 = 1$$
$$x = 0.9$$

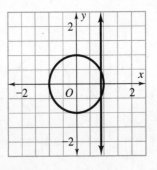

(c) 1 intersection

$$x^2 + y^2 = 1$$
$$x = 1$$

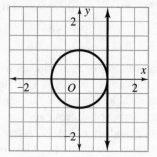

(d) no intersections

$$x^2 + y^2 = 1$$
$$x = 1.3$$

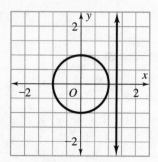

20. (a) 2 intersections

$$x^2 + y^2 = 1$$
$$y = 0.5$$

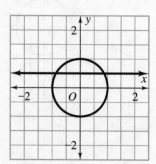

(b) 2 intersections

$$x^2 + y^2 = 1$$
$$y = -0.5$$

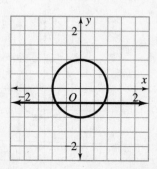

(c) 2 intersections

$$x^2 + y^2 = 1$$
$$y = -0.9$$

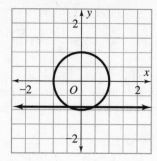

(d) 1 intersection

$$x^2 + y^2 = 1$$
$$y = -1$$

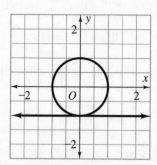

8.2 Extending the Domain, Part 1

Check Your Understanding

1. The equation of the unit circle is $x^2 + y^2 = 1$. If Jo's reasoning were correct, the point $\left(\frac{1}{2}, \frac{1}{2}\right)$ should be on the unit circle. $\left(\frac{1}{2}\right)^2 + \left(\frac{1}{2}\right)^2 = \frac{1}{4} + \frac{1}{4} = \frac{2}{4} \neq 1$, so it is not on the unit circle.

2. Since the magnitude is 1, $a = \cos 70° \approx 0.342$, and $y = \sin 70° \approx 0.940$.

$$a + bi = 0.342 + 0.940i$$

3. $-\frac{\sqrt{3}}{2} - \frac{1}{2}i \approx -0.866 - 0.5i$ You can use your calculator to get the decimal answers here. But since 210° makes a 30° angle with the real axis, you can find the expressions for the exact values by using a 30 − 60 − 90 triangle.

4. The points on the unit circle that correspond to θ and $\theta + 180°$ lie on a line that passes through the origin—they're the endpoints of a diameter and are exactly opposite each other on the circle. When one of the two points is in Quadrant I, the other is in Quadrant III. When one is in Quadrant II, the other is in Quadrant IV. Because of this, the sign of the x- and y-coordinates for one point will be the negatives of the coordinates for the other.

(a) $\cos\theta = -\cos(\theta + 180°)$
(b) $\sin\theta = -\sin(\theta + 180°)$
(c) $\tan\theta = \tan(\theta + 180°)$

5. Use your calculator. Both expressions equal 1.

6. The complex number would be on the unit circle. Some examples are $0 + 1i$, $1 + 0i$, and $-\frac{1}{2} + \frac{\sqrt{3}}{2}i$.

7. (a) $\sin\theta = 0$ at the points $(1, 0)$ and $(-1, 0)$, so
$\theta = 0°, 180°, 360°, 540°, \ldots$ or

$$\theta = 180° \cdot k, \text{ where } k \text{ is an integer.}$$

(b) $\cos\theta = 0$ at the points $(0, 1)$ and $(0, -1)$, so
$\theta = 90°, 270°, 450°, \ldots$ or

$$\theta = 90° + 180° \cdot k, \text{ where } k \text{ is an integer.}$$

(c) $\tan\theta = 0$ whenever $\sin\theta = 0$ so the answer is the same as for $\sin\theta = 0$ or

$$\theta = 180°, \text{ where } k \text{ is an integer.}$$

On Your Own

8. (a)

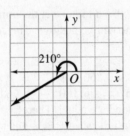

$\cos 210° = -\frac{\sqrt{3}}{2}$, $\sin 210° = -\frac{1}{2}$, $\tan 210° = \frac{-\frac{1}{2}}{-\frac{\sqrt{3}}{2}}$

$= \frac{1}{\sqrt{3}} = \frac{\sqrt{3}}{3}$

(b)

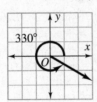

$\cos 330° = \frac{\sqrt{3}}{2}$, $\sin 330° = -\frac{1}{2}$, $\tan 330° = \frac{-\frac{1}{2}}{\frac{\sqrt{3}}{2}} =$

$-\frac{1}{\sqrt{3}} = -\frac{\sqrt{3}}{3}$

(c)

$\cos 40° \approx 0.766$, $\sin 40° \approx 0.643$, $\tan 40° \approx \frac{0.643}{0.766}$

≈ 0.839

(d)

$\cos 320° \approx 0.766$, $\sin 320° \approx -0.643$, $\tan 320° \approx \frac{-0.643}{0.766} \approx -0.839$

(e)

$\cos 360° = 1$, $\sin 360° = 0$, $\tan 360° = \frac{0}{1} = 0$

9. Since $\tan\theta = \frac{\sin\theta}{\cos\theta}$, it follows that

$$\cos\theta = \frac{\sin\theta}{\tan\theta} = \frac{0.57358}{0.70021} \approx 0.81915$$

The correct answer choice is B.

10.

angle θ	$\cos\theta$	$\sin\theta$	$\cos^2\theta$	$\sin^2\theta$
0°	1	0	1	0
30°	$\frac{\sqrt{3}}{2}$	$\frac{1}{2}$	$\frac{3}{4}$	$\frac{1}{4}$
45°	$\frac{\sqrt{2}}{2}$	$\frac{\sqrt{2}}{2}$	$\frac{1}{2}$	$\frac{1}{2}$
60°	$\frac{1}{2}$	$\frac{\sqrt{3}}{2}$	$\frac{1}{4}$	$\frac{3}{4}$
90°	0	1	0	1
120°	$-\frac{1}{2}$	$\frac{\sqrt{3}}{2}$	$\frac{1}{4}$	$\frac{3}{4}$
135°	$-\frac{\sqrt{2}}{2}$	$\frac{\sqrt{2}}{2}$	$\frac{1}{2}$	$\frac{1}{2}$
150°	$-\frac{\sqrt{3}}{2}$	$\frac{1}{2}$	$\frac{3}{4}$	$\frac{1}{4}$
180°	-1	0	1	0
210°	$-\frac{\sqrt{3}}{2}$	$-\frac{1}{2}$	$\frac{3}{4}$	$\frac{1}{4}$
225°	$-\frac{\sqrt{2}}{2}$	$-\frac{\sqrt{2}}{2}$	$\frac{1}{2}$	$\frac{1}{2}$
240°	$-\frac{1}{2}$	$-\frac{\sqrt{3}}{2}$	$\frac{1}{4}$	$\frac{3}{4}$
270°	0	-1	0	1
300°	$\frac{1}{2}$	$-\frac{\sqrt{3}}{2}$	$\frac{1}{4}$	$\frac{3}{4}$
315°	$\frac{\sqrt{2}}{2}$	$-\frac{\sqrt{2}}{2}$	$\frac{1}{2}$	$\frac{1}{2}$
330°	$\frac{\sqrt{3}}{2}$	$-\frac{1}{2}$	$\frac{3}{4}$	$\frac{1}{4}$
360°	1	0	1	0

11. $\sin 310° = -\sin 50°$ because $310°$ makes an angle of $50°$ with the positive x-axis. When you drop an altitude to the x-axis, the triangle formed is congruent to the one dropped from $50°$, but $50°$ is in Quadrant I where the sine is positive and $310°$ is in Quadrant IV where the sine is negative.

12. (a) $\sin 2\theta = \sin 2 \cdot 150° = \sin 300° = -\frac{\sqrt{3}}{2}$
(b) $2 \cdot \sin\theta \cdot \cos\theta = 2 \cdot \sin 150° \cdot \cos 150° =$
$2 \cdot \frac{1}{2} \cdot -\frac{\sqrt{3}}{2} = -\frac{\sqrt{3}}{2}$

13. (a) $\sin\theta = 1$ if θ intersects the unit circle at the point $(0, 1)$ so $\theta = 90°, 450°, 810°, \ldots$ and

$$\theta = 90° + 360° \cdot k \text{ (where } k \text{ is an integer)}$$

(b) $\cos\theta = 1$ if θ intersects the unit circle at the point $(1, 0)$, so $\theta = 0°, 360°, 720°, \ldots$ and

$$\theta = 360° \cdot k \text{ (where } k \text{ is an integer)}$$

(c) $\tan\theta = 1$ when $\cos\theta = \sin\theta$. This happens when θ intersects the unit circle at the point $\left(\frac{\sqrt{2}}{2}, \frac{\sqrt{2}}{2}\right)$ or at the point $\left(-\frac{\sqrt{2}}{2}, -\frac{\sqrt{2}}{2}\right)$, so $\theta = 45°, 225°, 405°, \ldots$ and

$$\theta = 45° + 180° \cdot k \text{ (where } k \text{ is an integer)}$$

14. (a) magnitude $= |-6\sqrt{3} + 6i| = \sqrt{(-6\sqrt{3})^2 + 6^2} = \sqrt{36 \cdot 3 + 36} = \sqrt{108 + 36} = \sqrt{144} = 12$

To find the direction, drop an altitude to the real axis. If θ is the acute angle formed, then the direction of $-6\sqrt{3} + 6i$ is $180° - \theta = 180° - \tan^{-1}\frac{6}{6\sqrt{3}} = 180° - \tan^{-1}\frac{1}{\sqrt{3}} = 180° - \tan^{-1}\frac{\sqrt{3}}{3} = 150°$

(b) Drop an altitude to the real axis. The triangle is a $30 - 60 - 90$ triangle, so the side opposite the $30°$ angle is $\frac{1}{2}$ the hypotenuse, $\frac{1}{2} \cdot 10 = 5$ and the other side is $5\sqrt{3}$. The complex number is $5\sqrt{3} + 5i$.

(c) Drop an altitude to the real axis. This is a $30 - 60 - 90$ triangle. The side opposite $60°$ is $\frac{1}{2}$ the hypotenuse times $\sqrt{3}$, $\frac{1}{2} \cdot 1 \cdot \sqrt{3} = \frac{\sqrt{3}}{2}$. The other side is $\frac{1}{2}$. The complex number is $\frac{1}{2} + \frac{\sqrt{3}}{2}i$.

Maintain Your Skills

15. In each of these parts, you are multiplying two complex numbers. Remember that to multiply two complex numbers, you add their directions and multiply their magnitudes. In each case, when you compute the magnitude, you find that it is 1. These points are all of the form $(\cos\theta, \sin\theta)$, so you're on the unit circle. Since $1 \cdot 1 = 1$, the product is also on the unit circle. All you need to do is add the angles.

(a) $\theta = 40° + 50° = 90°$

(b) $\theta = 40° + 20° = 60°$

(c) $\theta = 40° + 80° = 120°$

(d) $\theta = 45° + 45° = 90°$

8.3 Extending the Domain of Sine, Cosine, Tangent, Part 2

Check Your Understanding

1. $160°$ and $20°$ both make a $20°$ angle when you drop an altitude to the x-axis, but $160°$ is in Quadrant II where the cosine is negative and the sine is positive. $20°$ is in Quadrant I where cosine and sine are both positive. So, the cosines are opposites and the sines are equal.

2. (a) θ could be in Quadrant I or Quadrant II because the sine is positive there.

(b) Use $(\cos\theta)^2 + (\sin\theta)^2 = 1$:

$$(\cos\theta)^2 + \left(\frac{20}{29}\right)^2 = 1$$

$$(\cos\theta)^2 + \frac{400}{841} = 1$$

$$(\cos\theta)^2 = 1 - \frac{400}{841}$$

$$(\cos\theta)^2 = \frac{441}{841}$$

$$\cos\theta = \pm\sqrt{\frac{441}{841}}$$

$$\cos\theta = \pm\frac{21}{29}$$

(c) $\tan\theta = \frac{\sin\theta}{\cos\theta} = \frac{\frac{20}{29}}{\pm\frac{21}{29}} = \pm\frac{20}{21}$

3. Since $\tan\theta = \frac{\sin\theta}{\cos\theta}$, $\tan\theta$ will get larger as the denominator $(\cos\theta)$ gets closer to 0. In the first quadrant, this happens as θ gets closer to $90°$. By trying some values close to $90°$, you can find an angle θ where $\tan\theta > 100$. For example, $\tan 89.428° = 100.164$. Angles greater than $89.428°$ but less than $90°$ will also work. There are also possible solutions in Quadrant III as θ gets close to $270°$. For example, $\tan 269.428° = 100.164$.

4. Since $-60°$ will intersect the unit circle in Quadrant IV, the cosine will be positive. The correct answer is $\cos -60° = \frac{1}{2}$.

5. $\tan 110° \approx -2.747$, $\cos 120° = \sin 210° = -0.5$, $\sin 120° \approx 0.866$, $\cos 720° = 1$, $\tan 70° \approx 2.747$

6. Since $\sin\theta = \sin(180° - \theta)$, you want two numbers that add to 1 and are equal. Therefore, you want an angle whose sin is $\frac{1}{2}$. $\sin 30° = \frac{1}{2}$ and $\sin 150° = \frac{1}{2}$. If $\theta = 30°$, then $180° - \theta = 150°$. If $\theta = 150°$, then $180° - \theta = 30°$.

7. Each of the first four parts make an angle of $50°$ with the x-axis, so their sine and cosine will only differ from $\sin 50°$ and $\cos 50°$ by the sign, which is determined by the Quadrant the angle is in.

(a) $\sin 130° = \sin 50° \approx 0.7660$

(b) $\cos 130° = -\cos 50° \approx -0.6428$

(c) $\cos 230° = -\cos 50° \approx -0.6428$

(d) $\sin 310° = -\sin 50° \approx -0.7660$

(e) $\cos^2 230° + \sin^2 230° = 1$

On the unit circle, $x^2 + y^2 = 1$.

(f) $\sin 40° = \cos 50° \approx 0.6428$. When you drop an altitude to the x-axis, the right triangle will have acute angles of $40°$ and $50°$. $\sin 40° = \cos 50°$.

8. (a) $\tan^2\theta + 1 = \frac{1}{\cos^2\theta}$

(b)

$$\tan^2\theta + 1 = \frac{\sin^2\theta}{\cos^2\theta} + 1$$

$$= \frac{\sin^2\theta}{\cos^2\theta} + \frac{\cos^2\theta}{\cos^2\theta}$$

$$= \frac{\sin^2\theta + \cos^2\theta}{\cos^2\theta}$$

$$= \frac{1}{\cos^2\theta}$$

On Your Own

9. $\cos(-30°) = \cos(30°) = \frac{\sqrt{3}}{2}$, $\sin(-30°) =$
$-\sin(30°) = -\frac{1}{2}$, $\tan(-30°) = \frac{\sin(-30°)}{\cos(-30°)} = \frac{-\frac{1}{2}}{\frac{\sqrt{3}}{2}} =$
$-\frac{1}{\sqrt{3}} = -\frac{\sqrt{3}}{3}$

10. (a) $\sin 400° = \sin(40° + 360°) = \sin 40°$
  (b) $\cos 400° = \cos(40° + 360°) = \cos 40°$
  (c) $\cos 300° = \cos(360° + (-60°)) = \cos(-60°) =$
  $\cos 60°$
  (d) $\sin 315° = \sin(360° + (-45°)) = \sin(-45°) =$
  $-\sin 45°$
  (e) $\sin(-100°) = -\sin 100° = -\sin 80°$

11. In each case, draw a picture to show where θ is in relation to the angle for which you're finding the function value.

  (a) $\sin(180° - \theta) = \sin\theta$
  (b) $\cos(180° - \theta) = -\cos\theta$
  (c) $\sin(180° + \theta) = -\sin\theta$
  (d) $\cos(180° + \theta) = -\cos\theta$
  (e) $\sin(270° - \theta) = -\cos\theta$
  (f) $\cos(270° - \theta) = -\sin\theta$
  (g) $\sin(270° + \theta) = -\cos\theta$
  (h) $\cos(270° + \theta) = \sin\theta$

12. The statement is false. You can find a counterexample to show that it is not true. For example,

$$\sin(30° + 60°) \overset{?}{=} \sin 30° + \sin 60°$$

$$\sin(90°) \overset{?}{=} \frac{1}{2} + \frac{\sqrt{3}}{2}$$

$$1 \neq \frac{1 + \sqrt{3}}{2}$$

Similarly, you can show that the statement is not true for cosine:

$$\cos(30° + 60°) \overset{?}{=} \cos 30° + \cos 60°$$

$$\cos(90°) \overset{?}{=} \frac{\sqrt{3}}{2} + \frac{1}{2}$$

$$0 \neq \frac{\sqrt{3} + 1}{2}$$

13. (a) Positive, because the cosine is positive in Quadrant IV.
  (b) Negative, because the sine is negative in Quadrant IV.
  (c) Negative, because $\tan\theta = \frac{\sin\theta}{\cos\theta} = \frac{\text{negative}}{\text{positive}} = $ negative.
  (d) Positive. This expression is equal to 1, which is positive.
  (e) Negative. A negative number cubed is negative.

14. $\cos 120° + \sin 120° = -\frac{1}{2} + \frac{\sqrt{3}}{2} = \frac{-1+\sqrt{3}}{2} = \frac{\sqrt{3}-1}{2}$, which is choice **B**.

15. $\sin 60° + \sin 120° + \sin 180° + \sin 240° + \sin 300° + \sin 360° = \frac{\sqrt{3}}{2} + \frac{\sqrt{3}}{2} + 0 + \left(-\frac{\sqrt{3}}{2}\right) + \left(-\frac{\sqrt{3}}{2}\right) + 0 = 0$

16. You can find the exact value, if the angle formed when you drop an altitude is part of a "special right triangle" or if the angle falls on one of the axes.
$0°, 30°, 45°, 60°, 90°, 120°, 135°, 150°, 180°, 210°,$
$225°, 240°, 270°, 300°, 315°, 330°, 360°$

17. (a)

$$(\cos\theta)^2 + (\sin\theta)^2 = 1$$

$$(\cos\theta)^2 + \left(\frac{35}{37}\right)^2 = 1$$

$$(\cos\theta)^2 + \frac{1225}{1369} = 1$$

$$(\cos\theta)^2 = 1 - \frac{1225}{1369}$$

$$(\cos\theta)^2 = \frac{144}{1369}$$

$$\cos\theta = \pm\sqrt{\frac{144}{1369}}$$

$$\cos\theta = \pm\frac{12}{37}$$

Since θ is in Quadrant II, cos is negative, so $\cos\theta = -\frac{12}{37}$.

  (b) $\tan\theta = \frac{\sin\theta}{\cos\theta} = \frac{\frac{35}{37}}{-\frac{12}{37}} = -\frac{35}{12}$
  (c) $\theta = \cos^{-1}\left(-\frac{12}{37}\right) \approx 109°$

18. (a) $\frac{1}{\tan^2\theta} = \frac{1}{\sin^2\theta} - 1$
  (b)

$$\frac{1}{\sin^2\theta} - 1 = \frac{1}{\sin^2\theta} - \frac{\sin^2\theta}{\sin^2\theta}$$

$$= \frac{1 - \sin^2\theta}{\sin^2\theta}$$

$$= \frac{\cos^2\theta + \sin^2\theta - \sin^2\theta}{\sin^2\theta}$$

$$= \frac{\cos^2\theta}{\sin^2\theta}$$

$$= \frac{1}{\frac{\sin^2\theta}{\cos^2\theta}}$$

$$= \frac{1}{\tan^2\theta}$$

19. Both A and C are false (try 30° in A and 0° in C). In a right triangle, the side opposite $90 - \theta = $ the side adjacent to θ, so $\sin(90° - \theta) = \cos\theta$. The correct answer is **B**.

Maintain Your Skills

20. (a) $\cos 330° = \cos 30°$ The cosine is positive in Quadrants I and IV.
  (b) $\sin 150° = \sin 30°$ The sine is positive in Quadrants I and II.
  (c) $\tan 210° = \tan 30°$ The tangent is positive in Quadrants I and III.
  (d) You can find other solutions by adding multiples of 360° to either 30° or 330°.

Check Your Understanding

1. To find $\cos q$, use the Pythagorean Identity:

$$\cos^2 q + \sin^2 q = 1$$
$$\cos^2 q + (0.72)^2 = 1$$
$$\cos^2 q + 0.5184 = 1$$
$$\cos^2 q = 0.4816$$
$$\cos q = \pm\sqrt{0.4816}$$
$$\cos q \approx \pm 0.69$$

Choose $\cos q = -0.69$, because q is in the second quadrant and the cosine is negative there. To find q use $\sin^{-1}(0.72)$ which is about $46°$. Since q is in Quadrant II, the angle you are looking for is $180° - 46° = 134°$. (*Note*: You can also use $\cos^{-1}(-0.69)$, which will give you $134°$ directly.)

2. (a) When $\cos x = \frac{1}{2}$, the acute angle formed when you drop an altitude to the horizontal axes is $60°$. Since the cosine is positive in Quadrants I and IV, the angle could be $60°$, or $360° - 60° = 300°$

   (b) $\sin 60° = \frac{\sqrt{3}}{2}$, $\sin 300° = -\frac{\sqrt{3}}{2}$

   (c) $\left(\pm\frac{\sqrt{3}}{2}\right)^2 = \frac{3}{4}$

3.

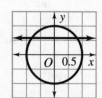

4.

$$x^2 + y^2 = 1$$
$$x^2 + (0.6)^2 = 1$$
$$x^2 + 0.36 = 1$$
$$x^2 = 0.64$$
$$x = \pm\sqrt{0.64} = \pm 0.8$$

5. (a) $\cos^{-1}(0.6) \approx 53.1°$. But, x could also be in Quadrant IV. $360° - 53.1° = 306.9°$

   (b) $\sin 53.1 \approx 0.8$ and $\sin 306.9° \approx -0.8$

   (c) $(\pm 0.8)^2 = 0.64$

6.

$$\frac{1}{z} = \frac{1}{\cos 30° + i \sin 30°}$$
$$= \frac{1}{\frac{\sqrt{3}}{2} + \frac{1}{2}i}$$
$$= \frac{1}{\frac{\sqrt{3}}{2} + \frac{1}{2}i} \cdot \frac{\frac{\sqrt{3}}{2} - \frac{1}{2}i}{\frac{\sqrt{3}}{2} - \frac{1}{2}i}$$
$$= \frac{\frac{\sqrt{3}}{2} - \frac{1}{2}i}{\left(\frac{\sqrt{3}}{2}\right)^2 - \left(\frac{1}{2}\right)^2 i^2}$$
$$= \frac{\frac{\sqrt{3}}{2} - \frac{1}{2}i}{\frac{3}{4} + \frac{1}{4}}$$
$$= \frac{\frac{\sqrt{3}}{2} - \frac{1}{2}i}{1}$$
$$= \frac{\sqrt{3}}{2} - \frac{1}{2}i$$
$$= \bar{z}$$

On Your Own

7. If $z\bar{z} = 1$, then $\frac{1}{z} = \bar{z}$. You can calculate $z\bar{z}$ as follows.

$$z\bar{z} = (\cos\theta + i\sin\theta)(\cos\theta - i\sin\theta)$$
$$= \cos^2\theta + \sin^2\theta$$
$$= 1$$

8. (a) The sine is positive in Quadrants I and II. $x = 45°$ or $x = 135°$

   (b) The sine and the cosine are both positive in Quadrant I only. $x = 45°$

   (c) The sine is positive *and* the cosine is negative in Quadrant II only. $x = 135°$

   (d) The sine and cosine are both negative in Quadrant III only $x = 225°$

9. You can find four solutions by using the points where the axes intersect the unit circle:

$$(1, 0), (0, 1), (-1, 0), (0, -1)$$

To find other points that are rational, consider some Pythagorean triples. To write a 3-4-5 triple with hypotenuse of length 1, divide by 5: $\frac{3}{5} - \frac{4}{5} - \frac{5}{5}$ are the sides of a right triangle with hypotenuse 1 and $\left(\frac{3}{5}\right)^2 + \left(\frac{4}{5}\right)^2 = 1^2 = 1$. Eight more ordered pairs are

$$\left(\pm\frac{3}{5}, \pm\frac{4}{5}\right), \left(\pm\frac{4}{5}, \pm\frac{3}{5}\right)$$

You can find other rational numbers (a, b) by using other triples. For example, $5 - 12 - 13$ will give $\frac{5}{13} - \frac{12}{13} - 1$ and a possible ordered pair is $\left(\frac{5}{13}, \frac{12}{13}\right)$.

10. Yes, as long as a and b represent real numbers. The point (a, b) will be on the unit circle, and if you connect it to the origin, that segment and the x-axis form the angle θ.

11. (a) To show that the statement is true, evaluate each side of the equation and show that they are equal.

$$\tan^2 30° = \frac{1}{\cos^2 30°} - 1$$

$$\left(\frac{\sqrt{3}}{3}\right)^2 = \frac{1}{\left(\frac{\sqrt{3}}{2}\right)^2} - 1$$

$$\frac{3}{9} = \frac{1}{\frac{3}{4}} - 1$$

$$\frac{1}{3} = \frac{4}{3} - 1$$

$$\frac{1}{3} = \frac{1}{3}$$

(b) This statement is true as long as $\cos \alpha \neq 0$.

$$\tan^2 \alpha = \frac{1}{\cos^2 \alpha} - 1$$

$$= \frac{1}{\cos^2 \alpha} - \frac{\cos^2 \alpha}{\cos^2 \alpha}$$

$$= \frac{1 - \cos^2 \alpha}{\cos^2 \alpha}$$

$$= \frac{\cos^2 \alpha + \sin^2 \alpha - \cos^2 \alpha}{\cos^2 \alpha}$$

$$= \frac{\sin^2 \alpha}{\cos^2 \alpha}$$

$$= \tan^2 \alpha, \quad \cos \alpha \neq 0$$

12. (a) $\cos^2 30° - \sin^2 30° = \left(\frac{\sqrt{3}}{2}\right)^2 - \left(\frac{1}{2}\right)^2 = \frac{3}{4} - \frac{1}{4} = \frac{2}{4} = \frac{1}{2}$

(b) $\cos^4 30° - \sin^4 30° = \left(\frac{\sqrt{3}}{2}\right)^4 - \left(\frac{1}{2}\right)^4 = \frac{9}{16} - \frac{1}{16} = \frac{8}{16} = \frac{1}{2}$

(c) You might choose $\theta = 45°$. Then

$$\cos^2 \theta - \sin^2 \theta = \cos^4 \theta - \sin^4 \theta$$

becomes

$$\cos^2 45° - \sin^2 45° = \cos^4 45° - \sin^4 45°$$

$$\left(\frac{\sqrt{2}}{2}\right)^2 - \left(\frac{\sqrt{2}}{2}\right)^2 = \left(\frac{\sqrt{2}}{2}\right)^4 - \left(\frac{\sqrt{2}}{2}\right)^4$$

$$\frac{2}{4} - \frac{2}{4} = \frac{4}{16} - \frac{4}{16}$$

$$0 = 0$$

(d) To prove that this works for any angle θ, factor the right side:

$$\cos^4 \theta - \sin^4 \theta = (\cos^2 \theta - \sin^2 \theta)(\cos^2 \theta + \sin^2 \theta)$$

$$= (\cos^2 \theta - \sin^2 \theta)(1)$$

$$= (\cos^2 \theta - \sin^2 \theta)$$

13. $\sin^2 \theta + \left(\frac{1}{3}\right)^2 = 1$, so $\sin^2 \theta = 1 - \frac{1}{9} = \frac{8}{9}$, and thus $\sin \theta = \pm\sqrt{\frac{8}{9}} = \pm\frac{2}{3}\sqrt{2}$. Since θ is in the first quadrant, the correct answer choice is **C**.

Maintain Your Skills

14.

angle θ	$\cos \theta$	$\sin \theta$	$\tan \theta$
0°	1	0	0
30°	$\frac{\sqrt{3}}{2}$	$\frac{1}{2}$	$\frac{1}{\sqrt{3}} = \frac{\sqrt{3}}{3}$
45°	$\frac{\sqrt{2}}{2}$	$\frac{\sqrt{2}}{2}$	1
60°	$\frac{1}{2}$	$\frac{\sqrt{3}}{2}$	$\sqrt{3}$
90°	0	1	undefined
120°	$-\frac{1}{2}$	$\frac{\sqrt{3}}{2}$	$-\sqrt{3}$
135°	$-\frac{\sqrt{2}}{2}$	$\frac{\sqrt{2}}{2}$	-1
150°	$-\frac{\sqrt{3}}{2}$	$\frac{1}{2}$	$-\frac{1}{\sqrt{3}} = -\frac{\sqrt{3}}{3}$
180°	-1	0	0
210°	$-\frac{\sqrt{3}}{2}$	$-\frac{1}{2}$	$\frac{1}{\sqrt{3}} = \frac{\sqrt{3}}{3}$
225°	$-\frac{\sqrt{2}}{2}$	$-\frac{\sqrt{2}}{2}$	1
240°	$-\frac{1}{2}$	$-\frac{\sqrt{3}}{2}$	$\sqrt{3}$
270°	0	-1	undefined
300°	$\frac{1}{2}$	$-\frac{\sqrt{3}}{2}$	$-\sqrt{3}$
315°	$\frac{\sqrt{2}}{2}$	$-\frac{\sqrt{2}}{2}$	-1
330°	$\frac{\sqrt{3}}{2}$	$-\frac{1}{2}$	$-\frac{1}{\sqrt{3}} = -\frac{\sqrt{3}}{3}$
360°	1	0	0

8.5 Solving Trigonometric Equations

Check Your Understanding

1. Since the sine is positive in Quadrants I and II, the values of x between 0° and 360° are 50° and $180° - 50° = 130°$. But, x can also be greater than 360° or less than 0°. You have to add multiples of 360°:

$$x = 50° + 360° \cdot k$$

or

$$x = 130° + 360° \cdot k$$

where k is an integer.

2. (a) Use your calculator: $\sin^{-1} 0.6 = 37°$. The angle could be in Quadrant I or II, so another solution is $180° - 37° = 143°$.

(b) The sine function is negative in Quadrants III and IV, so the angles are $180° + 37° = 217°$ and $360° - 37° = 323°$.

3. (a) Use your calculator: $\cos^{-1} 0.8 = 37°$. The cosine is also positive in Quadrant IV: $360° - 37° = 323°$.

(b) The cosine function is never less than -1, so there are no solutions.

4. (a)

$$3\cos x + 4 = 0$$

$$3\cos x = -4$$

$$\cos x = -\frac{4}{3}$$

There is no solution because cosine is never less than -1 for any angle x.

(b)

$$6 \sin x - 1 = 3$$
$$6 \sin x = 4$$
$$\sin x = \frac{2}{3}$$
$$x = \sin^{-1} \frac{2}{3}$$

$$x = 41.8° \text{ or } x = 180° - 41.8° = 138.2°$$

(c)

$$4 \sin^2 x = 1$$
$$\sin^2 x = \frac{1}{4}$$
$$\sin x = \pm \frac{1}{2}$$
$$x = \sin^{-1} \pm \frac{1}{2}$$

$$x = 30° \text{ or } 180° - 30° = 150° \text{ or } 180° + 30° = 210°$$
$$\text{or } 360° - 30° = 330°$$

(d)

$$4 \sin^2 x = 4 \sin x + 3$$
$$4 \sin^2 x - 4 \sin x - 3 = 0$$
$$(2 \sin x + 1)(2 \sin x - 3) = 0$$
$$\sin x = -\frac{1}{2} \text{ or } \sin x = \frac{3}{2}$$

$\sin x \neq \frac{3}{2}$, because sine can't be greater than 1, so
$x = \sin^{-1} -\frac{1}{2}$ and $x = 210°$ or $x = 330°$.

5. (a) $\sin x = \cos x$ when $1 = \frac{\sin x}{\cos x} = \tan x$, so $x = 45°$ (Quadrant I) or $x = 225°$ (Quadrant III).

(b) $\sin x = -\cos x$ when $x = 135°$ (Quadrant II) or $x = 315°$ (Quadrant IV).

(c)

$$\sin x = \tan x$$
$$\sin x = \frac{\sin x}{\cos x}$$
$$\sin x \cdot \cos x = \sin x$$
$$\sin x \cdot \cos x - \sin x = 0$$
$$\sin x (\cos x - 1) = 0$$
$$\sin x = 0 \text{ or } \cos x = 1$$

$$x = 0°, 180°, 360°$$

6. First solve $\cos^2 x + \sin^2 x = 1$ for $\cos^2 x$.

$$\cos^2 x = 1 - \sin^2 x$$

Substitute into the given equation and solve the resulting equation that is in quadratic form.

$$6 \cos^2 x + \sin x - 5 = 0$$
$$6(1 - \sin^2 x) + \sin x - 5 = 0$$
$$6 - 6 \sin^2 x + \sin x - 5 = 0$$
$$-6 \sin^2 x + \sin x + 1 = 0$$
$$6 \sin^2 x - \sin x - 1 = 0$$
$$(3 \sin x + 1)(2 \sin x - 1) = 0$$
$$3 \sin x + 1 = 0 \text{ or } 2 \sin x - 1 = 0$$
$$\sin x = -\frac{1}{3} \text{ or } \sin x = \frac{1}{2}$$
$$x = \sin^{-1}\left(-\frac{1}{3}\right) \text{ or } x = \sin^{-1}\frac{1}{2}$$
$$x = 199.47°, 340.53° \text{ or } x = 30°, 150°$$

7. If $z = a + bi$, then $\bar{z} = a - bi$. To find the sum $z + \bar{z}$, use the Parallelogram Law from Chapter 3. The points $(0, 0)$, (a, b), and $(a, -b)$ are three vertices of a parallelogram. The fourth is $(2a, 0)$, which you can find by constructing a segment parallel and congruent to the one from $(0, 0)$ to (a, b), but starting at $(a, -b)$ or similarly, by constructing a segment parallel and congruent to the one from $(0, 0)$ to $(a, -b)$, but starting at (a, b). This means that $z + \bar{z} = 2a$. If the complex number $z = a + bi$ has argument θ, you know that $\cos \theta = \frac{a}{|z|}$. This means that $a = |z| \cdot \cos \theta$. Substitute this value for a into the expression you got for $z + \bar{z}$ to get $z + \bar{z} = 2|z| \cdot \cos \theta$.

8. First, drop an altitude from O to $\overline{AB}$ intersecting at point C. In right triangle, $\triangle OAC$, $\angle A = \frac{180° - 36°}{2} = 72°$ and $\cos 72° = \frac{\text{adjacent}}{\text{hypotenuse}} = \frac{CA}{1} = CA$ Since $\triangle BOA$ is isosceles, the altitude divided $\overline{AB}$ into two congruent segments. $AB = 2 \cdot CA = 2 \cdot \cos 72°$.

On Your Own

9. (a) $\cos x = -\frac{4}{5} \Rightarrow x = \cos^{-1}\left(-\frac{4}{5}\right) = 143.13°$ or $216.87°$

(b) $\sin x = \frac{4}{\sqrt{2}} \approx 2.83 \Rightarrow$ No solution; $\sin x$ cannot be greater than 1.

(c) $4 \cos^2 x = 1 \Rightarrow \cos x = \pm \frac{1}{2} \Rightarrow x = \cos^{-1}\left(\pm \frac{1}{2}\right) = 60°, 120°, 240°, 300°$

(d)

$$4 \cos^2 x = 4 \cos x + 3$$
$$4 \cos^2 x - 4 \cos x - 3 = 0$$
$$(2 \cos x + 1)(2 \cos x - 3) = 0$$
$$2 \cos x + 1 = 0 \text{ or } 2 \cos x - 3 = 0$$
$$\cos x = -\frac{1}{2} \text{ or } \cos x = \frac{3}{2}$$
$$x = \cos^{-1}\left(-\frac{1}{2}\right)$$
$$x = 120°, 240°$$

10. (a) $2\cos x + 1 = 0 \Rightarrow \cos x = -\frac{1}{2} \Rightarrow x = 120°, 240°$

(b) $\tan x - 1 = 0 \Rightarrow \tan x = 1 \Rightarrow x = 45°, 225°$

(c)

$$1 - 3\sin x + 2\sin^2 x = 0$$
$$(1 - 2\sin x)(1 - \sin x) = 0$$
$$1 - 2\sin x = 0 \text{ or } 1 - \sin x = 0$$
$$\sin x = \frac{1}{2} \text{ or } \sin x = 1$$
$$x = 30°, 90°, 150°$$

(d)

$$2\cos^2 x - 5\cos x = 2$$
$$2\cos^2 x - 5\cos x - 2 = 0$$

Use the quadratic formula:

$$\cos x = \frac{5 \pm \sqrt{41}}{4}$$
$$\cos x = -0.3508 \text{ or } \cos x = 2.8508$$
$$x = \cos^{-1}(-0.3508) = 110.54°, 249.47°$$

11.

$$2\sin^2 \alpha + 5\cos \alpha = 2$$
$$2(1 - \cos^2 \alpha) + 5\cos \alpha - 2 = 0$$
$$2 - 2\cos^2 \alpha + 5\cos \alpha - 2 = 0$$
$$-2\cos^2 \alpha + 5\cos \alpha = 0$$
$$\cos \alpha(-2\cos \alpha + 5) = 0$$
$$\cos \alpha = 0 \text{ or } \cos \alpha = \frac{5}{2}$$
$$\alpha = \cos^{-1} 0 = 90°, 270°$$

12. Remember $a = \cos \theta$ and $b = \sin \theta$.

(a) $\cos 20° + \sin 20° \cdot i \approx 0.940 + 0.342i$

(b) $\cos 330° + \sin 330° \cdot i = \frac{\sqrt{3}}{2} - \frac{1}{2}i$

(c) $\cos(-30°) + \sin(-30°) \cdot i = \frac{\sqrt{3}}{2} - \frac{1}{2}i$

(d) $\cos 100° + \sin 100° \cdot i \approx -0.174 + 0.985i$

(e) $\cos 227° + \sin 227° \cdot i \approx -0.682 - 0.731i$

(f) $\cos 75° + \sin 75° \cdot i \approx 0.259 + 0.966i$

13. Since these are all unit vectors, you can use $\cos^{-1} a$, where $z = a + bi$. In general, $\arg z$ is found from $\tan^{-1} \frac{b}{a}$.

(a) $\cos^{-1}\left(\frac{4}{5}\right) = 36.87°$

(b) $\cos^{-1}\left(\frac{3}{5}\right) = 53.13°$

(c) $\cos^{-1}\left(-\frac{3}{5}\right) = 126.87°$ but you want the angle in Quadrant III where the cosine and sine are both negative. $360° - 126.87° = 233.13°$

(d) $\cos^{-1}\left(-\frac{4}{5}\right) = 143.13°$

14.

$$2\sin^3 x - \sin^2 x - 2\sin x + 1 = 0$$
$$\sin^2 x(2\sin x - 1) - (2\sin x - 1) = 0$$
$$(2\sin x - 1)(\sin^2 x - 1) = 0$$
$$(2\sin x - 1)(\sin x - 1)(\sin x + 1) = 0$$
$$2\sin x - 1 = 0 \text{ or } \sin x - 1 = 0 \text{ or } \sin x + 1 = 0$$
$$\sin x = \frac{1}{2} \text{ or } \sin x = 1 \text{ or } \sin x = -1$$
$$x = \sin^{-1}\frac{1}{2} \text{ or } x = \sin^{-1} 1 \text{ or } x = \sin^{-1} -1$$
$$x = 30°, 90°, 150°, 270°$$

15. (a) $m\angle BOA = m\angle ABC = 36°$, and $\angle CAB$ is just another name for $\angle OAB$. This means that $\triangle OAB \sim \triangle BCA$ by AA Similarity test. Since $\triangle OAB$ is isosceles, so is $\triangle BCA$, and $BC = z$. Use the side ratios between the two similar triangles to find AC.

$$\frac{OB}{BA} = \frac{BA}{AC}$$
$$\frac{1}{z} = \frac{z}{AC}$$
$$AC = z^2$$

This means that $OC = 1 - z^2$. $\triangle OCB$ is isosceles because $m\angle COB = m\angle CBO = 36°$, so $1 - z^2 = z$.

(b) The equation $1 - z^2 = z$ is a quadratic equation. Use the quadratic formula to solve it.

$$1 - z^2 = z$$
$$0 = z^2 + z - 1$$
$$z = \frac{-1 \pm \sqrt{1^2 - 4(1)(-1)}}{2(1)}$$
$$z = \frac{-1 \pm \sqrt{5}}{2}$$

In this context, z is a length, so only the positive solution makes sense. $z = \frac{-1+\sqrt{5}}{2}$

(c) In Exercise 8, you showed that $z = 2\cos 72°$. This gives you $\cos 72° = \frac{z}{2} = \frac{-1+\sqrt{5}}{4}$.

(d) To find $\sin 72°$, use the Pythagorean Identity.

$$\sin^2 72° + \cos^2 72° = 1$$
$$\sin^2 72° = 1 - \cos^2 72°$$
$$\sin^2 72° = 1 - \left(\frac{-1+\sqrt{5}}{4}\right)^2$$
$$\sin^2 72° = 1 - \frac{6 - 2\sqrt{5}}{16}$$
$$\sin^2 72° = \frac{10 + 2\sqrt{5}}{16}$$
$$\sin 72° = \sqrt{\frac{5 + \sqrt{5}}{8}}$$

16.

$$5 \cos 2x + 6 = 9$$

$$\cos 2x = \frac{3}{5}$$

Now $\cos^{-1} \frac{3}{5} = 53.13°$, So

$$2x = 53.13° + 360°k \text{ or } 306.87° + 360°k$$

$$x = 26.57° + 180°k \text{ or } 153.44° + 180°k$$

$$x = 26.57°, 206.57°, 153.44°, 333.44°$$

17. The equation implies that $2 \tan x = 10$, $\tan x = 5$, $x = \tan^{-1} 5 \approx 78.69°$. The correct answer choice is **C**.

Maintain Your Skills

18. (a) $(1, 0)$

(b) The equation of line ℓ is $y = 2x - 1$. Substituting into $x^2 + y^2 = 1$ gives $x^2 + (2x - 1)^2 = 1 \Rightarrow x^2 + 4x^2 - 4x + 1 = 1 \Rightarrow 5x^2 - 4x = 0 \Rightarrow x(5x - 4) = 0$ $x = 0$ or $x = \frac{4}{5}$. The x value is $\frac{4}{5}$ and the y value is $2 \cdot \frac{4}{5} - 1 = \frac{8}{5} - 1 = \frac{3}{5}$. The point is

$$\left(\frac{4}{5}, \frac{3}{5}\right)$$

(c) The equation of line ℓ is $y = \frac{3}{2}x - 1$.

$$x^2 + \left(\frac{3}{2}x - 1\right)^2 = 1 \Rightarrow x^2 + \frac{9}{4}x^2 - 3x + 1 = 1$$

$$\Rightarrow \frac{13}{4}x^2 - 3x = 0 \Rightarrow x\left(\frac{13}{4}x - 3\right) = 0.$$

$x = 0$ or $x = \frac{12}{13}$ The x value is $\frac{12}{13}$ and the y value is $\frac{3}{2}\left(\frac{12}{13}\right) - 1 = \frac{5}{13}$.

$$\left(\frac{12}{13}, \frac{5}{13}\right)$$

(d) The equation of line ℓ is $y = 4x - 1$.

$$x^2 + (4x - 1)^2 = 1 \Rightarrow x^2 + 16x^2 - 8x + 1 = 1$$

$$\Rightarrow 17x^2 - 8x = 0 \Rightarrow x(17x - 8) = 0.$$

$x = 0$ or $x = \frac{8}{17}$ The x value is $\frac{8}{17}$ and the y value is $4\left(\frac{8}{17}\right) - 1 = \frac{15}{17}$.

$$\left(\frac{8}{17}, \frac{15}{17}\right)$$

(e) The equation of line ℓ is $y = \frac{6}{5}x - 1$.

$$x^2 + \left(\frac{6}{5}x - 1\right)^2 = 1 \Rightarrow x^2 + \frac{36}{25}x^2 - \frac{12}{5}x + 1 = 1$$

$$\Rightarrow \frac{61}{25}x^2 - \frac{12}{5}x = 0 \Rightarrow x\left(\frac{61}{25}x - \frac{12}{5}\right) = 0.$$

$x = 0$ or $x = \frac{60}{61}$ The x value is $\frac{60}{61}$ and the y value is $\frac{6}{5}\left(\frac{60}{61}\right) - 1 = \frac{11}{61}$.

$$\left(\frac{60}{61}, \frac{11}{61}\right)$$

(f) The equation of line ℓ is $y = \frac{r}{s}x - 1$.

$$x^2 + \left(\frac{r}{s}x - 1\right)^2 = 1 \Rightarrow x^2 + \frac{r^2}{s^2}x^2 - 2\frac{r}{s}x + 1 = 1$$

$$\Rightarrow \left(1 + \frac{r^2}{s^2}\right)x^2 - 2\frac{r}{s}x = 0 \Rightarrow x\left(\left(1 + \frac{r^2}{s^2}\right)x - \frac{2r}{s}\right) = 0$$

$x = 0$ or $x = \frac{\frac{2r}{s}}{1 + \frac{r^2}{s^2}} = \frac{2rs}{r^2 + s^2}$. The x value is $\frac{2rs}{r^2+s^2}$ and the y value is $\frac{r}{s}\left(\frac{2rs}{r^2+s^2}\right) - 1 = \frac{2r^2}{r^2+s^2} - 1 = \frac{2r^2}{r^2+s^2} - \frac{r^2+s^2}{r^2+s^2} = \frac{r^2-s^2}{r^2+s^2}$.

$$\left(\frac{2rs}{r^2 + s^2}, \frac{r^2 - s^2}{r^2 + s^2}\right)$$

8A   MATHEMATICAL REFLECTIONS

1. The intersection point in Quadrant I will have coordinates $(\cos 30°, \sin 30°)$ or $\left(\frac{\sqrt{3}}{2}, \frac{1}{2}\right)$. The intersection point in Quadrant III will have coordinates $(\cos 210°, \sin 210°)$ or $\left(-\frac{\sqrt{3}}{2}, -\frac{1}{2}\right)$.

2. When you draw each angle in standard position, you can see that each forms one of the special right triangles with the x-axis. You can use what you know about the sidelengths of those triangles as well as about the sign of coordinates in each quadrant to evaluate the trigonometric functions.

(a)

$$\sin 150° = \frac{1}{2}, \ \cos 150° = -\frac{\sqrt{3}}{2}, \ \tan 150° = -\frac{\sqrt{3}}{3}$$

(b)

$$\sin 315° = -\frac{\sqrt{2}}{2}, \ \cos 315° = \frac{\sqrt{2}}{2}, \ \tan 315° = -1$$

(c)

$$\sin 240° = -\frac{\sqrt{3}}{2}, \ \cos 240° = -\frac{1}{2}, \ \tan 240° = \sqrt{3}$$

3. $\sin^{-1}(-1) = -90°$, so any angle of the form $-90° + k \cdot 360°$, where k is an integer, will solve the equation.

4. (a) Sketch a right triangle with a side of length 12 opposite angle θ and hypotenuse 13. Use the Pythagorean Theorem to find the length of the other leg. $\sqrt{13^2 - 12^2} = \sqrt{25} = 5$. This tells you that $\cos \theta$ is $\frac{5}{13}$ for θ in Quadrant I. But sine is also positive in

Quadrant II, so for the angle in Quadrant II that has $\sin\theta = \frac{12}{13}$, $\cos\theta = -\frac{5}{13}$.

(b) In Quadrant I, $\tan\theta = \frac{\frac{12}{13}}{\frac{5}{13}} = \frac{12}{5}$. In Quadrant II, $\tan\theta = -\frac{12}{5}$.

(c) On your calculator, you can find $\sin^{-1}\theta \approx 67.4°$. The Quadrant II angle with the same sine is $180° - 67.4° \approx 112.6°$.

5. Multiply through by 10.

$$100\cos^2\alpha + 10\cos\alpha - 30 = 0$$

Substitute $z = 10\cos\alpha$ and factor.

$$z^2 + z - 30 = 0$$
$$(z+6)(z-5) = 0$$

Unsubstitute and divide through by 10.

$$(10\cos\alpha + 6)(10\cos\alpha - 5) = 0$$
$$2(5\cos\alpha + 3)5(2\cos\alpha - 1) = 0$$
$$(5\cos\alpha + 3)(2\cos\alpha - 1) = 0$$

Now you have $\cos\alpha = -\frac{3}{5}$, or $\frac{1}{2}$.

Cosine is negative in Quadrants II and III. The inverse cosine function on your calculator gives you the Quadrant II solution. $\cos^{-1}\left(-\frac{3}{5}\right) \approx 126.87°$. Since this is equal to $180° - 53.13°$, the Quadrant III solution will be $180° + 53.13° = 233.13°$.

Cosine is positive in Quadrants I and IV. The inverse cosine function on your calculator (or your memory of the special angle values for trigonometric functions) gives you the Quadrant I solution. $\cos^{-1}\left(\frac{1}{2}\right) = 60°$. The Quadrant IV solution will be $360° - 60° = 300°$.

6. Change the definitions of cosine and sine to be the x- and y-coordinates, respectively, of the point on the unit circle intersected by the left side of the angle when the angle is in standard position. Then you define tangent to be the sine divided by the cosine for the angle. (You can also think of tangent as the slope of the left side of the angle in standard position.)

This definition leaves all the values for the trigonometric functions of acute angles unchanged, and allows key properties of right-triangle trigonometry to continue to hold.

7. The trigonometric function values are tied to the coordinates of points in the same quadrant. The x-coordinates in Quadrant IV are positive, so the cosine is positive, because it is the x-coordinate of the intersection of the angle and the unit circle. The y-coordinates in Quadrant IV are negative, so the sine is negative, because it is the y-coordinate of the intersection of the angle and the unit circle. Finally, the tangent is the quotient of sine and cosine, so it is negative. When you divide a negative number by a positive number, the quotient is negative.

8. The equation of the unit circle is $x^2 + y^2 = 1$. By definition, the coordinates of the intersection between the left side of angle θ in standard position and the unit circle are $(\cos\theta, \sin\theta)$. These coordinates must satisfy the equation of the circle, so $\cos^2\theta + \sin^2\theta = 1$, which is the Pythagorean Identity.

INVESTIGATION 8B   GRAPHS OF TRIGONOMETRIC FUNCTIONS

8.6   Getting Started

For You to Explore

1. $\cos 30° = \frac{\sqrt{3}}{2}$, $\sin 30° = \frac{1}{2}$
2. $\cos 45° = \frac{\sqrt{2}}{2}$, $\sin 45° = \frac{\sqrt{2}}{2}$
3. (a) $\cos^2 30° = (\cos 30°)^2 = \left(\frac{\sqrt{3}}{2}\right)^2 = \frac{3}{4}$

   (b) $\sin^2 30° = (\sin 30°)^2 = \left(\frac{1}{2}\right)^2 = \frac{1}{4}$

   (c) $\cos^2 45° = (\cos 45°)^2 = \left(\frac{\sqrt{2}}{2}\right)^2 = \frac{2}{4} = \frac{1}{2}$

   (d) $\sin^2 45° = (\sin 45°)^2 = \left(\frac{\sqrt{2}}{2}\right)^2 = \frac{2}{4} = \frac{1}{2}$

   (e) $\cos^2 30° + \sin^2 30° = \frac{3}{4} + \frac{1}{4} = 1$

   (f) $\cos^2 45° + \sin^2 45° = \frac{1}{2} + \frac{1}{2} = 1$
4. $\cos 60° = \sin 30°$ and $\sin 60° = \cos 30°$
5. $\cos 150° = -\cos 30°$ and $\sin 150° = \sin 30°$

On Your Own

6.

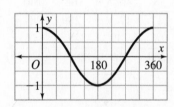

7. $\cos 230° > \cos 190°$ because the graph is increasing from $x = 190°$ to $x = 230°$.

8.

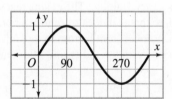

9. $\sin 230° < \sin 190°$ because the graph is decreasing from $x = 190°$ to $x = 230°$.

10. $\sin(180° + \theta) = -\sin\theta$

11.

$$\tan 190° < \tan 230°$$

$\tan\theta = \frac{\sin\theta}{\cos\theta}$. You know that $\cos\theta$ is increasing from $x = 190°$ to $x = 230°$ *and* $\cos\theta < 0$. So, $|\cos\theta|$ is decreasing. At the same time, the $|\sin\theta|$ is increasing. The fraction $\frac{\sin\theta}{\cos\theta}$ is increasing from $x = 190°$ to $x = 230°$ if the absolute value of the numerator is increasing and the absolute value of the denominator is decreasing.

You could also use the fact that $\tan\theta = \frac{\sin\theta}{\cos\theta}$ to realize that $\tan\theta$ is equal to the slope of a line passing through the point on the unit circle that corresponds to the angle θ and the origin. A quick sketch of the two lines for these two angles shows you which has the larger slope.

Maintain Your Skills

12. (a) magnitude $= \sqrt{3^2 + 2^2} = \sqrt{9+4} = \sqrt{13}$,
    direction $= \tan^{-1} \frac{2}{3} \approx 33.7°$

    (b)
    $$(3+2i)^2 = 9 + 12i + 4i^2 = 9 + 12i - 4 = 5 + 12i$$

    magnitude $= \sqrt{5^2 + 12^2} = \sqrt{25 + 144} = \sqrt{169} = 13$, direction $= \tan^{-1} \frac{12}{5} \approx 67.4°$

    (c) magnitude $= \sqrt{1^2 + 2^2} = \sqrt{1+4} = \sqrt{5}$,
    direction $= \tan^{-1} \frac{2}{1} \approx 63.4°$

    (d)
    $$(1+2i)^2 = 1 + 4i + 4i^2 = 1 + 4i - 4 = -3 + 4i$$

    magnitude $= \sqrt{(-3)^2 + 4^2} = \sqrt{9 + 16} = \sqrt{25} = 5$, direction $= 180° - \tan^{-1} \frac{4}{3} = 126.9°$

    (e) magnitude $= \sqrt{\left(-\frac{8}{17}\right)^2 + \left(\frac{15}{17}\right)^2} = \sqrt{\frac{64}{289} + \frac{225}{289}} = \sqrt{\frac{289}{289}} = 1$, direction $= 180° - \tan^{-1} \frac{15}{8} \approx 118.1°$

    (f)
    $$\left(-\frac{8}{17} + \frac{15}{17}i\right)^2 = \frac{64}{289} - \frac{240}{289}i + \frac{225}{289}i^2$$
    $$= \frac{64}{289} - \frac{240}{289}i - \frac{225}{289} = -\frac{161}{289} - \frac{240}{289}i$$

    magnitude $= \sqrt{\left(-\frac{161}{289}\right)^2 + \left(-\frac{240}{289}\right)^2} = \sqrt{\frac{25921}{83521} + \frac{57600}{83521}} = \sqrt{\frac{83521}{83521}} = 1$, direction $= 180° + \tan^{-1} \frac{240}{161} \approx 236.1°$

    (g) $5^2 = 25, 2 \cdot 100° = 200°$

13. Answers may vary. Sample: The cosine reads the same from bottom to top as it does from top to bottom. If you read the sine column from bottom to top, it is the negative of what you get from top to bottom. The same is true for tangent.

8.7 Graphing the Cosine and Sine Functions

Check Your Understanding

1. (a) $\sin(-50°) = -\sin 50°$
    You can see this relationship using the unit circle. $50°$ is a counterclockwise rotation, while $-50°$ is a clockwise rotation of the same magnitude. $50°$ is a Quadrant I angle that intersects the unit circle at a point $(\cos 50°, \sin 50°)$. $-50°$ is a Quadrant IV angle that intersects the unit circle at $(\cos(-50°), \sin(-50°))$. Use the symmetry of the unit circle to see that the cosines are equal and the sines are opposites.

(b) $\sin(-50°) = -\sin 50°$
    You can see this relationship by looking at the graph of $y = \sin x$. To find $\sin 50°$, look at an x-coordinate of $50°$ and see that the corresponding y-coordinate is approximately 0.8. To find $\sin(-50°)$, look at an x coordinate of -50. The corresponding y coordinate is approximately -0.8.

2. Derman is only looking at a small part of the domain, and all the y-values he sees are close to 0. (Try it!) In order to see a good picture of $y = \sin x$, he should include at least one full rotation around the unit circle. So, a better choice for the width of his window would be 0 to 360, or -360 to 360. You might also choose a smaller height for his window.

3.

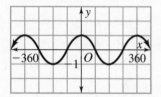

The graph looks *exactly* like the graph of $y = \cos x$ because angles that are 360° apart have the same coordinates on the unit circle. The graph of $g(x) = \sin(x + 360°)$ would also look just like the graph of $y = \sin x$.

4. (a) There are infinitely many x intercepts. The graph of $y = \cos x$ intersects the x axis at $\pm 90°$, $\pm 270°$, $\pm 450°, \ldots$

    (b) A polynomial function of degree n can't have more than n zeroes, so a polynomial match to this function would have to have infinite degree.

    (c) The tangent function is undefined whenever the cosine is 0 because $\tan x = \frac{\sin x}{\cos x}$ and division by 0 is undefined. Therefore, the tangent is undefined for $x = \pm 90°, \pm 270°, \pm 450°, \ldots$

5.

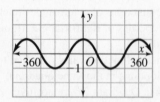

6.

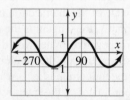

7. Using the symmetry of the graph, the next solution is 53° less than 180°, or 127°, and the one after that is 53° more than 360°, or 413°.

8.

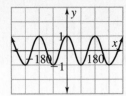

9. (a)

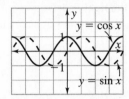

(b) 45° and 225° or any angle of the form $45° + k \cdot 180°$ for any integer k.

10. (a) $\tan 45° = \dfrac{\sin 45°}{\cos 45°} = \dfrac{\frac{\sqrt{2}}{2}}{\frac{\sqrt{2}}{2}} = 1$, $\tan 225° = \dfrac{\sin 225°}{\cos 225°} = $

$\dfrac{-\frac{\sqrt{2}}{2}}{-\frac{\sqrt{2}}{2}} = 1$

(b) Note that is $\cos \theta = 0$, then $\sin \theta = \pm 1$. Therefore, any solution of this equation will have $\cos \theta \neq 0$.

$$\sin \theta = \cos \theta$$
$$\frac{\sin \theta}{\cos \theta} = \frac{\cos \theta}{\cos \theta} \qquad \text{Divide both sides by } \cos \theta,$$
$$\tan \theta = 1$$

On Your Own

11.

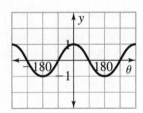

If you use the unit circle to see why $\cos(-\theta) = \cos \theta$, you should see that a rotation of x degrees counterclockwise and a rotation of x degrees clockwise will result in intersections with the unit circle that have the same x-coordinate (cosine) but y coordinates (sine) that are opposites. If you use the graph of $y = \cos x$, you can see that the graph is symmetric with respect to the y-axis. The points that are x units to the right of the y-axis and x units to the left will have the same y-coordinate.

12.

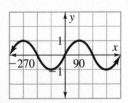

If you use the unit circle to see why $\sin(-\theta) = -\sin \theta$,

you should see that a rotation of x degrees counterclockwise and a rotation of x degrees clockwise will result in intersections with the unit circle that have the same x-coordinate (cosine) but y coordinates (sine) that are negatives of each other. If you use the graph of $y = \sin x$, you can see that the graph is symmetric with respect to the origin. x units to the right and x units to the left will have y-coordinates that are negatives of each other.

13.

14. The first choice does not even make sense, as it is a sum of degrees plus an ordinary number. No function could have $f(x) = -f(x)$, unless it was identically 0, so the second choice doesn't work. The last choice has values ranging from –2 to 2, so it doesn't work. The third choice is a horizontal translation of $\sin x$ by one full period, so it matches the original. The correct answer choice is **C**.

15. Using the symmetry of the graph, one solution will be $360° - 37° = 323°$, and the other will be $360° + 37° = 397°$.

16. (a)

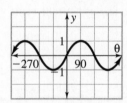

$\sin(180° - \theta) = \sin \theta$ You can see that the y-coordinates corresponding to these angles on the unit circle must be the same. On the graph of $y = \sin x$, the line $x = 90°$ is a line of symmetry for the graph, so since these two angles are an equal x-distance from that line of symmetry, they must produce the same y-value.

(b)

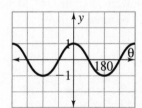

$\cos(180° - \theta) = -\cos \theta$ In the same picture of the unit circle as for the previous part, you can see that these two angles have x-coordinates on the unit circle that are opposite in sign. The graph of $y = \cos x$ is not symmetric about the line $x = 90°$, but a rotation by 180° of the graph around the point $(90°, 0)$ will map the graph onto itself. This means that these two values of cosine have opposite signs, but the same distance from the x-axis.

(c)

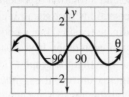

sin $(180° + \theta) = -\sin\theta$. In a similar argument, the y-coordinates corresponding to these angles on the unit circle have opposite sign but are the same distance from the x-axis. On the graph, if you look at angles that are 180° apart, they have opposite sign but the same distance from the x-axis.

(d)

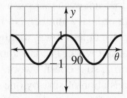

cos $(360° - \theta) = \cos\theta$. On the unit circle, the points corresponding to these angles are reflections of each other over the x-axis, so they have the same x-coordinate. On the graph of $y = \cos x$, you can see that these two angles have the same value for the function.

(e)

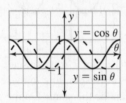

$\sin\theta = \cos(\theta - 90°)$ If you graph sine and cosine on the same set of axes, and look at an angle x on the sine graph, it will have the same value as the angle $x - 90°$ on the cosine graph. In other words, if the cosine graph were translated 90° to the right, its image would be the sine graph.

(f)

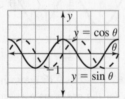

$\cos\theta = -\sin(\theta - 90)$ As in the previous part, on the graph of both functions, the value of the cosine graph at an angle x is the opposite as the value of sine at the angle $x - 90°$. If the sine graph were translated 90° to the right and then reflected over the x-axis, its image would be the same as the cosine graph.

17.

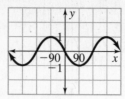

18. The graph of $h(x) = -\sin x$ is a translation of $g(x) = \sin x$ by 180° to the right *or* left.
19. The following three functions all have the same graph.
   (a) $j(x) = \cos^2 x - \sin^2 x$
   (b) $r(x) = \cos(2x)$
   (c) $k(x) = \cos^4 x - \sin^4 x$

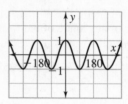

Maintain Your Skills

20. $A = (-360, 1)$, $B = (-180, -1)$, $C = (0, 1)$, $D = (90, 0)$, $E = (360, 1)$, $F = (540, -1)$
21. $G = (-270, 1)$, $H = (-90, -1)$, $I = (90, 1)$, $J = (180, 0)$, $K = (450, 1)$, $L = (630, -1)$

8.8 Graphing the Tangent Function

Check Your Understanding

1. (a) If you use the unit circle, adding 180° to x will bring you half way around the unit circle. The coordinates of the intersection with the unit circle will be the opposite of where you started. cos $(180° + x) = -\cos x$. If you use the graph of $y = \cos x$, cos $(180° + x)$ is a translation 180° to the left and the y-coordinates will be opposites.
   (b) If you use the unit circle, adding 180° to x will bring you half way around the unit circle. The coordinates of the intersection with the unit circle will be the opposite of where you started. sin $(180° + x) = -\sin x$. If you use the graph of $y = \sin x$, sin $(180° + x)$ is a translation 180° to the left and the y-coordinates will be opposites.

2. Since $\tan x = \frac{\sin x}{\cos x}$,

$$\tan(180° + x) = \frac{\sin(180° + x)}{\cos(180° + x)} = \frac{-\sin x}{-\cos x} = \frac{\sin x}{\cos x} = \tan x$$

3. (a)

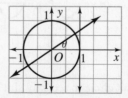

(b) The coordinates of the point where θ intersects the line tangent to the unit circle at $(1, 0)$ are $(1, \tan\theta) = (1, \frac{2}{3})$. If you consider the right triangle with legs 1 and $\frac{2}{3}$, the hypotenuse will be $\sqrt{1^2 + \left(\frac{2}{3}\right)^2} = \sqrt{1 + \frac{4}{9}} = \sqrt{\frac{13}{9}} = \frac{\sqrt{13}}{3}$. Then,

$$\sin\theta = \frac{\text{opposite}}{\text{hypotenuse}} = \frac{\frac{2}{3}}{\frac{\sqrt{13}}{3}} = \frac{2}{\sqrt{13}} = \frac{2\sqrt{13}}{13}$$

$$\cos\theta = \frac{\text{adjacent}}{\text{hypotenuse}} = \frac{1}{\frac{\sqrt{13}}{3}} = \frac{3}{\sqrt{13}} = \frac{3\sqrt{13}}{13}$$

4. (a) You can think of the graph of $y = \sin(90° + x)$ as a translation of 90 units to the left of the graph of $y = \sin x$ which is $y = \cos x$. So, $\sin(90° + x) = \cos x$. Similarly, $\cos(90° + x) = -\sin x$, and

$$\tan(90° + \theta) = \frac{\sin(90° + \theta)}{\cos(90° + \theta)} = \frac{\cos\theta}{-\sin\theta} = \frac{-1}{\frac{\sin\theta}{\cos\theta}}$$
$$= \frac{-1}{\tan\theta} = \frac{-1}{\frac{2}{3}} = -\frac{3}{2}$$

(b) First think of ℓ as a line through the origin. Then, you know that, unless it is vertical, it intersects the line tangent to the unit circle at $(1, 0)$ at the point $T(1, \tan\theta)$ where θ is the angle from the positive x-axis to ℓ, measured counter clockwise. You can find the slope of ℓ by finding the slope between the origin and T, and that slope is $\tan\theta$.

What if ℓ doesn't go through the origin? You can construct the unique line m parallel to ℓ through the origin and find its slope. ℓ and m form the same angle θ with the x-axis, because those angles are corresponding angles for the two parallel lines. They also have the same slope, because parallel lines have equal slope. So you can conclude that even if ℓ doesn't go through the origin, its slope is equal to $\tan\theta$, where θ is the angle if forms with the x-axis.

(c) First, realize that by using a similar argument to the one in the previous part, you can assume that your two lines intersect at the origin. If they don't, you can construct the unique parallels to your lines that *do* pass through the origin. Those two lines have the same slope as your original lines, so if *their* slopes are negative reciprocals, that's enough to prove the result for any pair of lines.

Start with two lines that are perpendicular to each other and intersect at the origin. As you measure the angle formed by each line from the positive x-axis, call the first line you hit ℓ and the angle it forms θ. Then the second line m has angle $90° + \theta$ with the positive x-axis. By the previous result, the slope of ℓ is $\tan\theta$, and the slope of m is $\tan(90° + \theta)$.

$$\tan(90° + \theta) = \frac{\sin(90° + \theta)}{\cos(90° + \theta)}$$
$$= \frac{\cos\theta}{-\sin\theta}$$
$$= \frac{\cos\theta}{-\sin\theta} \frac{\frac{1}{\cos\theta}}{\frac{1}{\cos\theta}}$$
$$= \frac{-1}{\frac{\sin\theta}{\cos\theta}}$$
$$= \frac{-1}{\tan\theta}$$

So the slope of m is the negative reciprocal of the slope of ℓ and perpendicular lines have negative reciprocal slope.

5. The cosine is 0 when $\theta = 90°$, $90° + 180° = 270°$, $270° + 180° = 450°$, $\ldots$ These are the odd multiples of $90°$.

6. (a) $\tan^{-1}\left(\frac{1}{4}\right) \approx 14°$
   (b) $(4 + i)^2 = 16 + 8i + i^2 = 16 + 8i + (-1) = 15 + 8i$. The argument is $\tan^{-1}\left(\frac{8}{15}\right) \approx 28°$. You also know that when you multiply two complex numbers, you add their arguments. $14° + 14° = 28°$
   (c) The argument will be in Quadrant II, so you must subtract from $180°$.

$$180° - \tan^{-1}\left(\frac{4}{1}\right) \approx 104°$$

   (d) You are multiplying, so add the arguments.

$$104° + 104° = 208°$$

7. (a) $\tan^{-1}\left(\frac{1}{4}\right) \approx 14°$
   (b) $\tan^{-1}\left(\frac{8}{15}\right) \approx 28°$
   (c) $180° - \tan^{-1}(4) \approx 104°$
   (d) $180° + \tan^{-1}\left(\frac{8}{15}\right) \approx 208°$
8. (a) $(x + yi)^2 = x^2 + 2xyi + y^2 \cdot i^2 = x^2 + 2xyi + y^2 \cdot -1 = (x^2 - y^2) + (2xy)i$
   (b) You add the arguments when you multiply two complex numbers. The complex number with argument θ and whose tangent is $\frac{y}{x}$ is $x + yi$. The argument of $(x + yi)^2 = (x^2 - y^2) + (2xy)i$ is 2θ. So, $\tan 2\theta = \frac{2xy}{x^2 - y^2}$.

On Your Own

9. Here are two possible explanations.

   (a) Since $\tan x = \frac{\sin x}{\cos x}$, the tangent will be negative if the sine and cosine have different signs, and positive if they have the same sign. Tangent is negative in Quadrant II because the sine is positive and the cosine is negative. Tangent is positive in Quadrant III because sine and cosine are *both* negative.
   (b) If θ is in Quadrant II, the line through the origin at angle θ will intersect the tangent drawn to the unit circle at $(1, 0)$ at the point $(1, \tan\theta)$ in Quadrant IV,

so tan θ must be negative. If θ is in Quadrant III, the line through the origin at angle θ will intersect the tangent line in Quadrant I, so tan θ is positive.

10. (a) The tangent is undefined whenever $\cos x = 0$. The domain will consist of all $\mathbb{R}$, except for those x where $\cos x = 0$. The domain for the tangent is: x is a real number and $x \neq 90° + 180° \cdot k$, where k is an integer.

    (b) As $\cos x$ gets closer to 0, tan x gets very large. The range of the tangent is all $\mathbb{R}$.

11. (a) Draw the horizontal line $y = 2$ and approximate the points of intersection. $x \approx 65° + 180° \cdot k$

    (b) Draw the horizontal line $y = -2$ and approximate the points of intersection. $x \approx 115° + 180° \cdot k$

12. Each "branch" of the graph repeats every 180°. If you take any x-value and add 180°, the y-values of the two points will be the same.

13.

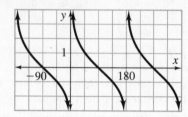

14. Substituting $A = B = \theta$ yields

$$\tan 2\theta = \frac{2\tan\theta}{1 - (\tan\theta)^2} = \frac{2 \cdot \frac{1}{2}}{1 - \left(\frac{1}{2}\right)^2} = \frac{1}{\frac{3}{4}} = \frac{4}{3}$$

The correct answer choice is **C**.

Maintain Your Skills

15. (a) $\sin(120° + 0°) = \sin 120° = \frac{\sqrt{3}}{2}$

    (b) $\sin(120° + 30°) = \sin 150° = \frac{1}{2}$

    (c) $\sin(120° + 60°) = \sin 180° = 0$

    (d) $\sin(120° + 90°) = \sin 210° = -\frac{1}{2}$

    (e) If $\sin(120° + 0°) = A\cos 0° + B\sin 0° = A \cdot 1 + B \cdot 0$, then $A = \sin 120° = \frac{\sqrt{3}}{2} = \sin 120°$. If $\sin(120° + 90°) = A\cos 90° + B\sin 90° = \frac{\sqrt{3}}{2} \cdot 0 + B \cdot 1$, then $B = \sin 210° = -\frac{1}{2} = \cos 120°$.

8.9 The Angle-Sum Identities

Check Your Understanding

1. (a)

$$\cos(a - b) = \cos(a + (-b))$$
$$= \cos a \cdot \cos(-b) - \sin a \cdot \sin(-b)$$
$$\text{(Use the identity for } \cos(\alpha + \beta).)$$
$$= \cos a \cdot \cos b - \sin a \cdot (-\sin b)$$
$$(\cos(-x) = \cos x, \sin(-x) = -\sin x)$$
$$= \cos a \cdot \cos b + \sin a \cdot \sin b$$

(b)

$$\cos(a - b) = \cos a \cos b + \sin a \sin b$$
$$\text{(the given identity)}$$
$$\cos(a - a) = \cos a \cos a + \sin a \sin a$$
$$\text{(Let } b = a)$$
$$\cos 0 = \cos^2 a + \sin^2 a$$
$$1 = \cos^2 a + \sin^2 a$$
$$\text{(the Pythagorean identity)}$$

(c)

$$\cos 15° = \cos(45° - 30°)$$
$$= \cos 45° \cos 30° + \sin 45° \sin 30°$$
$$= \frac{\sqrt{2}}{2} \cdot \frac{\sqrt{3}}{2} + \frac{\sqrt{2}}{2} \cdot \frac{1}{2}$$
$$= \frac{\sqrt{6}}{4} + \frac{\sqrt{2}}{4}$$
$$= \frac{\sqrt{6} + \sqrt{2}}{4}$$

2. (a)

$$\cos 2x = \cos(x + x)$$
$$= \cos x \cos x - \sin x \sin x$$
$$= \cos^2 x - \sin^2 x$$

(b)

$$\sin 2x = \sin(x + x)$$
$$= \sin x \cos x + \cos x \sin x$$
$$= \sin x \cos x + \sin x \cos x$$
$$= 2 \sin x \cos x$$

(c)

$$\cos 2x = \cos^2 x - \sin^2 x$$
$$= \cos^2 x - (1 - \cos^2 x)$$
$$= \cos^2 x - 1 + \cos^2 x$$
$$= 2\cos^2 x - 1$$

3. (a) Remember that you only want to consider positive solutions for z, because $z = \cos 15°$.

$$\frac{\sqrt{3}}{2} = 2z^2 - 1$$

Add 1 to each side.

$$\frac{2 + \sqrt{3}}{2} = 2z^2$$

Divide each side by 2.

$$\frac{2 + \sqrt{3}}{4} = z^2$$

Take the square root of each side.

$$\frac{\sqrt{2 + \sqrt{3}}}{2} = z$$

(b) Again, since you know that both sides are positive to begin with, if their squares are equal, the two original numbers were equal. (Otherwise you'd have to consider that they might be negatives of each other.)

$$\frac{\sqrt{2+\sqrt{3}}}{2} \stackrel{?}{=} \frac{\sqrt{6}+\sqrt{2}}{4}$$

$$2(\sqrt{2+\sqrt{3}}) \stackrel{?}{=} \sqrt{6}+\sqrt{2}$$

$$4(2+\sqrt{3}) \stackrel{?}{=} 6+2\sqrt{12}+2$$

$$8+4\sqrt{3} \stackrel{?}{=} 8+2\sqrt{12}$$

$$8+4\sqrt{3} = 8+4\sqrt{3}$$

4. (a)

$$\cos 3x = \cos(2x+x)$$
$$= \cos 2x \cos x - \sin 2x \sin x$$
$$= (\cos^2 x - \sin^2 x)\cos x - (2\sin x \cos x)\sin x$$
$$= \cos^3 x - \sin^2 x \cos x - 2\sin^2 x \cos x$$
$$= \cos^3 x - 3\sin^2 x \cos x$$

(b)

$$\sin 3x = \sin(2x+x)$$
$$= \sin 2x \cos x + \cos 2x \sin x$$
$$= (2\sin x \cos x)\cos x + (\cos^2 x - \sin^2 x)\sin x$$
$$= 2\sin x \cos^2 x + \sin x \cos^2 x - \sin^3 x$$
$$= 3\sin x \cos^2 x - \sin^3 x$$

5. Remember that when you multiply two complex numbers, you multiply their magnitudes and add their arguments. Since $z^2 = z \cdot z$, the magnitude of z^2 will be the magnitude of z squared. The magnitude of z is $\sqrt{1} = 1$. The argument of z^2 will be $\arg(z) + \arg(z) = 2\arg(z)$. The $\arg(z^2) = 60° = 2\arg(z)$. Therefore, $\arg(z) = 30°$ and z is on the unit circle. $z = \cos 30° + i \sin 30° = \frac{\sqrt{3}}{2} + \frac{1}{2}i$

6. (a) $\sin 10° = 0.1736$, $\sin 50° = 0.7660$, $\sin 70° = 0.9397$ $0.1736 + 0.7660 = 0.9396 \approx 0.9397$

(b) $\sin 20° = 0.3420$, $\sin 40° = 0.6428$, $0.3420 + 0.6428 = 0.9848$, $x = \sin^{-1} 0.9848 = 80°$

(c) $x = \sin^{-1}(\sin 5° + \sin 55°) = 65°$

7. In each case, the sum of the two angles on the left side of the equation is $60°$. That means that you can find a number B so that the first angle is $30° - B$ and the second is $30° + B$, and you might even be able to see that the last angle is $90° - B$.

You're looking for an identity of the form $\sin(A+B) + \sin(A-B)$ equals something, so start there and use the angle-sum identities.

$$\sin(A+B) + \sin(A-B)$$
$$= \sin A \cos B + \cos A \sin B + \sin A \cos B - \sin A \cos B$$
$$= 2\sin A \cos B$$

In this specific case, $A = 30°$, so the expression on the right becomes $2\left(\frac{1}{2}\right)\cos B$ or $\cos B$, which is equal to $\sin(90° - B)$.

Another way to approach this exercise is to show that

$$\sin x + \sin(60° - x) = \sin(60° + x)$$

$$\sin x + \sin(60° - x) \stackrel{?}{=} \sin(60° + x)$$

$$\sin x + \sin 60° \cos x - \cos 60° \sin x \stackrel{?}{=} \sin 60° \cos x + \cos 60° \sin x$$

$$\sin x + \frac{\sqrt{3}}{2}\cos x - \frac{1}{2}\sin x \stackrel{?}{=} \frac{\sqrt{3}}{2}\cos x + \frac{1}{2}\sin x$$

$$\frac{\sqrt{3}}{2}\cos x + \frac{1}{2}\sin x = \frac{\sqrt{3}}{2}\cos x + \frac{1}{2}\sin x$$

On Your Own

8. $\cos(90° - \theta) = \cos 90° \cos\theta + \sin 90° \sin\theta = 0 \cdot \cos\theta + 1 \cdot \sin\theta = \sin\theta$. The correct answer choice is **C**.

9. $\sin(\alpha - \beta) = \sin(\alpha + (-\beta)) = \sin\alpha\cos(-\beta) + \cos\alpha\sin(-\beta) = \sin\alpha\cos\beta + \cos\alpha\cdot(-\sin\beta) = \sin\alpha\cos\beta - \cos\alpha\sin\beta$

10.

$$\cos(180° + \theta) = \cos 180° \cos\theta - \sin 180° \sin\theta$$
$$= -1\cdot\cos\theta - 0\cdot\sin\theta = -\cos\theta$$
$$\sin(180° + \theta) = \sin 180° \cos\theta + \cos 180° \sin\theta$$
$$= 0\cdot\cos\theta + (-1)\cdot\sin\theta = -\sin\theta$$

11. (a) $\sin(360° + x) = \sin 360° \cos x + \cos 360° \sin x = 0\cdot\cos x + 1\cdot\sin x = \sin x$

(b) $\sin(90° + x) = \sin 90° \cos x + \cos 90° \sin x = 1\cdot\cos x + 0\cdot\sin x = \cos x$

(c) $\cos(90° + x) = \cos 90° \cos x - \sin 90° \sin x = 0\cdot\cos x - 1\cdot\sin x = -\sin x$

(d) $\sin(90° - x) = \sin 90° \cos x - \cos 90° \sin x = 1\cdot\cos x - 0\cdot\sin x = \cos x$

(e) $\sin(180° - x) = \sin 180° \cos x - \cos 180° \sin x = 0\cdot\cos x - (-1)\cdot\sin x = \sin x$

12.

A	Correct choice from B
$x \mapsto 2^x$	$f(a+b) = f(a)\,f(b)$ because $2^{a+b} = 2^a \cdot 2^b$
$z \mapsto |z|$	$f(ab) = f(a)\,f(b)$ because $|ab| = |a|\cdot|b|$
$z \mapsto \arg z$	$f(ab) = f(a) + f(b)$ because $\arg(ab) = \arg a + \arg b$
$x \mapsto 2x$	$f(a+b) = f(a) + f(b)$ because $2(a+b) = 2a + 2b$
$x \mapsto \log_3(x)$	$f(ab) = f(a) + f(b)$ because $\log_3(ab) = \log_3(a) + \log_3(b)$

13.

$$\tan(45° + x) = \frac{\sin(45° + x)}{\cos(45° + x)}$$
$$= \frac{\sin 45° \cos x + \cos 45° \sin x}{\cos 45° \cos x - \sin 45° \sin x}$$
$$= \frac{\frac{\sqrt{2}}{2}\cos x + \frac{\sqrt{2}}{2}\sin x}{\frac{\sqrt{2}}{2}\cos x - \frac{\sqrt{2}}{2}\sin x}$$
$$= \frac{\frac{\sqrt{2}}{2}(\cos x + \sin x)}{\frac{\sqrt{2}}{2}(\cos x - \sin x)}$$
$$= \frac{\cos x + \sin x}{\cos x - \sin x}$$

14. When you first use the angle-sum identities, you'll get an expression involving $\sin x$, $\sin y$, $\cos x$, and $\cos y$ all mixed together. You can't factor it or cancel anything out. But, since your goal is to write this in terms of $\tan x$ and $\tan y$, you might think of dividing the top and bottom of the fraction by $\cos x \cos y$. This will cause some cosines to cancel out and others to combine with sines to make tangents.

$$\tan(x + y) = \frac{\sin(x + y)}{\cos(x + y)}$$
$$= \frac{\sin x \cos y + \cos x \sin y}{\cos x \cos y - \sin x \sin y}$$

Now divide the numerator and denominator by $\cos x \cos y$.

$$\tan(x + y) = \frac{\frac{\sin x \cos y}{\cos x \cos y} + \frac{\cos x \sin y}{\cos x \cos y}}{\frac{\cos x \cos y}{\cos x \cos y} - \frac{\sin x \sin y}{\cos x \cos y}}$$
$$= \frac{\tan x + \tan y}{1 - \tan x \tan y}$$

15. Answers will vary depending on the proof that students chose. The following shows the derivation with the complex numbers.

Choose $z = \cos \alpha + i \cdot \sin \alpha$, so that it has magnitude 1 and argument α. Choose $w = \cos(-\beta) + i \cdot \sin(-\beta) = \cos \beta - i \sin \beta$, so that it also has magnitude 1, but argument is $-\beta$. Then the product zw will have magnitude 1 and argument $\alpha - \beta$ and will be of the form $zw = \cos(\alpha - \beta) + i \cdot \sin(\alpha - \beta)$.

$$zw = (\cos \alpha + i \cdot \sin \alpha)(\cos \beta - i \sin \beta)$$
$$= \cos \alpha \cos \beta - i \cos \alpha \sin \beta + i \sin \alpha \cos \beta + \sin \alpha \sin \beta$$
$$= (\cos \alpha \cos \beta + \sin \alpha \sin \beta) + i(\sin \alpha \cos \beta - \cos \alpha \sin \beta)$$

This gives you the expected result.

$$\cos(\alpha - \beta) = \cos \alpha \cos \beta + \sin \alpha \sin \beta$$
$$\sin(\alpha - \beta) = \sin \alpha \cos \beta - \cos \alpha \sin \beta$$

16. From the identity $\cos 2A = \cos^2 A - \sin^2 A$, it follows that

$$\frac{1}{\cos^2 A - \sin^2 A} = \frac{1}{\cos 2A} = \frac{1}{\frac{5}{8}} = \frac{8}{5}$$

The correct answer choice is **C**.

Maintain Your Skills

17. (a)

$$\sin(30° + \theta) = \sin 30° \cos \theta + \cos 30° \sin \theta$$
$$= \frac{1}{2} \cos \theta + \frac{\sqrt{3}}{2} \sin \theta$$

(b)

$$\sin(45° + \theta) = \sin 45° \cos \theta + \cos 45° \sin \theta$$
$$= \frac{\sqrt{2}}{2} \cos \theta + \frac{\sqrt{2}}{2} \sin \theta$$

(c)

$$\sin(60° + \theta) = \sin 60° \cos \theta + \cos 60° \sin \theta$$
$$= \frac{\sqrt{3}}{2} \cos \theta + \frac{1}{2} \sin \theta$$

(d)

$$\sin(120° + \theta) = \sin 120° \cos \theta + \cos 120° \sin \theta$$
$$= \frac{\sqrt{3}}{2} \cos \theta + \left(-\frac{1}{2}\right) \sin \theta$$

(e)

$$\sin(150° + \theta) = \sin 150° \cos \theta + \cos 150° \sin \theta$$
$$= \frac{1}{2} \cos \theta + \left(-\frac{\sqrt{3}}{2}\right) \sin \theta$$

8B   MATHEMATICAL REFLECTIONS

1.

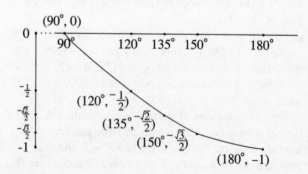

2. To decide whether the value of sine is positive or negative, increasing or decreasing, you can either look at the y-coordinates of points on the unit circle as the angle turns through the given interval or you can look at a graph of $y = \sin x$ and see how its y-coordinates behave as you move from left to right through the interval.

(a) $\sin x > 0$, increasing
(b) $\sin x > 0$, decreasing
(c) $\sin x < 0$, decreasing
(d) $\sin x < 0$, increasing

3.

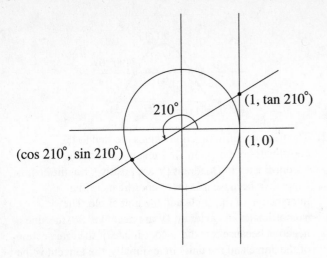

4.

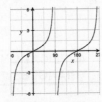

5. You can simplify these expressions either by using the angle-sum identities from Lesson 8.9 or by looking at the unit circle or the graphs of $y = \sin x$ and $y = \cos x$.

(a)

$$\sin (270° - x) = \sin 270° \cos (-x) + \cos 270° \sin (-x)$$
$$= (-1)(\cos x) + (0)(- \sin x)$$
$$= - \cos x$$

(b)

$$\cos (180° - x) = \cos 180° \cos (-x) - \sin 180° \sin (-x)$$
$$= (-1)(\cos x) - (0)(- \sin x)$$
$$= - \cos x$$

6. Answers will vary. The graph of sine looks like a sequence of hills and valleys, with height one and depth one, respectively. Every increase of x by 360° brings a repeat of the pattern (the graph is periodic). The graph of cosine looks exactly like the graph of sine, just shifted 90° to the left.

7. The tangent function is equal to the slope of the line passing through the origin and the point P on the unit circle with coordinates $(\cos \theta, \sin \theta)$. The ray $\overrightarrow{OP}$ forms an angle θ measured counterclockwise from the positive x-axis. However, there's another point Q with coordinates $(- \cos \theta, - \sin \theta)$ that's also on this line. The ray $\overrightarrow{OQ}$ forms an angle $\theta + 180°$ measured counterclockwise from the positive x-axis. The slopes for θ and $180° + \theta$

(and thus the tangents for these angles) must be the same, because they are the slopes of the same line.

8.

$$\cos(90° + \theta) = \cos 90° \cos \theta - \sin 90° \sin \theta$$
$$= (0)(\cos \theta) - (1)(\sin \theta)$$
$$= - \sin \theta$$

You could also use the unit circle to show this result.

MID-CHAPTER TEST

1. The only ordered pair that satisfies $x^2 + y^2 = 1$ is choice **C**, $\left(\frac{3}{5}, -\frac{4}{5}\right)$.

$$\left(\frac{3}{5}\right)^2 + \left(-\frac{4}{5}\right)^2 = \frac{9}{25} + \frac{16}{25} = \frac{25}{25} = 1$$

2. The $\cos 180° = -1$, not 0. So, the correct choice is **B**.

3. Since $260° = 180° + 80°$, the $\sin 260° = - \sin 80°$. You use the symmetry of the unit circle and recognize that $260°$ is in Quadrant III, so the sine is negative. The correct answer choice is **A**.

4. This is an example of the Pythagorean Identity: $\cos^2 \theta + \sin^2 \theta = 1$. The correct choice is **D**.

5. Sketch a graph of $y = \cos x$ and $y = -0.4$, where $-90° \le x \le 180°$ and $-2 \le y \le 2$. There will be only one point of intersection.

Or, recognize that the cosine is positive in Quadrants IV and I, when $-90° < x < 90°$. The cosine is negative in Quadrant II, when $90° < x < 180°$. So, the only time that the $\cos x = -0.4$ on the given domain is when x is in Quadrant II.

The correct choice is **B**, 1.

6. (a) $\sin 145° = \sin(180° - 35°) = \sin 35°$ (The sine is positive in Quadrant II.)
(b) $\cos 260° = \cos(180° + 80°) = - \cos 80°$. (The cosine is negative in Quadrant III.)
(c) $\cos 740° = \cos(360° + 360° + 20°) = \cos 20°$. (The cosine is positive in Quadrant I.)
(d) $\sin(-78)° = - \sin 78°$. (The sine is negative in Quadrant IV.)

7. In each case, draw a picture to show where α is in relation to the angle for which you are finding the function value. Or, use the angle-sum identities:

(a) $\sin (180° + \alpha) = \sin 180° \cdot \cos \alpha + \cos 180° \cdot \sin \alpha = 0 \cdot \cos \alpha + (-1) \cdot \sin \alpha = - \sin \alpha$
(b) $\cos (360° - \alpha) = \cos 360° \cdot \cos \alpha + \sin 360° \cdot \sin \alpha = 1 \cdot \cos \alpha + 0 \cdot \sin \alpha = \cos \alpha$

8. (a) Use the Pythagorean identity:

$$\cos^2\theta + \sin^2\theta = 1$$

$$\left(\frac{3}{5}\right)^2 + \sin^2\theta = 1$$

$$\frac{9}{25} + \sin^2\theta = 1$$

$$\sin^2\theta = 1 - \frac{9}{25}$$

$$\sin^2\theta = \frac{16}{25}$$

$$\sin\theta = \pm\sqrt{\frac{16}{25}}$$

$$= \pm\frac{4}{5}$$

θ could be in Quadrant I or Quadrant IV because the cosine is positive there. The sine is positive in Quadrant I and negative in Quadrant IV. So, $\sin\theta = \pm\frac{4}{5}$.

(b) $\tan\theta = \frac{\sin\theta}{\cos\theta} = \frac{\frac{4}{5}}{\frac{3}{5}} = \frac{4}{3}$ if θ is in the first quadrant.

$\tan\theta = \frac{-\frac{4}{5}}{\frac{3}{5}} = -\frac{4}{3}$ if θ is in the fourth quadrant. So, $\tan\theta = \pm\frac{4}{3}$.

(c) $\cos^{-1}\frac{3}{5} \approx 53.1°$ So, $\theta \approx 53.1°$ if θ is in Quadrant I. $\theta = 360° - 53.1° = 306.9°$ if θ is in Quadrant IV.

9. (a)

$$2\cos x - 1 = 0$$

$$2\cos x = 1$$

$$\cos x = \frac{1}{2}$$

$$x = 60° \text{ or } x = 300°$$

(b)

$$2\cos^2 x - 1 = 0$$

$$2\cos^2 x = 1$$

$$\cos^2 x = \frac{1}{2}$$

$$\cos x = \pm\sqrt{\frac{1}{2}}$$

$$\cos x = \pm\frac{\sqrt{2}}{2}$$

$$x = 45° \text{ or } x = 135° \text{ or } x = 225° \text{ or } x = 315°$$

(c)

$$2\sin^2 x - 3\sin x = 5$$

$$2\sin^2 x - 3\sin x - 5 = 0$$

$$(\sin x + 1)(2\sin x - 5) = 0$$

$$\sin x = -1 \text{ or } \sin x = \frac{5}{2}$$

Since the $\sin x$ cannot be greater than 1, $\sin x \neq \frac{5}{2}$. So, $\sin x = -1$ and $x = 270°$.

10. Some possible points are highlighted:

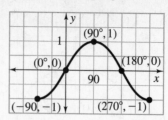

11. The trigonometric function values are tied to the coordinates of points in the same quadrant. The x-coordinates in Quadrant IV are positive. So, the cosine is positive because it is the x-coordinate of the intersection of the angle and the unit circle. The y-coordinates in Quadrant IV are negative. So, the sine is negative because it is the y-coordinate of the intersection of the angle and the unit circle. Finally, the tangent is the quotient of sine and cosine. So, it is negative because a negative number divided by a positive number is a negative number.

INVESTIGATION 8C APPLICATIONS TO TRIANGLES

8.10 Getting Started

For You to Explore

1. In order to find the area, you need to know the height of the triangle. You can draw an altitude from any of the three vertices to the opposite side. For example, you could drop an altitude from point B to $\overline{CA}$. Call the foot of the perpendicular D. To find the length of $\overline{BD}$, use $\sin 41° = \frac{BD}{6}$, $BD = 6 \cdot \sin 41° \approx 6 \cdot 0.6561 = 3.9366 \approx 3.9$. Since area $= \frac{1}{2} \cdot$ base $\cdot$ height, area $= \frac{1}{2} \cdot 5 \cdot 3.9 = 9.75$.

2. (a)

$$\sin 50° = \frac{BH}{12}$$

$$BH = 12 \cdot \sin 50° = 12 \cdot 0.7660\cdots \approx 9.19$$

(b)

$$\text{area} = \frac{1}{2}(10)(9.19) = 45.95$$

(c)

$$\cos 50° = \frac{CH}{12}$$

$$CH = 12 \cdot \cos 50° \approx 12(0.6428) \approx 7.71$$

$$HA = 10 - CH = 2.29$$

$$AB^2 = HA^2 + HB^2 = 2.29^2 + 9.19^2 = 89.7002$$

$$AB = \sqrt{89.7002} \approx 9.47$$

3. (a)

$$\angle HZY = 180° - 100° = 80°$$

$$\sin 80° = \frac{YH}{12}$$

$$YH = 12 \sin 80° \approx 12(0.9848) \approx 11.82$$

(b)

$$\text{area} = \frac{1}{2}(10)(11.82) = 59.1$$

(c)

$$\cos 80° = \frac{HZ}{12}$$

$$HZ = 12 \cos 80° \approx 12(0.1736) \approx 2.08$$

$$HX = 10 + HZ = 10 + 2.08 = 12.08$$

$$XY^2 = HY^2 + HX^2 = 11.82^2 + 12.08^2 = 285.639$$

$$XY = \sqrt{285.639} \approx 16.9$$

4. (a)

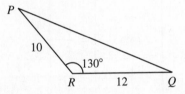

(b) $\triangle PQR$ has the greater perimeter. Two sides of $\triangle PQR$ are equal in length to two sides of $\triangle XYZ$. The third side of $\triangle PQR$ is longer than the third side of $\triangle XYZ$ because the angle between the congruent sides is greater. $130° > 100° \implies PQ > XY \implies$ perimeter of $\triangle PQR >$ perimeter of $\triangle XYZ$

(c) $\triangle XYZ$ has the greater area. If you consider either the side of length 10 or the side of length 12 as the base, the height to that base is smaller with a 130° angle than with a 100° angle, so $\triangle PQR$ has a smaller area.

5. (a) True, because the larger side has the effect of pushing the sides of the angle farther apart and increasing its measure.

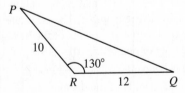

(b) True, because as the angle between the two known sides opens up, the endpoints of the third side of the triangle become farther apart.

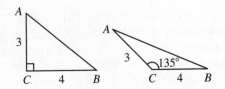

(c) False, because the height relative to $\overline{BC}$ can decrease as angle C increases.

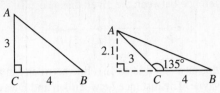

(d) The triangle on the left can be split into two 3-4-5 right triangles. It has area $\frac{1}{2} \cdot 8 \cdot 3 = 12$. The height of the second triangle (using the Pythagorean Theorem) is $\sqrt{7^2 - 2^2} = \sqrt{45} = 3\sqrt{5}$. Its area is $\frac{1}{2} \cdot 4 \cdot 3\sqrt{5} = 6\sqrt{5} \neq 12$, because $\sqrt{5} \neq 2$.

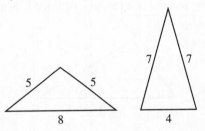

6. No. Take, for example, one triangle with sides 29, 29, and 40 and another triangle with sides 37, 37, and 24. The triangles are not congruent but have the same perimeter, $P_1 = 29 + 29 + 40 = 98$ and $P_2 = 37 + 37 + 24 = 98$. To verify that they have the same area, drop an altitude from the vertex of each isosceles triangle which will be perpendicular to the base. In the first triangle, use the Pythagorean Theorem to find the height:

$$h_1^2 = 29^2 - 20^2 = 441$$

$$h_1 = \sqrt{441} = 21$$

Do the same thing in the second triangle:

$$h_2^2 = 37^2 - 12^2 = 1225$$

$$h_2 = \sqrt{1225} = 35$$

The area of the first triangle is

$$A_1 = \frac{1}{2}(40)(21) = 420$$

The area of the second triangle is

$$A_2 = \frac{1}{2}(24)(35) = 420$$

Since $P_1 = P_2$ and $A_1 = A_2$, but the two triangles are *not* congruent, you can say that two triangles with the same area and perimeter are not necessarily congruent.

On Your Own

7. $\theta = 50°$ or $\theta = 130°$. Since $\sin 50° > 0$, θ must be in Quadrant I or II.

8. $\theta = 50°$ or $\theta = 310°$. Since $\cos 50° > 0$, θ must be in Quadrant I or IV.

9. Since $70°$ is in Quadrant I, and $110°$ is in Quadrant II, and they both make an angle of $70°$ with the x-axis, their sin, cos, and tan will have the same absolute value. Only the sine will have the same sign (positive). The answer is **B**.

10. (a) In this case, Jan, lives on a line between Dwayne and Paul. The distance between Jan and Dwayne is the difference between the given distances: $8 - 5 = 3$.

(b) In this case, Paul lives on a line between Jan and Dwayne. The distance between Jan and Dwayne is the sum of the given distances: $8 + 5 = 13$.

(c) Yes, it is possible. In this case, the three houses would be the vertices of a triangle with side 8, 5, and 10.

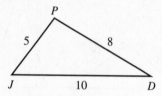

11. (a) $\triangle BHI$ is a 30-60-90 triangle.

$$BI = 2 \cdot 1 = 2$$
$$BH = (\sqrt{3}) \cdot 1 = \sqrt{3}$$

$\triangle GHI$ is a 45-45-90 triangle.

$$HG = 1$$
$$IG = (\sqrt{2}) \cdot 1 = \sqrt{2}$$
$$BG = BH + HG = \sqrt{3} + 1$$

(b) area
$$(\triangle BIG) = \tfrac{1}{2}(BG)(HI) = \tfrac{1}{2}(\sqrt{3} + 1) \cdot 1 = \tfrac{\sqrt{3}+1}{2}$$

12. Draw an altitude from B to $\overline{AC}$ intersecting $\overline{AC}$ at point D. In right $\triangle BDC$, $\sin C = \frac{BD}{a} \implies BD = a \sin C$ So, area $(\triangle ABC) = \tfrac{1}{2}(CA)(BD) = \tfrac{1}{2}(b)(a \sin C) = \tfrac{1}{2}ab \sin C$. By dropping an altitude from the other vertices, you can show that area $= \tfrac{1}{2}bc \sin A$, and area $= \tfrac{1}{2}ac \sin B$

Maintain Your Skills

13. Remember that the sum of any two side lengths of a triangle must be greater than the length of the third side.

(a) $8 + 6 > 10, 8 + 10 > 6, 10 + 6 > 8 \rightarrow$ Yes, a triangle
(b) $8 + 6 > 12, 8 + 12 > 6, 12 + 6 > 8 \rightarrow$ Yes, a triangle
(c) $8 + 6 = 14 \rightarrow$ No, not a triangle
(d) $8 + 6 < 16 \rightarrow$ No, not a triangle
(e) $8 + 6 > 9, 8 + 9 > 6, 9 + 6 > 8 \rightarrow$ Yes, a triangle
(f) $8 + 6 > 5, 8 + 5 > 6, 5 + 6 > 8 \rightarrow$ Yes, a triangle
(g) $8 + 6 > 3, 8 + 3 > 6, 3 + 6 > 8 \rightarrow$ Yes, a triangle
(h) $2 + 6 = 8 \rightarrow$ No, not a triangle
(i) $1 + 6 < 8 \rightarrow$ No, not a triangle

8.11 The Area of a Triangle

Check Your Understanding

1. Possible answers are

$$\frac{1}{2}(8)(5) \sin 60° = 20 \cdot \frac{\sqrt{3}}{2} = 10\sqrt{3} \approx 17.3$$
$$\frac{1}{2}(5)(7) \sin 82° = \frac{35}{2} \sin 82° \approx 17.3$$
$$\frac{1}{2}(8)(7) \sin 38° = 28 \sin 38° \approx 17.2$$

2. (a) base $= \sqrt{3} + 1$ and height $= 1$. The area of
$\triangle BIG = \tfrac{1}{2}(\sqrt{3} + 1)(1) = \tfrac{\sqrt{3}+1}{2}$
(b) $a = 2$ and $b = \sqrt{2}$.

$$A = \frac{1}{2}(2)(\sqrt{2}) \sin 105° = \sqrt{2} \sin 105°$$

(c)

$$\sqrt{2} \sin 105° = \frac{\sqrt{3} + 1}{2}$$
$$\frac{1}{\sqrt{2}} \cdot \sqrt{2} \sin 105° = \frac{1}{\sqrt{2}} \cdot \frac{\sqrt{3} + 1}{2}$$
$$\sin 105° = \frac{\sqrt{3} + 1}{2\sqrt{2}}$$
$$= \frac{\sqrt{3} + 1}{2\sqrt{2}} \cdot \frac{\sqrt{2}}{\sqrt{2}}$$
$$= \frac{\sqrt{6} + \sqrt{2}}{4}$$

3. Each central angle is $\frac{360}{5} = 72°$. You can find the area of each of the five congruent triangles: A (one triangle) $= \tfrac{1}{2}(1)(1) \sin 72° = \tfrac{1}{2} \sin 72°$. The area of the pentagon will be A(pentagon) $= 5(\cdot \tfrac{1}{2} \sin 72°) = \tfrac{5}{2} \sin 72° \approx 2.3776$.

4. Divide the hexagon into six congruent triangles. Each central angle is $\frac{360}{6} = 60°$, and each triangle is equilateral with each side having length 1. The perimeter of the hexagon is $6 \cdot 1 = 6$ and the area of the hexagon is 6 times the area of one of the triangles:
$A = 6(\tfrac{1}{2}(1)(1) \sin 60°) = 6(\tfrac{1}{2} \cdot \tfrac{\sqrt{3}}{2}) = \tfrac{3\sqrt{3}}{2} \approx 2.5981$

5. (a) Each central angle of the decagon is $\frac{360}{10} = 36°$. To find the area of the decagon, multiply the area of one triangle by 10. $A = 10$ (area of one triangle) $= 10(\tfrac{1}{2} \cdot 1 \cdot 1 \cdot \sin 36°) = 5 \sin 36° \approx 2.9389$

(b) The derivation of the exact value of $\sin 72°$, which is $\sqrt{\frac{5 + \sqrt{5}}{8}}$, was done in Exercise 15 in Lesson 8.5. You also know that $\sin 72° = \cos (90° - 72°) = \cos 18°$. You can use the Pythagorean identity to find an exact value for $\sin 18°$, and then the angle-sum identity for sine to find $\sin (36°) = \sin (18° + 18°)$.

$$\cos 18° = \sqrt{\frac{5 + \sqrt{5}}{8}}$$

$$\sin^2 18° = 1 - \cos^2 18°$$

$$= 1 - \frac{5 + \sqrt{5}}{8}$$

$$= \frac{3 - \sqrt{5}}{8}$$

$$\sin 18° = \sqrt{\frac{3 - \sqrt{5}}{8}}$$

$$\sin 36° = \sin(18° + 18°)$$

$$= \sin 18° \cos 18° + \cos 18° \sin 18°$$

$$= 2 \sin 18° \cos 18°$$

$$= 2\sqrt{\frac{3 - \sqrt{5}}{8}}\sqrt{\frac{5 + \sqrt{5}}{8}}$$

$$= \frac{\sqrt{10 - 2\sqrt{5}}}{4}$$

So the exact value of the area of one of the triangles is $\frac{1}{2}(1)(1)\frac{\sqrt{10-2\sqrt{5}}}{4} = \frac{\sqrt{10-2\sqrt{5}}}{8}$. There are ten such triangles in the decagon, so its total area is $\frac{5\sqrt{10-2\sqrt{5}}}{4}$.

6. (a) $A = \frac{n}{2} \cdot \sin \frac{360°}{n}$

   (b)

Sides: n	Area: $A(n)$
4	$2 \sin 90° = 2$
5	$\frac{5}{2} \sin 72° \approx 2.3776$
6	$3 \sin 60° = \frac{3\sqrt{3}}{2} \approx 2.5981$
10	$5 \sin 36° \approx 2.9389$
12	$6 \sin 30° = 6 \cdot \frac{1}{2} = 3$
20	$10 \sin 18° \approx 3.0902$
30	$15 \sin 12° \approx 3.1187$
50	$25 \sin 7.2° \approx 3.1333$
100	$50 \sin 3.6° \approx 3.1395$
360	$180 \sin 1° \approx 3.1414$

7. The area of the n-gons is getting closer and closer to π. The areas are getting closer and closer to the area of a circle with radius 1. The area of a circle with radius 1 is π.

On Your Own

8. The area is $A = \frac{1}{2} \cdot 10 \cdot 12 \sin I$. The maximum value will be when $\sin I$ is greatest. This will be when $I = 90°$ and $\sin 90° = 1$. The maximum area is $A = \frac{1}{2} \cdot 10 \cdot 12 \cdot \sin 90° = \frac{1}{2} \cdot 10 \cdot 12 \cdot 1 = 60$.

9. $\cos x = \sin(90° - x)$, so $\cos 20° = \sin(90° - 20°) = \sin 70°$. **D** is the correct choice.

10. (a) Use $\triangle HIG$ to find the height: $\cos x° = \frac{HI}{1} = HI$. To find the base, $\sin x° = \frac{HG}{1} = HG$. $BG = 2 \cdot HG = 2 \cdot \sin x°$

$$A = \frac{1}{2}bh = \frac{1}{2} \cdot BG \cdot HI = \frac{1}{2} \cdot 2 \sin x° \cdot \cos x°$$

$$= \sin x° \cos x°$$

(b)
$$A = \frac{1}{2} \cdot 1 \cdot 1 \cdot \sin(x° + x°) = \frac{1}{2}\sin(2x°)$$

(c)
$$\frac{1}{2}\sin(2x) = \sin x \cos x$$
$$\sin(2x) = 2 \sin x \cos x$$

11. (a) No, one side can be 10 times as long as *one* of the other two sides but then the third side will be nearly as long as the first. You can't have one extremely long side paired with two extremely short sides, or there won't be any way for the two short sides to "reach across" from the endpoints of the long side to touch each other and form the third vertex of the triangle. This is a consequence of the Triangle Inequality, which states that the sum of any two sides of a triangle must be greater than the third side.

   (b) Yes. You could have angles measuring 1°, 2°, and 177°. The largest angle is much more than ten times each of the others.

12. (a) Any triangle with sides of 7 and 15 and the included angle measuring 60° would be congruent to $\triangle ONE$ by SAS. So, there is only one such triangle.

   (b) Call the foot of the perpendicular from O to $\overline{EN}$ point T. $\triangle OTE$ is a $30 - 60 - 90$ triangle with a hypotenuse of length 7. $ET = \frac{1}{2}(7) = \frac{7}{2}$ and $OT = \frac{7}{2}\sqrt{3}$ using the relationships in a $30 - 60 - 90$ triangle. $TN = EN - ET = 15 - \frac{7}{2} = \frac{23}{2}$. To find ON, use the Pythagorean Theorem and $\triangle OTN$.

$$ON^2 = OT^2 + TN^2$$

$$ON^2 = \left(\frac{7}{2}\sqrt{3}\right)^2 + \left(\frac{23}{2}\right)^2$$

$$ON^2 = \frac{49 \cdot 3}{4} + \frac{529}{4}$$

$$ON^2 = \frac{147}{4} + \frac{529}{4}$$

$$ON^2 = \frac{676}{4}$$

$$ON = \sqrt{\frac{676}{4}}$$

$$ON = \frac{26}{2} = 13$$

13. (a) The area of a parallelogram is bh, where h is the height relative to base b. Assume you have a parallelogram with adjacent sides measuring a and b, and with their included angle θ, then the height h relative to base b is $a \sin \theta$, so the area of the parallelogram is $ab \sin \theta$.

   (b) A rhombus is a parallelogram with four equal sides. Let s = the length of a side. Every rhombus is also a parallelogram, so you can use the formula for a parallelogram and AREA $= s^2 \cdot \sin$ (any angle of the rhombus).

14. Both area formulas are correct because in a parallelogram, any two adjacent angles are supplementary. So, $P = 180° - L$ and $\sin L = \sin(180° - L) = \sin P$. Derman's reasoning is incorrect because the fact that one angle is bigger than the other angle does *not* imply that the sine of the angle is bigger.

15. The area of a rhombus is $s^2 \cdot \sin$ (angle of rhombus). If the perimeter is 36, $s = 9$ and $A = 9^2 \sin$ (angle). This value will be greatest when the sine is at its greatest. The maximum value for the sine is 1, so the greatest area is $9^2 \cdot 1 = 81$.

16. The area is

$$\tfrac{1}{2} \cdot 8 \cdot 12 \cdot \sin 65° = 48 \cdot \sin 65° \approx 43.50$$

The correct answer choice is **C**.

Maintain Your Skills

17. If $a^2 + b^2 = c^2$, where c is the length of the longest side, the triangle is a right triangle. If $a^2 + b^2 > c^2$, the triangle will be acute. If $a^2 + b^2 < c^2$, the triangle will be obtuse.

(a) $8^2 + 6^2 = 64 + 36 = 100 = 10^2$; right
(b) $8^2 + 6^2 = 64 + 36 = 100 < 12^2 = 144$; obtuse
(c) $8^2 + 6^2 = 64 + 36 = 100 < 13^2 = 169$; obtuse
(d) $8^2 + 6^2 = 64 + 36 = 100 > 9^2 = 81$; acute
(e) $8^2 + 6^2 = 64 + 36 = 100 > 8^2 = 64$; acute
(f) $7^2 + 6^2 = 49 + 36 = 85 > 8^2 = 64$; acute
(g) $6^2 + 6^2 = 36 + 36 = 72 > 8^2 = 64$; acute
(h) $5^2 + 6^2 = 25 + 36 = 61 < 8^2 = 64$; obtuse

8.12   The Law of Sines

Check Your Understanding

1. Use the Law of Sines.

$$\frac{12}{\sin 30°} = \frac{MB}{\sin I}$$
$$\frac{12}{\frac{1}{2}} = \frac{MB}{\sin I}$$
$$24 = \frac{MB}{\sin I}$$
$$24 \cdot \sin I = MB$$

Since $\sin I$ cannot be more than 1, 24 is the maximum length.

2. Find $m\angle T = 180° - (110° + 40°) = 30°$ and apply the Law of Sines.

$$\frac{15}{\sin 110°} = \frac{AR}{\sin 30°} = \frac{RT}{\sin 40°}$$
$$\frac{AR}{\sin 30°} = \frac{15}{\sin 110°}$$
$$\frac{AR}{\frac{1}{2}} \approx \frac{15}{0.9397}$$
$$AR \approx \frac{1}{2} \cdot \frac{15}{0.9397}$$
$$AR \approx 8.0$$
$$\frac{RT}{\sin 40°} = \frac{15}{\sin 110°}$$
$$\frac{RT}{0.6428} \approx \frac{15}{0.9397}$$
$$RT \approx 0.6428 \cdot \frac{15}{0.9397}$$
$$RT \approx 10.3$$

3. Find $m\angle X = 180° - (40° + 70°) = 70°$. The triangle is isosceles, and $OX = OS = 12$. To find XS, apply the Law of Sines:

$$\frac{XS}{\sin 40°} = \frac{12}{\sin 70°}$$
$$XS = \sin 40° \cdot \frac{12}{\sin 70°}$$
$$XS \approx 0.6428 \cdot \frac{12}{0.9397}$$
$$XS \approx 8.2$$

4. Apply the Law of Sines:

$$\frac{8}{\sin K} = \frac{5}{\sin 30°}$$
$$\frac{8}{\sin K} = \frac{5}{\frac{1}{2}} = 10$$
$$8 = \sin K \cdot 10$$
$$0.8 = \sin K$$
$$K = \sin^{-1} 0.8$$
$$K \approx 53.1° \text{ or } 180° - 53.1° = 126.9°$$

There are two possible values for $\angle K$ because the sine is positive in Quadrants I and II. The triangle is not unique because the given angle is not between the given sides.

5. In Exercise 2, you are given two angles and a side not included between them. Since you only get *one* triangle, this is a congruence theorem, namely AAS. In Exercise 3, you are given two angles and the included side. Since you only get *one* triangle, this is a congruence theorem, namely ASA. In Exercise 4, you are given two sides and an angle *not* included between them. Since you get two possible solutions, SSA is *not* a congruence theorem.

6. (a) $\angle ABD$ is inscribed in a semicircle since $\overline{AD}$ is a diameter. Any angle inscribed in a semicircle is a right angle, so $\angle ABD$ is a right angle.
(b) $\angle C$ and $\angle D$ are inscribed angles and they intercept the same arc, arc AB. Therefore, they are congruent.
(c) $\angle C \cong \angle D \Rightarrow m\angle C = m\angle D \Rightarrow \sin C = \sin D$

(d) Using $\triangle ABD$ and the Law of Sines, $\frac{c}{\sin D} = \frac{AD}{\sin \angle ABD}$. But, $\angle ABD$ is a right angle and $\sin \angle ABD = \sin 90° = 1$, and $m\angle D = m\angle C$. So, $\frac{c}{\sin C} = \frac{AD}{1} \Rightarrow AD = \frac{c}{\sin C}$.

7. Drop an altitude from B intersecting $\overline{CA}$ at D. In right $\triangle CDB$, $\sin C = \frac{BD}{a} \Rightarrow CA = a \sin C$. In right $\triangle ADB$, $\sin A = \frac{BD}{c} \Rightarrow BD = c \sin A$. Therefore,

$$a \sin C = c \sin A \Rightarrow \frac{a}{\sin A} = \frac{c}{\sin C}$$

If you drop an altitude from a different vertex, you can show that this is the same as $\frac{b}{\sin B}$.

8. Drop an altitude from W to $\overline{OT}$ intersecting $\overline{OT}$ at E. $\triangle OWE$ is an isosceles right triangle because one of its acute angles is $45°$. Each leg is $OE = WE = \frac{1}{2} \cdot 10\sqrt{2} = 5\sqrt{2}$. $ET = OT - OE = 15 - 5\sqrt{2}$. Use the Pythagorean Theorem to find WT:

$$
\begin{aligned}
WT^2 &= WE^2 + ET^2 \\
&= (5\sqrt{2})^2 + (15 - 5\sqrt{2})^2 \\
&= (25 \cdot 2) + 15^2 - 2 \cdot 15 \cdot 5\sqrt{2} + (25 \cdot 2) \\
&= 50 + 225 - 150\sqrt{2} + 50 \\
&= 325 - 150\sqrt{2} \\
WT &= \sqrt{325 - 150\sqrt{2}}
\end{aligned}
$$

9. Drop an altitude from B, intersecting $\overline{CA}$ at D. In right $\triangle CDB$, $\cos C = \frac{CD}{a} \Rightarrow CD = a \cos C$ and $\sin C = \frac{BD}{a} \Rightarrow BD = a \sin C$. $DA = CA - CD = b - a \cos C$. Apply the Pythagorean Theorem to right $\triangle ADB$:

$$
\begin{aligned}
AB^2 &= BD^2 + DA^2 \\
&= (a \sin C)^2 + (b - a \cos C)^2 \\
&= a^2 \sin^2 C + b^2 - 2ab \cos C + a^2 \cos^2 C \\
&= a^2 \sin^2 C + a^2 \cos^2 C + b^2 - 2ab \cos C \\
&= a^2 (\sin^2 C + \cos^2 C) + b^2 - 2ab \cos C \\
&= a^2 \cdot (1) + b^2 - 2ab \cos C \\
&= a^2 + b^2 - 2ab \cos C \\
AB &= \sqrt{a^2 + b^2 - 2ab \cos C}
\end{aligned}
$$

On Your Own

10. In right $\triangle ABC$ with right angle at C, let $m\angle A = 30°$ and the side opposite $\angle A$ be a, $m\angle B = 60°$, the side opposite $\angle B$ be b, and the hypotenuse be c. Apply the Law of Sines:

$$\frac{a}{\sin 30°} = \frac{b}{\sin 60°} = \frac{c}{\sin 90°}$$

Then,

$$
\begin{aligned}
\frac{a}{\sin 30°} &= \frac{c}{\sin 90°} \\
(\sin 90°)(a) &= (\sin 30°)(c) \\
1 \cdot a &= \frac{1}{2} \cdot c \\
a &= \frac{1}{2}c
\end{aligned}
$$

The side opposite the $30°$ angle is $\frac{1}{2}$ the hypotenuse.

$$
\begin{aligned}
\frac{b}{\sin 60°} &= \frac{c}{\sin 90°} \\
(\sin 90°)(b) &= (\sin 60°)(c) \\
1 \cdot b &= \frac{\sqrt{3}}{2} \cdot c \\
b &= \frac{\sqrt{3}}{2}c
\end{aligned}
$$

The side opposite the $60°$ angle is $\frac{\sqrt{3}}{2}$ times the hypotenuse.

11. A 45-45-90 right triangle is isosceles. Let the hypotenuse have length c and each leg have length ℓ. Apply the Law of Sines:

$$\frac{c}{\sin 90°} = \frac{\ell}{\sin 45°} = \frac{\ell}{\sin 45°}$$

Then,

$$
\begin{aligned}
\frac{\ell}{\sin 45°} &= \frac{c}{\sin 90°} \\
(\sin 90°)(\ell) &= (\sin 45°)(c) \\
1 \cdot \ell &= \frac{\sqrt{2}}{2} \cdot c \\
\ell &= \frac{\sqrt{2}}{2}c
\end{aligned}
$$

Each leg is $\frac{\sqrt{2}}{2}$ times the hypotenuse.

12. The Law of Sines gives

$$\frac{BC}{\sin 60°} = \frac{15}{\sin B} = \frac{7}{\sin C}$$

No matter how you pair the equations, there are two unknowns and you cannot find a solution. To use the Law of Sines, you need to know (or be able to find out) at least one side with its opposite angle. In this case, there's no way to find B or C from the given information.

13. First use the Law of Sines to find $m\angle B$:

$$
\begin{aligned}
\frac{14}{\sin 110°} &= \frac{10}{\sin B} \\
\sin B &= \frac{10 \cdot \sin 110°}{14} \approx 0.6712 \\
m\angle B &= \sin^{-1} 0.6712 \approx 42.16°
\end{aligned}
$$

Note that $\angle B$ could not be in Quadrant II, since the triangle already has an obtuse angle. This implies that $m\angle A \approx 27.84°$, and thus

$$
\begin{aligned}
\frac{BC}{\sin 27.84°} &= \frac{14}{\sin 110°} \\
BC &= \frac{14 \cdot \sin 27.84°}{\sin 110°} \approx 6.96 \text{ cm}
\end{aligned}
$$

The correct answer choice is **C**.

14. (a)

$$\frac{10}{\sin 40^\circ} = \frac{12}{\sin C}$$
$$10 \sin C = 12 \sin 40^\circ$$
$$\sin C = \frac{12 \sin 40^\circ}{10}$$
$$\sin C \approx 0.7713$$

(b) $C = \sin^{-1} 0.7713 \approx 50.4748^\circ$. Or, C could be a second quadrant angle: $C = 180^\circ - 50.4748^\circ \approx 129.5252^\circ$

(c) If $C = 50.4748^\circ$, then $A = 180^\circ - (50.4748^\circ + 40^\circ) = 89.5252^\circ$. Apply the Law of Sines to find BC:

$$\frac{BC}{\sin 89.5252^\circ} = \frac{10}{\sin 40^\circ}$$
$$BC = \frac{10 \sin 89.5252^\circ}{\sin 40^\circ} \approx 15.5567$$

If $C = 129.5252^\circ$, then $A = 180^\circ - (129.5252^\circ + 40^\circ) = 10.4748^\circ$. Apply the Law of Sines to find BC:

$$\frac{BC}{\sin 10.4748^\circ} = \frac{10}{\sin 40^\circ}$$
$$BC = \frac{10 \sin 10.4748^\circ}{\sin 40^\circ} \approx 2.8284$$

15. (a)

$$\frac{12}{\sin 40^\circ} = \frac{10}{\sin B}$$
$$12 \sin B = 10 \sin 40^\circ$$
$$\sin B = \frac{10 \sin 40^\circ}{12}$$
$$\sin B \approx 0.536$$

(b) $B = \sin^{-1} 0.536 = 32^\circ$. Or, B could be a second quadrant angle: $B = 180^\circ - 32^\circ = 148^\circ$

(c) If $B = 32^\circ$, then $A = 180^\circ - (32^\circ + 40^\circ) = 108^\circ$. Apply the Law of Sines to find BC:

$$\frac{BC}{\sin 108^\circ} = \frac{12}{\sin 40^\circ}$$
$$BC = \frac{12 \sin 108^\circ}{\sin 40^\circ} \approx 17.8$$

If $B = 148^\circ$, then $A = 180^\circ - (148^\circ + 40^\circ) = -8^\circ$. This is not possible. There is only one solution.

16. (a) Apply the Law of Sines:

$$\frac{10}{\sin 70^\circ} = \frac{12}{\sin C}$$
$$10 \sin C = 12 \sin 70^\circ$$
$$\sin C = \frac{12 \sin 70^\circ}{10} \approx 1.128$$

Sine *cannot* be greater than 1, so there is no solution.

(b) No solution

(c) No solution

17. Tyler is not correct. Although there will not be two solutions, there could be one or zero solutions. There will be no solution if the side opposite the given angle is less than the given adjacent side.

18. Assume that you're given angle A, and sides a and b, with a opposite A in the triangle. When A is acute, b determines limits on a if there is to be a solution. If $a < b \sin A$, then there is no solution. If $a = b \sin A$ or $a > b$, there will be one solution. If $b \sin A < a < b$ there will be two solutions.

If the given angle A is right or obtuse, and $a > b$, there is one solution. If $a \leq b$, there are no solutions.

Maintain Your Skills

19. (a) First find $\angle C$:

$$m\angle C = 180^\circ - (30^\circ + 45^\circ) = 105^\circ$$

Then apply the Law of Sines to find the missing sides:

$$\frac{10}{\sin 30^\circ} = \frac{AB}{\sin 105^\circ} = \frac{AC}{\sin 45^\circ}$$
$$\frac{AC}{\sin 45^\circ} = \frac{10}{\sin 30^\circ}$$
$$AC \cdot \sin 30^\circ = 10 \cdot \sin 45^\circ$$
$$AC \cdot \frac{1}{2} = 10 \cdot \frac{\sqrt{2}}{2}$$
$$AC = 2 \cdot 10 \cdot \frac{\sqrt{2}}{2}$$
$$AC = 10\sqrt{2} \approx 14.1$$

$$\frac{AB}{\sin 105^\circ} = \frac{10}{\sin 30^\circ}$$
$$AB \cdot \sin 30^\circ = 10 \cdot \sin 105^\circ$$
$$AB \cdot \frac{1}{2} = 10 \cdot \sin 105^\circ$$
$$AB = 2 \cdot 10 \cdot \sin 105^\circ$$
$$AB \approx 19.3$$

(b) First find $\angle C$:

$$m\angle C = 180^\circ - (30^\circ + 45^\circ) = 105^\circ$$

Then apply the Law of Sines to find the missing sides:

$$\frac{20}{\sin 30^\circ} = \frac{AB}{\sin 105^\circ} = \frac{AC}{\sin 45^\circ}$$
$$\frac{AC}{\sin 45^\circ} = \frac{20}{\sin 30^\circ}$$
$$AC \cdot \sin 30^\circ = 20 \cdot \sin 45^\circ$$
$$AC \cdot \frac{1}{2} = 20 \cdot \frac{\sqrt{2}}{2}$$
$$AC = 2 \cdot 20 \cdot \frac{\sqrt{2}}{2}$$
$$AC = 20\sqrt{2} \approx 28.3$$

$$\frac{AB}{\sin 105°} = \frac{20}{\sin 30°}$$
$$AB \cdot \sin 30° = 20 \cdot \sin 105°$$
$$AB \cdot \frac{1}{2} = 20 \cdot \sin 105°$$
$$AB = 2 \cdot 20 \cdot \sin 105°$$
$$AB = 40 \cdot \sin 105° \approx 38.6$$

(c) First find $\angle C$:

$$m\angle C = 180° - (30° + 45°) = 105°$$

Then apply the Law of Sines to find the missing sides:

$$\frac{BC}{\sin 30°} = \frac{AB}{\sin 105°} = \frac{10}{\sin 45°}$$
$$\frac{BC}{\sin 30°} = \frac{10}{\sin 45°}$$
$$BC \cdot \sin 45° = 10 \cdot \sin 30°$$
$$BC \cdot \frac{\sqrt{2}}{2} = 10 \cdot \frac{1}{2}$$
$$BC = 10 \cdot \frac{1}{2} \cdot \frac{2}{\sqrt{2}}$$
$$BC = \frac{10}{\sqrt{2}}$$
$$BC = \frac{10\sqrt{2}}{2} = 5\sqrt{2} \approx 7.07$$

$$\frac{AB}{\sin 105°} = \frac{10}{\sin 45°}$$
$$AB \cdot \sin 45° = 10 \cdot \sin 105°$$
$$AB \cdot \frac{\sqrt{2}}{2} = 10 \cdot \sin 105°$$
$$AB = \frac{2}{\sqrt{2}} \cdot 10 \cdot \sin 105°$$
$$AB = \frac{2\sqrt{2}}{2} \cdot 10 \sin 105°$$
$$AB = 10\sqrt{2} \sin 105° \approx 13.7$$

(d) First find $\angle C$:

$$m\angle C = 180° - (30° + 60°) = 90°$$

This is a 30-60-90 triangle, so you do not need to apply the Law of Sines. $\overline{AC}$ is the side opposite the 60° angle, $\overline{BC}$ is the side opposite the 30° angle, and $\overline{AB}$ is the hypotenuse.

$$BC \cdot \sqrt{3} = AC \Rightarrow BC = \frac{10}{\sqrt{3}} = \frac{10\sqrt{3}}{3} \approx 5.8$$
$$AB = 2 \cdot BC = 2 \cdot \frac{10\sqrt{3}}{3} = \frac{20\sqrt{3}}{3} \approx 11.5$$

(e) First find $\angle C$:

$$m\angle C = 180° - (30° + 120°) = 30°$$

Then apply the Law of Sines to find the missing sides:

$$\frac{BC}{\sin 30°} = \frac{AB}{\sin 30°} = \frac{10}{\sin 120°}$$

$$\frac{BC}{\sin 30°} = \frac{10}{\sin 120°}$$
$$BC \sin 120° = 10 \sin 30°$$
$$BC \cdot \frac{\sqrt{3}}{2} = 10 \cdot \frac{1}{2}$$
$$BC = 10 \cdot \frac{1}{2} \cdot \frac{2}{\sqrt{3}}$$
$$BC = \frac{10}{\sqrt{3}}$$
$$BC = \frac{10\sqrt{3}}{3} \approx 5.8$$

This triangle is isosceles, so $AB = BC = \frac{10\sqrt{3}}{3} \approx 5.8$

8.13 The Law of Cosines

Check Your Understanding

1. $AB = c = \sqrt{a^2 + b^2 - 2ab \cos C}$
2. The range of the cosine function is $-1 \le \cos x \le 1$. The largest value for AB will be when the cosine is smallest (because you are subtracting $2ab \cos C$) or when $\cos C = -1$. This gives you

$$AB = c = \sqrt{a^2 + b^2 - 2ab(-1)} = \sqrt{a^2 + 2ab + b^2}$$
$$= \sqrt{(a+b)^2} = |a + b| = a + b$$

$a + b$ is an upper bound and $c < a + b$. Note that $\cos C \ne -1$, because this would mean that $m\angle C = 180°$ and that is not possible. The smallest value for AB will be when $\cos C = 1$. This gives you

$$AB = c = \sqrt{a^2 + b^2 - 2ab(1)} = \sqrt{a^2 - 2ab + b^2}$$
$$= \sqrt{(a-b)^2} = |a - b|$$

$|a - b|$ is a lower bound and $c > |a - b|$. $\cos C \ne 1$, because this would mean that $m\angle C = 0°$ and that would not result in a triangle.

3. Since $\angle B$ is obtuse, $90° < m\angle B < 180°$. The lower bound for OT will be when $m\angle B = 90°$ and $\triangle OBT$ is a right triangle. Since you are given the legs are 3 and 4, the hypotenuse would be 5.

$$OT > 5$$

Using the results of Exercise 2, the upper bound is

$$OT < 3 + 4 \rightarrow OT < 7$$

4. Since $\angle C$ is acute, $0° < m\angle C < 90°$. The upper bound is when $m\angle C = 90°$, so $AU < 5$. The lower bound is when $m\angle C = 0°$, so $AU > |3 - 4| = 1$.

5. If just $\angle M$ were required to be acute, $FB < \sqrt{5^2 + 12^2} = 13$ and $FB > |12 - 5| = 7$. However, you must consider that the other angles are also less than $90°$ and $a^2 + b^2 > c^2$ where c is the side opposite the acute angle. In $\triangle FMB$, you need to check $\angle B$ and $\angle F$. In order for $\triangle FMB$ to be acute,

$$FB^2 + MB^2 > FM^2 \Rightarrow FB^2 + 5^2 > 12^2$$
$$\Rightarrow FB^2 > 12^2 - 5^2$$
$$\Rightarrow FB^2 > 119$$
$$\Rightarrow FB > \sqrt{119}$$

and

$$FB^2 + FM^2 > MB^2 \Rightarrow FB^2 + 12^2 > 5^2$$
$$\Rightarrow FB^2 + 144 > 25$$
$$\Rightarrow FB^2 > -119 \text{ (always true)}$$

So, $FB < 13$ and $FB > \sqrt{119}$.

6. (a) First use the Law of Cosines to find one of the angles of the triangle. Then use either the Law of Cosines or the Law of Sines to find a second angle. Once you have two angles, you can subtract their sum from $180°$ to find the final angle.

(b) First use the Law of Cosines to find the missing side. Then use the Law of Sines or the Law of Cosines to find one of the missing angles. To find the last angle, subtract the sum of the other two angles from $180°$.

(c) First use the Law of Sines to find the angle opposite a given side. Remember that you may get zero, one, or two possible solutions. Subtract the sum of the known angles from $180°$ to find the third angle. Use the Law of Sines or the Law of Cosines to find the final side.

(d) First find the missing angle by subtracting the sum of the known angles from $180°$. Then use the Law of Sines to find a missing side. Use the Law of Sines or the Law of Cosines to find the final side.

(e) First find the missing angle by subtracting the sum of the known angles from $180°$. Then use the Law of Sines to find a missing side. Use the Law of Sines or the Law of Cosines to find the final side.

(f) This cannot be solved. The triangle will not be unique because you are not given the length of a side. If the angles of one triangle are congruent to the angles of another triangle, the triangles are similar but not necessarily congruent.

7. (a) Let the side opposite $\angle A$ be 13, the side opposite $\angle B$ be 14, and the side opposite $\angle C$ be 15. Then,

$$\cos A = \frac{14^2 + 15^2 - 13^2}{2 \cdot 14 \cdot 15} = 0.6000$$
$$\cos B = \frac{13^2 + 15^2 - 14^2}{2 \cdot 13 \cdot 15} \approx 0.5077$$
$$\cos C = \frac{13^2 + 14^2 - 15^2}{2 \cdot 13 \cdot 14} \approx 0.3846$$

(b) The largest angle is $\angle C$ (opposite the longest side). $\angle C$ has the smallest cosine.

(c) Use $\angle A$ and let h be the altitude: $\sin A = \sqrt{1 - \cos^2 A} = \sqrt{0.64} = 0.8 = \frac{h}{15} \Rightarrow h = 15 \cdot 0.8 = 12.0$

(d) $A = \frac{1}{2}bh \approx \frac{1}{2} \cdot 14 \cdot 12.0 = 84$

8. (a) $\cos C = \frac{a^2 + b^2 - c^2}{2ab}$ If a, b, and c are integers, this expression, which is the sum, product, and quotient of integers, will be rational.

(b) area $= \frac{1}{2}ab \sin C$ where a and b are integers. $\sin^2 C + \cos^2 C = 1 \Rightarrow \sin C = \sqrt{1 - \cos^2 C}$. You have shown that $\cos C$ is rational. so $\sin C$ will be the square root of a rational number. The resulting area of the triangle is $\frac{1}{2}$(integer)(integer)($\sqrt{\text{rational number}}$). This expression can be simplified to an expression in the form $x\sqrt{y}$ where x is rational and y is an integer.

On Your Own

9. You can use the Law of Cosines:

$$MT^2 = 10^2 + 3^2 - 2 \cdot 10 \cdot 3 \cdot \cos 60°$$
$$MT^2 = 100 + 9 - 60 \cdot \frac{1}{2}$$
$$MT^2 = 79$$
$$MT = \sqrt{79}$$

The correct choice is **B**.

10. Use the Law of Cosines:

$$AB^2 = 3^2 + 10^2 - 2 \cdot 3 \cdot 10 \cdot \cos C = 109 - 60 \cdot \cos C$$
$$AB = \sqrt{109 - 60 \cdot \cos C}$$

11. The maximum and minimum values for cosine are 1 and -1. Use these to find the upper and lower bounds.
upper Bound:

$$UB = \sqrt{109 - 60 \cdot (-1)} = \sqrt{109 + 60} = \sqrt{169} = 13$$

lower Bound:

$$LB + \sqrt{109 - 60 \cdot 1} = \sqrt{109 - 60} = \sqrt{49} = 7$$

12. The smallest angle will be opposite the shortest side, 10. Use the Law of Cosines to find the angle :

$$\cos A = \frac{12^2 + 15^2 - 10^2}{2 \cdot 12 \cdot 15}$$
$$\cos A = \frac{144 + 225 - 100}{360}$$
$$\cos A = \frac{269}{360}$$
$$\cos A \approx 0.7472$$
$$A \approx \cos^{-1} 0.7472$$
$$A \approx 42°$$

13. (a) $m\angle O = 60°$. If $\angle O$ was the smallest angle, at least one of the other two angles would be more than $60°$ and the sum would be more than $180°$, which is impossible. Therefore, $\angle O$ cannot be the smallest angle.

(b) First find the missing side, FM, using the Law of Cosines:

$$FM = \sqrt{12^2 + 20^2 - 2 \cdot 12 \cdot 20 \cdot \cos 60°}$$

$$= \sqrt{144 + 400 - 480 \cdot \frac{1}{2}} = \sqrt{304} \approx 17.4$$

The smallest angle is opposite the shortest side, FO. Find the smallest angle, $\angle M$, using the Law of Sines:

$$\frac{17.4}{\sin 60°} = \frac{12}{\sin M}$$
$$17.4 \cdot \sin M = 12 \cdot \sin 60°$$
$$\sin M = \frac{12 \cdot \frac{\sqrt{3}}{2}}{17.4}$$
$$\sin M \approx 0.5973$$
$$M \approx \sin^{-1} 0.5973$$
$$M \approx 37°$$

14. (a) False. If θ is between 90° and 180°, $\cos \theta < 0$.
    (b) True
    (c) False. $\sin^2 \theta = 1 - \cos^2 \theta$
    (d) True

15. (a) Use the Law of Cosines to find the first angle:

$$\cos A = \frac{12^2 + 7^2 - 10^2}{2 \cdot 12 \cdot 7} = \frac{93}{168} \approx 0.5536$$
$$A = \cos^{-1} 0.5536 \approx 56.4°$$

Use the Law of Sines to find the next angle:

$$\frac{10}{\sin 56.4°} = \frac{12}{\sin B}$$
$$10 \sin B = 12 \sin 56.4°$$
$$\sin B = \frac{12 \sin 56.4°}{10}$$
$$\approx 0.9995$$
$$B = \sin^{-1} 0.9995$$
$$\approx 88°$$

To find the third angle, subtract the sum of the other two from 180°:

$$C = 180° - (56° + 88°) = 36°$$

(b)

$$\sin 56° = \frac{h}{7} \Rightarrow h = 7 \cdot \sin 56.4° \approx 5.83$$
$$\cos 56° = \frac{x}{7} \Rightarrow x = 7 \cdot \cos 56.4° \approx 3.87$$

(c) $Area = \frac{1}{2}bh = \frac{1}{2}(12)(5.83) = 34.98$

16. The solution uses the identity $\cos (a + b) = \cos a \cos b - \sin a \sin b$. First note that $\cos a \cos b = \frac{4}{5} \cdot \frac{5}{13} = \frac{20}{65}$. To find $\sin a$ and $\sin b$, use the identity $\sin^2 \theta = 1 - \cos^2 \theta$.

$$\sin^2 a = 1 - (\frac{4}{5})^2 = 1 - \frac{16}{25} = \frac{9}{25} \Rightarrow \sin a = \sqrt{\frac{9}{25}} = \frac{3}{5}.$$

$$\sin^2 b = 1 - (\frac{5}{13})^2 = 1 - \frac{25}{169} = \frac{144}{169} \Rightarrow \sin b = \sqrt{\frac{144}{169}} = \frac{12}{13}$$

$$\sin a \sin b = \frac{3}{5} \cdot \frac{12}{13} = \frac{36}{65}$$

Here, $\cos(a + b) = \frac{20}{65} - \frac{36}{65} = \frac{-16}{65}$. The third angle in the triangle isn't $(a + b)$, it's $180° - (a + b)$. The identity $\cos(180° - \theta) = -\cos \theta$ is used here, so the cosine of the third angle is exactly $\frac{16}{65}$.

17. Let C = the smallest angle, which is opposite the side of length 5. From the Law of Cosines,

$$5^2 = 8^2 + 7^2 - 2 \cdot 8 \cdot 7 \cdot \cos C$$
$$25 = 64 + 49 - 112 \cdot \cos C$$
$$112 \cdot \cos C = 88$$
$$\cos C = \frac{88}{112} \approx 0.7857$$
$$C \approx \cos^{-1}(0.7857) \approx 38.21°$$

The correct answer choice is **C**.

18. (a)

$$c = AB$$
$$= AD + DB$$
$$= b \cos A + a \cos B$$

(b) Drop an altitude from B to $\overline{AC}$ at E.

$$b = AC$$
$$= AE + EC$$
$$= c \cos A + a \cos C$$

(c) Drop an altitude from A to $\overline{BC}$ at F.

$$a = BC$$
$$= BF + FC$$
$$= c \cos B + b \cos C$$

19. Multiply each side of the equation on the left by the inverse of the first matrix. You can find the inverse either by hand or with your calculator. The inverse is

$$\begin{pmatrix} \frac{1}{2b} & \frac{1}{2c} & \frac{-a}{2bc} \\ \frac{1}{2a} & \frac{-b}{2ac} & \frac{1}{2c} \\ \frac{-c}{2ab} & \frac{1}{2a} & \frac{1}{2b} \end{pmatrix}$$

So on the right side of the equation, you have

$$\begin{pmatrix} \frac{1}{2b} & \frac{1}{2c} & \frac{-a}{2bc} \\ \frac{1}{2a} & \frac{-b}{2ac} & \frac{1}{2c} \\ \frac{-c}{2ab} & \frac{1}{2a} & \frac{1}{2b} \end{pmatrix} \begin{pmatrix} c \\ b \\ a \end{pmatrix}$$

This gives you the following equation:

$$\begin{pmatrix} \cos A \\ \cos B \\ \cos C \end{pmatrix} = \begin{pmatrix} \frac{c}{2b} + \frac{b}{2c} - \frac{a^2}{2bc} \\ \frac{c}{2a} - \frac{b^2}{2ac} + \frac{a}{2c} \\ \frac{-c^2}{2ab} + \frac{b}{2a} + \frac{a}{2b} \end{pmatrix}$$

Since these two matrices are the same size, their corresponding entries must be equal. This leads to a series of three equations, each of which becomes one of the Law of Cosines equations in the following manner:

$$\cos A = \frac{c}{2b} + \frac{b}{2c} - \frac{a^2}{2bc}$$
$$2bc \cos A = c^2 + b^2 - a^2$$
$$a^2 = b^2 + c^2 - 2bc \cos A$$

Maintain Your Skills

20. (a) $AB = \sqrt{8^2 + 13^2 - 2 \cdot 8 \cdot 13 \cdot \cos 1°} \approx 5.00$
    (b) $AB = \sqrt{8^2 + 13^2 - 2 \cdot 8 \cdot 13 \cdot \cos 10°} \approx 5.31$
    (c) $AB = \sqrt{8^2 + 13^2 - 2 \cdot 8 \cdot 13 \cdot \cos 50°} \approx 9.96$
    (d) $AB = \sqrt{8^2 + 13^2 - 2 \cdot 8 \cdot 13 \cdot \cos 90°} \approx 15.26$
    (e) $AB = \sqrt{8^2 + 13^2 - 2 \cdot 8 \cdot 13 \cdot \cos 130°} \approx 19.15$
    (f) $AB = \sqrt{8^2 + 13^2 - 2 \cdot 8 \cdot 13 \cdot \cos 170°} \approx 20.92$
    (g) $AB = \sqrt{8^2 + 13^2 - 2 \cdot 8 \cdot 13 \cdot \cos 179°} \approx 21.00$
    (h) AB increases from 5.00 to 21.00. These are the sidelength limits imposed by the Triangle Inequality.

8.14 Heron's Formula

Check Your Understanding

1. (a) $s = \frac{x+8+6}{2} = \frac{x+14}{2}$
   (b) Apply Heron's Formula:

$$A(x) = \sqrt{\left(\frac{x+14}{2}\right)\left(\frac{x+14}{2} - x\right)\left(\frac{x+14}{2} - 8\right)\left(\frac{x+14}{2} - 6\right)}$$

$$= \sqrt{\left(\frac{x+14}{2}\right)\left(\frac{x+14-2x}{2}\right)\left(\frac{x+14-16}{2}\right)\left(\frac{x+14-12}{2}\right)}$$

$$= \sqrt{\left(\frac{x+14}{2}\right)\left(\frac{-x+14}{2}\right)\left(\frac{x-2}{2}\right)\left(\frac{x+2}{2}\right)}$$

$$= \frac{1}{4}\sqrt{(x+14)(-x+14)(x-2)(x+2)}$$

   (c) The domain of $A(x)$ is $2 \le x \le 14$. The zeros are the values of x that make $A(x) = 0$. $x = 2$ or $x = 14$.
   (d) Use your graphing calculator to determine that the maximum value for $A(x)$ is 24 and this occurs when $x = 10$.

2. (a) Since the perimeter is 18, $EU = 18 - QE - QU = 18 - 6 - x = 12 - x$.
   (b) $A(x) = \sqrt{9(9-6)(9-x)(9-(12-x))} = \sqrt{27(9-x)(-3+x)}$
   (c) The domain for $A(x)$ is $3 \le x \le 9$. The zeros are $x = 3$ or $x = 9$.
   (d) Use your graphing calculator to find that the maximum value of $A(x)$ is $A(x) = 9\sqrt{3} \approx 15.6$. The value of x that produces this area is $x = 6$.

3. Draw a diagonal to form two triangles. One triangle will have as its sides 7, 15, and the diagonal. The other will

have sides 8, 8, and the diagonal. Use the Law of Cosines to find the length of the diagonal:

$$d^2 = 7^2 + 15^2 - 2 \cdot 7 \cdot 15 \cos 60° = 49 + 225 - 210 \cdot \frac{1}{2}$$

$$= 274 - 105 = 169$$

$$d = \sqrt{169} = 13$$

Since you know an angle in the first triangle, use the formula $A = \frac{1}{2}ab \sin C = \frac{1}{2} \cdot 7 \cdot 15 \cdot \sin 60° = \frac{105}{2} \cdot \frac{\sqrt{3}}{2} = \frac{105\sqrt{3}}{4} \approx 45.5$.

To find the area of the second triangle, use Heron's Formula, where $s = \frac{8+8+13}{2} = \frac{29}{2}$.

$$A = \sqrt{\frac{29}{2}\left(\frac{29}{2} - 8\right)\left(\frac{29}{2} - 8\right)\left(\frac{29}{2} - 13\right)}$$

$$= \sqrt{\frac{29}{2}\left(\frac{13}{2}\right)\left(\frac{13}{2}\right)\left(\frac{3}{2}\right)}$$

$$= \sqrt{\frac{29 \cdot 13 \cdot 13 \cdot 3}{16}}$$

$$= \frac{13\sqrt{87}}{4}$$

$$\approx 30.3$$

$A(\text{quad}) = \frac{105\sqrt{3} + 13\sqrt{87}}{4} \approx 75.8$

4. (a)

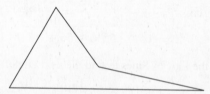

   (b) This particular quadrilateral cannot be concave, because if you collapse the sides of length 8 in towards the center of the triangle without changing any of the other measurements, the result is not a quadrilateral.

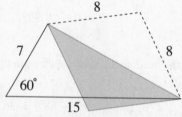

   To confirm this numerically, realize that the sides of length 7 and 15 and the 60° angle between them determine a triangle. The Law of Cosines can be used to show that the third side of this triangle has length 13. The measure of the angle in this triangle opposite the side of length 7 is about 27.8°, by the Law of Sines, but a base angle in an isosceles triangle with sides 8, 8, and 13 is about 35.7° (according to the Law of Cosines). When you "flip" the isosceles triangle over the side of length 13, you'll cross the side of length 15 because the base angle of the isosceles triangle is bigger than this angle of the triangle with sides 7, 13, and 15.

5. (a)

$$\frac{\sqrt{(b+c+a)(b+c-a)(a-b+c)(a+b-c)}}{4}$$

$$= \frac{\sqrt{(b+c+a)(b+c-a)(a-b+c)(a+b-c)}}{\sqrt{16}}$$

$$= \sqrt{\frac{(b+c+a)(b+c-a)(a-b+c)(a+b-c)}{16}}$$

$$= \sqrt{\frac{b+c+a}{2} \cdot \frac{b+c-a}{2} \cdot \frac{a-b+c}{2} \cdot \frac{a+b-c}{2}}$$

(b)

$$\sqrt{\frac{b+c+a}{2} \cdot \frac{b+c-a}{2} \cdot \frac{a-b+c}{2} \cdot \frac{a+b-c}{2}}$$

$$= \sqrt{\frac{b+c+a}{2} \cdot \frac{b+c+a-2a}{2} \cdot \frac{a+b-2b+c}{2} \cdot \frac{a+b+c-2c}{2}}$$

$$= \sqrt{\frac{b+c+a}{2} \cdot \left(\frac{b+c+a}{2} - \frac{2a}{2}\right)\left(\frac{a+b+c}{2} - \frac{2b}{2}\right)\left(\frac{a+b+c}{2} - \frac{2c}{2}\right)}$$

$$= \sqrt{s(s-a)(s-b)(s-c)}$$

On Your Own

6. The semiperimeter would be $s = \frac{12+25+11}{2} = \frac{48}{2} = 24$. If you apply Heron's formula, you get

$$A = \sqrt{24(24-12)(24-25)(24-11)}$$
$$= \sqrt{(24)(12)(-1)(13)} = \sqrt{-3744}$$

which is not a real number and therefore is not a suitable answer for an area. You would expect not to get an area here, because this is not a triangle, according to the Triangle Inequality. $(11 + 12 < 25)$

7. (a) Since each angle of an equilateral triangle is 60°, the area $A = \frac{1}{2} \cdot 10 \cdot 10 \cdot \sin 60° = 50 \cdot \frac{\sqrt{3}}{2} = 25\sqrt{3} \approx 43.3$

(b) The semiperimeter is $s = \frac{10+10+10}{2} = 15$. Using Heron's formula,

$$A = \sqrt{15(15-10)(15-10)(15-10)}$$
$$= \sqrt{3(5)(5)(5)(5)} = 25\sqrt{3}$$

(c) The semiperimeter is $s = \frac{x+x+x}{2} = \frac{3x}{2}$. Apply Heron's formula:

$$A = \sqrt{\frac{3x}{2}\left(\frac{3x}{2} - x\right)\left(\frac{3x}{2} - x\right)\left(\frac{3x}{2} - x\right)}$$

$$= \sqrt{\frac{3x}{2}\left(\frac{x}{2}\right)\left(\frac{x}{2}\right)\left(\frac{x}{2}\right)}$$

$$= \sqrt{\frac{3x^4}{16}}$$

$$= \frac{x^2\sqrt{3}}{4}$$

8. (a)

$$s = \frac{7+10+12}{2} = \frac{29}{2} = 14.5$$

$$A = \sqrt{14.5(14.5-7)(14.5-10)(14.5-12)}$$
$$= \sqrt{14.5(7.5)(4.5)(2.5)} = \sqrt{1223.44}$$

The area is not an integer, so the triangle is not a Heronian triangle.

(b)

$$s = \frac{6+8+9}{2} = \frac{23}{2} = 11.5$$

$$A = \sqrt{11.5(11.5-6)(11.5-8)(11.5-9)}$$
$$= \sqrt{11.5(5.5)(3.5)(2.5)} = \sqrt{553.438}$$

The area is not an integer, so the triangle is not a Heronian triangle.

(c)

$$s = \frac{10+15+20}{2} = \frac{45}{2} = 22.5$$

$$A = \sqrt{22.5(22.5-10)(22.5-15)(22.5-20)}$$
$$= \sqrt{22.5(12.5)(7.5)(2.5)} = \sqrt{5273.44}$$

The area is not an integer, so the triangle is not a Heronian triangle.

(d)

$$s = \frac{10+17+21}{2} = \frac{48}{2} = 24$$

$$A = \sqrt{24(24-10)(24-17)(24-21)}$$
$$= \sqrt{24(14)(7)(3)} = \sqrt{7056} = 84$$

The area is an integer, so this is a Heronian triangle.

9. The area of A = $\sqrt{18 \cdot 8 \cdot 5 \cdot 5} = \sqrt{3600} = 60$. The area of B = $\sqrt{18.5 \cdot 9.5 \cdot 6.5 \cdot 2.5} = \sqrt{2855.9375} \neq$ an integer. The area of **C** = $\sqrt{48 \cdot 33 \cdot 11 \cdot 4} = \sqrt{69,696} = 264$. The area of D = $\sqrt{32 \cdot 27 \cdot 3 \cdot 2} = \sqrt{5184} = 72$. The correct answer choice is **B**.

10. If an equilateral triangle were Heronian, both its sides and its area would have to be integers. If the side , x, is an integer then the area, $\frac{x^2\sqrt{3}}{4}$ would be irrational because of $\sqrt{3}$.

11. When you match the two legs of length 20 together to form a new triangle, the height of this new triangle is 20 and its base measures $15 + 21 = 36$. Its other two sides still measure 25 and 29. The area of the big triangle will be $A = \frac{1}{2}(20)(36) = 360$, so it is a Heronian triangle.

12. The next one (besides 3, 4, 5) is (51, 52, 53), a triangle with area 1170. The ones after that are (193, 194, 195), with area 16,296, and (723, 724, 725), with area 226,974. The only other one with side lengths less than 10,000 is (2701, 2702, 2703) which has area 3,161,340.

Maintain Your Skills

13. **(a)** Use Heron's formula with $s = \frac{5+12+c}{2} = \frac{17+c}{2}$ and

$$A(c) = \sqrt{\frac{17+c}{2}\left(\frac{17+c}{2}-5\right)\left(\frac{17+c}{2}-12\right)\left(\frac{17+c}{2}-c\right)}$$

$$A(c) = \sqrt{\left(\frac{17+c}{2}\right)\left(\frac{7+c}{2}\right)\left(\frac{c-7}{2}\right)\left(\frac{17-c}{2}\right)}$$

Here is the completed table:

c	$A(c)$
7	0
8	14.52
9	20.40
10	24.54
11	27.50
12	29.34
13	30
14	29.23
15	26.53
16	20.66
17	0

(b) It appears that the maximum area occurs when $c = 13$, $A(13) = 30$. This is when the triangle is a *right* triangle.

8C   MATHEMATICAL REFLECTIONS

1. $A_{DOG} = \frac{1}{2}(10)(8)\sin 20° \approx 13.7$

2. Apply the Law of Cosines to find DO.

$$DO^2 = 8^2 + 10^2 - 2(8)(10)\cos 20°$$
$$\approx 13.6492$$
$$DO \approx 3.7$$

Use the Law of Sines to find angle D.

$$\frac{8}{\sin D} \approx \frac{3.7}{\sin 20°}$$
$$\sin D \approx \frac{8\sin 20°}{3.7}$$
$$D \approx 47.7°$$

Since the sum of the angles in a triangle must be 180°, $O \approx 180° - 20° - 47.7° \approx 112.3°$.

3. Use the Law of Sines to find $m\angle P$.

$$\frac{7}{\sin 40°} = \frac{8}{\sin P}$$
$$\sin P = \frac{8\sin 40°}{7}$$
$$P \approx 47.3° \text{ or } 180° - 47.3° \approx 132.7°$$

This means that there will be two solutions. If angle P measures 47.3°, then angle I measures $180° - 40° - 47.3° \approx 92.7°$ and you can use the Law of Cosines to find PG.

$$PG^2 \approx 8^2 + 7^2 - 2(8)(7)\cos 92.7°$$
$$PG \approx 10.9$$

If, however, angle P measures 132.7°, then angle I measures $180° - 40° - 132.7° \approx 7.3°$. You can still use the Law of Cosines to find PG.

$$PG^2 \approx 8^2 + 7^2 - 2(8)(7)\cos 7.3°$$
$$PG \approx 1.4$$

4. Apply the Law of Cosines to find angle C.

$$\cos C = \frac{-4^2 + 6^2 + 8^2}{2(6)(8)}$$
$$\cos C \approx 0.875$$
$$C \approx 29.0°$$

Apply the Law of Cosines to find angle A.

$$\cos A = \frac{-8^2 + 4^2 + 6^2}{2(4)(6)}$$
$$\cos A \approx -0.25$$
$$A \approx 104.5°$$

Apply the Law of Cosines to find angle T.

$$\cos T = \frac{-6^2 + 4^2 + 8^2}{2(4)(8)}$$
$$\cos T \approx 0.6875$$
$$T \approx 46.6°$$

5. You could use any of the area formulas of the form $A = \frac{1}{2}ab\sin\theta$, or Heron's Formula.

$$s = \frac{4+6+8}{2} = 9$$

$$A_{CAT} = \sqrt{9(9-4)(9-6)(9-8)} = \sqrt{135} \approx 11.6$$

6. You need to know at least one side. Even if you know all three angles, that's only enough to define a class of similar triangles, not enough to determine a side length.

If you know one side length, you need to know two angle measures, but the side needn't be included between the two angles. This is because once you know two angle measures, you automatically know the third, because the sum of the angles in a triangle is always 180°.

If you know two side lengths, and their included angle, the triangle is completely determined. However, if you know a non-included angle, there could be zero, one, or two triangles with your given information. You might need another piece of information—such as, this is an acute triangle—to completely determine it in this case.

If you know three side lengths, the triangle is completely determined. However, for there to *be* a triangle, the side lengths must satisfy the Triangle Inequality.

7. If you have enough information to completely determine a triangle, you can also find its area.

8. The largest angle θ will be opposite the largest side.

$$\cos\theta = \frac{-10^2 + 5^2 + 8^2}{2(5)(8)}$$
$$\cos\theta \approx -0.1375$$
$$\theta \approx 97.9°$$

1. (a) Drop an altitude from the point (x, y) to make a right triangle with sides $|x|$, $|y|$, and 1 (hypotenuse). Then, the angle that the hypotenuse makes with the x-axis is $240° - 180° = 60°$. The triangle is a $30 - 60 - 90$. The hypotenuse has length 1, x is opposite the $30°$, and y is opposite the $60°$ angle. So, the other sides are $\frac{1}{2}$ and $\frac{\sqrt{3}}{2}$. Since you are in Quadrant III, the cosine and sine are both negative. The point is $\left(-\frac{1}{2}, -\frac{\sqrt{3}}{2}\right)$.

(b) To find the angle, use $\cos\theta = \frac{5}{13}$. So, $\cos^{-1}\left(\frac{5}{13}\right) \approx 67°$. The point is in Quadrant IV because x is positive and y is negative. So, the angle is $360° - 67° = 293°$.

2. (a)

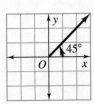

$$\cos 45° = \sin 45° = \frac{\sqrt{2}}{2}, \tan 45° = \frac{\frac{\sqrt{2}}{2}}{\frac{\sqrt{2}}{2}} = 1$$

(b)

$\cos 90° = 0$, $\sin 90° = 1$, $\tan 90° = \frac{1}{0}$ So, the tangent is undefined.

(c)

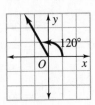

$$\cos 120° = -\frac{1}{2}, \sin 120° = \frac{\sqrt{3}}{2},$$
$$\tan 120° = \frac{\frac{\sqrt{3}}{2}}{-\frac{1}{2}} = -\sqrt{3}$$

(d)

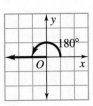

$$\cos 180° = -1, \sin 180° = 0, \tan 180° = \frac{0}{-1} = 0$$

(e)

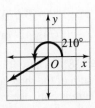

$$\cos 210° = -\frac{\sqrt{3}}{2}, \sin 210° = -\frac{1}{2}, \tan 210° =$$
$$\frac{-\frac{1}{2}}{-\frac{\sqrt{3}}{2}} = \frac{\sqrt{3}}{3}$$

(f) $\cos 330° = \frac{\sqrt{3}}{2}, \sin 330° = -\frac{1}{2}, \tan 330° =$
$$\frac{-\frac{1}{2}}{\frac{\sqrt{3}}{2}} = -\frac{\sqrt{3}}{3}$$

3. (a)

$$\sin\alpha - 1 = 0$$
$$\sin\alpha = 1$$
$$\alpha = 90°$$

(b)

$$2\sin\alpha = \sqrt{2}$$
$$\sin\alpha = \frac{\sqrt{2}}{2}$$
$$\alpha = 45° \text{ or } 135°$$

(c)

$$4\cos^2\alpha - 1 = 0$$
$$4\cos^2\alpha = 1$$
$$\cos^2\alpha = \frac{1}{4}$$
$$\cos\alpha = \pm\sqrt{\frac{1}{4}}$$
$$\cos\alpha = \pm\frac{1}{2}$$
$$\alpha = 60° \text{ or } 120° \text{ or } 240° \text{ or } 300°$$

(d)

$$3\cos^2\alpha + 2\cos\alpha = 1$$
$$3\cos^2\alpha + 2\cos\alpha - 1 = 0$$
$$(\cos\alpha + 1)(3\cos\alpha - 1) = 0$$
$$\cos\alpha = -1 \text{ or } \cos\alpha = \frac{1}{3}$$
$$\alpha = 180° \text{ or } \alpha = \cos^{-1}\frac{1}{3}$$
$$\alpha = 180° \text{ or } \alpha \approx 70.5° \text{ or } 289.5°$$

4. (a)

x	$\sin x$
0°	0
30°	$\frac{1}{2}$
45°	$\frac{\sqrt{2}}{2}$
90°	1
120°	$\frac{\sqrt{3}}{2}$
180°	0
210°	$-\frac{1}{2}$
240°	$-\frac{\sqrt{3}}{2}$
270°	-1
315°	$-\frac{\sqrt{2}}{2}$

(b)

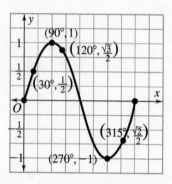

5. (a)

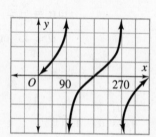

(b) The graph of $y = \frac{1}{2}$ intersects the graph of the tangent twice within the given domain. There are 2 solutions.

(c) $\tan^{-1}\left(\frac{1}{2}\right) = x \approx 27°$. The tangent is also positive in the third quadrant. So, $x = 180° + 27° = 207°$

6. (a) $\cos(180° + x) = \cos 180° \cos x - \sin 180° \sin x =$
$(-1)(\cos x) - (0)(\sin x) = -\cos x$

(b) $\sin(180° + x) = \sin 180° \cos x + \cos 180° \sin x =$
$(0)(\cos x) + (-1)(\sin x) = -\sin x$

(c) $\tan(180° + x) = \frac{\sin(180°+x)}{\cos(180°+x)} = \frac{-\sin x}{-\cos x} = \tan x$

7. (a)

$$m\angle C = 180° - (50° + 60°) = 70°$$

Use the Law of Sines to find AC and BC:

$$\frac{AC}{\sin 60°} = \frac{6}{\sin 70°}$$
$$AC = \frac{6 \sin 60°}{\sin 70°}$$
$$\approx 5.5$$

$$\frac{BC}{\sin 50°} = \frac{6}{\sin 70°}$$
$$BC = \frac{6 \sin 50°}{\sin 70°}$$
$$\approx 4.9$$

(b) Since $\triangle CHB$ is a 30-60-90 triangle, you know that $CH = \frac{1}{2}(4.9)(\sqrt{3}) \approx 4.24$. The area is $\frac{1}{2}bh = \frac{1}{2}(6)(4.24) = 12.7$.

8. (a) The largest angle is opposite the longest side. $\overline{DE}$ is the longest side. So, $\angle F$ is the largest angle. Use the Law of Cosines:

$$12^2 = 9^2 + 10^2 - 2(9)(10)(\cos \angle F)$$
$$144 - 81 - 100 = -180 \cos \angle F$$
$$\frac{-37}{-180} = \cos \angle F$$
$$\angle F = \cos^{-1}\left(\frac{37}{180}\right)$$
$$\angle F \approx 78°$$

(b) First find the semiperimeter: $s = \frac{12+10+9}{2} = \frac{31}{2} = 15.5$. Then use Heron's Formula to find the area:

$$A = \sqrt{15.5(15.5 - 12)(15.5 - 10)(15.5 - 9)}$$
$$= \sqrt{15.5(3.5)(5.5)(6.5)} = \sqrt{1939.44} \approx 44$$

9. (a) Use the Law of Cosines:

$$7^2 = 3^2 + 8^2 - 2(3)(8) \cos \angle G$$
$$49 - 9 - 64 = -48 \cos \angle G$$
$$-24 = -48 \cos \angle G$$
$$\frac{1}{2} = \cos \angle G$$
$$m\angle G = \cos^{-1} \frac{1}{2}$$
$$m\angle G = 60°$$

(b) Use the Law of Sines:

$$\frac{8}{\sin 50°} = \frac{7}{\sin \angle G}$$
$$8 \sin \angle G = 7 \sin 50°$$
$$\sin \angle G = \frac{7 \sin 50°}{8}$$
$$\approx 0.670289$$
$$m\angle G \approx 42° \text{ or } 180° - 42° = 138°$$

$m\angle G \neq 138°$ because it is too large. $138 + 50 > 180$ and the sum of the three angles of a triangle must be 180°. There is only one value for $m\angle G$, namely 42°.

(c) Use the Law of Sines:

$$\frac{18}{\sin 52°} = \frac{21}{\sin \angle G}$$

$$18 \sin \angle G = 21 \sin 52°$$

$$\sin \angle G = \frac{21 \sin 52°}{18}$$

$$\sin \angle G \approx 0.919346$$

$$m\angle G \approx 67° \text{ or } 180° - 67° = 113°$$

If $m\angle G = 67°$, then $m\angle I = 180° - 52° - 67° = 61°$.
If $m\angle G = 113°$, then $m\angle I = 180° - 113° - 52° = 15°$. So, there are two values for $m\angle G$: 67° or 113°.

(d) Use the Law of Sines:

$$\frac{6}{\sin 75°} = \frac{7}{\sin \angle G}$$

$$6 \sin \angle G = 7 \sin 75°$$

$$\sin \angle G = \frac{7 \sin 75°}{6}$$

$$\approx 1.12691$$

Since the sine of an angle can never be greater than 1, there is no solution.

CHAPTER TEST

1. Since the cosine is positive and the sine is negative, the angle is in Quadrant IV. The correct choice is **D**.
2. Use the Pythagorean Identity, $\cos^2 \alpha + \sin^2 \alpha = 1$:

$$\cos^2 \alpha + \sin^2 \alpha = 1$$

$$\cos^2 \alpha + \left(\frac{15}{17}\right)^2 = 1$$

$$\cos^2 \alpha + \frac{225}{289} = 1$$

$$\cos^2 \alpha = 1 - \frac{225}{289}$$

$$\cos^2 \alpha = \frac{64}{289}$$

$$\cos \alpha = \pm\sqrt{\frac{64}{289}}$$

$$= \pm\frac{8}{175}$$

Since α is in Quadrant II, the cosine is negative: $\cos \alpha = -\frac{8}{17}$. The correct choice is **B**.

3. For the given interval, $y = \cos x$ is below the x-axis. So, the $\cos x$ is negative. The values of the cosine decrease from $\cos 90° = 0$ to $\cos 180° = -1$. So, the $\cos x$ is decreasing. The correct choice is D, negative and decreasing.

4. Use the angle-sum identities:

$$\cos 200° = \cos(180° + 20°)$$

$$= \cos 180° \cos 20° - \sin 180° \sin 20°$$

$$= (-1)(\cos 20°) - (0)(\sin 20°) = \cos 20°.$$

The correct choice is **B**.

5. Use Heron's Formula. First find the semiperimeter: $s = \frac{5+9+8}{2} = \frac{22}{2} = 11$. Then,

$$A = \sqrt{11(11-5)(11-9)(11-8)} = \sqrt{11(6)(2)(3)} = 6\sqrt{11}$$

The correct choice is **D**.

6. (a)

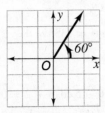

$$\cos 60° = \frac{1}{2}, \sin 60° = \frac{\sqrt{3}}{2}, \tan 60° = \sqrt{3}$$

(b)

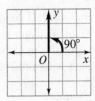

$\cos 90° = 0$, $\sin 90° = 1$, and $\tan 90°$ is undefined.

(c)

$$\cos 150° = -\frac{\sqrt{3}}{2}, \sin 150° = \frac{1}{2}, \tan 150° = -\frac{\sqrt{3}}{3}$$

(d)

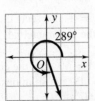

$\cos 289° \approx 0.33$, $\sin 289° \approx -0.95$,
$\tan 289° \approx -2.90$

7. (a)

$$2\sin\theta + 1 = 0$$

$$2\sin\theta = -1$$

$$\sin\theta = -\frac{1}{2}$$

$$\theta = 210° \text{ or } \theta = 330°$$

(b)

$$2\cos^2\theta - 1 = 0$$
$$2\cos^2\theta = 1$$
$$\cos^2\theta = \frac{1}{2}$$
$$\cos\theta = \pm\sqrt{\frac{1}{2}}$$
$$\cos\theta = \pm\frac{\sqrt{2}}{2}$$
$$\theta = 45° \text{ or } \theta = 135° \text{ or } \theta = 225° \text{ or } \theta = 315°$$

(c)

$$3\cos^2\theta - 5\cos\theta + 2 = 0$$
$$(\cos\theta - 1)(3\cos\theta - 2) = 0$$
$$\cos\theta - 1 = 0 \text{ or } 3\cos\theta - 2 = 0$$
$$\cos\theta = 1 \text{ or } \cos\theta = \frac{2}{3}$$

If $\cos\theta = 1$, then $\theta = 0°$. If $\cos\theta = \frac{2}{3}$, then $\theta = \cos^{-1}\left(\frac{2}{3}\right)$. Your calculator gives $\theta \approx 48°$. But, the cosine is also positive in Quadrant IV. So, $360° - 48° = 312°$ is also a solution. The three solutions are $0°$, $48°$, and $312°$.

8. Use the angle-sum identities:
   (a) $\sin(180° - x) = \sin 180° \cos x - \cos 180° \sin x = (0)\cos x - (-1)\sin x = \sin x$
   (b) $\cos(180° + x) = \cos 180° \cos x - \sin 180° \sin x = (-1)\cos x - (0)\sin x = -\cos x$
   (c) $\sin(270° + x) = \sin 270° \cos x + \cos 270° \sin x = (-1)\cos x + (0)\sin x = -\cos x$

9. (a)

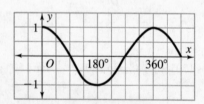

   (b) The graph of $y = \frac{1}{2}$ intersects the graph of $y = \cos x$ three times in the given interval. There are three solutions.
   (c) Since $\cos^{-1}\left(\frac{1}{2}\right) = 60°$ and the cosine is positive in Quadrants I and IV, the solutions are $60°$, $360° - 60° = 300°$, $360° + 60° = 420°$.

10. (a) Use the Law of Cosines to find two of the missing angles. Then subtract from $180°$ to find the third angle.

$$12^2 = 8^2 + 16^2 - 2(8)(16)\cos\angle A$$
$$144 - 64 - 256 = -256\cos\angle A$$
$$\frac{-176}{-256} = \cos\angle A$$
$$m\angle A = \cos^{-1}\left(\frac{176}{256}\right)$$
$$\approx 47°$$

$$8^2 = 12^2 + 16^2 - 2(12)(16)\cos\angle B$$
$$64 - 144 - 256 = -384\cos\angle B$$
$$\frac{-336}{-384} = \cos\angle B$$
$$m\angle B = \cos^{-1}\left(\frac{336}{384}\right)$$
$$\approx 29°$$

The third angle is $180° - 47° - 29° = 104°$

(b) Use the Law of Sines:

$$\frac{5}{\sin 34°} = \frac{7}{\sin\angle B}$$
$$5\sin\angle B = 7\sin 34°$$
$$\sin\angle B = \frac{7\sin 34°}{5}$$
$$m\angle B = \sin^{-1}\left(\frac{7\sin 34°}{5}\right)$$
$$\approx 52° \text{ or } 180° - 52° = 128°$$

There are two solutions for $\triangle ABC$:

(i) If $m\angle B = 52°$, $m\angle C = 180° - 52° - 34° = 94°$. Use the Law of Cosines to find AB:

$$AB^2 = 7^2 + 5^2 - 2(7)(5)\cos 94°$$
$$= 49 + 25 - 70\cos 94°$$
$$\approx 78.88$$
$$AB \approx \sqrt{78.88}$$
$$\approx 8.9$$

(ii) If $m\angle B = 128°$, $m\angle C = 180° - 128° - 34° = 18°$. Use the Law of Cosines to find AB:

$$AB^2 = 7^2 + 5^2 - 2(7)(5)\cos 18°$$
$$= 49 + 25 - 70\cos 18°$$
$$\approx 7.426$$
$$AB \approx \sqrt{7.426}$$
$$\approx 2.7$$

11. If you have enough information to completely determine a triangle, you can also find its area. Any combination of three sides and angles, other than AAA, will do.

CUMULATIVE REVIEW

1. If you add them forward and backward,

$$S = 9 + 11 + \ldots + 99 + 101$$
$$S = 101 + 99 + \ldots + 11 + 9$$
$$2S = 110 + 110 + \ldots + 110 + 110$$

There are 47 numbers in this sum, so $2S = 47 \cdot 110 = 5170$, and $S = 2585$. The correct answer choice is **C**.

2. If $\binom{20}{k} = 1$, then $k = 0$ or 20. The correct answer choice is **A**.

3. This is a geometric series:

$$\frac{13}{100} + \frac{13}{100} \cdot \frac{1}{100} + \frac{13}{100} \cdot \left(\frac{1}{100}\right)^2 + \ldots$$

$$= \frac{\frac{13}{100}}{1 - \frac{1}{100}} = \frac{\frac{13}{100}}{\frac{99}{100}} = \frac{13}{100} \cdot \frac{100}{99} = \frac{13}{99}$$

The correct answer choice is **C**.

4. Let a = the first term and d = the common difference. Then $a + 2d = 19$, while $a + 7d = 574$. Subtracting the first from the second yields $5d = 555$, $d = 111$. The sixth term is

$$a + 5d = (a + 2d) + 3d = 19 + 333 = 352$$

The correct answer choice is **B**.

5. This would be the 9th term in the 12th row of Pascal's triangle, which is $\binom{12}{8}$. The correct answer choice is **C**.

6. $\cos\theta > 0$ in quadrants I and IV, while $\sin\theta < 0$ in quadrants III and IV. The correct answer choice is **D**.

7. In Quadrant IV, sine is negative. Now

$$\sin^2\alpha + \cos^2\alpha = 1$$

$$\sin^2\alpha + \left(\frac{5}{13}\right)^2 = 1$$

$$\sin^2\alpha = 1 - \left(\frac{5}{13}\right)^2 = 1 - \frac{25}{169} = \frac{144}{169}$$

$$\sin\alpha = -\sqrt{\frac{144}{169}} = -\frac{12}{13}$$

The correct answer choice is **D**.

8. As stated in Exercise 6, cosine is positive in these quadrants. The sine function increases from –1 to 1. The correct answer choice is **A**.

9. In general, $\cos\theta = \sin(90° - \theta)$, so $\cos 42° = \sin(90° - 42°) = \sin 48°$. The correct answer choice is **C**.

10. Use Heron's formula. First, $s = \frac{16+23+21}{2} = 30$, so the area is

$$\sqrt{30(30 - 16)(30 - 23)(30 - 21)}$$

$$= \sqrt{30 \cdot 14 \cdot 7 \cdot 9}$$

$$= \sqrt{26,460} \approx 162.7$$

The correct answer choice is **C**.

11. (a)

$$\sum_{k=1}^{10}(3k - 1) = \sum_{k=1}^{10}3k - \sum_{k=1}^{10}1$$

$$= 3\sum_{k=1}^{10}k - \sum_{k=1}^{10}1$$

$$= 3 \cdot \frac{10 \cdot 11}{2} - 10$$

$$= 165 - 10 = 155$$

(b)

$$\sum_{k=0}^{4}6(-2)^k = 6\sum_{k=0}^{4}(-2)^k$$

$$= 6 \cdot \frac{(-2)^5 - 1}{-2 - 1}$$

$$= 6 \cdot \frac{-33}{-3} = 6 \cdot 11 = 66$$

12.

$$\sum_{k=0}^{n}(6k + 4) = \sum_{k=0}^{n}6k + \sum_{k=0}^{n}4$$

$$= 6\sum_{k=0}^{n}k + \sum_{k=0}^{n}4$$

$$= 6 \cdot \frac{n(n + 1)}{2} + 4(n + 1)$$

$$= (n + 1)(3n + 4)$$

13. A recursive rule would be

$$H(n) = \begin{cases} 2 & \text{if } n = 0 \\ H(n - 1) + (6n + 2) & \text{if } n \geq 1 \end{cases}$$

The closed form is obtained from

$$H(n) = \sum_{k=0}^{n}(6k + 2)$$

This is almost identical to the previous exercise; just replace 4 with 2 to obtain $(n + 1)(3n + 2)$.

14. (a)

n	$g(n)$
0	8
1	12
2	18
3	27
4	$\frac{81}{2}$

(b) $g(n) = 8 \cdot \left(\frac{3}{2}\right)^n$

15. The entries in the fifth row are 1, 5, 10, 10, 5, and 1, so

$$(3x - 2y)^5 = (3x)^5 + 5(3x)^4(-2y) + 10(3x)^3(-2y)^2 + $$
$$10(3x)^2(-2y)^3 + 5(3x)(-2y)^4 + (-2y)^5$$
$$= 243x^5 - 810x^4y + 1080x^3y^2 - 720x^2y^3 + $$
$$240xy^4 - 32y^5$$

16. (a)

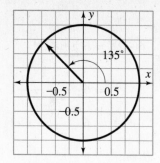

$$\sin 135° = \sin 45° = \frac{\sqrt{2}}{2}, \cos 135° = -\cos 45°$$
$$= -\frac{\sqrt{2}}{2}, \tan 135° = -\tan 45° = -1$$

(b)

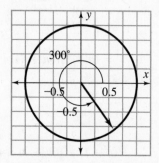

$$\sin 300° = -\sin 60° = -\frac{\sqrt{3}}{2}, \cos 300° = \cos 60°$$
$$= \frac{1}{2}, \tan 300° = -\tan 60° = -\sqrt{3}$$

17. (a) $\cos \theta + 1 = 0, \cos \theta = -1, \theta = 180°$

(b) $\sqrt{2} \sin \theta + 1 = 0, \sqrt{2} \sin \theta = -1,$
$\sin \theta = -\frac{1}{\sqrt{2}} = -\frac{\sqrt{2}}{2}$. Now $\sin 45° = \frac{\sqrt{2}}{2}$, and sine is negative in Quadrants III and IV, so $\theta = 225°$ and $315°$.

(b)

$$\sin^2 \theta - 3 \sin \theta + 2 = 0$$

$$(\sin \theta - 1)(\sin \theta - 2) = 0$$

$$\sin \theta - 1 = 0 \quad \text{or} \quad \sin \theta - 2 = 0$$

$$\sin \theta = 1 \quad \text{or} \quad \sin \theta = 2$$

$$\theta = 90° \qquad \text{(no solution)}$$

18. (a)

$$\cos(360° - x) = \cos 360° \cos x + \sin 360° \sin x$$

$$= 1 \cdot \cos x + 0 \cdot \sin x = \cos x$$

(b)

$$\sin(90 - x) = \sin 90° \cdot \cos x - \cos 90° \cdot \sin x$$

$$= 1 \cdot \cos x - 0 \cdot \sin x = \cos x$$

(c)

$$\sin(180° - x) = \sin 180° \cdot \cos x - \cos 180° \cdot \sin x$$

$$= 0 \cdot \cos x - (-1) \cdot \sin x = \sin x$$

19. (a) $\sin 135° = \sin 45°$

(b) $\cos 330° = \cos 30°$

(c) $\tan 240° = \tan 60°$

20. First note that the sine is negative in Quadrants III and IV.

(a) Since θ is in Quadrant III or IV, cosine could be negative or positive. Now

$$\sin^2 \theta + \cos^2 \theta = 1$$

$$\cos^2 \theta = 1 - \sin^2 \theta = 1 - \left(-\frac{12}{13}\right)^2 = 1 - \frac{144}{169} = \frac{25}{169}$$

$$\cos \theta = \pm \frac{5}{13}$$

(b) It follows that

$$\tan \theta = \frac{\sin \theta}{\cos \theta} = \frac{-\frac{12}{13}}{\pm \frac{5}{13}} = \pm \frac{12}{5}$$

(c) First find the reference angle:

$$\sin^{-1}\left(\frac{12}{13}\right) \approx 67.4°$$

This yields angles $180° + 67.4° = 247.4°$ and $360° - 67.4° = 292.6°$.

21. If $(x - a)^2 + (y - b)^2 = r^2$, then the graph is a circle with center (a, b) and radius r. Therefore, the center of the given circle is $(3, -4)$ and the radius is 6.

22. Since

$$g(-x) = 2(-x)^3 - (-x) = -2x^3 + x = -(2x^3 - x) = -g(x)$$

this is an odd function.

23. Replacing x by $x + 1$ shifts the graph 1 unit to the left, while replacing y by $y + 2$ shifts the graph 2 units down.

24. (a) If you multiply y by a constant, the graph is dilated vertically by the reciprocal. If you subtract a constant from y, it is shifted up. So the equation is $2(y - 3) = x^2$ or $y = \frac{1}{2}x^2 + 3$.

(b)

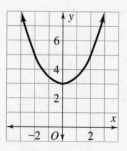

25. (a) $D_5 \circ T_{-3}(x) = D_5(x - 3) = 5(x - 3) = 5x - 15 = \mathcal{A}_{(5,-15)}$

(b)

$$D_2 \circ D_6 \circ T_3(x) = D_2 \circ D_6(x+3)$$
$$= D_2(6(x+3)) = 2 \cdot 6(x+3)$$

$$= 12(x+3) = 12x + 36 = A_{(\infty\in,\ni)}$$

(c) $A_{(3,-2)}A_{(6,3)}(x) = A_{(3,-2)}(6x+3) = 3(6x+3) - 2 = 18x + 9 - 2 = 18x + 7 = A_{(18,7)}$.

26. (a)

$$8^{-\frac{5}{3}} = \frac{1}{8^{\frac{5}{3}}} = \frac{1}{(\sqrt[3]{8})^5} = \frac{1}{2^5} = \frac{1}{32}$$

(b)

$$\frac{x^{-3}y^{-7}}{x^{-5}y^{-1}} = x^{-3-(-5)}y^{-7-(-1)} = x^2 y^{-6}$$

27. (a) If d = the common difference, then $15 + 3d = 120$. Therefore, $3d = 105$, $d = 35$. The sequence is thus 15, 50, 85, 120.

(b) If r = the common ratio, then $15 \cdot r^3 = 120$. Therefore, $r^3 = 8$, $r = 2$. The sequence is thus 15, 30, 60, 120.

28. (a) By definition, $f^{-1}(x) = \log_5 x$.

(b) $g^{-1}(x) = 3^x$

29. Multiply the second equation by 3 and add to the first:

$$
\begin{aligned}
2x + 3y &= 12 \\
-9x - 3y &= 9 \\
\hline
-7x &= 21 \\
x &= -3
\end{aligned}
$$

Substituting into the first equation yields

$$
\begin{aligned}
-6 + 3y &= 12 \\
3y &= 18 \\
y &= 6
\end{aligned}
$$

30.

$$(2, -1, 5) \cdot (6, -2, 0) = 2 \cdot 6 + (-1)(-2) + 5 \cdot 0$$
$$= 12 + 2 + 0 = 14$$

31. (a)

$$\sqrt{40} \cdot \sqrt{-5} = \sqrt{-200} = \sqrt{100} \cdot \sqrt{2} \cdot \sqrt{-1} = 10\sqrt{2}i$$

(b)

$$(3 - 2i)^2 = 9 - 12i + 4i^2 = 9 - 12i - 4 = 5 - 12i$$

32.

$$|6 + 2i| = \sqrt{6^2 + 2^2} = \sqrt{36 + 4} = \sqrt{40} \text{ or } 2\sqrt{10}$$

33. The function $g(x)$ is the inverse of $f(x)$. This can be found using algebra, or by describing what $f(x)$ does and reversing it. The first way, switch the input and output:

$$x = -2 \cdot g(x) + 4$$

$$2 \cdot g(x) = -x + 4$$

$$g(x) = -\tfrac{1}{2}x + 2$$

Alternatively, you could say that f multiplies the input by -2, then adds 4. The inverse subtracts 4, then divides by -2:

$$g(x) = \frac{x - 4}{-2} = -\tfrac{1}{2}x + 2$$

34. First find the balance point, by finding the average of the x-values and the average of the y-values: $(\frac{12}{4}, \frac{35}{4}) = (3, 8.75)$. Next, set up an equation of a line passing through this:

$$y = m(x - 3) + 8.75$$

Now the y-values for $x = -1, 2, 4, 7$ are

$$-4m + 8.75, \ -m + 8.75, \ m + 8.75, \ 4m + 8.75$$

The sum of the squares of the "errors" are

$$(-4m + 4.75)^2 + (-m + 1.75)^2 + (m - 1.25)^2 + (4m - 5.25)^2$$

$$= 16m^2 - 38m + m^2 - 3.5m + m^2 - 2.5m + 16m^2 - 42m + \text{constant}$$

$$= 34m^2 - 86m + \text{constant}$$

The graph of this is an upturned parabola, and the minimum value occurs at the vertex. That point has $m = \frac{-(-86)}{2\cdot34} = \frac{86}{68} \approx 1.265$. Therefore, the line of best fit is

$$y = 1.265(x - 3) + 8.75$$
$$= 1.265x + 4.955$$